Complete Solutions Manual
for
Gustafson and Frisk's
College Algebra
Eighth Edition

Complete Solutions Manual
for
Gustafson and Frisk's
College Algebra
Eighth Edition

Michael G. Welden
Rock Valley College

THOMSON
BROOKS/COLE
Australia • Canada • Mexico • Singapore • Spain • United Kingdom • United States

Printed in Canada
1 2 3 4 5 6 7 07 06 05 04 03

Printer: Transcontinental Printing/Louiseville

ISBN: 0-534-40071-X

For more information about our products, contact us at:
Thomson Learning Academic Resource Center
1-800-423-0563

For permission to use material from this text, contact us by:
Phone: 1-800-730-2214
Fax: 1-800-731-2215
Web: http://www.thomsonrights.com

Asia
Thomson Learning
5 Shenton Way #01-01
UIC Building
Singapore 068808

Australia/New Zealand
Thomson Learning
102 Dodds Street
Southbank, Victoria 3006
Australia

Canada
Nelson
1120 Birchmount Road
Toronto, Ontario M1K 5G4
Canada

Europe/Middle East/South Africa
Thomson Learning
High Holborn House
50/51 Bedford Row
London WC1R 4LR
United Kingdom

Latin America
Thomson Learning
Seneca, 53
Colonia Polanco
11560 Mexico D.F.
Mexico

Spain/Portugal
Paraninfo
Calle/Magallanes, 25
28015 Madrid, Spain

Contents

Preface

This manual contains detailed solutions to all of the exercises of the text *College Algebra*, eighth edition, by R. David Gustafson and Peter D. Frisk.

Many of the exercises in the text may be solved using more than one method, but it is not feasible to list all possible solutions in this manual. Also, some of the exercises may have been solved in this manual using a method that differs slightly from that presented in the text. There are a few exercises in the text whose solutions may vary from person to person. Some of these solutions may not have been included in this manual. For the solution to an exercise like this, the notation "answers may vary" has been included.

If you are a student using this manual, please remember that only reading a solution does not teach you how to solve a problem. To repeat a commonly used phrase, mathematics is not a spectator sport. You MUST make an honest attempt to solve each exercise in the text without using this manual first. This manual should be viewed more or less as a last resort. Above all, DO NOT simply copy the solution from this manual onto your own paper. Doing so will not help you learn how to do the exercise, nor will it help you to do better on quizzes or tests.

I would like to thank the members of the mathematics faculty at Rock Valley College and Rachael Sturgeon of Brooks/Cole Publishing Company for their help and support. This solutions manual was prepared using EXP 5.0.

This book is dedicated to John, who helps me to realize that mathematics cannot describe everything in life.

May your study of this material be successful and rewarding.

Michael G. Welden

Exercise 0.1 (page 13)

1. decimal

2. variable

3. 2

4. even

5. composite

6. rational

7. decimals

8. $\leq$

9. negative

10. 0

11. $x + (y + z)$

12. yx

13. $5m + 5 \cdot 2$

14. commutative, multiplication

15. interval

16. no

17. two

18. half-open

19. positive

20. distance

21. Every natural number is a whole number, so $\mathbf{N} \subseteq \mathbf{W}$. **TRUE**

22. Every rational number is a real number, so $\mathbf{Q} \subseteq \mathbf{R}$. **TRUE**

23. The rational number $\frac{1}{2}$ is **not** a natural number, so $\mathbf{Q} \nsubseteq \mathbf{N}$. **FALSE**

24. Every integer is a rational number, so $\mathbf{Z} \subseteq \mathbf{Q}$. **TRUE**

25. Every whole number is an integer, so $\mathbf{W} \subseteq \mathbf{Z}$. **TRUE**

26. The real number $\sqrt{2}$ is **not** an integer, so $\mathbf{R} \nsubseteq \mathbf{Z}$. **FALSE**

27. natural: 1, 2, 6, 7

28. whole: 0, 1, 2, 6, 7

29. integers: $-5, -4, 0, 1, 2, 6, 7$

30. rational: $-5, -4, -\frac{2}{3}, 0, 1, 2, 2.75, 6, 7$

31. irrational: $\sqrt{2}$

32. prime: 2, 7

33. composite: 6

34. even: $-4, 0, 2, 6$

35. odd: $-5, 1, 7$

36. negative: $-5, -4, -\frac{2}{3}$

37.

38.

39.

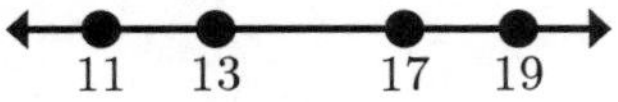

40.

41.

42.

43.

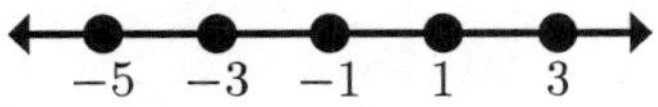

44.

45. $x > 2 \rightarrow (2, \infty)$

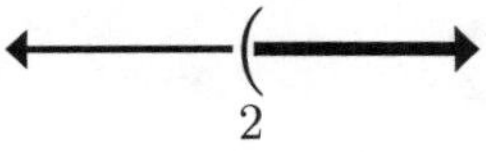

46. $x < 4 \rightarrow (-\infty, 4)$

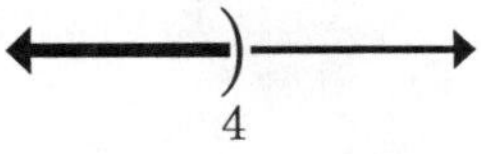

47. $0 < x < 5 \rightarrow (0, 5)$

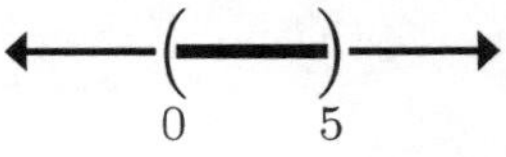

48. $-2 < x < 3 \rightarrow (-2, 3)$

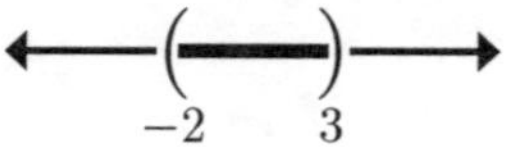

49. $x > -4 \rightarrow (-4, \infty)$

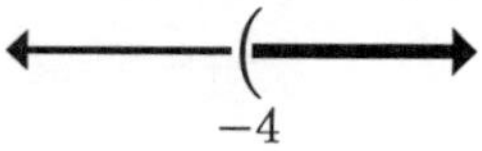

50. $x < 3 \rightarrow (-\infty, 3)$

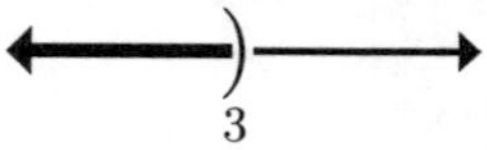

51. $-2 \le x < 2 \rightarrow [-2, 2)$

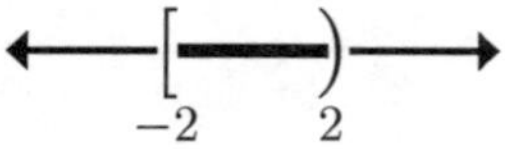

52. $-4 < x \le 1 \rightarrow (-4, 1]$

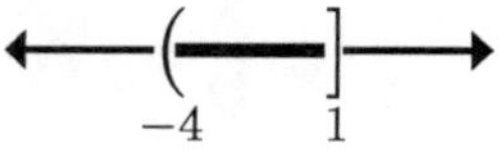

53. $x \le 5 \rightarrow (-\infty, 5]$

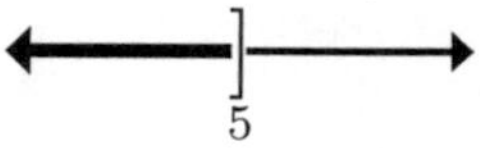

54. $x \ge -1 \rightarrow [-1, \infty)$

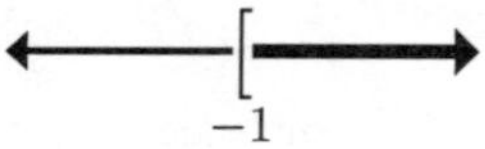

55. $-5 < x \le 0 \rightarrow (-5, 0]$

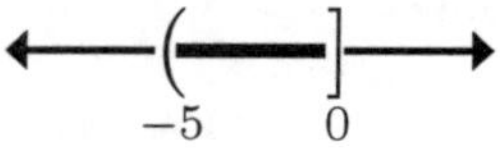

56. $-3 \le x < 4 \rightarrow [-3, 4)$

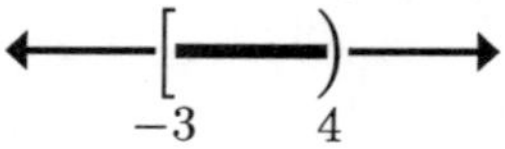

57. $-2 \le x \le 3 \rightarrow [-2, 3]$

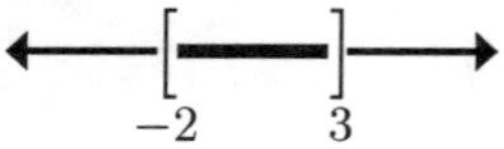

58. $-4 \le x \le 4 \rightarrow [-4, 4]$

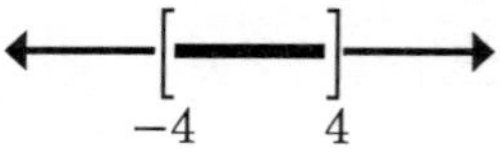

59. $6 \ge x \ge 2 \rightarrow 2 \le x \le 6 \rightarrow [2, 6]$

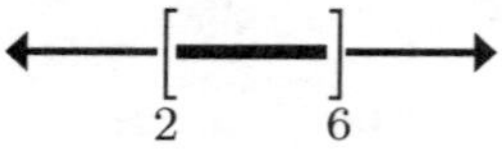

60. $3 \ge x \ge -2 \rightarrow -2 \le x \le 3 \rightarrow [-2, 3]$

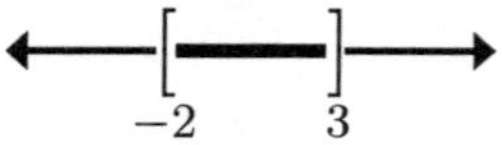

61. $x > -5$ and $x < 4 \rightarrow (-5, \infty) \cap (-\infty, 4)$

$(-5, \infty)$

$(-\infty, 4)$

$(-5, \infty) \cap (-\infty, 4)$

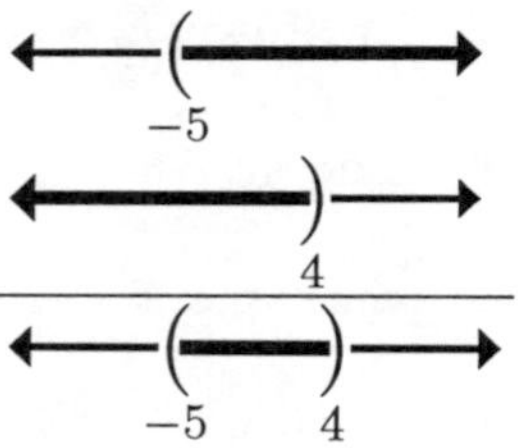

62. $x \ge -3$ and $x < 6 \rightarrow [-3, \infty) \cap (-\infty, 6)$

$[-3, \infty)$

$(-\infty, 6)$

$[-3, \infty) \cap (-\infty, 6)$

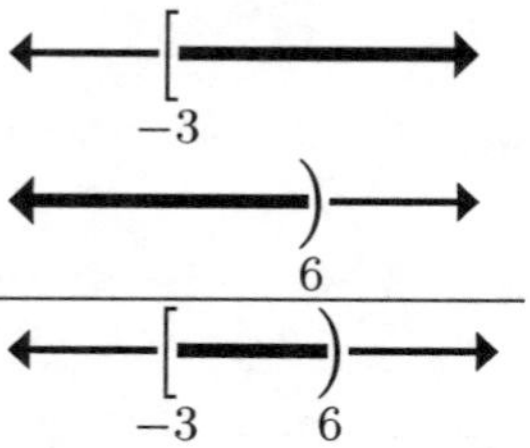

63. $x \geq -8$ and $x \leq -3 \rightarrow [-8, \infty) \cap (-\infty, -3]$

$[-8, \infty)$
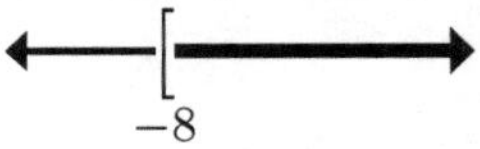

$(-\infty, -3]$
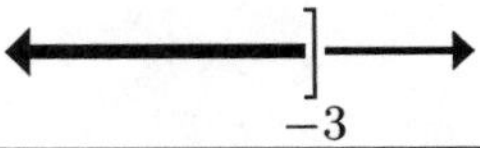

$[-8, \infty) \cap (-\infty, -3]$
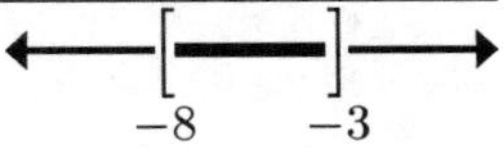

64. $x > 1$ and $x \leq 7 \rightarrow (1, \infty) \cap (-\infty, 7]$

$(1, \infty)$
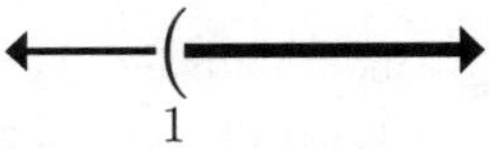

$(-\infty, 7]$
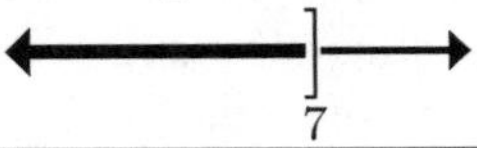

$(1, \infty) \cap (-\infty, 7]$
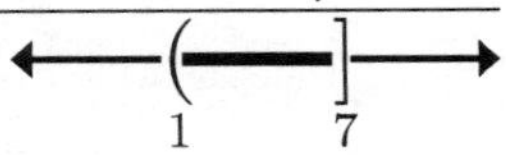

65. $x < -2$ or $x > 2 \rightarrow (-\infty, -2) \cup (2, \infty)$

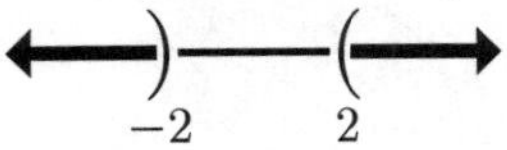

66. $x \leq -5$ or $x > 0 \rightarrow (-\infty, -5] \cup (0, \infty)$

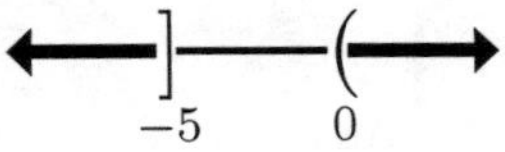

67. $x \leq -1$ or $x \geq 3 \rightarrow (-\infty, -1] \cup [3, \infty)$

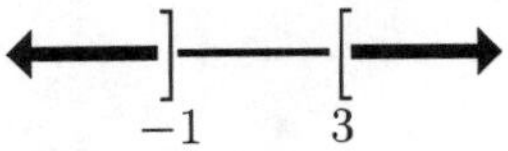

68. $x < -3$ or $x \geq 2 \rightarrow (-\infty, -3) \cup [2, \infty)$

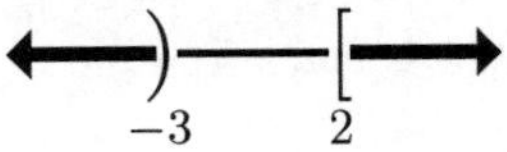

69. Since $13 \geq 0$, $|13| = 13$.

70. Since $-17 < 0$, $|-17| = -(-17) = 17$.

71. Since $0 \geq 0$, $|0| = 0$.

72. Since $63 \geq 0$, $|63| = 63$.
$-|63| = -(63) = -63$

73. Since $-8 < 0$, $|-8| = -(-8) = 8$.
$-|-8| = -(8) = -8$

74. Since $-25 < 0$, $|-25| = -(-25) = 25$.

75. Since $32 \geq 0$, $|32| = 32$.
$-|32| = -(32) = -32$

76. Since $-6 < 0$, $|-6| = -(-6) = 6$.
$-|-6| = -(6) = -6$

77. Since $\pi - 5 < 0$,
$|\pi - 5| = -(\pi - 5) = -\pi + 5 = 5 - \pi$.

78. Since $8 - \pi \geq 0$, $|8 - \pi| = 8 - \pi$.

79. $|\pi - \pi| = |0| = 0$

80. Since $2\pi \geq 0$, $|2\pi| = 2\pi$.

81. If $x \geq 2$, then $x + 1 \geq 0$. Then
$|x + 1| = x + 1$.

82. If $x \leq -2$, then $x + 1 < 0$. Then
$|x + 1| = -(x + 1)$.

83. If $x < 0$, then $x - 4 < 0$. Then $|x - 4| = -(x - 4)$.

84. If $x > 10$, then $x - 7 \geq 0$. Then $|x - 7| = x - 7$.

85. distance $= |3 - 8| = |-5| = 5$

86. distance $= |-5 - 12| = |-17| = 17$

87. distance $= |-8 - (-3)| = |-5| = 5$

88. distance $= |6 - (-20)| = |26| = 26$

89. Since population must be positive and never has a fractional part, the set of **natural numbers** should be used.

90. Since the subdivisions on a ruler are measured in fractions of an inch, the set of **rational numbers** should be used.

91. Since temperatures are usually reported without fractional parts and may be either positive or negative (or zero), the set of **integers** should be used.

92. Since the financial condition of a business is usually described in terms of dollars and cents (fractional parts of a dollar), the set of **rational numbers** should be used.

93. $-x$ will represent a positive number if x itself is negative. For instance, if $x = -3$, then $-x = -(-3) = 3$, which is a positive number.

94. Every integer is a rational number because every integer is equal to itself over 1.

95. The statement is always true.

96. The statement is always true.

97. The statement is not always true. (For example, let $a = 5$ and $b = -2$.)

98. The statement will be true if $a \geq 0$ and $b \geq 0$, or if $a \leq 0$ and $b \leq 0$.

99. The statement $a < b > c$ could be interpreted to mean that $a > c$, when this is not necessarily true.

100. $|b - a| = |-1(a - b)| = |-1| \cdot |a - b|$
$= |a - b|$

Exercise 0.2 (page 24)

1. factor

2. natural

3. 3, $2x$

4. exponential

5. scientific, integer

6. multiplications (and divisions)

7. $x^m x^n = x^{m+n}$

8. $(x^m)^n = x^{mn}$

9. $(xy)^n = x^n y^n$

10. $\frac{x^m}{x^n} = x^{m-n}$

11. $x^0 = 1$

12. $x^{-n} = \frac{1}{x^n}$

13. $13^2 = 13 \cdot 13 = 169$

14. $10^3 = 10 \cdot 10 \cdot 10 = 1{,}000$

15. $-5^2 = -1 \cdot 5 \cdot 5 = -25$

16. $(-5)^2 = (-5)(-5) = 25$

17. $4x^3 = 4 \cdot x \cdot x \cdot x$

18. $(4x)^3 = (4x)(4x)(4x)$

19. $(-5x)^4 = (-5x)(-5x)(-5x)(-5x)$

20. $-6x^2 = -6 \cdot x \cdot x$

21. $7xxx = 7x^3$

22. $-8yyyy = -8y^4$

23. $(-x)(-x) = (-1)(-1)x^2 = x^2$

24. $(2a)(2a)(2a) = 2 \cdot 2 \cdot 2 \cdot a^3 = 8a^3$

25. $(3t)(3t)(-3t) = (3)(3)(-3)t^3 = -27t^3$

26. $-(2b)(2b)(2b)(2b) = -1 \cdot 2 \cdot 2 \cdot 2 \cdot 2 \cdot b^4 = -16b^4$

27. $xxxyy = x^3y^2$

28. $aaabbbb = a^3b^4$

29. $2.2^3 = 10.648$

30. $7.1^4 = 2541.1681$

31. $-0.5^4 = -0.0625$

32. $(-0.2)^4 = 0.0016$

33. $x^2x^3 = x^{2+3} = x^5$

34. $y^3y^4 = y^{3+4} = y^7$

35. $(z^2)^3 = z^{2 \cdot 3} = z^6$

36. $(t^6)^7 = t^{6 \cdot 7} = t^{42}$

37. $(y^5y^2)^3 = (y^7)^3 = y^{21}$

38. $(a^3a^6)a^4 = a^9a^4 = a^{13}$

39. $(z^2)^3(z^4)^5 = z^6z^{20} = z^{26}$

40. $(t^3)^4(t^5)^2 = t^{12}t^{10} = t^{22}$

41. $(a^2)^3(a^4)^2 = a^6a^8 = a^{14}$

42. $(a^2)^4(a^3)^3 = a^8a^9 = a^{17}$

43. $(3x)^3 = 3^3x^3 = 27x^3$

44. $(-2y)^4 = (-2)^4y^4 = 16y^4$

45. $(x^2y)^3 = (x^2)^3y^3 = x^6y^3$

46. $(x^3z^4)^6 = (x^3)^6(z^4)^6 = x^{18}z^{24}$

47. $\left(\frac{a^2}{b}\right)^3 = \frac{(a^2)^3}{b^3} = \frac{a^6}{b^3}$

48. $\left(\frac{x}{y^3}\right)^4 = \frac{x^4}{(y^3)^4} = \frac{x^4}{y^{12}}$

49. $(-x)^0 = 1$

50. $4x^0 = 4 \cdot 1 = 4$

51. $(4x)^0 = 1$

52. $-2x^0 = -2 \cdot 1 = -2$

53. $z^{-4} = \frac{1}{z^4}$

54. $\frac{1}{t^{-2}} = t^2$

55. $y^{-2}y^{-3} = y^{-5} = \frac{1}{y^5}$

56. $-m^{-2}m^3 = -m^1 = -m$

57. $(x^3x^{-4})^{-2} = (x^{-1})^{-2} = x^2$

58. $(y^{-2}y^3)^{-4} = (y^1)^{-4} = y^{-4} = \frac{1}{y^4}$

59. $\frac{x^7}{x^3} = x^{7-3} = x^4$

60. $\frac{r^5}{r^2} = r^{5-2} = r^3$

61. $\frac{a^{21}}{a^{17}} = a^{21-17} = a^4$

62. $\frac{t^{13}}{t^4} = t^{13-4} = t^9$

63. $\dfrac{(x^2)^2}{x^2x} = \dfrac{x^4}{x^3} = x^{4-3} = x^1 = x$

64. $\dfrac{s^9s^3}{(s^2)^2} = \dfrac{s^{12}}{s^4} = s^{12-4} = s^8$

65. $\left(\dfrac{m^3}{n^2}\right)^3 = \dfrac{(m^3)^3}{(n^2)^3} = \dfrac{m^9}{n^6}$

66. $\left(\dfrac{t^4}{t^3}\right)^3 = \left(t^{4-3}\right)^3 = \left(t^1\right)^3 = t^3$

67. $\dfrac{(a^3)^{-2}}{aa^2} = \dfrac{a^{-6}}{a^3} = a^{-6-3} = a^{-9} = \dfrac{1}{a^9}$

68. $\dfrac{r^9r^{-3}}{(r^{-2})^3} = \dfrac{r^6}{r^{-6}} = r^{6-(-6)} = r^{12}$

69. $\left(\dfrac{a^{-3}}{b^{-1}}\right)^{-4} = \dfrac{(a^{-3})^{-4}}{(b^{-1})^{-4}} = \dfrac{a^{12}}{b^4}$

70. $\left(\dfrac{t^{-4}}{t^{-3}}\right)^{-2} = \dfrac{(t^{-4})^{-2}}{(t^{-3})^{-2}} = \dfrac{t^8}{t^6} = t^2$

71. $\left(\dfrac{r^4r^{-6}}{r^3r^{-3}}\right)^2 = \left(\dfrac{r^{-2}}{r^0}\right)^2 = \left(r^{-2}\right)^2 = r^{-4} = \dfrac{1}{r^4}$

72. $\dfrac{(x^{-3}x^2)^2}{(x^2x^{-5})^{-3}} = \dfrac{(x^{-1})^2}{(x^{-3})^{-3}} = \dfrac{x^{-2}}{x^9} = x^{-11} = \dfrac{1}{x^{11}}$

73. $\left(\dfrac{x^5y^{-2}}{x^{-3}y^2}\right)^4 = \left(\dfrac{x^5x^3}{y^2y^2}\right)^4 = \left(\dfrac{x^8}{y^4}\right)^4 = \dfrac{x^{32}}{y^{16}}$

74. $\left(\dfrac{x^{-7}y^5}{x^7y^{-4}}\right)^3 = \left(\dfrac{y^5y^4}{x^7x^7}\right)^3 = \left(\dfrac{y^9}{x^{14}}\right)^3 = \dfrac{y^{27}}{x^{42}}$

75. $\left(\dfrac{5x^{-3}y^{-2}}{3x^2y^{-3}}\right)^{-2} = \left(\dfrac{3x^2y^{-3}}{5x^{-3}y^{-2}}\right)^2 = \left(\dfrac{3x^2x^3y^2}{5y^3}\right)^2 = \left(\dfrac{3x^5}{5y}\right)^2 = \dfrac{9x^{10}}{25y^2}$

76. $\left(\dfrac{3x^2y^{-5}}{2x^{-2}y^{-6}}\right)^{-3} = \left(\dfrac{2x^{-2}y^{-6}}{3x^2y^{-5}}\right)^3 = \left(\dfrac{2y^5}{3x^2x^2y^6}\right)^3 = \left(\dfrac{2}{3x^4y}\right)^3 = \dfrac{8}{27x^{12}y^3}$

77. $\left(\dfrac{3x^5y^{-3}}{6x^{-5}y^3}\right)^{-2} = \left(\dfrac{6x^{-5}y^3}{3x^5y^{-3}}\right)^2 = \left(\dfrac{2y^3y^3}{1x^5x^5}\right)^2 = \left(\dfrac{2y^6}{x^{10}}\right)^2 = \dfrac{4y^{12}}{x^{20}}$

78. $\left(\dfrac{12x^{-4}y^3z^{-5}}{4x^4y^{-3}z^5}\right)^3 = \left(\dfrac{3y^3y^3}{1x^4x^4z^5z^5}\right)^3 = \left(\dfrac{3y^6}{x^8z^{10}}\right)^3 = \dfrac{27y^{18}}{x^{24}z^{30}}$

79. $\dfrac{(8^{-2}z^{-3}y)^{-1}}{(5y^2z^{-2})^3(5yz^{-2})^{-1}} = \dfrac{8^2z^3y^{-1}}{5^3y^6z^{-6}\cdot 5^{-1}y^{-1}z^2} = \dfrac{64z^3y^{-1}}{5^2y^5z^{-4}} = \dfrac{64z^3z^4}{25y^5y^1} = \dfrac{64z^7}{25y^6}$

80. $\dfrac{(m^{-2}n^3p^4)^{-2}(mn^{-2}p^3)^4}{(mn^{-2}p^3)^{-4}(mn^2p)^{-1}} = \dfrac{m^4n^{-6}p^{-8}\cdot m^4n^{-8}p^{12}}{m^{-4}n^8p^{-12}\cdot m^{-1}n^{-2}p^{-1}} = \dfrac{m^8n^{-14}p^4}{m^{-5}n^6p^{-13}} = \dfrac{m^8m^5p^4p^{13}}{n^6n^{14}} = \dfrac{m^{13}p^{17}}{n^{20}}$

81. $-\dfrac{5[6^2+(9-5)]}{4(2-3)} = -\dfrac{5[36+4]}{4(-1)} = -\dfrac{5[40]}{-4} = -\dfrac{200}{-4} = -(-50) = 50$

82. $\dfrac{6\left[3-(4-7)^2\right]}{-5(2-4^2)} = \dfrac{6\left[3-(-3)^2\right]}{-5(2-16)} = \dfrac{6[3-9]}{-5(-14)} = \dfrac{6[-6]}{70} = \dfrac{-36}{70} = -\dfrac{18}{35}$

83. $x^2 = (-2)^2 = 4$

84. $-x^2 = -(-2)^2 = -1 \cdot 4 = -4$

85. $x^3 = (-2)^3 = -8$

86. $-x^3 = -(-2)^3 = -1 \cdot (-8) = 8$

87. $(-xz)^3 = [-1 \cdot (-2) \cdot 3]^3 = 6^3 = 216$

88. $-xz^3 = -1 \cdot (-2) \cdot 3^3 = 2 \cdot 27 = 54$

89. $\dfrac{-(x^2z^3)}{z^2 - y^2} = \dfrac{-\left[(-2)^2 \cdot 3^3\right]}{3^2 - 0^2} = \dfrac{-[4 \cdot 27]}{9 - 0} = \dfrac{-108}{9} = -12$

90. $\dfrac{z^2(x^2 - y^2)}{x^3 z} = \dfrac{3^2\left[(-2)^2 - 0^2\right]}{(-2)^3(3)} = \dfrac{9(4-0)}{(-8)(3)} = \dfrac{9(4)}{-24} = \dfrac{36}{-24} = -\dfrac{3}{2}$

91. $5x^2 - 3y^3z = 5(-2)^2 - 3(0)^3(3) = 5(4) - 3(0)(3) = 20 - 0 = 20$

92. $3(x-z)^2 + 2(y-z)^3 = 3(-2-3)^2 + 2(0-3)^3 = 3(-5)^2 + 2(-3)^3 = 3(25) + 2(-27)$
$= 75 + (-54) = 21$

93. $\dfrac{-3x^{-3}z^{-2}}{6x^2z^{-3}} = \dfrac{-1z^3}{2x^2x^3z^2} = \dfrac{-z}{2x^5} = \dfrac{-3}{2(-2)^5} = \dfrac{-3}{2(-32)} = \dfrac{-3}{-64} = \dfrac{3}{64}$

94. $\dfrac{(-5x^2z^{-3})^2}{5xz^{-2}} = \dfrac{25x^4z^{-6}}{5xz^{-2}} = \dfrac{5x^4}{xz^{-2}z^6} = \dfrac{5x^3}{z^4} = \dfrac{5(-2)^3}{3^4} = \dfrac{5(-8)}{81} = \dfrac{-40}{81} = -\dfrac{40}{81}$

95. $372{,}000 = 3.72 \times 10^5$

96. $89{,}500 = 8.95 \times 10^4$

97. $-177{,}000{,}000 = -1.77 \times 10^8$

98. $-23{,}470{,}000{,}000 = -2.347 \times 10^{10}$

99. $0.007 = 7 \times 10^{-3}$

100. $0.00052 = 5.2 \times 10^{-4}$

101. $-0.000000693 = -6.93 \times 10^{-7}$

102. $-0.000000089 = -8.9 \times 10^{-8}$

103. $1{,}000{,}000{,}000{,}000 = 1 \times 10^{12}$

104. $0.000001 = 1 \times 10^{-6}$

105. $9.37 \times 10^5 = 937{,}000$

106. $4.26 \times 10^9 = 4{,}260{,}000{,}000$

107. $2.21 \times 10^{-5} = 0.0000221$

108. $2.774 \times 10^{-2} = 0.02774$

109. $0.00032 \times 10^4 = 3.2$

110. $9300.0 \times 10^{-4} = 0.93$

111. $-3.2 \times 10^{-3} = -0.0032$

112. $-7.25 \times 10^3 = -7{,}250$

113. $\dfrac{(65{,}000)(45{,}000)}{250{,}000} = \dfrac{(6.5 \times 10^4)(4.5 \times 10^4)}{2.5 \times 10^5} = \dfrac{(6.5)(4.5)}{2.5} \times 10^{4+4-5} = 11.7 \times 10^3$
$= 1.17 \times 10^1 \times 10^3$
$= 1.17 \times 10^4$

114. $\dfrac{(0.000000045)(0.00000012)}{45{,}000{,}000} = \dfrac{(4.5 \times 10^{-8})(1.2 \times 10^{-7})}{4.5 \times 10^{7}} = \dfrac{(4.5)(1.2)}{4.5} \times 10^{(-8)+(-7)-7}$
$= 1.2 \times 10^{-22}$

115. $\dfrac{(0.00000035)(170{,}000)}{0.00000085} = \dfrac{(3.5 \times 10^{-7})(1.7 \times 10^{5})}{8.5 \times 10^{-7}} = \dfrac{(3.5)(1.7)}{8.5} \times 10^{(-7)+5-(-7)}$
$= 0.7 \times 10^{5}$
$= 7 \times 10^{-1} \times 10^{5} = 7 \times 10^{4}$

116. $\dfrac{(0.0000000144)(12{,}000)}{600{,}000} = \dfrac{(1.44 \times 10^{-8})(1.2 \times 10^{4})}{6 \times 10^{5}} = \dfrac{(1.44)(1.2)}{6} \times 10^{(-8)+4-5}$
$= 0.288 \times 10^{-9}$
$= 2.88 \times 10^{-1} \times 10^{-9} = 2.88 \times 10^{-10}$

117. $\dfrac{(45{,}000{,}000{,}000)(212{,}000)}{0.00018} = \dfrac{(4.5 \times 10^{10})(2.12 \times 10^{5})}{1.8 \times 10^{-4}} = \dfrac{(4.5)(2.12)}{1.8} \times 10^{10+5-(-4)}$
$= 5.3 \times 10^{19}$

118. $\dfrac{(0.00000000275)(4{,}750)}{500{,}000{,}000{,}000} = \dfrac{(2.75 \times 10^{-9})(4.75 \times 10^{3})}{5 \times 10^{11}} = \dfrac{(2.75)(4.75)}{5} \times 10^{(-9)+3-11}$
$= 2.6125 \times 10^{-17}$

119. $3.31 \times 10^{4}\text{ cm/sec} = \dfrac{3.31 \times 10^{4}\text{ cm}}{1\text{ sec}} \cdot \dfrac{1\text{ m}}{100\text{ cm}} \cdot \dfrac{60\text{ sec}}{1\text{ min}} = \dfrac{(3.31 \times 10^{4})(6 \times 10^{1})}{1 \times 10^{2}}\text{ m/min}$
$= \dfrac{(3.31)(6)}{1} \times 10^{4+1-2}\text{ m/min}$
$= 19.86 \times 10^{3}\text{ m/min}$
$= 1.986 \times 10^{4}\text{ m/min}$

120. $V = lwh = (6{,}000\text{ mm})(9{,}700\text{ mm})(4{,}700\text{ mm}) = \left(6 \times 10^{3}\right)\left(9.7 \times 10^{3}\right)\left(4.7 \times 10^{3}\right)\text{ mm}^{3}$
$= (6)(9.7)(4.7) \times 10^{3+3+3}\text{ mm}^{3}$
$= 273.54 \times 10^{9}\text{ mm}^{3}$
$= 2.7354 \times 10^{11}\text{ mm}^{3}$

121. $\text{mass} = 1{,}000{,}000{,}000(0.00000000000000000000000167248\text{ g})$
$= \left(1 \times 10^{9}\right)\left(1.67248 \times 10^{-24}\text{ g}\right) = 1.67248 \times 10^{-15}\text{ g}$

122. $30{,}000{,}000{,}000 \text{ cm/sec} = \dfrac{30{,}000{,}000{,}000 \text{ cm}}{1 \text{ sec}} \cdot \dfrac{1 \text{ mile}}{160{,}934.4 \text{ cm}} \cdot \dfrac{60 \text{ sec}}{1 \text{ min}} \cdot \dfrac{60 \text{ min}}{1 \text{ hr}}$

$$= \frac{(3 \times 10^{10})(6 \times 10^1)(6 \times 10^1)}{1.609344 \times 10^5} \text{ mile/hr}$$

$$= \frac{(3)(6)(6)}{1.609344} \times 10^{10+1+1-5} \text{ mile/hr}$$

$$\approx 67.11 \times 10^7 \text{ mile/hr} = 6.711 \times 10^8 \text{ mile/hr}$$

123. $x^n x^2 = x^{n+2}$

124. $\dfrac{x^m}{x^3} = x^{m-3}$

125. $\dfrac{x^m x^2}{x^3} = \dfrac{x^{m+2}}{x^3} = x^{m+2-3} = x^{m-1}$

126. $\dfrac{x^{3m+5}}{x^2} = x^{3m+5-2} = x^{3m+3}$

127. $x^{m+1}x^3 = x^{m+1+3} = x^{m+4}$

128. $a^{n-3}a^3 = a^{n-3+3} = a^n$

129. In the expression $-x^4$, the base of the exponent is x, while in the expression $(-x)^4$, the base of the exponent is $-x$.

130. 32×10^2 is not in scientific notation because 32 is not a number between 1 and 10.

131. $(-2, 4) \Rightarrow$ 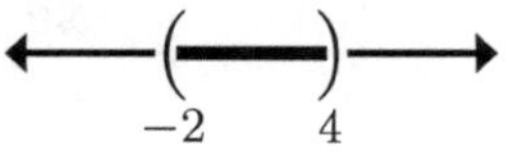

132. $(-\infty, -3] \cup [3, \infty) \Rightarrow$
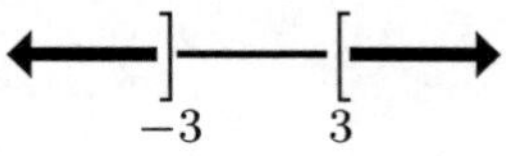

133. Since $\pi - 5 < 0$,
$|\pi - 5| = -(\pi - 5) = -\pi + 5 = 5 - \pi$.

134. distance $= |-7 - (-5)| = |-2| = 2$

Exercise 0.3 (page 36)

1. 0

2. positive

3. not

4. $(6^2)^{1/3}$, $(6^{1/3})^2$

5. $a^{1/n}$

6. $|a|$

7. $\sqrt[n]{ab}$

8. $\dfrac{\sqrt[n]{a}}{\sqrt[n]{b}}$

9. $\neq$

10. $\sqrt[mn]{x}$

11. $9^{1/2} = (3^2)^{1/2} = 3$

12. $8^{1/3} = (2^3)^{1/3} = 2$

13. $\left(\dfrac{1}{25}\right)^{1/2} = \left[\left(\dfrac{1}{5}\right)^2\right]^{1/2} = \dfrac{1}{5}$

14. $\left(\dfrac{16}{625}\right)^{1/4} = \left[\left(\dfrac{2}{5}\right)^4\right]^{1/4} = \dfrac{2}{5}$

15. $-81^{1/4} = -(3^4)^{1/4} = -3$

16. $-\left(\frac{8}{27}\right)^{1/3} = -\left[\left(\frac{2}{3}\right)^3\right]^{1/3} = -\frac{2}{3}$

17. $(10{,}000)^{1/4} = (10^4)^{1/4} = 10$

18. $(1024)^{1/5} = (4^5)^{1/5} = 4$

19. $-64^{1/3} = -(4^3)^{1/3} = -4$

20. $\left(-\frac{27}{8}\right)^{1/3} = \left[\left(-\frac{3}{2}\right)^3\right]^{1/3} = -\frac{3}{2}$

21. $64^{1/3} = (4^3)^{1/3} = 4$

22. $(-125)^{1/3} = \left[(-5)^3\right]^{1/3} = -5$

23. $(16a^2)^{1/2} = \left[(4a)^2\right]^{1/2} = 4|a|$

24. $(25a^4)^{1/2} = \left[(5a^2)^2\right]^{1/2} = 5|a^2| = 5a^2$

25. $(16a^4)^{1/4} = \left[(2a)^4\right]^{1/4} = 2|a|$

26. $(-64a^3)^{1/3} = \left[(-4a)^3\right]^{1/3} = -4a$

27. $(-32a^5)^{1/5} = \left[(-2a)^5\right]^{1/5} = -2a$

28. $(64a^6)^{1/6} = \left[(2a)^6\right]^{1/6} = 2|a|$

29. $(-216b^6)^{1/3} = \left[(-6b^2)^3\right]^{1/3} = -6b^2$

30. $(256t^8)^{1/4} = \left[(4t^2)^4\right]^{1/4} = 4|t^2| = 4t^2$

31. $\left(\frac{16a^4}{25b^2}\right)^{1/2} = \left[\left(\frac{4a^2}{5b}\right)^2\right]^{1/2} = \left|\frac{4a^2}{5b}\right| = \frac{4a^2}{5|b|}$

32. $\left(-\frac{a^5}{32b^{10}}\right)^{1/5} = \left[\left(-\frac{a}{2b^2}\right)^5\right]^{1/5} = -\frac{a}{2b^2}$

33. $\left(-\frac{1{,}000x^6}{27y^3}\right)^{1/3} = \left[\left(-\frac{10x^2}{3y}\right)^3\right]^{1/3} = -\frac{10x^2}{3y}$

34. $\left(\frac{49t^2}{100z^4}\right)^{1/2} = \left[\left(\frac{7t}{10z^2}\right)^2\right]^{1/2} = \left|\frac{7t}{10z^2}\right| = \frac{7|t|}{10z^2}$

35. $4^{3/2} = \left(4^{1/2}\right)^3 = 2^3 = 8$

36. $8^{2/3} = \left(8^{1/3}\right)^2 = 2^2 = 4$

37. $-16^{3/2} = -\left(16^{1/2}\right)^3 = -(4)^3 = -64$

38. $(-8)^{2/3} = \left[(-8)^{1/3}\right]^2 = (-2)^2 = 4$

39. $-1000^{2/3} = -\left(1000^{1/3}\right)^2 = -(10)^2 = -100$

40. $100^{3/2} = \left(100^{1/2}\right)^3 = 10^3 = 1{,}000$

41. $64^{-1/2} = \frac{1}{64^{1/2}} = \frac{1}{8}$

42. $25^{-1/2} = \frac{1}{25^{1/2}} = \frac{1}{5}$

43. $64^{-3/2} = \dfrac{1}{64^{3/2}} = \dfrac{1}{\left(64^{1/2}\right)^3} = \dfrac{1}{8^3} = \dfrac{1}{512}$

44. $49^{-3/2} = \dfrac{1}{49^{3/2}} = \dfrac{1}{\left(49^{1/2}\right)^3} = \dfrac{1}{7^3} = \dfrac{1}{343}$

45. $-9^{-3/2} = -\dfrac{1}{9^{3/2}} = -\dfrac{1}{\left(9^{1/2}\right)^3} = -\dfrac{1}{3^3} = -\dfrac{1}{27}$

46. $(-27)^{-2/3} = \dfrac{1}{(-27)^{2/3}} = \dfrac{1}{\left[(-27)^{1/3}\right]^2} = \dfrac{1}{(-3)^2} = \dfrac{1}{9}$

47. $\left(\dfrac{4}{9}\right)^{5/2} = \left[\left(\dfrac{4}{9}\right)^{1/2}\right]^5 = \left(\dfrac{2}{3}\right)^5 = \dfrac{32}{243}$

48. $\left(\dfrac{25}{81}\right)^{3/2} = \left[\left(\dfrac{25}{81}\right)^{1/2}\right]^3 = \left(\dfrac{5}{9}\right)^3 = \dfrac{125}{729}$

49. $\left(-\dfrac{27}{64}\right)^{-2/3} = \left(-\dfrac{64}{27}\right)^{2/3} = \left[\left(-\dfrac{64}{27}\right)^{1/3}\right]^2 = \left(-\dfrac{4}{3}\right)^2 = \dfrac{16}{9}$

50. $\left(\dfrac{125}{8}\right)^{-4/3} = \left(\dfrac{8}{125}\right)^{4/3} = \left[\left(\dfrac{8}{125}\right)^{1/3}\right]^4 = \left(\dfrac{2}{5}\right)^4 = \dfrac{16}{625}$

51. $\left(100s^4\right)^{1/2} = 100^{1/2}\left(s^4\right)^{1/2} = 10s^2$

52. $\left(64u^6v^3\right)^{1/3} = 64^{1/3}\left(u^6\right)^{1/3}\left(v^3\right)^{1/3} = 4u^2v$

53. $\left(32y^{10}z^5\right)^{-1/5} = \dfrac{1}{\left(32y^{10}z^5\right)^{1/5}} = \dfrac{1}{32^{1/5}\left(y^{10}\right)^{1/5}\left(z^5\right)^{1/5}} = \dfrac{1}{2y^2z}$

54. $\left(625a^4b^8\right)^{-1/4} = \dfrac{1}{\left(625a^4b^8\right)^{1/4}} = \dfrac{1}{625^{1/4}\left(a^4\right)^{1/4}\left(b^8\right)^{1/4}} = \dfrac{1}{5ab^2}$

55. $\left(x^{10}y^5\right)^{3/5} = x^{30/5}y^{15/5} = x^6y^3$

56. $\left(64a^6b^{12}\right)^{5/6} = 64^{5/6}a^{30/6}b^{60/6} = \left(64^{1/6}\right)^5 a^5b^{10} = 2^5a^5b^{10} = 32a^5b^{10}$

57. $\left(r^8s^{16}\right)^{-3/4} = r^{-24/4}s^{-48/4} = r^{-6}s^{-12} = \dfrac{1}{r^6s^{12}}$

58. $\left(-8x^9y^{12}\right)^{-2/3} = (-8)^{-2/3}x^{-18/3}y^{-24/3} = \dfrac{1}{(-8)^{2/3}}x^{-6}y^{-8} = \dfrac{1}{(-2)^2x^6y^8} = \dfrac{1}{4x^6y^8}$

59. $\left(-\dfrac{8a^6}{125b^9}\right)^{2/3} = \dfrac{(-8)^{2/3}a^{12/3}}{125^{2/3}b^{18/3}} = \dfrac{(-2)^2a^4}{5^2b^6} = \dfrac{4a^4}{25b^6}$

60. $\left(\dfrac{16x^4}{625y^8}\right)^{3/4} = \dfrac{16^{3/4}x^{12/4}}{625^{3/4}y^{24/4}} = \dfrac{2^3x^3}{5^3y^3} = \dfrac{8x^3}{125y^6}$

61. $\left(\dfrac{27r^6}{1000s^{12}}\right)^{-2/3}=\left(\dfrac{1000s^{12}}{27r^6}\right)^{2/3}=\dfrac{1000^{2/3}s^{24/3}}{27^{2/3}r^{12/3}}=\dfrac{10^2s^8}{3^2r^4}=\dfrac{100s^8}{9r^4}$

62. $\left(-\dfrac{32m^{10}}{243n^{15}}\right)^{-2/5}=\left(\dfrac{-243n^{15}}{32m^{10}}\right)^{2/5}=\dfrac{(-243)^{2/5}n^{30/5}}{32^{2/5}m^{20/5}}=\dfrac{(-3)^2n^6}{2^2m^4}=\dfrac{9n^6}{4m^4}$

63. $\dfrac{a^{2/5}a^{4/5}}{a^{1/5}}=\dfrac{a^{6/5}}{a^{1/5}}=a^{5/5}=a$

64. $\dfrac{x^{6/7}x^{3/7}}{x^{2/7}x^{5/7}}=\dfrac{x^{9/7}}{x^{7/7}}=x^{2/7}$

65. $\sqrt{49}=\sqrt{7^2}=7$

66. $\sqrt{81}=\sqrt{9^2}=9$

67. $\sqrt[3]{125}=\sqrt[3]{5^3}=5$

68. $\sqrt[3]{-64}=\sqrt[3]{(-4)^3}=-4$

69. $-\sqrt[4]{81}=-\sqrt[4]{3^4}=-3$

70. $\sqrt[5]{-243}=\sqrt[5]{(-3)^5}=-3$

71. $\sqrt[5]{-\dfrac{32}{100{,}000}}=\sqrt[5]{\left(-\dfrac{2}{10}\right)^5}=-\dfrac{2}{10}=-\dfrac{1}{5}$

72. $\sqrt[4]{\dfrac{256}{625}}=\sqrt[4]{\left(\dfrac{4}{5}\right)^4}=\dfrac{4}{5}$

73. $\sqrt{36x^2}=\sqrt{(6x)^2}=|6x|=6|x|$

74. $-\sqrt{25y^2}=-\sqrt{(5y)^2}=-|5y|=-5|y|$

75. $\sqrt{9y^4}=\sqrt{(3y^2)^2}=|3y^2|=3y^2$

76. $\sqrt{a^4b^8}=\sqrt{(a^2b^4)^2}=|a^2b^4|=a^2b^4$

77. $\sqrt[3]{8y^3}=\sqrt[3]{(2y)^3}=2y$

78. $\sqrt[3]{-27z^9}=\sqrt[3]{(-3z^3)^3}=-3z^3$

79. $\sqrt[4]{\dfrac{x^4y^8}{z^{12}}}=\sqrt[4]{\left(\dfrac{xy^2}{z^3}\right)^4}=\left|\dfrac{xy^2}{z^3}\right|=\dfrac{|x|y^2}{|z^3|}$

80. $\sqrt[5]{\dfrac{a^{10}b^5}{c^{15}}}=\sqrt[5]{\left(\dfrac{a^2b}{c^3}\right)^5}=\dfrac{a^2b}{c^3}$

81. $\sqrt{8}-\sqrt{2}=\sqrt{4}\sqrt{2}-\sqrt{2}=2\sqrt{2}-\sqrt{2}=\sqrt{2}$

82. $\sqrt{75}-2\sqrt{27}=\sqrt{25}\sqrt{3}-2\sqrt{9}\sqrt{3}=5\sqrt{3}-2(3)\sqrt{3}=5\sqrt{3}-6\sqrt{3}=-\sqrt{3}$

83. $\sqrt{200x^2}+\sqrt{98x^2}=\sqrt{100x^2}\sqrt{2}+\sqrt{49x^2}\sqrt{2}=10x\sqrt{2}+7x\sqrt{2}=17x\sqrt{2}$

84. $\sqrt{128a^3}-a\sqrt{162a}=\sqrt{64a^2}\sqrt{2a}-a\sqrt{81}\sqrt{2a}=8a\sqrt{2a}-9a\sqrt{2a}=-a\sqrt{2a}$

85. $2\sqrt{48y^5}-3y\sqrt{12y^3}=2\sqrt{16y^4}\sqrt{3y}-3y\sqrt{4y^2}\sqrt{3y}=2\left(4y^2\right)\sqrt{3y}-3y(2y)\sqrt{3y}$
$=8y^2\sqrt{3y}-6y^2\sqrt{3y}=2y^2\sqrt{3y}$

86. $y\sqrt{112y}+4\sqrt{175y^3}=y\sqrt{16}\sqrt{7y}+4\sqrt{25y^2}\sqrt{7y}=y(4)\sqrt{7y}+4(5y)\sqrt{7y}$
$=4y\sqrt{7y}+20y\sqrt{7y}=24y\sqrt{7y}$

87. $2\sqrt[3]{81}+3\sqrt[3]{24}=2\sqrt[3]{27}\sqrt[3]{3}+3\sqrt[3]{8}\sqrt[3]{3}=2(3)\sqrt[3]{3}+3(2)\sqrt[3]{3}=6\sqrt[3]{3}+6\sqrt[3]{3}=12\sqrt[3]{3}$

88. $3\sqrt[4]{32}-2\sqrt[4]{162}=3\sqrt[4]{16}\sqrt[4]{2}-2\sqrt[4]{81}\sqrt[4]{2}=3(2)\sqrt[4]{2}-2(3)\sqrt[4]{2}=6\sqrt[4]{2}-6\sqrt[4]{2}=0$

89. $\sqrt[4]{768z^5}+\sqrt[4]{48z^5}=\sqrt[4]{256z^4}\sqrt[4]{3z}+\sqrt[4]{16z^4}\sqrt[4]{3z}=4z\sqrt[4]{3z}+2z\sqrt[4]{3z}=6z\sqrt[4]{3z}$

90. $$\begin{aligned}-2\sqrt[5]{64y^2}+3\sqrt[5]{486y^2}&=-2\sqrt[5]{32}\sqrt[5]{2y^2}+3\sqrt[5]{243}\sqrt[5]{2y^2}=-2(2)\sqrt[5]{2y^2}+3(3)\sqrt[5]{2y^2}\\&=-4\sqrt[5]{2y^2}+9\sqrt[5]{2y^2}=5\sqrt[5]{2y^2}\end{aligned}$$

91. $$\begin{aligned}\sqrt{8x^2y}-x\sqrt{2y}+\sqrt{50x^2y}&=\sqrt{4x^2}\sqrt{2y}-x\sqrt{2y}+\sqrt{25x^2}\sqrt{2y}\\&=2x\sqrt{2y}-x\sqrt{2y}+5x\sqrt{2y}=6x\sqrt{2y}\end{aligned}$$

92. $$\begin{aligned}3x\sqrt{18x}+2\sqrt{2x^3}-\sqrt{72x^3}&=3x\sqrt{9}\sqrt{2x}+2\sqrt{x^2}\sqrt{2x}-\sqrt{36x^2}\sqrt{2x}\\&=3x(3)\sqrt{2x}+2x\sqrt{2x}-6x\sqrt{2x}\\&=9x\sqrt{2x}+2x\sqrt{2x}-6x\sqrt{2x}=5x\sqrt{2x}\end{aligned}$$

93. $$\begin{aligned}\sqrt[3]{16xy^4}+y\sqrt[3]{2xy}-\sqrt[3]{54xy^4}&=\sqrt[3]{8y^3}\sqrt[3]{2xy}+y\sqrt[3]{2xy}-\sqrt[3]{27y^3}\sqrt[3]{2xy}\\&=2y\sqrt[3]{2xy}+y\sqrt[3]{2xy}-3y\sqrt[3]{2xy}=0\end{aligned}$$

94. $$\begin{aligned}\sqrt[4]{512x^5}-\sqrt[4]{32x^5}+\sqrt[4]{1250x^5}&=\sqrt[4]{256x^4}\sqrt[4]{2x}-\sqrt[4]{16x^4}\sqrt[4]{2x}+\sqrt[4]{625x^4}\sqrt[4]{2x}\\&=4x\sqrt[4]{2x}-2x\sqrt[4]{2x}+5x\sqrt[4]{2x}=7x\sqrt[4]{2x}\end{aligned}$$

95. $\dfrac{3}{\sqrt{3}}=\dfrac{3}{\sqrt{3}}\cdot\dfrac{\sqrt{3}}{\sqrt{3}}=\dfrac{3\sqrt{3}}{3}=\sqrt{3}$

96. $\dfrac{2}{\sqrt{x}}=\dfrac{2}{\sqrt{x}}\cdot\dfrac{\sqrt{x}}{\sqrt{x}}=\dfrac{2\sqrt{x}}{x}$

97. $\dfrac{2}{\sqrt[3]{2}}=\dfrac{2}{\sqrt[3]{2}}\cdot\dfrac{\sqrt[3]{4}}{\sqrt[3]{4}}=\dfrac{2\sqrt[3]{4}}{\sqrt[3]{8}}=\dfrac{2\sqrt[3]{4}}{2}=\sqrt[3]{4}$

98. $\dfrac{5a}{\sqrt[3]{25a}}=\dfrac{5a}{\sqrt[3]{25a}}\cdot\dfrac{\sqrt[3]{5a^2}}{\sqrt[3]{5a^2}}=\dfrac{5a\sqrt[3]{5a^2}}{\sqrt[3]{125a^3}}=\dfrac{5a\sqrt[3]{5a^2}}{5a}=\sqrt[3]{5a^2}$

99. $\dfrac{2b}{\sqrt[4]{3a^2}}=\dfrac{2b}{\sqrt[4]{3a^2}}\cdot\dfrac{\sqrt[4]{27a^2}}{\sqrt[4]{27a^2}}=\dfrac{2b\sqrt[4]{27a^2}}{\sqrt[4]{81a^4}}=\dfrac{2b\sqrt[4]{27a^2}}{3a}$

100. $\sqrt{\dfrac{x}{2y}}=\dfrac{\sqrt{x}}{\sqrt{2y}}=\dfrac{\sqrt{x}}{\sqrt{2y}}\cdot\dfrac{\sqrt{2y}}{\sqrt{2y}}=\dfrac{\sqrt{2xy}}{2y}$

101. $\sqrt[3]{\dfrac{2u^4}{9v}}=\dfrac{\sqrt[3]{2u^4}}{\sqrt[3]{9v}}=\dfrac{\sqrt[3]{u^3}\sqrt[3]{2u}}{\sqrt[3]{9v}}\cdot\dfrac{\sqrt[3]{3v^2}}{\sqrt[3]{3v^2}}=\dfrac{u\sqrt[3]{6uv^2}}{\sqrt[3]{27v^3}}=\dfrac{u\sqrt[3]{6uv^2}}{3v}$

102. $\sqrt[3]{-\dfrac{3s^5}{4r^2}}=\dfrac{\sqrt[3]{-3s^5}}{\sqrt[3]{4r^2}}=\dfrac{\sqrt[3]{-s^3}\sqrt[3]{3s^2}}{\sqrt[3]{4r^2}}\cdot\dfrac{\sqrt[3]{2r}}{\sqrt[3]{2r}}=\dfrac{-s\sqrt[3]{6rs^2}}{\sqrt[3]{8r^3}}=-\dfrac{s\sqrt[3]{6rs^2}}{2r}$

103. $\dfrac{\sqrt{5}}{10} = \dfrac{\sqrt{5}}{10} \cdot \dfrac{\sqrt{5}}{\sqrt{5}} = \dfrac{5}{10\sqrt{5}} = \dfrac{1}{2\sqrt{5}}$

104. $\dfrac{\sqrt{y}}{3} = \dfrac{\sqrt{y}}{3} \cdot \dfrac{\sqrt{y}}{\sqrt{y}} = \dfrac{y}{3\sqrt{y}}$

105. $\dfrac{\sqrt[3]{9}}{3} = \dfrac{\sqrt[3]{9}}{3} \cdot \dfrac{\sqrt[3]{3}}{\sqrt[3]{3}} = \dfrac{\sqrt[3]{27}}{3\sqrt[3]{3}} = \dfrac{3}{3\sqrt[3]{3}} = \dfrac{1}{\sqrt[3]{3}}$

106. $\dfrac{\sqrt[3]{16b^2}}{16} = \dfrac{\sqrt[3]{16b^2}}{16} \cdot \dfrac{\sqrt[3]{4b}}{\sqrt[3]{4b}} = \dfrac{\sqrt[3]{64b^3}}{16\sqrt[3]{4b}} = \dfrac{4b}{16\sqrt[3]{4b}} = \dfrac{b}{4\sqrt[3]{4b}}$

107. $\dfrac{\sqrt[5]{16b^3}}{64a} = \dfrac{\sqrt[5]{16b^3}}{64a} \cdot \dfrac{\sqrt[5]{2b^2}}{\sqrt[5]{2b^2}} = \dfrac{\sqrt[5]{32b^5}}{64a\sqrt[5]{2b^2}} = \dfrac{2b}{64a\sqrt[5]{2b^2}} = \dfrac{b}{32a\sqrt[5]{2b^2}}$

108. $\sqrt{\dfrac{3x}{57}} = \dfrac{\sqrt{3x}}{\sqrt{57}} = \dfrac{\sqrt{3x}}{\sqrt{57}} \cdot \dfrac{\sqrt{3x}}{\sqrt{3x}} = \dfrac{3x}{\sqrt{171x}} = \dfrac{3x}{\sqrt{9}\sqrt{19x}} = \dfrac{3x}{3\sqrt{19x}} = \dfrac{x}{\sqrt{19x}}$

109. $\sqrt{\dfrac{1}{3}} - \sqrt{\dfrac{1}{27}} = \dfrac{\sqrt{1}}{\sqrt{3}} - \dfrac{\sqrt{1}}{\sqrt{27}} = \dfrac{1}{\sqrt{3}} \cdot \dfrac{\sqrt{3}}{\sqrt{3}} - \dfrac{1}{\sqrt{27}} \cdot \dfrac{\sqrt{3}}{\sqrt{3}} = \dfrac{\sqrt{3}}{3} - \dfrac{\sqrt{3}}{\sqrt{81}} = \dfrac{\sqrt{3}}{3} - \dfrac{\sqrt{3}}{9}$

$= \dfrac{3\sqrt{3}}{9} - \dfrac{\sqrt{3}}{9} = \dfrac{2\sqrt{3}}{9}$

110. $\sqrt[3]{\dfrac{1}{2}} + \sqrt[3]{\dfrac{1}{16}} = \dfrac{\sqrt[3]{1}}{\sqrt[3]{2}} + \dfrac{\sqrt[3]{1}}{\sqrt[3]{16}} = \dfrac{1}{\sqrt[3]{2}} \cdot \dfrac{\sqrt[3]{4}}{\sqrt[3]{4}} + \dfrac{1}{\sqrt[3]{16}} \cdot \dfrac{\sqrt[3]{4}}{\sqrt[3]{4}} = \dfrac{\sqrt[3]{4}}{\sqrt[3]{8}} + \dfrac{\sqrt[3]{4}}{\sqrt[3]{64}} = \dfrac{\sqrt[3]{4}}{2} + \dfrac{\sqrt[3]{4}}{4}$

$= \dfrac{2\sqrt[3]{4}}{4} + \dfrac{\sqrt[3]{4}}{4} = \dfrac{3\sqrt[3]{4}}{4}$

111. $\sqrt{\dfrac{x}{8}} - \sqrt{\dfrac{x}{2}} + \sqrt{\dfrac{x}{32}} = \dfrac{\sqrt{x}}{\sqrt{8}} - \dfrac{\sqrt{x}}{\sqrt{2}} + \dfrac{\sqrt{x}}{\sqrt{32}} = \dfrac{\sqrt{x}}{\sqrt{8}} \cdot \dfrac{\sqrt{2}}{\sqrt{2}} - \dfrac{\sqrt{x}}{\sqrt{2}} \cdot \dfrac{\sqrt{2}}{\sqrt{2}} + \dfrac{\sqrt{x}}{\sqrt{32}} \cdot \dfrac{\sqrt{2}}{\sqrt{2}}$

$= \dfrac{\sqrt{2x}}{\sqrt{16}} - \dfrac{\sqrt{2x}}{\sqrt{4}} + \dfrac{\sqrt{2x}}{\sqrt{64}}$

$= \dfrac{\sqrt{2x}}{4} - \dfrac{\sqrt{2x}}{2} + \dfrac{\sqrt{2x}}{8}$

$= \dfrac{2\sqrt{2x}}{8} - \dfrac{4\sqrt{2x}}{8} + \dfrac{\sqrt{2x}}{8} = -\dfrac{\sqrt{2x}}{8}$

112. $\sqrt[3]{\frac{y}{4}} + \sqrt[3]{\frac{y}{32}} - \sqrt[3]{\frac{y}{500}} = \frac{\sqrt[3]{y}}{\sqrt[3]{4}} + \frac{\sqrt[3]{y}}{\sqrt[3]{32}} - \frac{\sqrt[3]{y}}{\sqrt[3]{500}} = \frac{\sqrt[3]{y}}{\sqrt[3]{4}} \cdot \frac{\sqrt[3]{2}}{\sqrt[3]{2}} + \frac{\sqrt[3]{y}}{\sqrt[3]{32}} \cdot \frac{\sqrt[3]{2}}{\sqrt[3]{2}} - \frac{\sqrt[3]{y}}{\sqrt[3]{500}} \cdot \frac{\sqrt[3]{2}}{\sqrt[3]{2}}$

$$= \frac{\sqrt[3]{2y}}{\sqrt[3]{8}} + \frac{\sqrt[3]{2y}}{\sqrt[3]{64}} - \frac{\sqrt[3]{2y}}{\sqrt[3]{1{,}000}}$$

$$= \frac{\sqrt[3]{2y}}{2} + \frac{\sqrt[3]{2y}}{4} - \frac{\sqrt[3]{2y}}{10}$$

$$= \frac{10\sqrt[3]{2y}}{20} + \frac{5\sqrt[3]{2y}}{20} - \frac{2\sqrt[3]{2y}}{20} = \frac{13\sqrt[3]{2y}}{20}$$

113. $\sqrt[4]{9} = 9^{1/4} = (3^2)^{1/4} = 3^{2/4} = 3^{1/2} = \sqrt{3}$

114. $\sqrt[6]{27} = 27^{1/6} = (3^3)^{1/6} = 3^{3/6} = 3^{1/2} = \sqrt{3}$

115. $\sqrt[10]{16x^6} = (16x^6)^{1/10} = (2^4x^6)^{1/10} = 2^{4/10}x^{6/10} = 2^{2/5}x^{3/5} = (2^2x^3)^{1/5} = \sqrt[5]{4x^3}$

116. $\sqrt[6]{27x^9} = (27x^9)^{1/6} = (3^3x^9)^{1/6} = 3^{3/6}x^{9/6} = 3^{1/2}x^{3/2} = (3x^3)^{1/2} = \sqrt{3x^3} = x\sqrt{3x}$

117. $\sqrt{2}\sqrt[3]{2} = 2^{1/2} \cdot 2^{1/3} = 2^{3/6} \cdot 2^{2/6} = \sqrt[6]{2^3}\sqrt[6]{2^2} = \sqrt[6]{8}\sqrt[6]{4} = \sqrt[6]{32}$

118. $\sqrt{3}\sqrt[3]{5} = 3^{1/2}5^{1/3} = 3^{3/6}5^{2/6} = \sqrt[6]{3^3}\sqrt[6]{5^2} = \sqrt[6]{27}\sqrt[6]{25} = \sqrt[6]{675}$

119. $\frac{\sqrt[4]{3}}{\sqrt{2}} = \frac{3^{1/4}}{2^{1/2}} = \frac{3^{1/4}}{2^{2/4}} = \frac{\sqrt[4]{3}}{\sqrt[4]{2^2}} = \frac{\sqrt[4]{3}}{\sqrt[4]{4}} = \frac{\sqrt[4]{3}}{\sqrt[4]{4}} \cdot \frac{\sqrt[4]{4}}{\sqrt[4]{4}} = \frac{\sqrt[4]{12}}{\sqrt[4]{16}} = \frac{\sqrt[4]{12}}{2}$

120. $\frac{\sqrt[3]{2}}{\sqrt{5}} = \frac{2^{1/3}}{5^{1/2}} = \frac{2^{2/6}}{5^{3/6}} = \frac{\sqrt[6]{2^2}}{\sqrt[6]{5^3}} = \frac{\sqrt[6]{4}}{\sqrt[6]{125}} = \frac{\sqrt[6]{4}}{\sqrt[6]{125}} \cdot \frac{\sqrt[6]{125}}{\sqrt[6]{125}} = \frac{\sqrt[6]{500}}{\sqrt[6]{15{,}625}} = \frac{\sqrt[6]{500}}{5}$

121. $\sqrt[4]{x^4} = |x|$. Since $|x| = x$ if $x \geq 0$, then $\sqrt[4]{x^4} = x$ if $x \geq 0$.

122. $\sqrt[n]{\frac{x}{y}} = \left(\frac{x}{y}\right)^{1/n} = \frac{x^{1/n}}{y^{1/n}} = \frac{\sqrt[n]{x}}{\sqrt[n]{y}}$

123. $\left(\frac{x}{y}\right)^{-m/n} = \frac{x^{-m/n}}{y^{-m/n}} = \frac{x^{-m/n}}{y^{-m/n}} \cdot \frac{x^{m/n}y^{m/n}}{x^{m/n}y^{m/n}} = \frac{y^{m/n}}{x^{m/n}} = \frac{(y^m)^{1/n}}{(x^m)^{1/n}} = \left(\frac{y^m}{x^m}\right)^{1/n} = \sqrt[n]{\frac{y^m}{x^m}}$

124. Consider the case when n is even, m is odd and x is negative. Then $x^{m/n} = \left(x^{1/n}\right)^m = \left(\sqrt[n]{x}\right)^m$. Thus, $\sqrt[n]{x}$ must be a real number for the expression to be defined.

125. $-2 < x \leq 5 \Rightarrow (-2, 5]$

126. If $x > 4$, then $3 - x < 0$. Then $|3 - x| = -(3 - x) = -3 + x = x - 3$.

127. $x^2 - y^2 = (-2)^2 - 3^2 = 4 - 9 = -5$

128. $\frac{xy+4y}{x} = \frac{-2(3)+4(3)}{-2} = \frac{-6+12}{-2} = \frac{6}{-2} = -3$

129. $617{,}000{,}000 = 6.17 \times 10^8$

130. $0.00235 \times 10^4 = 23.5$

Exercise 0.4 (page 47)

1. monomial, variables

2. degree, variables

3. trinomial

4. binomial

5. one

6. zero

7. like

8. degree

9. coefficients, variables

10. $3\sqrt{x}-2$

11. yes, trinomial, 2nd degree

12. yes, binomial, 3rd degree

13. no

14. no

15. yes, binomial, 3rd degree

16. yes, monomial, 5th degree

17. yes, monomial, 0th degree

18. no

19. yes, monomial, no degree

20. yes, none, 3rd degree

21. $(x^3-3x^2)+(5x^3-8x) = x^3-3x^2+5x^3-8x = x^3+5x^3-3x^2-8x = 6x^3-3x^2-8x$

22.
$$\begin{aligned}(2x^4-5x^3)+(7x^3-x^4+2x) &= 2x^4-5x^3+7x^3-x^4+2x\\ &= 2x^4-x^4-5x^3+7x^3+2x = x^4+2x^3+2x\end{aligned}$$

23.
$$\begin{aligned}(y^5+2y^3+7)-(y^5-2y^3-7) &= y^5+2y^3+7-y^5+2y^3+7\\ &= y^5-y^5+2y^3+2y^3+7+7 = 4y^3+14\end{aligned}$$

24.
$$\begin{aligned}(3t^7-7t^3+3)-(7t^7-3t^3+7) &= 3t^7-7t^3+3-7t^7+3t^3-7\\ &= 3t^7-7t^7-7t^3+3t^3+3-7 = -4t^7-4t^3-4\end{aligned}$$

25.
$$\begin{aligned}2(x^2+3x-1)-3(x^2+2x-4)+4 &= 2(x^2)+2(3x)+2(-1)-3(x^2)-3(2x)-3(-4)+4\\ &= 2x^2+6x-2-3x^2-6x+12+4\\ &= 2x^2-3x^2+6x-6x-2+12+4 = -x^2+14\end{aligned}$$

26.
$$\begin{aligned}5(x^3-8x+3)+2(3x^2+5x)-7 &= 5(x^3)+5(-8x)+5(3)+2(3x^2)+2(5x)-7\\ &= 5x^3-40x+15+6x^2+10x-7\\ &= 5x^3+6x^2-40x+10x+15-7 = 5x^3+6x^2-30x+8\end{aligned}$$

27.
$$\begin{aligned}&8(t^2-2t+5)+4(t^2-3t+2)-6(2t^2-8)\\ &\quad= 8(t^2)+8(-2t)+8(5)+4(t^2)+4(-3t)+4(2)-6(2t^2)-6(-8)\\ &\quad= 8t^2-16t+40+4t^2-12t+8-12t^2+48\\ &\quad= 8t^2+4t^2-12t^2-16t-12t+40+8+48 = -28t+96\end{aligned}$$

28. $$-3(x^3-x)+2(x^2+x)+3(x^3-2x) = -3(x^3)-3(-x)+2(x^2)+2(x)+3(x^3)+3(-2x)$$
$$= -3x^3+3x+2x^2+2x+3x^3-6x$$
$$= -3x^3+3x^3+2x^2+3x+2x-6x = 2x^2-x$$

29. $$y(y^2-1)-y^2(y+2)-y(2y-2) = y(y^2)+y(-1)-y^2(y)-y^2(2)-y(2y)-y(-2)$$
$$= y^3-y-y^3-2y^2-2y^2+2y$$
$$= y^3-y^3-2y^2-2y^2-y+2y = -4y^2+y$$

30. $$-4a^2(a+1)+3a(a^2-4)-a^2(a+2)$$
$$= -4a^2(a)-4a^2(1)+3a(a^2)+3a(-4)-a^2(a)-a^2(2)$$
$$= -4a^3-4a^2+3a^3-12a-a^3-2a^2$$
$$= -4a^3+3a^3-a^3-4a^2-2a^2-12a = -2a^3-6a^2-12a$$

31. $$xy(x-4y)-y(x^2+3xy)+xy(2x+3y)$$
$$= xy(x)+xy(-4y)-y(x^2)-y(3xy)+xy(2x)+xy(3y)$$
$$= x^2y-4xy^2-x^2y-3xy^2+2x^2y+3xy^2$$
$$= x^2y-x^2y+2x^2y-4xy^2-3xy^2+3xy^2 = 2x^2y-4xy^2$$

32. $$3mn(m+2n)-6m(3mn+1)-2n(4mn-1)$$
$$= 3mn(m)+3mn(2n)-6m(3mn)-6m(1)-2n(4mn)-2n(-1)$$
$$= 3m^2n+6mn^2-18m^2n-6m-8mn^2+2n$$
$$= 3m^2n-18m^2n+6mn^2-8mn^2-6m+2n = -15m^2n-2mn^2-6m+2n$$

33. $$2x^2y^3(4xy^4) = 2(4)x^2xy^3y^4 = 8x^3y^7$$

34. $$-15a^3b(-2a^2b^3) = -15(-2)a^3a^2bb^3$$
$$= 30a^5b^4$$

35. $$-3m^2n(2mn^2)\left(-\frac{mn}{12}\right) = (-3)(2)\left(-\frac{1}{12}\right)m^2mmnn^2n = \frac{6}{12}m^4n^4 = \frac{m^4n^4}{2}$$

36. $$-\frac{3r^2s^3}{5}\left(\frac{2r^2s}{3}\right)\left(\frac{15rs^2}{2}\right) = \left(-\frac{3}{5}\right)\left(\frac{2}{3}\right)\left(\frac{15}{2}\right)r^2r^2rs^3ss^2 = -3r^5s^6$$

37. $$-4rs(r^2+s^2) = -4rs(r^2)-4rs(s^2) = -4r^3s-4rs^3$$

38. $$6u^2v(2uv^3-y) = 6u^2v(2uv^3)+6u^2v(-y) = 12u^3v^4-6u^2vy$$

39. $$6ab^2c(2ac+3bc^2-4ab^2c) = 6ab^2c(2ac)+6ab^2c(3bc^2)+6ab^2c(-4ab^2c)$$
$$= 12a^2b^2c^2+18ab^3c^3-24a^2b^4c^2$$

40. $$-\frac{mn^2}{2}(4mn-6m^2-8) = -\frac{mn^2}{2}(4mn)-\frac{mn^2}{2}(-6m^2)-\frac{mn^2}{2}(-8)$$
$$= -2m^2n^3+3m^3n^2+4mn^2$$

41. $(a+2)(a+2) = a^2 + 2a + 2a + 4$
$= a^2 + 4a + 4$

42. $(y-5)(y-5) = y^2 - 5y - 5y + 25$
$= y^2 - 10y + 25$

43. $(a-6)^2 = (a-6)(a-6)$
$= a^2 - 6a - 6a + 36$
$= a^2 - 12a + 36$

44. $(t+9)^2 = (t+9)(t+9)$
$= t^2 + 9t + 9t + 81$
$= t^2 + 18t + 81$

45. $(x+4)(x-4) = x^2 - 4x + 4x - 16$
$= x^2 - 16$

46. $(z+7)(z-7) = z^2 - 7z + 7z - 49$
$= z^2 - 49$

47. $(x-3)(x+5) = x^2 + 5x - 3x - 15$
$= x^2 + 2x - 15$

48. $(z+4)(z-6) = z^2 - 6z + 4z - 24$
$= z^2 - 2z - 24$

49. $(u+2)(3u-2) = 3u^2 - 2u + 6u - 4$
$= 3u^2 + 4u - 4$

50. $(4x+1)(2x-3) = 8x^2 - 12x + 2x - 3$
$= 8x^2 - 10x - 3$

51. $(5x-1)(2x+3) = 10x^2 + 15x - 2x - 3$
$= 10x^2 + 13x - 3$

52. $(4x-1)(2x-7) = 8x^2 - 28x - 2x + 7$
$= 8x^2 - 30x + 7$

53. $(3a-2b)^2 = (3a-2b)(3a-2b) = 9a^2 - 6ab - 6ab + 4b^2 = 9a^2 - 12ab + 4b^2$

54. $(4a+5b)(4a-5b) = 16a^2 - 20ab + 20ab - 25b^2 = 16a^2 - 25b^2$

55. $(3m+4n)(3m-4n) = 9m^2 - 12mn + 12mn - 16n^2 = 9m^2 - 16n^2$

56. $(4r+3s)^2 = (4r+3s)(4r+3s) = 16r^2 + 12rs + 12rs + 9s^2 = 16r^2 + 24rs + 9s^2$

57. $(2y-4x)(3y-2x) = 6y^2 - 4xy - 12xy + 8x^2 = 6y^2 - 16xy + 8x^2$

58. $(-2x+3y)(3x+y) = -6x^2 - 2xy + 9xy + 3y^2 = -6x^2 + 7xy + 3y^2$

59. $(9x-y)(x^2-3y) = 9x^3 - 27xy - x^2y + 3y^2$

60. $(8a^2+b)(a+2b) = 8a^3 + 16a^2b + ab + 2b^2$

61. $(5z+2t)(z^2-t) = 5z^3 - 5tz + 2tz^2 - 2t^2$

62. $(y-2x^2)(x^2+3y) = x^2y + 3y^2 - 2x^4 - 6x^2y = -2x^4 - 5x^2y + 3y^2$

63. $(3x-1)^3 = (3x-1)(3x-1)(3x-1)$
$= \left(9x^2 - 3x - 3x + 1\right)(3x-1)$
$= \left(9x^2 - 6x + 1\right)(3x-1)$
$= 9x^2(3x) + 9x^2(-1) - 6x(3x) - 6x(-1) + 1(3x) + 1(-1)$
$= 27x^3 - 9x^2 - 18x^2 + 6x + 3x - 1 = 27x^3 - 27x^2 + 9x - 1$

64. $$\begin{aligned}(2x-3)^3 &= (2x-3)(2x-3)(2x-3)\\ &= \left(4x^2-6x-6x+9\right)(2x-3)\\ &= \left(4x^2-12x+9\right)(2x-3)\\ &= 4x^2(2x)+4x^2(-3)-12x(2x)-12x(-3)+9(2x)+9(-3)\\ &= 8x^3-12x^2-24x^2+36x+18x-27 = 8x^3-36x^2+54x-27\end{aligned}$$

65. $$\begin{aligned}(3x+1)\left(2x^2+4x-3\right) &= 3x\left(2x^2\right)+3x(4x)+3x(-3)+1\left(2x^2\right)+1(4x)+1(-3)\\ &= 6x^3+12x^2-9x+2x^2+4x-3 = 6x^3+14x^2-5x-3\end{aligned}$$

66. $$\begin{aligned}(2x-5)\left(x^2-3x+2\right) &= 2x\left(x^2\right)+2x(-3x)+2x(2)-5\left(x^2\right)-5(-3x)-5(2)\\ &= 2x^3-6x^2+4x-5x^2+15x-10 = 2x^3-11x^2+19x-10\end{aligned}$$

67. $$\begin{aligned}&(3x+2y)\left(2x^2-3xy+4y^2\right)\\ &\quad= 3x\left(2x^2\right)+3x(-3xy)+3x\left(4y^2\right)+2y\left(2x^2\right)+2y(-3xy)+2y\left(4y^2\right)\\ &\quad= 6x^3-9x^2y+12xy^2+4x^2y-6xy^2+8y^3 = 6x^3-5x^2y+6xy^2+8y^3\end{aligned}$$

68. $$\begin{aligned}&(4r-3s)\left(2r^2+4rs-2s^2\right)\\ &\quad= 4r\left(2r^2\right)+4r(4rs)+4r\left(-2s^2\right)-3s\left(2r^2\right)-3s(4rs)-3s\left(-2s^2\right)\\ &\quad= 8r^3+16r^2s-8rs^2-6r^2s-12rs^2+6s^3 = 8r^3+10r^2s-20rs^2+6s^3\end{aligned}$$

69. $2y^n(3y^n+y^{-n}) = 2y^n(3y^n)+2y^n(y^{-n}) = 6y^{n+n}+2y^{n+(-n)} = 6y^{2n}+2y^0 = 6y^{2n}+2$

70. $$\begin{aligned}3a^{-n}\left(2a^n+3a^{n-1}\right) = 3a^{-n}(2a^n)+3a^{-n}\left(3a^{n-1}\right) = 6a^{-n+n}+9a^{-n+n-1} &= 6a^0+9a^{-1}\\ &= 6+\frac{9}{a}\end{aligned}$$

71. $$\begin{aligned}-5x^{2n}y^n\left(2x^{2n}y^{-n}+3x^{-2n}y^n\right) &= -5x^{2n}y^n\left(2x^{2n}y^{-n}\right)-5x^{2n}y^n\left(3x^{-2n}y^n\right)\\ &= -10x^{2n+2n}y^{n+(-n)}-15x^{2n+(-2n)}y^{n+n}\\ &= -10x^{4n}y^0-15x^0y^{2n} = -10x^{4n}-15y^{2n}\end{aligned}$$

72. $$\begin{aligned}-2a^{3n}b^{2n}\left(5a^{-3n}b-ab^{-2n}\right) &= -2a^{3n}b^{2n}\left(5a^{-3n}b\right)-2a^{3n}b^{2n}\left(-ab^{-2n}\right)\\ &= -10a^{3n+(-3n)}b^{2n+1}+2a^{3n+1}b^{2n+(-2n)}\\ &= -10a^0b^{2n+1}+2a^{3n+1}b^0 = -10b^{2n+1}+2a^{3n+1}\end{aligned}$$

73. $(x^n+3)(x^n-4) = x^nx^n-4x^n+3x^n-12 = x^{2n}-x^n-12$

74. $(a^n-5)(a^n-3) = a^na^n-3a^n-5a^n+15 = a^{2n}-8a^n+15$

75. $$\begin{aligned}(2r^n-7)(3r^n-2) &= 2r^n(3r^n)-2r^n(2)-7(3r^n)+14\\ &= 6r^{2n}-4r^n-21r^n+14 = 6r^{2n}-25r^n+14\end{aligned}$$

76. $(4z^n+3)(3z^n+1) = 4z^n(3z^n)+4z^n(1)+3(3z^n)+3$
$= 12z^{2n}+4z^n+9z^n+3 = 12z^{2n}+13z^n+3$

77. $x^{1/2}\left(x^{1/2}y+xy^{1/2}\right) = x^{1/2}x^{1/2}y+x^{1/2}xy^{1/2} = x^{2/2}y+x^{3/2}y^{1/2} = xy+x^{3/2}y^{1/2}$

78. $ab^{1/2}\left(a^{1/2}b^{1/2}+b^{1/2}\right) = ab^{1/2}a^{1/2}b^{1/2}+ab^{1/2}b^{1/2} = a^{3/2}b^{2/2}+ab^{2/2} = a^{3/2}b+ab$

79. $\left(a^{1/2}+b^{1/2}\right)\left(a^{1/2}-b^{1/2}\right) = a^{1/2}a^{1/2}-a^{1/2}b^{1/2}+a^{1/2}b^{1/2}-b^{1/2}b^{1/2}$
$= a^{2/2}-b^{2/2} = a-b$

80. $\left(x^{3/2}+y^{1/2}\right)^2 = \left(x^{3/2}+y^{1/2}\right)\left(x^{3/2}+y^{1/2}\right) = x^{3/2}x^{3/2}+x^{3/2}y^{1/2}+x^{3/2}y^{1/2}+y^{1/2}y^{1/2}$
$= x^{6/2}+2x^{3/2}y^{1/2}+y^{2/2}$
$= x^3+2x^{3/2}y^{1/2}+y$

81. $\dfrac{2}{\sqrt{3}-1} = \dfrac{2}{\sqrt{3}-1}\cdot\dfrac{\sqrt{3}+1}{\sqrt{3}+1} = \dfrac{2\left(\sqrt{3}+1\right)}{\left(\sqrt{3}\right)^2-1^2} = \dfrac{2\left(\sqrt{3}+1\right)}{3-1} = \dfrac{2\left(\sqrt{3}+1\right)}{2} = \sqrt{3}+1$

82. $\dfrac{1}{\sqrt{5}+2} = \dfrac{1}{\sqrt{5}+2}\cdot\dfrac{\sqrt{5}-2}{\sqrt{5}-2} = \dfrac{1\left(\sqrt{5}-2\right)}{\left(\sqrt{5}\right)^2-2^2} = \dfrac{\sqrt{5}-2}{5-4} = \dfrac{\sqrt{5}-2}{1} = \sqrt{5}-2$

83. $\dfrac{3x}{\sqrt{7}+2} = \dfrac{3x}{\sqrt{7}+2}\cdot\dfrac{\sqrt{7}-2}{\sqrt{7}-2} = \dfrac{3x\left(\sqrt{7}-2\right)}{\left(\sqrt{7}\right)^2-2^2} = \dfrac{3x\left(\sqrt{7}-2\right)}{7-4} = \dfrac{3x\left(\sqrt{7}-2\right)}{3} = x\left(\sqrt{7}-2\right)$

84. $\dfrac{14y}{\sqrt{2}-3} = \dfrac{14y}{\sqrt{2}-3}\cdot\dfrac{\sqrt{2}+3}{\sqrt{2}+3} = \dfrac{14y\left(\sqrt{2}+3\right)}{\left(\sqrt{2}\right)^2-3^2} = \dfrac{14y\left(\sqrt{2}+3\right)}{2-9} = -2y\left(\sqrt{2}+3\right)$

85. $\dfrac{x}{x-\sqrt{3}} = \dfrac{x}{x-\sqrt{3}}\cdot\dfrac{x+\sqrt{3}}{x+\sqrt{3}} = \dfrac{x\left(x+\sqrt{3}\right)}{x^2-\left(\sqrt{3}\right)^2} = \dfrac{x\left(x+\sqrt{3}\right)}{x^2-3}$

86. $\dfrac{y}{2y+\sqrt{7}} = \dfrac{y}{2y+\sqrt{7}}\cdot\dfrac{2y-\sqrt{7}}{2y-\sqrt{7}} = \dfrac{y\left(2y-\sqrt{7}\right)}{(2y)^2-\left(\sqrt{7}\right)^2} = \dfrac{y\left(2y-\sqrt{7}\right)}{4y^2-7}$

87. $\dfrac{y+\sqrt{2}}{y-\sqrt{2}} = \dfrac{y+\sqrt{2}}{y-\sqrt{2}}\cdot\dfrac{y+\sqrt{2}}{y+\sqrt{2}} = \dfrac{\left(y+\sqrt{2}\right)\left(y+\sqrt{2}\right)}{y^2-\left(\sqrt{2}\right)^2} = \dfrac{y^2+2y\sqrt{2}+2}{y^2-2}$

88. $\dfrac{x-\sqrt{3}}{x+\sqrt{3}}=\dfrac{x-\sqrt{3}}{x+\sqrt{3}}\cdot\dfrac{x-\sqrt{3}}{x-\sqrt{3}}=\dfrac{\left(x-\sqrt{3}\right)\left(x-\sqrt{3}\right)}{x^2-\left(\sqrt{3}\right)^2}=\dfrac{x^2-2x\sqrt{3}+3}{x^2-3}$

89. $\dfrac{\sqrt{2}-\sqrt{3}}{1-\sqrt{3}}=\dfrac{\sqrt{2}-\sqrt{3}}{1-\sqrt{3}}\cdot\dfrac{1+\sqrt{3}}{1+\sqrt{3}}=\dfrac{\sqrt{2}+\sqrt{6}-\sqrt{3}-\left(\sqrt{3}\right)^2}{1^2-\left(\sqrt{3}\right)^2}=\dfrac{\sqrt{2}+\sqrt{6}-\sqrt{3}-3}{1-3}$

$=\dfrac{\sqrt{2}+\sqrt{6}-\sqrt{3}-3}{-2}$

$=\dfrac{-\left(\sqrt{2}+\sqrt{6}-\sqrt{3}-3\right)}{2}$

$=\dfrac{\sqrt{3}+3-\sqrt{2}-\sqrt{6}}{2}$

90. $\dfrac{\sqrt{3}-\sqrt{2}}{1+\sqrt{2}}=\dfrac{\sqrt{3}-\sqrt{2}}{1+\sqrt{2}}\cdot\dfrac{1-\sqrt{2}}{1-\sqrt{2}}=\dfrac{\sqrt{3}-\sqrt{6}-\sqrt{2}+\left(\sqrt{2}\right)^2}{1^2-\left(\sqrt{2}\right)^2}=\dfrac{\sqrt{3}-\sqrt{6}-\sqrt{2}+2}{1-2}$

$=\dfrac{\sqrt{3}-\sqrt{6}-\sqrt{2}+2}{-1}$

$=-\left(\sqrt{3}-\sqrt{6}-\sqrt{2}+2\right)$

$=\sqrt{6}+\sqrt{2}-\sqrt{3}-2$

91. $\dfrac{\sqrt{x}-\sqrt{y}}{\sqrt{x}+\sqrt{y}}=\dfrac{\sqrt{x}-\sqrt{y}}{\sqrt{x}+\sqrt{y}}\cdot\dfrac{\sqrt{x}-\sqrt{y}}{\sqrt{x}-\sqrt{y}}=\dfrac{\sqrt{x^2}-\sqrt{xy}-\sqrt{xy}+\sqrt{y^2}}{\left(\sqrt{x}\right)^2-\left(\sqrt{y}\right)^2}=\dfrac{x-2\sqrt{xy}+y}{x-y}$

92. $\dfrac{\sqrt{2x}+y}{\sqrt{2x}-y}=\dfrac{\sqrt{2x}+y}{\sqrt{2x}-y}\cdot\dfrac{\sqrt{2x}+y}{\sqrt{2x}+y}=\dfrac{\sqrt{4x^2}+y\sqrt{2x}+y\sqrt{2x}+y^2}{\left(\sqrt{2x}\right)^2-y^2}=\dfrac{2x+2y\sqrt{2x}+y^2}{2x-y^2}$

93. $\dfrac{\sqrt{2}+1}{2}=\dfrac{\sqrt{2}+1}{2}\cdot\dfrac{\sqrt{2}-1}{\sqrt{2}-1}=\dfrac{\left(\sqrt{2}\right)^2-1^2}{2\left(\sqrt{2}-1\right)}=\dfrac{2-1}{2\left(\sqrt{2}-1\right)}=\dfrac{1}{2\left(\sqrt{2}-1\right)}$

94. $\dfrac{\sqrt{x}-3}{3}=\dfrac{\sqrt{x}-3}{3}\cdot\dfrac{\sqrt{x}+3}{\sqrt{x}+3}=\dfrac{\left(\sqrt{x}\right)^2-3^2}{3\left(\sqrt{x}+3\right)}=\dfrac{x-9}{3\left(\sqrt{x}+3\right)}$

95. $\dfrac{y-\sqrt{3}}{y+\sqrt{3}}=\dfrac{y-\sqrt{3}}{y+\sqrt{3}}\cdot\dfrac{y+\sqrt{3}}{y+\sqrt{3}}=\dfrac{y^2-\left(\sqrt{3}\right)^2}{y^2+y\sqrt{3}+y\sqrt{3}+\sqrt{9}}=\dfrac{y^2-3}{y^2+2y\sqrt{3}+3}$

96. $$\frac{\sqrt{a}-\sqrt{b}}{\sqrt{a}+\sqrt{b}} = \frac{\sqrt{a}-\sqrt{b}}{\sqrt{a}+\sqrt{b}} \cdot \frac{\sqrt{a}+\sqrt{b}}{\sqrt{a}+\sqrt{b}} = \frac{\left(\sqrt{a}\right)^2-\left(\sqrt{b}\right)^2}{\sqrt{a^2}+\sqrt{ab}+\sqrt{ab}+\sqrt{b^2}} = \frac{a-b}{a+2\sqrt{ab}+b}$$

97. $$\frac{\sqrt{x+3}-\sqrt{x}}{3} = \frac{\sqrt{x+3}-\sqrt{x}}{3} \cdot \frac{\sqrt{x+3}+\sqrt{x}}{\sqrt{x+3}+\sqrt{x}} = \frac{\left(\sqrt{x+3}\right)^2-\left(\sqrt{x}\right)^2}{3\left(\sqrt{x+3}+\sqrt{x}\right)}$$
$$= \frac{x+3-x}{3\left(\sqrt{x+3}+\sqrt{x}\right)}$$
$$= \frac{3}{3\left(\sqrt{x+3}+\sqrt{x}\right)} = \frac{1}{\sqrt{x+3}+\sqrt{x}}$$

98. $$\frac{\sqrt{2+h}-\sqrt{2}}{h} = \frac{\sqrt{2+h}-\sqrt{2}}{h} \cdot \frac{\sqrt{2+h}+\sqrt{2}}{\sqrt{2+h}+\sqrt{2}} = \frac{\left(\sqrt{2+h}\right)^2-\left(\sqrt{2}\right)^2}{h\left(\sqrt{2+h}+\sqrt{2}\right)}$$
$$= \frac{2+h-2}{h\left(\sqrt{2+h}+\sqrt{2}\right)}$$
$$= \frac{h}{h\left(\sqrt{2+h}+\sqrt{2}\right)} = \frac{1}{\sqrt{2+h}+\sqrt{2}}$$

99. $$\frac{36a^2b^3}{18ab^6} = 2a^{2-1}b^{3-6} = 2a^1b^{-3} = \frac{2a}{b^3}$$

100. $$\frac{-45r^2s^5t^3}{27r^6s^2t^8} = -\frac{5}{3}r^{2-6}s^{5-2}t^{3-8} = -\frac{5}{3}r^{-4}s^3t^{-5} = -\frac{5s^3}{3r^4t^5}$$

101. $$\frac{16x^6y^4z^9}{-24x^9y^6z^0} = -\frac{2}{3}x^{6-9}y^{4-6}z^{9-0} = -\frac{2}{3}x^{-3}y^{-2}z^9 = -\frac{2z^9}{3x^3y^2}$$

102. $$\frac{32m^6n^4p^2}{26m^6n^7p^2} = \frac{16}{13}m^{6-6}n^{4-7}p^{2-2} = \frac{16}{13}m^0n^{-3}p^0 = \frac{16}{13n^3}$$

103. $$\frac{5x^3y^2+15x^3y^4}{10x^2y^3} = \frac{5x^3y^2}{10x^2y^3} + \frac{15x^3y^4}{10x^2y^3}$$
$$= \frac{x}{2y} + \frac{3xy}{2}$$

104. $$\frac{9m^4n^9-6m^3n^4}{12m^3n^3} = \frac{9m^4n^9}{12m^3n^3} - \frac{6m^3n^4}{12m^3n^3}$$
$$= \frac{3mn^6}{4} - \frac{n}{2}$$

105. $$\frac{24x^5y^7-36x^2y^5+12xy}{60x^5y^4} = \frac{24x^5y^7}{60x^5y^4} - \frac{36x^2y^5}{60x^5y^4} + \frac{12xy}{60x^5y^4} = \frac{2y^3}{5} - \frac{3y}{5x^3} + \frac{1}{5x^4y^3}$$

106. $$\frac{9a^3b^4+27a^2b^4-18a^2b^3}{18a^2b^7} = \frac{9a^3b^4}{18a^2b^7} + \frac{27a^2b^4}{18a^2b^7} - \frac{18a^2b^3}{18a^2b^7} = \frac{a}{2b^3} + \frac{3}{2b^3} - \frac{1}{b^4}$$

107.

$$\begin{array}{r|l} & 3x+2 \\ \hline x+3 & 3x^2+11x+6 \\ & \underline{3x^2+9x} \\ & \qquad 2x+6 \\ & \qquad \underline{2x+6} \\ & \qquad\qquad 0 \end{array}$$

108.

$$\begin{array}{r|l} & x+3 \\ \hline 3x+2 & 3x^2+11x+6 \\ & \underline{3x^2+2x} \\ & \qquad 9x+6 \\ & \qquad \underline{9x+6} \\ & \qquad\qquad 0 \end{array}$$

109.

$$\begin{array}{r|l} & x-7+\frac{2}{2x-5} \\ \hline 2x-5 & 2x^2-19x+37 \\ & \underline{2x^2-5x} \\ & \quad -14x+37 \\ & \quad \underline{-14x+35} \\ & \qquad\qquad 2 \end{array}$$

110.

$$\begin{array}{r|l} & 2x-5 \\ \hline x-7 & 2x^2-19x+35 \\ & \underline{2x^2-14x} \\ & \quad -5x+35 \\ & \quad \underline{-5x+35} \\ & \qquad\qquad 0 \end{array}$$

111.

$$\begin{array}{r|l} & x-3 \\ \hline x^2+x-1 & x^3-2x^2-4x+3 \\ & \underline{x^3+x^2-x} \\ & \quad -3x^2-3x+3 \\ & \quad \underline{-3x^2-3x+3} \\ & \qquad\qquad 0 \end{array}$$

112.

$$\begin{array}{r|l} & x-2+\frac{-x-1}{x^2-3} \\ \hline x^2-3 & x^3-2x^2-4x+5 \\ & \underline{x^3-3x} \\ & \quad -2x^2-x+5 \\ & \quad \underline{-2x^2+6} \\ & \qquad -x-1 \end{array}$$

113.

$$\begin{array}{r|l} & x^2-2+\frac{-x^2+5}{x^3-2} \\ \hline x^3-2 & x^5+0x^4-2x^3-3x^2+0x+9 \\ & \underline{x^5-2x^2} \\ & \quad -2x^3-x^2+0x+9 \\ & \quad \underline{-2x^3+4} \\ & \qquad -x^2+5 \end{array}$$

114.

$$\begin{array}{r|l} & x^2-2+\frac{3}{x^3-3} \\ \hline x^3-3 & x^5+0x^4-2x^3-3x^2+0x+9 \\ & \underline{x^5-3x^2} \\ & \quad -2x^3+0x+9 \\ & \quad \underline{-2x^3+6} \\ & \qquad\qquad 3 \end{array}$$

115.

$$\begin{array}{r|l} & x^4+2x^3+4x^2+8x+16 \\ \hline x-2 & x^5+0x^4+0x^3+0x^2+0x-32 \\ & \underline{x^5-2x^4} \\ & \quad 2x^4+0x^3 \\ & \quad \underline{2x^4-4x^3} \\ & \qquad 4x^3+0x^2 \\ & \qquad \underline{4x^3-8x^2} \\ & \qquad\quad 8x^2+0x \\ & \qquad\quad \underline{8x^2-16x} \\ & \qquad\qquad 16x-32 \\ & \qquad\qquad \underline{16x-32} \\ & \qquad\qquad\qquad 0 \end{array}$$

116.

$$\begin{array}{r|l} & x^3-x^2+x-1 \\ \hline x+1 & x^4+0x^3+0x^2+0x-1 \\ & \underline{x^4+x^3} \\ & \quad -x^3+0x^2 \\ & \quad \underline{-x^3-x^2} \\ & \qquad x^2+0x \\ & \qquad \underline{x^2+x} \\ & \qquad\quad -x-1 \\ & \qquad\quad \underline{-x-1} \\ & \qquad\qquad 0 \end{array}$$

117.

$$\begin{array}{r|l} & 6x^2+x-12 \\ \hline 6x^2+11x-10 & 36x^4+72x^3-121x^2-142x+120 \\ & \underline{36x^4+66x^3-60x^2} \\ & \quad 6x^3-61x^2-142x \\ & \quad \underline{6x^3+11x^2-10x} \\ & \qquad -72x^2-132x+120 \\ & \qquad \underline{-72x^2-132x+120} \\ & \qquad\qquad 0 \end{array}$$

118.

$$\begin{array}{r|l} & 6x^2 + 11x - 10 \\ \hline 6x^2 + x - 12 & 36x^4 + 72x^3 - 121x^2 - 142x + 120 \\ & \underline{36x^4 + 6x^3 - 72x^2} \\ & \quad 66x^3 - 49x^2 - 142x \\ & \quad \underline{66x^3 + 11x^2 - 132x} \\ & \qquad - 60x^2 - 10x + 120 \\ & \qquad \underline{- 60x^2 - 10x + 120} \\ & \qquad\qquad 0 \end{array}$$

119. Area = length · width = $(x+5)(x-2)$ ft^2 = $(x^2 - 2x + 5x - 10)$ ft^2 = $(x^2 + 3x - 10)$ ft^2

120.

$$\begin{aligned} \text{Area} &= \frac{1}{2} \cdot \text{base} \cdot \text{height} \\ x^2 + 3x - 40 &= \frac{1}{2}(x+8) \cdot \text{height} \\ 2\left(x^2 + 3x - 40\right) &= (x+8) \cdot \text{height} \\ 2x^2 + 6x - 80 &= (x+8) \cdot \text{height} \\ \frac{2x^2 + 6x - 80}{x+8} &= \text{height} \end{aligned}$$

$$\begin{array}{r|l} & 2x - 10 \\ \hline x + 8 & 2x^2 + 6x - 80 \\ & \underline{2x^2 + 16x} \\ & \quad - 10x - 80 \\ & \quad \underline{- 10x - 80} \\ & \qquad 0 \end{array}$$

The height is $(2x - 10)$ ft.

121. $$\begin{aligned} (a+b+c)^2 = (a+b+c)(a+b+c) &= a(a+b+c) + b(a+b+c) + c(a+b+c) \\ &= a^2 + ab + ac + ab + b^2 + bc + ac + bc + c^2 \\ &= a^2 + b^2 + c^2 + 2ab + 2bc + 2ac \end{aligned}$$

122. $$\begin{aligned} (a+b+c+d)^2 &= (a+b+c+d)(a+b+c+d) \\ &= a(a+b+c+d) + b(a+b+c+d) + c(a+b+c+d) + d(a+b+c+d) \\ &= a^2 + ab + ac + ad + ab + b^2 + bc + bd + ac + bc + c^2 + cd + ad + bd + cd + d^2 \\ &= a^2 + b^2 + c^2 + d^2 + 2ab + 2ac + 2ad + 2bc + 2bd + 2cd \end{aligned}$$

123. Answers may vary.

124. Answers may vary.

125. Check the formula with $a = 1$ and $b = 2$.

126. Check the formula with $a = 3$ and $b = 4$.

127. $9^{3/2} = \left(9^{1/2}\right)^3 = 3^3 = 27$

128. $$\left(\frac{8}{125}\right)^{-2/3} = \left(\frac{125}{8}\right)^{2/3} = \left(\left(\frac{125}{8}\right)^{1/3}\right)^2 = \left(\frac{5}{2}\right)^2 = \frac{25}{4}$$

129. $$\left(\frac{625x^4}{16y^8}\right)^{3/4} = \frac{625^{3/4}\left(x^4\right)^{3/4}}{16^{3/4}\left(y^8\right)^{3/4}} = \frac{125x^3}{8y^6}$$

130. $\sqrt{80x^4} = \sqrt{16x^4}\sqrt{5} = 4x^2\sqrt{5}$

131. $$\begin{aligned} \sqrt[3]{16ab^4} - b\sqrt[3]{54ab} = \sqrt[3]{8b^3}\sqrt[3]{2ab} - b\sqrt[3]{27}\sqrt[3]{2ab} = 2b\sqrt[3]{2ab} - b(3)\sqrt[3]{2ab} &= 2b\sqrt[3]{2ab} - 3b\sqrt[3]{2ab} \\ &= -b\sqrt[3]{2ab} \end{aligned}$$

132. $x\sqrt[4]{1280x}+\sqrt[4]{80x^5}=x\sqrt[4]{256}\sqrt[4]{5x}+\sqrt[4]{16x^4}\sqrt[4]{5x}=4x\sqrt[4]{5x}+2x\sqrt[4]{5x}=6x\sqrt[4]{5x}$

Exercise 0.5 (page 56)

1. factor

2. integer, prime

3. $ax+bx=x(a+b)$

4. $x^2-y^2=(x+y)(x-y)$

5. $x^2+2xy+y^2=(x+y)(x+y)$

6. $x^2-2xy+y^2=(x-y)(x-y)$

7. $x^3+y^3=(x+y)(x^2-xy+y^2)$

8. $x^3-y^3=(x-y)(x^2+xy+y^2)$

9. $3x-6=3(x-2)$

10. $5y-15=5(y-3)$

11. $8x^2+4x^3=4x^2(2+x)$

12. $9y^3+6y^2=3y^2(3y+2)$

13. $7x^2y^2+14x^3y^2=7x^2y^2(1+2x)$

14. $25y^2z-15yz^2=5yz(5y-3z)$

15. $3a^2bc+6ab^2c+9abc^2=3abc(a+2b+3c)$

16. $5x^3y^3z^3+25x^2y^2z^2-125xyz=5xyz(x^2y^2z^2+5xyz-25)$

17. $a(x+y)+b(x+y)=(x+y)(a+b)$

18. $b(x-y)+a(x-y)=(x-y)(b+a)$

19. $4a+b-12a^2-3ab=4a+b-3a(4a+b)=1(4a+b)-3a(4a+b)=(4a+b)(1-3a)$

20. $x^2+4x+xy+4y=x(x+4)+y(x+4)=(x+4)(x+y)$

21. $3x^3+3x^2-x-1=3x^2(x+1)-1(x+1)=(x+1)(3x^2-1)$

22. $4x+6xy-9y-6=2x(2+3y)-3(3y+2)=(3y+2)(2x-3)$

23. $2txy+2ctx-3ty-3ct=t(2xy+2cx-3y-3c)=t[2x(y+c)-3(y+c)]=t(y+c)(2x-3)$

24. $2ax+4ay-bx-2by=2a(x+2y)-b(x+2y)=(x+2y)(2a-b)$

25. $ax+bx+ay+by+az+bz=x(a+b)+y(a+b)+z(a+b)=(a+b)(x+y+z)$

26. $$6x^2y^3+18xy+3x^2y^2+9x=3x(2xy^3+6y+xy^2+3)=3x[2y(xy^2+3)+1(xy^2+3)]$$
$$=3x(xy^2+3)(2y+1)$$

27. $4x^2-9=(2x)^2-3^2=(2x+3)(2x-3)$

28. $36z^2-49=(6z)^2-7^2=(6z+7)(6z-7)$

29. $4-9r^2=2^2-(3r)^2=(2+3r)(2-3r)$

30. $16-49x^2=4^2-(7x)^2=(4+7x)(4-7x)$

31. $(x+z)^2 - 25 = (x+z)^2 - 5^2$
$= (x+z+5)(x+z-5)$

32. $(x-y)^2 - 9 = (x-y)^2 - 3^2$
$= (x-y+3)(x-y-3)$

33. $25x^4 + 1 = (5x^2)^2 + 1^2$
prime (sum of squares)

34. $36t^4 + 121 = (6t^2)^2 + 11^2$
prime (sum of squares)

35. $x^2 - (y-z)^2 = [x+(y-z)][x-(y-z)]$
$= (x+y-z)(x-y+z)$

36. $z^2 - (y+3)^2 = [z+(y+3)][z-(y+3)]$
$= (z+y+3)(z-y-3)$

37. $(x-y)^2 - (x+y)^2 = [(x-y)+(x+y)][(x-y)-(x+y)] = (x-y+x+y)(x-y-x-y)$
$= (2x)(-2y) = -4xy$

38. $(2a+3)^2 - (2a-3)^2 = [(2a+3)+(2a-3)][(2a+3)-(2a-3)]$
$= (2a+3+2a-3)(2a+3-2a+3) = (4a)(6) = 24a$

39. $x^4 - y^4 = (x^2)^2 - (y^2)^2 = (x^2+y^2)(x^2-y^2) = (x^2+y^2)(x+y)(x-y)$

40. $z^4 - 81 = (z^2)^2 - 9^2 = (z^2+9)(z^2-9) = (z^2+9)(z^2-3^2) = (z^2+9)(z+3)(z-3)$

41. $3x^2 - 12 = 3(x^2-4) = 3(x+2)(x-2)$

42. $3x^3y - 3xy = 3xy(x^2-1)$
$= 3xy(x+1)(x-1)$

43. $18xy^2 - 8x = 2x(9y^2-4)$
$= 2x(3y+2)(3y-2)$

44. $27x^2 - 12 = 3(9x^2-4)$
$= 3(3x+2)(3x-2)$

45. $x^2 + 8x + 16 = (x+4)(x+4) = (x+4)^2$

46. $a^2 - 12a + 36 = (a-6)(a-6) = (a-6)^2$

47. $b^2 - 10b + 25 = (b-5)(b-5) = (b-5)^2$

48. $y^2 + 14y + 49 = (y+7)(y+7) = (y+7)^2$

49. $m^2 + 4mn + 4n^2 = (m+2n)(m+2n)$
$= (m+2n)^2$

50. $r^2 - 8rs + 16s^2 = (r-4s)(r-4s)$
$= (r-4s)^2$

51. $x^2 + 10x + 21 = (x+3)(x+7)$

52. $x^2 + 7x + 10 = (x+2)(x+5)$

53. $x^2 - 4x - 12 = (x-6)(x+2)$

54. $x^2 - 2x - 63 = (x-9)(x+7)$

55. $x^2 - 2x + 15 \Rightarrow$ prime

56. $x^2 + x + 2 \Rightarrow$ prime

57. $12x^2 - xy - 6y^2 = (4x-3y)(3x+2y)$

58. $8x^2 - 10xy - 3y^2 = (4x+y)(2x-3y)$

59. $-15 + 2a + 24a^2 = 24a^2 + 2a - 15$
$= (6a+5)(4a-3)$

60. $-32 - 68x + 9x^2 = 9x^2 - 68x - 32$
$= (9x+4)(x-8)$

61. $6x^2 + 29xy + 35y^2 = (3x+7y)(2x+5y)$

62. $10x^2 - 17xy + 6y^2 = (5x-6y)(2x-y)$

63. $12p^2 - 58pq - 70q^2 = 2(6p^2 - 29pq - 35q^2) = 2(6p - 35q)(p + q)$

64. $3x^2 - 6xy - 9y^2 = 3(x^2 - 2xy - 3y^2) = 3(x - 3y)(x + y)$

65. $-6m^2 + 47mn - 35n^2 = -(6m^2 - 47mn + 35n^2) = -(6m - 5n)(m - 7n)$

66. $-14r^2 - 11rs + 15s^2 = -(14r^2 + 11rs - 15s^2) = -(7r - 5s)(2r + 3s)$

67. $-6x^3 + 23x^2 + 35x = -x(6x^2 - 23x - 35) = -x(6x + 7)(x - 5)$

68. $-y^3 - y^2 + 90y = -y(y^2 + y - 90) = -y(y + 10)(y - 9)$

69. $6x^4 - 11x^3 - 35x^2 = x^2(6x^2 - 11x - 35) = x^2(2x - 7)(3x + 5)$

70. $12x + 17x^2 - 7x^3 = -7x^3 + 17x^2 + 12x = -x(7x^2 - 17x - 12) = -x(x - 3)(7x + 4)$

71. $x^4 + 2x^2 - 15 = (x^2 + 5)(x^2 - 3)$

72. $x^4 - x^2 - 6 = (x^2 - 3)(x^2 + 2)$

73. $a^{2n} - 2a^n - 3 = (a^n - 3)(a^n + 1)$

74. $a^{2n} + 6a^n + 8 = (a^n + 4)(a^n + 2)$

75. $6x^{2n} - 7x^n + 2 = (3x^n - 2)(2x^n - 1)$

76. $9x^{2n} + 9x^n + 2 = (3x^n + 2)(3x^n + 1)$

77. $$\begin{aligned} 4x^{2n} - 9y^{2n} &= (2x^n)^2 - (3y^n)^2 \\ &= (2x^n + 3y^n)(2x^n - 3y^n) \end{aligned}$$

78. $8x^{2n} - 2x^n - 3 = (4x^n - 3)(2x^n + 1)$

79. $10y^{2n} - 11y^n - 6 = (5y^n + 2)(2y^n - 3)$

80. $$\begin{aligned} 16y^{4n} - 25y^{2n} &= y^{2n}\left(16y^{2n} - 25\right) \\ &= y^{2n}\left[(4y^n)^2 - 5^2\right] \\ &= y^{2n}(4y^n + 5)(4y^n - 5) \end{aligned}$$

81. $8z^3 - 27 = (2z)^3 - 3^3 = (2z - 3)\left[(2z)^2 + (2z)(3) + 3^2\right] = (2z - 3)(4z^2 + 6z + 9)$

82. $125a^3 - 64 = (5a)^3 - 4^3 = (5a - 4)\left[(5a)^2 + (5a)(4) + 4^2\right] = (5a - 4)(25a^2 + 20a + 16)$

83. $2x^3 + 2000 = 2(x^3 + 1000) = 2(x^3 + 10^3) = 2(x + 10)(x^2 - 10x + 100)$

84. $3y^3 + 648 = 3(y^3 + 216) = 3(y^3 + 6^3) = 3(y + 6)(y^2 - 6y + 36)$

85. $$\begin{aligned} (x + y)^3 - 64 = (x + y)^3 - 4^3 &= [(x + y) - 4]\left[(x + y)^2 + 4(x + y) + 4^2\right] \\ &= (x + y - 4)\left(x^2 + 2xy + y^2 + 4x + 4y + 16\right) \end{aligned}$$

86. $$\begin{aligned} (x - y)^3 + 27 = (x - y)^3 + 3^3 &= [(x - y) + 3]\left[(x - y)^2 - 3(x - y) + 3^2\right] \\ &= (x - y + 3)\left(x^2 - 2xy + y^2 - 3x + 3y + 9\right) \end{aligned}$$

87. $64a^6 - y^6 = (8a^3)^2 - (y^3)^2 = (8a^3 + y^3)(8a^3 - y^3)$
$= (2a + y)(4a^2 - 2ay + y^2)(2a - y)(4a^2 + 2ay + y^2)$

88. $a^6 + b^6 = (a^2)^3 + (b^2)^3 = (a^2 + b^2)\left((a^2)^2 - a^2b^2 + (b^2)^2\right) = (a^2 + b^2)(a^4 - a^2b^2 + b^4)$

89. $a^3 - b^3 + a - b = (a - b)(a^2 + ab + b^2) + (a - b)1 = (a - b)(a^2 + ab + b^2 + 1)$

90. $a^2 - y^2 - 5(a + y) = (a + y)(a - y) - 5(a + y) = (a + y)(a - y - 5)$

91. $64x^6 + y^6 = (4x^2)^3 + (y^2)^3 = (4x^2 + y^2)\left((4x^2)^2 - 4x^2y^2 + (y^2)^2\right)$
$= (4x^2 + y^2)(16x^4 - 4x^2y^2 + y^4)$

92. $z^2 + 6z + 9 - 225y^2 = (z + 3)(z + 3) - 225y^2 = (z + 3)^2 - (15y)^2$
$= (z + 3 + 15y)(z + 3 - 15y)$

93. $x^2 - 6x + 9 - 144y^2 = (x - 3)(x - 3) - 144y^2 = (x - 3)^2 - (12y)^2$
$= (x - 3 + 12y)(x - 3 - 12y)$

94. $x^2 + 2x - 9y^2 + 1 = x^2 + 2x + 1 - 9y^2 = (x + 1)(x + 1) - 9y^2$
$= (x + 1)^2 - (3y)^2 = (x + 1 + 3y)(x + 1 - 3y)$

95. $(a + b)^2 - 3(a + b) - 10 = [(a + b) - 5][(a + b) + 2] = (a + b - 5)(a + b + 2)$

96. $2(a + b)^2 - 5(a + b) - 3 = [2(a + b) + 1][(a + b) - 3] = (2a + 2b + 1)(a + b - 3)$

97. $x^6 + 7x^3 - 8 = (x^3 + 8)(x^3 - 1) = (x + 2)(x^2 - 2x + 4)(x - 1)(x^2 + x + 1)$

98. $x^6 - 13x^4 + 36x^2 = x^2(x^4 - 13x^2 + 36) = x^2(x^2 - 9)(x^2 - 4) = x^2(x + 3)(x - 3)(x + 2)(x - 2)$

99. $x^4 + 3x^2 + 4 = x^4 + 4x^2 + 4 - x^2$
$= (x^2 + 2)(x^2 + 2) - x^2$
$= (x^2 + 2)^2 - x^2$
$= (x^2 + 2 + x)(x^2 + 2 - x)$

100. $x^4 + x^2 + 1 = x^4 + 2x^2 + 1 - x^2$
$= (x^2 + 1)(x^2 + 1) - x^2$
$= (x^2 + 1)^2 - x^2$
$= (x^2 + 1 + x)(x^2 + 1 - x)$

101. $x^4 + 7x^2 + 16 = x^4 + 8x^2 + 16 - x^2$
$= (x^2 + 4)(x^2 + 4) - x^2$
$= (x^2 + 4)^2 - x^2$
$= (x^2 + 4 + x)(x^2 + 4 - x)$

102. $y^4 + 2y^2 + 9 = y^4 + 6y^2 + 9 - 4y^2$
$= (y^2 + 3)(y^2 + 3) - 4y^2$
$= (y^2 + 3)^2 - (2y)^2$
$= (y^2 + 3 + 2y)(y^2 + 3 - 2y)$

103. $4a^4 + 1 + 3a^2 = 4a^4 + 4a^2 + 1 - a^2 = (2a^2 + 1)(2a^2 + 1) - a^2 = (2a^2 + 1)^2 - a^2$
$= (2a^2 + 1 + a)(2a^2 + 1 - a)$

104. $x^4 + 25 + 6x^2 = x^4 + 10x^2 + 25 - 4x^2 = (x^2+5)(x^2+5) - 4x^2$
$= (x^2+5)^2 - (2x)^2 = (x^2+5+2x)(x^2+5-2x)$

105. Answers may vary.

106. Answers may vary.

107. Answers may vary.

108. Answers may vary.

109. $3x + 2 = 2\left(\frac{3}{2}x + 1\right)$

110. $5x - 3 = 5\left(x - \frac{3}{5}\right)$

111. $x^2 + 2x + 4 = 2\left(\frac{1}{2}x^2 + x + 2\right)$

112. $3x^2 - 2x - 5 = 3\left(x^2 - \frac{2}{3}x - \frac{5}{3}\right)$

113. $a + b = a\left(1 + \frac{b}{a}\right)$

114. $a - b = b\left(\frac{a}{b} - 1\right)$

115. $x + x^{1/2} = x^{1/2}\left(x^{1/2} + 1\right)$

116. $x^{3/2} - x^{1/2} = x^{1/2}(x - 1)$

117. $2x + \sqrt{2}y = \sqrt{2}\left(\sqrt{2}x + y\right)$

118. $\sqrt{3}a - 3b = \sqrt{3}\left(a - \sqrt{3}b\right)$

119. $ab^{3/2} - a^{3/2}b = ab\left(b^{1/2} - a^{1/2}\right)$

120. $ab^2 + b = b^{-1}(ab^3 + b^2)$

121. $x^2 + x - 6 + xy - 2y = (x+3)(x-2) + y(x-2) = (x-2)(x+3+y)$

122. $2x^2 + 5x + 2 - xy - 2y = (2x+1)(x+2) - y(x+2) = (x+2)(2x+1-y)$

123. $a^4 + 2a^3 + a^2 + a + 1 = a^2(a^2+2a+1) + a + 1 = a^2(a+1)(a+1) + 1(a+1)$
$= (a+1)\left[a^2(a+1) + 1\right]$
$= (a+1)(a^3 + a^2 + 1)$

124. $a^4 + a^3 - 2a^2 + a - 1 = a^2(a^2 + a - 2) + a - 1 = a^2(a+2)(a-1) + 1(a-1)$
$= (a-1)\left[a^2(a+2) + 1\right]$
$= (a-1)(a^3 + 2a^2 + 1)$

125. The number 1 is neither prime nor composite.

126. $[-2, 3) \Rightarrow$ 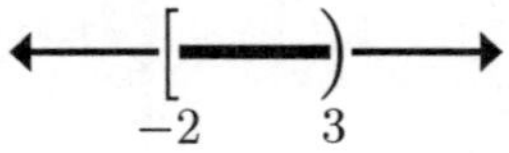

127. $(x^3x^2)^4 = (x^5)^4 = x^{20}$

128. $\dfrac{(a^3)^3(a^2)^4}{(a^2a^3)^3} = \dfrac{a^9a^8}{(a^5)^3} = \dfrac{a^{17}}{a^{15}} = a^2$

129. $\left(\dfrac{3x^4x^3}{6x^{-2}x^4}\right)^0 = 1$

130. $\sqrt{20x^5} = \sqrt{4x^4}\sqrt{5x} = 2x^2\sqrt{5x}$

131. $\sqrt{20x} - \sqrt{125x} = \sqrt{4}\sqrt{5x} - \sqrt{25}\sqrt{5x} = 2\sqrt{5x} - 5\sqrt{5x} = -3\sqrt{5x}$

132. $\frac{3}{\sqrt[3]{3}} = \frac{3}{\sqrt[3]{3}} \cdot \frac{\sqrt[3]{9}}{\sqrt[3]{9}} = \frac{3\sqrt[3]{9}}{\sqrt[3]{27}} = \frac{3\sqrt[3]{9}}{3} = \sqrt[3]{9}$

Exercise 0.6 (page 66)

1. numerator

2. denominator

3. $ad = bc$

4. zero

5. $\frac{ac}{bd}$

6. $\frac{ad}{bc}$

7. $\frac{a+c}{b}$

8. $\frac{a-c}{b}$

9.
$$\frac{8x}{3y} \stackrel{?}{=} \frac{16x}{6y}$$
$$8x \cdot 6y \stackrel{?}{=} 3y \cdot 16x$$
$$48xy = 48xy$$
EQUAL

10.
$$\frac{3x^2}{4y^2} \stackrel{?}{=} \frac{12y^2}{16x^2}$$
$$3x^2 \cdot 16x^2 \stackrel{?}{=} 4y^2 \cdot 12y^2$$
$$48x^4 \neq 48y^4$$
NOT EQUAL

11.
$$\frac{25xyz}{12ab^2c} \stackrel{?}{=} \frac{50a^2bc}{24xyz}$$
$$25xyz \cdot 24xyz \stackrel{?}{=} 12ab^2c \cdot 50a^2bc$$
$$600x^2y^2z^2 \neq 600a^3b^3c^2$$
NOT EQUAL

12.
$$\frac{15rs^2}{4rs^2} \stackrel{?}{=} \frac{37.5a^3}{10a^3}$$
$$15rs^2 \cdot 10a^3 \stackrel{?}{=} 4rs^2 \cdot 37.5a^3$$
$$150rs^2a^3 = 150rs^2a^3$$
EQUAL

13. $\frac{7a^2b}{21ab^2} = \frac{a \cdot 7ab}{3b \cdot 7ab} = \frac{a}{3b} \cdot \frac{7ab}{7ab} = \frac{a}{3b}$

14. $\frac{35p^3q^2}{49p^4q} = \frac{5q \cdot 7p^3q}{7p \cdot 7p^3q} = \frac{5q}{7p} \cdot \frac{7p^3q}{7p^3q} = \frac{5q}{7p}$

15. $\frac{4x}{7} \cdot \frac{2}{5a} = \frac{4x \cdot 2}{7 \cdot 5a} = \frac{8x}{35a}$

16. $\frac{-5y}{2z} \cdot \frac{4}{y^2} = \frac{-5y \cdot 4}{2z \cdot y^2} = \frac{-20y}{2y^2z} = -\frac{10}{zy}$

17. $\frac{8m}{5n} \div \frac{3m}{10n} = \frac{8m}{5n} \cdot \frac{10n}{3m} = \frac{80mn}{15mn} = \frac{16}{3}$

18. $\frac{15p}{8q} \div \frac{-5p}{16q^2} = \frac{15p}{8q} \cdot \frac{16q^2}{-5p} = \frac{240pq^2}{-40pq} = -6q$

19. $\frac{3z}{5c} + \frac{2z}{5c} = \frac{3z + 2z}{5c} = \frac{5z}{5c} = \frac{z}{c}$

20. $\frac{7a}{4b} - \frac{3a}{4b} = \frac{7a - 3a}{4b} = \frac{4a}{4b} = \frac{a}{b}$

21. $\frac{15x^2y}{7a^2b^3} - \frac{x^2y}{7a^2b^3} = \frac{14x^2y}{7a^2b^3} = \frac{2x^2y}{a^2b^3}$

22. $\frac{8rst^2}{15m^4t^2} + \frac{7rst^2}{15m^4t^2} = \frac{15rst^2}{15m^4t^2} = \frac{rs}{m^4}$

23. $\frac{2x-4}{x^2-4} = \frac{2(x-2)}{(x+2)(x-2)} = \frac{2}{x+2}$

24. $\frac{x^2-16}{x^2-8x+16} = \frac{(x+4)(x-4)}{(x-4)(x-4)} = \frac{x+4}{x-4}$

25.
$$\frac{25-x^2}{x^2+10x+25} = \frac{(5+x)(5-x)}{(x+5)(x+5)}$$
$$= \frac{5-x}{x+5} = -\frac{x-5}{x+5}$$

26.
$$\frac{4-x^2}{x^2-5x+6} = \frac{(2+x)(2-x)}{(x-3)(x-2)} = -\frac{x+2}{x-3}$$
$$= \frac{x+2}{3-x}$$

27. $$\frac{6x^3+x^2-12x}{4x^3+4x^2-3x}=\frac{x(6x^2+x-12)}{x(4x^2+4x-3)}=\frac{x(2x+3)(3x-4)}{x(2x+3)(2x-1)}=\frac{3x-4}{2x-1}$$

28. $$\frac{6x^4-5x^3-6x^2}{2x^3-7x^2-15x}=\frac{x^2(6x^2-5x-6)}{x(2x^2-7x-15)}=\frac{x^2(2x-3)(3x+2)}{x(2x+3)(x-5)}=\frac{x(2x-3)(3x+2)}{(2x+3)(x-5)}$$

29. $$\frac{x^3-8}{x^2+ax-2x-2a}=\frac{x^3-2^3}{x(x+a)-2(x+a)}=\frac{(x-2)(x^2+2x+4)}{(x+a)(x-2)}=\frac{x^2+2x+4}{x+a}$$

30. $$\frac{xy+2x+3y+6}{x^3+27}=\frac{x(y+2)+3(y+2)}{x^3+3^3}=\frac{(y+2)(x+3)}{(x+3)(x^2-3x+9)}=\frac{y+2}{x^2-3x+9}$$

31. $$\frac{x^2-1}{x}\cdot\frac{x^2}{x^2+2x+1}=\frac{(x+1)(x-1)}{x}\cdot\frac{x^2}{(x+1)(x+1)}=\frac{x(x-1)}{x+1}$$

32. $$\frac{y^2-2y+1}{y}\cdot\frac{y+2}{y^2+y-2}=\frac{(y-1)(y-1)}{y}\cdot\frac{y+2}{(y+2)(y-1)}=\frac{y-1}{y}$$

33. $$\frac{3x^2+7x+2}{x^2+2x}\cdot\frac{x^2-x}{3x^2+x}=\frac{(3x+1)(x+2)}{x(x+2)}\cdot\frac{x(x-1)}{x(3x+1)}=\frac{x-1}{x}$$

34. $$\frac{x^2+x}{2x^2+3x}\cdot\frac{2x^2+x-3}{x^2-1}=\frac{x(x+1)}{x(2x+3)}\cdot\frac{(2x+3)(x-1)}{(x+1)(x-1)}=1$$

35. $$\frac{x^2+x}{x-1}\cdot\frac{x^2-1}{x+2}=\frac{x(x+1)}{x-1}\cdot\frac{(x+1)(x-1)}{x+2}=\frac{x(x+1)^2}{x+2}$$

36. $$\frac{x^2+5x+6}{x^2+6x+9}\cdot\frac{x+2}{x^2-4}=\frac{(x+2)(x+3)}{(x+3)(x+3)}\cdot\frac{x+2}{(x+2)(x-2)}=\frac{x+2}{(x+3)(x-2)}$$

37. $$\frac{2x^2+32}{8}\div\frac{x^2+16}{2}=\frac{2x^2+32}{8}\cdot\frac{2}{x^2+16}=\frac{2(x^2+16)}{8}\cdot\frac{2}{x^2+16}=\frac{1}{2}$$

38. $$\frac{x^2+x-6}{x^2-6x+9}\div\frac{x^2-4}{x^2-9}=\frac{x^2+x-6}{x^2-6x+9}\cdot\frac{x^2-9}{x^2-4}=\frac{(x+3)(x-2)}{(x-3)(x-3)}\cdot\frac{(x+3)(x-3)}{(x+2)(x-2)}$$
$$=\frac{(x+3)^2}{(x-3)(x+2)}$$

39. $$\frac{z^2+z-20}{z^2-4}\div\frac{z^2-25}{z-5}=\frac{z^2+z-20}{z^2-4}\cdot\frac{z-5}{z^2-25}=\frac{(z+5)(z-4)}{(z+2)(z-2)}\cdot\frac{z-5}{(z+5)(z-5)}$$
$$=\frac{z-4}{(z+2)(z-2)}$$

40. $$\frac{ax+bx+a+b}{a^2+2ab+b^2} \div \frac{x^2-1}{x^2-2x+1} = \frac{ax+bx+a+b}{a^2+2ab+b^2} \cdot \frac{x^2-2x+1}{x^2-1}$$
$$= \frac{x(a+b)+1(a+b)}{(a+b)(a+b)} \cdot \frac{(x-1)(x-1)}{(x+1)(x-1)}$$
$$= \frac{(a+b)(x+1)}{(a+b)(a+b)} \cdot \frac{(x-1)(x-1)}{(x+1)(x-1)} = \frac{x-1}{a+b}$$

41. $$\frac{3x^2+5x-2}{x^3+2x^2} \div \frac{6x^2+13x-5}{2x^3+5x^2} = \frac{3x^2+5x-2}{x^3+2x^2} \cdot \frac{2x^3+5x^2}{6x^2+13x-5}$$
$$= \frac{(3x-1)(x+2)}{x^2(x+2)} \cdot \frac{x^2(2x+5)}{(3x-1)(2x+5)} = 1$$

42. $$\frac{x^2+13x+12}{8x^2-6x-5} \div \frac{2x^2-x-3}{8x^2-14x+5} = \frac{x^2+13x+12}{8x^2-6x-5} \cdot \frac{8x^2-14x+5}{2x^2-x-3}$$
$$= \frac{(x+12)(x+1)}{(4x-5)(2x+1)} \cdot \frac{(4x-5)(2x-1)}{(2x-3)(x+1)} = \frac{(x+12)(2x-1)}{(2x+1)(2x-3)}$$

43. $$\frac{x^2+7x+12}{x^3-x^2-6x} \cdot \frac{x^2-3x-10}{x^2+2x-3} \cdot \frac{x^3-4x^2+3x}{x^2-x-20}$$
$$= \frac{(x+3)(x+4)}{x(x-3)(x+2)} \cdot \frac{(x-5)(x+2)}{(x+3)(x-1)} \cdot \frac{x(x-3)(x-1)}{(x-5)(x+4)} = 1$$

44. $$\frac{x^2-2x-3}{21x^2-50x-16} \cdot \frac{3x-8}{x-3} \div \frac{x^2+6x+5}{7x^2-33x-10} = \frac{x^2-2x-3}{21x^2-50x-16} \cdot \frac{3x-8}{x-3} \cdot \frac{7x^2-33x-10}{x^2+6x+5}$$
$$= \frac{(x-3)(x+1)}{(7x+2)(3x-8)} \cdot \frac{3x-8}{x-3} \cdot \frac{(7x+2)(x-5)}{(x+5)(x+1)}$$
$$= \frac{x-5}{x+5}$$

45. $$\frac{x^3+27}{x^2-4} \div \left(\frac{x^2+4x+3}{x^2+2x} \div \frac{x^2+x-6}{x^2-3x+9}\right) = \frac{x^3+27}{x^2-4} \div \left(\frac{x^2+4x+3}{x^2+2x} \cdot \frac{x^2-3x+9}{x^2+x-6}\right)$$
$$= \frac{x^3+27}{x^2-4} \div \left(\frac{(x+3)(x+1)}{x(x+2)} \cdot \frac{x^2-3x+9}{(x+3)(x-2)}\right)$$
$$= \frac{x^3+27}{x^2-4} \div \frac{(x+1)(x^2-3x+9)}{x(x+2)(x-2)}$$
$$= \frac{(x+3)(x^2-3x+9)}{(x+2)(x-2)} \cdot \frac{x(x+2)(x-2)}{(x+1)(x^2-3x+9)}$$
$$= \frac{x(x+3)}{x+1}$$

46. $$\frac{x(x-2)-3}{x(x+7)-3(x-1)}\cdot\frac{x(x+1)-2}{x(x-7)+3(x+1)}=\frac{x^2-2x-3}{x^2+7x-3x+3}\cdot\frac{x^2+x-2}{x^2-7x+3x+3}$$
$$=\frac{x^2-2x-3}{x^2+4x+3}\cdot\frac{x^2+x-2}{x^2-4x+3}$$
$$=\frac{(x-3)(x+1)}{(x+3)(x+1)}\cdot\frac{(x+2)(x-1)}{(x-3)(x-1)}=\frac{x+2}{x+3}$$

47. $$\frac{3}{x+3}+\frac{x+2}{x+3}=\frac{3+x+2}{x+3}=\frac{x+5}{x+3}$$

48. $$\frac{3}{x+1}+\frac{x+2}{x+1}=\frac{3+x+2}{x+1}=\frac{x+5}{x+1}$$

49. $$\frac{4x}{x-1}-\frac{4}{x-1}=\frac{4x-4}{x-1}=\frac{4(x-1)}{x-1}=4$$

50. $$\frac{6x}{x-2}-\frac{3}{x-2}=\frac{6x-3}{x-2}=\frac{3(2x-1)}{x-2}$$

51. $$\frac{2}{5-x}+\frac{1}{x-5}=\frac{-2}{x-5}+\frac{1}{x-5}=\frac{-1}{x-5}$$

52. $$\frac{3}{x-6}-\frac{2}{6-x}=\frac{3}{x-6}-\frac{-2}{x-6}=\frac{5}{x-6}$$

53. $$\frac{3}{x+1}+\frac{2}{x-1}=\frac{3(x-1)}{(x+1)(x-1)}+\frac{2(x+1)}{(x-1)(x+1)}=\frac{3x-3}{(x+1)(x-1)}+\frac{2x+2}{(x-1)(x+1)}$$
$$=\frac{5x-1}{(x+1)(x-1)}$$

54. $$\frac{3}{x+4}+\frac{x}{x-4}=\frac{3(x-4)}{(x+4)(x-4)}+\frac{x(x+4)}{(x-4)(x+4)}=\frac{3x-12}{(x+4)(x-4)}+\frac{x^2+4x}{(x-4)(x+4)}$$
$$=\frac{x^2+7x-12}{(x+4)(x-4)}$$

55. $$\frac{a+3}{a^2+7a+12}+\frac{a}{a^2-16}=\frac{a+3}{(a+3)(a+4)}+\frac{a}{(a+4)(a-4)}$$
$$=\frac{1}{a+4}+\frac{a}{(a+4)(a-4)}$$
$$=\frac{1(a-4)}{(a+4)(a-4)}+\frac{a}{(a+4)(a-4)}$$
$$=\frac{a-4}{(a+4)(a-4)}+\frac{a}{(a+4)(a-4)}=\frac{2a-4}{(a+4)(a-4)}$$

56. $$\frac{a}{a^2+a-2}+\frac{2}{a^2-5a+4}=\frac{a}{(a+2)(a-1)}+\frac{2}{(a-4)(a-1)}$$
$$=\frac{a(a-4)}{(a+2)(a-1)(a-4)}+\frac{2(a+2)}{(a-4)(a-1)(a+2)}$$
$$=\frac{a^2-4a}{(a+2)(a-1)(a-4)}+\frac{2a+4}{(a+2)(a-1)(a-4)}$$
$$=\frac{a^2-2a+4}{(a+2)(a-1)(a-4)}$$

57. $$\frac{x}{x^2-4}-\frac{1}{x+2}=\frac{x}{(x+2)(x-2)}-\frac{1}{x+2}=\frac{x}{(x+2)(x-2)}-\frac{1(x-2)}{(x+2)(x-2)}$$
$$=\frac{x}{(x+2)(x-2)}-\frac{x-2}{(x+2)(x-2)}$$
$$=\frac{2}{(x+2)(x-2)}$$

58. $$\frac{b^2}{b^2-4}-\frac{4}{b^2+2b}=\frac{b^2}{(b+2)(b-2)}-\frac{4}{b(b+2)}=\frac{b^2(b)}{b(b+2)(b-2)}-\frac{4(b-2)}{b(b+2)(b-2)}$$
$$=\frac{b^3}{b(b+2)(b-2)}-\frac{4b-8}{b(b+2)(b-2)}$$
$$=\frac{b^3-4b+8}{b(b+2)(b-2)}$$

59. $$\frac{3x-2}{x^2+2x+1}-\frac{x}{x^2-1}=\frac{3x-2}{(x+1)(x+1)}-\frac{x}{(x+1)(x-1)}$$
$$=\frac{(3x-2)(x-1)}{(x+1)(x+1)(x-1)}-\frac{x(x+1)}{(x+1)(x-1)(x+1)}$$
$$=\frac{3x^2-5x+2}{(x+1)(x+1)(x-1)}-\frac{x^2+x}{(x+1)(x+1)(x-1)}$$
$$=\frac{2x^2-6x+2}{(x+1)(x+1)(x-1)}=\frac{2(x^2-3x+1)}{(x+1)^2(x-1)}$$

60. $$\frac{2t}{t^2-25}-\frac{t+1}{t^2+5t}=\frac{2t}{(t+5)(t-5)}-\frac{t+1}{t(t+5)}=\frac{2t(t)}{t(t+5)(t-5)}-\frac{(t+1)(t-5)}{t(t+5)(t-5)}$$
$$=\frac{2t^2}{t(t+5)(t-5)}-\frac{t^2-4t-5}{t(t+5)(t-5)}$$
$$=\frac{t^2+4t+5}{t(t+5)(t-5)}$$

61. $$\frac{2}{y^2-1}+3+\frac{1}{y+1}=\frac{2}{(y+1)(y-1)}+\frac{3}{1}+\frac{1}{y+1}$$
$$=\frac{2}{(y+1)(y-1)}+\frac{3(y+1)(y-1)}{1(y+1)(y-1)}+\frac{1(y-1)}{(y+1)(y-1)}$$
$$=\frac{2}{(y+1)(y-1)}+\frac{3y^2-3}{(y+1)(y-1)}+\frac{y-1}{(y+1)(y-1)}$$
$$=\frac{3y^2+y-2}{(y+1)(y-1)}=\frac{(3y-2)(y+1)}{(y+1)(y-1)}=\frac{3y-2}{y-1}$$

62. $$2+\frac{4}{t^2-4}-\frac{1}{t-2}=\frac{2}{1}+\frac{4}{(t+2)(t-2)}-\frac{1}{t-2}$$
$$=\frac{2(t+2)(t-2)}{1(t+2)(t-2)}+\frac{4}{(t+2)(t-2)}-\frac{1(t+2)}{(t+2)(t-2)}$$
$$=\frac{2t^2-8}{(t+2)(t-2)}+\frac{4}{(t+2)(t-2)}-\frac{t+2}{(t+2)(t-2)}$$
$$=\frac{2t^2-t-6}{(t+2)(t-2)}=\frac{(2t+3)(t-2)}{(t+2)(t-2)}=\frac{2t+3}{t+2}$$

63. $$\frac{1}{x-2}+\frac{3}{x+2}-\frac{3x-2}{x^2-4}=\frac{1}{x-2}+\frac{3}{x+2}-\frac{3x-2}{(x+2)(x-2)}$$
$$=\frac{1(x+2)}{(x-2)(x+2)}+\frac{3(x-2)}{(x+2)(x-2)}-\frac{3x-2}{(x+2)(x-2)}$$
$$=\frac{x+2}{(x+2)(x-2)}+\frac{3x-6}{(x+2)(x-2)}-\frac{3x-2}{(x+2)(x-2)}$$
$$=\frac{x-2}{(x+2)(x-2)}=\frac{1}{x+2}$$

64. $$\frac{x}{x-3}-\frac{5}{x+3}+\frac{3(3x-1)}{x^2-9}=\frac{x}{x-3}-\frac{5}{x+3}+\frac{9x-3}{(x+3)(x-3)}$$
$$=\frac{x(x+3)}{(x-3)(x+3)}-\frac{5(x-3)}{(x+3)(x-3)}+\frac{9x-3}{(x+3)(x-3)}$$
$$=\frac{x^2+3x}{(x+3)(x-3)}-\frac{5x-15}{(x+3)(x-3)}+\frac{9x-3}{(x+3)(x-3)}$$
$$=\frac{x^2+7x+12}{(x+3)(x-3)}=\frac{(x+3)(x+4)}{(x+3)(x-3)}=\frac{x+4}{x-3}$$

65. $$\left(\frac{1}{x-2}+\frac{1}{x-3}\right)\cdot\frac{x-3}{2x}=\left(\frac{1(x-3)}{(x-2)(x-3)}+\frac{1(x-2)}{(x-3)(x-2)}\right)\cdot\frac{x-3}{2x}$$
$$=\left(\frac{x-3}{(x-2)(x-3)}+\frac{x-2}{(x-2)(x-3)}\right)\cdot\frac{x-3}{2x}$$
$$=\frac{2x-5}{(x-2)(x-3)}\cdot\frac{x-3}{2x}=\frac{2x-5}{2x(x-2)}$$

66. $$\left(\frac{1}{x+1}-\frac{1}{x-2}\right)\div\frac{1}{x-2}=\left(\frac{1(x-2)}{(x+1)(x-2)}-\frac{1(x+1)}{(x-2)(x+1)}\right)\cdot\frac{x-2}{1}$$
$$=\left(\frac{x-2}{(x+1)(x-2)}-\frac{x+1}{(x+1)(x-2)}\right)\cdot\frac{x-2}{1}$$
$$=\frac{-3}{(x+1)(x-2)}\cdot\frac{x-2}{1}=\frac{-3}{x+1}$$

67. $$\frac{3x}{x-4}-\frac{x}{x+4}-\frac{3x+1}{16-x^2}=\frac{3x}{x-4}-\frac{x}{x+4}-\frac{3x+1}{(4+x)(4-x)}$$
$$=\frac{3x}{x-4}-\frac{x}{x+4}+\frac{3x+1}{(x+4)(x-4)}$$
$$=\frac{3x(x+4)}{(x-4)(x+4)}-\frac{x(x-4)}{(x+4)(x-4)}+\frac{3x+1}{(x+4)(x-4)}$$
$$=\frac{3x^2+12x}{(x+4)(x-4)}-\frac{x^2-4x}{(x+4)(x-4)}+\frac{3x+1}{(x+4)(x-4)}$$
$$=\frac{2x^2+19x+1}{(x+4)(x-4)}$$

68. $$\frac{7x}{x-5}+\frac{3x}{5-x}+\frac{3x-1}{x^2-25}=\frac{7x}{x-5}+\frac{-3x}{x-5}+\frac{3x-1}{(x+5)(x-5)}$$
$$=\frac{4x}{x-5}+\frac{3x-1}{(x+5)(x-5)}$$
$$=\frac{4x(x+5)}{(x-5)(x+5)}+\frac{3x-1}{(x+5)(x-5)}$$
$$=\frac{4x^2+20x}{(x+5)(x-5)}+\frac{3x-1}{(x+5)(x-5)}=\frac{4x^2+23x-1}{(x+5)(x-5)}$$

69. $$\frac{1}{x^2+3x+2}-\frac{2}{x^2+4x+3}+\frac{1}{x^2+5x+6}\quad\cdots$$
$$=\frac{1}{(x+2)(x+1)}-\frac{2}{(x+3)(x+1)}+\frac{1}{(x+2)(x+3)}$$
$$=\frac{1(x+3)}{(x+2)(x+1)(x+3)}-\frac{2(x+2)}{(x+3)(x+1)(x+2)}+\frac{1(x+1)}{(x+2)(x+3)(x+1)}$$
$$=\frac{x+3}{(x+2)(x+1)(x+3)}-\frac{2x+4}{(x+2)(x+1)(x+3)}+\frac{x+1}{(x+2)(x+1)(x+3)}$$
$$=\frac{x+3-2x-4+x+1}{(x+2)(x+1)(x+3)}=\frac{0}{(x+2)(x+1)(x+3)}=0$$

70. $$\frac{-2}{x-y}+\frac{2}{x-z}-\frac{2z-2y}{(y-x)(z-x)}=\frac{2}{y-x}+\frac{-2}{z-x}-\frac{2z-2y}{(y-x)(z-x)}$$
$$=\frac{2(z-x)}{(y-x)(z-x)}+\frac{-2(y-x)}{(z-x)(y-x)}-\frac{2z-2y}{(y-x)(z-x)}$$
$$=\frac{2z-2x}{(y-x)(z-x)}+\frac{-2y+2x}{(y-x)(z-x)}-\frac{2z-2y}{(y-x)(z-x)}$$
$$=\frac{2z-2x-2y+2x-2z+2y}{(y-x)(z-x)}=\frac{0}{(y-x)(z-x)}=0$$

71. $$\frac{3x-2}{x^2+x-20}-\frac{4x^2+2}{x^2-25}+\frac{3x^2-25}{x^2-16}\;\cdots$$

$$=\frac{3x-2}{(x+5)(x-4)}-\frac{4x^2+2}{(x+5)(x-5)}+\frac{3x^2-25}{(x+4)(x-4)}$$

$$=\frac{(3x-2)(x-5)(x+4)}{(x+5)(x-4)(x-5)(x+4)}-\frac{(4x^2+2)(x-4)(x+4)}{(x+5)(x-5)(x-4)(x+4)}\;\cdots$$

$$+\frac{(3x^2-25)(x+5)(x-5)}{(x+4)(x-4)(x+5)(x-5)}$$

$$=\frac{3x^3-5x^2-58x+40}{(x+5)(x-4)(x-5)(x+4)}-\frac{4x^4-62x^2-32}{(x+5)(x-4)(x-5)(x+4)}\;\cdots$$

$$+\frac{3x^4-100x^2+625}{(x+5)(x-4)(x-5)(x+4)}$$

$$=\frac{3x^3-5x^2-58x+40-4x^4+62x^2+32+3x^4-100x^2+625}{(x+5)(x-4)(x-5)(x+4)}$$

$$=\frac{-x^4+3x^3-43x^2-58x+697}{(x+5)(x-4)(x-5)(x+4)}$$

72. $$\frac{3x+2}{8x^2-10x-3}+\frac{x+4}{6x^2-11x+3}-\frac{1}{4x+1}\;\cdots$$

$$=\frac{3x+2}{(4x+1)(2x-3)}+\frac{x+4}{(3x-1)(2x-3)}-\frac{1}{4x+1}$$

$$=\frac{(3x+2)(3x-1)}{(4x+1)(2x-3)(3x-1)}+\frac{(x+4)(4x+1)}{(3x-1)(2x-3)(4x+1)}-\frac{1(2x-3)(3x-1)}{(4x+1)(2x-3)(3x-1)}$$

$$=\frac{9x^2+3x-2}{(4x+1)(2x-3)(3x-1)}+\frac{4x^2+17x+4}{(4x+1)(2x-3)(3x-1)}-\frac{6x^2-11x+3}{(4x+1)(2x-3)(3x-1)}$$

$$=\frac{9x^2+3x-2+4x^2+17x+4-6x^2+11x-3}{(4x+1)(2x-3)(3x-1)}=\frac{7x^2+31x-1}{(4x+1)(2x-3)(3x-1)}$$

73. $$\frac{\frac{3a}{b}}{\frac{6ac}{b^2}}=\frac{3a}{b}\div\frac{6ac}{b^2}=\frac{3a}{b}\cdot\frac{b^2}{6ac}=\frac{b}{2c}$$

74. $$\frac{\frac{3t^2}{9x}}{\frac{t}{18x}}=\frac{3t^2}{9x}\div\frac{t}{18x}=\frac{3t^2}{9x}\cdot\frac{18x}{t}=6t$$

75. $$\frac{3a^2b}{\frac{ab}{27}}=\frac{3a^2b}{1}\div\frac{ab}{27}=\frac{3a^2b}{1}\cdot\frac{27}{ab}=81a$$

76. $$\frac{\frac{3u^2v}{4t}}{3uv}=\frac{3u^2v}{4t}\div\frac{3uv}{1}=\frac{3u^2v}{4t}\cdot\frac{1}{3uv}=\frac{u}{4t}$$

77. $$\frac{\frac{x-y}{ab}}{\frac{y-x}{ab}}=\frac{x-y}{ab}\div\frac{y-x}{ab}=\frac{x-y}{ab}\cdot\frac{ab}{y-x}=-1$$

78. $$\frac{\frac{x^2-5x+6}{2x^2y}}{\frac{x^2-9}{2x^2y}}=\frac{x^2-5x+6}{2x^2y}\div\frac{x^2-9}{2x^2y}=\frac{x^2-5x+6}{2x^2y}\cdot\frac{2x^2y}{x^2-9}$$

$$=\frac{(x-3)(x-2)}{2x^2y}\cdot\frac{2x^2y}{(x+3)(x-3)}=\frac{x-2}{x+3}$$

79. $$\frac{\frac{1}{x}+\frac{1}{y}}{xy}=\frac{xy\left(\frac{1}{x}+\frac{1}{y}\right)}{xy(xy)}=\frac{xy\left(\frac{1}{x}\right)+xy\left(\frac{1}{y}\right)}{x^2y^2}=\frac{y+x}{x^2y^2}$$

80. $$\frac{xy}{\frac{11}{x}+\frac{11}{y}}=\frac{xy(xy)}{xy\left(\frac{11}{x}+\frac{11}{y}\right)}=\frac{x^2y^2}{xy\left(\frac{11}{x}\right)+xy\left(\frac{11}{y}\right)}=\frac{x^2y^2}{11y+11x}=\frac{x^2y^2}{11(y+x)}$$

81. $$\frac{\frac{1}{x}+\frac{1}{y}}{\frac{1}{x}-\frac{1}{y}}=\frac{xy\left(\frac{1}{x}+\frac{1}{y}\right)}{xy\left(\frac{1}{x}-\frac{1}{y}\right)}=\frac{xy\left(\frac{1}{x}\right)+xy\left(\frac{1}{y}\right)}{xy\left(\frac{1}{x}\right)-xy\left(\frac{1}{y}\right)}=\frac{y+x}{y-x}$$

82. $$\frac{\frac{1}{x}-\frac{1}{y}}{\frac{1}{x}+\frac{1}{y}}=\frac{xy\left(\frac{1}{x}-\frac{1}{y}\right)}{xy\left(\frac{1}{x}+\frac{1}{y}\right)}=\frac{xy\left(\frac{1}{x}\right)-xy\left(\frac{1}{y}\right)}{xy\left(\frac{1}{x}\right)+xy\left(\frac{1}{y}\right)}=\frac{y-x}{y+x}$$

83. $$\frac{\frac{3a}{b}-\frac{4a^2}{x}}{\frac{1}{b}+\frac{1}{ax}}=\frac{abx\left(\frac{3a}{b}-\frac{4a^2}{x}\right)}{abx\left(\frac{1}{b}+\frac{1}{ax}\right)}=\frac{abx\left(\frac{3a}{b}\right)-abx\left(\frac{4a^2}{x}\right)}{abx\left(\frac{1}{b}\right)+abx\left(\frac{1}{ax}\right)}=\frac{3a^2x-4a^3b}{ax+b}=\frac{a^2(3x-4ab)}{ax+b}$$

84. $$\frac{1-\frac{x}{y}}{\frac{x^2}{y^2}-1}=\frac{y^2\left(1-\frac{x}{y}\right)}{y^2\left(\frac{x^2}{y^2}-1\right)}=\frac{y^2(1)-y^2\left(\frac{x}{y}\right)}{y^2\left(\frac{x^2}{y^2}\right)-y^2(1)}=\frac{y^2-xy}{x^2-y^2}=\frac{y(y-x)}{(x+y)(x-y)}=\frac{-y}{x+y}$$

85. $$\frac{x+1-\frac{6}{x}}{x+5+\frac{6}{x}}=\frac{x\left(x+1-\frac{6}{x}\right)}{x\left(x+5+\frac{6}{x}\right)}=\frac{x(x)+x(1)-x\left(\frac{6}{x}\right)}{x(x)+x(5)+x\left(\frac{6}{x}\right)}=\frac{x^2+x-6}{x^2+5x+6}=\frac{(x+3)(x-2)}{(x+2)(x+3)}=\frac{x-2}{x+2}$$

86. $$\frac{2z}{1-\frac{3}{z}}=\frac{z(2z)}{z\left(1-\frac{3}{z}\right)}=\frac{2z^2}{z(1)-z\left(\frac{3}{z}\right)}=\frac{2z^2}{z-3}$$

87. $$\frac{3xy}{1-\frac{1}{xy}}=\frac{xy(3xy)}{xy\left(1-\frac{1}{xy}\right)}=\frac{3x^2y^2}{xy(1)-xy\left(\frac{1}{xy}\right)}=\frac{3x^2y^2}{xy-1}$$

88. $$\frac{x-3+\frac{1}{x}}{-\frac{1}{x}-x+3}=\frac{x\left(x-3+\frac{1}{x}\right)}{x\left(-\frac{1}{x}-x+3\right)}=\frac{x^2-3x+1}{-1-x^2+3x}=\frac{x^2-3x+1}{-(x^2-3x+1)}=-1$$

89. $$\frac{3x}{x+\frac{1}{x}}=\frac{x(3x)}{x\left(x+\frac{1}{x}\right)}=\frac{3x^2}{x^2+1}$$

90. $$\frac{2x^2+4}{2+\frac{4x}{5}}=\frac{5(2x^2+4)}{5\left(2+\frac{4x}{5}\right)}=\frac{10x^2+20}{10+4x}=\frac{2(5x^2+10)}{2(5+2x)}=\frac{5x^2+10}{5+2x}$$

91. $$\frac{\frac{x}{x+2}-\frac{2}{x-1}}{\frac{3}{x+2}+\frac{x}{x-1}}=\frac{(x+2)(x-1)\left(\frac{x}{x+2}-\frac{2}{x-1}\right)}{(x+2)(x-1)\left(\frac{3}{x+2}+\frac{x}{x-1}\right)}=\frac{(x+2)(x-1)\left(\frac{x}{x+2}\right)-(x+2)(x-1)\left(\frac{2}{x-1}\right)}{(x+2)(x-1)\left(\frac{3}{x+2}\right)+(x+2)(x-1)\left(\frac{x}{x-1}\right)}$$
$$=\frac{(x-1)(x)-(x+2)(2)}{(x-1)(3)+(x+2)(x)}$$
$$=\frac{x^2-x-2x-4}{3x-3+x^2+2x}=\frac{x^2-3x-4}{x^2+5x-3}$$

92. $$\frac{\frac{2x}{x-3}+\frac{1}{x-2}}{\frac{3}{x-3}-\frac{x}{x-2}}=\frac{(x-3)(x-2)\left(\frac{2x}{x-3}+\frac{1}{x-2}\right)}{(x-3)(x-2)\left(\frac{3}{x-3}-\frac{x}{x-2}\right)}=\frac{(x-3)(x-2)\left(\frac{2x}{x-3}\right)+(x-3)(x-2)\left(\frac{1}{x-2}\right)}{(x-3)(x-2)\left(\frac{3}{x-3}\right)-(x-3)(x-2)\left(\frac{x}{x-2}\right)}$$
$$=\frac{(x-2)(2x)+(x-3)(1)}{(x-2)(3)-(x-3)(x)}$$
$$=\frac{2x^2-4x+x-3}{3x-6-x^2+3x}$$
$$=\frac{2x^2-3x-3}{-x^2+6x-6}=-\frac{2x^2-3x-3}{x^2-6x+6}$$

93. $$\frac{1}{1+x^{-1}}=\frac{1}{1+\frac{1}{x}}=\frac{x(1)}{x\left(1+\frac{1}{x}\right)}=\frac{x}{x+1}$$

94. $$\frac{y^{-1}}{x^{-1}+y^{-1}}=\frac{\frac{1}{y}}{\frac{1}{x}+\frac{1}{y}}=\frac{xy\left(\frac{1}{y}\right)}{xy\left(\frac{1}{x}+\frac{1}{y}\right)}=\frac{x}{y+x}$$

95. $$\frac{3(x+2)^{-1}+2(x-1)^{-1}}{(x+2)^{-1}}=\frac{\frac{3}{x+2}+\frac{2}{x-1}}{\frac{1}{x+2}}=\frac{(x+2)(x-1)\left(\frac{3}{x+2}+\frac{2}{x-1}\right)}{(x+2)(x-1)\left(\frac{1}{x+2}\right)}$$
$$=\frac{(x+2)(x-1)\left(\frac{3}{x+2}\right)+(x+2)(x-1)\left(\frac{2}{x-1}\right)}{x-1}$$
$$=\frac{(x-1)(3)+(x+2)(2)}{x-1}$$
$$=\frac{3x-3+2x+4}{x-1}=\frac{5x+1}{x-1}$$

96. $$\frac{2x(x-3)^{-1}-3(x+2)^{-1}}{(x-3)^{-1}(x+2)^{-1}}=\frac{\frac{2x}{x-3}-\frac{3}{x+2}}{\frac{1}{(x-3)(x+2)}}=\frac{(x-3)(x+2)\left(\frac{2x}{x-3}-\frac{3}{x+2}\right)}{(x-3)(x+2)\left(\frac{1}{(x-3)(x+2)}\right)}$$
$$=\frac{(x+2)(2x)-(x-3)(3)}{1}$$
$$=2x^2+4x-3x+9=2x^2+x+9$$

97. $$\frac{1}{\frac{1}{k_1}+\frac{1}{k_2}}=\frac{k_1k_2(1)}{k_1k_2\left(\frac{1}{k_1}+\frac{1}{k_2}\right)}=\frac{k_1k_2}{k_1k_2\left(\frac{1}{k_1}\right)+k_1k_2\left(\frac{1}{k_2}\right)}=\frac{k_1k_2}{k_2+k_1}$$

98. $$\frac{1}{\frac{1}{R_1}+\frac{1}{R_2}+\frac{1}{R_3}}=\frac{R_1R_2R_3(1)}{R_1R_2R_3\left(\frac{1}{R_1}+\frac{1}{R_2}+\frac{1}{R_3}\right)}=\frac{R_1R_2R_3}{R_1R_2R_3\left(\frac{1}{R_1}\right)+R_1R_2R_3\left(\frac{1}{R_2}\right)+R_1R_2R_3\left(\frac{1}{R_3}\right)}$$
$$=\frac{R_1R_2R_3}{R_2R_3+R_1R_3+R_1R_2}$$

99. $\dfrac{x}{1+\frac{1}{3x^{-1}}} = \dfrac{x}{1+\frac{1}{\frac{3}{x}}} = \dfrac{x}{1+\frac{x(1)}{x\left(\frac{3}{x}\right)}} = \dfrac{x}{1+\frac{x}{3}} = \dfrac{3x}{3\left(1+\frac{x}{3}\right)} = \dfrac{3x}{3+x}$

100. $\dfrac{ab}{2+\frac{3}{2a^{-1}}} = \dfrac{ab}{2+\frac{3}{\frac{2}{a}}} = \dfrac{ab}{2+\frac{a(3)}{a\left(\frac{2}{a}\right)}} = \dfrac{ab}{2+\frac{3a}{2}} = \dfrac{2ab}{2\left(2+\frac{3a}{2}\right)} = \dfrac{2ab}{4+3a}$

101. $\dfrac{1}{1+\frac{1}{1+\frac{1}{x}}} = \dfrac{1}{1+\frac{x(1)}{x\left(1+\frac{1}{x}\right)}} = \dfrac{1}{1+\frac{x}{x+1}} = \dfrac{(x+1)1}{(x+1)\left(1+\frac{x}{x+1}\right)} = \dfrac{x+1}{x+1+x} = \dfrac{x+1}{2x+1}$

102. $\dfrac{y}{2+\frac{2}{2+\frac{2}{y}}} = \dfrac{y}{2+\frac{y(2)}{y\left(2+\frac{2}{y}\right)}} = \dfrac{y}{2+\frac{2y}{2y+2}} = \dfrac{(2y+2)(y)}{(2y+2)\left(2+\frac{2y}{2y+2}\right)} = \dfrac{2y^2+2y}{(2y+2)(2)+2y}$

$= \dfrac{2y(y+1)}{4y+4+2y}$

$= \dfrac{2y(y+1)}{2(3y+2)} = \dfrac{y(y+1)}{3y+2}$

103. Answers may vary.

104. Answers may vary.

105. Answers may vary.

106. Answers may vary.

107. Since $-6<0$, $|-6| = -(-6) = 6$.

108. If $x<0$, then $5-x \geq 0$. Then $|5-x| = 5-x$.

109. $\left(\dfrac{x^3y^{-2}}{x^{-1}y}\right)^{-3} = \left(\dfrac{x^{-1}y}{x^3y^{-2}}\right)^3 = \left(\dfrac{y^2y}{x^3x}\right)^3 = \left(\dfrac{y^3}{x^4}\right)^3 = \dfrac{y^9}{x^{12}}$

110. $(27x^6)^{2/3} = 27^{2/3}(x^6)^{2/3} = \left(27^{1/3}\right)^2 x^{12/3} = 3^2x^4 = 9x^4$

111. $\sqrt{20}-\sqrt{45} = \sqrt{4}\sqrt{5}-\sqrt{9}\sqrt{5} = 2\sqrt{5}-3\sqrt{5} = -\sqrt{5}$

112. $2(x^2+4)-3(2x^2+5) = 2(x^2)+2(4)-3(2x^2)-3(5) = 2x^2+8-6x^2-15 = -4x^2-7$

Chapter 0 Summary (page 71)

1. **a.** natural: $3, 6, 8$

b. whole: $0, 3, 6, 8$

c. integers: $-6, -3, 0, 3, 6, 8$

d. rational: $-6, -3, 0, \frac{1}{2}, 3, 6, 8$

e. irrational: $\pi, \sqrt{5}$

f. real: $-6, -3, 0, \frac{1}{2}, 3, \pi, \sqrt{5}, 6, 8$

2. **a.** prime: 3

   b. composite: 6, 8

   c. even integers: $-6, 0, 6, 8$

   d. odd integers: $-3, 3$

3. **a.** associative property of addition

   b. commutative property of addition

   c. associative property of multiplication

   d. distributive property

   e. commutative property of multiplication

   f. commutative property of addition

   g. double negative rule

4. **a.** 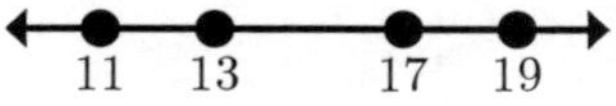

   b. 

5. **a.** $-3 < x \leq 5$

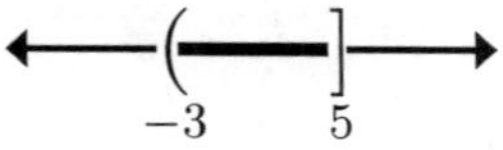

   b. $x \geq 0$ or $x < -1$

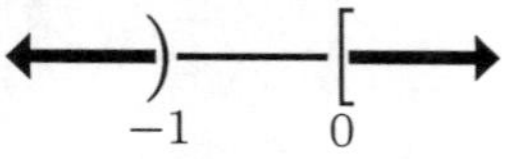

   c. $(-2, 4]$

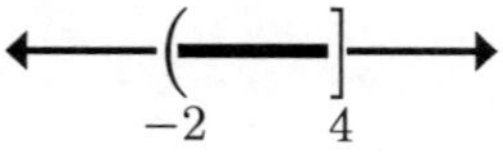

   d. $(-\infty, 2) \cap (-5, \infty)$

$(-\infty, 2)$ 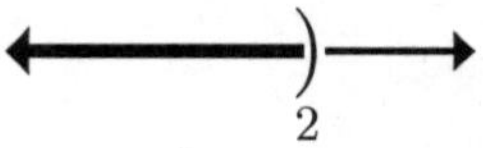

$(-5, \infty)$ 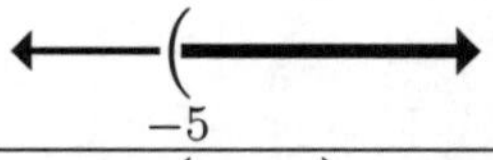

$(-\infty, 2) \cap (-5, \infty)$ 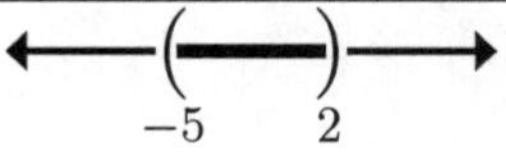

   e. $(-\infty, -4) \cup [6, \infty)$

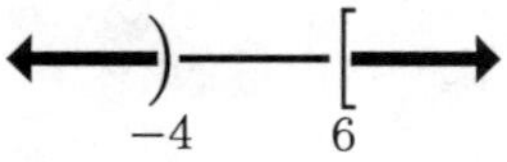

6. **a.** Since $6 \geq 0$, $|6| = 6$.

   b. Since $-25 < 0$, $|-25| = -(-25) = 25$.

   c. Since $1 - \sqrt{2} < 0$,
$\left|1 - \sqrt{2}\right| = -\left(1 - \sqrt{2}\right) = \sqrt{2} - 1$.

   d. Since $\sqrt{3} - 1 \geq 0$,
$\left|\sqrt{3} - 1\right| = \sqrt{3} - 1$.

7. distance $= |-5 - 7| = |-12| = 12$

8. **a.** $-5a^3 = -5aaa$

   b. $(-5a)^2 = (-5)(-5)aa = 25aa$

9. **a.** $3ttt = 3t^3$ **b.** $(-2b)(3b) = (-2)(3)bb = -6b^2$

10. **a.** $n^2n^4 = n^{2+4} = n^6$ **b.** $(p^3)^2 = p^{3\cdot 2} = p^6$

c. $(x^3y^2)^4 = (x^3)^4(y^2)^4 = x^{12}y^8$ **d.** $\left(\frac{a^4}{b^2}\right)^3 = \frac{(a^4)^3}{(b^2)^3} = \frac{a^{12}}{b^6}$

e. $(m^{-3}n^0)^2 = (m^{-3})^2(n^0)^2 = m^{-6}n^0 = m^{-6} = \frac{1}{m^6}$

f. $\left(\frac{p^{-2}q^2}{2}\right)^3 = \left(\frac{q^2}{2p^2}\right)^3 = \frac{(q^2)^3}{(2p^2)^3} = \frac{q^6}{8p^6}$

g. $\frac{a^5}{a^8} = a^{5-8} = a^{-3} = \frac{1}{a^3}$ **h.** $\left(\frac{a^2}{b^3}\right)^{-2} = \left(\frac{b^3}{a^2}\right)^2 = \frac{b^6}{a^4}$

i. $\left(\frac{3x^2y^{-2}}{x^2y^2}\right)^{-2} = \left(\frac{x^2y^2}{3x^2y^{-2}}\right)^2 = \left(\frac{x^2y^2y^2}{3x^2}\right)^2 = \left(\frac{y^4}{3}\right)^2 = \frac{y^8}{9}$

j. $\left(\frac{a^{-3}b^2}{ab^{-3}}\right)^{-2} = \left(\frac{ab^{-3}}{a^{-3}b^2}\right)^2 = \left(\frac{aa^3}{b^2b^3}\right)^2 = \left(\frac{a^4}{b^5}\right)^2 = \frac{a^8}{b^{10}}$

k. $\left(\frac{-3x^3y}{xy^3}\right)^{-2} = \left(\frac{xy^3}{-3x^3y}\right)^2 = \left(\frac{y^2}{-3x^2}\right)^2 = \frac{y^4}{9x^4}$

l. $\left(-\frac{2m^{-2}n^0}{4m^2n^{-1}}\right)^{-3} = \left(-\frac{4m^2n^{-1}}{2m^{-2}n^0}\right)^3 = \left(-\frac{2m^2m^2}{n^1n^0}\right)^3 = \left(-\frac{2m^4}{n}\right)^3 = -\frac{8m^{12}}{n^3}$

11. $-x^2 - xy^2 = -(-3)^2 - (-3)(3)^2 = -(+9) - (-3)(9) = -9 - (-27) = -9 + 27 = 18$

12. **a.** $6750 = 6.750 \times 10^3$ **b.** $0.00023 = 2.3 \times 10^{-4}$

13. **a.** $4.8 \times 10^2 = 480$ **b.** $0.25 \times 10^{-3} = 0.00025$

14.
$$\frac{(45{,}000)(350{,}000)}{0.000105} = \frac{(4.5 \times 10^4)(3.5 \times 10^5)}{1.05 \times 10^{-4}} = \frac{4.5 \times 3.5 \times 10^4 \times 10^5}{1.05 \times 10^{-4}} = \frac{15.75 \times 10^9}{1.05 \times 10^{-4}}$$
$$= 15 \times 10^{13}$$
$$= 1.5 \times 10^{14}$$

15. **a.** $121^{1/2} = (11^2)^{1/2} = 11$ **b.** $\left(\frac{27}{125}\right)^{1/3} = \left[\left(\frac{3}{5}\right)^3\right]^{1/3} = \frac{3}{5}$

c. $(32x^5)^{1/5} = 32^{1/5}(x^5)^{1/5} = 2x$

d. $(81a^4)^{1/4} = 81^{1/4}(a^4)^{1/4} = 3|a|$

e. $(-1000x^6)^{1/3} = (-1000)^{1/3}(x^6)^{1/3} = -10x^2$

f. $(-25x^2)^{1/2} = (-25)^{1/2}(x^2)^{1/2} \Rightarrow$ not a real number

g. $(x^{12}y^2)^{1/2} = (x^{12})^{1/2}(y^2)^{1/2} = x^6|y|$

h. $\left(\frac{x^{12}}{y^4}\right)^{-1/2} = \left(\frac{y^4}{x^{12}}\right)^{1/2} = \frac{y^2}{x^6}$

i. $\left(\frac{-c^{2/3}c^{5/3}}{c^{-2/3}}\right)^{1/3} = \left(\frac{-c^{7/3}}{c^{-2/3}}\right)^{1/3} = (-c^{9/3})^{1/3} = (-c^3)^{1/3} = -c$

j. $\left(\frac{a^{-1/4}a^{3/4}}{a^{9/2}}\right)^{-1/2} = \left(\frac{a^{9/2}}{a^{-1/4}a^{3/4}}\right)^{1/2} = \left(\frac{a^{9/2}}{a^{2/4}}\right)^{1/2} = \left(\frac{a^{9/2}}{a^{1/2}}\right)^{1/2} = (a^{8/2})^{1/2}$

$= (a^4)^{1/2} = a^2$

16. a. $64^{2/3} = (64^{1/3})^2 = 4^2 = 16$

b. $32^{-3/5} = \frac{1}{32^{3/5}} = \frac{1}{(32^{1/5})^3} = \frac{1}{2^3} = \frac{1}{8}$

c. $\left(\frac{16}{81}\right)^{3/4} = \frac{16^{3/4}}{81^{3/4}} = \frac{(16^{1/4})^3}{(81^{1/4})^3} = \frac{2^3}{3^3} = \frac{8}{27}$

d. $\left(\frac{32}{243}\right)^{2/5} = \frac{32^{2/5}}{243^{2/5}} = \frac{(32^{1/5})^2}{(243^{1/5})^2} = \frac{2^2}{3^2} = \frac{4}{9}$

e. $\left(\frac{8}{27}\right)^{-2/3} = \left(\frac{27}{8}\right)^{2/3} = \frac{27^{2/3}}{8^{2/3}} = \frac{(27^{1/3})^2}{(8^{1/3})^2} = \frac{3^2}{2^2} = \frac{9}{4}$

f. $\left(\frac{16}{625}\right)^{-3/4} = \left(\frac{625}{16}\right)^{3/4} = \frac{625^{3/4}}{16^{3/4}} = \frac{(625^{1/4})^3}{(16^{1/4})^3} = \frac{5^3}{2^3} = \frac{125}{8}$

g. $(-216x^3)^{2/3} = (-216)^{2/3}(x^3)^{2/3} = 36x^2$

h. $\frac{p^{a/2}p^{a/3}}{p^{a/6}} = \frac{p^{3a/6}p^{2a/6}}{p^{a/6}} = \frac{p^{5a/6}}{p^{a/6}} = p^{4a/6} = p^{2a/3}$

17. a. $\sqrt{36} = 6$

b. $-\sqrt{49} = -7$

c. $\sqrt{\frac{9}{25}} = \frac{\sqrt{9}}{\sqrt{25}} = \frac{3}{5}$

d. $\sqrt[3]{\frac{27}{125}} = \frac{\sqrt[3]{27}}{\sqrt[3]{125}} = \frac{3}{5}$

e. $\sqrt{x^2y^4} = \sqrt{x^2}\sqrt{y^4} = |x|y^2$

f. $\sqrt[3]{x^3} = x$

g. $\sqrt[4]{\dfrac{m^8n^4}{p^{16}}} = \dfrac{\sqrt[4]{m^8}\sqrt[4]{n^4}}{\sqrt[4]{p^{16}}} = \dfrac{m^2|n|}{p^4}$

h. $\sqrt[5]{\dfrac{a^{15}b^{10}}{c^5}} = \dfrac{\sqrt[5]{a^{15}}\sqrt[5]{b^{10}}}{\sqrt[5]{c^5}} = \dfrac{a^3b^2}{c}$

18. **a.** $\sqrt{50}+\sqrt{8} = \sqrt{25}\sqrt{2}+\sqrt{4}\sqrt{2} = 5\sqrt{2}+2\sqrt{2} = 7\sqrt{2}$

b. $\sqrt{12}+\sqrt{3}-\sqrt{27} = \sqrt{4}\sqrt{3}+\sqrt{3}-\sqrt{9}\sqrt{3} = 2\sqrt{3}+\sqrt{3}-3\sqrt{3} = 3\sqrt{3}-3\sqrt{3} = 0$

c. $\sqrt[3]{24x^4}-\sqrt[3]{3x^4} = \sqrt[3]{8x^3}\sqrt[3]{3x}-\sqrt[3]{x^3}\sqrt[3]{3x} = 2x\sqrt[3]{3x}-x\sqrt[3]{3x} = x\sqrt[3]{3x}$

19. **a.** $\dfrac{\sqrt{7}}{\sqrt{5}} = \dfrac{\sqrt{7}}{\sqrt{5}}\cdot\dfrac{\sqrt{5}}{\sqrt{5}} = \dfrac{\sqrt{35}}{5}$

b. $\dfrac{8}{\sqrt{8}} = \dfrac{8}{\sqrt{8}}\cdot\dfrac{\sqrt{2}}{\sqrt{2}} = \dfrac{8\sqrt{2}}{\sqrt{16}} = \dfrac{8\sqrt{2}}{4}$
$= 2\sqrt{2}$

c. $\dfrac{1}{\sqrt[3]{2}} = \dfrac{1}{\sqrt[3]{2}}\cdot\dfrac{\sqrt[3]{4}}{\sqrt[3]{4}} = \dfrac{\sqrt[3]{4}}{\sqrt[3]{8}} = \dfrac{\sqrt[3]{4}}{2}$

d. $\dfrac{2}{\sqrt[3]{25}} = \dfrac{2}{\sqrt[3]{25}}\cdot\dfrac{\sqrt[3]{5}}{\sqrt[3]{5}} = \dfrac{2\sqrt[3]{5}}{\sqrt[3]{125}} = \dfrac{2\sqrt[3]{5}}{5}$

20. **a.** $\dfrac{\sqrt{2}}{5} = \dfrac{\sqrt{2}}{5}\cdot\dfrac{\sqrt{2}}{\sqrt{2}} = \dfrac{2}{5\sqrt{2}}$

b. $\dfrac{\sqrt{5}}{5} = \dfrac{\sqrt{5}}{5}\cdot\dfrac{\sqrt{5}}{\sqrt{5}} = \dfrac{5}{5\sqrt{5}} = \dfrac{1}{\sqrt{5}}$

c. $\dfrac{\sqrt{2x}}{3} = \dfrac{\sqrt{2x}}{3}\cdot\dfrac{\sqrt{2x}}{\sqrt{2x}} = \dfrac{2x}{3\sqrt{2x}}$

d. $\dfrac{3\sqrt[3]{7x}}{2} = \dfrac{3\sqrt[3]{7x}}{2}\cdot\dfrac{\sqrt[3]{49x^2}}{\sqrt[3]{49x^2}} = \dfrac{3\sqrt[3]{343x^3}}{2\sqrt[3]{49x^2}}$
$= \dfrac{21x}{2\sqrt[3]{49x^2}}$

21. **a.** 3rd degree, binomial

b. 2nd degree, trinomial

c. 2nd degree, monomial

d. 4th degree, trinomial

22. **a.** $2(x+3)+3(x-4) = 2x+6+3x-12 = 5x-6$

b. $3x^2(x-1)-2x(x+3)-x^2(x+2) = 3x^3-3x^2-2x^2-6x-x^3-2x^2 = 2x^3-7x^2-6x$

c. $(3x+2)(3x+2) = 9x^2+6x+6x+4 = 9x^2+12x+4$

d. $(3x+y)(2x-3y) = 6x^2-9xy+2xy-3y^2 = 6x^2-7xy-3y^2$

e. $(4a+2b)(2a-3b) = 8a^2-12ab+4ab-6b^2 = 8a^2-8ab-6b^2$

f. $(z+3)(3z^2+z-1) = 3z^3+z^2-z+9z^2+3z-3 = 3z^3+10z^2+2z-3$

g. $(a^n+2)(a^n-1) = a^{2n}-a^n+2a^n-2 = a^{2n}+a^n-2$

h. $\left(\sqrt{2}+x\right)^2=\left(\sqrt{2}+x\right)\left(\sqrt{2}+x\right)=\left(\sqrt{2}\right)^2+x\sqrt{2}+x\sqrt{2}+x^2=2+2x\sqrt{2}+x^2$

i. $\left(\sqrt{2}+1\right)\left(\sqrt{3}+1\right)=\sqrt{6}+\sqrt{2}+\sqrt{3}+1$

j. $\left(\sqrt[3]{3}-2\right)\left(\sqrt[3]{9}+2\sqrt[3]{3}+4\right)=\sqrt[3]{27}+2\sqrt[3]{9}+4\sqrt[3]{3}-2\sqrt[3]{9}-4\sqrt[3]{3}-8=3-8=-5$

23. a. $\dfrac{2}{\sqrt{3}-1}=\dfrac{2}{\sqrt{3}-1}\cdot\dfrac{\sqrt{3}+1}{\sqrt{3}+1}=\dfrac{2\left(\sqrt{3}+1\right)}{\left(\sqrt{3}\right)^2-1^2}=\dfrac{2\left(\sqrt{3}+1\right)}{3-1}=\dfrac{2\left(\sqrt{3}+1\right)}{2}=\sqrt{3}+1$

b. $\dfrac{-2}{\sqrt{3}-\sqrt{2}}=\dfrac{-2}{\sqrt{3}-\sqrt{2}}\cdot\dfrac{\sqrt{3}+\sqrt{2}}{\sqrt{3}+\sqrt{2}}=\dfrac{-2\left(\sqrt{3}+\sqrt{2}\right)}{\left(\sqrt{3}\right)^2-\left(\sqrt{2}\right)^2}=\dfrac{-2\left(\sqrt{3}+\sqrt{2}\right)}{3-2}$

$=\dfrac{-2\left(\sqrt{3}+\sqrt{2}\right)}{1}$

$=-2\left(\sqrt{3}+\sqrt{2}\right)$

c. $\dfrac{2x}{\sqrt{x}-2}=\dfrac{2x}{\sqrt{x}-2}\cdot\dfrac{\sqrt{x}+2}{\sqrt{x}+2}=\dfrac{2x(\sqrt{x}+2)}{(\sqrt{x})^2-2^2}=\dfrac{2x(\sqrt{x}+2)}{x-4}$

d. $\dfrac{\sqrt{x}-\sqrt{y}}{\sqrt{x}+\sqrt{y}}=\dfrac{\sqrt{x}-\sqrt{y}}{\sqrt{x}+\sqrt{y}}\cdot\dfrac{\sqrt{x}-\sqrt{y}}{\sqrt{x}-\sqrt{y}}=\dfrac{\sqrt{x^2}-\sqrt{xy}-\sqrt{xy}+y}{(\sqrt{x})^2-\left(\sqrt{y}\right)^2}=\dfrac{x-2\sqrt{xy}+y}{x-y}$

24. a. $\dfrac{\sqrt{x}+2}{5}=\dfrac{\sqrt{x}+2}{5}\cdot\dfrac{\sqrt{x}-2}{\sqrt{x}-2}=\dfrac{\left(\sqrt{x}\right)^2-2^2}{5(\sqrt{x}-2)}=\dfrac{x-4}{5(\sqrt{x}-2)}$

b. $\dfrac{1-\sqrt{a}}{a}=\dfrac{1-\sqrt{a}}{a}\cdot\dfrac{1+\sqrt{a}}{1+\sqrt{a}}=\dfrac{1^2-(\sqrt{a})^2}{a(1+\sqrt{a})}=\dfrac{1-a}{a(1+\sqrt{a})}$

25. a. $\dfrac{3x^2y^2}{6x^3y}=\dfrac{y}{2x}$

b. $\dfrac{4a^2b^3+6ab^4}{2b^2}=\dfrac{4a^2b^3}{2b^2}+\dfrac{6ab^4}{2b^2}$

$=2a^2b+3ab^2$

c.

$$\begin{array}{r|l} & x^2 + 2x + 1 \\ \hline 2x+3 & 2x^3 + 7x^2 + 8x + 3 \\ & \underline{2x^3 + 3x^2} \\ & \quad 4x^2 + 8x \\ & \quad \underline{4x^2 + 6x} \\ & \qquad 2x + 3 \\ & \qquad \underline{2x + 3} \\ & \qquad\qquad 0 \end{array}$$

d.

$$\begin{array}{r|l} & x^3 + 2x - 3 + \frac{-6}{x^2-1} \\ \hline x^2-1 & x^5 + 0x^4 + x^3 - 3x^2 - 2x - 3 \\ & \underline{x^5 \qquad - x^3} \\ & \qquad 2x^3 - 3x^2 - 2x \\ & \qquad \underline{2x^3 \qquad - 2x} \\ & \qquad\quad -3x^2 \qquad -3 \\ & \qquad\quad \underline{-3x^2 \qquad +3} \\ & \qquad\qquad\qquad -6 \end{array}$$

26. a. $3t^3 - 3t = 3t(t^2 - 1) = 3t(t+1)(t-1)$

b. $5r^3 - 5 = 5(r^3 - 1) = 5(r^3 - 1^3) = 5(r-1)(r^2 + r + 1)$

c. $6x^2 + 7x - 24 = (3x+8)(2x-3)$

d. $3a^2 + ax - 3a - x = a(3a+x) - 1(3a+x) = (3a+x)(a-1)$

e. $8x^3 - 125 = (2x)^3 - 5^3 = (2x-5)\left[(2x)^2 + (2x)(5) + 5^2\right] = (2x-5)(4x^2 + 10x + 25)$

f. $6x^2 - 20x - 16 = 2(3x^2 - 10x - 8) = 2(3x+2)(x-4)$

g. $x^2 + 6x + 9 - t^2 = (x+3)(x+3) - t^2 = (x+3)^2 - t^2 = (x+3+t)(x+3-t)$

h. $3x^2 - 1 + 5x = 3x^2 + 5x - 1 \Rightarrow$ prime

i. $8z^3 + 343 = (2z)^3 + 7^3 = (2z+7)\left[(2z)^2 - (2z)(7) + 7^2\right] = (2z+7)(4z^2 - 14z + 49)$

j. $1 + 14b + 49b^2 = 49b^2 + 14b + 1 = (7b+1)(7b+1) = (7b+1)^2$

k. $121z^2 + 4 - 44z = 121z^2 - 44z + 4 = (11z-2)(11z-2) = (11z-2)^2$

l. $64y^3 - 1000 = 8(8y^3 - 125) = 8\left[(2y)^3 - 5^3\right] = 8(2y-5)(4y^2 + 10y + 25)$

m. $2xy - 4zx - wy + 2zw = 2x(y-2z) - w(y-2z) = (y-2z)(2x-w)$

n.

$$\begin{aligned} x^8 + x^4 + 1 = x^8 + 2x^4 + 1 - x^4 &= \left(x^4+1\right)\left(x^4+1\right) - x^4 \\ &= \left(x^4+1\right)^2 - \left(x^2\right)^2 \\ &= \left(x^4 + 1 + x^2\right)\left(x^4 + 1 - x^2\right) \\ &= \left(x^4 + 2x^2 + 1 - x^2\right)\left(x^4 - x^2 + 1\right) \\ &= \left[\left(x^2+1\right)\left(x^2+1\right) - x^2\right]\left(x^4 - x^2 + 1\right) \\ &= \left(x^2 + 1 + x\right)\left(x^2 + 1 - x\right)\left(x^4 - x^2 + 1\right) \end{aligned}$$

27. a. $\dfrac{x^2 - 4x + 4}{x+2} \cdot \dfrac{x^2 + 5x + 6}{x-2} = \dfrac{(x-2)(x-2)}{x+2} \cdot \dfrac{(x+2)(x+3)}{x-2} = (x-2)(x+3)$

b. $$\frac{2y^2-11y+15}{y^2-6y+8}\cdot\frac{y^2-2y-8}{y^2-y-6}=\frac{(2y-5)(y-3)}{(y-4)(y-2)}\cdot\frac{(y-4)(y+2)}{(y-3)(y+2)}=\frac{2y-5}{y-2}$$

c. $$\begin{aligned}\frac{2t^2+t-3}{3t^2-7t+4}\div\frac{10t+15}{3t^2-t-4}&=\frac{2t^2+t-3}{3t^2-7t+4}\cdot\frac{3t^2-t-4}{10t+15}\\&=\frac{(2t+3)(t-1)}{(3t-4)(t-1)}\cdot\frac{(3t-4)(t+1)}{5(2t+3)}=\frac{t+1}{5}\end{aligned}$$

d. $$\begin{aligned}\frac{p^2+7p+12}{p^3+8p^2+4p}\div\frac{p^2-9}{p^2}=\frac{p^2+7p+12}{p^3+8p^2+4p}\cdot\frac{p^2}{p^2-9}&=\frac{(p+3)(p+4)}{p(p^2+8p+4)}\cdot\frac{p^2}{(p+3)(p-3)}\\&=\frac{p(p+4)}{(p^2+8p+4)(p-3)}\end{aligned}$$

e. $$\begin{aligned}&\frac{x^2+x-6}{x^2-x-6}\cdot\frac{x^2-x-6}{x^2+x-2}\div\frac{x^2-4}{x^2-5x+6}\ \cdots\\&\quad=\frac{x^2+x-6}{x^2-x-6}\cdot\frac{x^2-x-6}{x^2+x-2}\cdot\frac{x^2-5x+6}{x^2-4}\\&\quad=\frac{(x+3)(x-2)}{(x-3)(x+2)}\cdot\frac{(x-3)(x+2)}{(x+2)(x-1)}\cdot\frac{(x-2)(x-3)}{(x+2)(x-2)}=\frac{(x+3)(x-2)(x-3)}{(x+2)^2(x-1)}\end{aligned}$$

f. $$\begin{aligned}\left(\frac{2x+6}{x+5}\div\frac{2x^2-2x-4}{x^2-25}\right)\frac{x^2-x-2}{x^2-2x-15}&=\frac{2x+6}{x+5}\cdot\frac{x^2-25}{2(x^2-x-2)}\cdot\frac{x^2-x-2}{x^2-2x-15}\\&=\frac{2(x+3)}{x+5}\cdot\frac{(x+5)(x-5)}{2(x-2)(x+1)}\cdot\frac{(x-2)(x+1)}{(x-5)(x+3)}\\&=1\end{aligned}$$

g. $$\begin{aligned}\frac{2}{x-4}+\frac{3x}{x+5}=\frac{2(x+5)}{(x-4)(x+5)}+\frac{3x(x-4)}{(x+5)(x-4)}&=\frac{2x+10}{(x-4)(x+5)}+\frac{3x^2-12x}{(x-4)(x+5)}\\&=\frac{3x^2-10x+10}{(x-4)(x+5)}\end{aligned}$$

h. $$\begin{aligned}\frac{5x}{x-2}-\frac{3x+7}{x+2}+\frac{2x+1}{x+2}&=\frac{5x}{x-2}+\frac{-x-6}{x+2}\\&=\frac{5x(x+2)}{(x-2)(x+2)}+\frac{(-x-6)(x-2)}{(x+2)(x-2)}\\&=\frac{5x^2+10x}{(x-2)(x+2)}+\frac{-x^2-4x+12}{(x-2)(x+2)}\\&=\frac{4x^2+6x+12}{(x-2)(x+2)}=\frac{2(2x^2+3x+6)}{(x-2)(x+2)}\end{aligned}$$

i. $$\frac{x}{x-1}+\frac{x}{x-2}+\frac{x}{x-3}$$
$$=\frac{x(x-2)(x-3)}{(x-1)(x-2)(x-3)}+\frac{x(x-1)(x-3)}{(x-2)(x-1)(x-3)}+\frac{x(x-1)(x-2)}{(x-3)(x-1)(x-2)}$$
$$=\frac{x^3-5x^2+6x}{(x-1)(x-2)(x-3)}+\frac{x^3-4x^2+3x}{(x-1)(x-2)(x-3)}+\frac{x^3-3x^2+2x}{(x-1)(x-2)(x-3)}$$
$$=\frac{3x^3-12x^2+11x}{(x-1)(x-2)(x-3)}=\frac{x(3x^2-12x+11)}{(x-1)(x-2)(x-3)}$$

j. $$\frac{x}{x+1}-\frac{3x+7}{x+2}+\frac{2x+1}{x+2}=\frac{x}{x+1}+\frac{-3x-7}{x+2}+\frac{2x+1}{x+2}$$
$$=\frac{x}{x+1}+\frac{-x-6}{x+2}$$
$$=\frac{x(x+2)}{(x+1)(x+2)}+\frac{(-x-6)(x+1)}{(x+2)(x+1)}$$
$$=\frac{x^2+2x}{(x+1)(x+2)}+\frac{-x^2-7x-6}{(x+1)(x+2)}=\frac{-5x-6}{(x+1)(x+2)}$$

k. $$\frac{3(x+1)}{x}-\frac{5(x^2+3)}{x^2}+\frac{x}{x+1}=\frac{3x(x+1)(x+1)}{x^2(x+1)}-\frac{5(x^2+3)(x+1)}{x^2(x+1)}+\frac{x(x^2)}{x^2(x+1)}$$
$$=\frac{3x^3+6x^2+3x}{x^2(x+1)}-\frac{5x^3+5x^2+15x+15}{x^2(x+1)}+\frac{x^3}{x^2(x+1)}$$
$$=\frac{-x^3+x^2-12x-15}{x^2(x+1)}$$

l. $$\frac{3x}{x+1}+\frac{x^2+4x+3}{x^2+3x+2}-\frac{x^2+x-6}{x^2-4}=\frac{3x}{x+1}+\frac{(x+3)(x+1)}{(x+1)(x+2)}-\frac{(x+3)(x-2)}{(x+2)(x-2)}$$
$$=\frac{3x}{x+1}+\frac{x+3}{x+2}-\frac{x+3}{x+2}=\frac{3x}{x+1}$$

28. **a.** $$\frac{\frac{5x}{2}}{\frac{3x^2}{8}}=\frac{5x}{2}\div\frac{3x^2}{8}=\frac{5x}{2}\cdot\frac{8}{3x^2}=\frac{20}{3x}$$

b. $$\frac{\frac{3x}{y}}{\frac{6x}{y^2}}=\frac{3x}{y}\div\frac{6x}{y^2}=\frac{3x}{y}\cdot\frac{y^2}{6x}=\frac{y}{2}$$

c. $$\frac{\frac{1}{x}+\frac{1}{y}}{x-y}=\frac{xy\left(\frac{1}{x}+\frac{1}{y}\right)}{xy(x-y)}=\frac{xy\left(\frac{1}{x}\right)+xy\left(\frac{1}{y}\right)}{xy(x-y)}=\frac{y+x}{xy(x-y)}$$

d. $$\frac{x^{-1}+y^{-1}}{y^{-1}-x^{-1}}=\frac{\frac{1}{x}+\frac{1}{y}}{\frac{1}{y}-\frac{1}{x}}=\frac{xy\left(\frac{1}{x}+\frac{1}{y}\right)}{xy\left(\frac{1}{y}-\frac{1}{x}\right)}=\frac{xy\left(\frac{1}{x}\right)+xy\left(\frac{1}{y}\right)}{xy\left(\frac{1}{y}\right)-xy\left(\frac{1}{x}\right)}=\frac{y+x}{x-y}$$

Chapter 0 Test (page 77)

1. odd integers: $-7, 1, 3$

2. prime numbers: 3

3. commutative property of addition

4. distributive property

5. $-4 < x \le 2 \Rightarrow$ 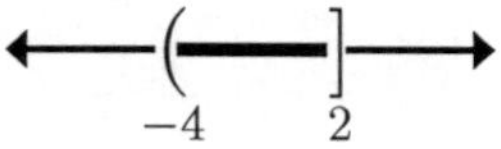

6. $(-\infty, -3) \cup [6, \infty) \Rightarrow$ 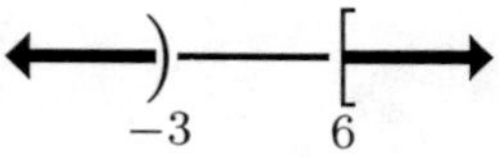

7. Since $-17 < 0$, $|-17| = -(-17) = 17$

8. If $x < 0$, then $x - 7 < 0$. Then $|x - 7| = -(x - 7)$.

9. distance $= |-4 - 12| = |-16| = 16$

10. distance $= |-20 - (-12)| = |-8| = 8$

11. $x^4x^5x^2 = x^{4+5+2} = x^{11}$

12. $\dfrac{r^2r^3s}{r^4s^2} = \dfrac{r^5s}{r^4s^2} = \dfrac{r}{s}$

13. $\dfrac{(a^{-1}a^2)^{-2}}{a^{-3}} = \dfrac{(a^1)^{-2}}{a^{-3}} = \dfrac{a^{-2}}{a^{-3}} = a$

14. $\left(\dfrac{x^0x^2}{x^{-2}}\right)^6 = \left(\dfrac{x^2}{x^{-2}}\right)^6 = (x^4)^6 = x^{24}$

15. $450{,}000 = 4.5 \times 10^5$

16. $0.000345 = 3.45 \times 10^{-4}$

17. $3.7 \times 10^3 = 3{,}700$

18. $1.2 \times 10^{-3} = 0.0012$

19. $(25a^4)^{1/2} = 25^{1/2}(a^4)^{1/2} = 5a^2$

20. $\left(\dfrac{36}{81}\right)^{3/2} = \dfrac{36^{3/2}}{81^{3/2}} = \dfrac{(36^{1/2})^3}{(81^{1/2})^3} = \dfrac{216}{729}$

21. $\left(\dfrac{8t^6}{27s^9}\right)^{-2/3} = \left(\dfrac{27s^9}{8t^6}\right)^{2/3} = \dfrac{27^{2/3}(s^9)^{2/3}}{8^{2/3}(t^6)^{2/3}} = \dfrac{(27^{1/3})^2s^6}{(8^{1/3})^2t^4} = \dfrac{9s^6}{4t^4}$

22. $\sqrt[3]{27a^6} = \sqrt[3]{27}\sqrt[3]{a^6} = 3a^2$

23. $\sqrt{12} + \sqrt{27} = \sqrt{4}\sqrt{3} + \sqrt{9}\sqrt{3}$
$= 2\sqrt{3} + 3\sqrt{3} = 5\sqrt{3}$

24. $2\sqrt[3]{3x^4} - 3x\sqrt[3]{24x} = 2\sqrt[3]{x^3}\sqrt[3]{3x} - 3x\sqrt[3]{8}\sqrt[3]{3x} = 2x\sqrt[3]{3x} - 3x(2)\sqrt[3]{3x} = 2x\sqrt[3]{3x} - 6x\sqrt[3]{3x}$
$= -4x\sqrt[3]{3x}$

25. $\dfrac{x}{\sqrt{x} - 2} = \dfrac{x}{\sqrt{x} - 2} \cdot \dfrac{\sqrt{x} + 2}{\sqrt{x} + 2} = \dfrac{x(\sqrt{x} + 2)}{(\sqrt{x})^2 - 2^2} = \dfrac{x(\sqrt{x} + 2)}{x - 4}$

26. $\dfrac{\sqrt{x} - \sqrt{y}}{\sqrt{x} + \sqrt{y}} = \dfrac{\sqrt{x} - \sqrt{y}}{\sqrt{x} + \sqrt{y}} \cdot \dfrac{\sqrt{x} + \sqrt{y}}{\sqrt{x} + \sqrt{y}} = \dfrac{(\sqrt{x})^2 - (\sqrt{y})^2}{\sqrt{x^2} + \sqrt{xy} + \sqrt{xy} + \sqrt{y^2}} = \dfrac{x - y}{x + 2\sqrt{xy} + y}$

27. $(a^2 + 3) - (2a^2 - 4) = a^2 + 3 - 2a^2 + 4$
$= -a^2 + 7$

28. $(3a^3b^2)(-2a^3b^4) = -6a^6b^6$

29. $\begin{aligned}(3x-4)(2x+7)&=6x^2+21x-8x-28\\&=6x^2+13x-28\end{aligned}$

30. $\begin{aligned}(a^n+2)(a^n-3)&=a^{2n}-3a^n+2a^n-6\\&=a^{2n}-a^n-6\end{aligned}$

31. $(x^2+4)(x^2-4)=x^4-4x^2+4x^2-16=x^4-16$

32. $(x^2-x+2)(2x-3)=2x^3-3x^2-2x^2+3x+4x-6=2x^3-5x^2+7x-6$

33.

$$\begin{array}{r|l} & 6x + 19 + \frac{34}{x-3} \\ \hline x-3 & 6x^2 + x - 23 \\ & \underline{6x^2 - 18x} \\ & \quad 19x - 23 \\ & \quad \underline{19x - 57} \\ & \qquad 34 \end{array}$$

34.

$$\begin{array}{r|l} & x^2 + 2x + 1 \\ \hline 2x-1 & 2x^3 + 3x^2 + 0x - 1 \\ & \underline{2x^3 - x^2} \\ & \quad 4x^2 + 0x \\ & \quad \underline{4x^2 - 2x} \\ & \qquad 2x - 1 \\ & \qquad \underline{2x - 1} \\ & \qquad\quad 0 \end{array}$$

35. $3x+6y=3(x+2y)$

36. $x^2-100=x^2-10^2=(x+10)(x-10)$

37. $10t^2-19tw+6w^2=(5t-2w)(2t-3w)$

38. $\begin{aligned}3a^3-648&=3\left(a^3-216\right)\\&=3(a-6)\left(a^2+6a+36\right)\end{aligned}$

39. $\begin{aligned}x^4-x^2-12&=\left(x^2-4\right)\left(x^2+3\right)\\&=(x+2)(x-2)\left(x^2+3\right)\end{aligned}$

40. $6x^4+11x^2-10=(3x^2-2)(2x^2+5)$

41. $\dfrac{x}{x+2}+\dfrac{2}{x+2}=\dfrac{x+2}{x+2}=1$

42. $\dfrac{x}{x+1}-\dfrac{x}{x-1}=\dfrac{x(x-1)}{(x+1)(x-1)}-\dfrac{x(x+1)}{(x+1)(x-1)}=\dfrac{x^2-x-x^2-x}{(x+1)(x-1)}=\dfrac{-2x}{(x+1)(x-1)}$

43. $\dfrac{x^2+x-20}{x^2-16}\cdot\dfrac{x^2-25}{x-5}=\dfrac{(x+5)(x-4)}{(x+4)(x-4)}\cdot\dfrac{(x+5)(x-5)}{x-5}=\dfrac{(x+5)^2}{x+4}$

44. $\dfrac{x+2}{x^2+2x+1}\div\dfrac{x^2-4}{x+1}==\dfrac{x+2}{(x+1)(x+1)}\cdot\dfrac{x+1}{(x+2)(x-2)}=\dfrac{1}{(x+1)(x-2)}$

45. $\dfrac{\frac{1}{a}+\frac{1}{b}}{\frac{1}{b}}=\dfrac{ab\left(\frac{1}{a}+\frac{1}{b}\right)}{ab\left(\frac{1}{b}\right)}=\dfrac{ab\left(\frac{1}{a}\right)+ab\left(\frac{1}{b}\right)}{a}=\dfrac{b+a}{a}$

46. $\dfrac{x^{-1}}{x^{-1}+y^{-1}}=\dfrac{\frac{1}{x}}{\frac{1}{x}+\frac{1}{y}}=\dfrac{xy\left(\frac{1}{x}\right)}{xy\left(\frac{1}{x}+\frac{1}{y}\right)}=\dfrac{y}{xy\left(\frac{1}{x}\right)+xy\left(\frac{1}{y}\right)}=\dfrac{y}{y+x}$

Exercise 1.1 (page 86)

1. root, solution

2. identity

3. no

4. conditional

5. linear

6. rational

7. one

8. denominator

9. $x + 3 = 1$
no restrictions

10. $\frac{1}{2}x - 7 = 14$
no restrictions

11. $\frac{1}{x} = 12$
$x \neq 0$

12. $\frac{3}{x-2}$
$x \neq 2$

13. $\sqrt{x} = 4$
$x \geq 0$

14. $\sqrt[3]{x} = 64$
no restrictions

15. $\frac{1}{x-3} = \frac{5}{x+2}$
$x \neq 3, x \neq -2$

16. $\frac{24}{\sqrt{x-3}}$
$x - 3 > 0 \Rightarrow x > 3$

17.
$$\begin{aligned} 2x + 5 &= 15 \\ 2x + 5 - 5 &= 15 - 5 \\ 2x &= 10 \\ \frac{2x}{2} &= \frac{10}{2} \\ x &= 5 \end{aligned}$$
conditional equation

18.
$$\begin{aligned} 3x + 2 &= x + 8 \\ 3x - x + 2 &= x - x + 8 \\ 2x + 2 &= 8 \\ 2x + 2 - 2 &= 8 - 2 \\ 2x &= 6 \\ \frac{2x}{2} &= \frac{6}{2} \\ x &= 3 \end{aligned}$$
conditional equation

19.
$$\begin{aligned} 2(n + 2) - 5 &= 2n \\ 2n + 4 - 5 &= 2n \\ 2n - 1 &= 2n \\ 2n - 2n - 1 &= 2n - 2n \\ -1 &\neq 0 \end{aligned}$$
no solution

20.
$$\begin{aligned} 3(m+2) &= 2(m+3)+m \\ 3m+6 &= 2m+6+m \\ 3m+6 &= 3m+6 \end{aligned}$$
identity

21.
$$\begin{aligned} \frac{x+7}{2} &= 7 \\ 2\cdot\frac{x+7}{2} &= 2(7) \\ x+7 &= 14 \\ x+7-7 &= 14-7 \\ x &= 7 \end{aligned}$$
conditional equation

22.
$$\begin{aligned} \frac{x}{2}-7 &= 14 \\ \frac{x}{2}-7+7 &= 14+7 \\ \frac{x}{2} &= 21 \\ 2\cdot\frac{x}{2} &= 2(21) \\ x &= 42 \end{aligned}$$
conditional equation

23.
$$\begin{aligned} 2(a+1) &= 3(a-2)-a \\ 2a+2 &= 3a-6-a \\ 2a+2 &= 2a-6 \\ 2a-2a+2 &= 2a-2a-6 \\ 2 &\neq -6 \end{aligned}$$
no solution

24.
$$\begin{aligned} x^2 &= (x+4)(x-4)+16 \\ x^2 &= x^2-16+16 \\ x^2 &= x^2 \end{aligned}$$
identity

25.
$$\begin{aligned} 3(x-3) &= \frac{6x-18}{2} \\ 3x-9 &= \frac{6x-18}{2} \\ 2(3x-9) &= 2\cdot\frac{6x-18}{2} \\ 6x-18 &= 6x-18 \end{aligned}$$
identity

26.
$$\begin{aligned} x(x+2) &= (x+1)^2 \\ x^2+2x &= (x+1)(x+1) \\ x^2+2x &= x^2+2x+1 \\ x^2-x^2+2x &= x^2-x^2+2x+1 \\ 2x &= 2x+1 \\ 2x-2x &= 2x-2x+1 \\ 0 &\neq 1 \end{aligned}$$
no solution

27.
$$\begin{aligned} \frac{3}{b-3} &= 1 \\ (b-3)\cdot\frac{3}{b-3} &= (b-3)(1) \\ 3 &= b-3 \\ 3+3 &= b-3+3 \\ 6 &= b \end{aligned}$$
conditional equation

28.
$$\begin{aligned} x^2-8x+15 &= (x-3)(x+5) \\ x^2-8x+15 &= x^2+2x-15 \\ x^2-x^2-8x+15 &= x^2-x^2+2x-15 \\ -8x+15 &= 2x-15 \\ -8x+8x+15 &= 2x+8x-15 \\ 15 &= 10x-15 \\ 15+15 &= 10x-15+15 \\ 30 &= 10x \\ \frac{30}{10} &= \frac{10x}{10} \\ 3 &= x \end{aligned}$$
conditional equation

29.
$$\begin{aligned}2x^2+5x-3&=(2x-1)(x+3)\\2x^2+5x-3&=2x^2+5x-3\end{aligned}$$
identity

30.
$$\begin{aligned}2x^2+5x-3&=2x\left(x+\frac{19}{2}\right)\\2x^2+5x-3&=2x^2+19x\\2x^2-2x^2+5x-3&=2x^2-2x^2+19x\\5x-3&=19x\\5x-5x-3&=19x-5x\\-3&=14x\\\frac{-3}{14}&=\frac{14x}{14}\\-\frac{3}{14}&=x\end{aligned}$$
conditional equation

31.
$$\begin{aligned}2x+7&=10-x\\3x+7&=10\\3x&=3\\x&=1\end{aligned}$$

32.
$$\begin{aligned}9a-3&=15+3a\\6a-3&=15\\6a&=18\\a&=3\end{aligned}$$

33.
$$\begin{aligned}\frac{5}{3}z-8&=7\\\frac{5}{3}z&=15\\3\cdot\frac{5}{3}z&=3(15)\\5z&=45\\z&=9\end{aligned}$$

34.
$$\begin{aligned}\frac{4}{3}y+12&=-4\\\frac{4}{3}y&=-16\\3\cdot\frac{4}{3}y&=3(-16)\\4y&=-48\\y&=-12\end{aligned}$$

35.
$$\begin{aligned}\frac{z}{5}+2&=4\\\frac{z}{5}&=2\\5\cdot\frac{z}{5}&=5(2)\\z&=10\end{aligned}$$

36.
$$\begin{aligned}\frac{3p}{7}-p&=-4\\7\left(\frac{3p}{7}-p\right)&=7(-4)\\3p-7p&=-28\\-4p&=-28\\p&=7\end{aligned}$$

37.
$$\begin{aligned}\frac{3x-2}{3}&=2x+\frac{7}{3}\\3\cdot\frac{3x-2}{3}&=3\left(2x+\frac{7}{3}\right)\\3x-2&=6x+7\\-3x-2&=7\\-3x&=9\\x&=-3\end{aligned}$$

38.
$$\begin{aligned}\frac{7}{2}x+5&=x+\frac{15}{2}\\2\left(\frac{7}{2}x+5\right)&=2\left(x+\frac{15}{2}\right)\\7x+10&=2x+15\\5x+10&=15\\5x&=5\\x&=1\end{aligned}$$

39.
$$\begin{aligned}5(x-2)&=2x+8\\5x-10&=2x+8\\3x-10&=8\\3x&=18\\x&=6\end{aligned}$$

40.
$$\begin{aligned}5(r-4)&=-5(r-4)\\5r-20&=-5r+20\\10r-20&=20\\10r&=40\\r&=4\end{aligned}$$

41.
$$\begin{aligned} 2(2x+1)-\frac{3x}{2} &= \frac{-3(4+x)}{2} \\ 2\left[2(2x+1)-\frac{3x}{2}\right] &= 2\cdot\frac{-3(4+x)}{2} \\ 4(2x+1)-3x &= -3(4+x) \\ 8x+4-3x &= -12-3x \\ 5x+4 &= -12-3x \\ 8x+4 &= -12 \\ 8x &= -16 \\ x &= -2 \end{aligned}$$

42.
$$\begin{aligned} (x-2)(x-3) &= (x+3)(x+4) \\ x^2-5x+6 &= x^2+7x+12 \\ -5x+6 &= 7x+12 \\ -12x+6 &= 12 \\ -12x &= 6 \\ x &= -\frac{6}{12} = -\frac{1}{2} \end{aligned}$$

43.
$$\begin{aligned} 7(2x+5)-6(x+8) &= 7 \\ 14x+35-6x-48 &= 7 \\ 8x-13 &= 7 \\ 8x &= 20 \\ x &= \frac{20}{8} = \frac{5}{2} \end{aligned}$$

44.
$$\begin{aligned} (t+1)(t-1) &= (t+2)(t-3)+4 \\ t^2-1 &= t^2-t-6+4 \\ -1 &= -t-2 \\ t-1 &= -2 \\ t &= -1 \end{aligned}$$

45.
$$\begin{aligned} (x-2)(x+5) &= (x-3)(x+2) \\ x^2+3x-10 &= x^2-x-6 \\ 3x-10 &= -x-6 \\ 4x-10 &= -6 \\ 4x &= 4 \\ x &= 1 \end{aligned}$$

46.
$$\begin{aligned} \frac{3x+1}{20} &= \frac{1}{2} \\ 20\cdot\frac{3x+1}{20} &= 20\cdot\frac{1}{2} \\ 3x+1 &= 10 \\ 3x &= 9 \\ x &= 3 \end{aligned}$$

47.
$$\begin{aligned} \frac{3}{2}(3x-2)-10x-4 &= 0 \\ 2\left[\frac{3}{2}(3x-2)-10x-4\right] &= 2(0) \\ 3(3x-2)-20x-8 &= 0 \\ 9x-6-20x-8 &= 0 \\ -11x-14 &= 0 \\ -11x &= 14 \\ x &= -\frac{14}{11} \end{aligned}$$

48.
$$\begin{aligned} a(a-3)+5 &= (a-1)^2 \\ a^2-3a+5 &= (a-1)(a-1) \\ a^2-3a+5 &= a^2-2a+1 \\ -3a+5 &= -2a+1 \\ 5 &= a+1 \\ 4 &= a \end{aligned}$$

49.
$$\begin{aligned} x(x+2) &= (x+1)^2 - 1 \\ x^2 + 2x &= (x+1)(x+1) - 1 \\ x^2 + 2x &= x^2 + 2x + 1 - 1 \\ x^2 + 2x &= x^2 + 2x \\ 0 &= 0 \Rightarrow \text{identity} \end{aligned}$$

50.
$$\begin{aligned} \frac{3+x}{3} + \frac{x+7}{2} &= 4x + 1 \\ 6\left(\frac{3+x}{3} + \frac{x+7}{2}\right) &= 6(4x+1) \\ 2(3+x) + 3(x+7) &= 24x + 6 \\ 6 + 2x + 3x + 21 &= 24x + 6 \\ 5x + 27 &= 24x + 6 \\ -19x + 27 &= 6 \\ -19x &= -21 \\ x &= \frac{21}{19} \end{aligned}$$

51.
$$\begin{aligned} \frac{(y+2)^2}{3} &= y + 2 + \frac{y^2}{3} \\ 3\left[\frac{(y+2)^2}{3}\right] &= 3\left(y + 2 + \frac{y^2}{3}\right) \\ (y+2)^2 &= 3y + 6 + y^2 \\ y^2 + 4y + 4 &= y^2 + 3y + 6 \\ 4y + 4 &= 3y + 6 \\ y + 4 &= 6 \\ y &= 2 \end{aligned}$$

52.
$$\begin{aligned} 2x - \frac{7}{6} + \frac{x}{6} &= \frac{4x+3}{6} \\ 6\left(2x - \frac{7}{6} + \frac{x}{6}\right) &= 6 \cdot \frac{4x+3}{6} \\ 12x - 7 + x &= 4x + 3 \\ 13x - 7 &= 4x + 3 \\ 9x - 7 &= 3 \\ 9x &= 10 \\ x &= \frac{10}{9} \end{aligned}$$

53.
$$\begin{aligned} 2(s+2) + (s+3)^2 &= s(s+5) + 2\left(\frac{17}{2} + s\right) \\ 2s + 4 + s^2 + 6s + 9 &= s^2 + 5s + 17 + 2s \\ s^2 + 8s + 13 &= s^2 + 7s + 17 \\ 8s + 13 &= 7s + 17 \\ s &= 4 \end{aligned}$$

54.
$$\begin{aligned} \frac{3}{x} + \frac{1}{2} &= \frac{4}{x} \\ 2x\left(\frac{3}{x} + \frac{1}{2}\right) &= 2x \cdot \frac{4}{x} \\ 6 + x &= 8 \\ x &= 2 \end{aligned}$$

55.
$$\begin{aligned} \frac{2}{x+1} + \frac{1}{3} &= \frac{1}{x+1} \\ 3(x+1)\left(\frac{2}{x+1} + \frac{1}{3}\right) &= 3(x+1) \cdot \frac{1}{x+1} \\ 6 + 1(x+1) &= 3(1) \\ 6 + x + 1 &= 3 \\ x + 7 &= 3 \\ x &= -4 \end{aligned}$$

56.

$$\frac{3}{x-2} + \frac{1}{x} = \frac{3}{x-2}$$
$$x(x-2)\left(\frac{3}{x-2} + \frac{1}{x}\right) = x(x-2) \cdot \frac{3}{x-2}$$
$$3x + 1(x-2) = 3x$$
$$3x + x - 2 = 3x$$
$$4x - 2 = 3x$$
$$x = 2$$

The answer does not check. $\Rightarrow$ no solution

57.

$$\frac{9t+6}{t(t+3)} = \frac{7}{t+3}$$
$$t(t+3)\left[\frac{9t+6}{t(t+3)}\right] = t(t+3) \cdot \frac{7}{t+3}$$
$$9t + 6 = 7t$$
$$2t + 6 = 0$$
$$2t = -6$$
$$t = -3$$

The answer does not check. $\Rightarrow$ no solution

58.

$$x + \frac{2(-2x+1)}{3x+5} = \frac{3x^2}{3x+5}$$
$$(3x+5)\left[x + \frac{2(-2x+1)}{3x+5}\right] = (3x+5) \cdot \frac{3x^2}{3x+5}$$
$$x(3x+5) + 2(-2x+1) = 3x^2$$
$$3x^2 + 5x - 4x + 2 = 3x^2$$
$$x + 2 = 0$$
$$x = -2$$

59.

$$\frac{2}{(a-7)(a+2)} = \frac{4}{(a+3)(a+2)}$$
$$(a-7)(a+2)(a+3) \cdot \frac{2}{(a-7)(a+2)} = (a-7)(a+2)(a+3) \cdot \frac{4}{(a+3)(a+2)}$$
$$2(a+3) = 4(a-7)$$
$$2a + 6 = 4a - 28$$
$$-2a = -34$$
$$a = 17$$

60.

$$\frac{2}{n-2} + \frac{1}{n+1} = \frac{1}{n^2 - n - 2}$$
$$\frac{2}{n-2} + \frac{1}{n+1} = \frac{1}{(n-2)(n+1)}$$
$$(n-2)(n+1)\left(\frac{2}{n-2} + \frac{1}{n+1}\right) = (n-2)(n+1) \cdot \frac{1}{(n-2)(n+1)}$$
$$2(n+1) + 1(n-2) = 1$$
$$2n + 2 + n - 2 = 1$$
$$3n = 1$$
$$n = \frac{1}{3}$$

61.

$$\begin{aligned}
\frac{2x+3}{x^2+5x+6}+\frac{3x-2}{x^2+x-6}&=\frac{5x-2}{x^2-4}\\
\frac{2x+3}{(x+3)(x+2)}+\frac{3x-2}{(x+3)(x-2)}&=\frac{5x-2}{(x+2)(x-2)}\\
(x-2)(2x+3)+(x+2)(3x-2)&=(x+3)(5x-2) \quad \{\text{multiply by common denominator}\}\\
2x^2-x-6+3x^2+4x-4&=5x^2+13x-6\\
5x^2+3x-10&=5x^2+13x-6\\
3x-10&=13x-6\\
-10x&=4\\
x&=-\frac{4}{10}=-\frac{2}{5}
\end{aligned}$$

62.

$$\begin{aligned}
\frac{3x}{x^2+x}-\frac{2x}{x^2+5x}&=\frac{x+2}{x^2+6x+5}\\
\frac{3x}{x(x+1)}-\frac{2x}{x(x+5)}&=\frac{x+2}{(x+5)(x+1)}\\
\frac{3}{x+1}-\frac{2}{x+5}&=\frac{x+2}{(x+5)(x+1)}\\
3(x+5)-2(x+1)&=x+2 \quad \{\text{multiply by common denominator}\}\\
3x+15-2x-2&=x+2\\
x+13&=x+2\\
13&\neq 2 \Rightarrow \text{no solution}
\end{aligned}$$

63.

$$\begin{aligned}
\frac{3x+5}{x^3+8}+\frac{3}{x^2-4}&=\frac{2(3x-2)}{(x-2)(x^2-2x+4)}\\
\frac{3x+5}{(x+2)(x^2-2x+4)}+\frac{3}{(x+2)(x-2)}&=\frac{2(3x-2)}{(x-2)(x^2-2x+4)}\\
(x-2)(3x+5)+\left(x^2-2x+4\right)(3)&=2(x+2)(3x-2) \quad \{\text{multiply by common denominator}\}\\
3x^2-x-10+3x^2-6x+12&=6x^2+8x-8\\
6x^2-7x+2&=6x^2+8x-8\\
-15x&=-10\\
x&=\frac{-10}{-15}=\frac{2}{3}
\end{aligned}$$

64.

$$\begin{aligned}
\frac{1}{n+8}-\frac{3n-4}{5n^2+42n+16}&=\frac{1}{5n+2}\\
\frac{1}{n+8}-\frac{3n-4}{(5n+2)(n+8)}&=\frac{1}{5n+2}\\
(5n+2)(1)-(3n-4)&=n+8 \quad \{\text{multiply by common denominator}\}\\
5n+2-3n+4&=n+8\\
2n+6&=n+8\\
n&=2
\end{aligned}$$

65.

$$\begin{aligned}
\frac{1}{11-n}-\frac{2(3n-1)}{-7n^2+74n+33}&=\frac{1}{7n+3}\\
\frac{-1}{n-11}+\frac{2(3n-1)}{7n^2-74n-33}&=\frac{1}{7n+3}\\
\frac{-1}{n-11}+\frac{6n-2}{(7n+3)(n-11)}&=\frac{1}{7n+3}\\
-(7n+3)+6n-2&=(n-11)1 \qquad \{\text{multiply by common denominator}\}\\
-7n-3+6n-2&=n-11\\
-n-5&=n-11\\
-2n&=-6\\
n&=3
\end{aligned}$$

66.

$$\begin{aligned}
\frac{4}{a^2-13a-48}-\frac{2}{a^2-18a+32}&=\frac{1}{a^2+a-6}\\
\frac{4}{(a-16)(a+3)}-\frac{2}{(a-16)(a-2)}&=\frac{1}{(a+3)(a-2)}\\
4(a-2)-2(a+3)&=1(a-16) \qquad \{\text{multiply by common denominator}\}\\
4a-8-2a-6&=a-16\\
2a-14&=a-16\\
a&=-2
\end{aligned}$$

67.

$$\begin{aligned}
\frac{5}{y+4}+\frac{2}{y+2}&=\frac{6}{y+2}-\frac{1}{y^2+6y+8}\\
\frac{5}{y+4}&=\frac{4}{y+2}-\frac{1}{(y+2)(y+4)}\\
5(y+2)&=4(y+4)-1 \qquad \{\text{multiply by common denominator}\}\\
5y+10&=4y+16-1\\
5y+10&=4y+15\\
y&=5
\end{aligned}$$

68.

$$\begin{aligned}
\frac{6}{2a-6}-\frac{3}{3-3a}&=\frac{1}{a^2-4a+3}\\
\frac{6}{2(a-3)}-\frac{3}{3(1-a)}&=\frac{1}{(a-3)(a-1)}\\
\frac{3}{a-3}+\frac{1}{a-1}&=\frac{1}{(a-3)(a-1)}\\
3(a-1)+1(a-3)&=1 \qquad \{\text{multiply by common denominator}\}\\
3a-3+a-3&=1\\
4a-6&=1\\
4a&=7\\
a&=\frac{7}{4}
\end{aligned}$$

69.

$$\frac{3y}{6-3y}+\frac{2y}{2y+4}=\frac{8}{4-y^2}$$
$$\frac{3y}{3(2-y)}+\frac{2y}{2(y+2)}=\frac{8}{(2+y)(2-y)}$$
$$\frac{y}{2-y}+\frac{y}{2+y}=\frac{8}{(2+y)(2-y)}$$
$$y(2+y)+y(2-y)=8 \qquad \text{\{multiply by common denominator\}}$$
$$2y+y^2+2y-y^2=8$$
$$4y=8$$
$$y=2 \Rightarrow \text{The solution does not check, so the equation has no solution.}$$

70.

$$\frac{3+2a}{a^2+6+5a}-\frac{2-3a}{a^2-6+a}=\frac{5a-2}{a^2-4}$$
$$\frac{2a+3}{(a+2)(a+3)}+\frac{3a-2}{(a+3)(a-2)}=\frac{5a-2}{(a+2)(a-2)}$$
$$(a-2)(2a+3)+(a+2)(3a-2)=(a+3)(5a-2) \qquad \text{\{multiply by common denominator\}}$$
$$2a^2-a-6+3a^2+4a-4=5a^2+13a-6$$
$$5a^2+3a-10=5a^2+13a-6$$
$$-10a=4$$
$$a=\frac{4}{-10}=-\frac{2}{5}$$

71.

$$\frac{a}{a+2}-1=-\frac{3a+2}{a^2+4a+4}$$
$$\frac{a}{a+2}-\frac{1}{1}=-\frac{3a+2}{(a+2)(a+2)}$$
$$(a+2)(a+2)\left[\frac{a}{a+2}-1\right]=(a+2)(a+2)\cdot\left[-\frac{3a+2}{(a+2)(a+2)}\right]$$
$$a(a+2)-(a+2)(a+2)=-(3a+2)$$
$$a^2+2a-\left(a^2+4a+4\right)=-3a-2$$
$$a^2+2a-a^2-4a-4=-3a-2$$
$$-2a-4=-3a-2$$
$$a=2$$

72.

$$\frac{x-1}{x+3}+\frac{x-2}{x-3}=\frac{1-2x}{3-x}$$
$$\frac{x-1}{x+3}+\frac{x-2}{x-3}=\frac{2x-1}{x-3}$$
$$(x-3)(x-1)+(x+3)(x-2)=(x+3)(2x-1) \qquad \text{\{multiply by common denominator\}}$$
$$x^2-4x+3+x^2+x-6=2x^2+5x-3$$
$$2x^2-3x-3=2x^2+5x-3$$
$$-8x=0$$
$$x=\frac{0}{-8}=0$$

73.
$$\begin{aligned} k &= 2.2p \\ \frac{k}{2.2} &= \frac{2.2p}{2.2} \\ \frac{k}{2.2} &= p \end{aligned}$$

74.
$$\begin{aligned} ax + b &= 0 \\ ax &= -b \\ x &= -\frac{b}{a} \end{aligned}$$

75.
$$\begin{aligned} p &= 2l + 2w \\ p - 2l &= 2w \\ \frac{p-2l}{2} &= \frac{2w}{2} \\ \frac{p-2l}{2} &= w \end{aligned}$$

76.
$$\begin{aligned} V &= \frac{1}{3}\pi r^2 h \\ 3V &= 3 \cdot \frac{1}{3}\pi r^2 h \\ 3V &= \pi r^2 h \\ \frac{3V}{\pi r^2} &= \frac{\pi r^2 h}{\pi r^2} \\ \frac{3V}{\pi r^2} &= h \end{aligned}$$

77.
$$\begin{aligned} V &= \frac{1}{3}\pi r^2 h \\ 3V &= 3 \cdot \frac{1}{3}\pi r^2 h \\ 3V &= \pi r^2 h \\ \frac{3V}{\pi h} &= \frac{\pi r^2 h}{\pi h} \\ \frac{3V}{\pi h} &= r^2 \end{aligned}$$

78.
$$\begin{aligned} z &= \frac{x-\mu}{\sigma} \\ z\sigma &= \frac{x-\mu}{\sigma} \cdot \sigma \\ z\sigma &= x - \mu \\ \mu + z\sigma &= x \\ \mu &= x - z\sigma \end{aligned}$$

79.
$$\begin{aligned} P_n &= L + \frac{si}{f} \\ P_n - L &= \frac{si}{f} \\ f(P_n - L) &= f \cdot \frac{si}{f} \\ f(P_n - L) &= si \\ \frac{f(P_n - L)}{i} &= \frac{si}{i} \\ \frac{f(P_n - L)}{i} &= s \end{aligned}$$

80.
$$\begin{aligned} P_n &= L + \frac{si}{f} \\ P_n - L &= \frac{si}{f} \\ f(P_n - L) &= f \cdot \frac{si}{f} \\ f(P_n - L) &= si \\ \frac{f(P_n - L)}{P_n - L} &= \frac{si}{P_n - L} \\ f &= \frac{si}{P_n - L} \end{aligned}$$

81.
$$\begin{aligned} F &= \frac{mMg}{r^2} \\ Fr^2 &= \frac{mMg}{r^2} \cdot r^2 \\ Fr^2 &= mMg \\ \frac{Fr^2}{Mg} &= \frac{mMg}{Mg} \\ \frac{Fr^2}{Mg} &= m \end{aligned}$$

82.
$$\begin{aligned} \frac{1}{f} &= \frac{1}{p} + \frac{1}{q} \\ fpq \cdot \frac{1}{f} &= fpq\left(\frac{1}{p} + \frac{1}{q}\right) \\ pq &= fq + fp \\ pq &= f(q+p) \\ \frac{pq}{q+p} &= \frac{f(q+p)}{q+p} \\ \frac{pq}{q+p} &= f \end{aligned}$$

83.
$$\begin{aligned} \frac{x}{a} + \frac{y}{b} &= 1 \\ \frac{y}{b} &= 1 - \frac{x}{a} \\ b \cdot \frac{y}{b} &= b\left(1 - \frac{x}{a}\right) \\ y &= b\left(1 - \frac{x}{a}\right) \end{aligned}$$

84.
$$\begin{aligned} \frac{x}{a} - \frac{y}{b} &= 1 \\ ab\left(\frac{x}{a} - \frac{y}{b}\right) &= ab \cdot 1 \\ bx - ay &= ab \\ bx &= ab + ay \\ bx &= a(b+y) \\ \frac{bx}{b+y} &= \frac{a(b+y)}{b+y} \\ \frac{bx}{b+y} &= a \end{aligned}$$

85.
$$\begin{aligned}\frac{1}{r} &= \frac{1}{r_1} + \frac{1}{r_2} \\ rr_1r_2 \cdot \frac{1}{r} &= rr_1r_2\left(\frac{1}{r_1} + \frac{1}{r_2}\right) \\ r_1r_2 &= rr_2 + rr_1 \\ r_1r_2 &= r(r_2 + r_1) \\ \frac{r_1r_2}{r_2 + r_1} &= \frac{r(r_2 + r_1)}{r_2 + r_1} \\ \frac{r_1r_2}{r_2 + r_1} &= r\end{aligned}$$

86.
$$\begin{aligned}\frac{1}{r} &= \frac{1}{r_1} + \frac{1}{r_2} \\ rr_1r_2 \cdot \frac{1}{r} &= rr_1r_2\left(\frac{1}{r_1} + \frac{1}{r_2}\right) \\ r_1r_2 &= rr_2 + rr_1 \\ r_1r_2 - rr_1 &= rr_2 \\ r_1(r_2 - r) &= rr_2 \\ \frac{r_1(r_2 - r)}{r_2 - r} &= \frac{rr_2}{r_2 - r} \\ r_1 &= \frac{rr_2}{r_2 - r}\end{aligned}$$

87.
$$\begin{aligned}l &= a + (n-1)d \\ l &= a + nd - d \\ l - a + d &= nd \\ \frac{l - a + d}{d} &= \frac{nd}{d} \\ \frac{l - a + d}{d} &= n\end{aligned}$$

88.
$$\begin{aligned}l &= a + (n-1)d \\ l - a &= (n-1)d \\ \frac{l - a}{n - 1} &= \frac{(n-1)d}{n-1} \\ \frac{l - a}{n - 1} &= d\end{aligned}$$

89.
$$\begin{aligned}a &= (n-2)\frac{180}{n} \\ an &= (n-2)\frac{180}{n} \cdot n \\ an &= (n-2)180 \\ an &= 180n - 360 \\ 360 &= 180n - an \\ 360 &= n(180 - a) \\ \frac{360}{180 - a} &= n\end{aligned}$$

90.
$$\begin{aligned}S &= \frac{a - lr}{1 - r} \\ S(1 - r) &= \frac{a - lr}{1 - r}(1 - r) \\ S(1 - r) &= a - lr \\ S - Sr + lr &= a\end{aligned}$$

91.
$$\begin{aligned}R &= \frac{1}{\frac{1}{r_1} + \frac{1}{r_2} + \frac{1}{r_3}} \\ R &= \frac{r_1r_2r_3(1)}{r_1r_2r_3\left(\frac{1}{r_1} + \frac{1}{r_2} + \frac{1}{r_3}\right)} \\ R &= \frac{r_1r_2r_3}{r_2r_3 + r_1r_3 + r_1r_2} \\ R(r_2r_3 + r_1r_3 + r_1r_2) &= r_1r_2r_3 \\ Rr_2r_3 + Rr_1r_3 + Rr_1r_2 &= r_1r_2r_3 \\ Rr_1r_3 + Rr_1r_2 - r_1r_2r_3 &= -Rr_2r_3 \\ r_1(Rr_3 + Rr_2 - r_2r_3) &= -Rr_2r_3 \\ r_1 &= \frac{-Rr_2r_3}{Rr_3 + Rr_2 - r_2r_3}\end{aligned}$$

92.
$$\begin{aligned}
R &= \frac{1}{\frac{1}{r_1}+\frac{1}{r_2}+\frac{1}{r_3}} \\
R &= \frac{r_1r_2r_3(1)}{r_1r_2r_3\left(\frac{1}{r_1}+\frac{1}{r_2}+\frac{1}{r_3}\right)} \\
R &= \frac{r_1r_2r_3}{r_2r_3+r_1r_3+r_1r_2} \\
R(r_2r_3+r_1r_3+r_1r_2) &= r_1r_2r_3 \\
Rr_2r_3+Rr_1r_3+Rr_1r_2 &= r_1r_2r_3 \\
Rr_2r_3+Rr_1r_3-r_1r_2r_3 &= -Rr_1r_2 \\
r_3(Rr_2+Rr_1-r_1r_2) &= -Rr_1r_2 \\
r_3 &= \frac{-Rr_1r_2}{Rr_2+Rr_1-r_1r_2}
\end{aligned}$$

93. Answers may vary.

94. Answers may vary.

95. $(25x^2)^{1/2} = \left[(5x)^2\right]^{1/2} = 5|x|$

96. $\left(\frac{25p^2}{16q^4}\right)^{1/2} = \left[\left(\frac{5p}{4q^2}\right)^2\right]^{1/2} = \frac{5|p|}{4q^2}$

97. $\left(\frac{125x^3}{8y^6}\right)^{-2/3} = \left(\frac{8y^6}{125x^3}\right)^{2/3} = \frac{8^{2/3}(y^6)^{2/3}}{125^{2/3}(x^3)^{2/3}} = \frac{4y^4}{25x^2}$

98. $\left(-\frac{27y^3}{1000x^6}\right)^{1/3} = \frac{(-27)^{1/3}(y^3)^{1/3}}{1000^{1/3}(x^6)^{1/3}} = \frac{-3y}{10x^2} = -\frac{3y}{10x^2}$

99. $\sqrt{25y^2} = \sqrt{(5y)^2} = 5|y|$

100. $\sqrt[3]{-125y^9} = \sqrt[3]{(-5y^3)^3} = -5y^3$

101. $\sqrt[4]{\frac{a^4b^{12}}{z^8}} = \sqrt[4]{\left(\frac{ab^3}{z^2}\right)^4} = \frac{|ab^3|}{z^2}$

102. $\sqrt[5]{\frac{x^{10}y^5}{z^{15}}} = \sqrt[5]{\left(\frac{x^2y}{z^3}\right)^5} = \frac{x^2y}{z^3}$

Exercise 1.2 (page 94)

1. add

2. perimeter

3. amount

4. break point

5. rate, time

6. $0.05(30) = 1.5$

7. Let $x =$ the score on the first exam. Then $x + 5 =$ the score on the midterm, and $x + 13 =$ the score on the final.

$$\frac{\boxed{\text{Sum of scores}}}{3} = 90$$
$$\frac{x + x + 5 + x + 13}{3} = 90$$
$$\frac{3x + 18}{3} = 90$$
$$3x + 18 = 270$$
$$3x = 252$$
$$x = 84$$

His score on the first exam was 84.

8. Let $x =$ the score on the first exam. Then her scores on the following tests were $x + 3$, $x + 6$ and $x + 9$.

$$\frac{\boxed{\text{Sum of scores}}}{4} = 69.5$$
$$\frac{x + x + 3 + x + 6 + x + 9}{4} = 69.5$$
$$\frac{4x + 18}{4} = 69.5$$
$$4x + 18 = 278$$
$$4x = 260$$
$$x = 65$$

Her score on the first exam was 65%.

9. Let $x =$ the program development score.

$$\frac{\boxed{\text{Sum of scores}}}{4} = 86$$
$$\frac{82 + 90 + x + 78}{4} = 86$$
$$\frac{x + 250}{4} = 86$$
$$x + 250 = 344$$
$$x = 94$$

The program development score was 94.

10. Let $x =$ the score on the final round.

$$\frac{\boxed{\text{Sum of scores}}}{4} = 72$$
$$\frac{76 + 68 + 70 + x}{4} = 72$$
$$\frac{x + 214}{4} = 72$$
$$x + 214 = 288$$
$$x = 74$$

She needs to shoot 74 on the final round.

11. Let $x =$ the number of locks replaced.

$$40 + 28 \cdot \boxed{\text{Number of locks}} = 236$$
$$40 + 28x = 236$$
$$28x = 196$$
$$x = 7$$

7 locks can be changed for \$236.

12. Let $x =$ the number of interviews.

$$20 + 0.75 \cdot \boxed{\text{Number of interviews}} = 56$$
$$20 + 0.75x = 56$$
$$0.75x = 36$$
$$x = 48$$

He interviewed 48 people.

13.

$$\boxed{\text{Perimeter}} = 14$$
$$x + (x + 2) + x + (x + 2) = 14$$
$$4x + 4 = 14$$
$$4x = 10$$
$$x = \frac{5}{2} = 2\frac{1}{2} \Rightarrow \text{The width is } 2\frac{1}{2} \text{ feet.}$$

14.

$$\boxed{\text{Total Fence Length}} = 2 \cdot \boxed{\text{Square Fence Length}}$$
$$x + (x + 24) + x + (x + 24) = 2 \cdot (x + x + x + x)$$
$$4x + 48 = 8x$$
$$48 = 4x$$
$$x = 12$$

The total fencing required is $4x + 48 = 4(12) + 48 = 96$ feet.

15.

$$\boxed{\text{Total Area}} = 2 \cdot \boxed{\text{Triangular Area}}$$
$$20x + \frac{1}{2}(16)(20) = 2 \cdot \frac{1}{2}(16)(20)$$
$$20x + 160 = 320$$
$$20x = 160$$
$$x = 8$$

The dimensions are 8 feet by 20 feet.

16.

$$\boxed{\text{Sum of angles}} = 180$$
$$x + x + 30 + x + 30 = 180$$
$$3x + 60 = 180$$
$$3x = 120$$
$$x = 40$$

The angles measure 40°, 70° and 70°.

17.

$$\boxed{\begin{array}{c}\text{New}\\\text{Area}\end{array}} = \boxed{\begin{array}{c}\text{Old}\\\text{Area}\end{array}} + 0.50 \cdot \boxed{\begin{array}{c}\text{Old}\\\text{Area}\end{array}}$$
$$12(x + 10) + 12x = 12(x + 10) + 0.50 \cdot 12(x + 10)$$
$$12x + 120 + 12x = 12x + 120 + 6x + 60$$
$$24x + 120 = 18x + 180$$
$$6x = 60$$

$x = 10 \Rightarrow$ The length of the living room is $x + 10 = 20$ feet.

18.

$$\boxed{\text{Area}} = 54$$
$$\frac{1}{2}d(12 + 8) = 54$$
$$10d = 54$$

$d = 5.4 \Rightarrow$ The depth is 5.4 inches

19. Let $x =$ the amount invested at 7%. Then $22000 - x =$ the amount invested at 6%.

$$\boxed{\text{Interest at 7\%}} + \boxed{\text{Interest at 6\%}} = \boxed{\text{Total interest}}$$
$$0.07x + 0.06(22000 - x) = 1420$$
$$0.07x + 1320 - 0.06x = 1420$$
$$0.01x = 100$$
$$x = 10000$$

\$10,000 was invested at 7% and \$12,000 was invested at 6%.

20. Let $x =$ the amount invested at 7%.

$$\boxed{\text{Interest at 7\%}} + \boxed{\text{Interest at 9\%}} = \boxed{\text{Total interest}}$$
$$0.07x + 0.09(20000) = 5000$$
$$0.07x + 1800 = 5000$$
$$0.07x = 3200$$
$$x \approx 45714.29$$

She needs to invest \$45,714.29 at 7% to reach her goal.

21. Let $x =$ the number of full-price tickets sold. Then $585 - x =$ the number of student tickets sold.

$$2.50 \cdot \boxed{\text{\# of full-price}} + 1.75 \cdot \boxed{\text{\# of student}} = 1217.25$$
$$2.50x + 1.75(585 - x) = 1217.25$$
$$2.50x + 1023.75 - 1.75x = 1217.25$$
$$0.75x = 193.50$$
$$x = 258 \Rightarrow \text{There were 327 student tickets sold.}$$

22. Let $x =$ the cost of a student ticket.

$$\boxed{\text{Cost of full-price}} \cdot \boxed{\text{\# of full-price}} + \boxed{\text{Cost of student}} \cdot \boxed{\text{\# of student}} = 2080$$
$$480(3) + x(800 - 480) = 2080$$
$$1440 + 320x = 2080$$
$$320x = 640$$
$$x = 2 \Rightarrow \text{A student ticket cost \$2.}$$

23. Let $x =$ the amount invested at 8%. Then $37{,}000 - x =$ the amount invested at $9\frac{1}{2}\%$.

$$\boxed{\text{Interest at } 9\tfrac{1}{2}\%} = \boxed{\text{Interest at 8\%}} + 452.50$$
$$0.095(37{,}000 - x) = 0.08x + 452.50$$
$$3515 - 0.095x = 0.08x + 452.50$$
$$3062.50 = 0.175x$$
$$17500 = x$$

\$17,500 is invested at 8% and \$19,500 is invested at $9\frac{1}{2}\%$.

24. Let $x =$ the amount invested at each rate.

$$\boxed{\text{Interest at 6\%}} + \boxed{\text{Interest at 7\%}} + \boxed{\text{Interest at 8\%}} = \boxed{\text{Total interest}}$$
$$0.06x + 0.07x + 0.08x = 2037$$
$$0.21x = 2037$$
$$x = 9700$$

\$9,700 was invested at each rate, for a total investment of \$29,100.

25. Let $p =$ the original price.

$$\boxed{\text{Original price}} - \boxed{\text{Discount}} = \boxed{\text{New price}}$$
$$p - 0.20p = 63.96$$
$$0.80p = 63.96$$
$$p = 79.95$$

The original price was \$79.95.

26. Let $w =$ the wholesale cost.

$$\boxed{\text{Wholesale cost}} + \boxed{\text{Markup}} = \boxed{\text{Selling price}}$$
$$w + 0.30w = 588.90$$
$$1.30w = 588.90$$
$$w = 453$$

The wholesale cost is \$453.

27. Let $x = \#$ of plates for equal costs.

$$\boxed{\text{Cost of 1st machine}} = \boxed{\text{Cost of 2nd machine}}$$
$$600 + 3x = 800 + 2x$$
$$x = 200$$

The break point is 200 plates.

28. Let $x = \#$ of fasteners for equal costs.

$$\boxed{\text{Cost of 1st machine}} = \boxed{\text{Cost of 2nd machine}}$$
$$1200 + 0.005x = 1500 + 0.0015x$$
$$0.0035x = 300$$
$$x \approx 85714$$

The break point is about 85,714 fasteners.

29. Let $x = \#$ of computers to break even.

$$\boxed{\text{Income}} = \boxed{\text{Expenses}}$$
$$1275x = 8925 + 850x$$
$$425x = 8925$$
$$x = 21$$

21 computers need to be sold to break even.

30. Let $x = \#$ of meals to break even.

$$\boxed{\text{Income}} = \boxed{\text{Expenses}}$$
$$6x = 137.50 + 4.75x$$
$$1.25x = 137.50$$
$$x = 110$$

More than 110 meals need to be sold to make a profit.

31. Let $x =$ hours for both working together.

$$\boxed{\text{Woman in 1 hour}} + \boxed{\text{Man in 1 hour}} = \boxed{\text{Total in 1 hour}}$$
$$\frac{1}{2} + \frac{1}{4} = \frac{1}{x}$$
$$4x\left(\frac{1}{2} + \frac{1}{4}\right) = 4x\left(\frac{1}{x}\right)$$
$$2x + x = 4$$
$$3x = 4$$
$$x = \frac{4}{3} = 1\frac{1}{3}$$

They can mow the lawn in $1\frac{1}{3}$ hours.

32. Let $x =$ days for both hoses to fill the pool.

$$\boxed{\text{1st hose in 1 day}} + \boxed{\text{2nd hose in 1 day}} = \boxed{\text{Total in 1 day}}$$
$$\frac{1}{3} + \frac{1}{2} = \frac{1}{x}$$
$$6x\left(\frac{1}{3} + \frac{1}{2}\right) = 6x\left(\frac{1}{x}\right)$$
$$2x + 3x = 6$$
$$5x = 6$$
$$x = \frac{6}{5} = 1\frac{1}{5}$$

The pool can be filled in $1\frac{1}{5}$ days.

33. Let $x =$ hours for pool to fill with drain open.

$$\boxed{\text{Pipe in 1 hour}} - \boxed{\text{Drain in 1 hour}} = \boxed{\text{Total in 1 hour}}$$
$$\frac{1}{10} - \frac{1}{19} = \frac{1}{x}$$
$$190x\left(\frac{1}{10} - \frac{1}{19}\right) = 190x\left(\frac{1}{x}\right)$$
$$19x - 10x = 190$$
$$9x = 190$$
$$x = \frac{190}{9} = 21\frac{1}{9}$$

The pool can be filled in $21\frac{1}{9}$ hours.

34. Let $x =$ hours for sister to stuff 1000 shrimp.

$$\boxed{\text{Sam in 1 hour}} + \boxed{\text{Sister in 1 hour}} = \boxed{\text{Total in 1 hour}}$$
$$\frac{1}{6} + \frac{1}{x} = \frac{1}{4}$$
$$24x\left(\frac{1}{6} + \frac{1}{x}\right) = 24x\left(\frac{1}{4}\right)$$
$$4x + 24 = 6x$$
$$24 = 2x$$
$$12 = x$$

She can stuff 1,000 shrimp in 12 hours, so she can stuff 500 shrimp in 6 hours.

35. Let $x =$ the liters of liquid replaced with pure antifreeze.

$$\boxed{\text{Liters of a.f. at start}} - \boxed{\text{Liters of a.f. removed}} + \boxed{\text{Liters of a.f. replaced}} = \boxed{\text{Liters of a.f. at end}}$$

$$\begin{aligned} 0.40(6) - 0.40x + x &= 0.50(6) \\ 2.4 + 0.6x &= 3 \\ 0.6x &= 0.6 \\ x &= 1 \Rightarrow \text{1 liter should be replaced with pure antifreeze.} \end{aligned}$$

36. Let $x =$ the liters of skimmed milk added.

$$\boxed{\text{Liters of butterfat at start}} + \boxed{\text{Liters of butterfat added}} = \boxed{\text{Liters of butterfat at end}}$$

$$\begin{aligned} 0.035(3) + 0(x) &= 0.02(3 + x) \\ 0.105 + 0 &= 0.06 + 0.02x \\ 0.045 &= 0.02x \\ 2.25 &= x \Rightarrow \text{2.25 liters of skimmed milk should be added.} \end{aligned}$$

37. Let $x =$ the liters of pure alcohol added.

$$\boxed{\text{Liters of alcohol at start}} + \boxed{\text{Liters of alcohol added}} = \boxed{\text{Liters of alcohol at end}}$$

$$\begin{aligned} 0.20(1) + x &= 0.25(1 + x) \\ 0.20 + x &= 0.25 + 0.25x \\ 0.75x &= 0.05 \\ x &= \frac{0.05}{0.75} = \frac{1}{15} \Rightarrow \frac{1}{15} \text{ of a liter of pure alcohol should be added.} \end{aligned}$$

38. Let $x =$ the cubic centimeters of water added.

$$\boxed{\text{Cubic centimeters of chemical at start}} + \boxed{\text{Cubic centimeters of chemical added}} = \boxed{\text{Cubic centimeters of chemical at end}}$$

$$\begin{aligned} 400 + 0 &= 0.25(1000 + x) \\ 400 &= 250 + 0.25x \\ 150 &= 0.25x \\ 600 &= x \Rightarrow \text{600 cubic centimeters of water should be added.} \end{aligned}$$

39. Let $x =$ the gallons of pure chlorine added.

$$\boxed{\text{Gallons of chlorine at start}} + \boxed{\text{Gallons of chlorine added}} = \boxed{\text{Gallons of chlorine at end}}$$

$$\begin{aligned} 0(15000) + x &= 0.0003(15000 + x) \\ x &= 4.5 + 0.0003x \\ 0.9997x &= 4.5 \\ x &\approx 4.5 \Rightarrow \text{About 4.5 gallons of pure chlorine should be added.} \end{aligned}$$

40. Let $x =$ the percentage of substitute fuel used. Then $1 - x =$ the percentage of gasoline used.

$$\boxed{\text{Percentage of gasoline used}} \cdot \boxed{\text{Cost per gallon of gasoline}} + \boxed{\text{Percentage of fuel used}} \cdot \boxed{\text{Cost per gallon of fuel}} = \boxed{\text{Cost per gallon of mixture}}$$

$$(1 - x)(1.50) + x(0.40) = 1$$
$$1.50 - 1.50x + 0.40x = 1$$
$$-1.10x = -0.50$$
$$x \approx 0.455$$

The substitute fuel should be about 45.5% of the mixture.

41. Let $x =$ the liters of water evaporated.

$$\boxed{\text{Liters of salt at start}} - \boxed{\text{Liters of salt evaporated}} = \boxed{\text{Liters of salt at end}}$$

$$0.24(12) - 0(x) = 0.36(12 - x)$$
$$2.88 - 0 = 4.32 - 0.36x$$
$$0.36x = 1.44$$
$$x = 4 \Rightarrow \text{4 liters of water should be evaporated.}$$

42. Let $x =$ the ounces of 1% cream used. Then $1 - x =$ the ounces of 5% cream used.

$$\boxed{\text{Ounces of h.c. in 1\% cream}} + \boxed{\text{Ounces of h.c. in 5\% cream}} = \boxed{\text{Ounces of h.c. in final cream}}$$

$$0.01x + 0.05(1 - x) = 0.02(1)$$
$$0.01x + 0.05 - 0.05x = 0.02$$
$$-0.04x = -0.03$$
$$x = 0.75$$

0.75 ounces of the 1% cream should be used with 0.25 ounces of the 5% cream.

43. Let $r =$ his first rate. Then $r + 26 =$ his return rate.

$$\boxed{\text{Distance to city}} = \boxed{\text{Return distance}}$$

$$5r = 3(r + 26)$$
$$5r = 3r + 78$$
$$2r = 78$$
$$r = 39 \Rightarrow \text{He drove 39 mph going and 65 mph returning.}$$

44. Let $t =$ the time Suzi and Jim travel.

$$\boxed{\text{Distance Suzi travels}} = \boxed{\text{Distance Jim travels}} + 60$$

$$60t = 48t + 60$$
$$12t = 60$$
$$t = 5 \Rightarrow \text{They traveled for 5 hours, so Suzi traveled 300 miles.}$$

45. Let $t =$ the time the cars travel.

$$\boxed{\text{Distance 1st car travels}} + \boxed{\text{Distance 2nd car travels}} = \boxed{\text{Total distance}}$$

$$60t + 64t = 310$$
$$124t = 310$$
$$t = 2.5 \Rightarrow \text{They will be 310 miles apart after 2.5 hours.}$$

46. Let $t =$ the hours the robbers travel. Then $t - \frac{10}{60} = t - \frac{1}{6} =$ the hours the police travel.

$$\boxed{\text{Distance robbers travel}} = \boxed{\text{Distance police travel}}$$

$$\begin{aligned} 70t &= 78\left(t - \frac{1}{6}\right) \\ 70t &= 78t - 13 \\ -8t &= -13 \\ t &= \frac{13}{8} = 1\frac{5}{8} = 1.625 \Rightarrow \text{The police will catch up after 1.625 hours.} \end{aligned}$$

47. Let $t =$ the time the runners run.

$$\boxed{\text{Distance 1st runs}} + \boxed{\text{Distance 2nd runs}} = \boxed{\text{Distance between them}}$$

$$\begin{aligned} 8t + 10t &= \frac{440}{1760} \\ 18t &= \frac{1}{4} \\ t &= \frac{1}{72} \text{ hour} = \frac{1}{72}(60) = \frac{5}{6} \text{ minute} = 50 \text{ seconds} \end{aligned}$$

They will meet after 50 seconds.

48. Let $r =$ the rate before lunch. Then $r + 10 =$ the rate after lunch.

$$\boxed{\text{Distance before lunch}} + \boxed{\text{Distance after lunch}} = \boxed{\text{Total distance}}$$

$$\begin{aligned} 5r + 3(r + 10) &= 430 \\ 5r + 3r + 30 &= 430 \\ 8r &= 400 \\ r &= 50 \Rightarrow \text{He drove 50 mph before lunch.} \end{aligned}$$

49. Let $r =$ the speed of the boat in still water.
Then the speed of the boat is $r + 2$ downstream and $r - 2$ upstream.

$$\boxed{\text{Time upstream}} = \boxed{\text{Time downstream}} \qquad \{\text{Note: Time} = \text{Distance} \div \text{Rate}\}$$

$$\begin{aligned} \frac{5}{r-2} &= \frac{7}{r+2} \\ (r+2)(r-2)\frac{5}{r-2} &= (r+2)(r-2)\frac{7}{r+2} \\ 5(r+2) &= 7(r-2) \\ 5r + 10 &= 7r - 14 \\ 24 &= 2r \\ 12 &= r \Rightarrow \text{The speed of the boat is 12 mph.} \end{aligned}$$

50. Let $w =$ the speed of the wind.

Then the speed of the plane is $340 + w$ downwind and $340 - w$ upwind.

$$\boxed{\text{Time upwind}} = \boxed{\text{Time downwind}}$$

$$\frac{140}{340 - w} = \frac{200}{340 + w}$$

$$(340 + w)(340 - w)\frac{140}{340 - w} = (340 + w)(340 - w)\frac{200}{340 + w}$$

$$140(340 + w) = 200(340 - w)$$

$$47{,}600 + 140w = 68{,}000 - 200w$$

$$340w = 20{,}400$$

$w = 60 \Rightarrow$ The speed of the wind is 60 mph.

51. Since the mixture is to be 25% barley, there will be $0.25(2400) = 600$ pounds of barley used.

Thus, the other 1800 pounds will be either oats or soybean meal.

Let $x =$ the number of pounds of oats used. Then $1800 - x =$ the number of pounds of meal used.

$$\boxed{\begin{array}{c}\text{Pounds of protein}\\\text{from barley}\end{array}} + \boxed{\begin{array}{c}\text{Pounds of protein}\\\text{from oats}\end{array}} + \boxed{\begin{array}{c}\text{Pounds of protein}\\\text{from soybean meal}\end{array}} = \boxed{\begin{array}{c}\text{Total pounds}\\\text{of protein}\end{array}}$$

$$0.117(600) + 0.118x + 0.445(1800 - x) = 0.14(2400)$$

$$70.2 + 0.118x + 801 - 0.445x = 336$$

$$871.2 - 0.327x = 336$$

$$-0.327x = -535.2$$

$$x \approx 1637$$

The farmer should use 600 pounds of barley, 1637 pounds of oats and 163 pounds of soybean meal.

52. Since the mixture is to be 20% barley, there will be $0.20(2400) = 480$ pounds of barley used.

Thus, the other 1920 pounds will be either oats or soybean meal.

Let $x =$ the number of pounds of oats used. Then $1920 - x =$ the number of pounds of meal used.

$$\boxed{\begin{array}{c}\text{Pounds of protein}\\\text{from barley}\end{array}} + \boxed{\begin{array}{c}\text{Pounds of protein}\\\text{from oats}\end{array}} + \boxed{\begin{array}{c}\text{Pounds of protein}\\\text{from soybean meal}\end{array}} = \boxed{\begin{array}{c}\text{Total pounds}\\\text{of protein}\end{array}}$$

$$0.117(480) + 0.118x + 0.445(1920 - x) = 0.14(2400)$$

$$56.16 + 0.118x + 854.4 - 0.445x = 336$$

$$910.56 - 0.327x = 336$$

$$-0.327x = -574.56$$

$$x \approx 1757$$

The farmer should use 480 pounds of barley, 1757 pounds of oats and 163 pounds of soybean meal.

53.
$$V = \pi r^2 h$$
$$712.51 = \pi(4.5)^2 d$$
$$\frac{712.51}{\pi(4.5)^2} = d$$
$$11.2 \approx d$$
The hole is about 11.2 millimeters deep.

54. Since the diameter of the semicircle is 6 feet, the radius of the semicircle is 3 feet.

Area of rectangle	+	Area of semicircle	=	Total area

$$6(h-3) + \tfrac{1}{2}\pi(3)^2 = 68.2$$
$$6h - 18 + 4.5\pi = 68.2$$
$$6h = 68.2 + 18 - 4.5\pi$$
$$6h \approx 72.0628$$
$$h \approx 12$$
The height of the window is about 12 feet.

55. **Answers may vary.**

56. **Answers may vary.**

57. $x^2 - 2x - 63 = (x-9)(x+7)$

58. $2x^2 + 11x - 21 = (2x-3)(x+7)$

59. $9x^2 - 12x - 5 = (3x+1)(3x-5)$

60. $9x^2 - 2x - 7 = (x-1)(9x+7)$

61. $x^2 + 6x + 9 = (x+3)(x+3)$

62. $x^2 - 10x + 25 = (x-5)(x-5)$

63.
$$x^3 + 8 = (x+2)(x^2 - 2x + 2^2)$$
$$= (x+2)(x^2 - 2x + 4)$$

64.
$$27a^3 - 64 = (3a-4)\left[(3a)^2 + (3a)(4) + 4^2\right]$$
$$= (3a-4)(9a^2 + 12a + 16)$$

Exercise 1.3 (page 106)

1. $ax^2 + bx + c = 0$

2. $ab = 0$

3. $\sqrt{c}, -\sqrt{c}$

4. $x = \dfrac{-b \pm \sqrt{b^2 - 4ac}}{2a}$

5. equal real numbers

6. not real numbers

7.
$$x^2 - x - 6 = 0$$
$$(x+2)(x-3) = 0$$
$$x + 2 = 0 \quad \textbf{or} \quad x - 3 = 0$$
$$x = -2 \qquad\qquad x = 3$$

8.
$$x^2 + 8x + 15 = 0$$
$$(x+5)(x+3) = 0$$
$$x + 5 = 0 \quad \textbf{or} \quad x + 3 = 0$$
$$x = -5 \qquad\qquad x = -3$$

9.
$$x^2 - 144 = 0$$
$$(x+12)(x-12) = 0$$
$$x + 12 = 0 \quad \textbf{or} \quad x - 12 = 0$$
$$x = -12 \qquad\qquad x = 12$$

10.
$$x^2 + 4x = 0$$
$$x(x+4) = 0$$
$$x = 0 \quad \textbf{or} \quad x + 4 = 0$$
$$x = 0 \qquad\qquad x = -4$$

11.
$$2x^2 + x - 10 = 0$$
$$(2x+5)(x-2) = 0$$
$$2x + 5 = 0 \quad \textbf{or} \quad x - 2 = 0$$
$$2x = -5 \qquad\qquad x = 2$$
$$x = -\tfrac{5}{2} \qquad\qquad x = 2$$

12.
$$3x^2 + 4x - 4 = 0$$
$$(3x-2)(x+2) = 0$$
$$3x - 2 = 0 \quad \textbf{or} \quad x + 2 = 0$$
$$3x = 2 \qquad\qquad x = -2$$
$$x = \tfrac{2}{3} \qquad\qquad x = -2$$

13.
$$\begin{aligned} 5x^2 - 13x + 6 &= 0 \\ (5x-3)(x-2) &= 0 \end{aligned}$$
$$\begin{array}{lcl} 5x - 3 = 0 & \textbf{or} & x - 2 = 0 \\ 5x = 3 & & x = 2 \\ x = \frac{3}{5} & & x = 2 \end{array}$$

14.
$$\begin{aligned} 2x^2 + 5x - 12 &= 0 \\ (2x-3)(x+4) &= 0 \end{aligned}$$
$$\begin{array}{lcl} 2x - 3 = 0 & \textbf{or} & x + 4 = 0 \\ 2x = 3 & & x = -4 \\ x = \frac{3}{2} & & x = -4 \end{array}$$

15.
$$\begin{aligned} 15x^2 + 16x &= 15 \\ 15x^2 + 16x - 15 &= 0 \\ (3x+5)(5x-3) &= 0 \end{aligned}$$
$$\begin{array}{lcl} 3x + 5 = 0 & \textbf{or} & 5x - 3 = 0 \\ 3x = -5 & & 5x = 3 \\ x = -\frac{5}{3} & & x = \frac{3}{5} \end{array}$$

16.
$$\begin{aligned} 6x^2 - 25x &= -25 \\ 6x^2 - 25x + 25 &= 0 \\ (3x-5)(2x-5) &= 0 \end{aligned}$$
$$\begin{array}{lcl} 3x - 5 = 0 & \textbf{or} & 2x - 5 = 0 \\ 3x = 5 & & 2x = 5 \\ x = \frac{5}{3} & & x = \frac{5}{2} \end{array}$$

17.
$$\begin{aligned} 12x^2 + 9 &= 24x \\ 12x^2 - 24x + 9 &= 0 \\ 3\left(4x^2 - 8x + 3\right) &= 0 \\ (2x-1)(2x-3) &= 0 \end{aligned}$$
$$\begin{array}{lcl} 2x - 1 = 0 & \textbf{or} & 2x - 3 = 0 \\ 2x = 1 & & 2x = 3 \\ x = \frac{1}{2} & & x = \frac{3}{2} \end{array}$$

18.
$$\begin{aligned} 24x^2 + 6 &= 24x \\ 24x^2 - 24x + 6 &= 0 \\ 6\left(4x^2 - 4x + 1\right) &= 0 \\ (2x-1)(2x-1) &= 0 \end{aligned}$$
$$\begin{array}{lcl} 2x - 1 = 0 & \textbf{or} & 2x - 1 = 0 \\ 2x = 1 & & 2x = 1 \\ x = \frac{1}{2} & & x = \frac{1}{2} \end{array}$$

19.
$$x^2 = 9$$
$$\begin{array}{lcl} x = \sqrt{9} & \textbf{or} & x = -\sqrt{9} \\ x = 3 & & x = -3 \end{array}$$

20.
$$x^2 = 20$$
$$\begin{array}{lcl} x = \sqrt{20} & \textbf{or} & x = -\sqrt{20} \\ x = 2\sqrt{5} & & x = -2\sqrt{5} \end{array}$$

21.
$$\begin{aligned} y^2 - 50 &= 0 \\ y^2 &= 50 \end{aligned}$$
$$\begin{array}{lcl} y = \sqrt{50} & \textbf{or} & y = -\sqrt{50} \\ y = 5\sqrt{2} & & y = -5\sqrt{2} \end{array}$$

22.
$$\begin{aligned} x^2 - 75 &= 0 \\ x^2 &= 75 \end{aligned}$$
$$\begin{array}{lcl} x = \sqrt{75} & \textbf{or} & x = -\sqrt{75} \\ x = 5\sqrt{3} & & x = -5\sqrt{3} \end{array}$$

23.
$$(x-1)^2 = 4$$
$$\begin{array}{lcl} x - 1 = \sqrt{4} & \textbf{or} & x - 1 = -\sqrt{4} \\ x - 1 = 2 & & x - 1 = -2 \\ x = 3 & & x = -1 \end{array}$$

24.
$$\begin{aligned} (y+2)^2 - 49 &= 0 \\ (y+2)^2 &= 49 \end{aligned}$$
$$\begin{array}{lcl} y + 2 = \sqrt{49} & \textbf{or} & y + 2 = -\sqrt{49} \\ y + 2 = 7 & & y + 2 = -7 \\ y = 5 & & y = -9 \end{array}$$

25.
$$\begin{aligned} a^2+2a+1&=9\\ (a+1)^2&=9 \end{aligned}$$
$$a+1=\sqrt{9} \quad \textbf{or} \quad a+1=-\sqrt{9}$$
$$a+1=3 \qquad a+1=-3$$
$$a=2 \qquad a=-4$$

26.
$$\begin{aligned} x^2-6x+9&=25\\ (x-3)^2&=25 \end{aligned}$$
$$x-3=\sqrt{25} \quad \textbf{or} \quad x-3=-\sqrt{25}$$
$$x-3=5 \qquad x-3=-5$$
$$x=8 \qquad x=-2$$

27. $$\begin{aligned} x^2+6x+\left[\tfrac{1}{2}(6)\right]^2&=x^2+6x+3^2\\ &=x^2+6x+9 \end{aligned}$$

28. $$\begin{aligned} x^2+8x+\left[\tfrac{1}{2}(8)\right]^2&=x^2+8x+4^2\\ &=x^2+8x+16 \end{aligned}$$

29. $$\begin{aligned} x^2-4x+\left[\tfrac{1}{2}(-4)\right]^2&=x^2-4x+(-2)^2\\ &=x^2-4x+4 \end{aligned}$$

30. $$\begin{aligned} x^2-12x+\left[\tfrac{1}{2}(-12)\right]^2&=x^2-12x+(-6)^2\\ &=x^2-12x+36 \end{aligned}$$

31. $$\begin{aligned} a^2+5a+\left[\tfrac{1}{2}(5)\right]^2&=a^2+5a+\left(\frac{5}{2}\right)^2\\ &=a^2+5a+\frac{25}{4} \end{aligned}$$

32. $$\begin{aligned} t^2+9t+\left[\tfrac{1}{2}(9)\right]^2&=t^2+9t+\left(\frac{9}{2}\right)^2\\ &=t^2+9t+\frac{81}{4} \end{aligned}$$

33. $$r^2-11r+\left[\tfrac{1}{2}(-11)\right]^2=r^2-11r+\left(\frac{-11}{2}\right)^2=r^2-11r+\frac{121}{4}$$

34. $$s^2-7s+\left[\tfrac{1}{2}(-7)\right]^2=s^2-7s+\left(\frac{-7}{2}\right)^2=s^2-7s+\frac{49}{4}$$

35. $$\begin{aligned} y^2+\frac{3}{4}y+\left[\frac{1}{2}\left(\frac{3}{4}\right)\right]^2&=y^2+\frac{3}{4}y+\left(\frac{3}{8}\right)^2\\ &=y^2+\frac{3}{4}y+\frac{9}{64} \end{aligned}$$

36. $$\begin{aligned} p^2+\frac{3}{2}p+\left[\frac{1}{2}\left(\frac{3}{2}\right)\right]^2&=p^2+\frac{3}{2}p+\left(\frac{3}{4}\right)^2\\ &=p^2+\frac{3}{2}p+\frac{9}{16} \end{aligned}$$

37. $$q^2-\frac{1}{5}q+\left[\frac{1}{2}\left(-\frac{1}{5}\right)\right]^2=q^2-\frac{1}{5}q+\left(\frac{-1}{10}\right)^2=q^2-\frac{1}{5}q+\frac{1}{100}$$

38. $$m^2-\frac{2}{3}m+\left[\frac{1}{2}\left(-\frac{2}{3}\right)\right]^2=m^2-\frac{2}{3}m+\left(\frac{-1}{3}\right)^2=m^2-\frac{2}{3}m+\frac{1}{9}$$

39.
$$\begin{aligned} x^2-8x+15&=0\\ x^2-8x&=-15\\ x^2-8x+16&=-15+16\\ (x-4)^2&=1 \end{aligned}$$
$$x-4=\sqrt{1} \quad \textbf{or} \quad x-4=-\sqrt{1}$$
$$x-4=1 \qquad x-4=-1$$
$$x=5 \qquad x=3$$

40.
$$\begin{aligned} x^2+10x+21&=0\\ x^2+10x&=-21\\ x^2+10x+25&=-21+25\\ (x+5)^2&=4 \end{aligned}$$
$$x+5=\sqrt{4} \quad \textbf{or} \quad x+5=-\sqrt{4}$$
$$x+5=2 \qquad x+5=-2$$
$$x=-3 \qquad x=-7$$

41.

$$\begin{aligned} x^2+x-6&=0\\ x^2+x&=6\\ x^2+x+\frac{1}{4}&=6+\frac{1}{4}\\ \left(x+\frac{1}{2}\right)^2&=\frac{25}{4} \end{aligned}$$

$$\begin{aligned} x+\frac{1}{2}&=\sqrt{\frac{25}{4}} \quad\textbf{or}\quad & x+\frac{1}{2}&=-\sqrt{\frac{25}{4}}\\ x+\frac{1}{2}&=\frac{5}{2} & x+\frac{1}{2}&=-\frac{5}{2}\\ x&=\frac{4}{2} & x&=-\frac{6}{2}\\ x&=2 & x&=-3 \end{aligned}$$

42.

$$\begin{aligned} x^2-9x+20&=0\\ x^2-9x&=-20\\ x^2-9x+\frac{81}{4}&=-20+\frac{81}{4}\\ \left(x-\frac{9}{2}\right)^2&=\frac{1}{4} \end{aligned}$$

$$\begin{aligned} x-\frac{9}{2}&=\sqrt{\frac{1}{4}} \quad\textbf{or}\quad & x-\frac{9}{2}&=-\sqrt{\frac{1}{4}}\\ x-\frac{9}{2}&=\frac{1}{2} & x-\frac{9}{2}&=-\frac{1}{2}\\ x&=\frac{10}{2} & x&=\frac{8}{2}\\ x&=5 & x&=4 \end{aligned}$$

43.

$$\begin{aligned} x^2-25x&=0\\ x^2-25x+\frac{625}{4}&=0+\frac{625}{4}\\ \left(x-\frac{25}{2}\right)^2&=\frac{625}{4} \end{aligned}$$

$$\begin{aligned} x-\tfrac{25}{2}&=\sqrt{\tfrac{625}{4}} \quad\textbf{or}\quad & x-\tfrac{25}{2}&=-\sqrt{\tfrac{625}{4}}\\ x-\frac{25}{2}&=\frac{25}{2} & x-\frac{25}{2}&=-\frac{25}{2}\\ x&=\frac{50}{2} & x&=0\\ x&=25 & x&=0 \end{aligned}$$

44.

$$\begin{aligned} x^2+x&=0\\ x^2+x+\frac{1}{4}&=0+\frac{1}{4}\\ \left(x+\frac{1}{2}\right)^2&=\frac{1}{4} \end{aligned}$$

$$\begin{aligned} x+\frac{1}{2}&=\sqrt{\frac{1}{4}} \quad\textbf{or}\quad & x+\frac{1}{2}&=-\sqrt{\frac{1}{4}}\\ x+\frac{1}{2}&=\frac{1}{2} & x+\frac{1}{2}&=-\frac{1}{2}\\ x&=0 & x&=-\frac{2}{2}\\ x&=0 & x&=-1 \end{aligned}$$

45.

$$\begin{aligned} 3x^2+4x&=4\\ x^2+\frac{4}{3}x&=\frac{4}{3}\\ x^2+\frac{4}{3}+\frac{4}{9}&=\frac{4}{3}+\frac{4}{9}\\ \left(x+\frac{2}{3}\right)^2&=\frac{16}{9} \end{aligned}$$

$$\begin{aligned} x+\frac{2}{3}&=\sqrt{\frac{16}{9}} \quad\textbf{or}\quad & x+\frac{2}{3}&=-\sqrt{\frac{16}{9}}\\ x+\frac{2}{3}&=\frac{4}{3} & x+\frac{2}{3}&=-\frac{4}{3}\\ x&=\frac{2}{3} & x&=-\frac{6}{3}\\ x&=\frac{2}{3} & x&=-2 \end{aligned}$$

46.

$$\begin{aligned} 2x^2+5x&=12\\ x^2+\frac{5}{2}x&=6\\ x^2+\frac{5}{2}+\frac{25}{16}&=6+\frac{25}{16}\\ \left(x+\frac{5}{4}\right)^2&=\frac{121}{16} \end{aligned}$$

$$\begin{aligned} x+\frac{5}{4}&=\sqrt{\frac{121}{16}} \quad\textbf{or}\quad & x+\frac{5}{4}&=-\sqrt{\frac{121}{16}}\\ x+\frac{5}{4}&=\frac{11}{4} & x+\frac{5}{4}&=-\frac{11}{4}\\ x&=\frac{6}{4} & x&=-\frac{16}{4}\\ x&=\frac{3}{2} & x&=-4 \end{aligned}$$

47.

$$x^2 + 5 = -5x$$
$$x^2 + 5x = -5$$
$$x^2 + 5x + \frac{25}{4} = -5 + \frac{25}{4}$$
$$\left(x + \frac{5}{2}\right)^2 = \frac{5}{4}$$

$$\left(x + \frac{5}{2}\right)^2 = \frac{5}{4}$$

$$x + \frac{5}{2} = \sqrt{\frac{5}{4}} \quad \textbf{or} \quad x + \frac{5}{2} = -\sqrt{\frac{5}{4}}$$
$$x + \frac{5}{2} = \frac{\sqrt{5}}{2} \qquad x + \frac{5}{2} = -\frac{\sqrt{5}}{2}$$
$$x = \frac{-5 + \sqrt{5}}{2} \qquad x = \frac{-5 - \sqrt{5}}{2}$$

48.

$$x^2 + 1 = -4x$$
$$x^2 + 4x = -1$$
$$x^2 + 4x + 4 = -1 + 4$$
$$(x + 2)^2 = 3$$
$$x + 2 = \sqrt{3} \quad \textbf{or} \quad x + 2 = -\sqrt{3}$$
$$x = -2 + \sqrt{3} \qquad x = -2 - \sqrt{3}$$

49.

$$3x^2 = 1 - 4x$$
$$3x^2 + 4x = 1$$
$$x^2 + \frac{4}{3}x = \frac{1}{3}$$
$$x^2 + \frac{4}{3}x + \frac{4}{9} = \frac{1}{3} + \frac{4}{9}$$
$$\left(x + \frac{2}{3}\right)^2 = \frac{7}{9}$$

$$\left(x + \frac{2}{3}\right)^2 = \frac{7}{9}$$

$$x + \frac{2}{3} = \sqrt{\frac{7}{9}} \quad \textbf{or} \quad x + \frac{2}{3} = -\sqrt{\frac{7}{9}}$$
$$x + \frac{2}{3} = \frac{\sqrt{7}}{3} \qquad x + \frac{2}{3} = -\frac{\sqrt{7}}{3}$$
$$x = \frac{-2 + \sqrt{7}}{3} \qquad x = \frac{-2 - \sqrt{7}}{3}$$

50.

$$2x^2 = 3x + 1$$
$$2x^2 - 3x = 1$$
$$x^2 - \frac{3}{2}x = \frac{1}{2}$$
$$x^2 - \frac{3}{2}x + \frac{9}{16} = \frac{1}{2} + \frac{9}{16}$$
$$\left(x - \frac{3}{4}\right)^2 = \frac{17}{16}$$

$$\left(x - \frac{3}{4}\right)^2 = \frac{17}{16}$$

$$x - \frac{3}{4} = \sqrt{\frac{17}{16}} \quad \textbf{or} \quad x - \frac{3}{4} = -\sqrt{\frac{17}{16}}$$
$$x - \frac{3}{4} = \frac{\sqrt{17}}{4} \qquad x - \frac{3}{4} = -\frac{\sqrt{17}}{4}$$
$$x = \frac{3 + \sqrt{17}}{4} \qquad x = \frac{3 - \sqrt{17}}{4}$$

51. $x^2 - 12 = 0 \Rightarrow a = 1, b = 0, c = -12$

$$x = \frac{-b \pm \sqrt{b^2 - 4ac}}{2a} = \frac{-(0) \pm \sqrt{(0)^2 - 4(1)(-12)}}{2(1)} = \frac{0 \pm \sqrt{0 + 48}}{2} = \frac{0 \pm \sqrt{48}}{2} = \frac{\pm\sqrt{48}}{2}$$

$$x = \frac{\sqrt{48}}{2} = \frac{4\sqrt{3}}{2} = 2\sqrt{3} \text{ or } x = \frac{-\sqrt{48}}{2} = \frac{-4\sqrt{3}}{2} = -2\sqrt{3}$$

52. $x^2 - 20 = 0 \Rightarrow a = 1, b = 0, c = -20$

$$x = \frac{-b \pm \sqrt{b^2 - 4ac}}{2a} = \frac{-(0) \pm \sqrt{(0)^2 - 4(1)(-20)}}{2(1)} = \frac{0 \pm \sqrt{0 + 80}}{2} = \frac{0 \pm \sqrt{80}}{2} = \frac{\pm \sqrt{80}}{2}$$

$$x = \frac{\sqrt{80}}{2} = \frac{4\sqrt{5}}{2} = 2\sqrt{5} \text{ or } x = \frac{-\sqrt{80}}{2} = \frac{-4\sqrt{5}}{2} = -2\sqrt{5}$$

53. $2x^2 - x - 15 = 0 \Rightarrow a = 2, b = -1, c = -15$

$$x = \frac{-b \pm \sqrt{b^2 - 4ac}}{2a} = \frac{-(-1) \pm \sqrt{(-1)^2 - 4(2)(-15)}}{2(2)} = \frac{1 \pm \sqrt{1 + 120}}{4} = \frac{1 \pm \sqrt{121}}{4} = \frac{1 \pm 11}{4}$$

$$x = \frac{1 + 11}{4} = \frac{12}{4} = 3 \text{ or } x = \frac{1 - 11}{4} = \frac{-10}{4} = -\frac{5}{2}$$

54. $6x^2 + x - 2 = 0 \Rightarrow a = 6, b = 1, c = -2$

$$x = \frac{-b \pm \sqrt{b^2 - 4ac}}{2a} = \frac{-(1) \pm \sqrt{(1)^2 - 4(6)(-2)}}{2(6)} = \frac{-1 \pm \sqrt{1 + 48}}{12} = \frac{-1 \pm \sqrt{49}}{12} = \frac{-1 \pm 7}{12}$$

$$x = \frac{-1 + 7}{12} = \frac{6}{12} = \frac{1}{2} \text{ or } x = \frac{-1 - 7}{12} = \frac{-8}{12} = -\frac{2}{3}$$

55. $5x^2 - 9x - 2 = 0 \Rightarrow a = 5, b = -9, c = -2$

$$x = \frac{-b \pm \sqrt{b^2 - 4ac}}{2a} = \frac{-(-9) \pm \sqrt{(-9)^2 - 4(5)(-2)}}{2(5)} = \frac{9 \pm \sqrt{81 + 40}}{10} = \frac{9 \pm \sqrt{121}}{10} = \frac{9 \pm 11}{10}$$

$$x = \frac{9 + 11}{10} = \frac{20}{10} = 2 \text{ or } x = \frac{9 - 11}{10} = \frac{-2}{10} = -\frac{1}{5}$$

56. $4x^2 - 4x - 3 = 0 \Rightarrow a = 4, b = -4, c = -3$

$$x = \frac{-b \pm \sqrt{b^2 - 4ac}}{2a} = \frac{-(-4) \pm \sqrt{(-4)^2 - 4(4)(-3)}}{2(4)} = \frac{4 \pm \sqrt{16 + 48}}{8} = \frac{4 \pm \sqrt{64}}{8} = \frac{4 \pm 8}{8}$$

$$x = \frac{4 + 8}{8} = \frac{12}{8} = \frac{3}{2} \text{ or } x = \frac{4 - 8}{8} = \frac{-4}{8} = -\frac{1}{2}$$

57. $2x^2 + 2x - 4 = 0 \Rightarrow a = 2, b = 2, c = -4$

$$x = \frac{-b \pm \sqrt{b^2 - 4ac}}{2a} = \frac{-(2) \pm \sqrt{(2)^2 - 4(2)(-4)}}{2(2)} = \frac{-2 \pm \sqrt{4 + 32}}{4} = \frac{-2 \pm \sqrt{36}}{4} = \frac{-2 \pm 6}{4}$$

$$x = \frac{-2 + 6}{4} = \frac{4}{4} = 1 \text{ or } x = \frac{-2 - 6}{4} = \frac{-8}{4} = -2$$

58. $3x^2 + 18x + 15 = 0 \Rightarrow a = 3,\, b = 18,\, c = 15$

$$x = \frac{-b \pm \sqrt{b^2 - 4ac}}{2a} = \frac{-(18) \pm \sqrt{(18)^2 - 4(3)(15)}}{2(3)} = \frac{-18 \pm \sqrt{324 - 180}}{6} = \frac{-18 \pm \sqrt{144}}{6}$$
$$= \frac{-18 \pm 12}{6}$$

$$x = \frac{-18 + 12}{6} = \frac{-6}{6} = -1 \text{ or } x = \frac{-18 - 12}{6} = \frac{-30}{6} = -5$$

59. $-3x^2 = 5x + 1 \Rightarrow -3x^2 - 5x - 1 = 0 \Rightarrow a = -3,\, b = -5,\, c = -1$

$$x = \frac{-b \pm \sqrt{b^2 - 4ac}}{2a} = \frac{-(-5) \pm \sqrt{(-5)^2 - 4(-3)(-1)}}{2(-3)} = \frac{5 \pm \sqrt{25 - 12}}{-6} = \frac{5 \pm \sqrt{13}}{-6}$$
$$= \frac{-5 \pm \sqrt{13}}{6}$$

60. $2x(x + 3) = -1 \Rightarrow 2x^2 + 6x + 1 = 0 \Rightarrow a = 2,\, b = 6,\, c = 1$

$$x = \frac{-b \pm \sqrt{b^2 - 4ac}}{2a} = \frac{-(6) \pm \sqrt{(6)^2 - 4(2)(1)}}{2(2)} = \frac{-6 \pm \sqrt{36 - 8}}{4} = \frac{-6 \pm \sqrt{28}}{4}$$
$$= \frac{-6 \pm 2\sqrt{7}}{4}$$
$$= \frac{-3 \pm \sqrt{7}}{2}$$

61. $5x\left(x + \frac{1}{5}\right) = 3 \Rightarrow 5x^2 + x - 3 = 0 \Rightarrow a = 5,\, b = 1,\, c = -3$

$$x = \frac{-b \pm \sqrt{b^2 - 4ac}}{2a} = \frac{-(1) \pm \sqrt{(1)^2 - 4(5)(-3)}}{2(5)} = \frac{-1 \pm \sqrt{1 + 60}}{10} = \frac{-1 \pm \sqrt{61}}{10}$$

62. $7x^2 = 2x + 2 \Rightarrow 7x^2 - 2x - 2 = 0 \Rightarrow a = 7,\, b = -2,\, c = -2$

$$x = \frac{-b \pm \sqrt{b^2 - 4ac}}{2a} = \frac{-(-2) \pm \sqrt{(-2)^2 - 4(7)(-2)}}{2(7)} = \frac{2 \pm \sqrt{4 + 56}}{14} = \frac{2 \pm \sqrt{60}}{14}$$
$$= \frac{2 \pm 2\sqrt{15}}{14}$$
$$= \frac{1 \pm \sqrt{15}}{7}$$

63. $h = \frac{1}{2}gt^2$

$2h = gt^2$

$\frac{2h}{g} = t^2 \Rightarrow t = \pm\sqrt{\frac{2h}{g}}$

64. $x^2 + y^2 = r^2$

$x^2 = r^2 - y^2$

$x = \pm\sqrt{r^2 - y^2}$

65.
$$h = 64t - 16t^2$$
$$16t^2 - 64t + h = 0;\ a = 16,\ b = -64,\ c = h$$
$$\begin{aligned} t &= \frac{-b \pm \sqrt{b^2 - 4ac}}{2a} \\ &= \frac{-(-64) \pm \sqrt{(-64)^2 - 4(16)h}}{2(16)} \\ &= \frac{64 \pm \sqrt{4096 - 64h}}{32} \\ &= \frac{64 \pm \sqrt{64(64 - h)}}{32} \\ &= \frac{64 \pm 8\sqrt{64 - h}}{32} = \frac{8 \pm \sqrt{64 - h}}{4} \end{aligned}$$

66.
$$\begin{aligned} y &= 16x^2 - 4 \\ y + 4 &= 16x^2 \\ \frac{y + 4}{16} &= x^2 \\ \pm\sqrt{\frac{y + 4}{16}} &= x \\ \frac{\pm\sqrt{y + 4}}{4} &= x \end{aligned}$$

67.
$$\begin{aligned} \frac{x^2}{a^2} + \frac{y^2}{b^2} &= 1 \\ \frac{y^2}{b^2} &= 1 - \frac{x^2}{a^2} \\ \frac{y^2}{b^2} &= \frac{a^2 - x^2}{a^2} \\ y^2 &= \frac{b^2(a^2 - x^2)}{a^2} \\ y &= \pm\sqrt{\frac{b^2(a^2 - x^2)}{a^2}} \\ y &= \pm\frac{b\sqrt{a^2 - x^2}}{a} \end{aligned}$$

68.
$$\begin{aligned} \frac{x^2}{a^2} - \frac{y^2}{b^2} &= 1 \\ \frac{x^2}{a^2} &= 1 + \frac{y^2}{b^2} \\ \frac{x^2}{a^2} &= \frac{b^2 + y^2}{b^2} \\ x^2 &= \frac{a^2(b^2 + y^2)}{b^2} \\ x &= \pm\sqrt{\frac{a^2(b^2 + y^2)}{b^2}} \\ x &= \pm\frac{a\sqrt{b^2 + y^2}}{b} \end{aligned}$$

69.
$$\begin{aligned} \frac{x^2}{a^2} - \frac{y^2}{b^2} &= 1 \\ a^2b^2\left(\frac{x^2}{a^2} - \frac{y^2}{b^2}\right) &= a^2b^2(1) \\ b^2x^2 - a^2y^2 &= a^2b^2 \\ b^2x^2 &= a^2b^2 + a^2y^2 \\ b^2x^2 &= a^2\left(b^2 + y^2\right) \\ \frac{b^2x^2}{b^2 + y^2} &= a^2 \\ \pm\sqrt{\frac{b^2x^2}{b^2 + y^2}} &= a \\ \pm\frac{bx\sqrt{b^2 + y^2}}{b^2 + y^2} &= a \end{aligned}$$

70.
$$\begin{aligned} \frac{x^2}{a^2} - \frac{y^2}{b^2} &= 1 \\ a^2b^2\left(\frac{x^2}{a^2} - \frac{y^2}{b^2}\right) &= a^2b^2(1) \\ b^2x^2 - a^2y^2 &= a^2b^2 \\ b^2x^2 - a^2b^2 &= a^2y^2 \\ b^2\left(x^2 - a^2\right) &= a^2y^2 \\ b^2 &= \frac{a^2y^2}{x^2 - a^2} \\ b &= \pm\sqrt{\frac{a^2y^2}{x^2 - a^2}} \\ b &= \pm\frac{ay\sqrt{x^2 - a^2}}{x^2 - a^2} \end{aligned}$$

71. $x^2 + xy - y^2 = 0 \Rightarrow a = 1, b = y, c = -y^2$

$$x = \frac{-b \pm \sqrt{b^2 - 4ac}}{2a} = \frac{-(y) \pm \sqrt{(y)^2 - 4(1)(-y^2)}}{2(1)} = \frac{-y \pm \sqrt{y^2 + 4y^2}}{2} = \frac{-y \pm \sqrt{5y^2}}{2} = \frac{-y \pm y\sqrt{5}}{2}$$

72. $x^2 - 3xy + y^2 = 0 \Rightarrow y^2 - 3xy + x^2 = 0$

$a = 1, b = -3x, c = x^2$

$$y = \frac{-b \pm \sqrt{b^2 - 4ac}}{2a} = \frac{-(-3x) \pm \sqrt{(-3x)^2 - 4(1)(x^2)}}{2(1)} = \frac{3x \pm \sqrt{9x^2 - 4x^2}}{2} = \frac{3x \pm \sqrt{5x^2}}{2} = \frac{3x \pm x\sqrt{5}}{2}$$

73. $x^2 + 6x + 9 = 0 \Rightarrow a = 1, b = 6, c = 9$

$b^2 - 4ac = 6^2 - 4(1)(9) = 36 - 36 = 0$

The solutions are rational and equal.

74. $x^2 - 5x + 2 = 0 \Rightarrow a = 1, b = -5, c = 2$

$b^2 - 4ac = (-5)^2 - 4(1)(2) = 25 - 8 = 17$

The solutions are irrational and unequal.

75. $3x^2 - 2x + 5 = 0 \Rightarrow a = 3, b = -2, c = 5$

$b^2 - 4ac = (-2)^2 - 4(3)(5)$

$= 4 - 60 = -56$

The solutions are not real numbers.

76. $9x^2 + 42x + 49 = 0$

$a = 9, b = 42, c = 49$

$b^2 - 4ac = (42)^2 - 4(9)(49)$

$= 1764 - 1764 = 0$

The solutions are rational and equal.

77. $10x^2 + 29x = 21 \Rightarrow 10x^2 + 29x - 21 = 0$

$a = 10, b = 29, c = -21$

$b^2 - 4ac = (29)^2 - 4(10)(-21)$

$= 841 + 840 = 1681$

The solutions are rational and unequal.

78. $10x^2 + x = 21 \Rightarrow 10x^2 + x - 21 = 0$

$a = 10, b = 1, c = -21$

$b^2 - 4ac = (1)^2 - 4(10)(-21)$

$= 1 + 840 = 841$

The solutions are rational and unequal.

79. $-3x^2 + 2x = 21 \Rightarrow -3x^2 + 2x - 21 = 0$

$a = -3, b = 2, c = -21$

$b^2 - 4ac = (2)^2 - 4(-3)(-21)$

$= 4 - 252 = -248$

The solutions are not real numbers.

80. $-8x^2 - 2x = 13 \Rightarrow -8x^2 - 2x - 13 = 0$

$a = -8, b = -2, c = -13$

$b^2 - 4ac = (-2)^2 - 4(-8)(-13)$

$= 4 - 416 = -412$

The solutions are not real numbers.

81. $1492x^2 + 1984x - 1776 = 0$

$a = 1492, b = 1984, c = -1776$

$b^2 - 4ac = (1984)^2 - 4(1492)(-1776)$

$= 3{,}936{,}256 + 10{,}599{,}168$

$= 14{,}535{,}424$

The solutions are real numbers.

82. $2004x^2 + 10x + 1994 = 0$

$a = 2004, b = 10, c = 1994$

$b^2 - 4ac = (10)^2 - 4(2004)(1994)$

$= 100 - 15{,}983{,}904$

$= -15{,}983{,}804$

The solutions are not real numbers.

83.
$$x^2 + kx + 3k - 5 = 0$$
$$a = 1, b = k, c = 3k - 5$$
Set the discriminant equal to 0:
$$b^2 - 4ac = 0$$
$$k^2 - 4(1)(3k - 5) = 0$$
$$k^2 - 4(3k - 5) = 0$$
$$k^2 - 12k + 20 = 0$$
$$(k - 2)(k - 10) = 0$$
$$k = 2 \text{ or } k = 10$$

84.
$$x^2 - 2bx + b^2 = 0$$
$$a = 1, b = -2b, c = b^2$$
Set the discriminant equal to 0:
$$b^2 - 4ac = 0$$
$$(-2b)^2 - 4(1)(b^2) = 0$$
$$4b^2 - 4b^2 = 0$$
$$0 = 0$$
True for all values of b

85.
$$x + 1 = \frac{12}{x}$$
$$x(x + 1) = x\left(\frac{12}{x}\right)$$
$$x^2 + x = 12$$
$$x^2 + x - 12 = 0$$
$$(x + 4)(x - 3) = 0$$
$$x + 4 = 0 \quad \textbf{or} \quad x - 3 = 0$$
$$x = -4 \qquad\qquad x = 3$$

86.
$$x - 2 = \frac{15}{x}$$
$$x(x - 2) = x\left(\frac{15}{x}\right)$$
$$x^2 - 2x = 15$$
$$x^2 - 2x - 15 = 0$$
$$(x + 3)(x - 5) = 0$$
$$x + 3 = 0 \quad \textbf{or} \quad x - 5 = 0$$
$$x = -3 \qquad\qquad x = 5$$

87.
$$8x - \frac{3}{x} = 10$$
$$x\left(8x - \frac{3}{x}\right) = x(10)$$
$$8x^2 - 3 = 10x$$
$$8x^2 - 10x - 3 = 0$$
$$(4x + 1)(2x - 3) = 0$$
$$4x + 1 = 0 \quad \textbf{or} \quad 2x - 3 = 0$$
$$4x = -1 \qquad\qquad 2x = 3$$
$$x = -\tfrac{1}{4} \qquad\qquad x = \tfrac{3}{2}$$

88.
$$15x - \frac{4}{x} = 4$$
$$x\left(15x - \frac{4}{x}\right) = x(4)$$
$$15x^2 - 4 = 4x$$
$$15x^2 - 4x - 4 = 0$$
$$(5x + 2)(3x - 2) = 0$$
$$5x + 2 = 0 \quad \textbf{or} \quad 3x - 2 = 0$$
$$5x = -2 \qquad\qquad 3x = 2$$
$$x = -\tfrac{2}{5} \qquad\qquad x = \tfrac{2}{3}$$

89.
$$\frac{5}{x} = \frac{4}{x^2} - 6$$
$$x^2\left(\frac{5}{x}\right) = x^2\left(\frac{4}{x^2} - 6\right)$$
$$5x = 4 - 6x^2$$
$$6x^2 + 5x - 4 = 0$$
$$(3x + 4)(2x - 1) = 0$$
$$3x + 4 = 0 \quad \textbf{or} \quad 2x - 1 = 0$$
$$3x = -4 \qquad\qquad 2x = 1$$
$$x = -\tfrac{4}{3} \qquad\qquad x = \tfrac{1}{2}$$

90.
$$\frac{6}{x^2} + \frac{1}{x} = 12$$
$$x^2\left(\frac{6}{x^2} + \frac{1}{x}\right) = x^2(12)$$
$$6 + x = 12x^2$$
$$0 = 12x^2 - x - 6$$
$$0 = (3x + 2)(4x - 3)$$
$$3x + 2 = 0 \quad \textbf{or} \quad 4x - 3 = 0$$
$$3x = -2 \qquad\qquad 4x = 3$$
$$x = -\tfrac{2}{3} \qquad\qquad x = \tfrac{3}{4}$$

91.
$$x\left(30-\frac{13}{x}\right)=\frac{10}{x}$$
$$30x-13=\frac{10}{x}$$
$$x(30x-13)=x\left(\frac{10}{x}\right)$$
$$30x^2-13x=10$$
$$30x^2-13x=10$$
$$30x^2-13x-10=0$$
$$(5x+2)(6x-5)=0$$
$5x+2=0$ **or** $6x-5=0$
$5x=-2$ $\quad$ $6x=5$
$x=-\frac{2}{5}$ $\quad$ $x=\frac{5}{6}$

92.
$$x\left(20-\frac{17}{x}\right)=\frac{10}{x}$$
$$20x-17=\frac{10}{x}$$
$$x(20x-17)=x\left(\frac{10}{x}\right)$$
$$20x^2-17x=10$$
$$20x^2-17x-10=0$$
$$(5x+2)(4x-5)=0$$
$5x+2=0$ **or** $4x-5=0$
$5x=-2$ $\quad$ $4x=5$
$x=-\frac{2}{5}$ $\quad$ $x=\frac{5}{4}$

93.
$$(a-2)(a+4)=2a(a-3)$$
$$a^2+2a-8=2a^2-6a$$
$$0=a^2-8a+8$$
$a=1,\ b=-8,\ c=8$
$$a=\frac{-b\pm\sqrt{b^2-4ac}}{2a}$$
$$=\frac{-(-8)\pm\sqrt{(-8)^2-4(1)(8)}}{2(1)}$$
$$=\frac{8\pm\sqrt{32}}{2}=\frac{8\pm4\sqrt{2}}{2}=4\pm2\sqrt{2}$$

94.
$$\frac{4+a}{2a}=\frac{a-2}{3}$$
$$6a\left(\frac{4+a}{2a}\right)=6a\left(\frac{a-2}{3}\right)$$
$$12+3a=2a^2-4a$$
$$0=2a^2-7a-12$$
$a=2,\ b=-7,\ c=-12$
$$a=\frac{-b\pm\sqrt{b^2-4ac}}{2a}$$
$$=\frac{-(-7)\pm\sqrt{(-7)^2-4(2)(-12)}}{2(2)}$$
$$=\frac{7\pm\sqrt{145}}{4}$$

95.
$$\frac{1}{x}+\frac{3}{x+2}=2$$
$$x(x+2)\left(\frac{1}{x}+\frac{3}{x+2}\right)=x(x+2)(2)$$
$$1(x+2)+3x=2x(x+2)$$
$$x+2+3x=2x^2+4x$$
$$0=2x^2-2$$
$$0=2(x+1)(x-1)$$
$x+1=0$ **or** $x-1=0$
$x=-1$ $\quad$ $x=1$

96.

$$\frac{1}{x-1}+\frac{1}{x-4}=\frac{5}{4}$$
$$4(x-1)(x-4)\left(\frac{1}{x-1}+\frac{1}{x-4}\right)=4(x-1)(x-4)\frac{5}{4}$$
$$4(x-4)+4(x-1)=5(x-1)(x-4)$$
$$4x-16+4x-4=5x^2-25x+20$$
$$0=5x^2-33x+40$$
$$0=(5x-8)(x-5)$$

$5x-8=0$ **or** $x-5=0$
$5x=8$ $\quad x=5$
$x=\frac{8}{5}$ $\quad x=5$

97.

$$\frac{1}{x+1}+\frac{5}{2x-4}=1$$
$$(x+1)(2x-4)\left(\frac{1}{x+1}+\frac{5}{2x-4}\right)=(x+1)(2x-4)1$$
$$1(2x-4)+5(x+1)=(x+1)(2x-4)$$
$$2x-4+5x+5=2x^2-2x-4$$
$$0=2x^2-9x-5$$
$$0=(2x+1)(x-5)$$

$2x+1=0$ **or** $x-5=0$
$2x=-1$ $\quad x=5$
$x=-\frac{1}{2}$ $\quad x=5$

98.

$$\frac{x(2x+1)}{x-2}=\frac{10}{x-2}$$
$$(x-2)\frac{x(2x+1)}{x-2}=(x-2)\frac{10}{x-2}$$
$$x(2x+1)=10$$
$$2x^2+x=10$$
$$2x^2+x-10=0$$
$$(2x+5)(x-2)=0$$

$2x+5=0$ **or** $x-2=0$
$2x=-5$ $\quad x=2$
$x=-\frac{5}{2}$ $\quad x=2$

Since $x=2$ does not check, the only solution is $x=-\frac{5}{2}$.

99.

$$x+1+\frac{x+2}{x-1}=\frac{3}{x-1}$$
$$(x-1)\left(\frac{x+1}{1}+\frac{x+2}{x-1}\right)=(x-1)\frac{3}{x-1}$$
$$(x-1)(x+1)+x+2=3$$
$$x^2-1+x+2=3$$
$$x^2+x-2=0$$
$$(x+2)(x-1)=0$$

$x+2=0$ **or** $x-1=0$
$x=-2$ $\quad x=1$

Since $x=1$ does not check, the only solution is $x=-2$.

100.
$$\frac{1}{4-y}=\frac{1}{4}+\frac{1}{y+2}$$
$$4(4-y)(y+2)\left(\frac{1}{4-y}\right)=4(4-y)(y+2)\left(\frac{1}{4}+\frac{1}{y+2}\right)$$
$$4(y+2)(1)=(4-y)(y+2)(1)+4(4-y)(1)$$
$$4y+8=-y^2+2y+8+16-4y$$
$$y^2+6y-16=0$$
$$(y+8)(y-2)=0$$
$$y+8=0 \quad \textbf{or} \quad y-2=0$$
$$y=-8 \qquad\qquad y=2$$

101.
$$\frac{24}{a}-11=\frac{-12}{a+1}$$
$$a(a+1)\left(\frac{24}{a}-11\right)=a(a+1)\frac{-12}{a+1}$$
$$24(a+1)-11a(a+1)=a(-12)$$
$$24a+24-11a^2-11a=-12a$$
$$0=11a^2-25a-24$$
$$0=(11a+8)(a-3)$$
$$11a+8=0 \quad \textbf{or} \quad a-3=0$$
$$11a=-8 \qquad\qquad a=3$$
$$a=-\tfrac{8}{11} \qquad\qquad a=3$$

102.
$$\frac{36}{b}-17=\frac{-24}{b+1}$$
$$b(b+1)\left(\frac{36}{b}-17\right)=b(b+1)\frac{-24}{b+1}$$
$$36(b+1)-17b(b+1)=b(-24)$$
$$36b+36-17b^2-17b=-24b$$
$$0=17b^2-43b-36 \Rightarrow a=17,\ b=-43,\ c=-36$$
$$b=\frac{-b\pm\sqrt{b^2-4ac}}{2a}=\frac{-(-43)\pm\sqrt{(-43)^2-4(17)(-36)}}{2(17)}=\frac{43\pm\sqrt{4297}}{34}$$

103. If r_1 and r_2 are the roots of $ax^2+bx+c=0$, then their values are
$$r_1=\frac{-b+\sqrt{b^2-4ac}}{2a} \text{ and } r_2=\frac{-b-\sqrt{b^2-4ac}}{2a}.$$
$$r_1+r_2=\frac{-b+\sqrt{b^2-4ac}}{2a}+\frac{-b-\sqrt{b^2-4ac}}{2a}=\frac{-2b}{2a}=-\frac{b}{a}$$

104. If r_1 and r_2 are the roots of $ax^2+bx+c=0$, then their values are

$$r_1=\frac{-b+\sqrt{b^2-4ac}}{2a} \text{ and } r_2=\frac{-b-\sqrt{b^2-4ac}}{2a}.$$

$$r_1r_2=\frac{-b+\sqrt{b^2-4ac}}{2a}\cdot\frac{-b-\sqrt{b^2-4ac}}{2a}$$

$$=\frac{\left(-b+\sqrt{b^2-4ac}\right)\left(-b-\sqrt{b^2-4ac}\right)}{4a^2}$$

$$=\frac{(-b)^2-\left(\sqrt{b^2-4ac}\right)^2}{4a^2}=\frac{b^2-(b^2-4ac)}{4a^2}=\frac{b^2-b^2+4ac}{4a^2}=\frac{4ac}{4a^2}=\frac{c}{a}$$

105. Rewrite the equation as $16t^2-v_0t+h=0$ and solve for t using the quadratic formula.
$a=16$, $b=-v_0$, $c=h$

$$t=\frac{-b\pm\sqrt{b^2-4ac}}{2a}=\frac{-(-v_0)\pm\sqrt{(-v_0)^2-4(16)(h)}}{2(16)}=\frac{v_0\pm\sqrt{v_0^2-64h}}{32}$$

Since t_1 and t_2 are the solutions to the equation, we have

$$t_1=\frac{v_0+\sqrt{v_0^2-64h}}{32} \text{ and } t_2=\frac{v_0-\sqrt{v_0^2-64h}}{32}. \text{ Calculate } 16t_1t_2:$$

$$16t_1t_2=16\cdot\frac{v_0+\sqrt{v_0^2-64h}}{32}\cdot\frac{v_0-\sqrt{v_0^2-64h}}{32}=16\cdot\frac{v_0^2-(v_0^2-64h)}{1024}$$

$$=\frac{16\cdot 64h}{1024}=\frac{1024h}{1024}=h$$

Thus, $h=16t_1t_2$.

106. Proceed as in **#105** to calculate t_1 and t_2. Then

$$16(t_1+t_2)=16\left(\frac{v_0+\sqrt{v_0^2-64h}}{32}+\frac{v_0-\sqrt{v_0^2-64h}}{32}\right)=16\left(\frac{2v_0}{32}\right)=\frac{32v_0}{32}=v_0.$$

Thus $v_0=16(t_1+t_2)$.

107. Answers may vary.

108. Answers may vary.

109. $5x(x-2)-x(3x-2)=5x^2-10x-3x^2+2x=2x^2-8x$

110. $(x+3)(x-9)-x(x-5)=x^2-6x-27-x^2+5x=-x-27$

111. $(m+3)^2-(m-3)^2=(m+3)(m+3)-(m-3)(m-3)$

$$=m^2+6m+9-\left(m^2-6m+9\right)$$

$$=m^2+6m+9-m^2+6m-9=12m$$

112. $[(y+z)(y-z)]^2=[y^2-z^2]^2=(y^2-z^2)(y^2-z^2)=y^4-2y^2z^2+z^4$

113. $\sqrt{50x^3}-x\sqrt{8x}=\sqrt{25x^2}\sqrt{2x}-x\sqrt{4}\sqrt{2x}=5x\sqrt{2x}-2x\sqrt{2x}=3x\sqrt{2x}$

114. $\frac{2x}{\sqrt{5}-2} = \frac{2x}{\sqrt{5}-2} \cdot \frac{\sqrt{5}+2}{\sqrt{5}+2} = \frac{2x\left(\sqrt{5}+2\right)}{\left(\sqrt{5}\right)^2 - 2^2} = \frac{2x\left(\sqrt{5}+2\right)}{5-4} = \frac{2x\left(\sqrt{5}+2\right)}{1} = 2x\left(\sqrt{5}+2\right)$

Exercise 1.4 (page 112)

1. $A = lw$

2. $d = rt$

3. Let $w =$ the width of the rectangle.
Then $w + 4 =$ the length.

$\boxed{\text{Width}} \cdot \boxed{\text{Length}} = \boxed{\text{Area}}$

$$w(w+4) = 32$$
$$w^2 + 4w = 32$$
$$w^2 + 4w - 32 = 0$$
$$(w+8)(w-4) = 0$$
$$w + 8 = 0 \quad \textbf{or} \quad w - 4 = 0$$
$$w = -8 \qquad\qquad w = 4$$

Since the width cannot be negative, the only reasonable solution is $w = 4$.
The dimensions are 4 feet by 8 feet.

4. Let $w =$ the width of the rectangle.
Then $5w =$ the length.

$\boxed{\text{Width}} \cdot \boxed{\text{Length}} = \boxed{\text{Area}}$

$$w \cdot 5w = 125$$
$$5w^2 = 125$$
$$w^2 = 25$$
$$w = \sqrt{25} \quad \textbf{or} \quad w = -\sqrt{25}$$
$$w = 5 \qquad\qquad w = -5$$

Since the width cannot be negative, the only reasonable solution is $w = 5$.
The dimensions are 5 feet by 25 feet, and the perimeter is 60 feet.

5. Let $s =$ the side of the second square.
Then $s - 4 =$ the side of the first square.

$\boxed{\text{Area of first}} + \boxed{\text{Area of second}} = 106$

$$(s-4)^2 + s^2 = 106$$
$$s^2 - 8s + 16 + s^2 = 106$$
$$2s^2 - 8s - 90 = 0$$
$$2\left(s^2 - 4s - 45\right) = 0$$
$$2(s+5)(s-9) = 0$$
$$s + 5 = 0 \quad \textbf{or} \quad s - 9 = 0$$
$$s = -5 \qquad\qquad s = 9$$

Since the side cannot be negative, the only reasonable solution is $s = 9$.
The larger square has a side of length 9 cm.

6. Let $h =$ the height of the triangle.
Then $\frac{1}{3}h =$ the base of the triangle.

$\frac{1}{2} \cdot \boxed{\text{Base}} \cdot \boxed{\text{Height}} = \boxed{\text{Area}}$

$$\tfrac{1}{2} \cdot \tfrac{1}{3}h \cdot h = 24$$
$$\tfrac{1}{6}h^2 = 24$$
$$h^2 = 144$$
$$h = \sqrt{144} \quad \textbf{or} \quad h = -\sqrt{144}$$
$$h = 12 \qquad\qquad h = -12$$

Since the height cannot be negative, the only reasonable solution is $h = 12$.
The base has a length of 4 meters.

7. The floor area of the box is a square with a side of length $12 - 2x$.

$$\boxed{\text{Floor area}} = 64$$
$$(12 - 2x)^2 = 64$$
$$144 - 48x + 4x^2 = 64$$
$$4x^2 - 48x + 80 = 0$$
$$4(x^2 - 12x + 20) = 0$$
$$4(x-2)(x-10) = 0$$
$$x - 2 = 0 \quad \textbf{or} \quad x - 10 = 0$$
$$x = 2 \qquad\qquad x = 10$$

The solution $x = 10$ does not make sense in the problem, so the depth is 2 inches.

8.

$$\boxed{\text{Cross-sectional area}} = 36$$
$$x(18 - 2x) = 36$$
$$18x - 2x^2 = 36$$
$$0 = 2x^2 - 18x + 36$$
$$0 = 2(x^2 - 9x + 18)$$
$$0 = 2(x-3)(x-6)$$
$$x - 3 = 0 \quad \textbf{or} \quad x - 6 = 0$$
$$x = 3 \qquad\qquad x = 6$$

Both solutions are valid, so the depth of the gutter is either 3 inches or 6 inches.

9. Let $x =$ the height of the tube. Then $x + 6 =$ the width. Use the Pythagorean Theorem:

$$\text{height}^2 + \text{width}^2 = \text{diagonal}^2$$
$$x^2 + (x+6)^2 = 52^2$$
$$x^2 + x^2 + 12x + 36 = 2704$$
$$2x^2 + 12x - 2668 = 0$$

$a = 2$, $b = 12$, $c = -2668$

$$x = \frac{-b \pm \sqrt{b^2 - 4ac}}{2a}$$
$$= \frac{-12 \pm \sqrt{12^2 - 4(2)(-2668)}}{2(2)}$$
$$= \frac{-12 \pm \sqrt{21488}}{4} \approx \frac{-12 \pm 146.588}{4}$$

The only positive solution is 33.6. The dimensions are 33.6 inches by 39.6 inches.

10. Let $x =$ the width of the rug. Then $x + 2 =$ the length. Use the Pythagorean Theorem:

$$\text{width}^2 + \text{length}^2 = \text{diagonal}^2$$
$$x^2 + (x+2)^2 = 12^2$$
$$x^2 + x^2 + 4x + 4 = 144$$
$$2x^2 + 4x - 140 = 0$$

$a = 2$, $b = 4$, $c = -140$

$$x = \frac{-b \pm \sqrt{b^2 - 4ac}}{2a}$$
$$= \frac{-4 \pm \sqrt{4^2 - 4(2)(-140)}}{2(2)}$$
$$= \frac{-4 \pm \sqrt{1136}}{4} \approx \frac{-4 \pm 33.705}{4}$$

The only positive solution is 7.4. The dimensions are 7.4 feet by 9.4 feet.

11. Let $r =$ the cyclist's rate from DeKalb to Rockford. Then his return rate is $r - 10$.

$\boxed{\text{Return time}} = \boxed{\text{First time}} + 2$

	Rate	Time	Dist.
First trip	r	$\frac{40}{r}$	40
Return trip	$r-10$	$\frac{40}{r-10}$	40

$$\frac{40}{r-10} = \frac{40}{r} + 2$$
$$r(r-10)\frac{40}{r-10} = r(r-10)\left(\frac{40}{r} + 2\right)$$
$$40r = 40(r-10) + 2r(r-10)$$
$$40r = 40r - 400 + 2r^2 - 20r$$
$$0 = 2r^2 - 20r - 400$$
$$0 = 2(r-20)(r+10)$$

$r - 20 = 0$ **or** $r + 10 = 0$ Since $r = -10$ does not make sense, the solution is $r = 20$.
$r = 20$ $r = -10$ The cyclist rides 20 mph going and 10 mph returning.

12. Let $r =$ the farmer's first rate. Then his return rate is $r + 10$.

$\boxed{\text{Return time}} = \boxed{\text{First time}} - 1$

	Rate	Time	Dist.
First trip	r	$\frac{120}{r}$	120
Return trip	$r+10$	$\frac{120}{r+10}$	120

$$\frac{120}{r+10} = \frac{120}{r} - 1$$
$$r(r+10)\frac{120}{r+10} = r(r+10)\left(\frac{120}{r} - 1\right)$$
$$120r = 120(r+10) - r(r+10)$$
$$120r = 120r + 1200 - r^2 - 10r$$
$$r^2 + 10r - 1200 = 0$$
$$(r-30)(r+40) = 0$$

$r - 30 = 0$ **or** $r + 40 = 0$ Since $r = -40$ does not make sense, the solution is $r = 30$.
$r = 30$ $r = -40$ The farmer drives 30 kph going and 40 kph returning.

13. Let $r =$ the slower rate. Then the faster rate is $r + 10$.

$\boxed{\text{Faster time}} = \boxed{\text{Slower time}} - 1$

	Rate	Time	Dist.
Slower trip	r	$\frac{420}{r}$	420
Faster trip	$r+10$	$\frac{420}{r+10}$	420

$$\frac{420}{r+10} = \frac{420}{r} - 1$$
$$r(r+10)\frac{420}{r+10} = r(r+10)\left(\frac{420}{r} - 1\right)$$
$$420r = 420(r+10) - r(r+10)$$
$$420r = 420r + 4200 - r^2 - 10r$$
$$r^2 + 10r - 4200 = 0$$
$$(r-60)(r+70) = 0$$

$r - 60 = 0$ **or** $r + 70 = 0$ Since $r = -70$ does not make sense, the solution is $r = 60$.
$r = 60$ $r = -70$ The slower speed results in a trip of length 7 hours.

14. Let r = the driver's slower rate. Then her faster rate is $r + 25$.

$$\boxed{\text{Faster time}} = \boxed{\text{Slower time}} - \frac{10}{60}$$

$$\frac{25}{r+25} = \frac{25}{r} - \frac{1}{6}$$

$$6r(r+25)\frac{25}{r+25} = 6r(r+25)\left(\frac{25}{r} - \frac{1}{6}\right)$$

$$150r = 150(r+25) - r(r+25)$$

$$150r = 150r + 3750 - r^2 - 25r$$

$$r^2 + 25r - 3750 = 0$$

$$(r-50)(r+75) = 0$$

$r - 50 = 0$ **or** $r + 75 = 0$

$r = 50$ $\quad$ $r = -75$

	Rate	Time	Dist.
Slower trip	r	$\frac{25}{r}$	25
Faster trip	$r+25$	$\frac{25}{r+25}$	25

Since $r = -75$ does not make sense, the solution is $r = 50$. The driver's usual speed is 50 kph.

15. Set $h = 0$:

$$h = -16t^2 + 400t$$

$$0 = -16t^2 + 400t$$

$$16t^2 - 400t = 0$$

$$16t(t-25) = 0$$

$16t = 0$ **or** $t - 25 = 0$

$t = 0$ $\quad$ $t = 25$

$t = 0$ represents when the projectile was fired, so it returns to earth after 25 seconds.

16. Set $h = 0$:

$$h = -16t^2 + 104t$$

$$0 = -16t^2 + 104t$$

$$16t^2 - 104t = 0$$

$$8t(2t-13) = 0$$

$8t = 0$ **or** $2t - 13 = 0$

$t = 0$ $\quad$ $t = \frac{13}{2} = 6.5$

$t = 0$ represents when the projectile was fired, so it returns after 6.5 seconds.

17. Set $s = 1454$:

$$s = 16t^2$$

$$1454 = 16t^2$$

$$\frac{1454}{16} = t^2$$

$t = \sqrt{\frac{1454}{16}}$ **or** $t = -\sqrt{\frac{1454}{16}}$

$t \approx 9.5$ $\quad$ $t \approx -9.5$

$t = -9.5$ does not make sense, so it takes the penny about 9.5 seconds to hit the ground.

18. Set $h = 16$:

$$h = -16t^2 + 32t$$

$$16 = -16t^2 + 32t$$

$$16t^2 - 32t + 16 = 0$$

$$16(t-1)(t-1) = 0$$

$t - 1 = 0$ **or** $t - 1 = 0$

$t = 1$ $\quad$ $t = 1$

It takes the object 1 second to reach a height of 16 feet.

19. Let $x =$ the number of nickel increases. The new fare $= 25 + 5x$ (in cents), while the number of passengers $= 3000 - 80x$.

$$\boxed{\text{Number of passengers}} \cdot \boxed{\text{Fare}} = \boxed{\text{Revenue}}$$

$$\begin{aligned}(3000 - 80x)(25 + 5x) &= 99400\\ 75000 + 13000x - 400x^2 &= 99400\\ 400x^2 - 13000x + 24400 &= 0\\ 200\left(2x^2 - 65x + 122\right) &= 0\\ 200(2x - 61)(x - 2) &= 0\end{aligned}$$

$$2x - 61 = 0 \quad \textbf{or} \quad x - 2 = 0$$
$$x = 30.5 \qquad\qquad x = 2$$

Since you cannot have half of a nickel increase, $x = 30.5$ does not make sense. Thus, there should be 2 nickel increases, for a fare increase of 10 cents.

20. Let $x =$ the number of dollar increases. The new price $= 12 + x$, while the number attending $= 500 - 50x$.

$$\boxed{\text{Number attending}} \cdot \boxed{\text{Price}} = \boxed{\text{Revenue}}$$

$$\begin{aligned}(500 - 50x)(12 + x) &= 5600\\ 6000 - 100x - 50x^2 &= 5600\\ 50x^2 + 100x - 400 &= 0\\ 50\left(x^2 + 2x - 8\right) &= 0\\ 50(x + 4)(x - 2) &= 0\end{aligned}$$

$$x + 4 = 0 \quad \textbf{or} \quad x - 2 = 0$$
$$x = -4 \qquad\qquad x = 2$$

Since you cannot have a negative number of increases, $x = -4$ does not make sense. Thus, there should be an increase of 2 dollars, for a ticket price of \$14.

21. Let $x =$ the number of \$0.50 decreases. The new price $= 15 - 0.5x$, while the number attending $= 1200 + 40x$.

$$\boxed{\text{Number attending}} \cdot \boxed{\text{Price}} = \boxed{\text{Revenue}}$$

$$\begin{aligned}(1200 + 40x)(15 - 0.5x) &= 17280\\ 18000 - 20x^2 &= 17280\\ 20x^2 &= 720\\ x^2 &= 36\end{aligned}$$

$$x = \sqrt{36} \quad \textbf{or} \quad x = -\sqrt{36}$$
$$x = 6 \qquad\qquad x = -6$$

$x = -6$ does not make sense. Thus, there should be six 50-cent decreases, for a ticket price of \$12 and an attendance of 1440 people.

22. Let $x =$ the number of subscribers over 3000. The new profit $= 20 + 0.01x$, while the number subscribing $= 3000 + x$.

$$\boxed{\text{Number subscribing}} \cdot \boxed{\text{Profit}} = \boxed{\text{Total profit}}$$

$$\begin{aligned}(3000 + x)(20 + 0.01x) &= 120000\\ 60000 + 50x + 0.01x^2 &= 120000\\ 0.01x^2 + 50x - 60000 &= 0\\ x^2 + 5000x - 6000000 &= 0\\ (x + 6000)(x - 1000) &= 0\end{aligned}$$

$$x + 6000 = 0 \quad \textbf{or} \quad x - 1000 = 0$$
$$x = -6000 \qquad\qquad x = 1000$$

$x = -6000$ does not make sense. The increase should be 1000, for a total of 4000.

23. Let $h = 15$:

$$\begin{aligned}\frac{l}{h} &= \frac{h}{l - h}\\ \frac{l}{15} &= \frac{15}{l - 15}\\ 15(l - 15) \cdot \frac{l}{15} &= 15(l - 15) \cdot \frac{15}{l - 15}\\ l(l - 15) &= 15^2\\ l^2 - 15l - 225 &= 0\end{aligned}$$

$a = 1, b = -15, c = -225$

$$\begin{aligned}l &= \frac{-b \pm \sqrt{b^2 - 4ac}}{2a}\\ &= \frac{-(-15) \pm \sqrt{(-15)^2 - 4(1)(-225)}}{2(1)}\\ &= \frac{15 \pm \sqrt{1125}}{2} \approx \frac{15 \pm 33.541}{2}\end{aligned}$$

The only positive solution is $l = 24.3$ ft.

24. If $AE = 1$, then $AD = BC = 1$ and $BE = x - 1$.

$$\frac{AB}{AD} = \frac{BC}{BE}$$
$$\frac{x}{1} = \frac{1}{x-1}$$
$$(x-1)\cdot\frac{x}{1} = (x-1)\cdot\frac{1}{x-1}$$
$$x^2 - x = 1$$
$$x^2 - x - 1 = 0$$

$a = 1, b = -1, c = -1$

$$x = \frac{-b \pm \sqrt{b^2 - 4ac}}{2a} = \frac{-(-1) \pm \sqrt{(-1)^2 - 4(1)(-1)}}{2(1)} = \frac{1 \pm \sqrt{5}}{2} \approx \frac{1 \pm 2.236}{2}$$

The only positive solution is $x = 1.618$.

The ratio is about $\frac{1.618}{1}$, or 1.618 to 1.

25. Let $x =$ time for the second pipe to fill tank.

$$\boxed{\text{First in 1 hour}} + \boxed{\text{Second in 1 hour}} = \boxed{\text{Total in 1 hour}}$$
$$\frac{1}{4} + \frac{1}{x} = \frac{1}{x-2}$$
$$4x(x-2)\left(\frac{1}{4} + \frac{1}{x}\right) = 4x(x-2)\cdot\frac{1}{x-2}$$
$$x(x-2) + 4(x-2) = 4x$$
$$x^2 - 2x + 4x - 8 = 4x$$
$$x^2 - 2x - 8 = 0$$
$$(x-4)(x+2) = 0$$
$$x - 4 = 0 \quad \textbf{or} \quad x + 2 = 0$$
$$x = 4 \qquad\qquad x = -2$$

Since $x = -2$ does not make sense, the solution is $x = 4$. It takes the second pipe 4 hours to fill the tank alone.

26. Let $x =$ time for the both hoses to fill pool.

$$\boxed{\text{First in 1 hour}} + \boxed{\text{Second in 1 hour}} = \boxed{\text{Total in 1 hour}}$$
$$\frac{1}{6} + \frac{1}{x+3} = \frac{1}{x}$$
$$6x(x+3)\left(\frac{1}{6} + \frac{1}{x+3}\right) = 6x(x+3)\cdot\frac{1}{x}$$
$$x(x+3) + 6x = 6(x+3)$$
$$x^2 + 3x + 6x = 6x + 18$$
$$x^2 + 3x - 18 = 0$$
$$(x-3)(x+6) = 0$$
$$x - 3 = 0 \quad \textbf{or} \quad x + 6 = 0$$
$$x = 3 \qquad\qquad x = -6$$

Since $x = -6$ does not make sense, the solution is $x = 3$. It takes the second hose 6 hours to fill the pool alone.

27. Let $x =$ time for the Steven to mow lawn.

$$\boxed{\text{Steven in 1 hour}} + \boxed{\text{Kristy in 1 hour}} = \boxed{\text{Total in 1 hour}}$$
$$\frac{1}{x} + \frac{1}{x-1} = \frac{1}{5}$$
$$5x(x-1)\left(\frac{1}{x} + \frac{1}{x-1}\right) = 5x(x-1)\cdot\frac{1}{5}$$
$$5(x-1) + 5x = x(x-1)$$
$$5x - 5 + 5x = x^2 - x$$
$$0 = x^2 - 11x + 5$$

$a = 1, b = -11, c = 5$

$$x = \frac{-b \pm \sqrt{b^2 - 4ac}}{2a} = \frac{-(-11) \pm \sqrt{(-11)^2 - 4(1)(5)}}{2(1)} = \frac{11 \pm \sqrt{101}}{2} \approx 10.5 \text{ or } 0.5$$

$x = 0.5$ does not make sense, so Kristy could mow the lawn in about 9.5 hours alone.

28. Let $x =$ time for the Sarah to milk cows.

$$\boxed{\text{Sarah in 1 hour}} + \boxed{\text{Heidi in 1 hour}} = \boxed{\text{Total in 1 hour}}$$

$$\frac{1}{x} + \frac{1}{x+3} = \frac{1}{2}$$

$$2x(x+3)\left(\frac{1}{x} + \frac{1}{x+3}\right) = 2x(x+3) \cdot \frac{1}{2}$$

$$2(x+3) + 2x = x(x+3)$$

$$2x + 6 + 2x = x^2 + 3x$$

$$0 = x^2 - x - 6$$

$$0 = (x-3)(x+2)$$

$$x - 3 = 0 \quad \textbf{or} \quad x + 2 = 0$$

$$x = 3 \qquad\qquad x = -2$$

$x = -2$ does not make sense. It would take Heidi 6 hours to milk the cows alone.

29. Let $x =$ the length of the diagonal.

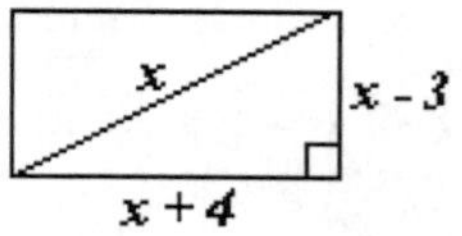

Using the Pythagorean Theorem:

$$(x+4)^2 + (x-3)^2 = x^2$$

$$x^2 + 8x + 16 + x^2 - 6x + 9 = x^2$$

$$x^2 + 2x + 25 = 0$$

$$a = 1, b = 2, c = 25$$

$$x = \frac{-b \pm \sqrt{b^2 - 4ac}}{2a}$$

$$= \frac{-2 \pm \sqrt{2^2 - 4(1)(25)}}{2(1)} = \frac{-2 \pm \sqrt{-96}}{2}$$

This does not equal a real number, so it is not possible.

30. Let $x =$ the side of the original square.

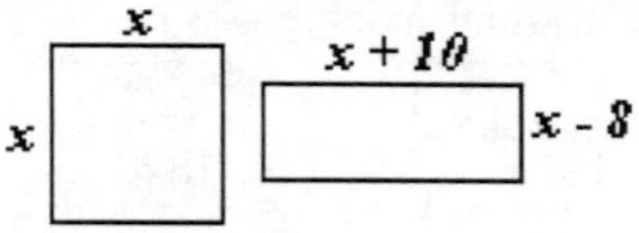

$$\boxed{\text{Area of rectangle}} = 63$$

$$(x+10)(x-8) = 63$$

$$x^2 + 2x - 80 = 63$$

$$x^2 + 2x - 143 = 0$$

$$x^2 + 2x - 143 = 0$$

$$(x-11)(x+13) = 0$$

$$x - 11 = 0 \quad \textbf{or} \quad x + 13 = 0$$

$$x = 11 \qquad\qquad x = -13$$

$x = -13$ does not make sense.

The original area was 121 square meters.

31. Let $x =$ Matilda's principal.

	I	P	r
Matilda	240	x	$\frac{240}{x}$
Maude	280	$x + 1000$	$\frac{280}{x+1000}$

$$\boxed{\text{Maude's rate}} = \boxed{\text{Matilda's rate}} - 0.01$$

$$\frac{280}{x+1000} = \frac{240}{x} - 0.01$$

$$x(x+1000)\frac{280}{x+1000} = x(x+1000)\left(\frac{240}{x} - 0.01\right)$$

$$280x = 240(x+1000) - 0.01x(x+1000)$$

$$0.01x^2 + 50x - 240{,}000 = 0$$

$$x^2 + 5000x - 24{,}000{,}000 = 0$$

$$(x-3000)(x+8000) = 0$$

$$x - 3000 = 0 \quad \textbf{or} \quad x + 8000 = 0$$

$$x = 3000 \qquad\qquad x = -8000 \Rightarrow$$

$x = -8000$ does not make sense. The principal amounts were \$3000 and \$4000. The interest rates were 8% for Matilda and 7% for Maude.

32. Let x = Laura's principal.

	I	P	r
Laura	400	x	$\frac{400}{x}$
Scott	800	$x+3000$	$\frac{800}{x+3000}$

$$\boxed{\text{Scott's rate}} = \boxed{\text{Laura's rate}} + 0.02$$

$$\frac{800}{x+3000} = \frac{400}{x} + 0.02$$

$$x(x+3000)\frac{800}{x+3000} = x(x+3000)\left(\frac{400}{x} + 0.02\right)$$

$$800x = 400(x+3000) + 0.02x(x+3000)$$

$$800x = 400x + 1{,}200{,}000 + 0.02x^2 + 60x$$

$$0.02x^2 - 340x + 1{,}200{,}000 = 0$$

$$2x^2 - 34{,}000x + 120{,}000{,}000 = 0$$

$$x^2 - 17{,}000x + 60{,}000{,}000 = 0$$

$$(x-5000)(x-12{,}000) = 0$$

$x - 5000 = 0$ **or** $x - 12{,}000 = 0$

$x = 5000$ $\quad$ $x = 12{,}000 \Rightarrow$ Laura invested either \$5000 or \$12,000, so Scott invested either \$8000 or \$15,000.

33. Let x = the total number of professors.

$$\boxed{\text{New share with lower number}} = \boxed{\text{Original share}} + 10$$

$$\frac{150}{x-4} = \frac{150}{x} + 10$$

$$x(x-4)\frac{150}{x-4} = x(x-4)\left(\frac{150}{x} + 10\right)$$

$$150x = 150(x-4) + 10x(x-4)$$

$$150x = 150x - 600 + 10x^2 - 40x$$

$$0 = 10x^2 - 40x - 600$$

$$0 = x^2 - 4x - 60$$

$$0 = (x-10)(x+6)$$

$x - 10 = 0$ **or** $x + 6 = 0$

$x = 10$ $\quad$ $x = -6$

$x = -6$ does not make sense, so there are 10 professors in the department.

34. Note that the number of trees needed equals the length of the row divided by the space between each two trees, plus 1.

Let x = the original spacing.

$$\boxed{\text{Original number}} - 44 = \boxed{\text{New number}}$$

$$\frac{1320}{x} + 1 - 44 = \frac{1320}{x+1} + 1$$

$$\frac{1320}{x} - 44 = \frac{1320}{x+1}$$

$$x(x+1)\left(\frac{1320}{x} - 44\right) = x(x+1)\frac{1320}{x+1}$$

$$1320(x+1) - 44x(x+1) = 1320x$$

$$44x^2 + 44x - 1320 = 0$$

$$x^2 + x - 30 = 0$$

$$(x-5)(x+6) = 0$$

$x - 5 = 0$ **or** $x + 6 = 0$

$x = 5$ $\quad$ $x = -6$

$x = -6$ does not make sense. The original spacing was 5 feet, resulting in 265 trees, so the new spacing will require 221 trees.

35. Let $x =$ the actual number of spokes.

$$\boxed{\text{Actual angles between spokes}} - 6 = \boxed{\text{New angle between spokes}}$$

$$\frac{360}{x} - 6 = \frac{360}{x+10}$$

$$x(x+10)\left(\frac{360}{x} - 6\right) = x(x+10)\frac{360}{x+10}$$

$$360(x+10) - 6x(x+10) = 360x$$

$$6x^2 + 60x - 3600 = 0$$

$$x^2 + 10x - 600 = 0$$

$$(x-20)(x+30) = 0$$

$x - 20 = 0$ **or** $x + 30 = 0$ $\quad$ $x = -30$ does not make sense, so there

$x = 20$ $\qquad$ $x = -30$ $\quad$ are 20 spokes.

36. Let $x =$ the actual number of calculators.

$$\boxed{\text{Actual price per calculator}} - 10 = \boxed{\text{New price per calculator}}$$

$$\frac{180}{x} - 10 = \frac{180}{x+3}$$

$$x(x+3)\left(\frac{180}{x} - 10\right) = x(x+3)\frac{180}{x+3}$$

$$180(x+3) - 10x(x+3) = 180x$$

$$10x^2 + 30x - 540 = 0$$

$$x^2 + 3x - 54 = 0$$

$$(x-6)(x+9) = 0$$

$x - 6 = 0$ **or** $x + 9 = 0$ $\quad$ $x = -9$ does not make sense, so there

$x = 6$ $\qquad$ $x = -9$ $\quad$ are 6 calculators, with each costing \$30.

37. Let x and $x - 14$ represent the two legs. Use the Pythagorean Theorem:

$$x^2 + (x-14)^2 = 26^2$$

$$x^2 + x^2 - 28x + 196 = 676$$

$$2x^2 - 28x - 480 = 0$$

$$x^2 - 14x - 240 = 0$$

$$(x-24)(x+10) = 0$$

$x - 24 = 0$ **or** $x + 10 = 0$

$x = 24$ $\qquad$ $x = -10$

$x = -10$ does not make sense. The legs have lengths of 24 meters and 10 meters.

38. Let $w =$ the width. Then $\frac{180}{w} =$ the length.

$$2w + 2\left(\frac{180}{w}\right) = 54$$

$$w\left(2w + \frac{360}{w}\right) = w(54)$$

$$2w^2 + 360 = 54w$$

$$2w^2 - 54w + 360 = 0$$

$$w^2 - 27w + 180 = 0$$

$$(w-12)(w-15) = 0$$

$w - 12 = 0$ **or** $w - 15 = 0$

$w = 12$ $\qquad$ $w = 15$

The dimensions are 12 cm by 15 cm.

39. **Answers may vary.**

40. **Answers may vary.**

41. $\frac{2}{x}-\frac{1}{x-3}=\frac{2(x-3)}{x(x-3)}-\frac{1(x)}{(x-3)(x)}=\frac{2x-6}{x(x-3)}-\frac{x}{x(x-3)}=\frac{x-6}{x(x-3)}$

42. $\frac{1}{x}\cdot\frac{x^2-5x}{x-3}=\frac{1}{x}\cdot\frac{x(x-5)}{x-3}=\frac{x-5}{x-3}$

43. $\frac{x+3}{x^2-x-6}\div\frac{x^2+3x}{x^2-9}=\frac{x+3}{x^2-x-6}\cdot\frac{x^2-9}{x^2+3x}=\frac{x+3}{(x-3)(x+2)}\cdot\frac{(x+3)(x-3)}{x(x+3)}=\frac{x+3}{x(x+2)}$

44. $\frac{\frac{1}{x}-\frac{1}{2}}{x-2}=\frac{\left(\frac{1}{x}-\frac{1}{2}\right)2x}{(x-2)2x}=\frac{2-x}{2x(x-2)}=-\frac{1}{2x}$

45. $\frac{\frac{1}{x}+\frac{1}{y}}{\frac{1}{x}-\frac{1}{y}}=\frac{xy\left(\frac{1}{x}+\frac{1}{y}\right)}{xy\left(\frac{1}{x}-\frac{1}{y}\right)}=\frac{xy\left(\frac{1}{x}\right)+xy\left(\frac{1}{y}\right)}{xy\left(\frac{1}{x}\right)-xy\left(\frac{1}{y}\right)}=\frac{y+x}{y-x}$

46.
$$\begin{aligned}\frac{x}{x+1}+\frac{x+1}{x}\cdot\frac{x^2-x}{3}=\frac{x}{x+1}+\frac{x+1}{x}\cdot\frac{x(x-1)}{3}&=\frac{x}{x+1}+\frac{(x+1)(x-1)}{3}\\&=\frac{x(3)}{(x+1)(3)}+\frac{(x+1)(x-1)(x+1)}{3(x+1)}\\&=\frac{3x}{3(x+1)}+\frac{x^3+x^2-x-1}{3(x+1)}\\&=\frac{x^3+x^2+2x-1}{3(x+1)}\end{aligned}$$

Exercise 1.5 (page 123)

1. imaginary **2.** real, imaginary **3.** imaginary **4.** real

5. $2-5i$ **6.** $\sqrt{a^2+b^2}$ **7.** real **8.** real

9. Equate real parts: $\boxed{x=3}$
Equate imaginary parts: $x+y=8$
$3+y=8$
$\boxed{y=5}$

10. Equate imaginary parts: $5=-y$
$\boxed{-5=y}$
Equate real parts: $x=y$
$\boxed{x=-5}$

11. Equate real parts: $3x=2$
$\boxed{x=\frac{2}{3}}$
Equate imaginary parts: $-2y=x+y$
$-3y=x$
$y=-\frac{1}{3}x$
$y=-\frac{1}{3}\cdot\frac{2}{3}$
$\boxed{y=-\frac{2}{9}}$

12. Equate real parts: $\boxed{x=2}$ Equate imaginary parts:

$$\begin{aligned} x+y&=-1\\ 2+y&=-1\\ \boxed{y=-3} \end{aligned}$$

13. $(2-7i)+(3+i)=2-7i+3+i$
$=5-6i$

14. $(-7+2i)+(2-8i)=-7+2i+2-8i$
$=-5-6i$

15. $(5-6i)-(7+4i)=5-6i-7-4i$
$=-2-10i$

16. $(11+2i)-(13-5i)=11+2i-13+5i$
$=-2+7i$

17. $(14i+2)+\left(2-\sqrt{-16}\right)=(14i+2)+(2-4i)=14i+2+2-4i=4+10i$

18. $\left(5+\sqrt{-64}\right)-(23i-32)=(5+8i)-(23i-32)=5+8i-23i+32=37-15i$

19. $\left(3+\sqrt{-4}\right)-\left(2+\sqrt{-9}\right)=(3+2i)-(2+3i)=3+2i-2-3i=1-i$

20. $\left(7-\sqrt{-25}\right)+\left(-8+\sqrt{-1}\right)=(7-5i)+(-8+i)=7-5i-8+i=-1-4i$

21. $(2+3i)(3+5i)=6+19i+15(-1)=6+19i-15=-9+19i$

22. $(5-7i)(2+i)=10-9i-7i^2=10-9i-7(-1)=10-9i+7=17-9i$

23. $(2+3i)^2=(2+3i)(2+3i)=4+12i+9i^2=4+12i+9(-1)=4+12i-9=-5+12i$

24. $(3-4i)^2=(3-4i)(3-4i)=9-24i+16i^2=9-24i+16(-1)=9-24i-16=-7-24i$

25. $\left(11+\sqrt{-25}\right)\left(2-\sqrt{-36}\right)=(11+5i)(2-6i)=22-56i-30i^2=22-56i-30(-1)$
$=22-56i+30=52-56i$

26. $\left(6+\sqrt{-49}\right)\left(6-\sqrt{-49}\right)=(6+7i)(6-7i)=36-49i^2=36-49(-1)=36+49=85+0i$

27. $\left(\sqrt{-16}+3\right)\left(2+\sqrt{-9}\right)=(4i+3)(2+3i)=6+17i+12i^2=6+17i+12(-1)$
$=6+17i-12=-6+17i$

28. $\left(12-\sqrt{-4}\right)\left(-7+\sqrt{-25}\right)=(12-2i)(-7+5i)=-84+74i-10i^2=-84+74i-10(-1)$
$=-84+74i+10$
$=-74+74i$

29. $\dfrac{1}{i^3}=\dfrac{1\cdot i}{i^3\cdot i}=\dfrac{i}{i^4}=\dfrac{i}{1}=i=0+i$

30. $\dfrac{3}{i^5}=\dfrac{3\cdot i^3}{i^5\cdot i^3}=\dfrac{3i^3}{i^8}=\dfrac{3i^3}{1}=3i^3=0-3i$

31. $\frac{-4}{i^{10}}=\frac{-4\cdot i^2}{i^{10}\cdot i^2}=\frac{-4i^2}{i^{12}}=\frac{-4i^2}{1}=-4(-1)=4+0i$

32. $\frac{-10}{i^{24}}=\frac{-10}{1}=-10=-10+0i$

33. $\frac{1}{2+i}=\frac{1(2-i)}{(2+i)(2-i)}=\frac{2-i}{2^2-i^2}=\frac{2-i}{4-(-1)}=\frac{2-i}{5}=\frac{2}{5}-\frac{1}{5}i$

34. $\frac{-2}{3-i}=\frac{-2(3+i)}{(3-i)(3+i)}=\frac{-2(3+i)}{3^2-i^2}=\frac{-2(3+i)}{9-(-1)}=\frac{-2(3+i)}{10}=\frac{-(3+i)}{5}=-\frac{3}{5}-\frac{1}{5}i$

35. $\frac{2i}{7+i}=\frac{2i(7-i)}{(7+i)(7-i)}=\frac{14i-2i^2}{7^2-i^2}=\frac{14i-2(-1)}{49-(-1)}=\frac{14i+2}{50}=\frac{7i+1}{25}=\frac{1}{25}+\frac{7}{25}i$

36. $\frac{-3i}{2+5i}=\frac{-3i(2-5i)}{(2+5i)(2-5i)}=\frac{-6i+15i^2}{2^2-(5i)^2}=\frac{-6i-15}{4-25i^2}=\frac{-6i-15}{29}=-\frac{15}{29}-\frac{6}{29}i$

37. $\frac{2+i}{3-i}=\frac{(2+i)(3+i)}{(3-i)(3+i)}=\frac{6+5i+i^2}{9-i^2}=\frac{5+5i}{10}=\frac{5}{10}+\frac{5}{10}i=\frac{1}{2}+\frac{1}{2}i$

38. $\frac{3-i}{1+i}=\frac{(3-i)(1-i)}{(1+i)(1-i)}=\frac{3-4i+i^2}{1-i^2}=\frac{2-4i}{2}=\frac{2}{2}-\frac{4}{2}i=1-2i$

39. $\frac{4-5i}{2+3i}=\frac{(4-5i)(2-3i)}{(2+3i)(2-3i)}=\frac{8-22i+15i^2}{4-9i^2}=\frac{-7-22i}{13}=-\frac{7}{13}-\frac{22}{13}i$

40. $\frac{34+2i}{2-4i}=\frac{(34+2i)(2+4i)}{(2-4i)(2+4i)}=\frac{68+140i+8i^2}{4-16i^2}=\frac{60+140i}{20}=\frac{60}{20}+\frac{140}{20}i=3+7i$

41. $\frac{5-\sqrt{-16}}{-8+\sqrt{-4}}=\frac{5-4i}{-8+2i}=\frac{(5-4i)(-8-2i)}{(-8+2i)(-8-2i)}=\frac{-40+22i+8i^2}{64-4i^2}=\frac{-48+22i}{68}=-\frac{48}{68}+\frac{22}{68}i$

$=-\frac{12}{17}+\frac{11}{34}i$

42. $\frac{3-\sqrt{-9}}{2-\sqrt{-1}}=\frac{3-3i}{2-i}=\frac{(3-3i)(2+i)}{(2-i)(2+i)}=\frac{6-3i-3i^2}{4-i^2}=\frac{9-3i}{5}=\frac{9}{5}-\frac{3}{5}i$

43. $\frac{2+i\sqrt{3}}{3+i}=\frac{\left(2+i\sqrt{3}\right)(3-i)}{(3+i)(3-i)}=\frac{6-2i+3i\sqrt{3}-i^2\sqrt{3}}{9-i^2}=\frac{6+\sqrt{3}+\left(3\sqrt{3}-2\right)i}{10}$

$=\frac{6+\sqrt{3}}{10}+\frac{3\sqrt{3}-2}{10}i$

44. $\dfrac{3+i}{4-i\sqrt{2}} = \dfrac{(3+i)\left(4+i\sqrt{2}\right)}{\left(4-i\sqrt{2}\right)\left(4+i\sqrt{2}\right)} = \dfrac{12+3i\sqrt{2}+4i+i^2\sqrt{2}}{16-2i^2} = \dfrac{12-\sqrt{2}+\left(3\sqrt{2}+4\right)i}{18}$

$= \dfrac{12-\sqrt{2}}{18} + \dfrac{4+3\sqrt{2}}{18}i$

45. $i^9 = i^8 i = (i^4)^2 i = 1^2 i = i$

46. $i^{27} = i^{24} i^3 = (i^4)^6 i^3 = 1^6 i^3 = i^3 = -i$

47. $i^{38} = i^{36} i^2 = (i^4)^9 i^2 = 1^9 i^2 = i^2 = -1$

48. $i^{99} = i^{96} i^3 = (i^4)^{24} i^3 = 1^{24} i^3 = i^3 = -i$

49. $i^{-6} = \dfrac{1}{i^6} = \dfrac{1 \cdot i^2}{i^6 \cdot i^2} = \dfrac{i^2}{i^8} = \dfrac{i^2}{1} = i^2 = -1$

50. $i^0 = 1$

51. $i^{-10} = \dfrac{1}{i^{10}} = \dfrac{1 \cdot i^2}{i^{10} \cdot i^2} = \dfrac{i^2}{i^{12}} = \dfrac{i^2}{1} = i^2$
$= -1$

52. $i^{-31} = \dfrac{1}{i^{31}} = \dfrac{1 \cdot i}{i^{31} \cdot i} = \dfrac{i}{i^{32}} = \dfrac{i}{1} = i$

53. $|3+4i| = \sqrt{3^2+4^2} = \sqrt{9+16}$
$= \sqrt{25} = 5$

54. $|5+12i| = \sqrt{5^2+12^2} = \sqrt{25+144}$
$= \sqrt{169} = 13$

55. $|2+3i| = \sqrt{2^2+3^2} = \sqrt{4+9} = \sqrt{13}$

56. $|5-i| = \sqrt{5^2+(-1)^2} = \sqrt{25+1} = \sqrt{26}$

57. $\left|-7+\sqrt{-49}\right| = |-7+7i| = \sqrt{(-7)^2+7^2} = \sqrt{49+49} = \sqrt{98} = 7\sqrt{2}$

58. $\left|-2-\sqrt{-16}\right| = |-2-4i| = \sqrt{(-2)^2+(-4)^2} = \sqrt{4+16} = \sqrt{20} = 2\sqrt{5}$

59. $\left|\dfrac{1}{2}+\dfrac{1}{2}i\right| = \sqrt{\left(\dfrac{1}{2}\right)^2+\left(\dfrac{1}{2}\right)^2} = \sqrt{\dfrac{1}{4}+\dfrac{1}{4}} = \sqrt{\dfrac{1}{2}} = \dfrac{\sqrt{2}}{2}$

60. $\left|\dfrac{1}{2}-\dfrac{1}{4}i\right| = \sqrt{\left(\dfrac{1}{2}\right)^2+\left(-\dfrac{1}{4}\right)^2} = \sqrt{\dfrac{1}{4}+\dfrac{1}{16}} = \sqrt{\dfrac{5}{16}} = \dfrac{\sqrt{5}}{4}$

61. $|-6i| = |0-6i| = \sqrt{0^2+(-6)^2} = \sqrt{0+36} = \sqrt{36} = 6$

62. $|5i| = |0+5i| = \sqrt{0^2+5^2} = \sqrt{0+25} = \sqrt{25} = 5$

63. $\left|\dfrac{2}{1+i}\right| = \left|\dfrac{2(1-i)}{(1+i)(1-i)}\right| = \left|\dfrac{2(1-i)}{1-i^2}\right| = \left|\dfrac{2(1-i)}{2}\right| = |1-i| = \sqrt{1^2+(-1)^2} = \sqrt{2}$

64. $$\left|\frac{3}{3+i}\right| = \left|\frac{3(3-i)}{(3+i)(3-i)}\right| = \left|\frac{3(3-i)}{9-i^2}\right| = \left|\frac{3(3-i)}{10}\right| = \left|\frac{9-3i}{10}\right| = \sqrt{\left(\frac{9}{10}\right)^2 + \left(-\frac{3}{10}\right)^2}$$
$$= \sqrt{\frac{81}{100} + \frac{9}{100}}$$
$$= \sqrt{\frac{90}{100}} = \sqrt{\frac{9}{10}} = \frac{3\sqrt{10}}{10}$$

65. $$\left|\frac{-3i}{2+i}\right| = \left|\frac{-3i(2-i)}{(2+i)(2-i)}\right| = \left|\frac{-3i(2-i)}{4-i^2}\right| = \left|\frac{-3i(2-i)}{5}\right| = \left|\frac{-6i+3i^2}{5}\right|$$
$$= \left|-\frac{3}{5} - \frac{6}{5}i\right|$$
$$= \sqrt{\left(-\frac{3}{5}\right)^2 + \left(-\frac{6}{5}\right)^2}$$
$$= \sqrt{\frac{9}{25} + \frac{36}{25}}$$
$$= \sqrt{\frac{45}{25}} = \frac{\sqrt{45}}{5} = \frac{3\sqrt{5}}{5}$$

66. $$\left|\frac{5i}{i-2}\right| = \left|\frac{5i}{-2+i}\right| = \left|\frac{5i(-2-i)}{(-2+i)(-2-i)}\right|\left|\frac{5i(-2-i)}{4-i^2}\right| = \left|\frac{5i(-2-i)}{5}\right| = \left|\frac{-10i-5i^2}{5}\right|$$
$$= |1-2i|$$
$$= \sqrt{1^2 + (-2)^2}$$
$$= \sqrt{1+4} = \sqrt{5}$$

67. $$\left|\frac{i+2}{i-2}\right| = \left|\frac{(i+2)(i+2)}{(i-2)(i+2)}\right| = \left|\frac{i^2+4i+4}{i^2-4}\right| = \left|\frac{3+4i}{5}\right| = \left|\frac{3}{5} + \frac{4}{5}i\right| = \sqrt{\left(\frac{3}{5}\right)^2 + \left(\frac{4}{5}\right)^2}$$
$$= \sqrt{\frac{9}{25} + \frac{16}{25}}$$
$$= \sqrt{\frac{25}{25}} = \sqrt{1} = 1$$

68. $$\left|\frac{2+i}{2-i}\right| = \left|\frac{(2+i)(2+i)}{(2-i)(2+i)}\right| = \left|\frac{4+4i+i^2}{4^2-i^2}\right| = \left|\frac{3+4i}{5}\right| = \left|\frac{3}{5} + \frac{4}{5}i\right| = \sqrt{\left(\frac{3}{5}\right)^2 + \left(\frac{4}{5}\right)^2}$$
$$= \sqrt{\frac{9}{25} + \frac{16}{25}}$$
$$= \sqrt{\frac{25}{25}} = \sqrt{1} = 1$$

69. $x^2 + 2x + 2 = 0 \Rightarrow a = 1, b = 2, c = 2$

$$x = \frac{-b \pm \sqrt{b^2 - 4ac}}{2a} = \frac{-2 \pm \sqrt{2^2 - 4(1)(2)}}{2(1)} = \frac{-2 \pm \sqrt{4-8}}{2} = \frac{-2 \pm \sqrt{-4}}{2} = \frac{-2 \pm 2i}{2}$$
$$= -1 \pm i$$

70. $a^2 + 4a + 8 = 0 \Rightarrow a = 1, b = 4, c = 8$

$$a = \frac{-b \pm \sqrt{b^2 - 4ac}}{2a} = \frac{-4 \pm \sqrt{4^2 - 4(1)(8)}}{2(1)} = \frac{-4 \pm \sqrt{16-32}}{2} = \frac{-4 \pm \sqrt{-16}}{2} = \frac{-4 \pm 4i}{2}$$
$$= -2 \pm 2i$$

71. $y^2 + 4y + 5 = 0 \Rightarrow a = 1, b = 4, c = 5$

$$y = \frac{-b \pm \sqrt{b^2 - 4ac}}{2a} = \frac{-4 \pm \sqrt{4^2 - 4(1)(5)}}{2(1)} = \frac{-4 \pm \sqrt{16-20}}{2} = \frac{-4 \pm \sqrt{-4}}{2} = \frac{-4 \pm 2i}{2}$$
$$= -2 \pm i$$

72. $x^2 + 2x + 5 = 0 \Rightarrow a = 1, b = 2, c = 5$

$$x = \frac{-b \pm \sqrt{b^2 - 4ac}}{2a} = \frac{-2 \pm \sqrt{2^2 - 4(1)(5)}}{2(1)} = \frac{-2 \pm \sqrt{4-20}}{2} = \frac{-2 \pm \sqrt{-16}}{2} = \frac{-2 \pm 4i}{2}$$
$$= -1 \pm 2i$$

73. $x^2 - 2x = -5 \Rightarrow x^2 - 2x + 5 = 0 \Rightarrow a = 1, b = -2, c = 5$

$$x = \frac{-b \pm \sqrt{b^2 - 4ac}}{2a} = \frac{-(-2) \pm \sqrt{(-2)^2 - 4(1)(5)}}{2(1)} = \frac{2 \pm \sqrt{4-20}}{2} = \frac{2 \pm \sqrt{-16}}{2} = \frac{2 \pm 4i}{2}$$
$$= 1 \pm 2i$$

74. $z^2 - 3z = -8 \Rightarrow z^2 - 3z + 8 = 0 \Rightarrow a = 1, b = -3, c = 8$

$$z = \frac{-b \pm \sqrt{b^2 - 4ac}}{2a} = \frac{-(-3) \pm \sqrt{(-3)^2 - 4(1)(8)}}{2(1)} = \frac{3 \pm \sqrt{9-32}}{2} = \frac{3 \pm \sqrt{-23}}{2}$$
$$= \frac{3}{2} \pm \frac{\sqrt{23}}{2}i$$

75. $x^2 - \frac{2}{3}x = -\frac{2}{9} \Rightarrow x^2 - \frac{2}{3}x + \frac{2}{9} = 0 \Rightarrow 9x^2 - 6x + 2 = 0 \Rightarrow a = 9, b = -6, c = 2$

$$x = \frac{-b \pm \sqrt{b^2 - 4ac}}{2a} = \frac{-(-6) \pm \sqrt{(-6)^2 - 4(9)(2)}}{2(9)} = \frac{6 \pm \sqrt{36-72}}{18} = \frac{6 \pm \sqrt{-36}}{18}$$
$$= \frac{6 \pm 6i}{18} = \frac{1}{3} \pm \frac{1}{3}i$$

76. $x^2 + \frac{5}{4} = x \Rightarrow x^2 - x + \frac{5}{4} = 0 \Rightarrow 4x^2 - 4x + 5 = 0 \Rightarrow a = 4, b = -4, c = 5$

$$x = \frac{-b \pm \sqrt{b^2 - 4ac}}{2a} = \frac{-(-4) \pm \sqrt{(-4)^2 - 4(4)(5)}}{2(4)} = \frac{4 \pm \sqrt{16 - 80}}{8} = \frac{4 \pm \sqrt{-64}}{8}$$
$$= \frac{4 \pm 8i}{8} = \frac{1}{2} \pm i$$

77. $x^2 + 4 = x^2 - (-4) = x^2 - (2i)^2 = (x + 2i)(x - 2i)$

78. $16a^2 + 9 = (4a)^2 - (-9) = (4a)^2 - (3i)^2 = (4a + 3i)(4a - 3i)$

79. $25p^2 + 36q^2 = (5p)^2 - (-36q^2) = (5p)^2 - (6qi)^2 = (5p + 6qi)(5p - 6qi)$

80. $100r^2 + 49s^2 = (10r)^2 - (-49s^2) = (10r)^2 - (7si)^2 = (10r + 7si)(10r - 7si)$

81. $2y^2 + 8z^2 = 2(y^2 + 4z^2) = 2[y^2 - (-4z^2)] = 2\left[y^2 - (2zi)^2\right] = 2(y + 2zi)(y - 2zi)$

82. $12b^2 + 75c^2 = 3(4b^2 + 25c^2) = 3\left[(2b)^2 - (-25c^2)\right] = 3\left[(2b)^2 - (5ci)^2\right] = 3(2b + 5ci)(2b - 5ci)$

83. $50m^2 + 2n^2 = 2(25m^2 + n^2) = 2\left[(5m)^2 - (-n^2)\right] = 2\left[(5m)^2 - (ni)^2\right] = 2(5m + ni)(5m - ni)$

84. $64a^4 + 4b^2 = 4(16a^4 + b^2) = 4\left[(4a^2)^2 - (-b^2)\right] = 4\left[(4a^2)^2 - (bi)^2\right] = 4(4a^2 + bi)(4a^2 - bi)$

85. $V = IR = (3 - 2i)(3 + 6i) = 9 + 18i - 6i - 12i^2 = 9 + 12i + 12 = 21 + 12i$

86. $R = \frac{V}{I} = \frac{21 + i}{2 - 3i} = \frac{(21 + i)(2 + 3i)}{(2 - 3i)(2 + 3i)} = \frac{42 + 63i + 2i + 3i^2}{4 - 9i^2} = \frac{39 + 65i}{13} = 3 + 5i$

87.
$$\begin{aligned}(a + bi) + (c + di) &= a + bi + c + di \\ &= a + c + bi + di \\ &= (a + c) + (b + d)i\end{aligned}$$
$$\begin{aligned}(c + di) + (a + bi) &= c + di + a + bi \\ &= c + a + di + bi \\ &= (c + a) + (d + b)i \\ &= (a + c) + (b + d)i\end{aligned}$$

88.
$$\begin{aligned}(a + bi)(c + di) &= ac + adi + bci + bdi^2 \\ &= ac + (ad + bc)i - bd \\ &= (ac - bd) + (ad + bc)i\end{aligned}$$
$$\begin{aligned}(c + di)(a + bi) &= ac + bci + adi + bdi^2 \\ &= ac + (bc + ad)i - bd \\ &= (ac - bd) + (ad + bc)i\end{aligned}$$

89.
$$\begin{aligned}[(a + bi) + (c + di)] + (e + fi) &= a + bi + c + di + e + fi \\ &= a + c + e + bi + di + fi \\ &= (a + c + e) + (b + d + f)i \\ (a + bi) + [(c + di) + (e + fi)] &= a + bi + c + di + e + fi \\ &= a + c + e + bi + di + fi \\ &= (a + c + e) + (b + d + f)i\end{aligned}$$

90.
$$a+bi=\frac{1}{a-bi}=\frac{1(a+bi)}{(a-bi)(a+bi)}=\frac{a+bi}{a^2-b^2i^2}=\frac{a+bi}{a^2+b^2}=\frac{a}{a^2+b^2}+\frac{b}{a^2+b^2}i$$

Thus, a must equal $\frac{a}{a^2+b^2}$ and b must equal $\frac{b}{a^2+b^2}$.
If $a^2+b^2=1$, then this will certainly be true.
Some solutions to $a^2+b^2=1$ are below:
$\begin{cases}a=1\\b=0\end{cases}$ $\begin{cases}a=-1\\b=0\end{cases}$ $\begin{cases}a=0\\b=1\end{cases}$ $\begin{cases}a=0\\b=-1\end{cases}$
Some complex numbers with the described property are then:
$1+0i, -1+0i, 0+i, 0-i$

There are many other possible solutions.

91. **Answers may vary.**

92. **Answers may vary.**

93. $\sqrt{8x^3}\sqrt{4x}=\sqrt{32x^4}=\sqrt{16x^4}\sqrt{2}=4x^2\sqrt{2}$

94. $\left(\sqrt{x}-5\right)^2=\left(\sqrt{x}-5\right)\left(\sqrt{x}-5\right)=x-10\sqrt{x}+25$

95. $\left(\sqrt{x+1}-2\right)^2=\left(\sqrt{x+1}-2\right)\left(\sqrt{x+1}-2\right)=x+1-4\sqrt{x+1}+4=x-4\sqrt{x+1}+5$

96. $\left(-3\sqrt{2x+1}\right)^2=(-3)^2\left(\sqrt{2x+1}\right)^2=9(2x+1)=18x+9$

97. $\frac{4}{\sqrt{5}-1}=\frac{4}{\sqrt{5}-1}\cdot\frac{\sqrt{5}+1}{\sqrt{5}+1}=\frac{4\left(\sqrt{5}+1\right)}{\left(\sqrt{5}\right)^2-1^2}=\frac{4\left(\sqrt{5}+1\right)}{5-1}=\frac{4\left(\sqrt{5}+1\right)}{4}=\sqrt{5}+1$

98. $\frac{x-4}{\sqrt{x}+2}=\frac{x-4}{\sqrt{x}+2}\cdot\frac{\sqrt{x}-2}{\sqrt{x}-2}=\frac{(x-4)\left(\sqrt{x}-2\right)}{\left(\sqrt{x}\right)^2-(2)^2}=\frac{(x-4)\left(\sqrt{x}-2\right)}{x-4}=\sqrt{x}-2$

Exercise 1.6 (page 130)

1. equal

2. b^2

3. extraneous

4. Radical, radicands

5.
$$x^3+9x^2+20x=0$$
$$x\left(x^2+9x+20\right)=0$$
$$x(x+5)(x+4)=0$$
$x=0$ **or** $x+5=0$ **or** $x+4=0$
$x=0$ $\quad x=-5$ $\quad x=-4$

6.
$$x^3+4x^2-21x=0$$
$$x\left(x^2+4x-21\right)=0$$
$$x(x+7)(x-3)=0$$
$x=0$ **or** $x+7=0$ **or** $x-3=0$
$x=0$ $\quad x=-7$ $\quad x=3$

7.

$$6a^3 - 5a^2 - 4a = 0$$
$$a(6a^2 - 5a - 4) = 0$$
$$a(2a+1)(3a-4) = 0$$
$$a = 0 \quad \textbf{or} \quad 2a + 1 = 0 \quad \textbf{or} \quad 3a - 4 = 0$$
$$a = 0 \qquad 2a = -1 \qquad 3a = 4$$
$$a = 0 \qquad a = -\tfrac{1}{2} \qquad a = \tfrac{4}{3}$$

8.

$$8b^3 - 10b^2 + 3b = 0$$
$$b(8b^2 - 10b + 3) = 0$$
$$b(4b-3)(2b-1) = 0$$
$$b = 0 \quad \textbf{or} \quad 4b - 3 = 0 \quad \textbf{or} \quad 2b - 1 = 0$$
$$b = 0 \qquad 4b = 3 \qquad 2b = 1$$
$$b = 0 \qquad b = \tfrac{3}{4} \qquad b = \tfrac{1}{2}$$

9.

$$y^4 - 26y^2 + 25 = 0$$
$$(y^2 - 25)(y^2 - 1) = 0$$
$$y^2 - 25 = 0 \quad \textbf{or} \quad y^2 - 1 = 0$$
$$y^2 = 25 \qquad y^2 = 1$$
$$y = \pm 5 \qquad y = \pm 1$$

10.

$$y^4 - 13y^2 + 36 = 0$$
$$(y^2 - 4)(y^2 - 9) = 0$$
$$y^2 - 4 = 0 \quad \textbf{or} \quad y^2 - 9 = 0$$
$$y^2 = 4 \qquad y^2 = 9$$
$$y = \pm 2 \qquad y = \pm 3$$

11.

$$x^4 - 37x^2 + 36 = 0$$
$$(x^2 - 36)(x^2 - 1) = 0$$
$$x^2 - 36 = 0 \quad \textbf{or} \quad x^2 - 1 = 0$$
$$x^2 = 36 \qquad x^2 = 1$$
$$x = \pm 6 \qquad x = \pm 1$$

12.

$$x^4 - 50x^2 + 49 = 0$$
$$(x^2 - 49)(x^2 - 1) = 0$$
$$x^2 - 49 = 0 \quad \textbf{or} \quad x^2 - 1 = 0$$
$$x^2 = 49 \qquad x^2 = 1$$
$$x = \pm 7 \qquad x = \pm 1$$

13.

$$2y^4 - 46y^2 = -180$$
$$2(y^4 - 23y^2 + 90) = 0$$
$$2(y^2 - 18)(y^2 - 5) = 0$$
$$y^2 - 18 = 0 \quad \textbf{or} \quad y^2 - 5 = 0$$
$$y^2 = 18 \qquad y^2 = 5$$
$$y = \pm\sqrt{18} \qquad y = \pm\sqrt{5}$$
$$y = \pm 3\sqrt{2} \qquad y = \pm\sqrt{5}$$

14.

$$2x^4 - 102x^2 = -196$$
$$2(x^4 - 51x^2 + 98) = 0$$
$$2(x^2 - 49)(x^2 - 2) = 0$$
$$x^2 - 49 = 0 \quad \textbf{or} \quad x^2 - 2 = 0$$
$$x^2 = 49 \qquad x^2 = 2$$
$$x = \pm 7 \qquad x = \pm\sqrt{2}$$

15.

$$z^{3/2} - z^{1/2} = 0$$
$$z^{1/2}(z^{2/2} - 1) = 0$$
$$z^{1/2}(z - 1) = 0$$
$$z^{1/2} = 0 \quad \textbf{or} \quad z - 1 = 0$$
$$\left(z^{1/2}\right)^2 = 0^2 \qquad z = 1$$
$$z = 0 \qquad z = 1$$

Both answers check.

16.

$$r^{5/2} - r^{3/2} = 0$$
$$r^{3/2}(r^{2/2} - 1) = 0$$
$$r^{3/2}(r - 1) = 0$$
$$r^{3/2} = 0 \quad \textbf{or} \quad r - 1 = 0$$
$$\left(r^{3/2}\right)^2 = 0^2 \qquad r = 1$$
$$r^3 = 0 \qquad r = 1$$
$$r = 0 \qquad r = 1$$

Both answers check.

17.
$$2m^{2/3} + 3m^{1/3} - 2 = 0$$
$$\left(2m^{1/3} - 1\right)\left(m^{1/3} + 2\right) = 0$$

$2m^{1/3} - 1 = 0$ **or** $m^{1/3} + 2 = 0$

$m^{1/3} = \frac{1}{2}$ | $m^{1/3} = -2$

$\left(m^{1/3}\right)^3 = \left(\frac{1}{2}\right)^3$ | $\left(m^{1/3}\right)^3 = (-2)^3$

$m = \frac{1}{8}$ | $m = -8$

Both answers check.

18.
$$6t^{2/5} + 11t^{1/5} + 3 = 0$$
$$\left(2t^{1/5} + 3\right)\left(3t^{1/5} + 1\right) = 0$$

$2t^{1/5} + 3 = 0$ **or** $3t^{1/5} + 1 = 0$

$t^{1/5} = -\frac{3}{2}$ | $t^{1/5} = -\frac{1}{3}$

$\left(t^{1/5}\right)^5 = \left(-\frac{3}{2}\right)^5$ | $\left(t^{1/5}\right)^5 = \left(-\frac{1}{3}\right)^5$

$t = -\frac{243}{32}$ | $t = -\frac{1}{243}$

Both answers check.

19.
$$x - 13x^{1/2} + 12 = 0$$
$$\left(x^{1/2} - 12\right)\left(x^{1/2} - 1\right) = 0$$

$x^{1/2} - 12 = 0$ **or** $x^{1/2} - 1 = 0$

$x^{1/2} = 12$ | $x^{1/2} = 1$

$\left(x^{1/2}\right)^2 = (12)^2$ | $\left(x^{1/2}\right)^2 = (1)^2$

$x = 144$ | $x = 1$

Both answers check.

20.
$$p + p^{1/2} - 20 = 0$$
$$\left(p^{1/2} + 5\right)\left(p^{1/2} - 4\right) = 0$$

$p^{1/2} + 5 = 0$ **or** $p^{1/2} - 4 = 0$

$p^{1/2} = -5$ | $p^{1/2} = 4$

$\left(p^{1/2}\right)^2 = (-5)^2$ | $\left(p^{1/2}\right)^2 = (4)^2$

$p = 25$ | $p = 16$

$p = 25$ does not check and is extraneous.

21.
$$2t^{1/3} + 3t^{1/6} - 2 = 0$$
$$\left(2t^{1/6} - 1\right)\left(t^{1/6} + 2\right) = 0$$

$2t^{1/6} - 1 = 0$ **or** $t^{1/6} + 2 = 0$

$t^{1/6} = \frac{1}{2}$ | $t^{1/6} = -2$

$\left(t^{1/6}\right)^6 = \left(\frac{1}{2}\right)^6$ | $\left(t^{1/6}\right)^6 = (-2)^6$

$t = \frac{1}{64}$ | $t = 64$

$t = 64$ does not check and is extraneous.

22.
$$z^3 - 7z^{3/2} - 8 = 0$$
$$\left(z^{3/2} + 1\right)\left(z^{3/2} - 8\right) = 0$$

$z^{3/2} + 1 = 0$ **or** $z^{3/2} - 8 = 0$

$z^{3/2} = -1$ | $z^{3/2} = 8$

$\left(z^{3/2}\right)^2 = (-1)^2$ | $\left(z^{3/2}\right)^2 = (8)^2$

$z^3 = 1$ | $z^3 = 64$

$z = 1$ | $z = 4$

$z = 1$ does not check and is extraneous.

23.
$$6p+p^{1/2}-1=0$$
$$(2p^{1/2}+1)(3p^{1/2}-1)=0$$

$$2p^{1/2}+1=0 \quad \textbf{or} \quad 3p^{1/2}-1=0$$
$$p^{1/2}=-\tfrac{1}{2} \qquad p^{1/2}=\tfrac{1}{3}$$
$$\left(p^{1/2}\right)^2=\left(-\tfrac{1}{2}\right)^2 \qquad \left(p^{1/2}\right)^2=\left(\tfrac{1}{3}\right)^2$$
$$p=\tfrac{1}{4} \qquad p=\tfrac{1}{9}$$

$p=\frac{1}{4}$ does not check and is extraneous.

24.
$$3r-r^{1/2}-2=0$$
$$(3r^{1/2}+2)(r^{1/2}-1)=0$$

$$3r^{1/2}+2=0 \quad \textbf{or} \quad r^{1/2}-1=0$$
$$r^{1/2}=-\tfrac{2}{3} \qquad r^{1/2}=1$$
$$\left(r^{1/2}\right)^2=\left(-\tfrac{2}{3}\right)^2 \qquad \left(r^{1/2}\right)^2=(1)^2$$
$$r=\tfrac{4}{9} \qquad r=1$$

$r=\frac{4}{9}$ does not check and is extraneous.

25.
$$\sqrt{x-2}=5$$
$$\left(\sqrt{x-2}\right)^2=5^2$$
$$x-2=25$$
$$x=27$$
The solution checks.

26.
$$\sqrt{a-3}-5=0$$
$$\sqrt{a-3}=5$$
$$\left(\sqrt{a-3}\right)^2=5^2$$
$$a-3=25$$
$$a=28$$
The solution checks.

27.
$$3\sqrt{x+1}=\sqrt{6}$$
$$\left(3\sqrt{x+1}\right)^2=\left(\sqrt{6}\right)^2$$
$$9(x+1)=6$$
$$9x+9=6$$
$$9x=-3$$
$$x=-\tfrac{1}{3}$$
The solution checks.

28.
$$\sqrt{x+3}=2\sqrt{x}$$
$$\left(\sqrt{x+3}\right)^2=\left(2\sqrt{x}\right)^2$$
$$x+3=4x$$
$$3=3x$$
$$1=x$$
The solution checks.

29.
$$\sqrt{5a-2}=\sqrt{a+6}$$
$$\left(\sqrt{5a-2}\right)^2=\left(\sqrt{a+6}\right)^2$$
$$5a-2=a+6$$
$$4a=8$$
$$a=2$$
The solution checks.

30.
$$\sqrt{16x+4}=\sqrt{x+4}$$
$$\left(\sqrt{16x+4}\right)^2=\left(\sqrt{x+4}\right)^2$$
$$16x+4=x+4$$
$$15x=0$$
$$x=0$$
The solution checks.

31.

$$\begin{aligned} 2\sqrt{x^2+3} &= \sqrt{-16x-3} \\ \left(2\sqrt{x^2+3}\right)^2 &= \left(\sqrt{-16x-3}\right)^2 \\ 4(x^2+3) &= -16x-3 \\ 4x^2+12 &= -16x-3 \\ 4x^2+16x+15 &= 0 \\ (2x+3)(2x+5) &= 0 \end{aligned}$$

$2x+3=0$ **or** $2x+5=0$

$x=-\frac{3}{2}$ $\qquad x=-\frac{5}{2}$

Both solutions check.

32.

$$\begin{aligned} \sqrt{x^2+1} &= \frac{\sqrt{-7x+11}}{\sqrt{6}} \\ \left(\sqrt{x^2+1}\right)^2 &= \left(\frac{\sqrt{-7x+11}}{\sqrt{6}}\right)^2 \\ x^2+1 &= \frac{-7x+11}{6} \\ 6x^2+6 &= -7x+11 \\ 6x^2+7x-5 &= 0 \\ (2x-1)(3x+5) &= 0 \end{aligned}$$

$2x-1=0$ **or** $3x+5=0$

$x=\frac{1}{2}$ $\qquad x=-\frac{5}{3}$

Both solutions check.

33.

$$\begin{aligned} \sqrt[3]{7x+1} &= 4 \\ \left(\sqrt[3]{7x+1}\right)^3 &= 4^3 \\ 7x+1 &= 64 \\ 7x &= 63 \\ x &= 9 \end{aligned}$$

The solution checks.

34.

$$\begin{aligned} \sqrt[3]{11a-40} &= 5 \\ \left(\sqrt[3]{11a-40}\right)^3 &= 5^3 \\ 11a-40 &= 125 \\ 11a &= 165 \\ a &= 15 \end{aligned}$$

The solution checks.

35.

$$\begin{aligned} \sqrt[4]{30t+25} &= 5 \\ \left(\sqrt[4]{30t+25}\right)^4 &= 5^4 \\ 30t+25 &= 625 \\ 30t &= 600 \\ t &= 20 \end{aligned}$$

The solution checks.

36.

$$\begin{aligned} \sqrt[4]{3z+1} &= 2 \\ \left(\sqrt[4]{3z+1}\right)^4 &= 2^4 \\ 3z+1 &= 16 \\ 3z &= 15 \\ z &= 5 \end{aligned}$$

The solution checks.

37.

$$\begin{aligned} \sqrt{x^2+21} &= x+3 \\ \left(\sqrt{x^2+21}\right)^2 &= (x+3)^2 \\ x^2+21 &= x^2+6x+9 \\ 21 &= 6x+9 \\ 12 &= 6x \\ 2 &= x \end{aligned}$$

The solution checks.

38.

$$\begin{aligned} \sqrt{5-x^2} &= -(x+1) \\ \left(\sqrt{5-x^2}\right)^2 &= [-(x+1)]^2 \\ 5-x^2 &= (x+1)^2 \\ 5-x^2 &= x^2+2x+1 \\ 0 &= 2x^2+2x-4 \\ 0 &= 2(x+2)(x-1) \end{aligned}$$

$x+2=0$ **or** $x-1=0$

$x=-2$ $\qquad x=1$

$x=1$ does not check and is extraneous.

39.
$$\begin{aligned}\sqrt{y+2} &= 4-y\\ \left(\sqrt{y+2}\right)^2 &= (4-y)^2\\ y+2 &= 16-8y+y^2\\ 0 &= y^2-9y+14\\ 0 &= (y-2)(y-7)\end{aligned}$$
$$y-2=0 \quad \textbf{or} \quad y-7=0$$
$$y=2 \qquad\qquad y=7$$
$y=7$ does not check and is extraneous.

40.
$$\begin{aligned}\sqrt{3z+1} &= z-1\\ \left(\sqrt{3z+1}\right)^2 &= (z-1)^2\\ 3z+1 &= z^2-2z+1\\ 0 &= z^2-5z\\ 0 &= z(z-5)\end{aligned}$$
$$z=0 \quad \textbf{or} \quad z-5=0$$
$$z=0 \qquad\qquad z=5$$
$z=0$ does not check and is extraneous.

41.
$$\begin{aligned}x-\sqrt{7x-12} &= 0\\ x &= \sqrt{7x-12}\\ x^2 &= \left(\sqrt{7x-12}\right)^2\\ x^2 &= 7x-12\\ x^2-7x+12 &= 0\\ (x-4)(x-3) &= 0\end{aligned}$$
$$x-4=0 \quad \textbf{or} \quad x-3=0$$
$$x=4 \qquad\qquad x=3$$
Both solutions check.

42.
$$\begin{aligned}x-\sqrt{4x-4} &= 0\\ x &= \sqrt{4x-4}\\ x^2 &= \left(\sqrt{4x-4}\right)^2\\ x^2 &= 4x-4\\ x^2-4x+4 &= 0\\ (x-2)(x-2) &= 0\end{aligned}$$
$$x-2=0 \quad \textbf{or} \quad x-2=0$$
$$x=2 \qquad\qquad x=2$$
The solution checks.

43.
$$\begin{aligned}x+4 &= \sqrt{\frac{6x+6}{5}}+3\\ x+1 &= \sqrt{\frac{6x+6}{5}}\\ (x+1)^2 &= \left(\sqrt{\frac{6x+6}{5}}\right)^2\\ x^2+2x+1 &= \frac{6x+6}{5}\\ 5x^2+10x+5 &= 6x+6\\ 5x^2+4x-1 &= 0\\ (5x-1)(x+1) &= 0\end{aligned}$$
$$5x-1=0 \quad \textbf{or} \quad x+1=0$$
$$x=\tfrac{1}{5} \qquad\qquad x=-1$$
Both solutions check.

44.
$$\begin{aligned}\sqrt{\frac{8x+43}{3}}-1 &= x\\ \sqrt{\frac{8x+43}{3}} &= x+1\\ \left(\sqrt{\frac{8x+43}{3}}\right)^2 &= (x+1)^2\\ \frac{8x+43}{3} &= x^2+2x+1\\ 8x+43 &= 3x^2+6x+3\\ 0 &= 3x^2-2x-40\\ 0 &= (3x+10)(x-4)\end{aligned}$$
$$3x+10=0 \quad \textbf{or} \quad x-4=0$$
$$x=-\tfrac{10}{3} \qquad\qquad x=4$$
$x=-\frac{10}{3}$ does not check and is extraneous.

45.
$$\sqrt{\frac{x^2-1}{x-2}} = 2\sqrt{2}$$
$$\left(\sqrt{\frac{x^2-1}{x-2}}\right)^2 = \left(2\sqrt{2}\right)^2$$
$$\frac{x^2-1}{x-2} = 8$$
$$x^2-1 = 8x-16$$
$$x^2-8x+15 = 0$$
$$(x-3)(x-5) = 0$$
$$x-3=0 \quad \textbf{or} \quad x-5=0$$
$$x=3 \qquad\qquad x=5$$
Both solutions check.

46.
$$\frac{\sqrt{x^2-1}}{\sqrt{3x-5}} = \sqrt{2}$$
$$\left(\frac{\sqrt{x^2-1}}{\sqrt{3x-5}}\right)^2 = \left(\sqrt{2}\right)^2$$
$$\frac{x^2-1}{3x-5} = 2$$
$$x^2-1 = 6x-10$$
$$x^2-6x+9 = 0$$
$$(x-3)(x-3) = 0$$
$$x-3=0 \quad \textbf{or} \quad x-3=0$$
$$x=3 \qquad\qquad x=3$$
The solution checks.

47.
$$\sqrt[3]{x^3+7} = x+1$$
$$\left(\sqrt[3]{x^3+7}\right)^3 = (x+1)^3$$
$$x^3+7 = x^3+3x^2+3x+1$$
$$0 = 3x^2+3x-6$$
$$0 = 3(x+2)(x-1)$$
$$x+2=0 \quad \textbf{or} \quad x-1=0$$
$$x=-2 \qquad\qquad x=1$$
Both solutions check.

48.
$$\sqrt[3]{x^3-7}+1 = x$$
$$\sqrt[3]{x^3-7} = x-1$$
$$\left(\sqrt[3]{x^3-7}\right)^3 = (x-1)^3$$
$$x^3-7 = x^3-3x^2+3x-1$$
$$3x^2-3x-6 = 0$$
$$3(x-2)(x+1) = 0$$
$$x-2=0 \quad \textbf{or} \quad x+1=0$$
$$x=2 \qquad\qquad x=-1$$
Both solutions check.

49.
$$\sqrt[3]{8x^3+61} = 2x+1$$
$$\left(\sqrt[3]{8x^3+61}\right)^3 = (2x+1)^3$$
$$8x^3+61 = 8x^3+12x^2+6x+1$$
$$0 = 12x^2+6x-60$$
$$0 = 6(2x+5)(x-2)$$
$$2x+5=0 \quad \textbf{or} \quad x-2=0$$
$$x=-\tfrac{5}{2} \qquad\qquad x=2$$
Both solutions check.

50.
$$\sqrt[3]{8x^3-37} = 2x-1$$
$$\left(\sqrt[3]{8x^3-37}\right)^3 = (2x-1)^3$$
$$8x^3-37 = 8x^3-12x^2+6x-1$$
$$12x^2-6x-36 = 0$$
$$6(2x+3)(x-2) = 0$$
$$2x+3=0 \quad \textbf{or} \quad x-2=0$$
$$x=-\tfrac{3}{2} \qquad\qquad x=2$$
Both solutions check.

51.
$$\sqrt{2p+1}-1=\sqrt{p}$$
$$\left(\sqrt{2p+1}-1\right)^2=\left(\sqrt{p}\right)^2$$
$$2p+1-2\sqrt{2p+1}+1=p$$
$$p+2=2\sqrt{2p+1}$$
$$(p+2)^2=\left(2\sqrt{2p+1}\right)^2$$
$$p^2+4p+4=4(2p+1)$$
$$p^2+4p+4=8p+4$$
$$p^2-4p=0$$
$$p(p-4)=0$$
$$p=0 \quad \textbf{or} \quad p-4=0$$
$$p=0 \qquad\qquad p=4$$
Both solutions check.

52.
$$\sqrt{r}+\sqrt{r+2}=2$$
$$\sqrt{r}=2-\sqrt{r+2}$$
$$\left(\sqrt{r}\right)^2=\left(2-\sqrt{r+2}\right)^2$$
$$r=4-4\sqrt{r+2}+r+2$$
$$4\sqrt{r+2}=6$$
$$\left(4\sqrt{r+2}\right)^2=6^2$$
$$16(r+2)=36$$
$$16r+32=36$$
$$16r=4$$
$$r=\tfrac{4}{16}=\tfrac{1}{4}$$
The solution checks.

53.
$$\sqrt{x+3}=\sqrt{2x+8}-1$$
$$\left(\sqrt{x+3}\right)^2=\left(\sqrt{2x+8}-1\right)^2$$
$$x+3=2x+8-2\sqrt{2x+8}+1$$
$$2\sqrt{2x+8}=x+6$$
$$\left(2\sqrt{2x+8}\right)^2=(x+6)^2$$
$$4(2x+8)=x^2+12x+36$$
$$8x+32=x^2+12x+36$$
$$0=x^2+4x+4$$
$$0=(x+2)(x+2)$$
$$x+2=0 \quad \textbf{or} \quad x+2=0$$
$$x=-2 \qquad\qquad x=-2$$
The solution checks.

54.
$$\sqrt{x+2}+1=\sqrt{2x+5}$$
$$\left(\sqrt{x+2}+1\right)^2=\left(\sqrt{2x+5}\right)^2$$
$$x+2+2\sqrt{x+2}+1=2x+5$$
$$2\sqrt{x+2}=x+2$$
$$\left(2\sqrt{x+2}\right)^2=(x+2)^2$$
$$4(x+2)=x^2+4x+4$$
$$4x+8=x^2+4x+4$$
$$0=x^2-4$$
$$0=(x+2)(x-2)$$
$$x+2=0 \quad \textbf{or} \quad x-2=0$$
$$x=-2 \qquad\qquad x=2$$
Both solutions check.

55.
$$\sqrt{y+8}-\sqrt{y-4}=-2$$
$$\sqrt{y+8}=\sqrt{y-4}-2$$
$$\left(\sqrt{y+8}\right)^2=\left(\sqrt{y-4}-2\right)^2$$
$$y+8=y-4-4\sqrt{y-4}+4$$
$$4\sqrt{y-4}=-8$$
$$\left(4\sqrt{y-4}\right)^2=(-8)^2$$
$$16(y-4)=64$$
$$16y-64=64$$
$$16y=128$$
$$y=8$$
The solution does not check.

56.
$$\sqrt{z+5}-2=\sqrt{z-3}$$
$$\left(\sqrt{z+5}-2\right)^2=\left(\sqrt{z-3}\right)^2$$
$$z+5-2(2)\sqrt{z+5}+4=z-3$$
$$12=4\sqrt{z+5}$$
$$12^2=\left(4\sqrt{z+5}\right)^2$$
$$144=16(z+5)$$
$$144=16z+80$$
$$64=16z$$
$$4=z$$
The solution checks.

57.

$$\begin{aligned}
\sqrt{2b+3}-\sqrt{b+1} &= \sqrt{b-2} \\
\left(\sqrt{2b+3}-\sqrt{b+1}\right)^2 &= \left(\sqrt{b-2}\right)^2 \\
2b+3-2\sqrt{(2b+3)(b+1)}+b+1 &= b-2 \\
3b+4-2\sqrt{2b^2+5b+3} &= b-2 \\
2b+6 &= 2\sqrt{2b^2+5b+3} \\
(2b+6)^2 &= \left(2\sqrt{2b^2+5b+3}\right)^2 \\
4b^2+24b+36 &= 4\left(2b^2+5b+3\right) \\
4b^2+24b+36 &= 8b^2+20b+12 \\
0 &= 4b^2-4b-24 \\
0 &= 4(b-3)(b+2)
\end{aligned}$$

$b-3=0$ **or** $b+2=0$ $\qquad$ $b=-2$ does not check, so it
$b=3$ $\qquad$ $b=-2$ $\qquad$ is an extraneous solution.

58.

$$\begin{aligned}
\sqrt{a+1}+\sqrt{3a} &= \sqrt{5a+1} \\
\left(\sqrt{a+1}+\sqrt{3a}\right)^2 &= \left(\sqrt{5a+1}\right)^2 \\
a+1+2\sqrt{3a(a+1)}+3a &= 5a+1 \\
4a+1+2\sqrt{3a^2+3a} &= 5a+1 \\
2\sqrt{3a^2+3a} &= a \\
\left(2\sqrt{3a^2+3a}\right)^2 &= a^2 \\
4\left(3a^2+3a\right) &= a^2 \\
12a^2+12a &= a^2 \\
11a^2+12a &= 0 \\
a(11a+12) &= 0
\end{aligned}$$

$a=0$ **or** $11a+12=0$ $\qquad$ $a=-\frac{12}{11}$ does not check, so it
$a=0$ $\qquad$ $a=-\frac{12}{11}$ $\qquad$ is an extraneous solution.

59.
$$\sqrt{\sqrt{b}+\sqrt{b+8}}=2$$
$$\left(\sqrt{\sqrt{b}+\sqrt{b+8}}\right)^2=2^2$$
$$\sqrt{b}+\sqrt{b+8}=4$$
$$\sqrt{b+8}=4-\sqrt{b}$$
$$\left(\sqrt{b+8}\right)^2=\left(4-\sqrt{b}\right)^2$$
$$b+8=16-8\sqrt{b}+b$$
$$8\sqrt{b}=8$$
$$\sqrt{b}=1$$
$$\left(\sqrt{b}\right)^2=1^2$$
$b=1 \Rightarrow$ The solution checks.

60.
$$\sqrt{\sqrt{x+19}-\sqrt{x-2}}=\sqrt{3}$$
$$\left(\sqrt{\sqrt{x+19}-\sqrt{x-2}}\right)^2=\left(\sqrt{3}\right)^2$$
$$\sqrt{x+19}-\sqrt{x-2}=3$$
$$\sqrt{x+19}=3+\sqrt{x-2}$$
$$\left(\sqrt{x+19}\right)^2=\left(3+\sqrt{x-2}\right)^2$$
$$x+19=9+6\sqrt{x-2}+x-2$$
$$12=6\sqrt{x-2}$$
$$2=\sqrt{x-2}$$
$$2^2=\left(\sqrt{x-2}\right)^2$$
$$4=x-2$$
$6=x \Rightarrow$ The solutions checks.

61.
$$t=\sqrt{\frac{d}{16}}$$
$$5=\sqrt{\frac{d}{16}}$$
$$5^2=\left(\sqrt{\frac{d}{16}}\right)^2$$
$$25=\frac{d}{16}$$
$400=d \Rightarrow$ The bridge is 400 feet high.

62.
$$d=1.4\sqrt{h}$$
$$30=1.4\sqrt{h}$$
$$\frac{30}{1.4}=\sqrt{h}$$
$$\left(\frac{30}{1.4}\right)^2=\left(\sqrt{h}\right)^2$$
$$460\approx h$$
The tower must be about 460 feet tall.

63.
$$l = \sqrt{f^2 + h^2}$$
$$10 = \sqrt{f^2 + 6^2}$$
$$10^2 = \left(\sqrt{f^2 + 36}\right)^2$$
$$100 = f^2 + 36$$
$$64 = f^2$$
$$\pm 8 = f$$
He should nail the brace to the floor 8 feet from the wall.

64.
$$v = \sqrt[3]{\frac{P}{0.02}}$$
$$v = \sqrt[3]{\frac{600}{0.02}}$$
$$v \approx 31$$
The wind velocity is about 31 mph.

65. **Answers may vary.**

66. **Answers may vary.**

67. Natural numbers between -4 and 4:

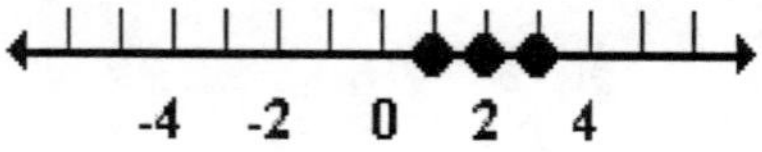

68. Integers between -4 and 4:

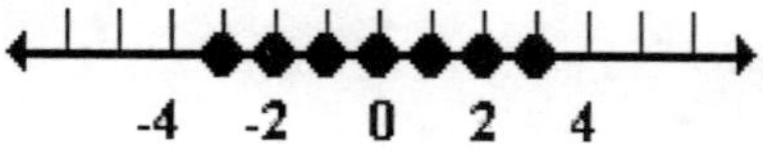

69. $x \geq 3 \Rightarrow [3, \infty)$

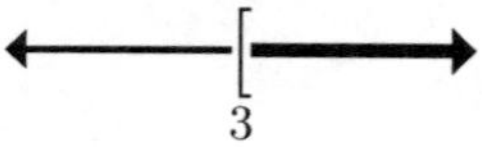

70. $x < -5 \Rightarrow (-\infty, -5)$

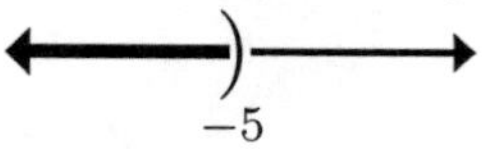

71. $-2 \leq x < 1 \Rightarrow [-2, 1)$

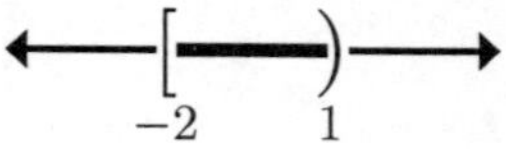

72. $-3 \leq x \leq 3 \Rightarrow [-3, 3]$

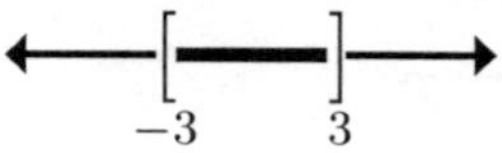

73. $x < 1$ or $x \geq 2$
$(-\infty, 1) \cup [2, \infty)$

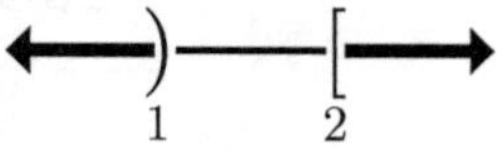

74. $x \leq 1$ or $x > 2$
$(-\infty, 1] \cup (2, \infty)$

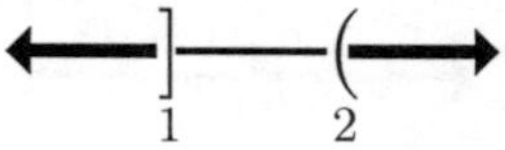

Exercise 1.7 (page 140)

1. right

2. $a = b$

3. $a < c$

4. $b + c$

5. $b - c$

6. $<$

7. $>$

8. $>$

9. linear

10. quadratic

11. equivalent

12. rational

13.
$$3x + 2 < 5$$
$$3x < 3$$
$$x < 1 \Rightarrow (-\infty, 1)$$

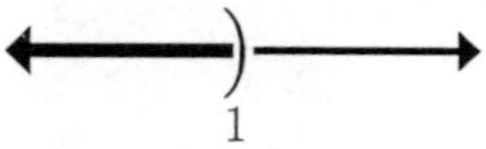

14.
$$-2x + 4 < 6$$
$$-2x < 2$$
$$x > -1 \Rightarrow (-1, \infty)$$

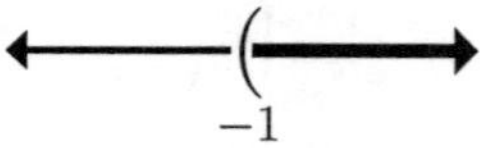

15. $3x + 2 \geq 5$
$3x \geq 3$
$x \geq 1 \Rightarrow [1, \infty)$

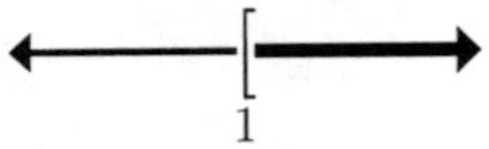

16. $-2x + 4 \geq 6$
$-2x \geq 2$
$x \leq -1 \Rightarrow (-\infty, -1]$

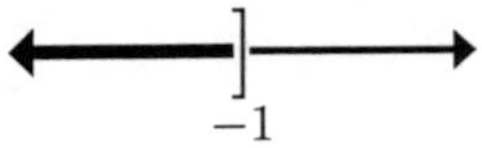

17. $-5x + 3 > -2$
$-5x > -5$
$x < 1 \Rightarrow (-\infty, 1)$

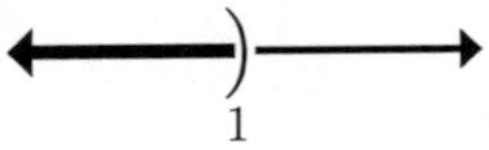

18. $4x - 3 > -4$
$4x > -1$
$x > -\frac{1}{4} \Rightarrow (-\frac{1}{4}, \infty)$

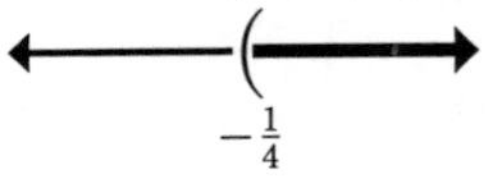

19. $-5x + 3 \leq -2$
$-5x \leq -5$
$x \geq 1 \Rightarrow [1, \infty)$

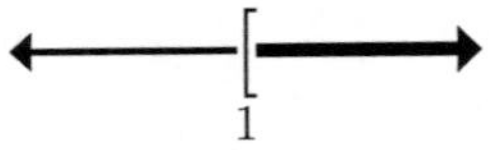

20. $4x - 3 \leq -4$
$4x \leq -1$
$x \leq -\frac{1}{4} \Rightarrow (-\infty, -\frac{1}{4}]$

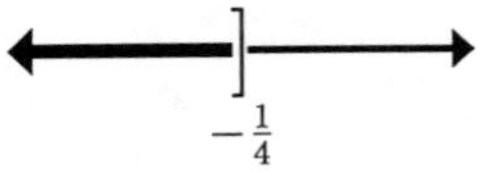

21. $2(x - 3) \leq -2(x - 3)$
$2x - 6 \leq -2x + 6$
$4x \leq 12$
$x \leq 3 \Rightarrow (-\infty, 3]$

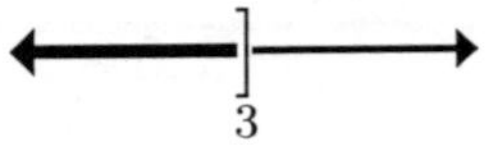

22. $3(x + 2) \leq 2(x + 5)$
$3x + 6 \leq 2x + 10$
$x \leq 4 \Rightarrow (-\infty, 4]$

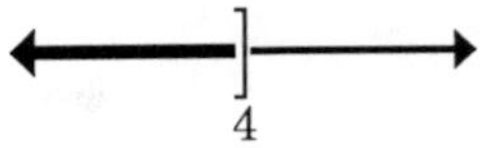

23. $\frac{3}{5}x + 4 > 2$
$5\left(\frac{3}{5}x + 4\right) > 5(2)$
$3x + 20 > 10$
$3x > -10$
$x > -\frac{10}{3} \Rightarrow (-\frac{10}{3}, \infty)$

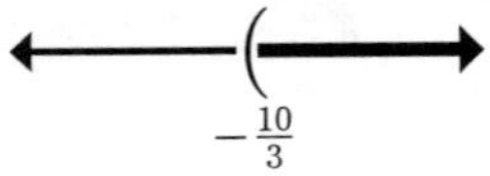

24. $\frac{1}{4}x - 3 > 5$
$4\left(\frac{1}{4}x - 3\right) > 4(5)$
$x - 12 > 20$
$x > 32 \Rightarrow (32, \infty)$

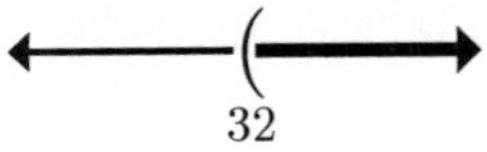

25.

$$\begin{aligned} \frac{x+3}{4} &< \frac{2x-4}{3} \\ 12\cdot\frac{x+3}{4} &< 12\cdot\frac{2x-4}{3} \\ 3(x+3) &< 4(2x-4) \\ 3x+9 &< 8x-16 \\ -5x &< -25 \\ x &> 5 \Rightarrow (5, \infty) \end{aligned}$$

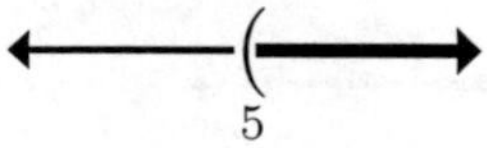

26.

$$\begin{aligned} \frac{x+2}{5} &> \frac{x-1}{2} \\ 10\cdot\frac{x+2}{5} &> 10\cdot\frac{x-1}{2} \\ 2(x+2) &> 5(x-1) \\ 2x+4 &> 5x-5 \\ -3x &> -9 \\ x &< 3 \Rightarrow (-\infty, 3) \end{aligned}$$

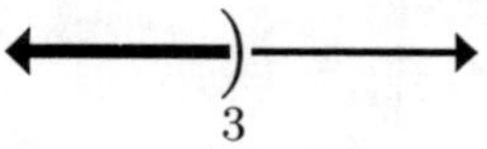

27.

$$\begin{aligned} \frac{6(x-4)}{5} &\ge \frac{3(x+2)}{4} \\ 20\cdot\frac{6x-24}{5} &\ge 20\cdot\frac{3x+6}{4} \\ 4(6x-24) &\ge 5(3x+6) \\ 24x-96 &\ge 15x+30 \\ 9x &\ge 126 \\ x &\ge 14 \Rightarrow [14, \infty) \end{aligned}$$

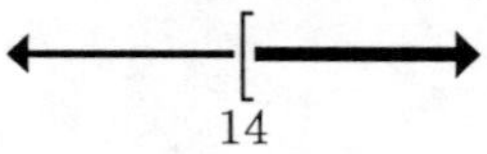

28.

$$\begin{aligned} \frac{3(x+3)}{2} &< \frac{2(x+7)}{3} \\ 6\cdot\frac{3x+9}{2} &< 6\cdot\frac{2x+14}{3} \\ 3(3x+9) &< 2(2x+14) \\ 9x+27 &< 4x+28 \\ 5x &< 1 \\ x &< \tfrac{1}{5} \Rightarrow (-\infty, \tfrac{1}{5}) \end{aligned}$$

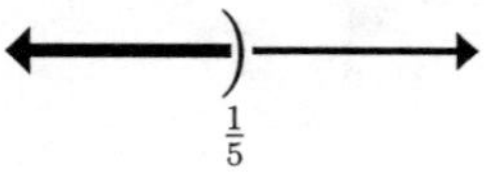

29.

$$\begin{aligned} \frac{5}{9}(a+3)-a &\ge \frac{4}{3}(a-3)-1 \\ 9\left[\frac{5}{9}(a+3)-a\right] &\ge 9\left[\frac{4}{3}(a-3)-1\right] \\ 5(a+3)-9a &\ge 12(a-3)-9 \\ 5a+15-9a &\ge 12a-36-9 \\ -16a &\ge -60 \\ a &\le \frac{-60}{-16} \\ a &\le \tfrac{15}{4} \Rightarrow (-\infty, \tfrac{15}{4}] \end{aligned}$$

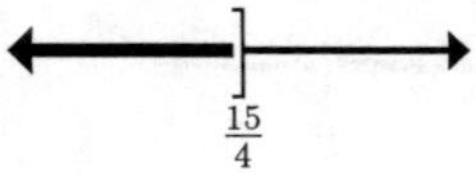

30.

$$\begin{aligned} \frac{2}{3}y-y &\le -\frac{3}{2}(y-5) \\ 6\left(\frac{2}{3}y-y\right) &\le 6\left[-\frac{3}{2}(y-5)\right] \\ 4y-6y &\le -9(y-5) \\ -2y &\le -9y+45 \\ 7y &\le 45 \\ y &\le \tfrac{45}{7} \Rightarrow (-\infty, \tfrac{45}{7}] \end{aligned}$$

31.
$$\frac{2}{3}a-\frac{3}{4}a<\frac{3}{5}\left(a+\frac{2}{3}\right)+\frac{1}{3}$$
$$60\left(\frac{2}{3}a-\frac{3}{4}a\right)<60\left[\frac{3}{5}\left(a+\frac{2}{3}\right)+\frac{1}{3}\right]$$
$$40a-45a<36\left(a+\frac{2}{3}\right)+20$$
$$-5a<36a+24+20$$
$$-41a<44$$
$$a>-\tfrac{44}{41}\Rightarrow\left(-\tfrac{44}{41},\infty\right)$$

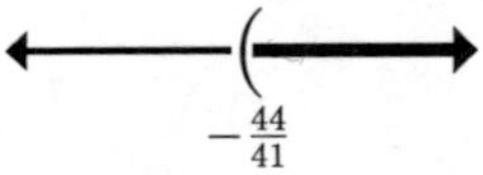

32.
$$\frac{1}{4}b+\frac{2}{3}b-\frac{1}{2}>\frac{1}{2}(b+1)+b$$
$$12\left(\frac{1}{4}b+\frac{2}{3}b-\frac{1}{2}\right)>12\left[\frac{1}{2}(b+1)+b\right]$$
$$3b+8b-6>6(b+1)+12b$$
$$11b-6>6b+6+12b$$
$$-7b>12$$
$$b<-\tfrac{12}{7}\Rightarrow\left(-\infty,-\tfrac{12}{7}\right)$$

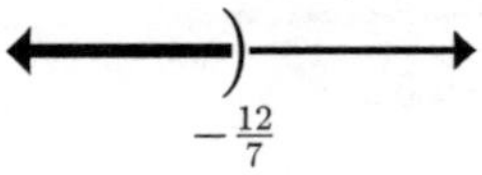

33.
$$4<2x-8\le 10$$
$$12<2x\le 18$$
$$6<x\le 9\Rightarrow(6,9]$$

34.
$$3\le 2x+2<6$$
$$1\le 2x<4$$
$$\tfrac{1}{2}\le x<2\Rightarrow\left[\tfrac{1}{2},2\right)$$

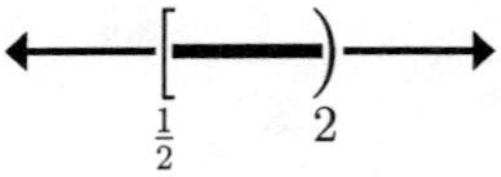

35.
$$9\ge\frac{x-4}{2}>2$$
$$18\ge x-4>4$$
$$22\ge x>8$$
$$8<x\le 22\Rightarrow(8,22]$$

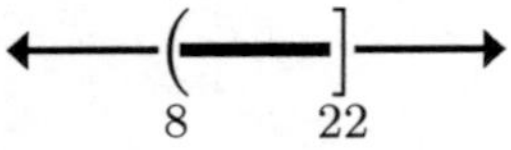

36.
$$5<\frac{x-2}{6}<6$$
$$30<x-2<36$$
$$32<x<38\Rightarrow(32,38)$$

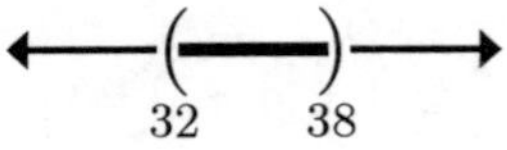

37.
$$0\le\frac{4-x}{3}\le 5$$
$$0\le 4-x\le 15$$
$$-4\le -x\le 11$$
$$4\ge x\ge -11$$
$$-11\le x\le 4\Rightarrow[-11,4]$$

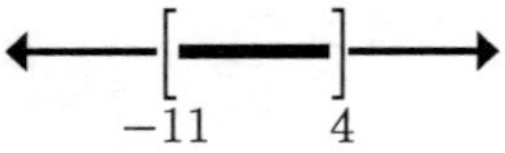

38.
$$0\ge\frac{5-x}{2}\ge -10$$
$$0\ge 5-x\ge -20$$
$$-5\ge -x\ge -25$$
$$5\le x\le 25\Rightarrow[5,25]$$

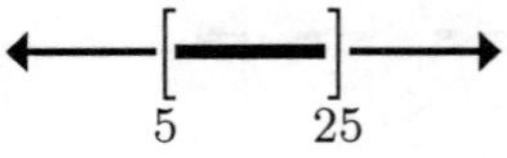

39.
$$\begin{aligned} -2 \geq \frac{1-x}{2} &\geq -10 \\ -4 \geq 1-x &\geq -20 \\ -5 \geq \ \ -x &\geq -21 \\ 5 \leq \ \ \ x &\leq 21 \Rightarrow [5, 21] \end{aligned}$$

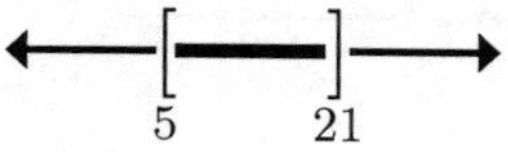

40.
$$\begin{aligned} -2 \leq \frac{1-x}{2} &< 10 \\ -4 \leq 1-x &< 20 \\ -5 \leq \ \ -x &< 19 \\ 5 \geq \ \ \ x &> -19 \\ -19 < \ \ \ x &\leq 5 \Rightarrow (-19, 5] \end{aligned}$$

41.
$$-3x > -2x > -x$$
$$\begin{array}{lcl} -3x > -2x & \textbf{and} & -2x > -x \\ -x > 0 & & -x > 0 \\ x < 0 & & x < 0 \end{array}$$
$$x < 0 \Rightarrow (-\infty, 0)$$

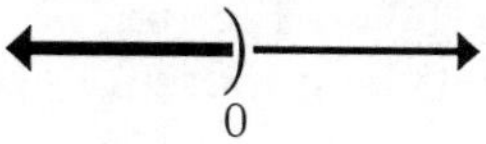

42.
$$-3x < -2x < -x$$
$$\begin{array}{lcl} -3x < -2x & \textbf{and} & -2x < -x \\ -x < 0 & & -x < 0 \\ x > 0 & & x > 0 \end{array}$$
$$x > 0 \Rightarrow (0, \infty)$$

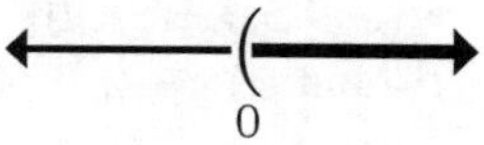

43.
$$x < 2x < 3x$$
$$\begin{array}{lcl} x < 2x & \textbf{and} & 2x < 3x \\ -x < 0 & & -x < 0 \\ x > 0 & & x > 0 \end{array}$$
$$x > 0 \Rightarrow (0, \infty)$$

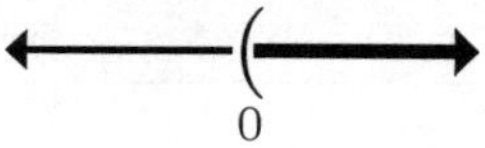

44.
$$x > 2x > 3x$$
$$\begin{array}{lcl} x > 2x & \textbf{and} & 2x > 3x \\ -x > 0 & & -x > 0 \\ x < 0 & & x < 0 \end{array}$$
$$x < 0 \Rightarrow (-\infty, 0)$$

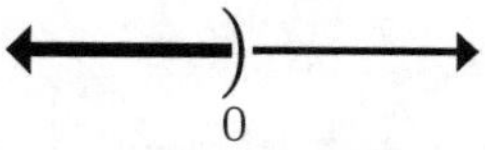

45.
$$2x + 1 < 3x - 2 < 12$$
$$\begin{array}{lcl} 2x + 1 < 3x - 2 & \textbf{and} & 3x - 2 < 12 \\ -x < -3 & & 3x < 14 \\ x > 3 & & x < \frac{14}{3} \end{array}$$

$x > 3$

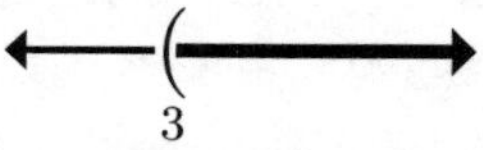

$x < \frac{14}{3}$

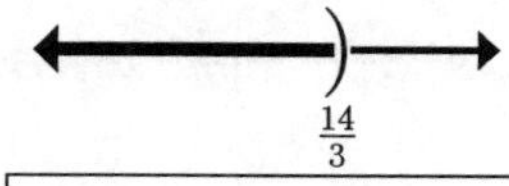

$x > 3$
and
$x < \frac{14}{3}$

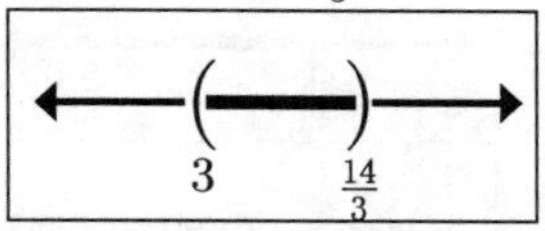

Solution set: $\left(3, \frac{14}{3}\right)$

46.
$$2 - x < 3x + 5 < 18$$
$$\begin{array}{lcl} 2 - x < 3x + 5 & \textbf{and} & 3x + 5 < 18 \\ -4x < 3 & & 3x < 13 \\ x > -\frac{3}{4} & & x < \frac{13}{3} \end{array}$$

$x > -\frac{3}{4}$

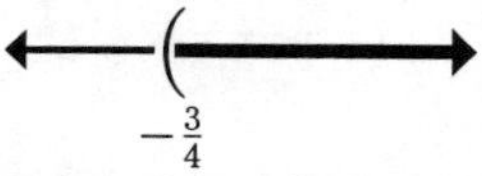

$x < \frac{13}{3}$

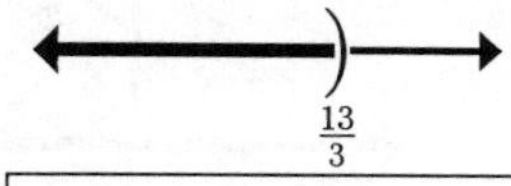

$x > -\frac{3}{4}$
and
$x < \frac{13}{3}$

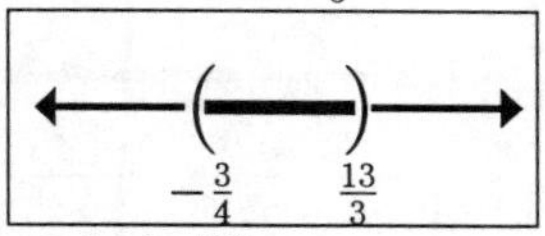

Solution set: $\left(-\frac{3}{4}, \frac{13}{3}\right)$

47. $2 + x < 3x - 2 < 5x + 2$

$2 + x < 3x - 2$ **and** $3x - 2 < 5x + 2$

$-2x < -4$ $\quad$ $-2x < 4$

$x > 2$ $\quad$ $x > -2$

$x > 2$

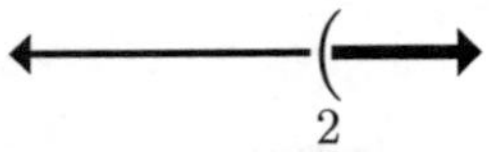

$x > -2$

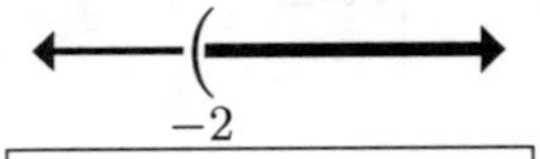

$x > 2$
and
$x > -2$

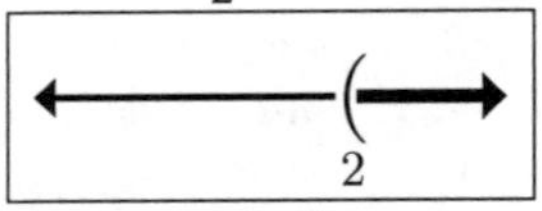

Solution set: $(2, \infty)$

48. $x > 2x + 3 > 4x - 7$

$x > 2x + 3$ **and** $2x + 3 > 4x - 7$

$-x > 3$ $\quad$ $-2x > -10$

$x < -3$ $\quad$ $x < 5$

$x < -3$

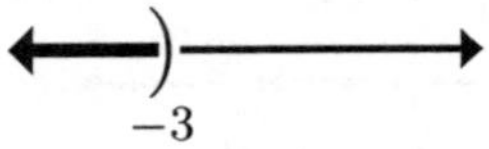

$x < 5$

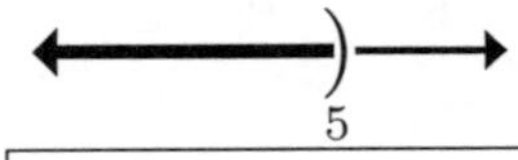

$x < -3$
and
$x < 5$

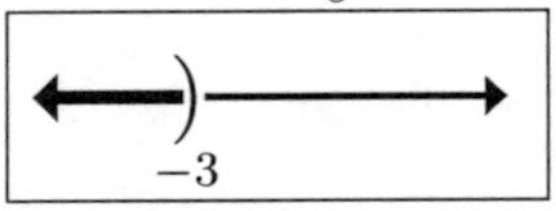

Solution set: $(-\infty, -3)$

49. $3 + x > 7x - 2 > 5x - 10$

$3 + x > 7x - 2$ **and** $7x - 2 > 5x - 10$

$-6x > -5$ $\quad$ $2x > -8$

$x < \frac{5}{6}$ $\quad$ $x > -4$

$x < \frac{5}{6}$

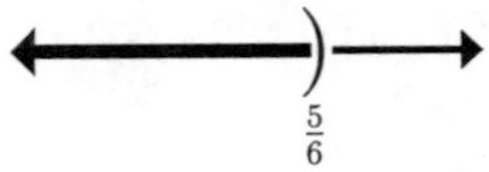

$x > -4$

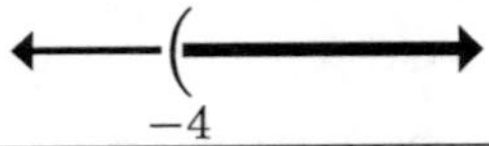

$x < \frac{5}{6}$
and
$x > -4$

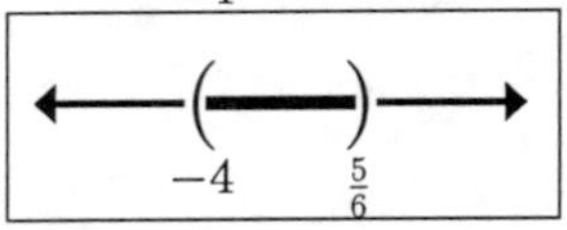

Solution set: $\left(-4, \frac{5}{6}\right)$

50. $2 - x < 3x + 1 < 10x$

$2 - x < 3x + 1$ **and** $3x + 1 < 10x$

$-4x < -1$ $\quad$ $-7x < -1$

$x > \frac{1}{4}$ $\quad$ $x > \frac{1}{7}$

$x > \frac{1}{4}$

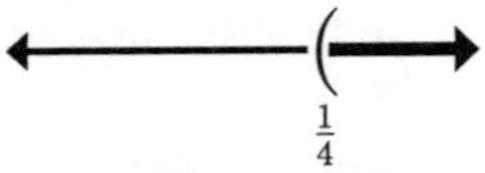

$x > \frac{1}{7}$

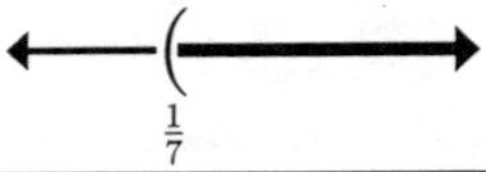

$x > \frac{1}{4}$
and
$x > \frac{1}{7}$

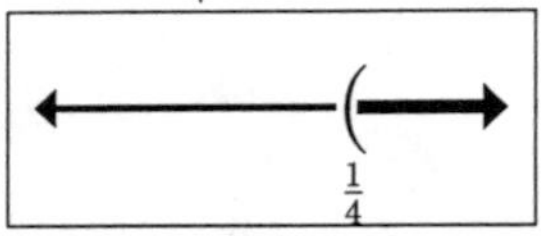

Solution set: $\left(\frac{1}{4}, \infty\right)$

51. $x \le x + 1 \le 2x + 3$

$x \le x + 1$ **and** $x + 1 \le 2x + 3$

$0 \le 1$ $\quad$ $-x \le 2$

true for all real numbers x $\quad$ $x \ge -2$

$0 \le 1$

$x \ge -2$

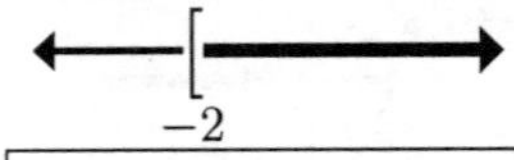

$0 \le 1$
and
$x \ge -2$

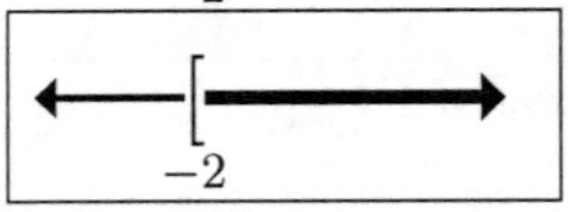

Solution set: $[-2, \infty)$

52. $-x \ge -2x + 1 \ge -3x + 1$

$-x \ge -2x + 1$ **and** $-2x + 1 \ge -3x + 1$

$x \ge 1$ $\quad$ $x \ge 0$

$x \ge 1$

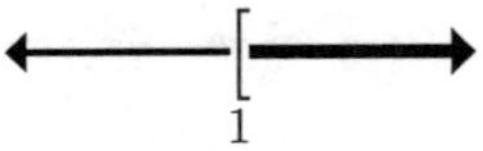

$x \ge 0$

$x \ge 1$
and
$x \ge 0$

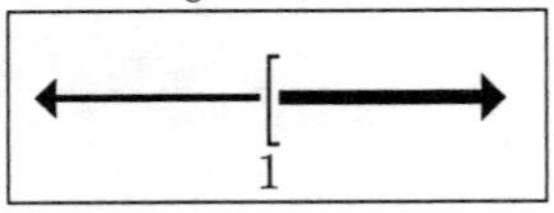

Solution set: $[1, \infty)$

53. $x^2 + 7x + 12 < 0$

$(x+3)(x+4) < 0$

factors $= 0$: $x = -3$, $x = -4$

intervals: $(-\infty, -4)$, $(-4, -3)$, $(-3, \infty)$

interval	test number	value of $x^2+7x+12$
$(-\infty, -4)$	-5	$+2$
$(-4, -3)$	-3.5	-0.25
$(-3, \infty)$	0	$+12$

Solution: $(-4, -3)$

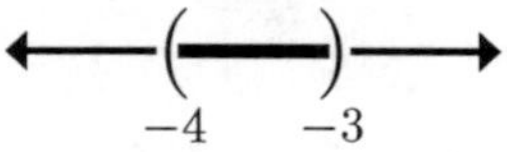

54. $x^2 - 13x + 12 \le 0$

$(x-12)(x-1) \le 0$

factors $= 0$: $x = 12$, $x = 1$

intervals: $(-\infty, 1)$, $(1, 12)$, $(12, \infty)$

interval	test number	value of $x^2-13x+12$
$(-\infty, 1)$	0	$+12$
$(1, 12)$	2	-10
$(12, \infty)$	13	$+12$

Solution: $[1, 12]$

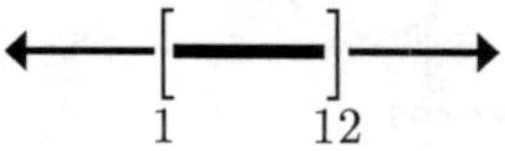

55. $x^2 - 5x + 6 \ge 0$

$(x-3)(x-2) \ge 0$

factors $= 0$: $x = 3$, $x = 2$

intervals: $(-\infty, 2)$, $(2, 3)$, $(3, \infty)$

interval	test number	value of x^2-5x+6
$(-\infty, 2)$	0	$+6$
$(2, 3)$	2.5	-0.25
$(3, \infty)$	4	$+2$

Solution: $(-\infty, 2] \cup [3, \infty)$

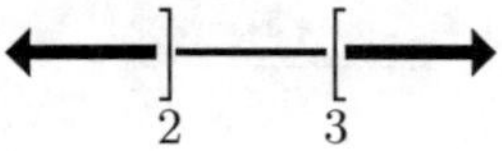

56. $6x^2 + 5x - 6 > 0$

$(2x+3)(3x-2) > 0$

factors $= 0$: $x = -\frac{3}{2}$, $x = \frac{2}{3}$

intervals: $(-\infty, -\frac{3}{2})$, $(-\frac{3}{2}, \frac{2}{3})$, $(\frac{2}{3}, \infty)$

interval	test number	value of $6x^2+5x-6$
$(-\infty, -\frac{3}{2})$	-2	$+8$
$(-\frac{3}{2}, \frac{2}{3})$	0	-6
$(\frac{2}{3}, \infty)$	1	$+5$

Solution: $(-\infty, -\frac{3}{2}) \cup (\frac{2}{3}, \infty)$

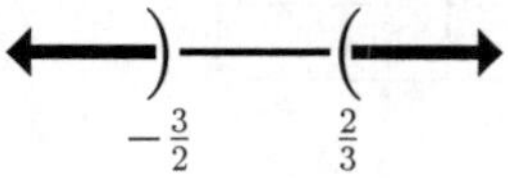

57. $x^2 + 5x + 6 < 0$

$(x+3)(x+2) < 0$

factors $= 0$: $x = -3$, $x = -2$

intervals: $(-\infty, -3)$, $(-3, -2)$, $(-2, \infty)$

interval	test number	value of x^2+5x+6
$(-\infty, -3)$	-4	$+2$
$(-3, -2)$	-2.5	-0.25
$(-2, \infty)$	0	$+6$

Solution: $(-3, -2)$

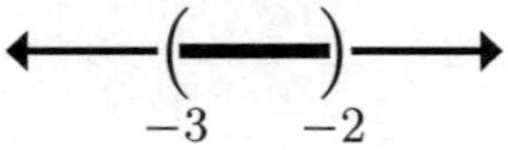

58. $x^2 + 9x + 20 \ge 0$

$(x+4)(x+5) \ge 0$

factors $= 0$: $x = -4$, $x = -5$

intervals: $(-\infty, -5)$, $(-5, -4)$, $(-4, \infty)$

interval	test number	value of $x^2+9x+20$
$(-\infty, -5)$	-6	$+2$
$(-5, -4)$	-4.5	-0.25
$(-4, \infty)$	0	$+20$

Solution: $(-\infty, -5] \cup [-4, \infty)$

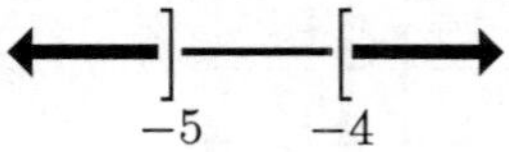

59. $6x^2 + 5x + 1 \geq 0$

$(2x+1)(3x+1) \geq 0$

factors $= 0$: $x = -\frac{1}{2}, x = -\frac{1}{3}$

intervals: $(-\infty, -\frac{1}{2}), (-\frac{1}{2}, -\frac{1}{3}), (-\frac{1}{3}, \infty)$

interval	test number	value of $6x^2+5x+1$
$(-\infty, -\frac{1}{2})$	-1	$+2$
$(-\frac{1}{2}, -\frac{1}{3})$	-0.4	-0.04
$(-\frac{1}{3}, \infty)$	0	$+1$

Solution: $(-\infty, -\frac{1}{2}] \cup [-\frac{1}{3}, \infty)$

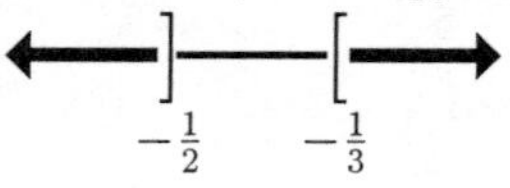

60. $x^2 + 9x + 20 < 0$

$(x+5)(x+4) < 0$

factors $= 0$: $x = -5, x = -4$

intervals: $(-\infty, -5), (-5, -4), (-4, \infty)$

interval	test number	value of $x^2+9x+20$
$(-\infty, -5)$	-6	$+2$
$(-5, -4)$	-4.5	-0.25
$(-4, \infty)$	0	$+20$

Solution: $(-5, -4)$

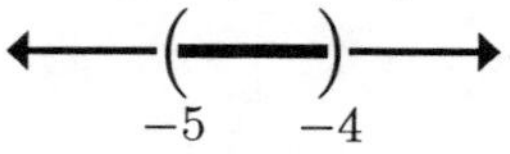

61. $6x^2 - 5x < -1$

$6x^2 - 5x + 1 < 0$

$(2x-1)(3x-1) < 0$

factors $= 0$: $x = \frac{1}{2}, x = \frac{1}{3}$

intervals: $(-\infty, \frac{1}{3}), (\frac{1}{3}, \frac{1}{2}), (\frac{1}{2}, \infty)$

interval	test number	value of $6x^2-5x+1$
$(-\infty, \frac{1}{3})$	0	$+1$
$(\frac{1}{3}, \frac{1}{2})$	0.4	-0.04
$(\frac{1}{2}, \infty)$	1	$+2$

Solution: $(\frac{1}{3}, \frac{1}{2})$

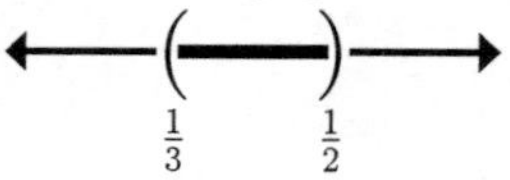

62. $9x^2 + 24x > -16$

$9x^2 + 24x + 16 > 0$

$(3x+4)(3x+4) > 0$

factors $= 0$: $x = -\frac{4}{3}, x = -\frac{4}{3}$

intervals: $(-\infty, -\frac{4}{3}), (-\frac{4}{3}, \infty)$

interval	test number	value of $9x^2+24x+16$
$(-\infty, -\frac{4}{3})$	-2	$+4$
$(-\frac{4}{3}, \infty)$	0	$+16$

Solution: $(-\infty, -\frac{4}{3}) \cup (-\frac{4}{3}, \infty)$

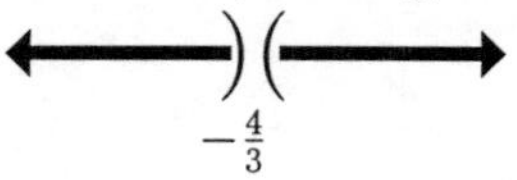

63. $2x^2 \geq 3 - x$

$2x^2 + x - 3 \geq 0$

$(2x+3)(x-1) \geq 0$

factors $= 0$: $x = -\frac{3}{2}, x = 1$

intervals: $(-\infty, -\frac{3}{2}), (-\frac{3}{2}, 1), (1, \infty)$

interval	test number	value of $2x^2+x-3$
$(-\infty, -\frac{3}{2})$	-2	$+3$
$(-\frac{3}{2}, 1)$	0	-3
$(1, \infty)$	2	$+7$

Solution: $(-\infty, -\frac{3}{2}] \cup [1, \infty)$

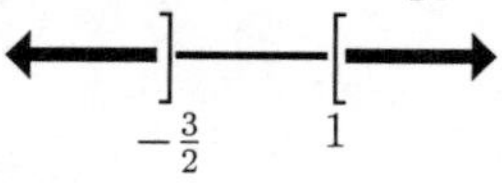

64. $9x^2 \leq 24x - 16$

$9x^2 - 24x + 16 \leq 0$

$(3x-4)(3x-4) \leq 0$

factors $= 0$: $x = \frac{4}{3}, x = \frac{4}{3}$

intervals: $(-\infty, \frac{4}{3}), (\frac{4}{3}, \infty)$

interval	test number	value of $9x^2-24x+16$
$(-\infty, \frac{4}{3})$	0	$+16$
$(\frac{4}{3}, \infty)$	2	$+4$

Solution: $x = \frac{4}{3}$, or $[\frac{4}{3}, \frac{4}{3}]$

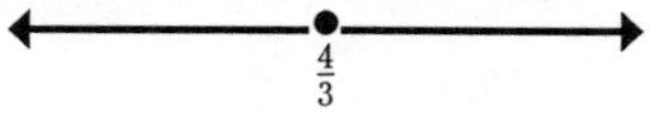

65. $\dfrac{x+3}{x-2} < 0$

factors $= 0$: $x = -3$, $x = 2$

intervals: $(-\infty, -3)$, $(-3, 2)$, $(2, \infty)$

interval	test number	sign of $\frac{x+3}{x-2}$
$(-\infty, -3)$	-4	$+$
$(-3, 2)$	0	$-$
$(2, \infty)$	3	$+$

Solution: $(-3, 2)$

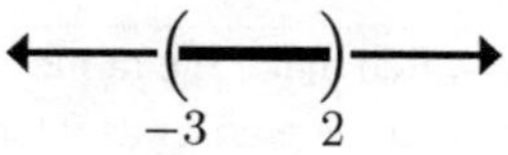

66. $\dfrac{x+3}{x-2} > 0$

factors $= 0$: $x = -3$, $x = 2$

intervals: $(-\infty, -3)$, $(-3, 2)$, $(2, \infty)$

interval	test number	sign of $\frac{x+3}{x-2}$
$(-\infty, -3)$	-4	$+$
$(-3, 2)$	0	$-$
$(2, \infty)$	3	$+$

Solution: $(-\infty, -3) \cup (2, \infty)$

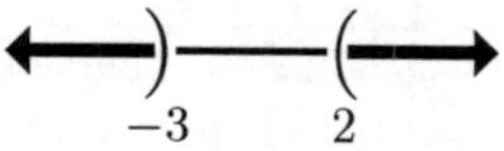

67. $\dfrac{x^2+x}{x^2-1} > 0$

$\dfrac{x(x+1)}{(x+1)(x-1)} > 0$

factors $= 0$: $x = 0$, $x = -1$, $x = 1$

intervals: $(-\infty, -1)$, $(-1, 0)$, $(0, 1)$, $(1, \infty)$

interval	test number	sign of $\frac{x^2+x}{x^2-1}$
$(-\infty, -1)$	-2	$+$
$(-1, 0)$	$-\frac{1}{2}$	$+$
$(0, 1)$	$\frac{1}{2}$	$-$
$(1, \infty)$	2	$+$

Solution: $(-\infty, -1) \cup (-1, 0) \cup (1, \infty)$

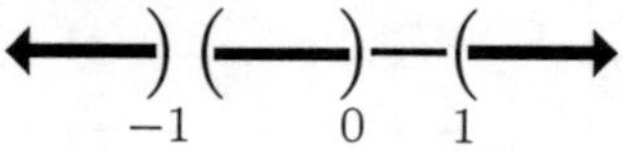

68. $\dfrac{x^2-4}{x^2-9} < 0 \Rightarrow \dfrac{(x+2)(x-2)}{(x+3)(x-3)} < 0$

factors $= 0$: $x = \pm 2$, $x = \pm 3$

intervals: $(-\infty, -3)$, $(-3, -2)$, $(-2, 2)$, $(2, 3)$, $(3, \infty)$

interval	test number	sign of $\frac{x^2-4}{x^2-9}$
$(-\infty, -3)$	-4	$+$
$(-3, -2)$	-2.5	$-$
$(-2, 2)$	0	$+$
$(2, 3)$	2.5	$-$
$(3, \infty)$	4	$+$

Solution: $(-3, -2) \cup (2, 3)$

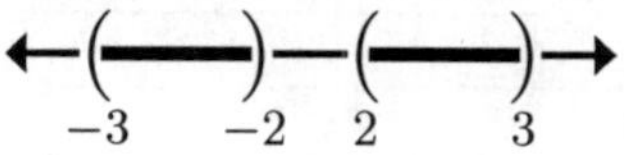

69. $\dfrac{x^2+5x+6}{x^2+x-6} \geq 0 \Rightarrow \dfrac{(x+3)(x+2)}{(x+3)(x-2)} \geq 0$

factors = 0: $x = -3$, $x = \pm 2$

intervals: $(-\infty, -3)$, $(-3, -2)$, $(-2, 2)$, $(2, \infty)$

interval	test number	sign of $\frac{x^2+5x+6}{x^2+x-6}$
$(-\infty, -3)$	-4	$+$
$(-3, -2)$	-2.5	$+$
$(-2, 2)$	0	$-$
$(2, \infty)$	3	$+$

Include endpoints which make the numerator equal to 0. Do not include endpoints which make the denominator equal to 0.

Solution: $(-\infty, -3) \cup (-3, -2] \cup (2, \infty)$

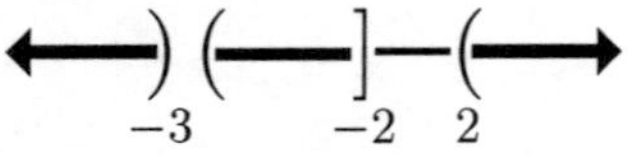

70. $\dfrac{x^2+10x+25}{x^2-x-12} \leq 0 \Rightarrow \dfrac{(x+5)(x+5)}{(x+3)(x-4)} \leq 0$

factors = 0: $x = -3$, $x = 4$, $x = -5$

intervals: $(-\infty, -5)$, $(-5, -3)$, $(-3, 4)$, $(4, \infty)$

interval	test number	sign of $\frac{x^2+10x+25}{x^2-x-12}$
$(-\infty, -5)$	-6	$+$
$(-5, -3)$	-4	$+$
$(-3, 4)$	0	$-$
$(4, \infty)$	5	$+$

Include endpoints which make the numerator equal to 0. Do not include endpoints which make the denominator equal to 0.

Solution: $[-5, -5] \cup (-3, 4)$

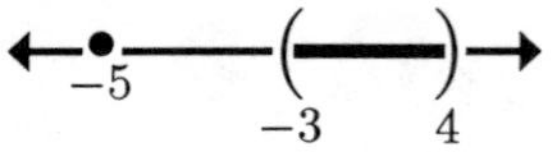

71. $\dfrac{6x^2-x-1}{x^2+4x+4} > 0 \Rightarrow \dfrac{(2x-1)(3x+1)}{(x+2)(x+2)} > 0$

factors = 0: $x = \frac{1}{2}$, $x = -\frac{1}{3}$, $x = -2$

intervals: $(-\infty, -2)$, $(-2, -\frac{1}{3})$, $(-\frac{1}{3}, \frac{1}{2})$, $(\frac{1}{2}, \infty)$

interval	test number	sign of $\frac{6x^2-x-1}{x^2+4x+4}$
$(-\infty, -2)$	-3	$+$
$(-2, -\frac{1}{3})$	-1	$+$
$(-\frac{1}{3}, \frac{1}{2})$	0	$-$
$(\frac{1}{2}, \infty)$	1	$+$

Solution: $(-\infty, -2) \cup (-2, -\frac{1}{3}) \cup (\frac{1}{2}, \infty)$

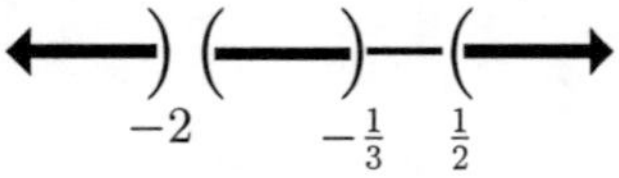

72. $\dfrac{6x^2-3x-3}{x^2-2x-8} < 0 \Rightarrow \dfrac{3(2x+1)(x-1)}{(x+2)(x-4)} < 0$

factors = 0: $x = -\frac{1}{2}$, $x = 1$, $x = -2$, $x = 4$

intervals: $(-\infty, -2)$, $(-2, -\frac{1}{2})$, $(-\frac{1}{2}, 1)$, $(1, 4)$, $(4, \infty)$

interval	test number	sign of $\frac{6x^2-3x-3}{x^2-2x-8}$
$(-\infty, -2)$	-3	$+$
$(-2, -\frac{1}{2})$	-1	$-$
$(-\frac{1}{2}, 1)$	0	$+$
$(1, 4)$	2	$-$
$(4, \infty)$	5	$+$

Solution: $(-2, -\frac{1}{2}) \cup (1, 4)$

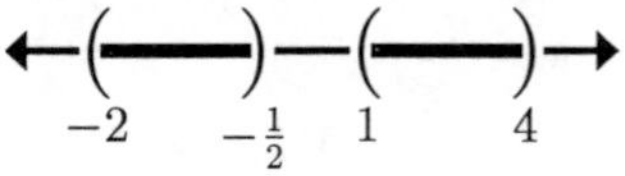

73.

$$\frac{3}{x} > 2$$

$$\frac{3}{x} - 2 > 0$$

$$\frac{3-2x}{x} > 0$$

factors = 0: $x = \frac{3}{2}$, $x = 0$

intervals: $(-\infty, 0)$, $(0, \frac{3}{2})$, $(\frac{3}{2}, \infty)$

interval	test number	sign of $\frac{3-2x}{x}$
$(-\infty, 0)$	-1	$-$
$(0, \frac{3}{2})$	1	$+$
$(\frac{3}{2}, \infty)$	2	$-$

Solution: $(0, \frac{3}{2})$

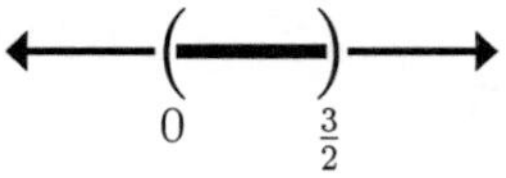

74.

$$\frac{3}{x} < 2$$
$$\frac{3}{x} - 2 < 0$$
$$\frac{3-2x}{x} < 0$$

factors = 0: $x = \frac{3}{2}$, $x = 0$

intervals: $(-\infty, 0)$, $(0, \frac{3}{2})$, $(\frac{3}{2}, \infty)$

interval	test number	sign of $\frac{3-2x}{x}$
$(-\infty, 0)$	-1	$-$
$(0, \frac{3}{2})$	1	$+$
$(\frac{3}{2}, \infty)$	2	$-$

Solution: $(-\infty, 0) \cup (\frac{3}{2}, \infty)$

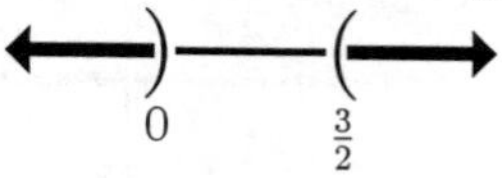

75.

$$\frac{6}{x} < 4$$
$$\frac{6}{x} - 4 < 0$$
$$\frac{6-4x}{x} < 0$$

factors = 0: $x = \frac{3}{2}$, $x = 0$

intervals: $(-\infty, 0)$, $(0, \frac{3}{2})$, $(\frac{3}{2}, \infty)$

interval	test number	sign of $\frac{6-4x}{x}$
$(-\infty, 0)$	-1	$-$
$(0, \frac{3}{2})$	1	$+$
$(\frac{3}{2}, \infty)$	2	$-$

Solution: $(-\infty, 0) \cup (\frac{3}{2}, \infty)$

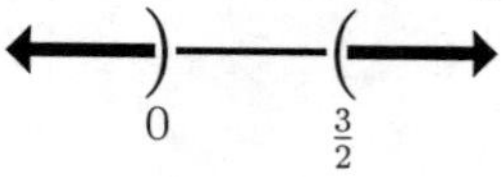

76.

$$\frac{6}{x} > 4$$
$$\frac{6}{x} - 4 > 0$$
$$\frac{6-4x}{x} > 0$$

factors = 0: $x = \frac{3}{2}$, $x = 0$

intervals: $(-\infty, 0)$, $(0, \frac{3}{2})$, $(\frac{3}{2}, \infty)$

interval	test number	sign of $\frac{6-4x}{x}$
$(-\infty, 0)$	-1	$-$
$(0, \frac{3}{2})$	1	$+$
$(\frac{3}{2}, \infty)$	2	$-$

Solution: $(0, \frac{3}{2})$

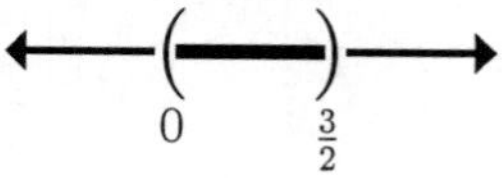

77.

$$\frac{3}{x-2} \le 5$$
$$\frac{3}{x-2} - 5 \le 0$$
$$\frac{3}{x-2} - \frac{5(x-2)}{x-2} \le 0$$
$$\frac{3-5x+10}{x-2} \le 0$$
$$\frac{13-5x}{x-2} \le 0$$

factors = 0: $x = \frac{13}{5}$, $x = 2$

intervals: $(-\infty, 2)$, $(2, \frac{13}{5})$, $(\frac{13}{5}, \infty)$

interval	test number	sign of $\frac{13-5x}{x-2}$
$(-\infty, 2)$	0	$-$
$(2, \frac{13}{5})$	$\frac{11}{5}$	$+$
$(\frac{13}{5}, \infty)$	3	$-$

Solution: $(-\infty, 2) \cup [\frac{13}{5}, \infty)$

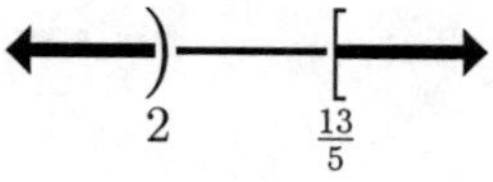

Include endpoints which make the numerator equal to 0. Do not include endpoints which make the denominator equal to 0.

78.
$$\frac{3}{x+2} \le 4$$
$$\frac{3}{x+2} - 4 \le 0$$
$$\frac{3}{x+2} - \frac{4(x+2)}{x+2} \le 0$$
$$\frac{3 - 4x - 8}{x+2} \le 0$$
$$\frac{-4x - 5}{x+2} \le 0$$

factors $= 0$: $x = -2, x = -\frac{5}{4}$

intervals: $(-\infty, -2)$, $\left(-2, -\frac{5}{4}\right)$, $\left(-\frac{5}{4}, \infty\right)$

interval	test number	sign of $\frac{-4x-5}{x+2}$
$(-\infty, -2)$	-3	$-$
$\left(-2, -\frac{5}{4}\right)$	$-\frac{7}{4}$	$+$
$\left(-\frac{5}{4}, \infty\right)$	0	$-$

Solution: $(-\infty, -2) \cup \left[-\frac{5}{4}, \infty\right)$

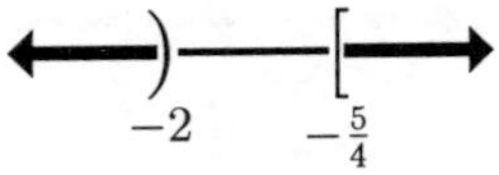

Include endpoints which make the the numerator equal to 0. Do not include endpoints which make the denominator equal to 0.

79.
$$\frac{6}{x^2-1} < 1$$
$$\frac{6}{x^2-1} - 1 < 0$$
$$\frac{6}{x^2-1} - \frac{x^2-1}{x^2-1} < 0$$
$$\frac{7-x^2}{x^2-1} < 0$$
$$\frac{7-x^2}{(x+1)(x-1)} < 0$$

factors $= 0$: $x = \pm\sqrt{7}, x = \pm 1$

intervals: $\left(-\infty, -\sqrt{7}\right)$, $\left(-\sqrt{7}, -1\right)$, $(-1, 1)$, $\left(1, \sqrt{7}\right)$, $\left(\sqrt{7}, \infty\right)$

interval	test number	sign of $\frac{7-x^2}{x^2-1}$
$\left(-\infty, -\sqrt{7}\right)$	-3	$-$
$\left(-\sqrt{7}, -1\right)$	-2	$+$
$(-1, 1)$	0	$-$
$\left(1, \sqrt{7}\right)$	2	$+$
$\left(\sqrt{7}, \infty\right)$	3	$-$

Sol'n: $\left(-\infty, -\sqrt{7}\right) \cup (-1, 1) \cup \left(\sqrt{7}, \infty\right)$

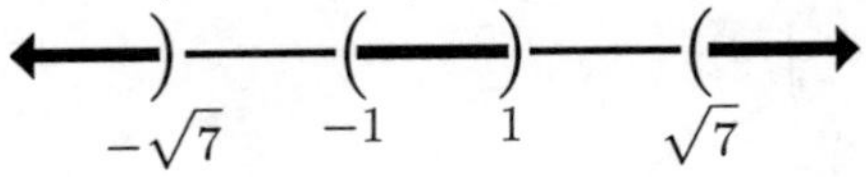

80.
$$\frac{6}{x^2-1} > 1$$
$$\frac{6}{x^2-1} - 1 > 0$$
$$\frac{6}{x^2-1} - \frac{x^2-1}{x^2-1} > 0$$
$$\frac{7-x^2}{x^2-1} > 0$$
$$\frac{7-x^2}{(x+1)(x-1)} > 0$$

factors $= 0$: $x = \pm\sqrt{7}, x = \pm 1$

intervals: $\left(-\infty, -\sqrt{7}\right)$, $\left(-\sqrt{7}, -1\right)$, $(-1, 1)$, $\left(1, \sqrt{7}\right)$, $\left(\sqrt{7}, \infty\right)$

interval	test number	sign of $\frac{7-x^2}{x^2-1}$
$\left(-\infty, -\sqrt{7}\right)$	-3	$-$
$\left(-\sqrt{7}, -1\right)$	-2	$+$
$(-1, 1)$	0	$-$
$\left(1, \sqrt{7}\right)$	2	$+$
$\left(\sqrt{7}, \infty\right)$	3	$-$

Sol'n: $\left(-\sqrt{7}, -1\right) \cup \left(1, \sqrt{7}\right)$

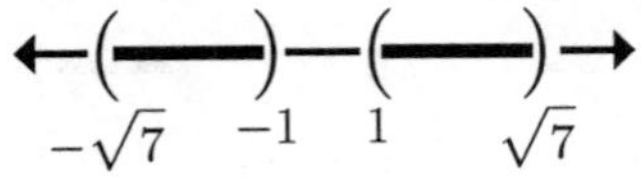

81. Let $x =$ the number of minutes after 3 minutes. The total cost $= 36 + 11x$ cents.

$$\boxed{\text{Total cost}} < 200$$
$$36 + 11x < 200$$
$$11x < 164$$
$$x < 14.9$$

A person can talk for up to 14 minutes after the initial 3 minutes, for a total of up to 17 minutes for less than \$2.

82. Let $x =$ the number of games. Then the total cost $= 1695.95 + 19.95x$.

$$\boxed{\text{Total cost}} < 2000$$
$$1695.95 + 19.95x < 2000$$
$$19.95x < 304.05$$
$$x < 15.2$$

She can buy up to 15 games.

83. Let $x =$ the number of CDs. Then the total cost $= 150 + 9.75x$.

$$\boxed{\text{Total cost}} < 275$$
$$150 + 9.75x < 275$$
$$9.75x < 125$$
$$x < 12.8$$

He can buy up to 12 disks.

84. Let $x =$ the number of disks. Then the total cost $= 425 + 7.50x$.

$$\boxed{\text{Total cost}} < 600$$
$$425 + 7.50x < 600$$
$$7.50x < 175$$
$$x < 23.3$$

She can buy up to 23 disks.

85. Let $p =$ the price of the refrigerator. Then the total cost $= p + 0.065p + 0.0025p$.

$$\boxed{\text{Total cost}} < 1200$$
$$p + 0.065p + 0.0025p < 1200$$
$$1.0675p < 1200$$
$$p < 1124.122$$
$$p \leq \$1124.12$$

86. Let $x =$ the number of hours after the first. Then the total cost $= 17.50 + 8.95x$.

$$\boxed{\text{Total cost}} < 75$$
$$17.50 + 8.95x < 75$$
$$8.95x < 57.50$$
$$x < 6.4$$

A person could have the rototiller for up to 6 hours after the first hour, for a total of up to 7 hours.

87. Let $a =$ the assessed value. Find when Method 1 < Method 2:

$$2200 + 0.04a < 1200 + 0.06a$$
$$1000 < 0.02a$$
$$50000 < a$$

The first method will benefit the taxpayer when $a >$ \$50,000.

88. Let $P =$ the perimeter. Then the length is equal to $\dfrac{P - 2w}{2}$, or $\dfrac{P - 80}{2}$.

$$180 < P < 200$$
$$180 - 80 < P - 80 < 200 - 80$$
$$100 < P - 80 < 120$$
$$\frac{100}{2} < \frac{P-80}{2} < \frac{120}{2}$$
$$50 < \text{length} < 60$$

The length is between 50 and 60 inches.

89. Let $P =$ the perimeter. Then the length of one side is equal to $\frac{P}{3}$.

$$\begin{aligned} 50 &< P < 60 \\ \tfrac{50}{3} &< \tfrac{P}{3} < \tfrac{60}{3} \\ 16\tfrac{2}{3} &< \text{length} < 20 \end{aligned}$$

The length of a side is between $16\frac{2}{3}$ and 20 cm.

90. Let $P =$ the perimeter. Then the length of one side is equal to $\frac{P}{4}$, so the area is equal to

$$A = s^2 = \left(\frac{P}{4}\right)^2$$

$$\begin{aligned} 25 &< P < 60 \\ \tfrac{25}{4} &< \tfrac{P}{4} < \tfrac{60}{4} \\ \left(\tfrac{25}{4}\right)^2 &< \left(\tfrac{P}{4}\right)^2 < 15^2 \\ \tfrac{625}{16} &< \text{Area} < 225 \end{aligned}$$

The area is between $\frac{625}{16}$ m^2 and 225 m^2.

91.
$$\begin{aligned} 20 &< l < 30 \\ 40 &< 2l < 60 \\ 40 + 2w &< 2l + 2w < 60 + 2w \\ 40 + 2w &< P < 60 + 2w \end{aligned}$$

92.
$$\begin{aligned} 10 &< C < 20 \\ \tfrac{9}{5}(10) &< \tfrac{9}{5}C < \tfrac{9}{5}(20) \\ 18 + 32 &< \tfrac{9}{5}C + 32 < 36 + 32 \\ 50 &< F < 68 \end{aligned}$$

93. **Answers may vary.**

94. **Answers may vary.**

95. even integers: $-2, 2$

96. natural numbers: 1, 2

97. prime numbers: 2

98. irrational numbers: $-\pi, \sqrt{7}$

99. real numbers: all in the list

100. rational numbers: $-9, -2, -\frac{1}{2}, 0, 1, 2, \frac{21}{2}$

Exercise 1.8 (page 148)

1. x

2. $-x$

3. $x = k$ or $x = -k$

4. $a = -b$

5. $-k < x < k$

6. $x < -k$ or $x > k$

7. $x \le -k$ or $x \ge k$

8. $|a|$

9. $|7| = 7$

10. $|-9| = 9$

11. $|0| = 0$

12. $|3 - 5| = |-2| = 2$

13. $|5| - |-3| = 5 - 3 = 2$

14. $|-3| + |5| = 3 + 5 = 8$

15. $|\pi - 2| = +(\pi - 2) = \pi - 2$

16. $|\pi - 4| = -(\pi - 4) = 4 - \pi$

17. $x > 5 \Rightarrow |x - 5| = x - 5$

18. $x < 5 \Rightarrow |x - 5| = -(x - 5) = 5 - x$

19. $|x^3| = \begin{cases} x^3 & \text{if } x \ge 0 \\ -x^3 & \text{if } x < 0 \end{cases}$

20. $|2x| = \begin{cases} 2x & \text{if } x \ge 0 \\ -2x & \text{if } x < 0 \end{cases}$

21.
$$|x + 2| = 2$$
$$\begin{aligned} x + 2 &= 2 \quad \textbf{or} \quad & x + 2 &= -2 \\ x &= 0 & x &= -4 \end{aligned}$$

22.
$$|2x + 5| = 3$$
$$\begin{aligned} 2x + 5 &= 3 \quad \textbf{or} \quad & 2x + 5 &= -3 \\ 2x &= -2 & 2x &= -8 \\ x &= -1 & x &= -4 \end{aligned}$$

23. $|3x-1|=5$

$3x-1=5$ **or** $3x-1=-5$

$3x=6$ $\quad$ $3x=-4$

$x=2$ $\quad$ $x=-\frac{4}{3}$

24. $|7x-5|=3$

$7x-5=3$ **or** $7x-5=-3$

$7x=8$ $\quad$ $7x=2$

$x=\frac{8}{7}$ $\quad$ $x=\frac{2}{7}$

25. $\left|\frac{3x-4}{2}\right|=5$

$\frac{3x-4}{2}=5$ **or** $\frac{3x-4}{2}=-5$

$3x-4=10$ $\quad$ $3x-4=-10$

$3x=14$ $\quad$ $3x=-6$

$x=\frac{14}{3}$ $\quad$ $x=-2$

26. $\left|\frac{10x+1}{2}\right|=\frac{9}{2}$

$\frac{10x+1}{2}=\frac{9}{2}$ **or** $\frac{10x+1}{2}=-\frac{9}{2}$

$10x+1=9$ $\quad$ $10x+1=-9$

$10x=8$ $\quad$ $10x=-10$

$x=\frac{8}{10}=\frac{4}{5}$ $\quad$ $x=-1$

27. $\left|\frac{2x-4}{5}\right|=2$

$\frac{2x-4}{5}=2$ **or** $\frac{2x-4}{5}=-2$

$2x-4=10$ $\quad$ $2x-4=-10$

$2x=14$ $\quad$ $2x=-6$

$x=7$ $\quad$ $x=-3$

28. $\left|\frac{3x+11}{7}\right|=1$

$\frac{3x+11}{7}=1$ **or** $\frac{3x+11}{7}=-1$

$3x+11=7$ $\quad$ $3x+11=-7$

$3x=-4$ $\quad$ $3x=-18$

$x=-\frac{4}{3}$ $\quad$ $x=-6$

29. $\left|\frac{x-3}{4}\right|=-2$

An absolute value can never equal a negative number.

no solution

30. $\left|\frac{x-5}{3}\right|=0$

$\frac{x-5}{3}=0$ **or** $\frac{x-5}{3}=-0$

$x-5=0$ $\quad$ $x-5=0$

$x=5$ $\quad$ $x=5$

31. $\left|\frac{4x-2}{x}\right|=3$

$\frac{4x-2}{x}=3$ **or** $\frac{4x-2}{x}=-3$

$4x-2=3x$ $\quad$ $4x-2=-3x$

$x=2$ $\quad$ $7x=2$

$x=2$ $\quad$ $x=\frac{2}{7}$

32. $\left|\frac{2(x-3)}{3x}\right|=6$

$\frac{2x-6}{3x}=6$ **or** $\frac{2x-6}{3x}=-6$

$2x-6=18x$ $\quad$ $2x-6=-18x$

$-16x=6$ $\quad$ $20x=6$

$x=-\frac{3}{8}$ $\quad$ $x=\frac{3}{10}$

33. $|x|=x$

True for all $x\geq 0$.

34. $|x|+x=2$

$|x|=-x+2$

$x=-x+2$ **or** $x=-(-x+2)$

$2x=2$ $\quad$ $x=x-2$

$x=1$ $\quad$ $0=-2\Rightarrow$ not true

35.

$$|x+3| = |x|$$

$x+3 = x$ **or** $x+3 = -x$

$0 = 3$ $\quad 2x = -3$

not true $\quad x = -\frac{3}{2}$

36.

$$|x+5| = |5-x|$$

$x+5 = 5-x$ **or** $x+5 = -(5-x)$

$2x = 0$ $\quad x+5 = -5+x$

$x = 0$ $\quad 0 = -10$

not true

37.

$$|x-3| = |2x+3|$$

$x-3 = 2x+3$ **or** $x-3 = -(2x+3)$

$-x = 6$ $\quad x-3 = -2x-3$

$x = -6$ $\quad 3x = 0$

$x = 0$

38.

$$|x-2| = |3x+8|$$

$x-2 = 3x+8$ **or** $x-2 = -(3x+8)$

$-2x = 10$ $\quad x-2 = -3x-8$

$x = -5$ $\quad 4x = -6$

$x = -\frac{3}{2}$

39.

$$|x+2| = |x-2|$$

$x+2 = x-2$ **or** $x+2 = -(x-2)$

$0 = -4$ $\quad x+2 = -x+2$

not true $\quad 2x = 0$

$x = 0$

40.

$$|2x-3| = |3x-5|$$

$2x-3 = 3x-5$ **or** $2x-3 = -(3x-5)$

$-x = -2$ $\quad 2x-3 = -3x+5$

$x = 2$ $\quad 5x = 8$

$x = \frac{8}{5}$

41.

$$\left|\frac{x+3}{2}\right| = |2x-3|$$

$\frac{x+3}{2} = 2x-3$ **or** $\frac{x+3}{2} = -(2x-3)$

$x+3 = 4x-6$ $\quad \frac{x+3}{2} = -2x+3$

$-3x = -9$ $\quad x+3 = -4x+6$

$x = 3$ $\quad 5x = 3$

$x = \frac{3}{5}$

42.

$$\left|\frac{x-2}{3}\right| = |6-x|$$

$\frac{x-2}{3} = 6-x$ **or** $\frac{x-2}{3} = -(6-x)$

$\frac{x-2}{3} = 6-x$ $\quad \frac{x-2}{3} = -6+x$

$x-2 = 18-3x$ $\quad x-2 = -18+3x$

$4x = 20$ $\quad -2x = -16$

$x = 5$ $\quad x = 8$

43.

$$\left|\frac{3x-1}{2}\right| = \left|\frac{2x+3}{3}\right|$$

$\frac{3x-1}{2} = \frac{2x+3}{3}$ **or** $\frac{3x-1}{2} = -\frac{2x+3}{3}$

$6\left(\frac{3x-1}{2} = \frac{2x+3}{3}\right)$ $\quad 6\left(\frac{3x-1}{2} = -\frac{2x+3}{3}\right)$

$3(3x-1) = 2(2x+3)$ $\quad 3(3x-1) = -2(2x+3)$

$9x-3 = 4x+6$ $\quad 9x-3 = -4x-6$

$5x = 9$ $\quad 13x = -3$

$x = \frac{9}{5}$ $\quad x = -\frac{3}{13}$

44.

$$\left|\frac{5x+2}{3}\right| = \left|\frac{x-1}{4}\right|$$

$$\frac{5x+2}{3} = \frac{x-1}{4} \quad \textbf{or} \quad \frac{5x+2}{3} = -\frac{x-1}{4}$$

$$12\left(\frac{5x+2}{3} = \frac{x-1}{4}\right) \qquad 12\left(\frac{5x+2}{3} = -\frac{x-1}{4}\right)$$

$$4(5x+2) = 3(x-1) \qquad 4(5x+2) = -3(x-1)$$

$$20x+8 = 3x-3 \qquad 20x+8 = -3x+3$$

$$17x = -11 \qquad 23x = -5$$

$$x = -\tfrac{11}{17} \qquad x = -\tfrac{5}{23}$$

45.

$$|x-3| < 6$$

$$-6 < x-3 < 6$$

$$-3 < \quad x \quad < 9$$

$$(-3, 9)$$

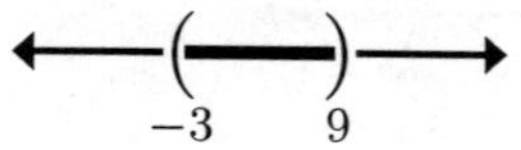

46.

$$|x-2| \geq 4$$

$$x-2 \geq 4 \quad \textbf{or} \quad x-2 \leq -4$$

$$x \geq 6 \qquad x \leq -2$$

$$(-\infty, -2] \cup [6, \infty)$$

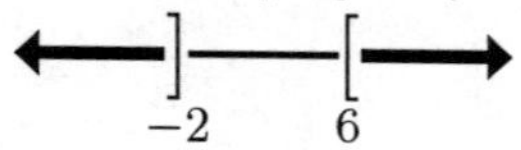

47.

$$|x+3| > 6$$

$$x+3 > 6 \quad \textbf{or} \quad x+3 < -6$$

$$x > 3 \qquad x < -9$$

$$(-\infty, -9) \cup (3, \infty)$$

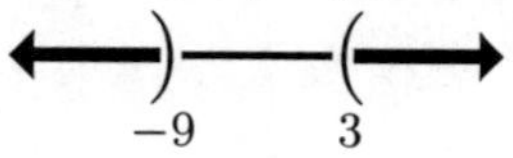

48.

$$|x+2| \leq 4$$

$$-4 \leq x+2 \leq 4$$

$$-6 \leq \quad x \quad \leq 2$$

$$[-6, 2]$$

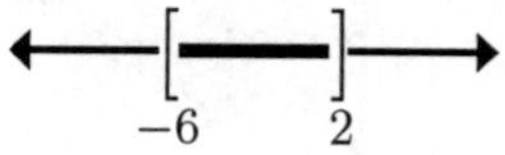

49.

$$|2x+4| \geq 10$$

$$2x+4 \geq 10 \quad \textbf{or} \quad 2x+4 \leq -10$$

$$2x \geq 6 \qquad 2x \leq -14$$

$$x \geq 3 \qquad x \leq -7$$

$$(-\infty, -7] \cup [3, \infty)$$

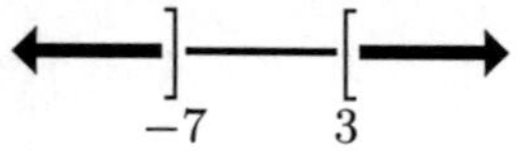

50.

$$|5x-2| < 7$$

$$-7 < 5x-2 < 7$$

$$-5 < \quad 5x \quad < 9$$

$$-1 < \quad x \quad < \tfrac{9}{5}$$

$$\left(-1, \tfrac{9}{5}\right)$$

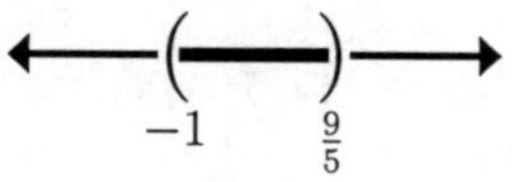

51.

$$|3x+5| + 1 \leq 9$$

$$|3x+5| \leq 8$$

$$-8 \leq 3x+5 \leq 8$$

$$-13 \leq \quad 3x \quad \leq 3$$

$$-\tfrac{13}{3} \leq \quad x \quad \leq 1$$

$$\left[-\tfrac{13}{3}, 1\right]$$

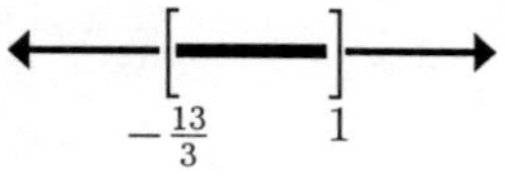

52.

$$|2x-7| - 3 > 2$$

$$|2x-7| > 5$$

$$2x-7 > 5 \quad \textbf{or} \quad 2x-7 < -5$$

$$2x > 12 \qquad 2x < 2$$

$$x > 6 \qquad x < 1$$

$$(-\infty, 1) \cup (6, \infty)$$

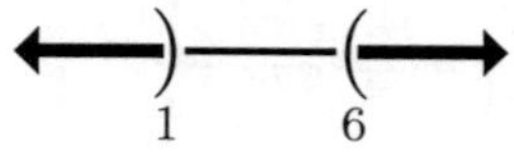

53.

$$|x+3| > 0$$
$$x+3>0 \quad \textbf{or} \quad x+3<-0$$
$$x>-3 \qquad\qquad x<-3$$
$$(-\infty,-3)\cup(-3,\infty)$$

-3

54.

$$|x-3| \le 0$$
$$-0 \le x-3 \le 0$$
$$3 \le x \le 3$$
$$[3, 3]$$

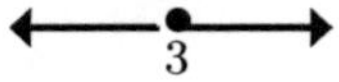

3

55.

$$\left|\tfrac{5x+2}{3}\right| < 1$$
$$-1 < \tfrac{5x+2}{3} < 1$$
$$-3 < 5x+2 < 3$$
$$-5 < 5x < 1$$
$$-1 < x < \tfrac{1}{5}$$
$$\left(-1, \tfrac{1}{5}\right)$$

-1 $\quad \frac{1}{5}$

56.

$$\left|\tfrac{3x+2}{4}\right| > 2$$
$$\tfrac{3x+2}{4} > 2 \quad \textbf{or} \quad \tfrac{3x+2}{4} < -2$$
$$3x+2>8 \qquad 3x+2<-8$$
$$3x>6 \qquad 3x<-10$$
$$x>2 \qquad x<-\tfrac{10}{3}$$
$$\left(-\infty,-\tfrac{10}{3}\right)\cup(2,\infty)$$

$-\frac{10}{3}$ $\quad 2$

57.

$$3\left|\tfrac{3x-1}{2}\right| > 5$$
$$\left|\tfrac{3x-1}{2}\right| > \tfrac{5}{3}$$
$$\tfrac{3x-1}{2} > \tfrac{5}{3} \quad \textbf{or} \quad \tfrac{3x-1}{2} < -\tfrac{5}{3}$$
$$6\cdot\tfrac{3x-1}{2} > 6\cdot\tfrac{5}{3} \qquad 6\cdot\tfrac{3x-1}{2} < 6\left(-\tfrac{5}{3}\right)$$
$$9x-3>10 \qquad 9x-3<-10$$
$$9x>13 \qquad 9x<-7$$
$$x>\tfrac{13}{9} \qquad x<-\tfrac{7}{9}$$
$$\left(-\infty,-\tfrac{7}{9}\right)\cup\left(\tfrac{13}{9},\infty\right)$$

$-\frac{7}{9}$ $\quad \frac{13}{9}$

58.

$$2\left|\tfrac{8x+2}{5}\right| \le 1$$
$$\left|\tfrac{8x+2}{5}\right| \le \tfrac{1}{2}$$
$$-\frac{1}{2} \le \frac{8x+2}{5} \le \frac{1}{2}$$
$$10\left(-\frac{1}{2}\right) \le 10\cdot\frac{8x+2}{5} \le 10\cdot\frac{1}{2}$$
$$-5 \le 16x+4 \le 5$$
$$-9 \le 16x \le 1$$
$$-\tfrac{9}{16} \le x \le \tfrac{1}{16}$$
$$\left[-\tfrac{9}{16}, \tfrac{1}{16}\right]$$

$-\frac{9}{16}$ $\quad \frac{1}{16}$

59.

$$\frac{|x-1|}{-2} > -3$$
$$|x-1| < 6$$
$$-6 < x-1 < 6$$
$$-5 < \quad x \quad < 7$$
$$(-5, 7)$$

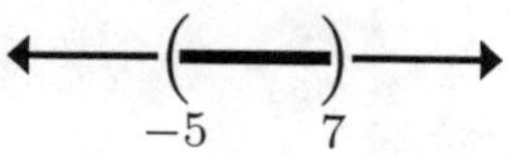

60.

$$\frac{|2x-3|}{-3} < -1$$
$$|2x-3| > 3$$
$$2x-3 > 3 \quad \textbf{or} \quad 2x-3 < -3$$
$$2x > 6 \qquad\qquad 2x < 0$$
$$x > 3 \qquad\qquad x < 0$$
$$(-\infty, 0) \cup (3, \infty)$$

61.

$$0 < |2x+1| < 3$$

$0 < |2x+1|$ **and** $|2x+1| < 3$

(1) $|2x+1| > 0$

$$2x+1 > 0 \quad \textbf{or} \quad 2x+1 < -0$$
$$2x > -1 \qquad\qquad 2x < -1$$
$$x > -\tfrac{1}{2} \qquad\qquad x < -\tfrac{1}{2}$$

(2) $|2x+1| < 3$

$$-3 < 2x+1 < 3$$
$$-4 < \quad 2x \quad < 2$$
$$-2 < \quad x \quad < 1$$

(1) 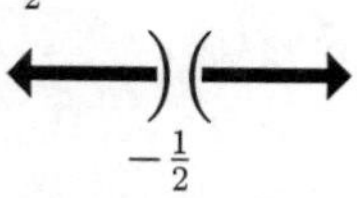

(2) 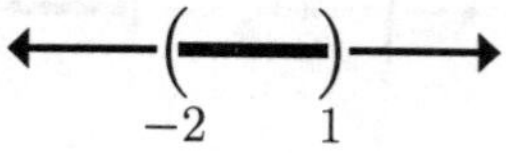

(1) 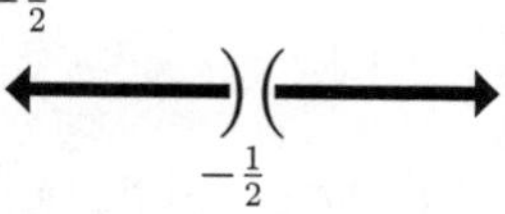

(2) 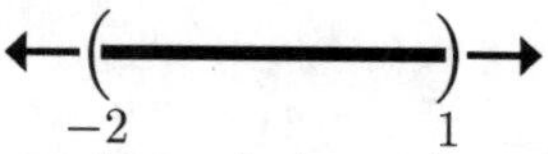

(1) and (2) 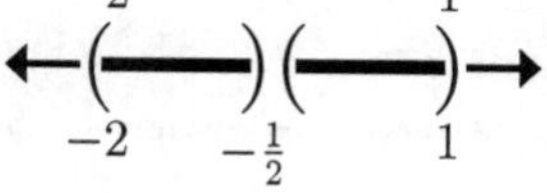

$\Rightarrow (-2, -\frac{1}{2}) \cup (-\frac{1}{2}, 1)$

62.

$$0 < |2x-3| < 1$$

$0 < |2x-3|$ **and** $|2x-3| < 1$

(1) $|2x-3| > 0$

$$2x-3 > 0 \quad \textbf{or} \quad 2x-3 < -0$$
$$2x > 3 \qquad\qquad 2x < 3$$
$$x > \tfrac{3}{2} \qquad\qquad x < \tfrac{3}{2}$$

(2) $|2x-3| < 1$

$$-1 < 2x-3 < 1$$
$$2 < \quad 2x \quad < 4$$
$$1 < \quad x \quad < 2$$

(1) 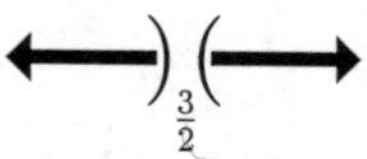

(2) 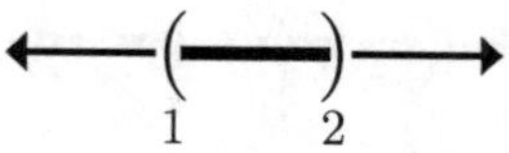

(1) 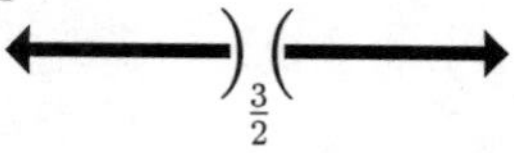

(2) 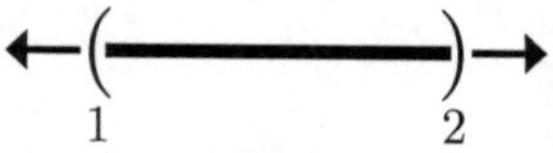

(1) and (2) 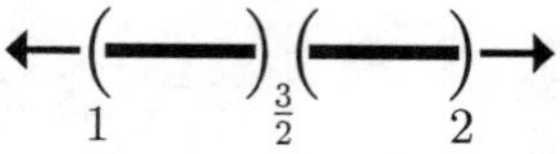

$\Rightarrow (1, \frac{3}{2}) \cup (\frac{3}{2}, 2)$

63. $$8 > |3x-1| > 3$$

$|3x-1| > 3$ **and** $8 > |3x-1|$

(1) $|3x-1| > 3$

$3x-1>3$ **or** $3x-1<-3$

$3x>4$ $\qquad$ $3x<-2$

$x>\frac{4}{3}$ $\qquad$ $x<-\frac{2}{3}$

(2) $|3x-1| < 8$

$-8 < 3x-1 < 8$

$-7 < 3x < 9$

$-\frac{7}{3} < x < 3$

(1) 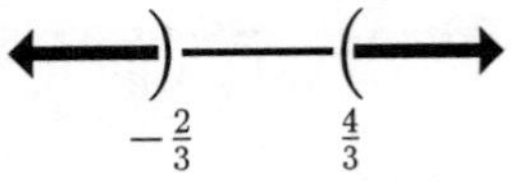

(2) 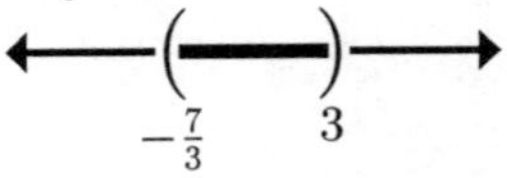

(1) 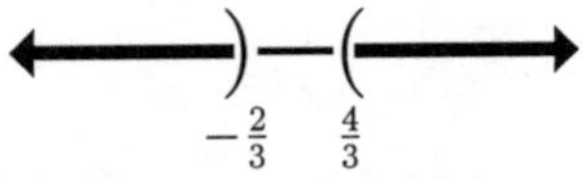

(2) 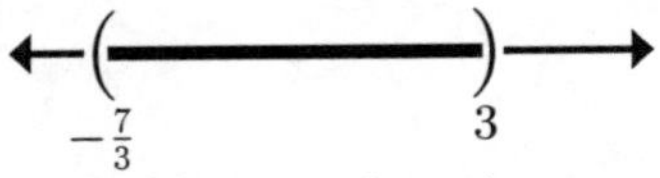

(1) and (2) 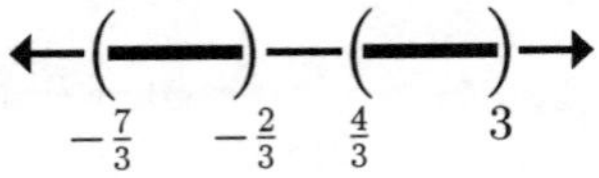

$\Rightarrow \left(-\frac{7}{3}, -\frac{2}{3}\right) \cup \left(\frac{4}{3}, 3\right)$

64. $$8 > |4x-1| > 5$$

$|4x-1| > 5$ **and** $8 > |4x-1|$

(1) $|4x-1| > 5$

$4x-1>5$ **or** $4x-1<-5$

$4x>6$ $\qquad$ $4x<-4$

$x>\frac{3}{2}$ $\qquad$ $x<-1$

(2) $|4x-1| < 8$

$-8 < 4x-1 < 8$

$-7 < 4x < 9$

$-\frac{7}{4} < x < \frac{9}{4}$

(1) 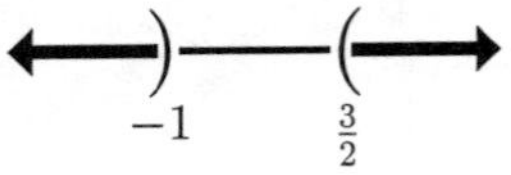

(2) 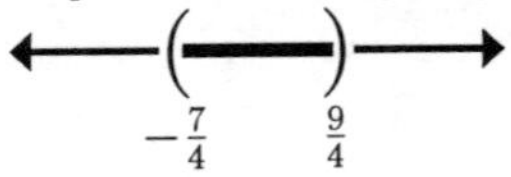

(1) 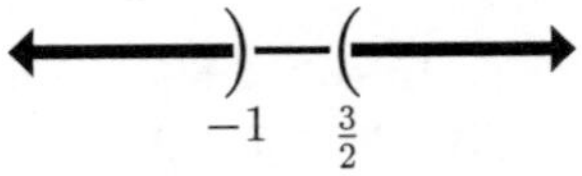

(2) 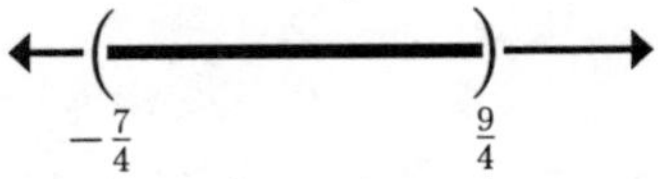

(1) and (2) 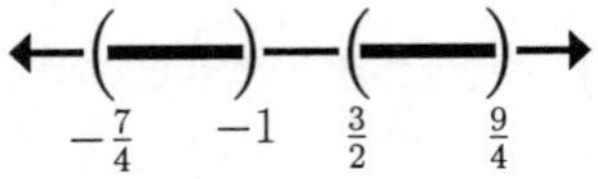

$\Rightarrow \left(-\frac{7}{4}, -1\right) \cup \left(\frac{3}{2}, \frac{9}{4}\right)$

65.

$$2 < \left|\frac{x-5}{3}\right| < 4$$

$2 < \left|\frac{x-5}{3}\right|$ **and** $\left|\frac{x-5}{3}\right| < 4$

(1) $\left|\frac{x-5}{3}\right| > 2$

$\frac{x-5}{3} > 2$ **or** $\frac{x-5}{3} < -2$

$x - 5 > 6$ $\quad$ $x - 5 < -6$

$x > 11$ $\quad$ $x < -1$

(1) 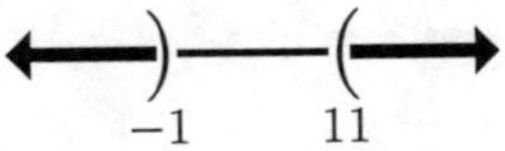

(2) $\left|\frac{x-5}{3}\right| < 4$

$-4 < \frac{x-5}{3} < 4$

$-12 < x - 5 < 12$

$-7 < x < 17$

(2) 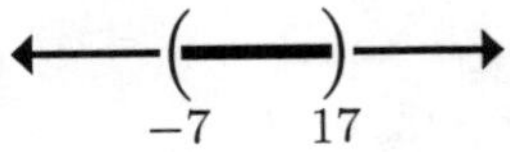

(1) 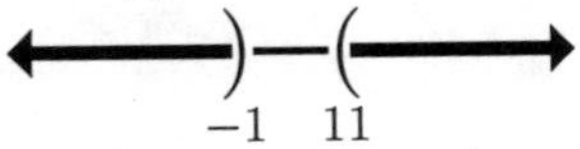

(2) 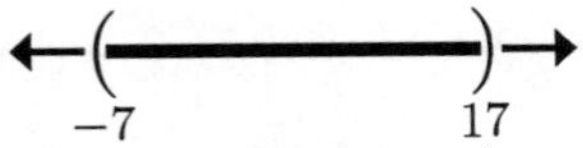

(1) and (2) 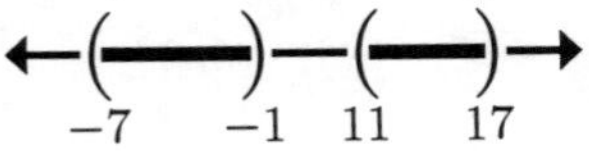

$\Rightarrow (-7, -1) \cup (11, 17)$

66.

$$3 < \left|\frac{x-3}{2}\right| < 5$$

$3 < \left|\frac{x-3}{2}\right|$ **and** $\left|\frac{x-3}{2}\right| < 5$

(1) $\left|\frac{x-3}{2}\right| > 3$

$\frac{x-3}{2} > 3$ **or** $\frac{x-3}{2} < -3$

$x - 3 > 6$ $\quad$ $x - 3 < -6$

$x > 9$ $\quad$ $x < -3$

(1) 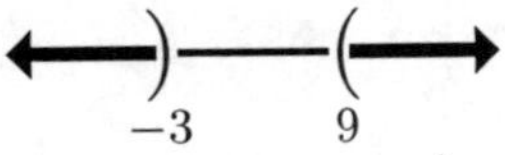

(2) $\left|\frac{x-3}{2}\right| < 5$

$-5 < \frac{x-3}{2} < 5$

$-10 < x - 3 < 10$

$-7 < x < 13$

(2) 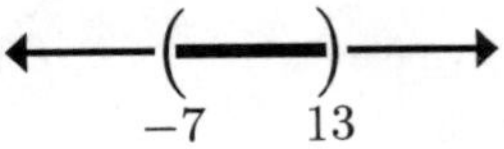

(1) 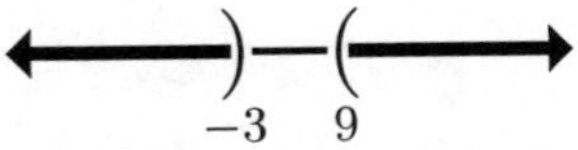

(2) 

(1) and (2) 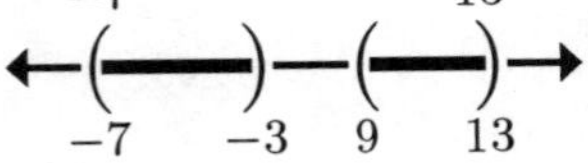

$\Rightarrow (-7, -3) \cup (9, 13)$

67.

$$10 > \left|\frac{x-2}{2}\right| > 4$$

$$\left|\frac{x-2}{2}\right| > 4 \quad \textbf{and} \quad 10 > \left|\frac{x-2}{2}\right|$$

(1) $\left|\frac{x-2}{2}\right| > 4$ **(2)** $\left|\frac{x-2}{2}\right| < 10$

$$\frac{x-2}{2} > 4 \quad \textbf{or} \quad \frac{x-2}{2} < -4 \qquad -10 < \frac{x-2}{2} < 10$$

$$x - 2 > 8 \qquad x - 2 < -8 \qquad -20 < x - 2 < 20$$

$$x > 10 \qquad x < -6 \qquad -18 < x < 22$$

(1) 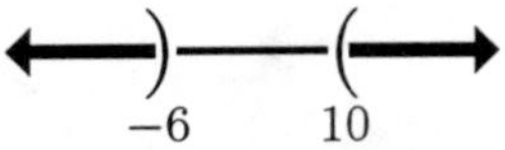

(2) 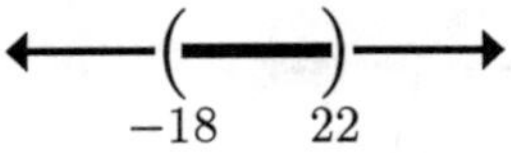

(1) 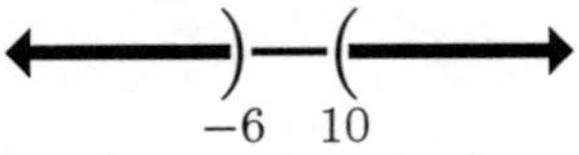

(2) 

(1) and (2) 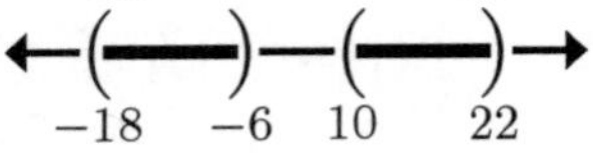

$\Rightarrow (-18, -6) \cup (10, 22)$

68.

$$5 \geq \left|\frac{x+2}{3}\right| > 1$$

$$\left|\frac{x+2}{3}\right| > 1 \quad \textbf{and} \quad 5 \geq \left|\frac{x+2}{3}\right|$$

(1) $\left|\frac{x+2}{3}\right| > 1$ **(2)** $\left|\frac{x+2}{3}\right| \leq 5$

$$\frac{x+2}{3} > 1 \quad \textbf{or} \quad \frac{x+2}{3} < -1 \qquad -5 \leq \frac{x+2}{3} \leq 5$$

$$x + 2 > 3 \qquad x + 2 < -3 \qquad -15 \leq x + 2 \leq 15$$

$$x > 1 \qquad x < -5 \qquad -17 \leq x \leq 13$$

(1) 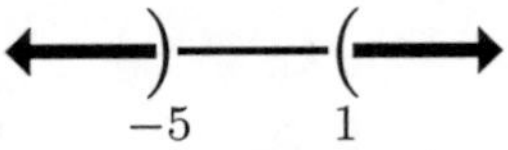

(2) 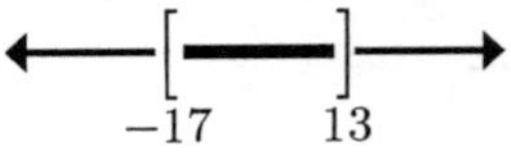

(1) 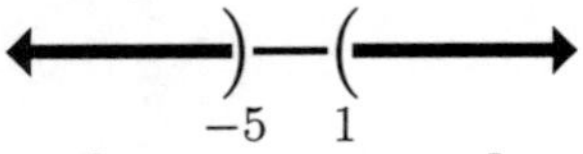

(2) 

(1) and (2) 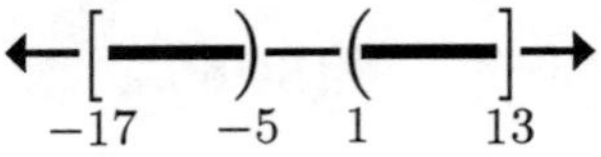

$\Rightarrow [-17, -5) \cup (1, 13]$

69.

$$2 \le \left|\frac{x+1}{3}\right| < 3$$

$$2 \le \left|\frac{x+1}{3}\right| \quad \textbf{and} \quad \left|\frac{x+1}{3}\right| < 3$$

(1) $\left|\frac{x+1}{3}\right| \ge 2$ **(2)** $\left|\frac{x+1}{3}\right| < 3$

$\frac{x+1}{3} \ge 2$ **or** $\frac{x+1}{3} \le -2$

$x+1 \ge 6$ $\quad x+1 \le -6$

$x \ge 5$ $\quad x \le -7$

$-3 < \frac{x+1}{3} < 3$

$-9 < x+1 < 9$

$-10 < x < 8$

(1) 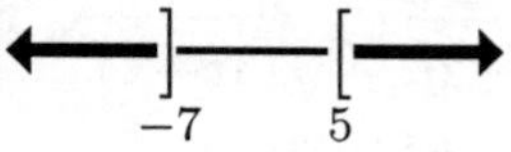

(2) 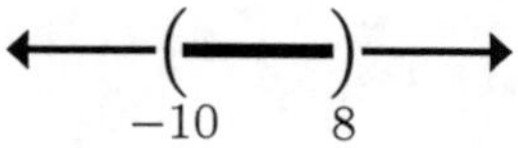

(1) 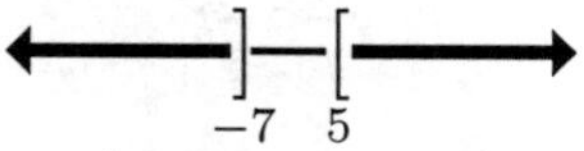

(2) 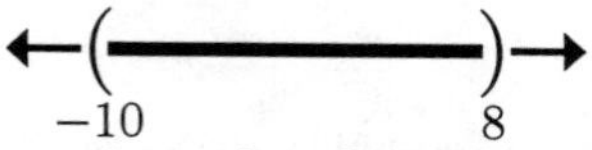

(1) and (2) 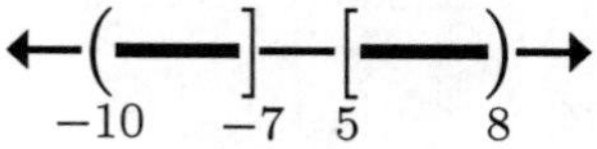

$\Rightarrow (-10, -7] \cup [5, 8)$

70.

$$8 > \left|\frac{3x+1}{2}\right| > 2$$

$$\left|\frac{3x+1}{2}\right| > 2 \quad \textbf{and} \quad 8 > \left|\frac{3x+1}{2}\right|$$

(1) $\left|\frac{3x+1}{2}\right| > 2$ **(2)** $\left|\frac{3x+1}{2}\right| < 8$

$\frac{3x+1}{2} > 2$ **or** $\frac{3x+1}{2} < -2$

$3x+1 > 4$ $\quad 3x+1 < -4$

$3x > 3$ $\quad 3x < -5$

$x > 1$ $\quad x < -\frac{5}{3}$

$-8 < \frac{3x+1}{2} < 8$

$-16 < 3x+1 < 16$

$-17 < 3x < 15$

$-\frac{17}{3} < x < 5$

(1) 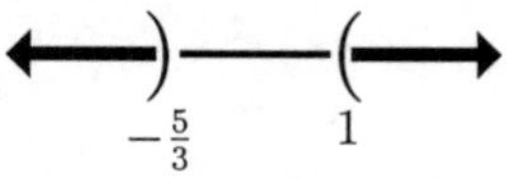

(2) 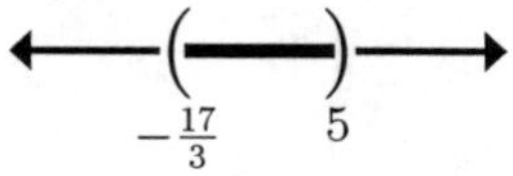

(1) 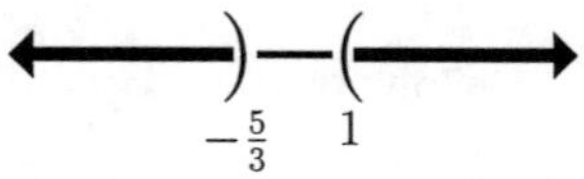

(2) 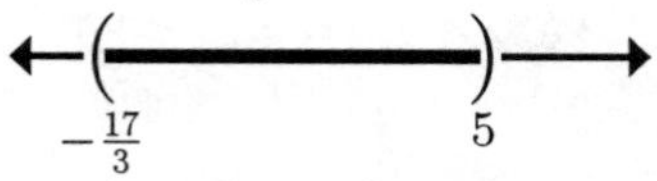

(1) and (2) 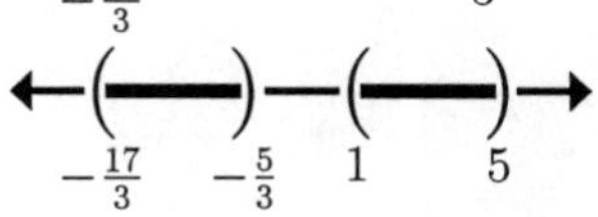

$\Rightarrow \left(-\frac{17}{3}, -\frac{5}{3}\right) \cup (1, 5)$

71.
$$\begin{aligned} |x+1| &\geq |x| \\ \sqrt{(x+1)^2} &\geq \sqrt{x^2} \\ (x+1)^2 &\geq x^2 \\ x^2+2x+1 &\geq x^2 \\ 2x &\geq -1 \\ x &\geq -\tfrac{1}{2} \end{aligned}$$
Solution: $\left[-\frac{1}{2}, \infty\right)$

72.
$$\begin{aligned} |x+1| &< |x+2| \\ \sqrt{(x+1)^2} &< \sqrt{(x+2)^2} \\ (x+1)^2 &< (x+2)^2 \\ x^2+2x+1 &< x^2+4x+4 \\ -2x &< 3 \\ x &> -\tfrac{3}{2} \end{aligned}$$
Solution: $\left(-\frac{3}{2}, \infty\right)$

73.
$$\begin{aligned} |2x+1| &< |2x-1| \\ \sqrt{(2x+1)^2} &< \sqrt{(2x-1)^2} \\ (2x+1)^2 &< (2x-1)^2 \\ 4x^2+4x+1 &< 4x^2-4x+1 \\ 8x &< 0 \\ x &< 0 \end{aligned}$$
Solution: $(-\infty, 0)$

74.
$$\begin{aligned} |3x-2| &\geq |3x+1| \\ \sqrt{(3x-2)^2} &\geq \sqrt{(3x+1)^2} \\ (3x-2)^2 &\geq (3x+1)^2 \\ 9x^2-12x+4 &\geq 9x^2+6x+1 \\ -18x &\geq -3 \\ x &\leq \tfrac{1}{6} \end{aligned}$$
Solution: $\left(-\infty, \frac{1}{6}\right]$

75.
$$\begin{aligned} |x+1| &< |x| \\ \sqrt{(x+1)^2} &< \sqrt{x^2} \\ (x+1)^2 &< x^2 \\ x^2+2x+1 &< x^2 \\ 2x &< -1 \\ x &< -\tfrac{1}{2} \end{aligned}$$
Solution: $\left(-\infty, -\frac{1}{2}\right)$

76.
$$\begin{aligned} |x+2| &\leq |x+1| \\ \sqrt{(x+2)^2} &\leq \sqrt{(x+1)^2} \\ (x+2)^2 &\leq (x+1)^2 \\ x^2+4x+4 &\leq x^2+2x+1 \\ 2x &\leq -3 \\ x &\leq -\tfrac{3}{2} \end{aligned}$$
Solution: $\left(-\infty, -\frac{3}{2}\right]$

77.
$$\begin{aligned} |2x+1| &\geq |2x-1| \\ \sqrt{(2x+1)^2} &\geq \sqrt{(2x-1)^2} \\ (2x+1)^2 &\geq (2x-1)^2 \\ 4x^2+4x+1 &\geq 4x^2-4x+1 \\ 8x &\geq 0 \\ x &\geq 0 \end{aligned}$$
Solution: $[0, \infty)$

78.
$$\begin{aligned} |3x-2| &< |3x+1| \\ \sqrt{(3x-2)^2} &< \sqrt{(3x+1)^2} \\ (3x-2)^2 &< (3x+1)^2 \\ 9x^2-12x+4 &< 9x^2+6x+1 \\ -18x &< -3 \\ x &> \tfrac{1}{6} \end{aligned}$$
Solution: $\left(\frac{1}{6}, \infty\right)$

79.
$$\begin{aligned} |t-78^\circ| &\leq 8^\circ \\ -8^\circ \leq t-78^\circ &\leq 8^\circ \\ 70^\circ \leq t &\leq 86^\circ \end{aligned}$$

80.
$$\begin{aligned} |t-40^\circ| &\leq 80^\circ \\ -80^\circ \leq t-40^\circ &\leq 80^\circ \\ -40^\circ \leq t &\leq 120^\circ \end{aligned}$$

81.
$$\begin{aligned} 0.6° + 0.5° &= 1.1° \\ 0.6° - 0.5° &= 0.1° \end{aligned}$$
$$\begin{aligned} 0.1° \leq &\quad c \quad \leq 1.1° \\ 0.6° - 0.5° \leq &\quad c \quad \leq 0.6° + 0.5° \\ -0.5° \leq &\ c - 0.6° \leq 0.5° \\ &|c - 0.6°| \leq 0.5° \end{aligned}$$

82.
$$\begin{aligned} 0.25 + 0.015 &= 0.265 \\ 0.25 - 0.015 &= 0.235 \end{aligned}$$
$$\begin{aligned} 0.235 \leq &\quad x \quad \leq 0.265 \\ 0.25 - 0.015 \leq &\quad x \quad \leq 0.25 + 0.015 \\ -0.015 \leq &\ x - 0.25 \leq 0.015 \\ &|x - 0.25| \leq 0.015 \text{ in.} \end{aligned}$$

83.
$$\frac{38 + 72}{2} = \frac{110}{2} = 55$$
$$\begin{aligned} 38 &= 55 - 17 \\ 72 &= 55 + 17 \end{aligned}$$
$$\begin{aligned} 38 < &\quad h \quad < 72 \\ 55 - 17 < &\quad h \quad < 55 + 17 \\ -17 < &\ h - 55 < 17 \\ &|h - 55| < 17 \end{aligned}$$

84.
$$\begin{aligned} &|h - 1500| \leq 200 \\ -200 \leq &\ h - 1500 \leq 200 \\ 1300 \leq &\quad h \quad \leq 1700 \end{aligned}$$

85. **Answers may vary.**

86. $|x| + 9 = 0$

$|x| = -9$

Since the absolute value of x can never equal a negative number, the equation has no solution.

87. **Answers may vary.**

88. **Answers may vary.**

89. $37{,}250 = 3.725 \times 10^4$

90. $0.0003725 = 3.725 \times 10^{-4}$

91. $5.23 \times 10^5 = 523{,}000$

92. $7.9 \times 10^{-4} = 0.00079$

93.
$$\begin{aligned} (x - y)^2 - (x + y)^2 = [(x - y)(x - y)] - [(x + y)(x + y)] &= \left[x^2 - 2xy + y^2\right] - \left[x^2 + 2xy + y^2\right] \\ &= x^2 - 2xy + y^2 - x^2 - 2xy - y^2 \\ &= -4xy \end{aligned}$$

94.
$$\begin{aligned} (p + q)^2 + (p - q)^2 = [(p + q)(p + q)] + [(p - q)(p - q)] &= \left[p^2 + 2pq + q^2\right] + \left[p^2 - 2pq + q^2\right] \\ &= p^2 + 2pq + q^2 + p^2 - 2pq + q^2 \\ &= 2p^2 + 2q^2 \end{aligned}$$

Chapter 1 Summary (page 152)

1. **a.** $3x + 7 = 4$

no restrictions on x

b. $x + \dfrac{1}{x} = 2$

restriction: $x \neq 0$

c. $\sqrt{x} = 4$

restriction: $x \geq 0$

d. $\dfrac{1}{x - 2} = \dfrac{2}{x - 3}$

restriction: $x \neq 2$, $x \neq 3$

2. **a.**

$$\begin{aligned} 3(9x+4) &= 28 \\ 27x+12 &= 28 \\ 27x &= 16 \\ x &= \tfrac{16}{27} \end{aligned}$$

conditional equation

b.

$$\begin{aligned} \tfrac{3}{2}a &= 7(a+11) \\ 2\cdot\tfrac{3}{2}a &= 2\cdot 7(a+11) \\ 3a &= 14a+154 \\ -11a &= 154 \\ a &= -\tfrac{154}{11} = -14 \end{aligned}$$

conditional equation

c.

$$\begin{aligned} 8(3x-5)-4(x+3) &= 12 \\ 24x-40-4x-12 &= 12 \\ 20x-52 &= 12 \\ 20x &= 64 \\ x &= \tfrac{64}{20} = \tfrac{16}{5} \Rightarrow \text{conditional equation} \end{aligned}$$

d.

$$\begin{aligned} \frac{x+3}{x+4}+\frac{x+3}{x+2} &= 2 \\ (x+4)(x+2)\left(\frac{x+3}{x+4}+\frac{x+3}{x+2}\right) &= (x+4)(x+2)\cdot 2 \\ (x+2)(x+3)+(x+4)(x+3) &= \left(x^2+6x+8\right)\cdot 2 \\ x^2+5x+6+x^2+7x+12 &= 2x^2+12x+16 \\ 2x^2+12x+18 &= 2x^2+12x+16 \\ 18 &\neq 16 \Rightarrow \text{no solution} \end{aligned}$$

e.

$$\begin{aligned} \frac{3}{x-1} &= \frac{1}{2} \\ 2(x-1)\cdot\frac{3}{x-1} &= 2(x-1)\cdot\frac{1}{2} \\ 6 &= x-1 \\ 7 &= x \end{aligned}$$

conditional equation

f.

$$\begin{aligned} \frac{8x^2+72x}{9+x} &= 8x \\ (9+x)\cdot\frac{8x^2+72x}{9+x} &= (9+x)\cdot 8x \\ 8x^2+72x &= 72x+8x^2 \end{aligned}$$

identity

g.

$$\begin{aligned} \frac{3x}{x-1}-\frac{5}{x+3} &= 3 \\ (x-1)(x+3)\left(\frac{3x}{x-1}-\frac{5}{x+3}\right) &= (x-1)(x+3)\cdot 3 \\ 3x(x+3)-5(x-1) &= \left(x^2+2x-3\right)\cdot 3 \\ 3x^2+9x-5x+5 &= 3x^2+6x-9 \\ 4x+5 &= 6x-9 \\ -2x &= -14 \\ x &= 7 \Rightarrow \text{conditional equation} \end{aligned}$$

h.

$$\begin{aligned} x + \frac{1}{2x-3} &= \frac{2x^2}{2x-3} \\ (2x-3)\left(x + \frac{1}{2x-3}\right) &= (2x-3) \cdot \frac{2x^2}{2x-3} \\ (2x-3)x + 1 &= 2x^2 \\ 2x^2 - 3x + 1 &= 2x^2 \\ -3x &= -1 \\ x &= \tfrac{1}{3} \Rightarrow \text{conditional equation} \end{aligned}$$

3. **a.**

$$\begin{aligned} C &= \frac{5}{9}(F-32) \\ \frac{9}{5}C &= \frac{9}{5} \cdot \frac{5}{9}(F-32) \\ \frac{9}{5}C &= F - 32 \\ \frac{9}{5}C + 32 &= F \end{aligned}$$

b.

$$\begin{aligned} P_n &= l + \frac{si}{f} \\ P_n - l &= \frac{si}{f} \\ f(P_n - l) &= f \cdot \frac{si}{f} \\ f(P_n - l) &= si \\ \frac{f(P_n - l)}{P_n - l} &= \frac{si}{P_n - l} \\ f &= \frac{si}{P_n - l} \end{aligned}$$

c.

$$\begin{aligned} \frac{1}{f} &= \frac{1}{f_1} + \frac{1}{f_2} \\ ff_1f_2 \cdot \frac{1}{f} &= ff_1f_2\left(\frac{1}{f_1} + \frac{1}{f_2}\right) \\ f_1f_2 &= ff_2 + ff_1 \\ f_1f_2 - ff_1 &= ff_2 \\ f_1(f_2 - f) &= ff_2 \\ \frac{f_1(f_2 - f)}{f_2 - f} &= \frac{ff_2}{f_2 - f} \\ f_1 &= \frac{ff_2}{f_2 - f} \end{aligned}$$

d.

$$\begin{aligned} S &= \frac{a - lr}{1 - r} \\ S(1-r) &= \frac{a - lr}{1 - r}(1 - r) \\ S(1-r) &= a - lr \\ S - Sr &= a - lr \\ lr &= a - S + Sr \\ \frac{lr}{r} &= \frac{a - S + Sr}{r} \\ l &= \frac{a - S + Sr}{r} \end{aligned}$$

4. Let $x =$ the liters of water added.

Liters of alcohol at start	+	Liters of alcohol added	=	Liters of alcohol at end

$$\begin{aligned} 0.50(1) + 0 &= 0.20(1 + x) \\ 0.50 &= 0.20 + 0.20x \\ 0.30 &= 0.20x \\ 1.5 &= x \Rightarrow \text{1.5 liters of water should be added.} \end{aligned}$$

5. Let x = hours for both working together.

$$\boxed{\text{Number Scott washes in 1 hour}} \cdot \boxed{\text{Number of hours}} + \boxed{\text{Number Bill washes in 1 hour}} \cdot \boxed{\text{Number of hours}} = \boxed{\text{100 windows}}$$

$$\begin{aligned} \frac{37}{3}x + \frac{27}{2}x &= 100 \\ 6\left(\frac{37}{3}x + \frac{27}{2}x\right) &= 6(100) \\ 74x + 81x &= 600 \\ 155x &= 600 \\ x &= \frac{600}{155} \approx 3.9 \end{aligned}$$

They can wash 100 windows together in about 3.9 hours.

6. Let x = hours for both pipes to fill the tank.

$$\boxed{\text{1st pipe in 1 hour}} + \boxed{\text{2nd pipe in 1 hour}} = \boxed{\text{Total in 1 hour}}$$

$$\begin{aligned} \frac{1}{9} + \frac{1}{12} &= \frac{1}{x} \\ 36x\left(\frac{1}{9} + \frac{1}{12}\right) &= 36x\left(\frac{1}{x}\right) \\ 4x + 3x &= 36 \\ 7x &= 36 \\ x &= \frac{36}{7} = 5\frac{1}{7} \end{aligned}$$

The tank can be filled in $5\frac{1}{7}$ hours.

7. Let x = the ounces of pure zinc added.

$$\boxed{\text{Ounces of zinc at start}} + \boxed{\text{Ounces of zinc added}} = \boxed{\text{Ounces of zinc at end}}$$

$$\begin{aligned} 0.30(20) + x &= 0.40(20 + x) \\ 6 + x &= 8 + 0.40x \\ 0.60x &= 2 \\ 6x &= 20 \\ x &= \frac{20}{6} = 3\frac{1}{3} \end{aligned}$$

$3\frac{1}{3}$ ounces of zinc should be added.

8. Let x = the amount invested at 11%. Then $10{,}000 - x$ = the amount invested at 14%.

$$\boxed{\text{Interest at 11\%}} + \boxed{\text{Interest at 14\%}} = \boxed{\text{Total interest}}$$

$$\begin{aligned} 0.11x + 0.14(10{,}000 - x) &= 1{,}265 \\ 0.11x + 1{,}400 - 0.14x &= 1{,}265 \\ -0.03x &= -135 \\ x &= 4{,}500 \end{aligned}$$

\$4,500 was invested at 11% and \$5,500 was invested at 14%.

9. Let x = # of rugs for equal costs.

$$\boxed{\text{Cost of 1st loom}} = \boxed{\text{Cost of 2nd loom}}$$

$$\begin{aligned} 750 + 115x &= 950 + 95x \\ 20x &= 200 \\ x &= 10 \end{aligned}$$

The costs are the same on either loom for 10 rugs.

10. **a.**

$$\begin{aligned} 2x^2 - x - 6 &= 0 \\ (2x + 3)(x - 2) &= 0 \end{aligned}$$

$$\begin{aligned} 2x + 3 = 0 \quad &\textbf{or} \quad x - 2 = 0 \\ 2x = -3 \quad & \quad x = 2 \\ x = -\tfrac{3}{2} \quad & \quad x = 2 \end{aligned}$$

b.

$$\begin{aligned} 12x^2 + 13x &= 4 \\ 12x^2 + 13x - 4 &= 0 \\ (4x - 1)(3x + 4) &= 0 \end{aligned}$$

$$\begin{aligned} 4x - 1 = 0 \quad &\textbf{or} \quad 3x + 4 = 0 \\ 4x = 1 \quad & \quad 3x = -4 \\ x = \tfrac{1}{4} \quad & \quad x = -\tfrac{4}{3} \end{aligned}$$

c.

$$\begin{aligned} 5x^2 - 8x &= 0 \\ x(5x-8) &= 0 \end{aligned}$$

$$\begin{array}{lll} x = 0 & \textbf{or} & 5x - 8 = 0 \\ x = 0 & & 5x = 8 \\ x = 0 & & x = \frac{8}{5} \end{array}$$

d.

$$\begin{aligned} 27x^2 &= 30x - 8 \\ 27x^2 - 30x + 8 &= 0 \\ (9x-4)(3x-2) &= 0 \end{aligned}$$

$$\begin{array}{lll} 9x - 4 = 0 & \textbf{or} & 3x - 2 = 0 \\ 9x = 4 & & 3x = 2 \\ x = \frac{4}{9} & & x = \frac{2}{3} \end{array}$$

11. a.

$$\begin{aligned} x^2 - 8x + 15 &= 0 \\ x^2 - 8x &= -15 \\ x^2 - 8x + 16 &= -15 + 16 \\ (x-4)^2 &= 1 \end{aligned}$$

$$\begin{array}{lll} x - 4 = \sqrt{1} & \textbf{or} & x - 4 = -\sqrt{1} \\ x - 4 = 1 & & x - 4 = -1 \\ x = 5 & & x = 3 \end{array}$$

b.

$$\begin{aligned} 3x^2 + 18x &= -24 \\ \frac{3x^2 + 18x}{3} &= \frac{-24}{3} \\ x^2 + 6x &= -8 \\ x^2 + 6x + 9 &= -8 + 9 \\ (x+3)^2 &= 1 \end{aligned}$$

$$\begin{array}{lll} x + 3 = \sqrt{1} & \textbf{or} & x + 3 = -\sqrt{1} \\ x + 3 = 1 & & x + 3 = -1 \\ x = -2 & & x = -4 \end{array}$$

c.

$$\begin{aligned} 5x^2 - x - 1 &= 0 \\ 5x^2 - x &= 1 \\ x^2 - \frac{1}{5}x &= \frac{1}{5} \\ x^2 - \frac{1}{5}x + \frac{1}{100} &= \frac{1}{5} + \frac{1}{100} \\ \left(x - \frac{1}{10}\right)^2 &= \frac{21}{100} \end{aligned}$$

$$\begin{array}{lll} x - \frac{1}{10} = \sqrt{\frac{21}{100}} & \textbf{or} & x - \frac{1}{10} = -\sqrt{\frac{21}{100}} \\ x - \frac{1}{10} = \frac{\sqrt{21}}{10} & & x - \frac{1}{10} = -\frac{\sqrt{21}}{10} \\ x = \frac{1 + \sqrt{21}}{10} & & x = \frac{1 - \sqrt{21}}{10} \end{array}$$

d.

$$5x^2 - x = 0$$
$$x^2 - \frac{1}{5}x = 0$$
$$x^2 - \frac{1}{5}x + \frac{1}{100} = 0 + \frac{1}{100}$$
$$\left(x - \frac{1}{10}\right)^2 = \frac{1}{100}$$
$$x - \frac{1}{10} = \sqrt{\frac{1}{100}} \quad \textbf{or} \quad x - \frac{1}{10} = -\sqrt{\frac{1}{100}}$$
$$x - \frac{1}{10} = \frac{1}{10} \qquad x - \frac{1}{10} = -\frac{1}{10}$$
$$x = \frac{2}{10} = \frac{1}{5} \qquad x = \frac{0}{10} = 0$$

12. a. $x^2 + 5x - 14 = 0 \Rightarrow a = 1, b = 5, c = -14$

$$x = \frac{-b \pm \sqrt{b^2 - 4ac}}{2a} = \frac{-(5) \pm \sqrt{(5)^2 - 4(1)(-14)}}{2(1)} = \frac{-5 \pm \sqrt{25 + 56}}{2} = \frac{-5 \pm \sqrt{81}}{2}$$
$$= \frac{-5 \pm 9}{2}$$

$$x = \frac{-5 + 9}{2} = \frac{4}{2} = 2 \text{ or } x = \frac{-5 - 9}{2} = \frac{-14}{2} = -7$$

b. $3x^2 - 25x = 18 \Rightarrow 3x^2 - 25x - 18 = 0 \Rightarrow a = 3, b = -25, c = -18$

$$x = \frac{-b \pm \sqrt{b^2 - 4ac}}{2a} = \frac{-(-25) \pm \sqrt{(-25)^2 - 4(3)(-18)}}{2(3)} = \frac{25 \pm \sqrt{625 + 216}}{6}$$
$$= \frac{25 \pm \sqrt{841}}{6} = \frac{25 \pm 29}{6}$$

$$x = \frac{25 + 29}{6} = \frac{54}{6} = 9 \text{ or } x = \frac{25 - 29}{6} = \frac{-4}{6} = -\frac{2}{3}$$

c. $5x^2 = 1 - x \Rightarrow 5x^2 + x - 1 = 0 \Rightarrow a = 5, b = 1, c = -1$

$$x = \frac{-b \pm \sqrt{b^2 - 4ac}}{2a} = \frac{-(1) \pm \sqrt{(1)^2 - 4(5)(-1)}}{2(5)} = \frac{-1 \pm \sqrt{1 + 20}}{10} = \frac{-1 \pm \sqrt{21}}{10}$$

d. $-5 = a^2 + 2a \Rightarrow a^2 + 2a + 5 = 0 \Rightarrow a = 1, b = 2, c = 5$

$$a = \frac{-b \pm \sqrt{b^2 - 4ac}}{2a} = \frac{-(2) \pm \sqrt{(2)^2 - 4(1)(5)}}{2(1)} = \frac{-2 \pm \sqrt{4 - 20}}{2} = \frac{-2 \pm \sqrt{-16}}{2}$$
$$= \frac{-2 \pm 4i}{2}$$
$$= -1 \pm 2i$$

13. $kx^2 + 4x + 12 = 0$

$a = k, b = 4, c = 12$

Set the discriminant equal to 0:

$$\begin{aligned} b^2 - 4ac &= 0 \\ 4^2 - 4(k)(12) &= 0 \\ 16 - 48k &= 0 \\ -48k &= -16 \\ k &= \frac{1}{3} \end{aligned}$$

14. $$\begin{aligned} 4y^2 + (k+2)y &= 1 - k \\ 4y^2 + (k+2)y - 1 + k &= 0 \end{aligned}$$

$a = 4, b = k + 2, c = -1 + k$

Set the discriminant equal to 0:

$$\begin{aligned} b^2 - 4ac &= 0 \\ (k+2)^2 - 4(4)(-1+k) &= 0 \\ k^2 + 4k + 4 + 16 - 16k &= 0 \\ k^2 - 12k + 20 &= 0 \\ (k-10)(k-2) &= 0 \end{aligned}$$

$k - 10 = 0$ **or** $k - 2 = 0$

$k = 10$ $\qquad$ $k = 2$

15. $$\begin{aligned} \frac{4}{a-4} + \frac{4}{a-1} &= 5 \\ (a-4)(a-1)\left(\frac{4}{a-4} + \frac{4}{a-1}\right) &= (a-4)(a-1)5 \\ 4(a-1) + 4(a-4) &= 5(a^2 - 5a + 4) \\ 4a - 4 + 4a - 16 &= 5a^2 - 25a + 20 \\ 0 &= 5a^2 - 33a + 40 \\ 0 &= (5a-8)(a-5) \end{aligned}$$

$5a - 8 = 0$ **or** $a - 5 = 0$

$5a = 8$ $\qquad$ $a = 5$

$a = \frac{8}{5}$ $\qquad$ $a = 5$

16. Let $x =$ one side of the garden.

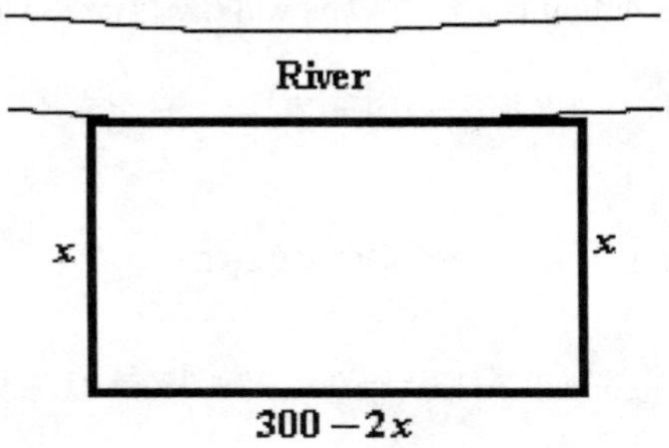

$$\begin{aligned} \text{Area} &= 10450 \\ x(300 - 2x) &= 10450 \\ -2x^2 + 300x &= 10450 \\ 0 &= 2x^2 - 300x + 10450 \\ 0 &= 2(x^2 - 150x + 5225) \\ 0 &= 2(x-95)(x-55) \end{aligned}$$

$x - 95 = 0$ **or** $x - 55 = 0$

$x = 95$ $\qquad$ $x = 55$

The dimensions are 95 yards by 110 yards or 55 yards by 190 yards.

17. Let $r =$ the rate of the propeller-driven plane. Then the rate of the jet plane is $r + 120$.

	Rate	Time	Dist.
Propeller	r	$\frac{3520}{r}$	3520
Jet	$r+120$	$\frac{3520}{r+120}$	3520

$$\boxed{\text{Jet time}} = \boxed{\text{Propeller time}} - 3$$

$$\frac{3520}{r+120} = \frac{3520}{r} - 3$$

$$r(r+120)\frac{3520}{r+120} = r(r+120)\left(\frac{3520}{r} - 3\right)$$

$$3520r = 3520(r+120) - 3r(r+120)$$

$$3520r = 3520r + 422400 - 3r^2 - 360r$$

$$3r^2 + 360r + 422{,}400 = 0$$

$$3(r-320)(r+440) = 0$$

$r - 320 = 0$ **or** $r + 440 = 0$

$r = 320$ $\quad r = -440$

Since $r = -440$ does not make sense, the solution is $r = 320$. The prop. plane's rate is 320 mph, while the jet plane's rate is 440 mph.

18. Set $h = 48$:

$$h = -16t^2 + 64t$$

$$48 = -16t^2 + 64t$$

$$16t^2 - 64t + 48 = 0$$

$$16(t-1)(t-3) = 0$$

$t - 1 = 0$ **or** $t - 3 = 0$

$t = 1$ $\quad t = 3$

The shortest time required for the ball to reach a height of 48 feet is 1 second.

19. Let $x =$ the width of the walk. Then the total dimensions are $16 + 2x$ by $20 + 2x$.

$$\boxed{\text{Total area}} - \boxed{\text{Area of pool}} = \boxed{\text{Area of walk}}$$

$$(16+2x)(20+2x) - (16)(20) = 117$$

$$320 + 72x + 4x^2 - 320 = 117$$

$$4x^2 + 72x - 117 = 0$$

$$(2x+39)(2x-3) = 0$$

$2x + 39 = 0$ **or** $2x - 3 = 0$

$x = -\frac{39}{2}$ $\quad x = \frac{3}{2}$

Since $x = -\frac{39}{2}$ does not make sense, the only solution is $x = \frac{3}{2}$. The walk is $1\frac{1}{2}$ feet wide.

20 **a.** $(2-3i) + (-4+2i) = 2 - 3i - 4 + 2i$
$= -2 - i$

b. $(2-3i) - (4+2i) = 2 - 3i - 4 - 2i$
$= -2 - 5i$

c. $\left(3 - \sqrt{-36}\right) + \left(\sqrt{-16} + 2\right) = (3-6i) + (4i+2) = 3 - 6i + 4i + 2 = 5 - 2i$

d. $\left(3 + \sqrt{-9}\right)\left(2 - \sqrt{-25}\right) = (3+3i)(2-5i) = 6 - 9i - 15i^2 = 6 - 9i + 15 = 21 - 9i$

e. $\frac{3}{i} = \frac{3i}{ii} = \frac{3i}{i^2} = \frac{3i}{-1} = 0 - 3i$

f. $-\frac{2}{i^3} = -\frac{2i}{i^3 i} = -\frac{2i}{i^4} = -\frac{2i}{1} = 0 - 2i$

g. $\frac{3}{1+i} = \frac{3(1-i)}{(1+i)(1-i)} = \frac{3(1-i)}{1^2 - i^2} = \frac{3-3i}{2} = \frac{3}{2} - \frac{3}{2}i$

h. $\frac{2i}{2-i} = \frac{2i(2+i)}{(2-i)(2+i)} = \frac{4i + 2i^2}{2^2 - i^2} = \frac{-2+4i}{5} = -\frac{2}{5} + \frac{4}{5}i$

i. $\dfrac{3+i}{3-i}=\dfrac{(3+i)(3+i)}{(3-i)(3+i)}=\dfrac{9+6i+i^2}{3^2-i^2}=\dfrac{8+6i}{10}=\dfrac{8}{10}+\dfrac{6}{10}i=\dfrac{4}{5}+\dfrac{3}{5}i$

j. $\dfrac{3-2i}{1+i}=\dfrac{(3-2i)(1-i)}{(1+i)(1-i)}=\dfrac{3-5i+2i^2}{1^2-i^2}=\dfrac{1-5i}{2}=\dfrac{1}{2}-\dfrac{5}{2}i$

k. $i^{53}=i^{52}i=\left(i^4\right)^{13}i=1^{13}i=0+i$

l. $i^{103}=i^{100}i^3=\left(i^4\right)^{25}i^3=1^{25}i^3=0-i$

m. $|3-i|=\sqrt{3^2+(-1)^2}=\sqrt{9+1}=\sqrt{10}$

n. $\left|\dfrac{1+i}{1-i}\right|=\left|\dfrac{(1+i)(1+i)}{(1-i)(1+i)}\right|=\left|\dfrac{1+2i+i^2}{1^2-i^2}\right|=\left|\dfrac{2i}{2}\right|=|0+i|=\sqrt{0^2+1^2}=1$

21. a.

$$\begin{aligned}\frac{3x}{2}-\frac{2x}{x-1}&=x-3\\ 2(x-1)\left(\frac{3x}{2}-\frac{2x}{x-1}\right)&=2(x-1)(x-3)\\ 3x(x-1)-2(2x)&=2\left(x^2-4x+3\right)\\ 3x^2-3x-4x&=2x^2-8x+6\\ x^2+x-6&=0\\ (x+3)(x-2)&=0\end{aligned}$$

$x+3=0$ **or** $x-2=0$

$x=-3$ $\quad$ $x=2$

b.

$$\begin{aligned}\frac{12}{x}-\frac{x}{2}&=x-3\\ 2x\left(\frac{12}{x}-\frac{x}{2}\right)&=2x(x-3)\\ 2(12)-x(x)&=2x^2-6x\\ 24-x^2&=2x^2-6x\\ 0&=3x^2-6x-24\\ 0&=3(x+2)(x-4)\end{aligned}$$

$x+2=0$ **or** $x-4=0$

$x=-2$ $\quad$ $x=4$

c.

$$\begin{aligned}x^4-2x^2+1&=0\\ \left(x^2-1\right)\left(x^2-1\right)&=0\end{aligned}$$

$x^2-1=0$ **or** $x^2-1=0$

$x^2=1$ $\quad$ $x^2=1$

$x=\pm1$ $\quad$ $x=\pm1$

d.

$$\begin{aligned}x^4+36&=37x^2\\ x^4-37x^2+36&=0\\ \left(x^2-36\right)\left(x^2-1\right)&=0\end{aligned}$$

$x^2-36=0$ **or** $x^2-1=0$

$x^2=36$ $\quad$ $x^2=1$

$x=\pm6$ $\quad$ $x=\pm1$

e.

$$\begin{aligned}a-a^{1/2}-6&=0\\ \left(a^{1/2}+2\right)\left(a^{1/2}-3\right)&=0\end{aligned}$$

$a^{1/2}+2=0$ **or** $a^{1/2}-3=0$

$a^{1/2}=-2$ $\quad$ $a^{1/2}=3$

$\left(a^{1/2}\right)^2=(-2)^2$ $\quad$ $\left(a^{1/2}\right)^2=(3)^2$

$a=4$ $\quad$ $a=9$

$a=4$ does not check and is extraneous.

f.

$$\begin{aligned}x^{2/3}+x^{1/3}-6&=0\\ \left(x^{1/3}-2\right)\left(x^{1/3}+3\right)&=0\end{aligned}$$

$x^{1/3}-2=0$ **or** $x^{1/3}+3=0$

$x^{1/3}=2$ $\quad$ $x^{1/3}=-3$

$\left(x^{1/3}\right)^3=(2)^3$ $\quad$ $\left(x^{1/3}\right)^3=(-3)^3$

$x=8$ $\quad$ $x=-27$

Both answers check.

g.
$$\begin{aligned} \sqrt{x-1}+x &= 7 \\ \sqrt{x-1} &= 7-x \\ \left(\sqrt{x-1}\right)^2 &= (7-x)^2 \\ x-1 &= 49-14x+x^2 \\ 0 &= x^2-15x+50 \\ 0 &= (x-5)(x-10) \end{aligned}$$
$$x-5=0 \quad \textbf{or} \quad x-10=0$$
$$x=5 \qquad\qquad x=10$$
$x=10$ does not check and is extraneous.

h.
$$\begin{aligned} \sqrt{a+9}-\sqrt{a} &= 3 \\ \sqrt{a+9} &= 3+\sqrt{a} \\ \left(\sqrt{a+9}\right)^2 &= \left(3+\sqrt{a}\right)^2 \\ a+9 &= 9+6\sqrt{a}+a \\ 0 &= 6\sqrt{a} \\ 0^2 &= \left(6\sqrt{a}\right)^2 \\ 0 &= 36a \Rightarrow a=0 \end{aligned}$$
The solution checks.

i.
$$\begin{aligned} \sqrt{5-x}+\sqrt{5+x} &= 4 \\ \sqrt{5+x} &= 4-\sqrt{5-x} \\ \left(\sqrt{5+x}\right)^2 &= \left(4-\sqrt{5-x}\right)^2 \\ 5+x &= 16-8\sqrt{5-x}+5-x \\ 8\sqrt{5-x} &= 16-2x \\ \left(8\sqrt{5-x}\right)^2 &= (16-2x)^2 \\ 64(5-x) &= 256-64x+4x^2 \\ 320-64x &= 4x^2-64x+256 \\ 0 &= 4x^2-64 \\ 0 &= 4(x+4)(x-4) \end{aligned}$$
$$x+4=0 \quad \textbf{or} \quad x-4=0$$
$$x=-4 \qquad\qquad x=4$$
Both solutions check.

j.
$$\begin{aligned} \sqrt{y+5}+\sqrt{y} &= 1 \\ \sqrt{y+5} &= 1-\sqrt{y} \\ \left(\sqrt{y+5}\right)^2 &= \left(1-\sqrt{y}\right)^2 \\ y+5 &= 1-2\sqrt{y}+y \\ 2\sqrt{y} &= -4 \\ \left(2\sqrt{y}\right)^2 &= (-4)^2 \\ 4y &= 16 \\ y &= 4 \end{aligned}$$
The solution does not check.

22. **a.**
$$\begin{aligned} 2x-9 &< 5 \\ 2x &< 14 \\ x &< 7 \Rightarrow (-\infty, 7) \end{aligned}$$
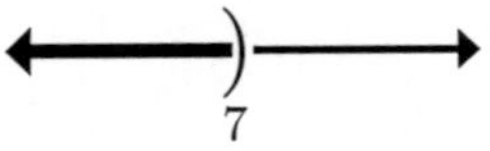

b.
$$\begin{aligned} 5x+3 &\geq 2 \\ 5x &\geq -1 \\ x &\geq -\tfrac{1}{5} \Rightarrow \left[-\tfrac{1}{5}, \infty\right) \end{aligned}$$
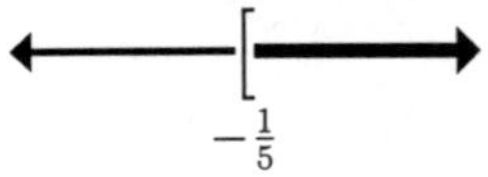

c.
$$\begin{aligned} \frac{5(x-1)}{2} &< x \\ 5(x-1) &< 2x \\ 5x-5 &< 2x \\ 3x &< 5 \\ x &< \tfrac{5}{3} \Rightarrow \left(-\infty, \tfrac{5}{3}\right) \end{aligned}$$
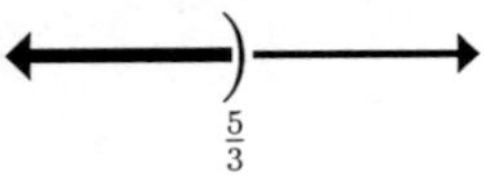

d.
$$\begin{aligned} 0 \leq \frac{3+x}{2} &< 4 \\ 0 \leq 3+x &< 8 \\ -3 \leq x &< 5 \Rightarrow [-3, 5) \end{aligned}$$
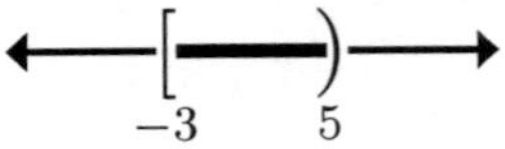

e. $(x+2)(x-4) > 0$

factors = 0: $x=-2$, $x=4$

intervals: $(-\infty, -2)$, $(-2, 4)$, $(4, \infty)$

interval	test number	value of $(x+2)(x-4)$
$(-\infty, -2)$	-3	$+7$
$(-2, 4)$	0	-8
$(4, \infty)$	5	$+10$

Solution: $(-\infty, -2) \cup (4, \infty)$

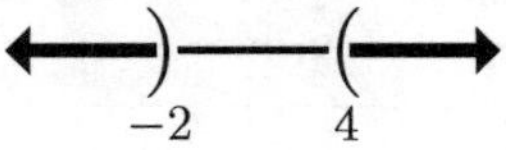

f. $(x-1)(x+4) < 0$

factors = 0: $x=1$, $x=-4$

intervals: $(-\infty, -4)$, $(-4, 1)$, $(1, \infty)$

interval	test number	value of $(x-1)(x+4)$
$(-\infty, -4)$	-5	$+6$
$(-4, 1)$	0	-4
$(1, \infty)$	2	$+8$

Solution: $(-4, 1)$

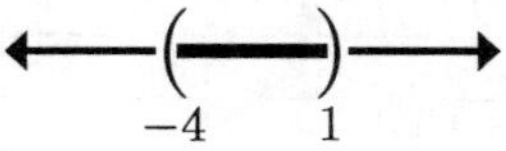

g. $x^2-2x-3 < 0$

$(x-3)(x+1) < 0$

factors = 0: $x=3$, $x=-1$

intervals: $(-\infty, -1)$, $(-1, 3)$, $(3, \infty)$

interval	test number	value of x^2-2x-3
$(-\infty, -1)$	-2	$+5$
$(-1, 3)$	0	-3
$(3, \infty)$	4	$+5$

Solution: $(-1, 3)$

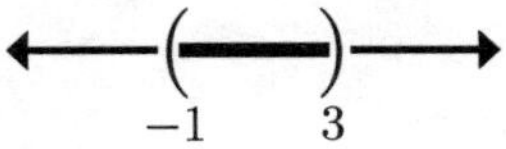

h. $2x^2+x-3 > 0$

$(2x+3)(x-1) > 0$

factors = 0: $x=-\frac{3}{2}$, $x=1$

intervals: $(-\infty, -\frac{3}{2})$, $(-\frac{3}{2}, 1)$, $(1, \infty)$

interval	test number	value of $2x^2+x-3$
$(-\infty, -\frac{3}{2})$	-2	$+3$
$(-\frac{3}{2}, 1)$	0	-3
$(1, \infty)$	2	$+7$

Solution: $(-\infty, -\frac{3}{2}) \cup (1, \infty)$

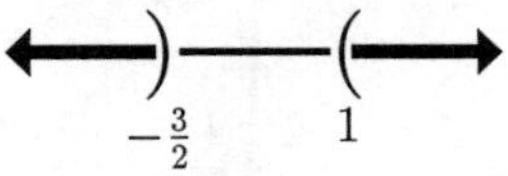

i. $\dfrac{x+2}{x-3} \geq 0$

factors = 0: $x=-2$, $x=3$

intervals: $(-\infty, -2)$, $(-2, 3)$, $(3, \infty)$

interval	test number	sign of $\frac{x+2}{x-3}$
$(-\infty, -2)$	-3	$+$
$(-2, 3)$	0	$-$
$(3, \infty)$	4	$+$

Include endpoints which make the numerator equal to 0. Do not include endpoints which make the denominator equal to 0.

Solution: $(-\infty, -2] \cup (3, \infty)$

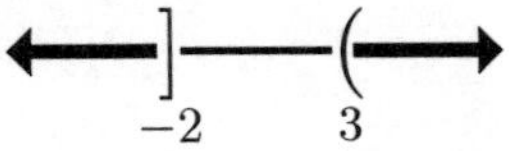

j. $\dfrac{x-1}{x+4} \leq 0$

factors = 0: $x=1$, $x=-4$

intervals: $(-\infty, -4)$, $(-4, 1)$, $(1, \infty)$

interval	test number	sign of $\frac{x-1}{x+4}$
$(-\infty, -4)$	-5	$+$
$(-4, 1)$	0	$-$
$(1, \infty)$	2	$+$

Include endpoints which make the numerator equal to 0. Do not include endpoints which make the denominator equal to 0.

Solution: $(-4, 1]$

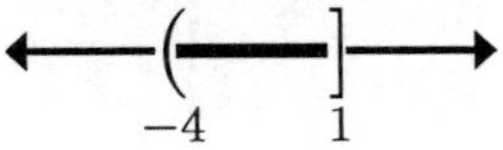

k.

$$\frac{x^2+x-2}{x-3} \geq 0$$

$$\frac{(x+2)(x-1)}{x-3} \geq 0$$

factors $= 0$: $x = -2, x = 1, x = 3$

int.: $(-\infty, -2), (-2, 1), (1, 3), (3, \infty)$

interval	test number	sign of $\frac{x^2+x-2}{x-3}$
$(-\infty, -2)$	-3	$-$
$(-2, 1)$	0	$+$
$(1, 3)$	2	$-$
$(3, \infty)$	4	$+$

Include endpoints which make the numerator equal to 0. Do not include endpoints which make the denominator equal to 0.

Solution: $[-2, 1] \cup (3, \infty)$

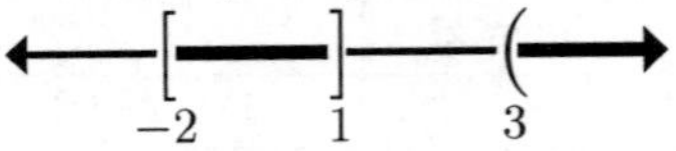

l.

$$\frac{5}{x} < 2$$

$$\frac{5}{x} - 2 < 0$$

$$\frac{5-2x}{x} < 0$$

factors $= 0$: $x = \frac{5}{2}, x = 0$

intervals: $(-\infty, 0), \left(0, \frac{5}{2}\right), \left(\frac{5}{2}, \infty\right)$

interval	test number	value of $\frac{5-2x}{x}$
$(-\infty, 0)$	-1	-7
$\left(0, \frac{5}{2}\right)$	1	$+3$
$\left(\frac{5}{2}, \infty\right)$	3	$-\frac{1}{3}$

Solution: $(-\infty, 0) \cup \left(\frac{5}{2}, \infty\right)$

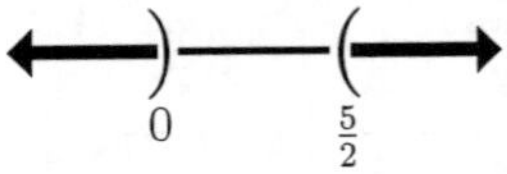

23. a.

$$|x+1| = 6$$

$x + 1 = 6$ **or** $x + 1 = -6$

$x = 5 \qquad x = -7$

b.

$$|2x-1| = |2x+1|$$

$2x - 1 = 2x + 1$ **or** $2x - 1 = -(2x+1)$

$0 = 2 \qquad 2x - 1 = -2x - 1$

never true $\qquad 4x = 0$

$x = 0$

c.

$$|x+3| < 3$$

$$-3 < x + 3 < 3$$

$$-6 < x < 0$$

$$(-6, 0)$$

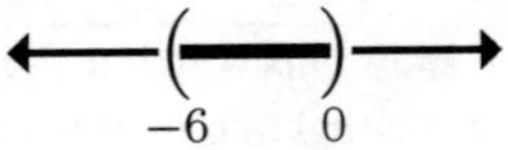

d.

$$|3x-7| \geq 1$$

$3x - 7 \geq 1$ **or** $3x - 7 \leq -1$

$3x \geq 8 \qquad 3x \leq 6$

$x \geq \frac{8}{3} \qquad x \leq 2$

$$(-\infty, 2] \cup \left[\frac{8}{3}, \infty\right)$$

e.

$$\left|\tfrac{x+2}{3}\right| < 1$$
$$-1 < \tfrac{x+2}{3} < 1$$
$$-3 < x+2 < 3$$
$$-5 < x < 1$$
$$(-5, 1)$$

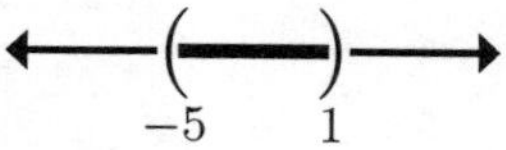

f.

$$\left|\tfrac{x-3}{4}\right| > 8$$
$$\tfrac{x-3}{4} > 8 \quad \textbf{or} \quad \tfrac{x-3}{4} < -8$$
$$x-3 > 32 \qquad x-3 < -32$$
$$x > 35 \qquad x < -29$$
$$(-\infty, -29) \cup (35, \infty)$$

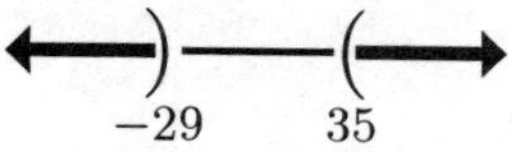

g.

$$1 < |2x+3| < 4$$

$1 < |2x+3|$ **and** $|2x+3| < 4$

(1) $|2x+3| > 1$

$$2x+3 > 1 \quad \textbf{or} \quad 2x+3 < -1$$
$$2x > -2 \qquad 2x < -4$$
$$x > -1 \qquad x < -2$$

(1) 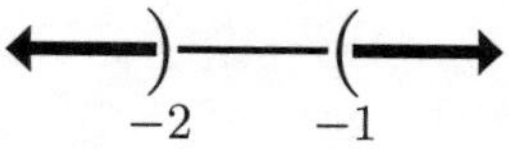

(2) $|2x+3| < 4$

$$-4 < 2x+3 < 4$$
$$-7 < 2x < 1$$
$$-\tfrac{7}{2} < x < \tfrac{1}{2}$$

(2) 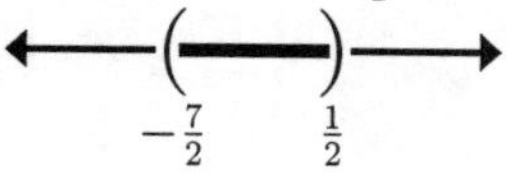

(1) 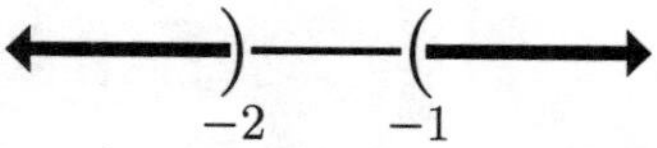

(2) 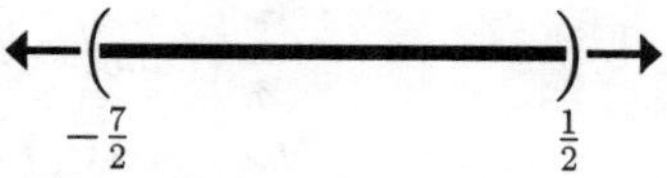

(1) and (2) 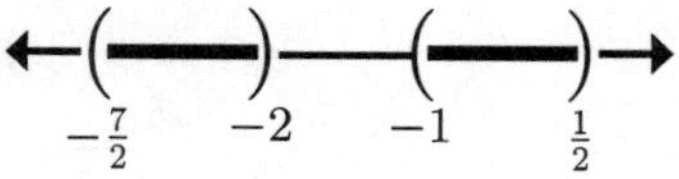

$\Rightarrow \left(-\tfrac{7}{2}, -2\right) \cup \left(-1, \tfrac{1}{2}\right)$

h.

$$0 < |3x-4| < 7$$

$0 < |3x-4|$ **and** $|3x-4| < 7$

(1) $|3x-4| > 0$

$$3x-4 > 0 \quad \textbf{or} \quad 3x-4 < -0$$
$$3x > 4 \qquad 3x < 4$$
$$x > \tfrac{4}{3} \qquad x < \tfrac{4}{3}$$

(1) 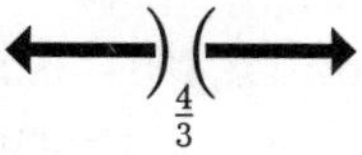

(2) $|3x-4| < 7$

$$-7 < 3x-4 < 7$$
$$-3 < 3x < 11$$
$$-1 < x < \tfrac{11}{3}$$

(2) 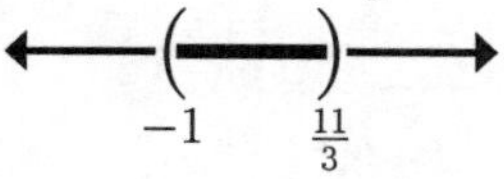

(1) 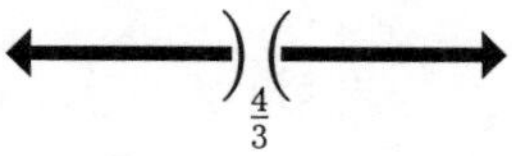

(2) 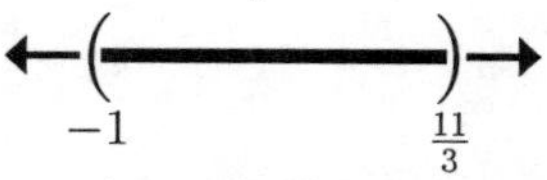

(1) and (2) 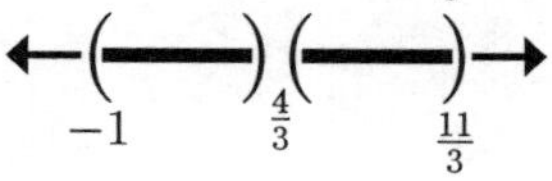

$\Rightarrow \left(-1, \tfrac{4}{3}\right) \cup \left(\tfrac{4}{3}, \tfrac{11}{3}\right)$

Chapter 1 Test (page 157)

1. $\dfrac{x}{x(x-1)}$
restrictions: $x \neq 0$, $x \neq 1$

2. $\sqrt{x}$
restrictions: $x \geq 0$

3.
$$\begin{aligned} 7(2a+5)-7 &= 6(a+8) \\ 14a+35-7 &= 6a+48 \\ 8a &= 20 \\ a &= \frac{20}{8} = \frac{5}{2} \end{aligned}$$

4.
$$\begin{aligned} \frac{3}{x^2-5x-14} &= \frac{4}{x^2+5x+6} \\ \frac{3}{(x-7)(x+2)} &= \frac{4}{(x+2)(x+3)} \\ (x-7)(x+2)(x+3)\frac{3}{(x-7)(x+2)} &= (x-7)(x+2)(x+3)\frac{4}{(x+2)(x+3)} \\ 3(x+3) &= 4(x-7) \\ 3x+9 &= 4x-28 \\ 37 &= x \end{aligned}$$

5.
$$\begin{aligned} z &= \frac{x-\mu}{\sigma} \\ \sigma z &= \sigma \cdot \frac{x-\mu}{\sigma} \\ z\sigma &= x-\mu \\ z\sigma+\mu &= x \end{aligned}$$

6.
$$\begin{aligned} \frac{1}{a} &= \frac{1}{b}+\frac{1}{c} \\ abc\cdot\frac{1}{a} &= abc\left(\frac{1}{b}+\frac{1}{c}\right) \\ bc &= ac+ab \\ bc &= a(c+b) \\ \frac{bc}{c+b} &= \frac{a(c+b)}{c+b} \\ \frac{bc}{c+b} &= a \end{aligned}$$

7. Let $x =$ the score on the final.
Note: This score is counted twice.
$$\begin{aligned} \frac{\boxed{\text{Sum of scores}}}{5} &= 80 \\ \frac{75+75+75+x+x}{5} &= 80 \\ \frac{2x+225}{5} &= 80 \\ 2x+225 &= 400 \\ 2x &= 175 \\ x &= 87.5 \end{aligned}$$
The student needs to score 87.5.

8. Let $x =$ the amount invested at 6%. Then $20{,}000 - x =$ the amount invested at 7%.
$$\boxed{\text{Interest at 6\%}} + \boxed{\text{Interest at 7\%}} = \boxed{\text{Total interest}}$$
$$\begin{aligned} 0.06x+0.07(20{,}000-x) &= 1{,}260 \\ 0.06x+1{,}400-0.07x &= 1{,}260 \\ -0.01x &= -140 \\ x &= 14{,}000 \end{aligned}$$
\$14,000 was invested at 6%.

9.
$$4x^2 - 8x + 3 = 0$$
$$(2x-3)(2x-1) = 0$$
$$2x - 3 = 0 \quad \textbf{or} \quad 2x - 1 = 0$$
$$2x = 3 \qquad 2x = 1$$
$$x = \tfrac{3}{2} \qquad x = \tfrac{1}{2}$$

10.
$$2b^2 - 12 = -5b$$
$$2b^2 + 5b - 12 = 0$$
$$(2b-3)(b+4) = 0$$
$$2b - 3 = 0 \quad \textbf{or} \quad b + 4 = 0$$
$$2b = 3 \qquad b = -4$$
$$b = \tfrac{3}{2} \qquad b = -4$$

11. $x = \dfrac{-b \pm \sqrt{b^2 - 4ac}}{2a}$

12. $3x^2 - 5x - 9 = 0 \Rightarrow a = 3, b = -5, c = -9$

$$x = \frac{-b \pm \sqrt{b^2 - 4ac}}{2a} = \frac{-(-5) \pm \sqrt{(-5)^2 - 4(3)(-9)}}{2(3)} = \frac{5 \pm \sqrt{25 + 108}}{6} = \frac{5 \pm \sqrt{133}}{6}$$

13. $x^2 + (k+1)x + k + 4 = 0$

$a = 1, b = k + 1, c = k + 4$

Set the discriminant equal to 0:
$$b^2 - 4ac = 0$$
$$(k+1)^2 - 4(1)(k+4) = 0$$
$$k^2 + 2k + 1 - 4k - 16 = 0$$
$$k^2 - 2k - 15 = 0$$
$$(k-5)(k+3) = 0$$
$$k - 5 = 0 \quad \textbf{or} \quad k + 3 = 0$$
$$k = 5 \qquad k = -3$$

14. Set $h = 0$:
$$h = -16t^2 + 128t$$
$$0 = -16t^2 + 128t$$
$$0 = -16t(t-8)$$
$$-16t = 0 \quad \textbf{or} \quad t - 8 = 0$$
$$t = 0 \qquad t = 8$$

The ball will return after 8 seconds.

15. $(4-5i) - (-3+7i) = 4 - 5i + 3 - 7i$
$= 7 - 12i$

16. $(4-5i)(3-7i) = 12 - 43i + 35i^2$
$= 12 - 43i - 35$
$= -23 - 43i$

17. $\dfrac{2}{2-i} = \dfrac{2(2+i)}{(2-i)(2+i)} = \dfrac{4+2i}{2^2 - i^2} = \dfrac{4+2i}{5} = \dfrac{4}{5} + \dfrac{2}{5}i$

18. $\dfrac{1+i}{1-i} = \dfrac{(1+i)(1+i)}{(1-i)(1+i)} = \dfrac{1+2i+i^2}{1^2 - i^2} = \dfrac{2i}{2} = 0 + i$

19. $i^{13} = i^{12}i = (i^4)^3 i = 1^3 i = i$

20. $i^0 = 1$

21. $|5 - 12i| = \sqrt{5^2 + (-12)^2} = \sqrt{25 + 144} = \sqrt{169} = 13$

22. $\left|\frac{1}{3+i}\right| = \left|\frac{1(3-i)}{(3+i)(3-i)}\right| = \left|\frac{3-i}{3^2-i^2}\right| = \left|\frac{3-i}{10}\right| = \left|\frac{3}{10} - \frac{1}{10}i\right| = \sqrt{\left(\frac{3}{10}\right)^2 + \left(-\frac{1}{10}\right)^2}$

$$= \sqrt{\frac{9}{100} + \frac{1}{100}}$$

$$= \sqrt{\frac{10}{100}} = \frac{\sqrt{10}}{10}$$

23.

$$z^4 - 13z^2 + 36 = 0$$
$$(z^2-4)(z^2-9) = 0$$

$z^2 - 4 = 0$ **or** $z^2 - 9 = 0$

$z^2 = 4$ $\quad$ $z^2 = 9$

$z = \pm 2$ $\quad$ $z = \pm 3$

24.

$$2p^{2/5} - p^{1/5} - 1 = 0$$
$$(2p^{1/5}+1)(p^{1/5}-1) = 0$$

$2p^{1/5} + 1 = 0$ **or** $p^{1/5} - 1 = 0$

$p^{1/5} = -\frac{1}{2}$ $\quad$ $p^{1/5} = 1$

$(p^{1/5})^5 = (-\frac{1}{2})^5$ $\quad$ $(p^{1/5})^5 = (1)^5$

$p = -\frac{1}{32}$ $\quad$ $p = 1$

Both answers check.

25.

$$\sqrt{x+5} = 12$$
$$\left(\sqrt{x+5}\right)^2 = 12^2$$
$$x + 5 = 144$$
$$x = 139$$

The answer checks.

26.

$$\sqrt{2z+3} = 1 - \sqrt{z+1}$$
$$\left(\sqrt{2z+3}\right)^2 = \left(1-\sqrt{z+1}\right)^2$$
$$2z + 3 = 1 - 2\sqrt{z+1} + z + 1$$
$$2\sqrt{z+1} = -z - 1$$
$$\left(2\sqrt{z+1}\right)^2 = (-z-1)^2$$
$$4(z+1) = z^2 + 2z + 1$$
$$4z + 4 = z^2 + 2z + 1$$
$$0 = z^2 - 2z - 3$$
$$0 = (z+1)(z-3)$$

$z + 1 = 0$ **or** $z - 3 = 0$

$z = -1$ $\quad$ $z = 3$

The answer $z = 3$ is extraneous.

27.

$$5x - 3 \le 7$$
$$5x \le 10$$
$$x \le 2 \Rightarrow (-\infty, 2]$$

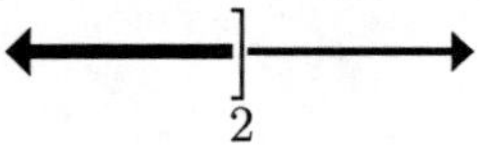

28.

$$\frac{x+3}{4} > \frac{2x-4}{3}$$
$$12 \cdot \tfrac{x+3}{4} > 12 \cdot \tfrac{2x-4}{3}$$
$$3(x+3) > 4(2x-4)$$
$$3x + 9 > 8x - 16$$
$$-5x > -25$$
$$x < 5 \Rightarrow (-\infty, 5)$$

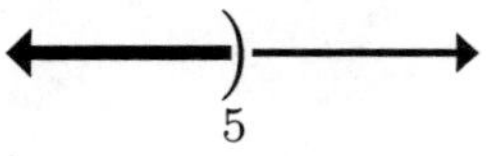

29. $1 + x < 3x - 3 < 4x - 2$

$1 + x < 3x - 3$ **and** $3x - 3 < 4x - 2$

$-2x < -4$ $\quad$ $-x < 1$

$x > 2$ $\quad$ $x > -1$

$x > 2$

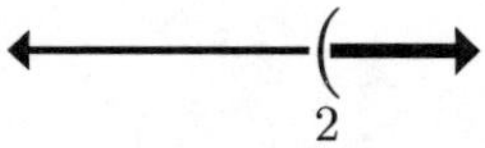

$x > -1$

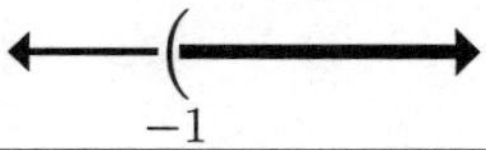

$x > 2$
and
$x > -1$

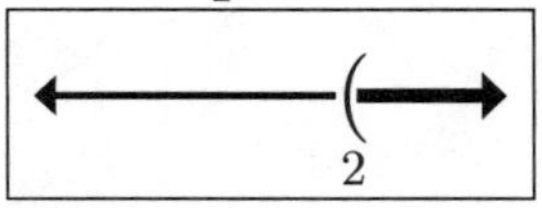

Solution set: $(2, \infty)$

30. $\dfrac{x+2}{x-1} \le 0$

factors $= 0$: $x = -2$, $x = 1$

intervals: $(-\infty, -2)$, $(-2, 1)$, $(1, \infty)$

interval	test number	sign of $\frac{x+2}{x-1}$
$(-\infty, -2)$	-3	$+$
$(-2, 1)$	0	$-$
$(1, \infty)$	2	$+$

Include endpoints which make the numerator equal to 0. Do not include endpoints which make the denominator equal to 0.

Solution: $[-2, 1)$

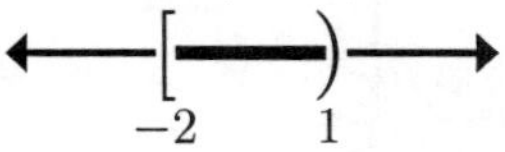

31. $\left|\dfrac{3x+2}{2}\right| = 4$

$\frac{3x+2}{2} = 4$ **or** $\frac{3x+2}{2} = -4$

$3x + 2 = 8$ $\quad$ $3x + 2 = -8$

$3x = 6$ $\quad$ $3x = -10$

$x = 2$ $\quad$ $x = -\frac{10}{3}$

32. $|x + 3| = |x - 3|$

$x + 3 = x - 3$ **or** $x + 3 = -(x - 3)$

$0 = -6$ $\quad$ $x + 3 = -x + 3$

not true $\quad$ $2x = 0$

$x = 0$

33. $|2x - 5| > 2$

$2x - 5 > 2$ **or** $2x - 5 < -2$

$2x > 7$ $\quad$ $2x < 3$

$x > \frac{7}{2}$ $\quad$ $x < \frac{3}{2}$

$(-\infty, \frac{3}{2}) \cup (\frac{7}{2}, \infty)$

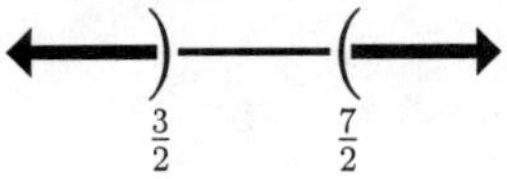

34. $\left|\dfrac{2x+3}{3}\right| \le 5$

$-5 \le \frac{2x+3}{3} \le 5$

$-15 \le 2x + 3 \le 15$

$-18 \le 2x \le 12$

$-9 \le x \le 6$

$[-9, 6]$

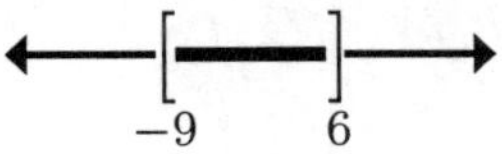

Cumulative Review Exercises (page 158)

1. even integers: $-2, 0, 2, 6$

2. prime numbers: $2, 11$

3. $-4 \le x < 7 \Rightarrow [-4, 7)$

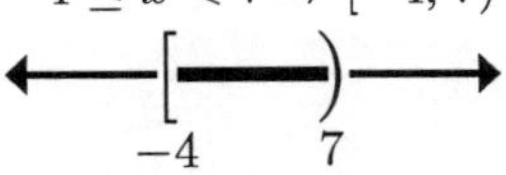

4. $x \ge 2$ or $x < 0 \Rightarrow (-\infty, 0) \cup [2, \infty)$

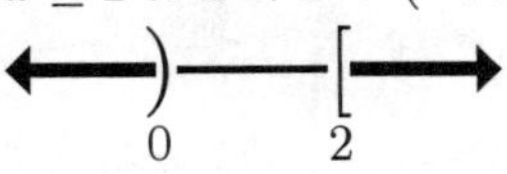

5. commutative property of addition

6. transitive property

7. $(81a^4)^{1/2} = \left[(9a^2)^2\right]^{1/2} = 9a^2$

8. $81(a^4)^{1/2} = 81\left[(a^2)^2\right]^{1/2} = 81a^2$

9. $(a^{-3}b^{-2})^{-2} = (a^{-3})^{-2}(b^{-2})^{-2} = a^6b^4$

10. $\left(\dfrac{4x^4}{12x^2y}\right)^{-2} = \left(\dfrac{12x^2y}{4x^4}\right)^2 = \left(\dfrac{3y}{x^2}\right)^2 = \dfrac{9y^2}{x^4}$

11. $\left(\dfrac{4x^0y^2}{x^2y}\right)^{-2} = \left(\dfrac{x^2y}{4x^0y^2}\right)^2 = \left(\dfrac{x^2}{4y}\right)^2 = \dfrac{x^4}{16y^2}$

12. $\left(\dfrac{4x^{-5}y^2}{6x^{-2}y^{-3}}\right)^2 = \left(\dfrac{2y^5}{3x^3}\right)^2 = \dfrac{4y^{10}}{9x^6}$

13. $(a^{1/2}b)^2(ab^{1/2})^2 = (ab^2)(a^2b) = a^3b^3$

14. $(a^{1/2}b^{1/2}c)^2 = abc^2$

15. $\dfrac{3}{\sqrt{3}} = \dfrac{3\sqrt{3}}{\sqrt{3}\sqrt{3}} = \dfrac{3\sqrt{3}}{3} = \sqrt{3}$

16. $\dfrac{2}{\sqrt[3]{4x}} = \dfrac{2\sqrt[3]{2x^2}}{\sqrt[3]{4x}\sqrt[3]{2x^2}} = \dfrac{2\sqrt[3]{2x^2}}{\sqrt[3]{8x^3}} = \dfrac{2\sqrt[3]{2x^2}}{2x} = \dfrac{\sqrt[3]{2x^2}}{x}$

17. $\dfrac{3}{y-\sqrt{3}} = \dfrac{3\left(y+\sqrt{3}\right)}{\left(y-\sqrt{3}\right)\left(y+\sqrt{3}\right)} = \dfrac{3\left(y+\sqrt{3}\right)}{y^2-\left(\sqrt{3}\right)^2} = \dfrac{3\left(y+\sqrt{3}\right)}{y^2-3}$

18. $\dfrac{3x}{\sqrt{x}-1} = \dfrac{3x(\sqrt{x}+1)}{(\sqrt{x}-1)(\sqrt{x}+1)} = \dfrac{3x(\sqrt{x}+1)}{(\sqrt{x})^2-1^2} = \dfrac{3x(\sqrt{x}+1)}{x-1}$

19. $\sqrt{75} - 3\sqrt{5} = \sqrt{25}\sqrt{3} - 3\sqrt{5} = 5\sqrt{3} - 3\sqrt{5}$

20. $\sqrt{18} + \sqrt{8} - 2\sqrt{2} = \sqrt{9}\sqrt{2} + \sqrt{4}\sqrt{2} - 2\sqrt{2} = 3\sqrt{2} + 2\sqrt{2} - 2\sqrt{2} = 3\sqrt{2}$

21. $\left(\sqrt{2}-\sqrt{3}\right)^2 = \left(\sqrt{2}-\sqrt{3}\right)\left(\sqrt{2}-\sqrt{3}\right) = \sqrt{4} - 2\sqrt{6} + \sqrt{9} = 5 - 2\sqrt{6}$

22. $\left(3-\sqrt{5}\right)\left(3+\sqrt{5}\right) = 9 - \sqrt{25} = 9 - 5 = 4$

23. $(3x^2 - 2x + 5) - 3(x^2 + 2x - 1) = 3x^2 - 2x + 5 - 3x^2 - 6x + 3 = -8x + 8$

24. $5x^2(2x^2 - x) + x(x^2 - x^3) = 10x^4 - 5x^3 + x^3 - x^4 = 9x^4 - 4x^3$

25. $(3x-5)(2x+7) = 6x^2 + 21x - 10x - 35 = 6x^2 + 11x - 35$

26. $(z+2)(z^2 - z + 2) = z^3 - z^2 + 2z + 2z^2 - 2z + 4 = z^3 + z^2 + 4$

27.

$$\begin{array}{r@{}l}
 & \quad 2x^2 - \quad x + \; 1 \\
3x+2 & \overline{)\,6x^3 + \; x^2 + \; x + 2} \\
 & \underline{6x^3 + 4x^2} \\
 & \quad - 3x^2 + \; x \\
 & \quad \underline{- 3x^2 - 2x} \\
 & \qquad\qquad 3x + 2 \\
 & \qquad\qquad \underline{3x + 2} \\
 & \qquad\qquad\quad 0
\end{array}$$

28.

$$\begin{array}{r@{}l}
 & \quad 3x^2 + \quad 1 + \; \frac{-x}{x^2+2} \\
x^2+2 & \overline{)\,3x^4 + 0x^3 + 7x^2 - x + 2} \\
 & \underline{3x^4 \qquad\quad + 6x^2} \\
 & \qquad\qquad x^2 - x + 2 \\
 & \qquad\qquad \underline{x^2 \qquad + 2} \\
 & \qquad\qquad\quad - x
\end{array}$$

29. $3t^2 - 6t = 3t(t-2)$

30. $3x^2 - 10x - 8 = (3x+2)(x-4)$

31.
$$\begin{aligned}
x^8 - 2x^4 + 1 = (x^4-1)(x^4-1) &= (x^2+1)(x^2-1)(x^2+1)(x^2-1) \\
&= (x^2+1)^2(x+1)(x-1)(x+1)(x-1) \\
&= (x^2+1)^2(x+1)^2(x-1)^2
\end{aligned}$$

32. $x^6 - 1 = (x^3)^2 - 1^2 = (x^3+1)(x^3-1) = (x+1)(x^2-x+1)(x-1)(x^2+x+1)$

33. $$\frac{x^2-4}{x^2+5x+6} \cdot \frac{x^2-2x-15}{x^2+3x-10} = \frac{(x+2)(x-2)}{(x+2)(x+3)} \cdot \frac{(x-5)(x+3)}{(x+5)(x-2)} = \frac{x-5}{x+5}$$

34.
$$\begin{aligned}
\frac{6x^3+x^2-x}{x+2} \div \frac{3x^2-x}{x^2+4x+4} &= \frac{x(6x^2+x-1)}{x+2} \cdot \frac{x^2+4x+4}{3x^2-x} \\
&= \frac{x(2x+1)(3x-1)}{x+2} \cdot \frac{(x+2)(x+2)}{x(3x-1)} = (2x+1)(x+2)
\end{aligned}$$

35.
$$\begin{aligned}
\frac{2}{x+3} + \frac{5x}{x-3} = \frac{2(x-3)}{(x+3)(x-3)} + \frac{5x(x+3)}{(x-3)(x+3)} &= \frac{2x-6}{(x+3)(x-3)} + \frac{5x^2+15x}{(x+3)(x-3)} \\
&= \frac{5x^2+17x-6}{(x+3)(x-3)}
\end{aligned}$$

36. $$\frac{x-2}{x+3}\left(\frac{x+3}{x^2-4} - 1\right) = \frac{x-2}{x+3}\left(\frac{x+3}{x^2-4} - \frac{x^2-4}{x^2-4}\right) = \frac{x-2}{x+3}\left(\frac{-x^2+x+7}{(x+2)(x-2)}\right) = \frac{-x^2+x+7}{(x+3)(x+2)}$$

37. $$\frac{\frac{1}{a}+\frac{1}{b}}{\frac{1}{ab}} = \frac{ab\left(\frac{1}{a}+\frac{1}{b}\right)}{ab\left(\frac{1}{ab}\right)} = \frac{b+a}{1} = b+a$$

38.
$$\begin{aligned}
\frac{x^{-1}-y^{-1}}{x-y} = \frac{\frac{1}{x}-\frac{1}{y}}{x-y} &= \frac{xy\left(\frac{1}{x}-\frac{1}{y}\right)}{xy(x-y)} \\
&= \frac{y-x}{xy(x-y)} = -\frac{1}{xy}
\end{aligned}$$

39.
$$\begin{aligned}\frac{3x}{x+5} &= \frac{x}{x-5}\\ 3x(x-5) &= x(x+5)\\ 3x^2-15x &= x^2+5x\\ 2x^2-20x &= 0\\ 2x(x-10) &= 0\\ 2x = 0 \quad &\textbf{or} \quad x-10=0\\ x = 0 \quad & \qquad\quad x = 10\end{aligned}$$

40.
$$\begin{aligned}8(2x-3)-3(5x+2) &= 4\\ 16x-24-15x-6 &= 4\\ x &= 34\end{aligned}$$

41.
$$\begin{aligned}\frac{1}{R} &= \frac{1}{R_1}+\frac{1}{R_2}\\ RR_1R_2\cdot\frac{1}{R} &= RR_1R_2\left(\frac{1}{R_1}+\frac{1}{R_2}\right)\\ R_1R_2 &= RR_2+RR_1\\ R_1R_2 &= R(R_2+R_1)\\ \frac{R_1R_2}{R_2+R_1} &= \frac{R(R_2+R_1)}{R_2+R_1}\\ \frac{R_1R_2}{R_2+R_1} &= R\end{aligned}$$

42.
$$\begin{aligned}S &= \frac{a-lr}{1-r}\\ S(1-r) &= \frac{a-lr}{1-r}(1-r)\\ S(1-r) &= a-lr\\ S-Sr &= a-lr\\ S-a &= Sr-lr\\ S-a &= r(S-l)\\ \frac{S-a}{S-l} &= r\end{aligned}$$

43.

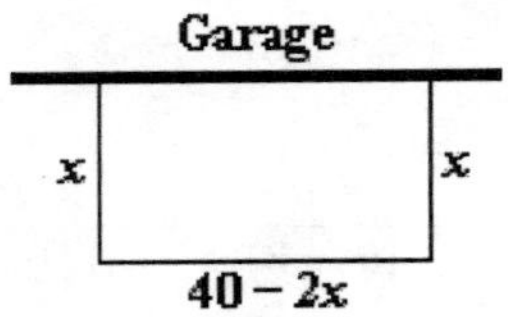

$$\begin{aligned}\text{Area} &= 192\\ x(40-2x) &= 192\\ 40x-2x^2 &= 192\\ 0 &= 2x^2-40x+192\\ 0 &= 2(x-8)(x-12)\\ x-8=0 \quad &\textbf{or} \quad x-12=0\\ x=8 \quad & \qquad\quad x=12\end{aligned}$$

If $x = 8$, then the dimensions are 8 feet by 24 feet.
If $x = 12$, then the dimensions are 12 feet by 16 feet.

44. Let $x =$ the amount invested at 6%. Then $25{,}000 - x =$ the amount invested at 7%.

$$\boxed{\text{Interest at 6\%}} + \boxed{\text{Interest at 7\%}} = \boxed{\text{Total interest}}$$

$$\begin{aligned}0.06x+0.07(25{,}000-x) &= 1{,}670\\ 0.06x+1{,}750-0.07x &= 1{,}670\\ -0.01x &= -80\\ x &= 8{,}000 \Rightarrow \text{\$8,000 was invested at 6\%.}\end{aligned}$$

45. $$\frac{2+i}{2-i} = \frac{(2+i)(2+i)}{(2-i)(2+i)} = \frac{4+4i+i^2}{4-i^2} = \frac{3+4i}{5} = \frac{3}{5}+\frac{4}{5}i$$

CUMULATIVE REVIEW EXERCISES

46. $$\frac{i(3-i)}{(1+i)(1+i)} = \frac{i(3-i)(1-i)(1-i)}{(1+i)(1-i)(1+i)(1-i)} = \frac{(3i-i^2)(1-2i+i^2)}{(1-i^2)(1-i^2)}$$
$$= \frac{(1+3i)(-2i)}{1-2i^2+i^4}$$
$$= \frac{-2i-6i^2}{4}$$
$$= \frac{6-2i}{4} = \frac{3}{2} - \frac{1}{2}i$$

47. $|3+4i| = \sqrt{3^2+4^2} = \sqrt{9+16} = \sqrt{25} = 5$

48. $\frac{5}{i^7} + 5i = \frac{5i}{i^7 i} + 5i = \frac{5i}{i^8} + 5i = \frac{5i}{(i^4)^2} + 5i = \frac{5i}{1^2} + 5i = 5i + 5i = 10i = 0 + 10i$

49.
$$\frac{x+3}{x-1} - \frac{6}{x} = 1$$
$$x(x-1)\left(\frac{x+3}{x-1} - \frac{6}{x}\right) = x(x-1)(1)$$
$$x(x+3) - 6(x-1) = x^2 - x$$
$$x^2 + 3x - 6x + 6 = x^2 - x$$
$$-2x = -6$$
$$x = 3$$

50.
$$x^4 + 36 = 13x^2$$
$$x^4 - 13x^2 + 36 = 0$$
$$(x^2-4)(x^2-9) = 0$$
$x^2 - 4 = 0$ **or** $x^2 - 9 = 0$
$x^2 = 4$ $\quad$ $x^2 = 9$
$x = \pm 2$ $\quad$ $x = \pm 3$

51.
$$\sqrt{y+2} + \sqrt{11-y} = 5$$
$$\sqrt{y+2} - 5 = -\sqrt{11-y}$$
$$\left(\sqrt{y+2} - 5\right)^2 = \left(-\sqrt{11-y}\right)^2$$
$$y + 2 - 10\sqrt{y+2} + 25 = 11 - y$$
$$-10\sqrt{y+2} = -2y - 16$$
$$\left(-10\sqrt{y+2}\right)^2 = (-2y+16)^2$$
$$100(y+2) = 4y^2 - 64y + 256$$
$$100y + 200 = 4y^2 - 64y + 256$$
$$0 = 4y^2 - 36y + 56$$
$$0 = 4(y-2)(y-7)$$
$y - 2 = 0$ **or** $y - 7 = 0$
$y = 2$ $\quad$ $y = 7$
Both solutions check.

52.
$$z^{2/3} - 13z^{1/3} + 36 = 0$$
$$\left(z^{1/3} - 4\right)\left(z^{1/3} - 9\right) = 0$$
$z^{1/3} - 4 = 0$ **or** $z^{1/3} - 9 = 0$
$z^{1/3} = 4$ $\quad$ $z^{1/3} = 9$
$\left(z^{1/3}\right)^3 = 4^3$ $\quad$ $\left(z^{1/3}\right)^3 = 9^3$
$z = 64$ $\quad$ $z = 729$
Both solutions check.

53. $5x - 7 \le 4$

$5x \le 11$

$x \le \frac{11}{5} \Rightarrow (-\infty, \frac{11}{5}]$

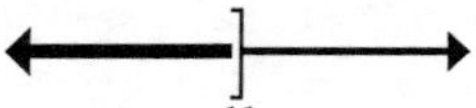

$\frac{11}{5}$

54. $x^2 - 8x + 15 > 0$

$(x-3)(x-5) > 0$

factors $= 0$: $x = 3$, $x = 5$

intervals: $(-\infty, 3)$, $(3, 5)$, $(5, \infty)$

interval	test number	value of $x^2-8x+15$
$(-\infty, 3)$	0	$+15$
$(3, 5)$	4	-1
$(5, \infty)$	6	$+3$

Solution: $(-\infty, 3) \cup (5, \infty)$

3 5

55. $\dfrac{x^2 + 4x + 3}{x - 2} \ge 0$

$\dfrac{(x+3)(x+1)}{x-2} \ge 0$

factors $= 0$: $x = -3$, $x = -1$, $x = 2$

int.: $(-\infty, -3)$, $(-3, -1)$, $(-1, 2)$, $(2, \infty)$

interval	test number	sign of $\frac{x^2+4x+3}{x-2}$
$(-\infty, -3)$	-4	$-$
$(-3, -1)$	-2	$+$
$(-1, 2)$	0	$-$
$(2, \infty)$	3	$+$

Include endpoints which make the numerator equal to 0. Do not include endpoints which make the denominator equal to 0.

Solution: $[-3, -1] \cup (2, \infty)$

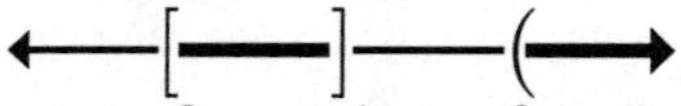

-3 -1 2

56. $\dfrac{9}{x} > x$

$\dfrac{9}{x} - x > 0$

$\dfrac{9 - x^2}{x} > 0$

$\dfrac{(3+x)(3-x)}{x} > 0$

factors $= 0$: $x = -3$, $x = 3$, $x = 0$

int.: $(-\infty, -3)$, $(-3, 0)$, $(0, 3)$, $(3, \infty)$

interval	test number	sign of $\frac{9-x^2}{x}$
$(-\infty, -3)$	-4	$+$
$(-3, 0)$	-1	$-$
$(0, 3)$	1	$+$
$(3, \infty)$	4	$-$

Solution: $(-\infty, -3) \cup (0, 3)$

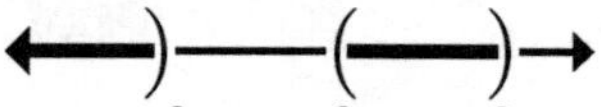

-3 0 3

57. $|2x - 3| \ge 5$

$2x - 3 \ge 5$ **or** $2x - 3 \le -5$

$2x \ge 8$ $\quad$ $2x \le -2$

$x \ge 4$ $\quad$ $x \le -1$

$(-\infty, -1] \cup [4, \infty)$

-1 4

58. $\left|\dfrac{3x-5}{2}\right| < 2$

$-2 < \dfrac{3x-5}{2} < 2$

$-4 < 3x - 5 < 4$

$1 < 3x < 9$

$\frac{1}{3} < x < 3$

$(\frac{1}{3}, 3)$

$\frac{1}{3}$ 3

Exercise 2.1 (page 173)

1. quadrants **2.** origin **3.** to the right **4.** upward

5. first **6.** second **7.** linear **8.** y-axis

9. x-intercept **10.** vertical **11.** horizontal

12. $\sqrt{(x_2 - x_1)^2 + (y_2 - y_1)^2}$ **13.** midpoint **14.** $M\left(\frac{x_1 + x_2}{2}, \frac{y_1 + y_2}{2}\right)$

15. $A(2, 3)$ **16.** $B(-3, 5)$ **17.** $C(-2, -3)$ **18.** $D(4, -5)$

19. $E(0, 0)$ **20.** $F(-4, 0)$ **21.** $G(-5, -5)$ **22.** $H(2, -2)$

23, 25, 27, 29.

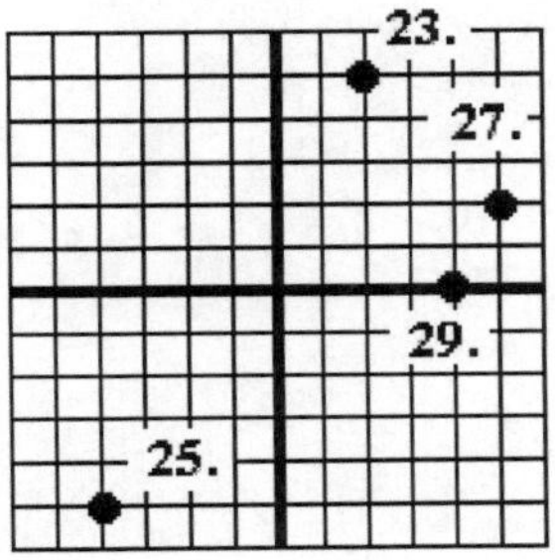

23. QI

25. QIII

27. QI

29. $+\,x$-axis

24, 26, 28, 30.

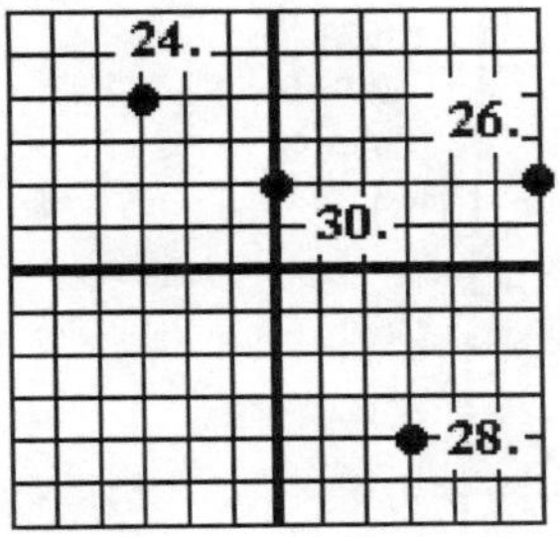

24. QII

26. QI

28. QIV

30. $+\,y$-axis

31.
$$\begin{aligned} x + y &= 5 \\ x + 0 &= 5 \\ x &= 5 \end{aligned} \qquad \begin{aligned} x + y &= 5 \\ 0 + y &= 5 \\ y &= 5 \end{aligned}$$
(5, 0) (0, 5)

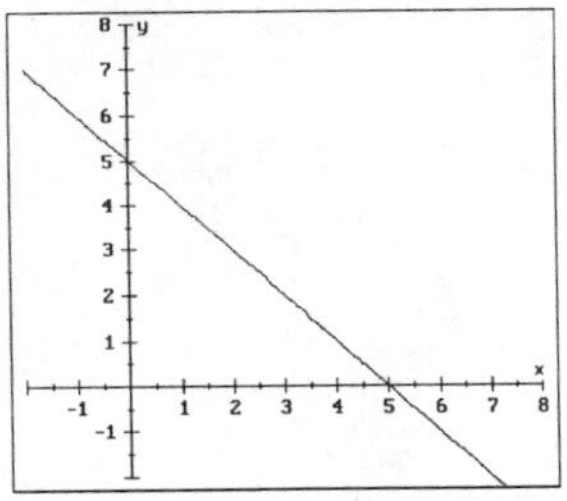

32.
$$\begin{aligned} x - y &= 3 \\ x - 0 &= 3 \\ x &= 3 \end{aligned} \qquad \begin{aligned} x - y &= 3 \\ 0 - y &= 3 \\ -y &= 3 \\ y &= -3 \end{aligned}$$
(3, 0) (0, −3)

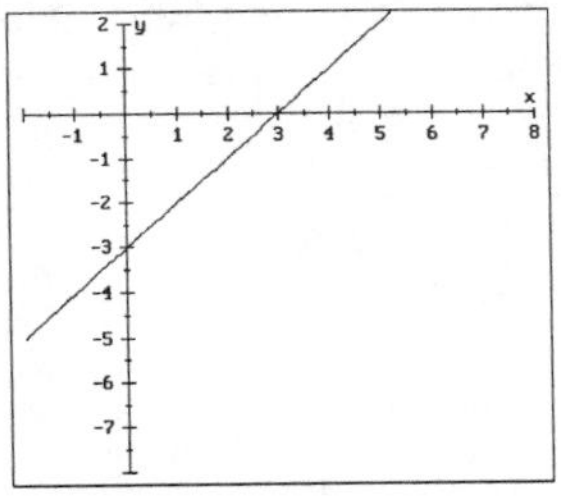

33.

$$\begin{aligned} 2x - y &= 4 \\ 2x - 0 &= 4 \\ 2x &= 4 \\ x &= 2 \end{aligned} \qquad \begin{aligned} 2x - y &= 4 \\ 2(0) - y &= 4 \\ -y &= 4 \\ y &= -4 \end{aligned}$$

$(2, 0)$ $\qquad$ $(0, -4)$

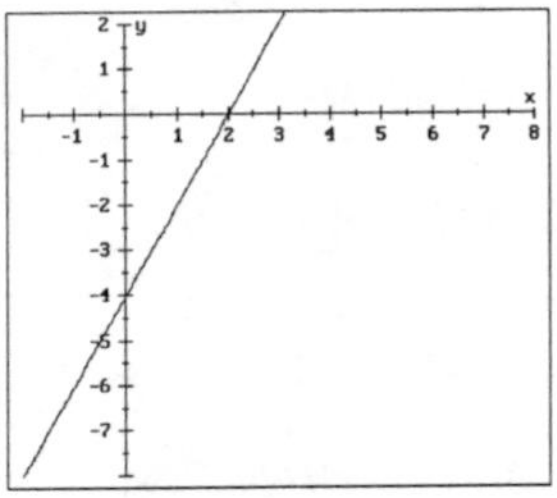

34.

$$\begin{aligned} 3x + y &= 9 \\ 3x + 0 &= 9 \\ 3x &= 9 \\ x &= 3 \end{aligned} \qquad \begin{aligned} 3x + y &= 9 \\ 3(0) + y &= 9 \\ y &= 9 \\ (0, 9)& \end{aligned}$$

$(3, 0)$

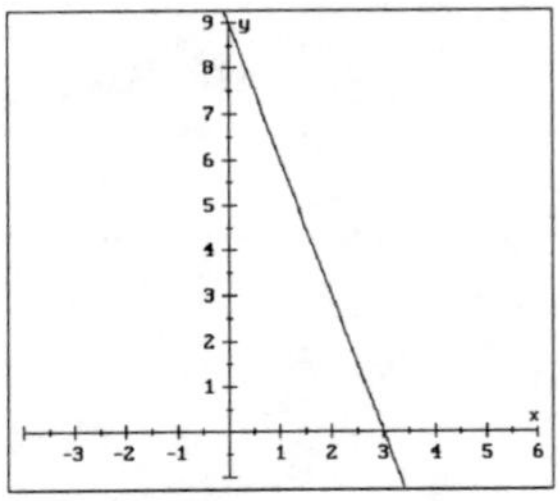

35.

$$\begin{aligned} 3x + 2y &= 6 \\ 3x + 2(0) &= 6 \\ 3x &= 6 \\ x &= 2 \end{aligned} \qquad \begin{aligned} 3x + 2y &= 6 \\ 3(0) + 2y &= 6 \\ 2y &= 6 \\ y &= 3 \end{aligned}$$

$(2, 0)$ $\qquad$ $(0, 3)$

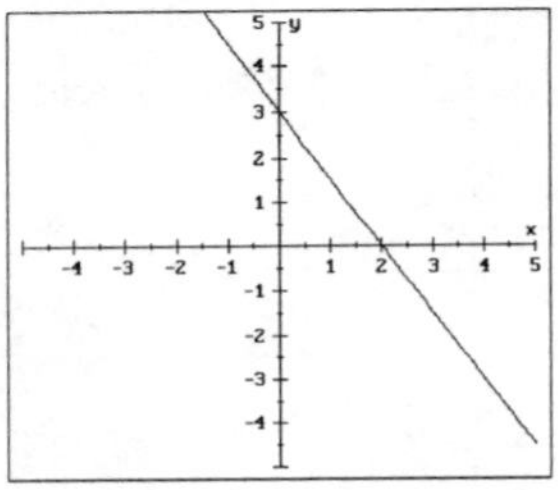

36.

$$\begin{aligned} 2x - 3y &= 6 \\ 2x - 3(0) &= 6 \\ 2x &= 6 \\ x &= 3 \end{aligned} \qquad \begin{aligned} 2x - 3y &= 6 \\ 2(0) - 3y &= 6 \\ -3y &= 6 \\ y &= -2 \end{aligned}$$

$(3, 0)$ $\qquad$ $(0, -2)$

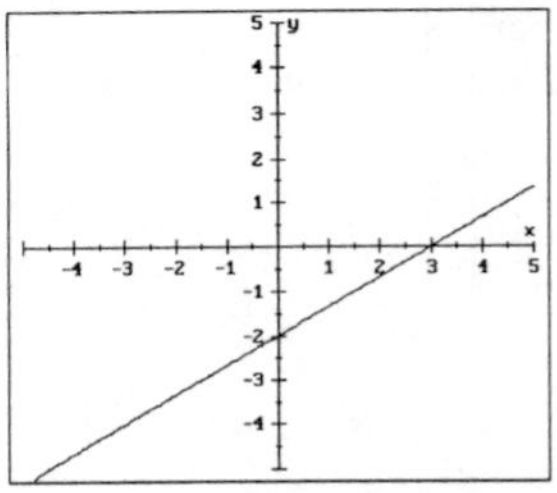

37.

$$\begin{aligned} 4x - 5y &= 20 \\ 4x - 5(0) &= 20 \\ 4x &= 20 \\ x &= 5 \end{aligned} \qquad \begin{aligned} 4x - 5y &= 20 \\ 4(0) - 5y &= 20 \\ -5y &= 20 \\ y &= -4 \end{aligned}$$

$(5, 0)$ $\qquad$ $(0, -4)$

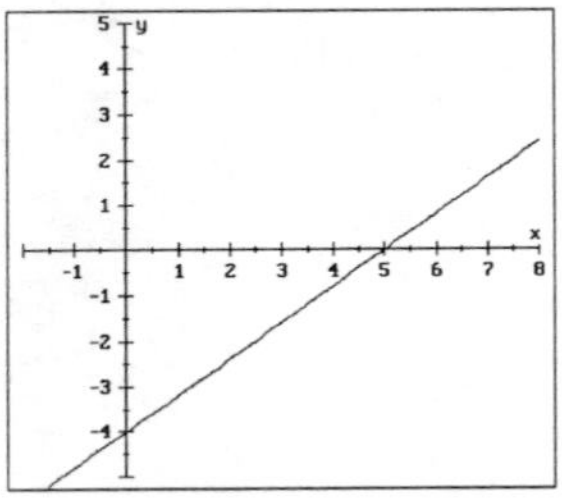

38.

$$\begin{aligned} 3x - 5y &= 15 \\ 3x - 5(0) &= 15 \\ 3x &= 15 \\ x &= 5 \end{aligned} \qquad \begin{aligned} 3x - 5y &= 15 \\ 3(0) - 5y &= 15 \\ -5y &= 15 \\ y &= -3 \end{aligned}$$

$(5, 0)$ $\qquad$ $(0, -3)$

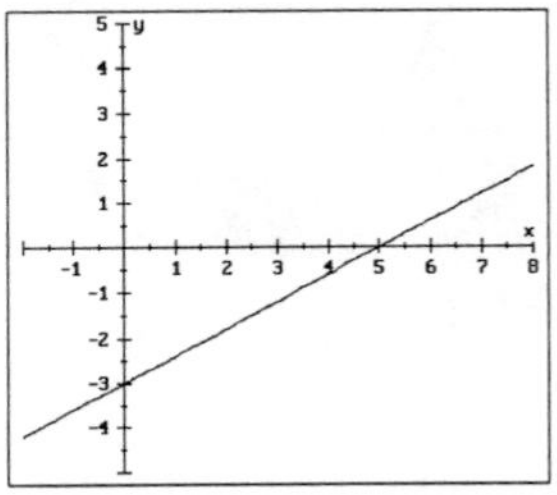

39. $y - 2x = 7$

$y = 2x + 7$

x	y
0	7
−2	3

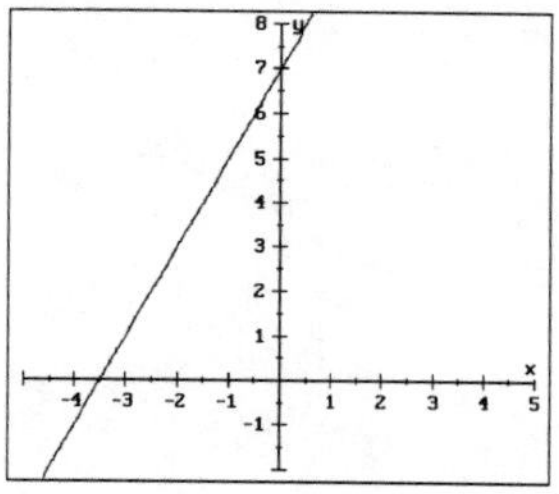

40. $y + 3 = -4x$

$y = -4x - 3$

x	y
0	−3
−1	1

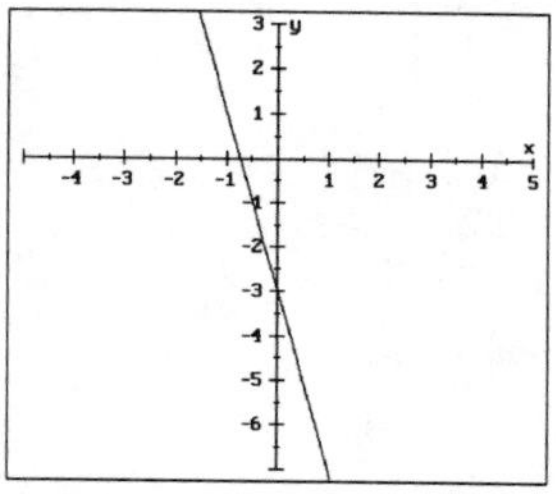

41. $y + 5x = 5$

$y = -5x + 5$

x	y
0	5
1	0

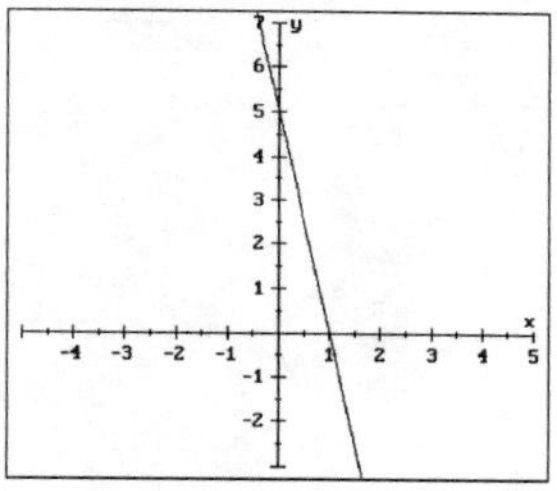

42. $y - 3x = 6$

$y = 3x + 6$

x	y
0	6
−2	0

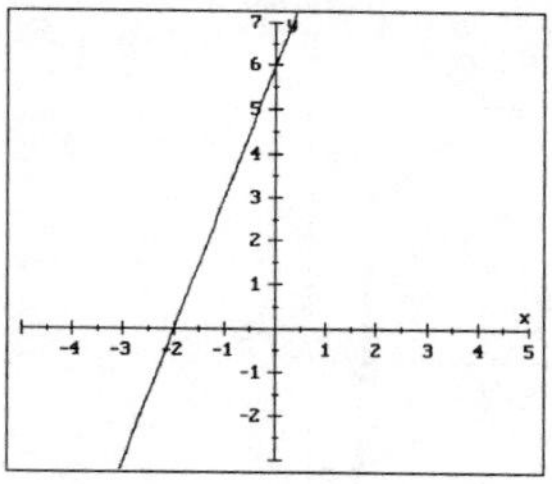

43. $6x - 3y = 10$

$-3y = -6x + 10$

$y = 2x - \frac{10}{3}$

x	y
0	$-\frac{10}{3}$
2	$\frac{2}{3}$

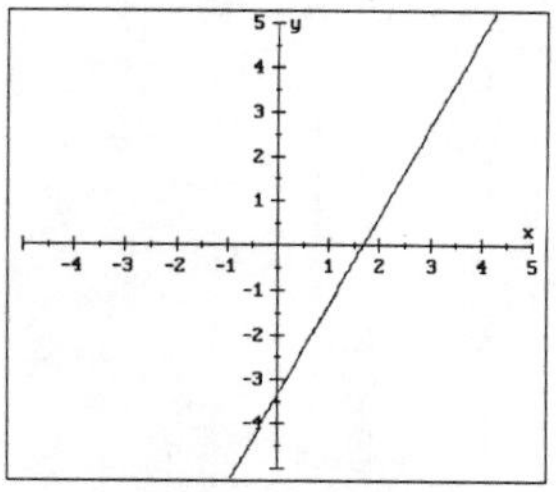

44. $4x + 8y - 1 = 0$

$8y = -4x + 1$

$y = -\frac{1}{2}x + \frac{1}{8}$

x	y
0	$\frac{1}{8}$
4	$-\frac{15}{8}$

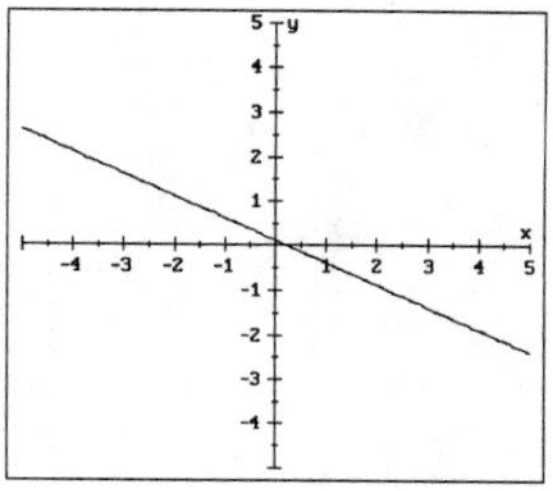

45.
$$3x = 6y - 1$$
$$-6y = -3x - 1$$
$$y = \tfrac{1}{2}x + \tfrac{1}{6}$$

x	y
0	$\frac{1}{6}$
-2	$-\frac{5}{6}$

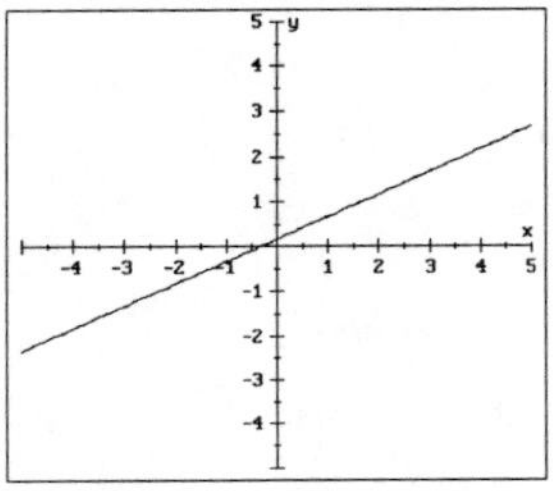

46.
$$2x + 1 = 4y$$
$$-4y = -2x - 1$$
$$y = \tfrac{1}{2}x + \tfrac{1}{4}$$

x	y
0	$\frac{1}{4}$
-2	$-\frac{3}{4}$

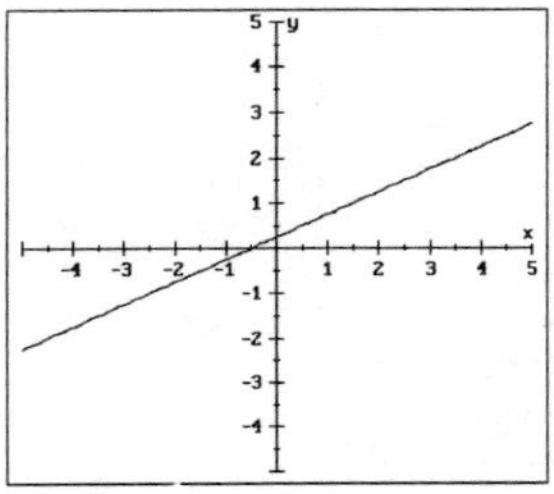

47.
$$2(x + y + 1) = x + 2$$
$$2x + 2y + 2 = x + 2$$
$$2y = -x$$
$$y = -\tfrac{1}{2}x$$

x	y
0	0
-2	1

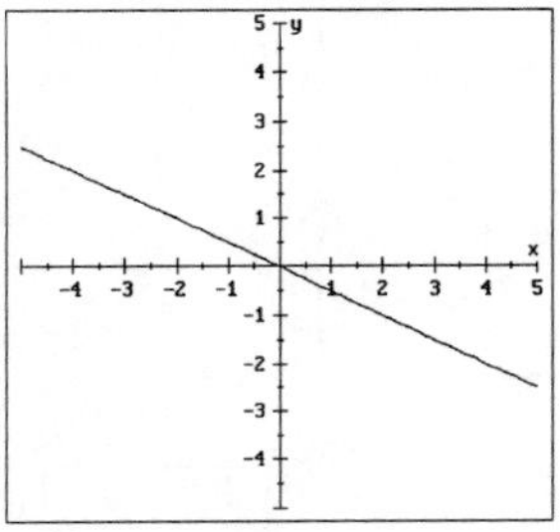

48.
$$5(x + 2) = 3y - x$$
$$5x + 10 = 3y - x$$
$$-3y = -6x - 10$$
$$y = 2x + \tfrac{10}{3}$$

x	y
0	$\frac{10}{3}$
-2	$-\frac{2}{3}$

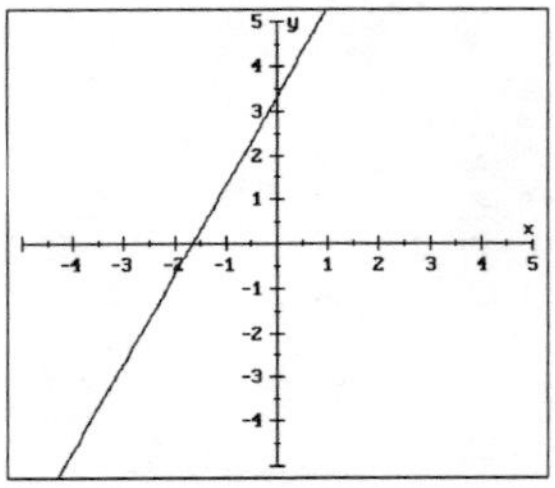

49. $y = 3$

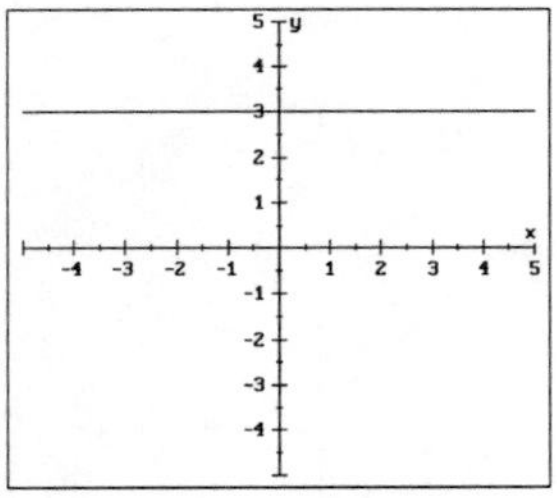

50. $x = -4$

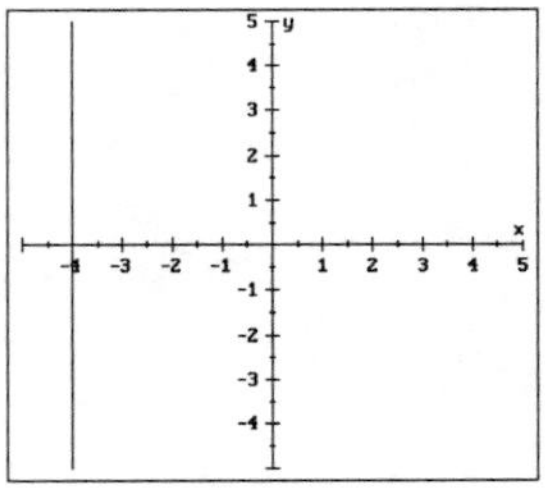

51.
$$3x + 5 = -1$$
$$3x = -6 \Rightarrow x = -2$$

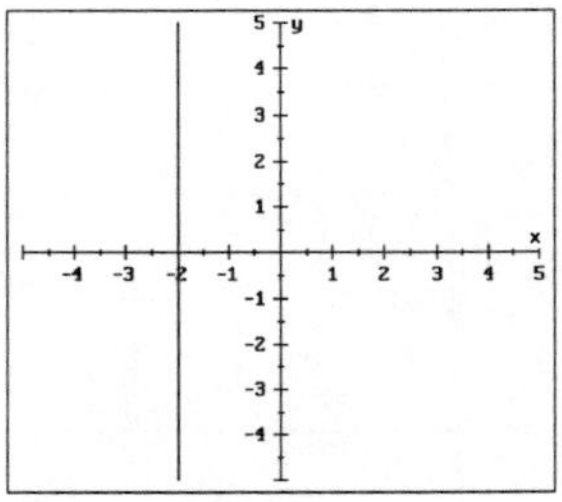

52. $7y - 1 = 6$

$7y = 7 \Rightarrow y = 1$

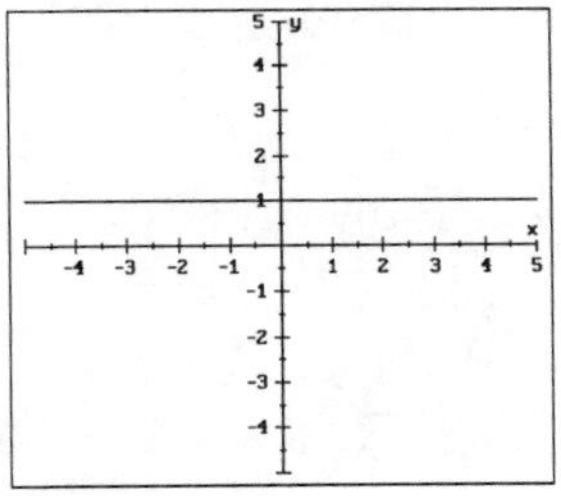

53. $3(y + 2) = y$

$3y + 6 = y$

$2y = -6 \Rightarrow y = -3$

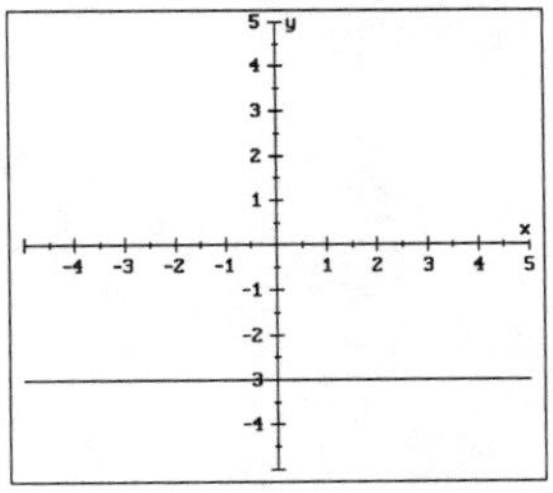

54. $4 + 3y = 3(x + y)$

$4 + 3y = 3x + 3y$

$4 = 3x \Rightarrow x = \frac{4}{3}$

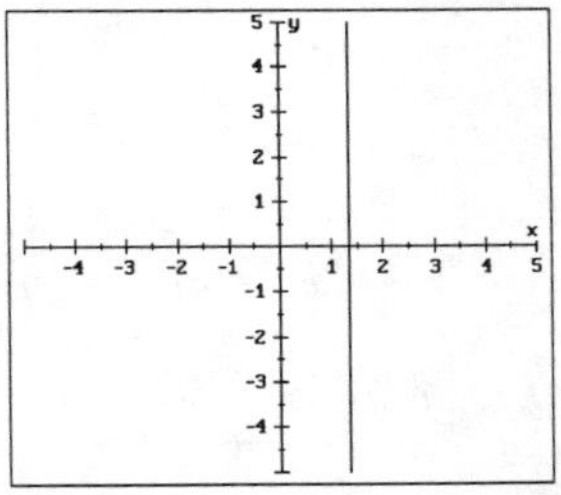

55. $3(y + 2x) = 6x + y$

$3y + 6x = 6x + y$

$2y = 0 \Rightarrow y = 0$

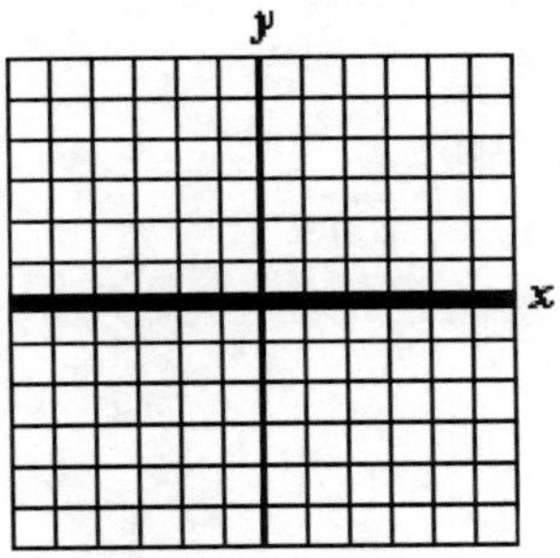

56. $5(y - x) = x + 5y$

$5y - 5x = x + 5y$

$0 = 6x \Rightarrow x = 0$

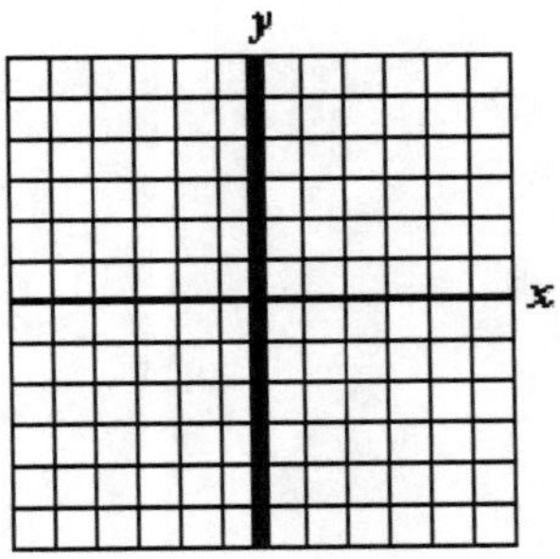

57. $y = 3.7x - 4.5$

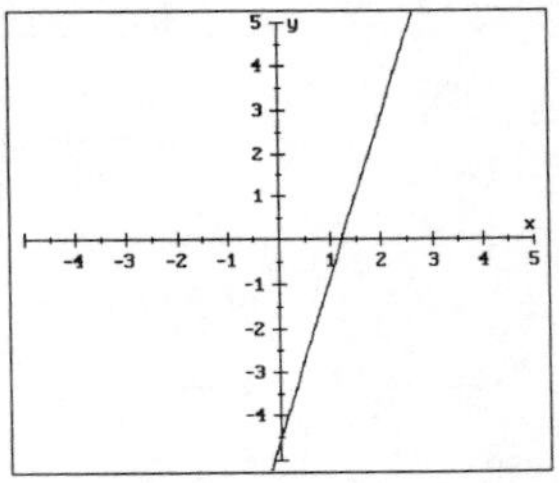

x-int: $x = 1.22$

58. $y = \dfrac{3}{5}x + \dfrac{5}{4}$

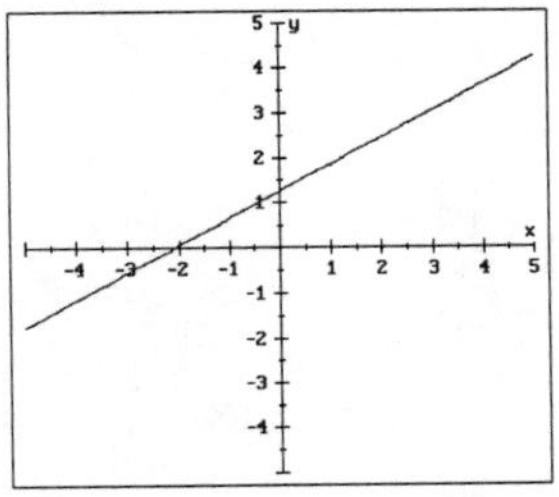

x-int: $x = -2.08$

59. $1.5x - 3y = 7$

$-3y = -1.5x + 7$

$y = 0.5x - \frac{7}{3}$

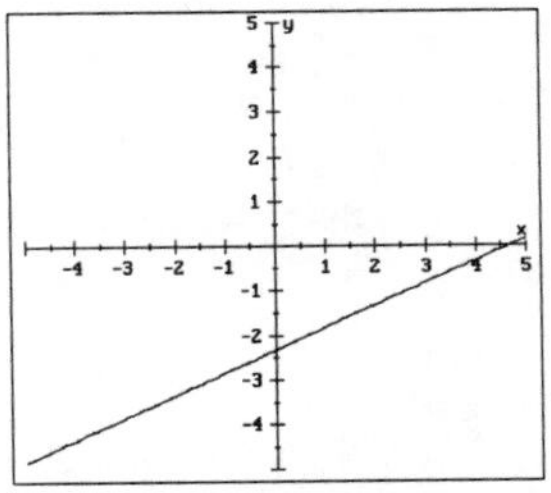

x-int: $x = 4.67$

60. $0.3x + y = 7.5$

$y = -0.3x + 7.5$

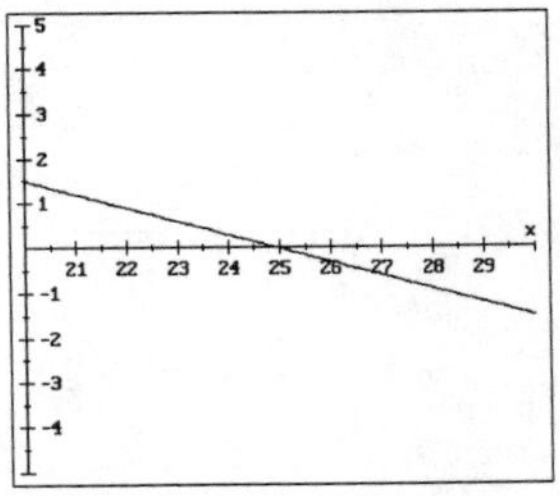

x-int: $x = 25.00$

61. $$\begin{aligned} d &= \sqrt{(x_2 - x_1)^2 + (y_2 - y_1)^2} \\ &= \sqrt{(4-0)^2 + (-3-0)^2} \\ &= \sqrt{4^2 + (-3)^2} \\ &= \sqrt{16+9} = \sqrt{25} = 5 \end{aligned}$$

62. $$\begin{aligned} d &= \sqrt{(x_2 - x_1)^2 + (y_2 - y_1)^2} \\ &= \sqrt{(-5-0)^2 + (12-0)^2} \\ &= \sqrt{(-5)^2 + (12)^2} \\ &= \sqrt{25+144} = \sqrt{169} = 13 \end{aligned}$$

63. $$\begin{aligned} d &= \sqrt{(x_2 - x_1)^2 + (y_2 - y_1)^2} \\ &= \sqrt{(-3-0)^2 + (2-0)^2} \\ &= \sqrt{(-3)^2 + (2)^2} \\ &= \sqrt{9+4} = \sqrt{13} \end{aligned}$$

64. $$\begin{aligned} d &= \sqrt{(x_2 - x_1)^2 + (y_2 - y_1)^2} \\ &= \sqrt{(5-0)^2 + (0-0)^2} \\ &= \sqrt{(5)^2 + (0)^2} \\ &= \sqrt{25+0} = \sqrt{25} = 5 \end{aligned}$$

65. $$\begin{aligned} d &= \sqrt{(x_2 - x_1)^2 + (y_2 - y_1)^2} \\ &= \sqrt{(1-0)^2 + (1-0)^2} \\ &= \sqrt{(1)^2 + (1)^2} \\ &= \sqrt{1+1} = \sqrt{2} \end{aligned}$$

66. $$\begin{aligned} d &= \sqrt{(x_2 - x_1)^2 + (y_2 - y_1)^2} \\ &= \sqrt{(6-0)^2 + (-8-0)^2} \\ &= \sqrt{(6)^2 + (-8)^2} \\ &= \sqrt{36+64} = \sqrt{100} = 10 \end{aligned}$$

67. $$\begin{aligned} d &= \sqrt{(x_2 - x_1)^2 + (y_2 - y_1)^2} \\ &= \sqrt{\left(\sqrt{3}-0\right)^2 + (1-0)^2} \\ &= \sqrt{\left(\sqrt{3}\right)^2 + (1)^2} \\ &= \sqrt{3+1} = \sqrt{4} = 2 \end{aligned}$$

68. $$\begin{aligned} d &= \sqrt{(x_2 - x_1)^2 + (y_2 - y_1)^2} \\ &= \sqrt{\left(\sqrt{7}-0\right)^2 + \left(\sqrt{2}-0\right)^2} \\ &= \sqrt{\left(\sqrt{7}\right)^2 + \left(\sqrt{2}\right)^2} \\ &= \sqrt{7+2} = \sqrt{9} = 3 \end{aligned}$$

69. $$\begin{aligned} d &= \sqrt{(x_2 - x_1)^2 + (y_2 - y_1)^2} \\ &= \sqrt{(3-6)^2 + (7-3)^2} \\ &= \sqrt{(-3)^2 + (4)^2} \\ &= \sqrt{9+16} = \sqrt{25} = 5 \end{aligned}$$

70. $$\begin{aligned} d &= \sqrt{(x_2 - x_1)^2 + (y_2 - y_1)^2} \\ &= \sqrt{(4-9)^2 + (9-21)^2} \\ &= \sqrt{(-5)^2 + (-12)^2} \\ &= \sqrt{25+144} = \sqrt{169} = 13 \end{aligned}$$

71. $$\begin{aligned} d &= \sqrt{(x_2 - x_1)^2 + (y_2 - y_1)^2} \\ &= \sqrt{[4-(-1)]^2 + [-6-6]^2} \\ &= \sqrt{(5)^2 + (-12)^2} \\ &= \sqrt{25+144} = \sqrt{169} = 13 \end{aligned}$$

72. $$\begin{aligned} d &= \sqrt{(x_2 - x_1)^2 + (y_2 - y_1)^2} \\ &= \sqrt{[0-6]^2 + [5-(-3)]^2} \\ &= \sqrt{(-6)^2 + (8)^2} \\ &= \sqrt{36+64} = \sqrt{100} = 10 \end{aligned}$$

73.
$$\begin{aligned} d &= \sqrt{(x_2-x_1)^2+(y_2-y_1)^2} \\ &= \sqrt{[-2-(-9)]^2+[-15-(-39)]^2} \\ &= \sqrt{(7)^2+(24)^2} \\ &= \sqrt{49+576} = \sqrt{625} = 25 \end{aligned}$$

74.
$$\begin{aligned} d &= \sqrt{(x_2-x_1)^2+(y_2-y_1)^2} \\ &= \sqrt{[-7-3]^2+[11-(-13)]^2} \\ &= \sqrt{(-10)^2+(24)^2} \\ &= \sqrt{100+576} = \sqrt{676} = 26 \end{aligned}$$

75.
$$\begin{aligned} d &= \sqrt{(x_2-x_1)^2+(y_2-y_1)^2} \\ &= \sqrt{[3-(-5)]^2+[-3-5]^2} \\ &= \sqrt{(8)^2+(-8)^2} \\ &= \sqrt{64+64} = \sqrt{128} = 8\sqrt{2} \end{aligned}$$

76.
$$\begin{aligned} d &= \sqrt{(x_2-x_1)^2+(y_2-y_1)^2} \\ &= \sqrt{[6-(-3)]^2+[-3-2]^2} \\ &= \sqrt{(9)^2+(-5)^2} \\ &= \sqrt{81+25} = \sqrt{106} \end{aligned}$$

77.
$$\begin{aligned} d &= \sqrt{(x_2-x_1)^2+(y_2-y_1)^2} \\ &= \sqrt{[\pi-\pi]^2+[-2-5]^2} \\ &= \sqrt{(0)^2+(-7)^2} \\ &= \sqrt{0+49} = \sqrt{49} = 7 \end{aligned}$$

78.
$$\begin{aligned} d &= \sqrt{(x_2-x_1)^2+(y_2-y_1)^2} \\ &= \sqrt{\left[\sqrt{5}-0\right]^2+[0-2]^2} \\ &= \sqrt{\left(\sqrt{5}\right)^2+(-2)^2} \\ &= \sqrt{5+4} = \sqrt{9} = 3 \end{aligned}$$

79. $M\left(\frac{x_1+x_2}{2}, \frac{y_1+y_2}{2}\right) = M\left(\frac{2+6}{2}, \frac{4+8}{2}\right) = M\left(\frac{8}{2}, \frac{12}{2}\right) = M(4, 6)$

80. $M\left(\frac{x_1+x_2}{2}, \frac{y_1+y_2}{2}\right) = M\left(\frac{3+(-1)}{2}, \frac{-6+(-6)}{2}\right) = M\left(\frac{2}{2}, \frac{-12}{2}\right) = M(1, -6)$

81. $M\left(\frac{x_1+x_2}{2}, \frac{y_1+y_2}{2}\right) = M\left(\frac{2+(-2)}{2}, \frac{-5+7}{2}\right) = M\left(\frac{0}{2}, \frac{2}{2}\right) = M(0, 1)$

82. $M\left(\frac{x_1+x_2}{2}, \frac{y_1+y_2}{2}\right) = M\left(\frac{0+(-10)}{2}, \frac{3+(-13)}{2}\right) = M\left(\frac{-10}{2}, \frac{-10}{2}\right) = M(-5, -5)$

83. $M\left(\frac{x_1+x_2}{2}, \frac{y_1+y_2}{2}\right) = M\left(\frac{-8+8}{2}, \frac{5+(-5)}{2}\right) = M\left(\frac{0}{2}, \frac{0}{2}\right) = M(0, 0)$

84. $M\left(\frac{x_1+x_2}{2}, \frac{y_1+y_2}{2}\right) = M\left(\frac{3+2}{2}, \frac{-2+(-3)}{2}\right) = M\left(\frac{5}{2}, \frac{-5}{2}\right) = M\left(\frac{5}{2}, -\frac{5}{2}\right)$

85. $M\left(\frac{x_1+x_2}{2}, \frac{y_1+y_2}{2}\right) = M\left(\frac{0+\sqrt{5}}{2}, \frac{0+\sqrt{5}}{2}\right) = M\left(\frac{\sqrt{5}}{2}, \frac{\sqrt{5}}{2}\right)$

86. $M\left(\frac{x_1+x_2}{2}, \frac{y_1+y_2}{2}\right) = M\left(\frac{\sqrt{3}+0}{2}, \frac{0+\left(-\sqrt{5}\right)}{2}\right) = M\left(\frac{\sqrt{3}}{2}, \frac{-\sqrt{5}}{2}\right) = M\left(\frac{\sqrt{3}}{2}, -\frac{\sqrt{5}}{2}\right)$

87. Let Q have coordinates (x, y):
$M\left(\frac{x_1+x_2}{2}, \frac{y_1+y_2}{2}\right) = (3, 5)$

$$\frac{x_1+x_2}{2} = 3 \qquad \frac{y_1+y_2}{2} = 5$$
$$\frac{1+x}{2} = 3 \qquad \frac{4+y}{2} = 5$$
$$1+x = 6 \qquad 4+y = 10$$
$$x = 5 \qquad y = 6$$

$Q(5, 6)$

88. Let Q have coordinates (x, y):
$M\left(\frac{x_1+x_2}{2}, \frac{y_1+y_2}{2}\right) = (-5, 6)$

$$\frac{x_1+x_2}{2} = -5 \qquad \frac{y_1+y_2}{2} = 6$$
$$\frac{2+x}{2} = -5 \qquad \frac{-7+y}{2} = 6$$
$$2+x = -10 \qquad -7+y = 12$$
$$x = -12 \qquad y = 19$$

$Q(-12, 19)$

89. Let Q have coordinates (x, y):
$M\left(\frac{x_1+x_2}{2}, \frac{y_1+y_2}{2}\right) = (5, 5)$

$$\frac{x_1+x_2}{2} = 5 \qquad \frac{y_1+y_2}{2} = 5$$
$$\frac{5+x}{2} = 5 \qquad \frac{-5+y}{2} = 5$$
$$5+x = 10 \qquad -5+y = 10$$
$$x = 5 \qquad y = 15$$

$Q(5, 15)$

90. Let Q have coordinates (x, y):
$M\left(\frac{x_1+x_2}{2}, \frac{y_1+y_2}{2}\right) = (0, 0)$

$$\frac{x_1+x_2}{2} = 0 \qquad \frac{y_1+y_2}{2} = 0$$
$$\frac{-7+x}{2} = 0 \qquad \frac{3+y}{2} = 0$$
$$-7+x = 0 \qquad 3+y = 0$$
$$x = 7 \qquad y = -3$$

$Q(7, -3)$

91. Let the points be identified as $A(13, -2)$, $B(9, -8)$ and $C(5, -2)$.

$AB = \sqrt{(x_2-x_1)^2+(y_2-y_1)^2} = \sqrt{(13-9)^2+(-2-(-8))^2} = \sqrt{16+36} = \sqrt{52} = 2\sqrt{13}$

$BC = \sqrt{(x_2-x_1)^2+(y_2-y_1)^2} = \sqrt{(9-5)^2+(-8-(-2))^2} = \sqrt{16+36} = \sqrt{52} = 2\sqrt{13}$

Since AB and BC have the same length, the triangle is isosceles.

92. Let the points be identified as $A(-1, 2)$, $B(3, 1)$ and $C(4, 5)$.

$AB = \sqrt{(x_2-x_1)^2+(y_2-y_1)^2} = \sqrt{(-1-3)^2+(2-1)^2} = \sqrt{16+1} = \sqrt{17}$

$BC = \sqrt{(x_2-x_1)^2+(y_2-y_1)^2} = \sqrt{(3-4)^2+(1-5)^2} = \sqrt{1+16} = \sqrt{17}$

Since AB and BC have the same length, the triangle is isosceles.

93. $M = \left(\frac{2+6}{2}, \frac{4+10}{2}\right) = \left(\frac{8}{2}, \frac{14}{2}\right) = (4, 7)$; $N = \left(\frac{4+6}{2}, \frac{6+10}{2}\right) = \left(\frac{10}{2}, \frac{16}{2}\right) = (5, 8)$

$MN = \sqrt{(x_2-x_1)^2+(y_2-y_1)^2} = \sqrt{(4-5)^2+(7-8)^2} = \sqrt{1+1} = \sqrt{2}$

94. $M = \left(\frac{0+b}{2}, \frac{0+c}{2}\right) = \left(\frac{b}{2}, \frac{c}{2}\right)$; $N = \left(\frac{a+b}{2}, \frac{0+c}{2}\right) = \left(\frac{a+b}{2}, \frac{c}{2}\right)$

$AB = \sqrt{(x_2-x_1)^2 + (y_2-y_1)^2} = \sqrt{(0-a)^2 + (0-0)^2} = \sqrt{a^2} = a$

$MN = \sqrt{(x_2-x_1)^2 + (y_2-y_1)^2} = \sqrt{\left(\frac{b}{2} - \frac{a+b}{2}\right)^2 + \left(\frac{c}{2} - \frac{c}{2}\right)^2} = \sqrt{\frac{a^2}{4} + 0} = \frac{a}{2} = \frac{1}{2}AB$

95. $M = \left(\frac{0+a}{2}, \frac{b+0}{2}\right) = \left(\frac{a}{2}, \frac{b}{2}\right)$; $L = \left(\frac{a}{2}, 0\right)$; $N = \left(0, \frac{b}{2}\right)$

Area of $AOB = \frac{1}{2} \cdot$ base $\cdot$ height $= \frac{1}{2}(OA)(OB) = \frac{1}{2}(a)(b) = \frac{1}{2}ab$

Area of $OLMN =$ length $\cdot$ width $= (OL)(ON) = \frac{a}{2} \cdot \frac{b}{2} = \frac{1}{4}ab = \frac{1}{2}$(Area of AOB)

96. Let $x =$ the width (from A to D). Then the length (from A to B) $= 2x$.

$$\begin{aligned} \text{Perimeter} &= 42 \\ x + 2x + x + 2x &= 42 \\ 6x &= 42 \\ x &= 7 \end{aligned}$$

Thus, the distance from A to D is 7 and the distance from A to B is $2(7) = 14$. Thus, the x-coordinate of C is $-3 + 14$, or 11. The y-coordinate of C is $-2 + 7$, or 5. Point C then has coordinates $(11, 5)$.

97.
$$\begin{aligned} y &= 7500x + 125{,}000 \\ y &= 7500(5) + 125{,}000 \\ y &= 37{,}500 + 125{,}000 \\ y &= 162{,}500 \end{aligned}$$

The value will be \$162,500.

98. Set $y = 0$:

$$\begin{aligned} y &= -1360x + 17{,}000 \\ 0 &= -1360x + 17{,}000 \\ 1360x &= 17{,}000 \\ x &= 12.5 \end{aligned}$$

The car will be worthless after 12.5 years.

99.
$$\begin{aligned} p &= -\frac{1}{10}q + 170 \\ 150 &= -\frac{1}{10}q + 170 \\ \frac{1}{10}q &= 20 \\ q &= 200 \end{aligned}$$

200 TVs will be sold.

100.
$$\begin{aligned} p &= \frac{1}{10}q + 130 \\ 150 &= \frac{1}{10}q + 130 \\ 20 &= \frac{1}{10}q \\ 200 &= q \end{aligned}$$

200 TVs will be produced.

101.
$$\begin{aligned} V &= \frac{nv}{N} \\ 60 &= \frac{12v}{20} \\ 1200 &= 12v \\ 100 &= v \end{aligned}$$

The smaller gear is spinning at 100 rpm.

102.
$$\begin{aligned} n &= 430 - 0.005d \\ 350 &= 430 - 0.005d \\ 0.005d &= 80 \\ d &= 16{,}000 \end{aligned}$$

\$16,000 would reduce the number to 350.

103.

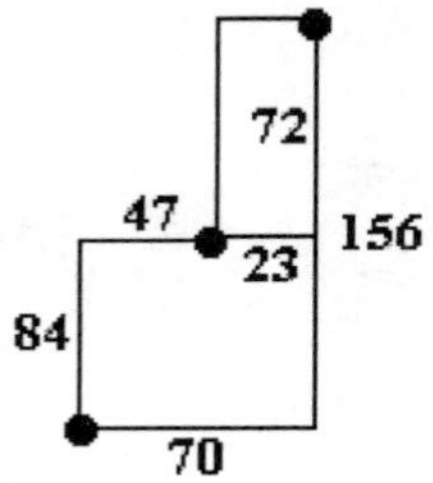

$$d^2 = 70^2 + 156^2$$
$$d^2 = 4900 + 24{,}336$$
$$d^2 = 29{,}236$$
$$d = \sqrt{29{,}236}$$
$$d \approx 170 \text{ miles}$$

104.

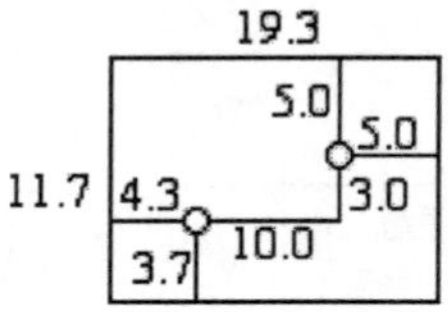

$$d^2 = 10^2 + 3^2$$
$$d^2 = 100 + 9$$
$$d^2 = 109$$
$$d = \sqrt{109}$$
$$d \approx 10.4 \text{ mm}$$

105. Answers may vary.

106. Answers may vary.

107. Answers may vary.

108. Answers may vary.

109. $[-3, 2)$

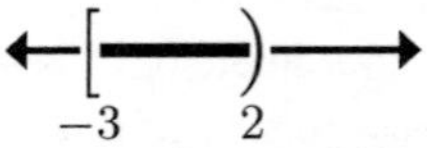

$(-2, 3]$

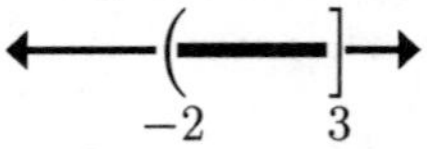

$[-3, 2) \cup (-2, 3]$

110. $(-1, 4)$

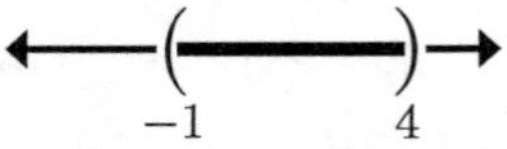

$[-2, 2]$

$(-1, 4) \cap [-2, 2]$

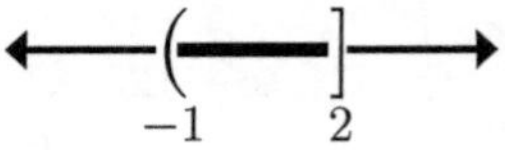

111. $[-3, -2)$

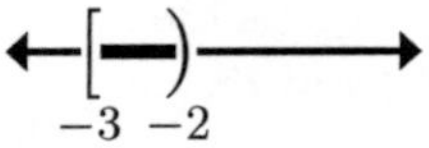

$(2, 3]$

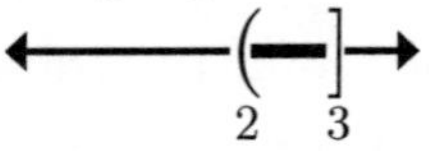

$[-3, 2) \cap (-2, 3]$ no intersection

112. $[-4, -3) \cup (2, 3]$

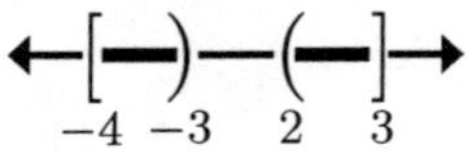

113.
$$\begin{aligned} \frac{3}{y+6} &= \frac{4}{y+4} \\ (y+6)(y+4)\cdot\frac{3}{y+6} &= (y+6)(y+4)\cdot\frac{4}{y+4} \\ 3(y+4) &= 4(y+6) \\ 3y+12 &= 4y+24 \\ -12 &= y \end{aligned}$$

114.
$$\begin{aligned} \frac{z+4}{z^2+z} - \frac{z+1}{z^2+2z} &= \frac{8}{z^2+3z+2} \\ \frac{z+4}{z(z+1)} - \frac{z+1}{z(z+2)} &= \frac{8}{(z+2)(z+1)} \\ (z+2)(z+4) - (z+1)(z+1) &= z(8) \qquad \{\text{multiply by common denominator}\} \\ \left(z^2+6z+8\right) - \left(z^2+2z+1\right) &= 8z \\ z^2+6z+8-z^2-2z-1 &= 8z \\ -4z = -7 &\Rightarrow z = \tfrac{7}{4} \end{aligned}$$

Exercise 2.2 (page 185)

1. divided
2. y
3. run
4. same order
5. the change in
6. horizontal
7. vertical
8. parallel
9. perpendicular
10. perpendicular, -1

11. $m = \dfrac{y_2 - y_1}{x_2 - x_1} = \dfrac{10-5}{3-2} = \dfrac{5}{1} = 5$

12. $m = \dfrac{y_2 - y_1}{x_2 - x_1} = \dfrac{3-(-1)}{5-3} = \dfrac{4}{2} = 2$

13. $m = \dfrac{y_2 - y_1}{x_2 - x_1} = \dfrac{5-(-2)}{-1-3} = \dfrac{7}{-4} = -\dfrac{7}{4}$

14. $m = \dfrac{y_2 - y_1}{x_2 - x_1} = \dfrac{16-7}{6-3} = \dfrac{9}{3} = 3$

15. $m = \dfrac{y_2 - y_1}{x_2 - x_1} = \dfrac{1-(-7)}{4-8} = \dfrac{8}{-4} = -2$

16. $m = \dfrac{y_2 - y_1}{x_2 - x_1} = \dfrac{17-17}{17-5} = \dfrac{0}{12} = 0$

17. $m = \dfrac{y_2 - y_1}{x_2 - x_1} = \dfrac{-3-3}{-4-(-4)} = \dfrac{-6}{0} \Rightarrow$ und.

18. $m = \dfrac{y_2 - y_1}{x_2 - x_1} = \dfrac{2-\sqrt{7}}{\sqrt{7}-2} = -1$

19. $m = \dfrac{y_2 - y_1}{x_2 - x_1} = \dfrac{\frac{7}{3} - \frac{2}{3}}{\frac{5}{2} - \frac{3}{2}} = \dfrac{\frac{5}{3}}{\frac{2}{2}} = \dfrac{\frac{5}{3}}{1} = \dfrac{5}{3}$

20. $m = \dfrac{y_2 - y_1}{x_2 - x_1} = \dfrac{-\frac{5}{3} - \frac{1}{3}}{\frac{3}{5} - \left(-\frac{2}{5}\right)} = \dfrac{-\frac{6}{3}}{\frac{5}{5}} = -2$

21. $m = \dfrac{y_2 - y_1}{x_2 - x_1} = \dfrac{a-c}{(b+c)-(a+b)}$
$= \dfrac{a-c}{c-a} = -1$

22. $m = \dfrac{y_2 - y_1}{x_2 - x_1} = \dfrac{a-0}{(a+b)-b} = \dfrac{a}{a} = 1$

23. $y = 3x + 2$

x	y
0	2
1	5

$m = \dfrac{y_2 - y_1}{x_2 - x_1} = \dfrac{5-2}{1-0}$
$= \dfrac{3}{1} = 3$

24. $y = 5x - 8$

x	y
0	-8
1	-3

$m = \dfrac{y_2 - y_1}{x_2 - x_1} = \dfrac{-3-(-8)}{1-0}$
$= \dfrac{5}{1} = 5$

25. $5x - 10y = 3$

x	y
0	$-\frac{3}{10}$
1	$\frac{1}{5}$

$m = \dfrac{y_2 - y_1}{x_2 - x_1}$
$= \dfrac{\frac{1}{5} - \left(-\frac{3}{10}\right)}{1-0}$
$= \dfrac{\frac{5}{10}}{1} = \dfrac{1}{2}$

26. $8y + 2x = 5$

x	y
0	$\frac{5}{8}$
1	$\frac{3}{8}$

$m = \dfrac{y_2 - y_1}{x_2 - x_1}$
$= \dfrac{\frac{3}{8} - \frac{5}{8}}{1-0}$
$= \dfrac{-\frac{2}{8}}{1} = -\dfrac{1}{4}$

27. $3(y+2) = 2x - 3$
$3y - 2x = -9$

x	y
0	-3
3	-1

$$m = \frac{y_2 - y_1}{x_2 - x_1} = \frac{-1-(-3)}{3-0} = \frac{2}{3}$$

28. $4(x-2) = 3y + 2$
$4x - 3y = 10$

x	y
0	$-\frac{10}{3}$
1	-2

$$m = \frac{y_2 - y_1}{x_2 - x_1} = \frac{-2-(-\frac{10}{3})}{1-0} = \frac{\frac{4}{3}}{1} = \frac{4}{3}$$

29. $3(y+x) = 3(x-1)$
$3y = -3$
$y = -1$

x	y
0	-1
1	-1

$$m = \frac{y_2 - y_1}{x_2 - x_1} = \frac{-1-(-1)}{1-0} = \frac{0}{1} = 0$$

30. $2x + 5 = 2(y+x)$
$5 = 2y$
$\frac{5}{2} = y$

x	y
0	$\frac{5}{2}$
1	$\frac{5}{2}$

$$m = \frac{y_2 - y_1}{x_2 - x_1} = \frac{\frac{5}{2} - \frac{5}{2}}{1-0} = \frac{0}{1} = 0$$

31. The slope is negative.

32. The slope is zero.

33. The slope is positive.

34. The slope is positive.

35. The slope is undefined.

36. The slope is negative.

37. $m_1 m_2 = 3\left(-\frac{1}{3}\right) = -1$
perpendicular

38. $m_1 \neq m_2;\ m_1 m_2 = \frac{2}{3} \cdot \frac{3}{2} = 1 \neq -1$
neither

39. $m_1 = \sqrt{8} = 2\sqrt{2} = m_2$
parallel

40. $m_1 m_2 = 1(-1) = -1$
perpendicular

41. $m_1 m_2 = -\sqrt{2}\left(\frac{\sqrt{2}}{2}\right) = -1$
perpendicular

42. $m_2 = \sqrt{28} = 2\sqrt{7} = m_1$
parallel

43. $m_1 m_2 = -0.125(8) = -1$
perpendicular

44. $m_1 = 0.125 = \frac{1}{8} = m_2$
parallel

45. $m_1 m_2 = ab^{-1}(-a^{-1}b) = -a^0 b^0 = -1$
perpendicular

46. $m_1 = \left(\frac{a}{b}\right)^{-1} = \frac{b}{a} \neq -\frac{b}{a} = m_2$
$m_1 m_2 = \frac{b}{a}\left(-\frac{b}{a}\right) \neq -1$
neither (assume $a \neq b$)

For Exercises 47-52 use the slope of line through R and S calculated below:

$$m_{RS} = \frac{y_2 - y_1}{x_2 - x_1} = \frac{7-5}{2-(-3)} = \frac{2}{5}$$

47. $m_{PQ} = \frac{y_2 - y_1}{x_2 - x_1} = \frac{6-4}{7-2} = \frac{2}{5} = m_{RS} \Rightarrow$ parallel

48. $m_{PQ} = \frac{y_2 - y_1}{x_2 - x_1} = \frac{4-8}{-13-(-3)} = \frac{-4}{-10} = \frac{2}{5} = m_{RS} \Rightarrow$ parallel

49. $m_{PQ} = \frac{y_2 - y_1}{x_2 - x_1} = \frac{1-6}{-2-(-4)} = \frac{-5}{2} = -\frac{5}{2} \Rightarrow$ perpendicular

50. $m_{PQ} = \frac{y_2 - y_1}{x_2 - x_1} = \frac{1-(-9)}{4-0} = \frac{10}{4} = \frac{5}{2} \Rightarrow$ neither

51. $m_{PQ} = \frac{y_2 - y_1}{x_2 - x_1} = \frac{6a-a}{3a-a} = \frac{5a}{2a} = \frac{5}{2} \Rightarrow$ neither

52. $m_{PQ} = \frac{y_2 - y_1}{x_2 - x_1} = \frac{6b-b}{-b-b} = \frac{5b}{-2b} = -\frac{5}{2} \Rightarrow$ perpendicular

53. $m_{PQ} = \frac{y_2 - y_1}{x_2 - x_1} = \frac{9-8}{-6-(-2)} = \frac{1}{-4} = -\frac{1}{4}$

$m_{PR} = \frac{y_2 - y_1}{x_2 - x_1} = \frac{5-8}{2-(-2)} = \frac{-3}{4} = -\frac{3}{4} \Rightarrow$ not on same line

54. $m_{PQ} = \frac{y_2 - y_1}{x_2 - x_1} = \frac{-2-(-1)}{3-1} = \frac{-1}{2} = -\frac{1}{2}$

$m_{PR} = \frac{y_2 - y_1}{x_2 - x_1} = \frac{0-(-1)}{-3-1} = \frac{1}{-4} = -\frac{1}{4} \Rightarrow$ not on same line

55. $m_{PQ} = \frac{y_2 - y_1}{x_2 - x_1} = \frac{0-a}{0-(-a)} = \frac{-a}{a} = -1$

$m_{PR} = \frac{y_2 - y_1}{x_2 - x_1} = \frac{-a-a}{a-(-a)} = \frac{-2a}{2a} = -1 \Rightarrow$ on same line

56. $m_{PQ} = \frac{y_2 - y_1}{x_2 - x_1} = \frac{b-(a+b)}{(a+b)-a} = \frac{-a}{b} = -\frac{a}{b}$

$m_{PR} = \frac{y_2 - y_1}{x_2 - x_1} = \frac{a-(a+b)}{(a-b)-a} = \frac{-b}{-b} = 1 \Rightarrow$ not on same line

57. $m_{PQ} = \dfrac{y_2 - y_1}{x_2 - x_1} = \dfrac{-5-4}{2-5} = \dfrac{-9}{-3} = 3$

$m_{PR} = \dfrac{y_2 - y_1}{x_2 - x_1} = \dfrac{-3-4}{8-5} = \dfrac{-7}{3} = -\dfrac{7}{3}$

$m_{QR} = \dfrac{y_2 - y_1}{x_2 - x_1} = \dfrac{-3-(-5)}{8-2} = \dfrac{2}{6} = \dfrac{1}{3} \Rightarrow$ None are perpendicular.

58. $m_{PQ} = \dfrac{y_2 - y_1}{x_2 - x_1} = \dfrac{6-(-2)}{4-8} = \dfrac{8}{-4} = -2$

$m_{PR} = \dfrac{y_2 - y_1}{x_2 - x_1} = \dfrac{7-(-2)}{6-8} = \dfrac{9}{-2} = -\dfrac{9}{2}$

$m_{QR} = \dfrac{y_2 - y_1}{x_2 - x_1} = \dfrac{7-6}{6-4} = \dfrac{1}{2} \Rightarrow PQ$ and QR are perpendicular.

59. $m_{PQ} = \dfrac{y_2 - y_1}{x_2 - x_1} = \dfrac{9-3}{1-1} = \dfrac{6}{0} \Rightarrow$ undefined $\Rightarrow$ vertical

$m_{PR} = \dfrac{y_2 - y_1}{x_2 - x_1} = \dfrac{3-3}{7-1} = \dfrac{0}{6} = 0 \Rightarrow$ horizontal

$m_{QR} = \dfrac{y_2 - y_1}{x_2 - x_1} = \dfrac{3-9}{7-1} = \dfrac{-6}{6} = -1 \Rightarrow PQ$ and PR are perpendicular.

60. $m_{PQ} = \dfrac{y_2 - y_1}{x_2 - x_1} = \dfrac{2-(-3)}{-3-2} = \dfrac{5}{-5} = -1$

$m_{PR} = \dfrac{y_2 - y_1}{x_2 - x_1} = \dfrac{8-(-3)}{3-2} = \dfrac{11}{1} = 11$

$m_{QR} = \dfrac{y_2 - y_1}{x_2 - x_1} = \dfrac{8-2}{3-(-3)} = \dfrac{6}{6} = 1 \Rightarrow PQ$ and QR are perpendicular.

61. $m_{PQ} = \dfrac{y_2 - y_1}{x_2 - x_1} = \dfrac{b-0}{a-0} = \dfrac{b}{a}$

$m_{PR} = \dfrac{y_2 - y_1}{x_2 - x_1} = \dfrac{a-0}{-b-0} = \dfrac{a}{-b} = -\dfrac{a}{b}$

$m_{QR} = \dfrac{y_2 - y_1}{x_2 - x_1} = \dfrac{a-b}{-b-a} = \dfrac{a-b}{-b-a} \Rightarrow PQ$ and PR are perpendicular.

62. $m_{PQ} = \dfrac{y_2 - y_1}{x_2 - x_1} = \dfrac{a-b}{-b-a} = \dfrac{a-b}{-(a+b)} = -\dfrac{a-b}{a+b}$

$m_{PR} = \dfrac{y_2 - y_1}{x_2 - x_1} = \dfrac{(a+b)-b}{(a-b)-a} = \dfrac{a}{-b} = -\dfrac{a}{b}$

$m_{QR} = \dfrac{y_2 - y_1}{x_2 - x_1} = \dfrac{(a+b)-a}{(a-b)-(-b)} = \dfrac{b}{a} \Rightarrow PR$ and QR are perpendicular.

63. $m_{AB} = \dfrac{y_2 - y_1}{x_2 - x_1} = \dfrac{4-(-1)}{-3-(-1)} = \dfrac{5}{-2} = -\dfrac{5}{2}$

$m_{AC} = \dfrac{y_2 - y_1}{x_2 - x_1} = \dfrac{1-(-1)}{4-(-1)} = \dfrac{2}{5} = \dfrac{2}{5} \Rightarrow AB$ and AC are perpendicular. $\Rightarrow$ right triangle

64. $m_{DE} = \dfrac{y_2 - y_1}{x_2 - x_1} = \dfrac{3-1}{-1-0} = \dfrac{2}{-1} = -2$

$m_{DF} = \dfrac{y_2 - y_1}{x_2 - x_1} = \dfrac{5-3}{3-(-1)} = \dfrac{2}{4} = \dfrac{1}{2} \Rightarrow DE$ and DF are perpendicular. $\Rightarrow$ right triangle

65. $m_{AB} = \dfrac{y_2 - y_1}{x_2 - x_1} = \dfrac{0-(-1)}{3-1} = \dfrac{1}{2}$; $d(A, B) = \sqrt{(1-3)^2 + (-1-0)^2} = \sqrt{5}$

$m_{BC} = \dfrac{y_2 - y_1}{x_2 - x_1} = \dfrac{2-0}{2-3} = \dfrac{2}{-1} = -2$; $d(B, C) = \sqrt{(3-2)^2 + (0-2)^2} = \sqrt{5}$

$m_{CD} = \dfrac{y_2 - y_1}{x_2 - x_1} = \dfrac{1-2}{0-2} = \dfrac{-1}{-2} = \dfrac{1}{2}$; $d(C, D) = \sqrt{(2-0)^2 + (2-1)^2} = \sqrt{5}$

$m_{DA} = \dfrac{y_2 - y_1}{x_2 - x_1} = \dfrac{1-(-1)}{0-1} = \dfrac{2}{-1} = -2$; $d(D, A) = \sqrt{(-1-1)^2 + (1-0)^2} = \sqrt{5}$

Adjacent sides are perpendicular and congruent, so the figure is a square.

66. $m_{EF} = \dfrac{y_2 - y_1}{x_2 - x_1} = \dfrac{0-(-1)}{3-(-1)} = \dfrac{1}{4}$; $d(E, F) = \sqrt{(-1-3)^2 + (-1-0)^2} = \sqrt{17}$

$m_{FG} = \dfrac{y_2 - y_1}{x_2 - x_1} = \dfrac{4-0}{2-3} = \dfrac{4}{-1} = -4$; $d(F, G) = \sqrt{(3-2)^2 + (0-4)^2} = \sqrt{17}$

$m_{GH} = \dfrac{y_2 - y_1}{x_2 - x_1} = \dfrac{3-4}{-2-2} = \dfrac{-1}{-4} = \dfrac{1}{4}$; $d(G, H) = \sqrt{(2-(-2))^2 + (4-3)^2} = \sqrt{17}$

$m_{HE} = \dfrac{y_2 - y_1}{x_2 - x_1} = \dfrac{3-(-1)}{-2-(-1)} = \dfrac{4}{-1} = -4$; $d(H, E) = \sqrt{(-1-(-2))^2 + (-1-3)^2} = \sqrt{17}$

Adjacent sides are perpendicular and congruent, so the figure is a square.

67. $m_{AB} = \dfrac{y_2 - y_1}{x_2 - x_1} = \dfrac{3-(-2)}{3-(-2)} = \dfrac{5}{5} = 1$

$m_{BC} = \dfrac{y_2 - y_1}{x_2 - x_1} = \dfrac{6-3}{2-3} = \dfrac{3}{-1} = -3$

$m_{CD} = \dfrac{y_2 - y_1}{x_2 - x_1} = \dfrac{1-6}{-3-2} = \dfrac{-5}{-5} = 1$

$m_{DA} = \dfrac{y_2 - y_1}{x_2 - x_1} = \dfrac{1-(-2)}{-3-(-2)} = \dfrac{3}{-1} = -3$

Opposite sides are parallel, so the figure is a parallelogram.

68. $m_{EF} = \dfrac{y_2 - y_1}{x_2 - x_1} = \dfrac{1-(-2)}{5-1} = \dfrac{3}{4}$

$m_{FG} = \dfrac{y_2 - y_1}{x_2 - x_1} = \dfrac{4-1}{3-5} = \dfrac{3}{-2} = -\dfrac{3}{2}$

$m_{GH} = \dfrac{y_2 - y_1}{x_2 - x_1} = \dfrac{4-4}{-3-3} = \dfrac{0}{-6} = 0$

$m_{HE} = \dfrac{y_2 - y_1}{x_2 - x_1} = \dfrac{4-(-2)}{-3-1} = \dfrac{6}{-4} = -\dfrac{3}{2}$

Exactly one pair of sides is parallel, so the figure is a trapezoid.

69. $M\left(\dfrac{5+7}{2}, \dfrac{9+5}{2}\right) = M\left(\dfrac{12}{2}, \dfrac{14}{2}\right) = M(6, 7)$; $N\left(\dfrac{1+7}{2}, \dfrac{3+5}{2}\right) = N\left(\dfrac{8}{2}, \dfrac{8}{2}\right) = N(4, 4)$

$m_{MN} = \dfrac{y_2 - y_1}{x_2 - x_1} = \dfrac{4-7}{4-6} = \dfrac{-3}{-2} = \dfrac{3}{2}$; $m_{AC} = \dfrac{y_2 - y_1}{x_2 - x_1} = \dfrac{9-3}{5-1} = \dfrac{6}{4} = \dfrac{3}{2} \Rightarrow MN \parallel AC$

70. $d(AB) = \sqrt{(0-a)^2 + (0-0)^2} = \sqrt{a^2 + 0^2} = \sqrt{a^2} = a$

$d(AC) = \sqrt{(0-b)^2 + (0-c)^2} = \sqrt{b^2 + c^2}$. From the given information, $a = \sqrt{b^2 + c^2}$.

$m_{AD} = \frac{y_2 - y_1}{x_2 - x_1} = \frac{c - 0}{(a+b) - 0} = \frac{c}{a+b}$; $m_{BC} = \frac{y_2 - y_1}{x_2 - x_1} = \frac{0 - c}{a - b} = \frac{-c}{a-b}$

$$m_{AD}m_{BC} = \frac{c}{a+b} \cdot \frac{-c}{a-b} = \frac{-c^2}{a^2 - b^2} = \frac{-c^2}{\left(\sqrt{b^2+c^2}\right)^2 - b^2} = \frac{-c^2}{b^2 + c^2 - b^2} = \frac{-c^2}{c^2} = -1$$

Thus, AD is perpendicular to BC.

71. $m = \frac{y_2 - y_1}{x_2 - x_1} = \frac{26 - 12}{5 - 1} = \frac{14}{4} = 3.5$

The rate of growth was 3.5 students per year.

72. $m = \frac{y_2 - y_1}{x_2 - x_1} = \frac{110{,}000 - 50{,}000}{3 - 1}$

$= \frac{60{,}000}{2} = 30{,}000$

The sales increased \$30,000 per year.

73. $m = \frac{y_2 - y_1}{x_2 - x_1} = \frac{6700 - 2200}{10 - 3}$

$= \frac{4500}{7} \approx 642.86$

The cost decreased about \$642.86 per year.

74. The cost absorbed by the hospital was \$245 in 1990, \$375 in 1995 and \$505 in 2000.

$m = \frac{y_2 - y_1}{x_2 - x_1} = \frac{505 - 245}{2000 - 1990} = \frac{260}{10} = 26$

The cost absorbed by the hospital increased by \$26 per year.

75. $\frac{\Delta T}{\Delta t}$ = the hourly rate of change of temperature.

(Let $t = x$ and $T = y$.)

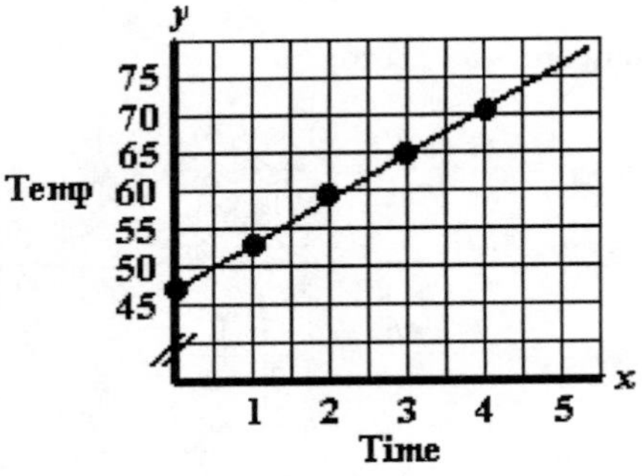

76. $\frac{\Delta D}{\Delta d}$ = the daily rate of change of the Dow Jones average.

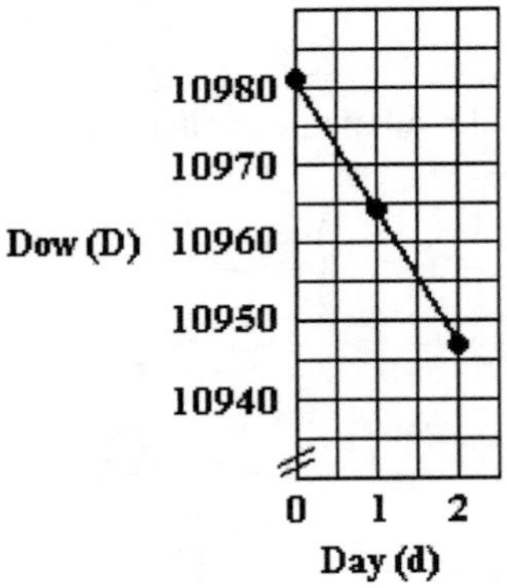

77. $D = 590t$; The slope is the speed of the plane.

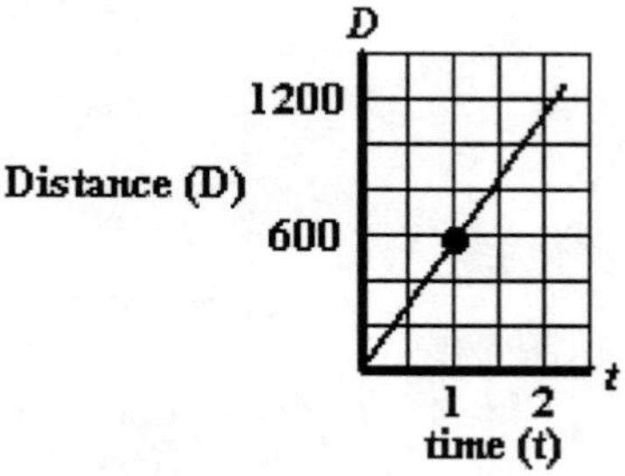

78. $A = 25n$; The slope is the monthly increase of the value of the account.

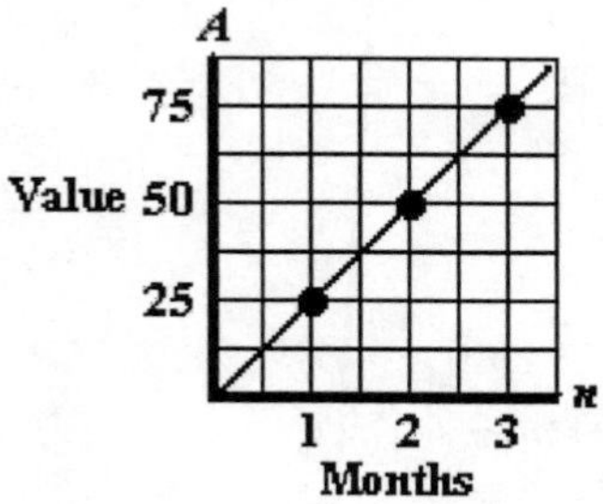

79. **Answers may vary.**

80. **Answers may vary.**

81.
$$\begin{aligned} 3x + 7y &= 21 \\ 7y &= -3x + 21 \\ \frac{7y}{7} &= \frac{-3x}{7} + \frac{21}{7} \\ y &= -\frac{3}{7}x + 3 \end{aligned}$$

82.
$$\begin{aligned} y - 3 &= 5(x + 2) \\ y - 3 &= 5x + 10 \\ y &= 5x + 13 \end{aligned}$$

83.
$$\begin{aligned} \frac{x}{5} + \frac{y}{2} &= 1 \\ 2\left(\frac{x}{5} + \frac{y}{2}\right) &= 2(1) \\ \frac{2}{5}x + y &= 2 \\ y &= -\frac{2}{5}x + 2 \end{aligned}$$

84.
$$\begin{aligned} x - 5y &= 15 \\ -5y &= -x + 15 \\ \frac{-5y}{-5} &= \frac{-x}{-5} + \frac{15}{-5} \\ y &= \frac{1}{5}x - 3 \end{aligned}$$

85. $6p^2 + p - 12 = (2p + 3)(3p - 4)$

86.
$$\begin{aligned} b^3 - 27 = b^3 - 3^3 &= (b - 3)\left(b^2 + b(3) + 3^2\right) \\ &= (b - 3)\left(b^2 + 3b + 9\right) \end{aligned}$$

87. $mp + mq + np + nq = m(p + q) + n(p + q) = (p + q)(m + n)$

88. $x^4 + x^2 - 2 = (x^2 + 2)(x^2 - 1) = (x^2 + 2)(x + 1)(x - 1)$

Exercise 2.3 (page 197)

1. $y - y_1 = m(x - x_1)$

2. m, y-intercept

3. slope-intercept

4. $Ax + By = C$

5. $-\frac{A}{B}$

6. $\left(0, \frac{C}{B}\right)$

7.
$$\begin{aligned} y - y_1 &= m(x - x_1) \\ y - 4 &= 2(x - 2) \\ y - 4 &= 2x - 4 \\ -2x + y &= 0 \\ 2x - y &= 0 \end{aligned}$$

8.
$$\begin{aligned} y - y_1 &= m(x - x_1) \\ y - 5 &= -3(x - 3) \\ y - 5 &= -3x + 9 \\ 3x + y &= 14 \end{aligned}$$

9.
$$\begin{aligned} y - y_1 &= m(x - x_1) \\ y - \frac{1}{2} &= 2\left(x + \frac{3}{2}\right) \\ y - \frac{1}{2} &= 2x + 3 \\ 2y - 1 &= 4x + 6 \\ -4x + 2y &= 7 \\ 4x - 2y &= -7 \end{aligned}$$

10.
$$\begin{aligned} y - y_1 &= m(x - x_1) \\ y + 2 &= -6\left(x - \frac{1}{4}\right) \\ y + 2 &= -6x + \frac{3}{2} \\ 2y + 4 &= -12x + 3 \\ 12x + 2y &= -1 \end{aligned}$$

11.
$$\begin{aligned} y - y_1 &= m(x - x_1) \\ y - 0 &= \pi(x - \pi) \\ y &= \pi x - \pi^2 \\ -\pi x + y &= -\pi^2 \\ \pi x - y &= \pi^2 \end{aligned}$$

12.
$$\begin{aligned} y - y_1 &= m(x - x_1) \\ y - \pi &= \pi(x - 0) \\ y - \pi &= \pi x \\ -\pi x + y &= \pi \\ \pi x - y &= -\pi \end{aligned}$$

13. From the graph, $m = \frac{2}{3}$ and the line passes through $(2, 5)$.
$$\begin{aligned} y - y_1 &= m(x - x_1) \\ y - 5 &= \frac{2}{3}(x - 2) \\ 3(y - 5) &= 3 \cdot \frac{2}{3}(x - 2) \\ 3y - 15 &= 2(x - 2) \\ 3y - 15 &= 2x - 4 \\ -2x + 3y &= 11 \\ 2x - 3y &= -11 \end{aligned}$$

14. From the graph, $m = -\frac{2}{3}$ and the line passes through $(-3, 2)$.
$$\begin{aligned} y - y_1 &= m(x - x_1) \\ y - 2 &= -\frac{2}{3}(x + 3) \\ 3(y - 2) &= 3 \cdot \left(-\frac{2}{3}\right)(x + 3) \\ 3y - 6 &= -2(x + 3) \\ 3y - 6 &= -2x - 6 \\ 2x + 3y &= 0 \end{aligned}$$

15. $m = \frac{y_2 - y_1}{x_2 - x_1} = \frac{4 - 0}{4 - 0} = \frac{4}{4} = 1$
$$\begin{aligned} y - y_1 &= m(x - x_1) \\ y - 0 &= 1(x - 0) \\ y &= x \end{aligned}$$

16. $m = \frac{y_2 - y_1}{x_2 - x_1} = \frac{0 - (-5)}{0 - (-5)} = \frac{5}{5} = 1$
$$\begin{aligned} y - y_1 &= m(x - x_1) \\ y - 0 &= 1(x - 0) \\ y &= x \end{aligned}$$

17. $m = \frac{y_2 - y_1}{x_2 - x_1} = \frac{-3 - 4}{0 - 3} = \frac{-7}{-3} = \frac{7}{3}$
$$\begin{aligned} y - y_1 &= m(x - x_1) \\ y + 3 &= \frac{7}{3}(x - 0) \\ y &= \frac{7}{3}x - 3 \end{aligned}$$

18. $m = \frac{y_2 - y_1}{x_2 - x_1} = \frac{-8 - 0}{6 - 4} = \frac{-8}{2} = -4$
$$\begin{aligned} y - y_1 &= m(x - x_1) \\ y - 0 &= -4(x - 4) \\ y &= -4x + 16 \end{aligned}$$

19. From the graph, $m = -\frac{9}{5}$ and the line passes through $(-2, 4)$

$$\begin{aligned} y - y_1 &= m(x - x_1) \\ y - 4 &= -\frac{9}{5}(x + 2) \\ y - 4 &= -\frac{9}{5}x - \frac{18}{5} \\ y &= -\frac{9}{5}x - \frac{18}{5} + 4 \\ y &= -\frac{9}{5}x + \frac{2}{5} \end{aligned}$$

20. From the graph, $m = \frac{8}{5}$ and the line passes through $(2, 3)$.

$$\begin{aligned} y - y_1 &= m(x - x_1) \\ y - 3 &= \frac{8}{5}(x - 2) \\ y - 3 &= \frac{8}{5}x - \frac{16}{5} \\ y &= \frac{8}{5}x - \frac{16}{5} + 3 \\ y &= \frac{8}{5}x - \frac{1}{5} \end{aligned}$$

21. $y = mx + b$
$y = 3x - 2$

22. $y = mx + b$
$y = -\frac{1}{3}x + \frac{2}{3}$

23. $y = mx + b$
$y = 5x - \frac{1}{5}$

24. $y = mx + b$
$y = \sqrt{2}x + \sqrt{2}$

25. $y = mx + b$
$y = ax + \frac{1}{a}$

26. $y = mx + b$
$y = ax + 2a$

27. $y = mx + b$
$y = ax + a$

28. $y = mx + b$
$y = \frac{1}{a}x + a$

29.

$$\begin{aligned} y &= mx + b \\ 0 &= \frac{3}{2}(0) + b \\ 0 &= b \end{aligned}$$

$$\begin{aligned} y &= mx + b \\ y &= \frac{3}{2}x + 0 \\ 2y &= 3x \\ -3x + 2y &= 0 \\ 3x - 2y &= 0 \end{aligned}$$

30.

$$\begin{aligned} y &= mx + b \\ -7 &= -\frac{2}{3}(-3) + b \\ -7 &= 2 + b \\ -9 &= b \end{aligned}$$

$$\begin{aligned} y &= mx + b \\ y &= -\frac{2}{3}x - 9 \\ 3y &= -2x - 27 \\ 2x + 3y &= -27 \end{aligned}$$

31.

$$\begin{aligned} y &= mx + b \\ 5 &= -3(-3) + b \\ 5 &= 9 + b \\ -4 &= b \end{aligned}$$

$$\begin{aligned} y &= mx + b \\ y &= -3x - 4 \\ 3x + y &= -4 \end{aligned}$$

32.

$$\begin{aligned} y &= mx + b \\ 1 &= 1(-5) + b \\ 1 &= -5 + b \\ 6 &= b \end{aligned}$$

$$\begin{aligned} y &= mx + b \\ y &= 1x + 6 \\ -x + y &= 6 \\ x - y &= -6 \end{aligned}$$

33.

$$\begin{aligned} y &= mx + b \\ \sqrt{2} &= \sqrt{2}(0) + b \\ \sqrt{2} &= b \end{aligned}$$

$$\begin{aligned} y &= mx + b \\ y &= \sqrt{2}x + \sqrt{2} \\ -\sqrt{2}x + y &= \sqrt{2} \\ \sqrt{2}x - y &= -\sqrt{2} \end{aligned}$$

34.

$$\begin{aligned} y &= mx + b \\ 0 &= 2\sqrt{3}\left(-\sqrt{3}\right) + b \\ 0 &= -6 + b \\ 6 &= b \end{aligned}$$

$$\begin{aligned} y &= mx + b \\ y &= 2\sqrt{3}x + 6 \\ -2\sqrt{3}x + y &= 6 \\ 2\sqrt{3}x - y &= -6 \end{aligned}$$

35. $y + 1 = x$

$y = x - 1 \Rightarrow m = 1, (0, -1)$

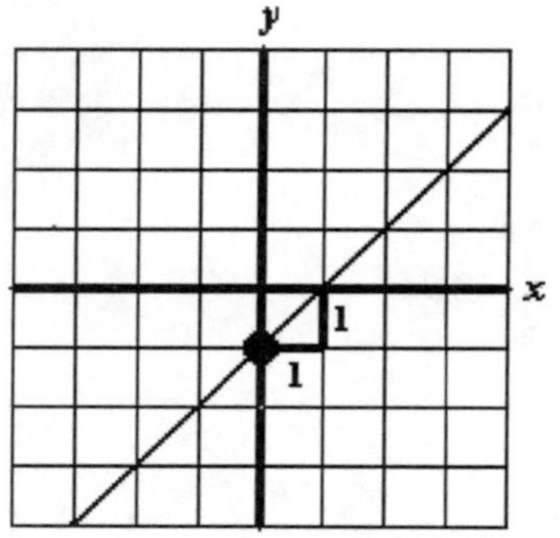

36. $x + y = 2$

$y = -x + 2 \Rightarrow m = -1, (0, 2)$

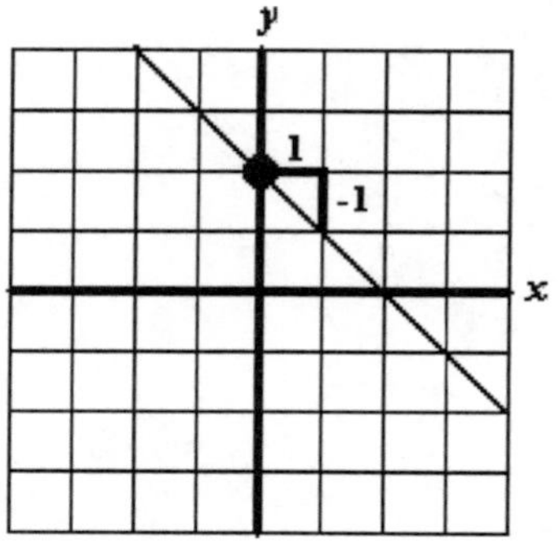

37.

$$x = \frac{3}{2}y - 3$$
$$2x = 3y - 6$$
$$-3y = -2x - 6$$
$$y = \frac{2}{3}x + 2 \Rightarrow m = \frac{2}{3}, (0, 2)$$

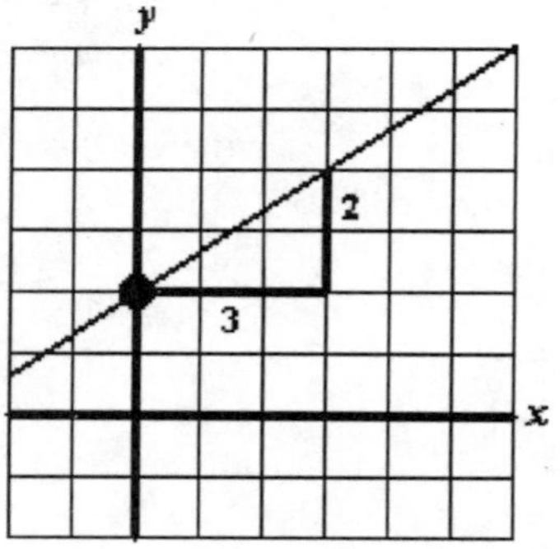

38.

$$x = -\frac{4}{5}y + 2$$
$$5x = -4y + 10$$
$$4y = -5x + 10$$
$$y = -\frac{5}{4}x + \frac{5}{2} \Rightarrow m = -\frac{5}{4}, \left(0, \frac{5}{2}\right)$$

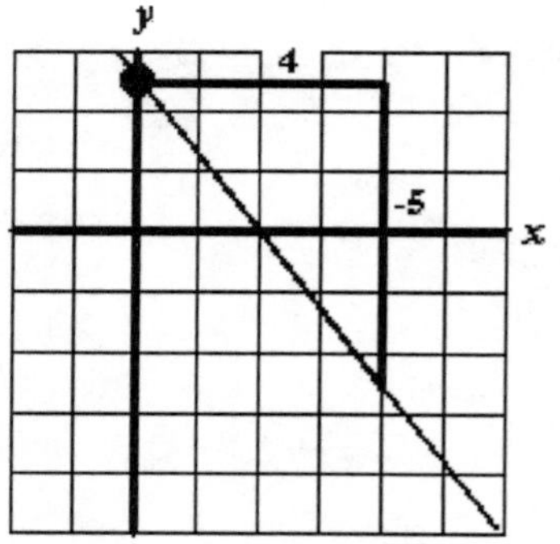

39. $3(y-4)=-2(x-3)$
$3y-12=-2x+6$
$3y=-2x+18$
$y=-\frac{2}{3}x+6 \Rightarrow m=-\frac{2}{3}, (0, 6)$

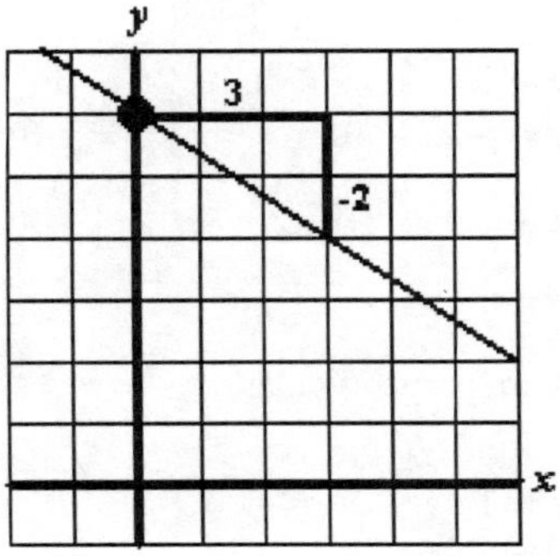

40. $-4(2x+3)=3(3y+8)$
$-8x-12=9y+24$
$-9y=8x+36$
$y=-\frac{8}{9}x-4$: $m=-\frac{8}{9}, (0, -4)$

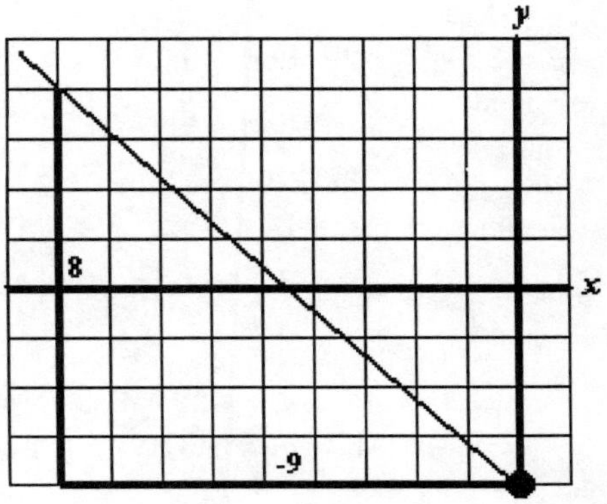

41. $3x-2y=8$
$-2y=-3x+8$
$y=\frac{3}{2}x-4$
$m=\frac{3}{2}, (0, -4)$

42. $-2x+4y=12$
$4y=2x+12$
$y=\frac{1}{2}x+3$
$m=\frac{1}{2}, (0, 3)$

43. $-2(x+3y)=5$
$-2x-6y=5$
$-6y=2x+5$
$y=-\frac{1}{3}x-\frac{5}{6}$
$m=-\frac{1}{3}, \left(0, -\frac{5}{6}\right)$

44. $5(2x-3y)=4$
$10x-15y=4$
$-15y=-10x+4$
$y=\frac{2}{3}x-\frac{4}{15}$
$m=\frac{2}{3}, \left(0, -\frac{4}{15}\right)$

45. $x=\frac{2y-4}{7}$
$7x=2y-4$
$-2y=-7x-4$
$y=\frac{7}{2}x+2$
$m=\frac{7}{2}, (0, 2)$

46. $3x+4=-\frac{2(y-3)}{5}$
$15x+20=-2(y-3)$
$15x+20=-2y+6$
$2y=-15x-14$
$y=-\frac{15}{2}x-7$
$m=-\frac{15}{2}, (0, -7)$

47. $y=3x+4$ $\quad y=3x-7$
$m=3$ $\quad m=3$
The lines are parallel.

48. $y=4x-13$ $\quad y=\frac{1}{4}x+13$
$m=4$ $\quad m=\frac{1}{4}$
The lines are neither.

49. $x+y=2$ $\quad y=x+5$

$y=-x+2$ $\quad m=1$

$m=-1$

The lines are perpendicular.

50. $x=y+2$ $\quad y=x+3$

$-y=-x+2$ $\quad m=1$

$y=x-2$

$m=1$

The lines are parallel.

51. $y=3x+7$ $\quad 2y=6x-9$

$m=3$ $\quad y=3x-\frac{9}{2}$

$m=3$

The lines are parallel.

52. $2x+3y=9$ $\quad 3x-2y=5$

$3y=-2x+9$ $\quad -2y=-3x+5$

$y=-\frac{2}{3}x+3$ $\quad y=\frac{3}{2}x-\frac{5}{2}$

$m=-\frac{2}{3}$ $\quad m=\frac{3}{2}$

The lines are perpendicular.

53. $x=3y+4$ $\quad y=-3x+7$

$-3y=-x+4$ $\quad m=-3$

$y=\frac{1}{3}x-\frac{4}{3}$

$m=\frac{1}{3}$

The lines are perpendicular.

54. $3x+6y=1$ $\quad y=\frac{1}{2}x$

$6y=-3x+1$ $\quad m=\frac{1}{2}$

$y=-\frac{1}{2}x+\frac{1}{6}$

$m=-\frac{1}{2}$

The lines are neither.

55. $y=3$ $\quad x=4$

horizontal vertical

The lines are perpendicular.

56. $y=-3$ $\quad y=-7$

horizontal horizontal

The lines are parallel.

57. $x=\frac{y-2}{3}$ $\quad 3(y-3)+x=0$

$3x=y-2$ $\quad 3y-9+x=0$

$-y=-3x-2$ $\quad 3y=-x+9$

$y=3x+2$ $\quad y=-\frac{1}{3}x+3$

$m=3$ $\quad m=-\frac{1}{3}$

The lines are perpendicular.

58. $2y=8$ $\quad 3(2+x)=3(y+2)$

$y=4$ $\quad 6+3x=3y+6$

horizontal $\quad -3y=-3x$

$y=x$

$m=1$

neither

59. $y=4x-7$ $\quad y-y_1=m(x-x_1)$

$m=4$ $\quad y-0=4(x-0)$

Use $m=4$. $\quad \boxed{y=4x}$

60. $x=-3y-12$ $\quad y-y_1=m(x-x_1)$

$3y=-x-12$ $\quad y-0=-\frac{1}{3}(x-0)$

$y=-\frac{1}{3}x-4$ $\quad \boxed{y=-\frac{1}{3}x}$

$m=-\frac{1}{3}$

Use $m=-\frac{1}{3}$.

61.
$$4x - y = 7$$
$$-y = -4x + 7$$
$$y = 4x - 7$$
$$m = 4$$
Use $m = 4$.
$$y - y_1 = m(x - x_1)$$
$$y - 5 = 4(x - 2)$$
$$y - 5 = 4x - 8$$
$$\boxed{y = 4x - 3}$$

62.
$$y + 3x = -12$$
$$y = -3x - 12$$
$$m = -3$$
Use $m = -3$.
$$y - y_1 = m(x - x_1)$$
$$y - 3 = -3(x + 6)$$
$$y - 3 = -3x - 18$$
$$\boxed{y = -3x - 15}$$

63.
$$x = \frac{5}{4}y - 2$$
$$4x = 5y - 8$$
$$-5y = -4x - 8$$
$$y = \frac{4}{5}x + \frac{8}{5}$$
$$m = \frac{4}{5}$$
Use $m = \frac{4}{5}$.
$$y - y_1 = m(x - x_1)$$
$$y + 2 = \frac{4}{5}(x - 4)$$
$$y + 2 = \frac{4}{5}x - \frac{16}{5}$$
$$\boxed{y = \frac{4}{5}x - \frac{26}{5}}$$

64.
$$x = -\frac{3}{4}y + 5$$
$$4x = -3y + 20$$
$$3y = -4x + 20$$
$$y = -\frac{4}{3}x + \frac{20}{3}$$
$$m = -\frac{4}{3}$$
Use $m = -\frac{4}{3}$.
$$y - y_1 = m(x - x_1)$$
$$y + 5 = -\frac{4}{3}(x - 1)$$
$$y + 5 = -\frac{4}{3}x + \frac{4}{3}$$
$$\boxed{y = -\frac{4}{3}x - \frac{11}{3}}$$

65.
$$y = 4x - 7$$
$$m = 4$$
Use $m = -\frac{1}{4}$.
$$y - y_1 = m(x - x_1)$$
$$y - 0 = -\frac{1}{4}(x - 0)$$
$$\boxed{y = -\frac{1}{4}x}$$

66.
$$x = -3y - 12$$
$$3y = -x - 12$$
$$y = -\frac{1}{3}x - 4$$
$$m = -\frac{1}{3}$$
Use $m = 3$.
$$y - y_1 = m(x - x_1)$$
$$y - 0 = 3(x - 0)$$
$$\boxed{y = 3x}$$

67.
$$4x - y = 7$$
$$-y = -4x + 7$$
$$y = 4x - 7$$
$$m = 4$$
Use $m = -\frac{1}{4}$.
$$y - y_1 = m(x - x_1)$$
$$y - 5 = -\frac{1}{4}(x - 2)$$
$$y - 5 = -\frac{1}{4}x + \frac{1}{2}$$
$$\boxed{y = -\frac{1}{4}x + \frac{11}{2}}$$

68.
$$y + 3x = -12$$
$$y = -3x - 12$$
$$m = -3$$
Use $m = \frac{1}{3}$.
$$y - y_1 = m(x - x_1)$$
$$y - 3 = \frac{1}{3}(x + 6)$$
$$y - 3 = \frac{1}{3}x + 2$$
$$\boxed{y = \frac{1}{3}x + 5}$$

69.
$$x = \frac{5}{4}y - 2$$
$$4x = 5y - 8$$
$$-5y = -4x - 8$$
$$y = \frac{4}{5}x + \frac{8}{5}$$
$$m = \frac{4}{5}$$
Use $m = -\frac{5}{4}$.
$$y - y_1 = m(x - x_1)$$
$$y + 2 = -\frac{5}{4}(x - 4)$$
$$y + 2 = -\frac{5}{4}x + 5$$
$$\boxed{y = -\frac{5}{4}x + 3}$$

70.
$$x = -\frac{3}{4}y + 5$$
$$4x = -3y + 20$$
$$3y = -4x + 20$$
$$y = -\frac{4}{3}x + \frac{20}{3}$$
$$m = -\frac{4}{3}$$
Use $m = \frac{3}{4}$.
$$y - y_1 = m(x - x_1)$$
$$y + 5 = \frac{3}{4}(x - 1)$$
$$y + 5 = \frac{3}{4}x - \frac{3}{4}$$
$$\boxed{y = \frac{3}{4}x - \frac{23}{4}}$$

71. $4x + 5y = 20 \Rightarrow A = 4, B = 5, C = 20$

$m = -\frac{A}{B} = -\frac{4}{5}$

$b = \frac{C}{B} = \frac{20}{5} = 4 \Rightarrow (0, 4)$

72. $9x - 12y = 17 \Rightarrow A = 9, B = -12, C = 17$

$m = -\frac{A}{B} = -\frac{9}{-12} = \frac{3}{4}$

$b = \frac{C}{B} = \frac{17}{-12} = -\frac{17}{12} \Rightarrow \left(0, -\frac{17}{12}\right)$

73. $2x + 3y = 12 \Rightarrow A = 2, B = 3, C = 12$

$m = -\frac{A}{B} = -\frac{2}{3}$

$b = \frac{C}{B} = \frac{12}{3} = 4 \Rightarrow (0, 4)$

74. $5x + 6y = 30 \Rightarrow A = 5, B = 6, C = 30$

$m = -\frac{A}{B} = -\frac{5}{6}$

$b = \frac{C}{B} = \frac{30}{6} = 5 \Rightarrow (0, 5)$

75. Since $y = 3$ is the equation of a horizontal line, any perpendicular line will be vertical.
Find the midpoint:

$x = \frac{2 + (-6)}{2} = -2;\ y = \frac{4 + 10}{2} = 7$

The vertical line through $(-2, 7)$ is $x = -2$.

76. Since $y = -8$ is the equation of a horizontal line, any parallel line will be horizontal.
Find the midpoint:

$x = \frac{-4 + (-2)}{2} = -3;\ y = \frac{2 + 8}{2} = 5$

The horizontal line through $(-3, 5)$ is $y = 5$.

77. Since $x = 3$ is the equation of a vertical line, any parallel line will be vertical.
Find the midpoint:

$x = \frac{2 + 8}{2} = 5;\ y = \frac{-4 + 12}{2} = 4$

The vertical line through $(5, 4)$ is $x = 5$.

78. Since $x = 3$ is the equation of a vertical line, any perpendicular line will be horizontal.
Find the midpoint:

$x = \frac{-2 + 4}{2} = 1;\ y = \frac{2 + (-8)}{2} = -3$

The horizontal line through $(1, -3)$: $y = -3$.

79. Let $x =$ the number of years the cab has been owned and let $y =$ the value of the cab. Then two points on the line are given: $(0, 24300)$ and $(7, 1900)$.

$m = \frac{24300 - 1900}{0 - 7} = \frac{22400}{-7} = -3200$

$$\begin{aligned} y - y_1 &= m(x - x_1) \\ y - 24300 &= -3200(x - 0) \\ y - 24300 &= -3200x \\ y &= -3200x + 24300 \end{aligned}$$

80. Let $x =$ the number of years the laptop has been owned and let $y =$ the value of the laptop. Then two points on the line are given: $(0, 2700)$ and $(4, 300)$.

$m = \frac{2700 - 300}{0 - 4} = \frac{2400}{-4} = -600$

$$\begin{aligned} y - y_1 &= m(x - x_1) \\ y - 2700 &= -600(x - 0) \\ y - 2700 &= -600x \\ y &= -600x + 2700 \end{aligned}$$

81. Let $x =$ the number of years the building has been owned and let $y =$ the value of the building. Then two points on the line are given: (0, 475000) and (10, 950000).

$$m = \frac{950000 - 475000}{10 - 0} = \frac{475000}{10} = 47500$$

$$\begin{aligned} y - y_1 &= m(x - x_1) \\ y - 475000 &= 47500(x - 0) \\ y - 475000 &= 47500x \\ y &= 47500x + 475000 \end{aligned}$$

82. Let $x =$ the number of years the house has been owned and let $y =$ the value of the house. Then two points on the line are given: (0, 112000) and (12, 224000).

$$m = \frac{224000 - 112000}{12 - 0} = \frac{112000}{12} = \frac{28000}{3}$$

$$\begin{aligned} y - y_1 &= m(x - x_1) \\ y - 112000 &= \frac{28000}{3}(x - 0) \\ y - 112000 &= \frac{28000}{3}x \\ y &= \frac{28000}{3}x + 112000 \end{aligned}$$

83. Let $x =$ the number of years the TV has been owned and let $y =$ the value of the TV. Then two points on the line are given: (0, 1900) and (3, 1190).

$$m = \frac{1900 - 1190}{0 - 3} = \frac{710}{-3} = -\frac{710}{3}$$

$$\begin{aligned} y - y_1 &= m(x - x_1) \\ y - 1900 &= -\frac{710}{3}(x - 0) \\ y - 1900 &= -\frac{710}{3}x \\ y &= -\frac{710}{3}x + 1900 \end{aligned}$$

84. Let $x =$ the number of years the processor has been owned and let $y =$ the value of the processor. Then two points on the line are given: (0, 555) and (5, 80).

$$m = \frac{555 - 80}{0 - 5} = \frac{475}{-5} = -95$$

$$\begin{aligned} y - y_1 &= m(x - x_1) \\ y - 555 &= -95(x - 0) \\ y - 555 &= -95x \\ y &= -95x + 555 \end{aligned}$$

Let $x = 3$ and find the value of y:

$$\begin{aligned} y &= -95x + 555 \\ &= -95(3) + 555 = 270 \end{aligned}$$

It will be worth \$270.

85. Let $x =$ the number of years the copier has been owned and let $y =$ the value of the copier. Then one point on the line is given: (0, 1050). Since the copier depreciates by \$120 per year, $m = -120$.

$$\begin{aligned} y - y_1 &= m(x - x_1) \\ y - 1050 &= -120(x - 0) \\ y - 1050 &= -120x \\ y &= -120x + 1050 \end{aligned}$$

Let $x = 8$ and find the value of y:

$$\begin{aligned} y &= -120x + 1050 \\ &= -120(8) + 1050 = 90 \end{aligned}$$

The salvage value will be \$90.

86. Let $x =$ the number of years the truck has been owned and let $y =$ the value of the truck. Then two points on the line are given: (0, 27600) and (12, 0).

$$m = \frac{27600 - 0}{0 - 12} = \frac{27600}{-12} = -2300$$

The truck depreciates at a rate of \$2300 per year.

87. Let x = the number of years the table has been owned and let y = the value of the table. Then one point on the line is given: $(2, 450)$. Since the table appreciates by \$40 per year, $m = 40$.

$$y - y_1 = m(x - x_1)$$
$$y - 450 = 40(x - 2)$$
$$y - 450 = 40x - 80$$
$$y = 40x + 370$$

Let $x = 13$ and find the value of y:

$$y = 40x + 370$$
$$= 40(13) + 370 = 890$$

The value will be \$890.

88. Let x = the number of years the clock has been owned and let y = the value of the clock. Then two points on the line are given: $(2, 350)$ and $(5, 530)$.

$$m = \frac{530 - 350}{5 - 2} = \frac{180}{3} = 60$$
$$y - y_1 = m(x - x_1)$$
$$y - 350 = 60(x - 2)$$
$$y - 350 = 60x - 120$$
$$y = 60x + 230$$

Let $x = 7$ and find the value of y:

$$y = 60x + 230$$
$$= 60(7) + 230 = 650$$

It will be worth \$650.

89. Let x = the number of years the cottage has been owned and let y = the value of the cottage. Then one point on the line is given: $(3, 47700)$. Since the cottage appreciates by \$3500 per year, $m = 3500$.

$$y - y_1 = m(x - x_1)$$
$$y - 47700 = 3500(x - 3)$$
$$y - 47700 = 3500x - 10500$$
$$y = 3500x + 37200$$

Let $x = 0$ and find the value of y:

$$y = 3500x + 37200$$
$$= 3500(0) + 37200 = 37200$$

The purchase price was \$37,200.

90. Let x = the number of hours of service needed and let y = the total charge. Then two points on the line are given: $(2, 70)$ and $(4, 105)$

$$m = \frac{105 - 70}{4 - 2} = \frac{35}{2} = 17.50$$
$$y - y_1 = m(x - x_1)$$
$$y - 70 = 17.50(x - 2)$$
$$y - 70 = 17.50x - 35$$
$$y = 17.50x + 35$$

The hourly charge is \$17.50.

91. Let x = the hours of labor and let y = the labor charge. Then m = the hourly charge.

$y = mx$	$y = 46x$
$69 = m(1.5)$	$y = 46(5) = 230$
$46 = m$	The charge will be \$230.

92. Let x = the number of hundreds of copies and let y = the total charge. Then m = the charge per copy and b = the fixed charge.

$y = mx + b$	$y = x + 45$
$y = 1x + b$	$y = 10 + 45 = 55$
$52 = 1(7) + b$	The charge will be \$55.
$45 = b$	

93. Let x = the number of fires and let y = the population. Then two points on the line are given: (300, 57000) and (325, 59000).

$$m = \frac{59000 - 57000}{325 - 300} = \frac{2000}{25} = 80$$
$$y - y_1 = m(x - x_1)$$
$$y - 57000 = 80(x - 300)$$
$$y - 57000 = 80x - 24000$$
$$y = 80x + 33000$$

Let $y = 100000$ and find the value of x:

$$y = 80x + 33000$$
$$100000 = 80x + 33000$$
$$67000 = 80x$$

$837.5 = x \Rightarrow$ There will be about 838 fires when the population is 100,000.

94. Let x = the number of feet of gutter and let y = the total charge. Then m = the charge per foot. One point on the line is given: (250, 435)

$$y = mx + b$$
$$435 = m(250) + 60$$
$$375 = 250m$$
$$1.5 = m$$

Let $x = 300$ and find the value of y:

$$y = 1.5x + 60$$
$$= 1.5(300) + 60 = 510$$

It will cost $510.

95. Let F replace x and C replace y. Then two points on the line are given: (32, 0) and (212, 100).

$$m = \frac{100 - 0}{212 - 32} = \frac{100}{180} = \frac{5}{9}$$
$$C - C_1 = m(F - F_1)$$
$$C - 0 = \frac{5}{9}(F - 32)$$
$$C = \frac{5}{9}(F - 32)$$

96. Two points on the line are given: (1, 88) and (0, 0).

$$m = \frac{88 - 0}{1 - 0} = \frac{88}{1} = 88$$
$$y - y_1 = m(x - x_1)$$
$$y - 0 = 88(x - 0)$$
$$y = 88x$$

97. Let y = the percent who smoke and let x = the # of years since 1974. Two points are given: (0, 47) and (20, 29).

$$m = \frac{29 - 47}{20 - 0} = \frac{-18}{20} = -\frac{9}{10}$$
$$y - y_1 = m(x - x_1)$$
$$y - 47 = -\frac{9}{10}(x - 0)$$
$$\boxed{y = -\frac{9}{10}x + 47}$$

Let $x = 30$:

$$y = -\frac{9}{10}(30) + 47 = -27 + 47 = 20$$

20% will smoke in 2004.

98. Let f replace x and h replace y. Then two points on the line are given: (62.5, 200) and (40.2, 150).

$$m = \frac{150 - 200}{40.2 - 62.5} = \frac{-50}{-22.3} \approx 2.242$$
$$h - h_1 = m(f - f_1)$$
$$h - 200 = 2.242(f - 62.5)$$
$$h - 200 = 2.242f - 140.125$$
$$\boxed{h = 2.242f + 59.875}$$

Let $f = 50$:

$$h = 2.242(50) + 59.875 \approx 172$$

He would be about 172 cm tall.

99. Two points on the line are given: $(0, 37.5)$ and $(2, 45)$.

$$m = \frac{45 - 37.5}{2 - 0} = \frac{7.5}{2} = 3.75$$

$$y - y_1 = m(x - x_1)$$
$$y - 37.5 = 3.75(x - 0)$$
$$y = 3.75x + 37.5$$

Let $x = 4$ and find the value of y:

$$y = 3.75x + 37.5$$
$$= 3.75(4) + 37.5$$
$$= 15 + 37.5 = 52.5$$

The price will be \$52.50 in the year 2000.

100. Let January be represented by $x = 0$, and later months by $x = 1, 2, 3, \ldots$ Let y represent the inventory. Then two points on the line are given: $(0, 375)$ and $(3, 264)$.

$$m = \frac{375 - 264}{0 - 3} = \frac{111}{-3} = -37$$

$$y - y_1 = m(x - x_1)$$
$$y - 375 = -37(x - 0)$$
$$y = -37x + 375$$

Let $x = 2$ and find the value of y:

$$y = -37x + 375$$
$$= -37(2) + 375 = 301$$

The March inventory will be about 301.

101. The equation describing the production is $y = -70x + 1900$, where x represents the number of years and y is the level of production. Let $x = 3\frac{1}{2} = \frac{7}{2}$.

$$y = -70x + 1900$$
$$= -70\left(\frac{7}{2}\right) + 1900 = 1655$$

The production will be 1655 barrels per day.

102. Let $x =$ the number of years the piping has been owned and let $y =$ the value of the piping. Then two points on the line are given: $(0, 137000)$ and $(12, -33000)$.

$$m = \frac{-33000 - 137000}{12 - 0} = -\frac{42500}{3}$$

$$y - y_1 = m(x - x_1)$$
$$y - 137000 = -\frac{42500}{3}(x - 0)$$
$$y = -\frac{42500}{3}x + 137000$$

103. **a.**

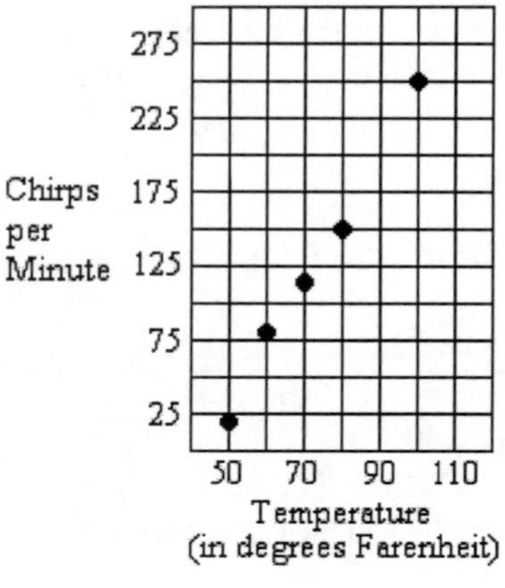

b. Use $(50, 20)$ and $(100, 250)$ for the regression line.

$$m = \frac{250 - 20}{100 - 50} = \frac{230}{50} = \frac{23}{5}$$

$$y - y_1 = m(x - x_1)$$
$$y - 20 = \frac{23}{5}(x - 50)$$
$$y - 20 = \frac{23}{5}x - 230$$
$$y = \frac{23}{5}x - 210$$

c. $y = \frac{23}{5}(90) - 210 = 204$

The rate will be about 204 chirps per minute.

104. a.

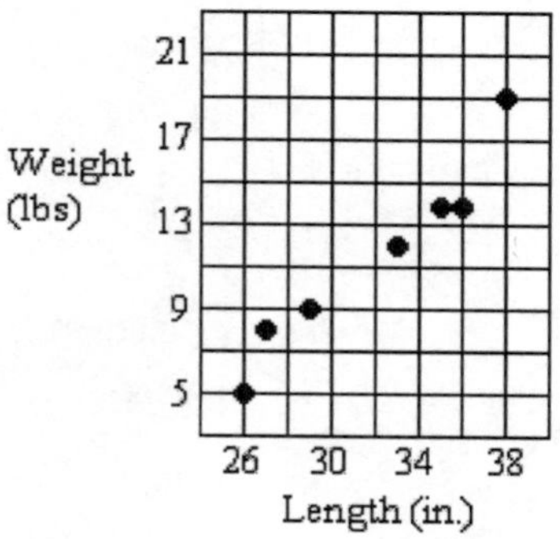

b. Use (26, 5) and (38, 19) for the regression line.

$$m = \frac{19-5}{38-26} = \frac{14}{12} = \frac{7}{6}$$
$$y - y_1 = m(x - x_1)$$
$$y - 5 = \frac{7}{6}(x - 26)$$
$$y - 5 = \frac{7}{6}x - \frac{91}{3}$$
$$y = \frac{7}{6}x - \frac{76}{3}$$

c. $y = \frac{7}{6}(32) - \frac{76}{3} = 12$

The weight will be about 12 pounds.

105. Answers may vary.

106. Answers may vary.

107. $m = \frac{b-0}{0-a} = -\frac{b}{a}$
$$y - y_1 = m(x - x_1)$$
$$y - b = -\frac{b}{a}(x - 0)$$
$$y - b = -\frac{b}{a}x$$
$$ay - ab = -bx$$
$$bx + ay = ab$$
$$\frac{bx + ay}{ab} = \frac{ab}{ab}$$
$$\frac{x}{a} + \frac{y}{b} = 1$$

108.

x-intercept	y-intercept
$bx + ay = ab$	$bx + ay = ab$
$bx + a(0) = ab$	$b(0) + ay = ab$
$bx = ab$	$ay = ab$
$x = a$	$y = b$
$(a, 0)$	$(0, b)$

109. Answers may vary.

110. Answers may vary.

111. Answers may vary.

112. Answers may vary.

113. Answers may vary.

114. Answers may vary.

115. $x^7x^3x^{-5} = x^{7+3-5} = x^5$

116. $\frac{y^3y^{-4}}{y^{-5}} = \frac{y^{-1}}{y^{-5}} = y^{-1-(-5)} = y^4$

117. $\left(\frac{81}{25}\right)^{-3/2} = \left(\frac{25}{81}\right)^{3/2} = \left[\frac{5}{9}\right]^3 = \frac{125}{729}$

118. $\sqrt[3]{27x^7} = \sqrt[3]{27x^6}\sqrt[3]{x} = 3x^2\sqrt[3]{x}$

119. $\sqrt{27} - 2\sqrt{12} = \sqrt{9}\sqrt{3} - 2\sqrt{4}\sqrt{3} = 3\sqrt{3} - 2(2)\sqrt{3} = 3\sqrt{3} - 4\sqrt{3} = -\sqrt{3}$

120. $\frac{5}{\sqrt{5}} = \frac{5\sqrt{5}}{\sqrt{5}\sqrt{5}} = \frac{5\sqrt{5}}{5} = \sqrt{5}$

121. $\dfrac{5}{\sqrt{x}+2} = \dfrac{5}{\sqrt{x}+2} \cdot \dfrac{\sqrt{x}-2}{\sqrt{x}-2} = \dfrac{5(\sqrt{x}-2)}{(\sqrt{x})^2 - 2^2} = \dfrac{5(\sqrt{x}-2)}{x-4}$

122. $(\sqrt{x}-2)^2 = (\sqrt{x}-2)(\sqrt{x}-2) = x - 2\sqrt{x} - 2\sqrt{x} + 4 = x - 4\sqrt{x} + 4$

Exercise 2.4 (page 213)

1. x-intercept

2. y-axis

3. axis of symmetry

4. y-axis

5. x-axis

6. origin

7. circle, center

8. radius

9. $x^2 + y^2 = r^2$

10. $(x-h)^2 + (y-k)^2 = r^2$

11.
$y = x^2 - 4$
$0 = (x+2)(x-2)$
$x = -2, x = 2$
x-int: $(-2, 0), (2, 0)$

$y = x^2 - 4$
$y = 0^2 - 4$
$y = -4$
y-int: $(0, -4)$

12.
$y = x^2 - 9$
$0 = x^2 - 9$
$0 = (x+3)(x-3)$
$x = -3, x = 3$
x-int: $(-3, 0), (3, 0)$

$y = x^2 - 9$
$y = 0^2 - 9$
$y = -9$
y-int: $(0, -9)$

13.
$y = 4x^2 - 2x$
$0 = 2x(2x-1)$
$x = 0, x = \frac{1}{2}$
x-int: $(0, 0), \left(\frac{1}{2}, 0\right)$

$y = 4x^2 - 2x$
$y = 4(0)^2 - 2(0)$
$y = 0$
y-int: $(0, 0)$

14.
$y = 2x - 4x^2$
$0 = 2x(1-2x)$
$x = 0, x = \frac{1}{2}$
x-int: $(0, 0), \left(\frac{1}{2}, 0\right)$

$y = 2x - 4x^2$
$y = 2(0) - 4(0)^2$
$y = 0$
y-int: $(0, 0)$

15.
$y = x^2 - 4x - 5$
$0 = (x+1)(x-5)$
$x = -1, x = 5$
x-int: $(-1, 0), (5, 0)$

$y = x^2 - 4x - 5$
$y = 0^2 - 4(0) - 5$
$y = -5$
y-int: $(0, -5)$

16.
$y = x^2 - 10x + 21$
$0 = (x-3)(x-7)$
$x = 3, x = 7$
x-int: $(3, 0), (7, 0)$

$y = x^2 - 10x + 21$
$y = 0^2 - 10(0) + 21$
$y = 21$
y-int: $(0, 21)$

17.
$y = x^2 + x - 2$
$0 = (x+2)(x-1)$
$x = -2, x = 1$
x-int: $(-2, 0), (1, 0)$

$y = x^2 + x - 2$
$y = 0^2 + 0 - 2$
$y = -2$
y-int: $(0, -2)$

18.
$y = x^2 + 2x - 3$
$0 = (x+3)(x-1)$
$x = -3, x = 1$
x-int: $(-3, 0), (1, 0)$

$y = x^2 + 2x - 3$
$y = 0^2 + 2(0) - 3$
$y = -3$
y-int: $(0, -3)$

19.
$y = x^3 - 9x$
$0 = x(x^2 - 9)$
$0 = x(x+3)(x-3)$
$x = 0, x = -3, x = 3$
x-int: $(0, 0), (-3, 0), (3, 0)$

$y = x^3 - 9x$
$y = 0^3 - 9(0)$
$y = 0$
y-int: $(0, 0)$

20.
$y = x^3 + x$
$0 = x(x^2 + 1)$
$x = 0, \{x^2 + 1 \neq 0\}$
x-int: $(0, 0)$

$y = x^3 + x$
$y = 0^3 + 0$
$y = 0$
y-int: $(0, 0)$

21. $y = x^4 - 1$
$0 = (x^2 + 1)(x^2 - 1)$
$0 = (x^2 + 1)(x + 1)(x - 1)$
$x = -1, x = 1$
x-int: $(-1, 0), (1, 0)$

$y = x^4 - 1$
$y = 0^4 - 1$
$y = -1$
y-int: $(0, -1)$

22. $y = x^4 - 25x^2$
$0 = x^2(x^2 - 25)$
$0 = x^2(x + 5)(x - 5)$
$x = 0, x = -5, x = 5$
x-int: $(0, 0), (-5, 0), (5, 0)$

$y = x^4 - 25x^2$
$y = 0^4 - 25(0)^2$
$y = 0$
y-int: $(0, 0)$

23. $y = x^2$
x-int: $(0, 0)$
y-int: $(0, 0)$

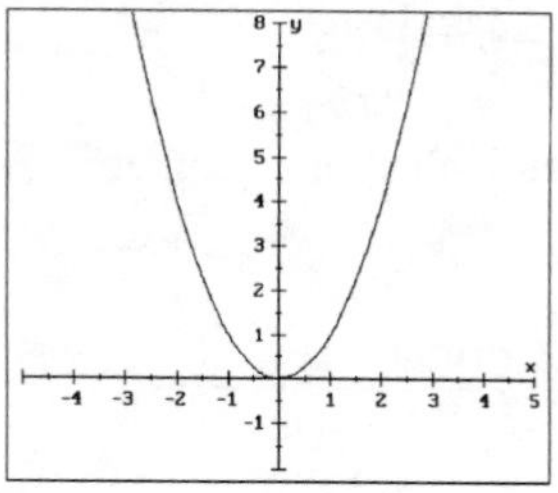

24. $y = -x^2$
x-int: $(0, 0)$
y-int: $(0, 0)$

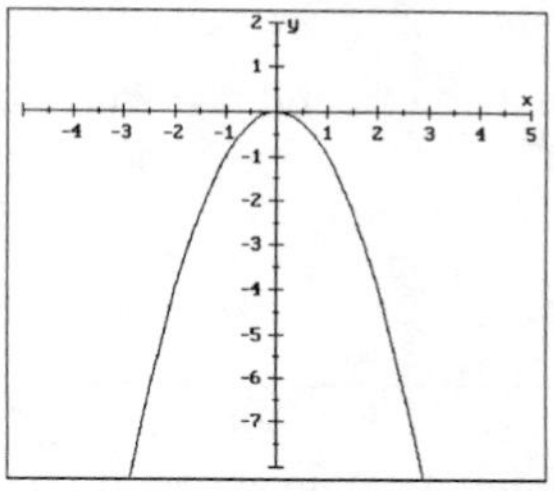

25. $y = -x^2 + 2$
x-int: $(\sqrt{2}, 0), (-\sqrt{2}, 0)$
y-int: $(0, 2)$

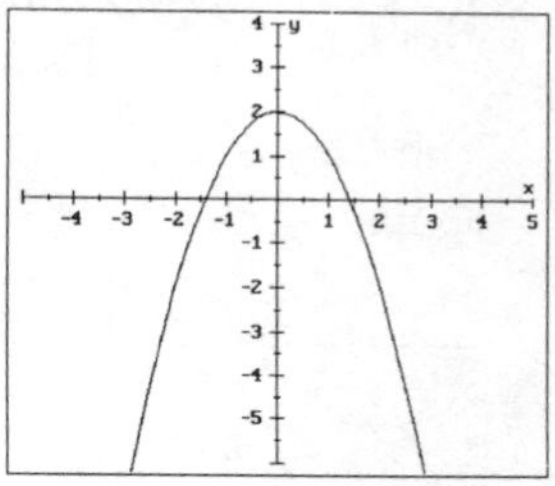

26. $y = x^2 - 1$
x-int: $(1, 0), (-1, 0)$
y-int: $(0, -1)$

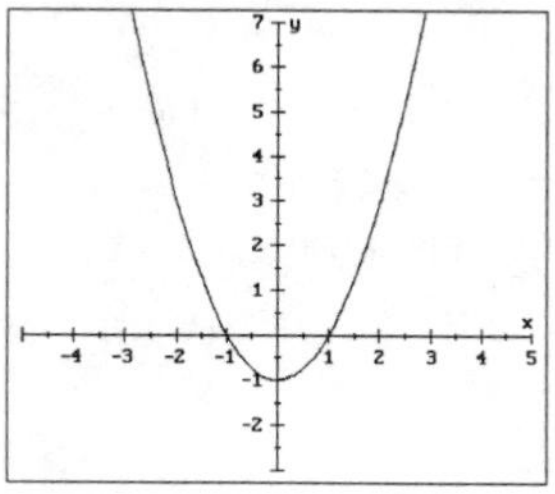

27. $y = x^2 - 4x$
x-int: $(0, 0), (4, 0)$
y-int: $(0, 0)$

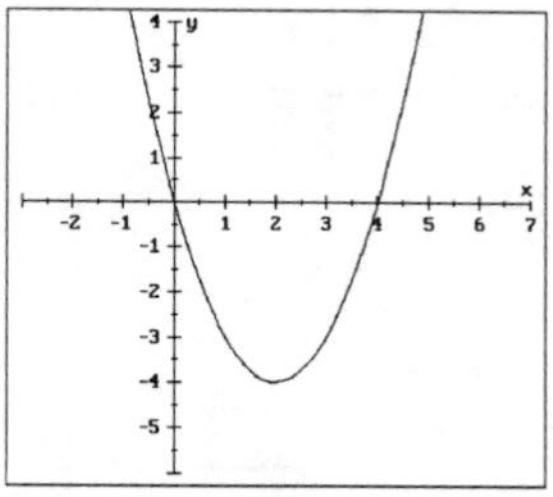

28. $y = x^2 + 2x$
x-int: $(0, 0), (-2, 0)$
y-int: $(0, 0)$

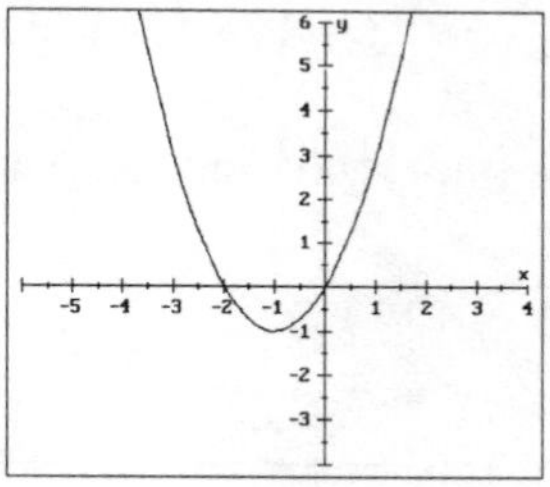

29. $y = \frac{1}{2}x^2 - 2x$
x-int: $(0, 0), (4, 0)$
y-int: $(0, 0)$

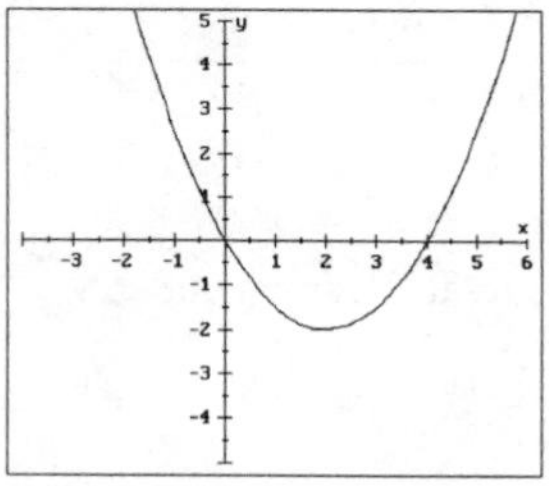

30. $y = \frac{1}{2}x^2 + 3$
x-int: none
y-int: $(0, 3)$

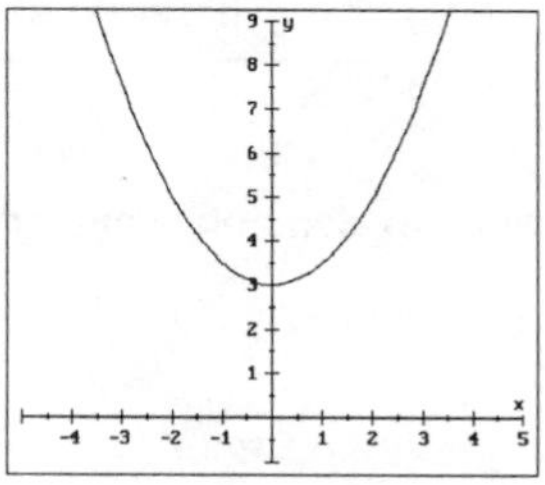

31. $y = x^2 + 2$

x-axis	y-axis	origin
$-y = x^2 + 2$	$y = (-x)^2 + 2$	$-y = (-x)^2 + 2$
not equivalent: no symmetry	$y = x^2 + 2$	$-y = x^2 + 2$
	equivalent: symmetry	not equivalent: no symmetry

32. $y = 3x + 2$

x-axis	y-axis	origin
$-y = 3x + 2$	$y = 3(-x) + 2$	$-y = 3(-x) + 2$
not equivalent: no symmetry	$y = -3x + 2$	$-y = -3x + 2$
	not equivalent: no symmetry	$y = 3x - 2$
		not equivalent: no symmetry

33. $y^2 + 1 = x$

x-axis	y-axis	origin
$(-y)^2 + 1 = x$	$y^2 + 1 = -x$	$(-y)^2 + 1 = -x$
$y^2 + 1 = x$	not equivalent: no symmetry	$y^2 + 1 = -x$
equivalent: symmetry		not equivalent: no symmetry

34. $y^2 + y = x$

x-axis	y-axis	origin
$(-y)^2 + (-y) = x$	$y^2 + y = -x$	$(-y)^2 + (-y) = -x$
$y^2 - y = x$	not equivalent: no symmetry	$y^2 - y = -x$
not equivalent: no symmetry		$-y^2 + y = x$
		not equivalent: no symmetry

35. $y^2 = x^2$

x-axis	y-axis	origin
$(-y)^2 = x^2$	$y^2 = (-x)^2$	$(-y)^2 = (-x)^2$
$y^2 = x^2$	$y^2 = x^2$	$y^2 = x^2$
equivalent: symmetry	equivalent: symmetry	equivalent: symmetry

36. $y = 3x + 7$

x-axis	y-axis	origin
$-y = 3x + 7$	$y = 3(-x) + 7$	$-y = 3(-x) + 7$
not equivalent: no symmetry	$y = -3x + 7$	$-y = -3x + 7$
	not equivalent: no symmetry	$y = 3x - 7$
		not equivalent: no symmetry

37. $y = 3x^2 + 7$

x-axis	y-axis	origin
$-y = 3x^2 + 7$	$y = 3(-x)^2 + 7$	$-y = 3(-x)^2 + 7$
not equivalent: no symmetry	$y = 3x^2 + 7$	$-y = 3x^2 + 7$
	equivalent: $\boxed{\text{symmetry}}$	not equivalent: no symmetry

38. $x^2 + y^2 = 1$

x-axis	y-axis	origin
$x^2 + (-y)^2 = 1$	$(-x)^2 + y^2 = 1$	$(-x)^2 + (-y)^2 = 1$
$x^2 + y^2 = 1$	$x^2 + y^2 = 1$	$x^2 + y^2 = 1$
equivalent: $\boxed{\text{symmetry}}$	equivalent: $\boxed{\text{symmetry}}$	equivalent: $\boxed{\text{symmetry}}$

39. $y = 3x^3 + 7$

x-axis	y-axis	origin
$-y = 3x^3 + 7$	$y = 3(-x)^3 + 7$	$-y = 3(-x)^3 + 7$
not equivalent: no symmetry	$y = -3x^3 + 7$	$-y = -3x^3 + 7$
	not equivalent: no symmetry	$y = 3x^3 - 7$
		not equivalent: no symmetry

40. $y = 3x^3 + 7x$

x-axis	y-axis	origin
$-y = 3x^3 + 7x$	$y = 3(-x)^3 + 7x$	$-y = 3(-x)^3 + 7(-x)$
not equivalent: no symmetry	$y = -3x^3 + 7x$	$-y = -3x - 7x$
	not equivalent: no symmetry	$y = 3x^3 + 7x$
		equivalent: $\boxed{\text{symmetry}}$

41. $y^2 = 3x$

x-axis	y-axis	origin
$(-y)^2 = 3x$	$y^2 + 1 = 3(-x)$	$(-y)^2 = 3(-x)$
$y^2 = 3x$	$y^2 + 1 = -3x$	$y^2 = -3x$
equivalent: $\boxed{\text{symmetry}}$	not equivalent: no symmetry	not equivalent: no symmetry

42. $y = 3x^4 + 7$

x-axis	y-axis	origin
$-y = 3x^4 + 7$	$y = 3(-x)^4 + 7$	$-y = 3(-x)^4 + 7$
not equivalent: no symmetry	$y = 3x^4 + 7$	$-y = 3x^4 + 7$
	equivalent: $\boxed{\text{symmetry}}$	not equivalent: no symmetry

43. $y = |x|$

x-axis	y-axis	origin
$-y = \|x\|$	$y = \|-x\|$	$-y = \|-x\|$
not equivalent: no symmetry	$y = \|-1\|\|x\|$	$-y = \|-1\|\|x\|$
	$y = \|x\|$	$-y = \|x\|$
	equivalent: **symmetry**	not equivalent: no symmetry

44. $y = |x+1|$

x-axis	y-axis	origin
$-y = \|x+1\|$	$y = \|-x+1\|$	$-y = \|-x+1\|$
not equivalent: no symmetry	not equivalent: no symmetry	not equivalent: no symmetry

45. $|y| = x$

x-axis	y-axis	origin
$\|-y\| = x$	$\|y\| = -x$	$\|-y\| = -x$
$\|-1\|\|y\| = x$	not equivalent: no symmetry	$\|-1\|\|y\| = -x$
$\|y\| = x$		$\|y\| = -x$
equivalent: **symmetry**		not equivalent: no symmetry

46. $|y| = |x|$

x-axis	y-axis	origin
$\|-y\| = \|x\|$	$\|y\| = \|-x\|$	$\|-y\| = \|-x\|$
$\|-1\|\|y\| = \|x\|$	$\|y\| = \|-1\|\|x\|$	$\|-1\|\|y\| = \|-1\|\|x\|$
$\|y\| = \|x\|$	$\|y\| = \|x\|$	$\|y\| = \|x\|$
equivalent: **symmetry**	equivalent: **symmetry**	equivalent: **symmetry**

47. $y = x^2 + 4x$
x-int: $(0, 0)$, $(-4, 0)$
y-int: $(0, 0)$
symmetry: none

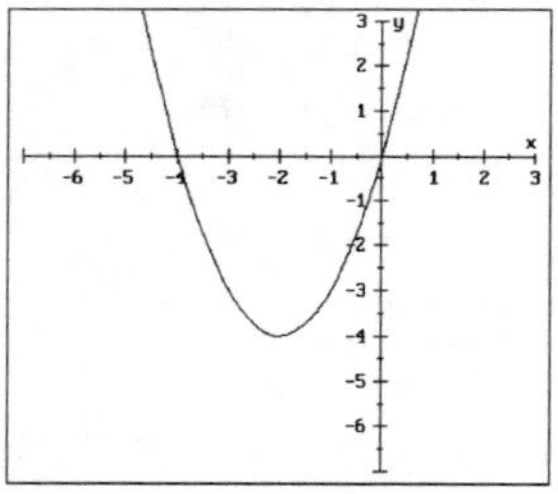

48. $y = x^2 - 6x$
x-int: $(0, 0)$, $(6, 0)$
y-int: $(0, 0)$
symmetry: none

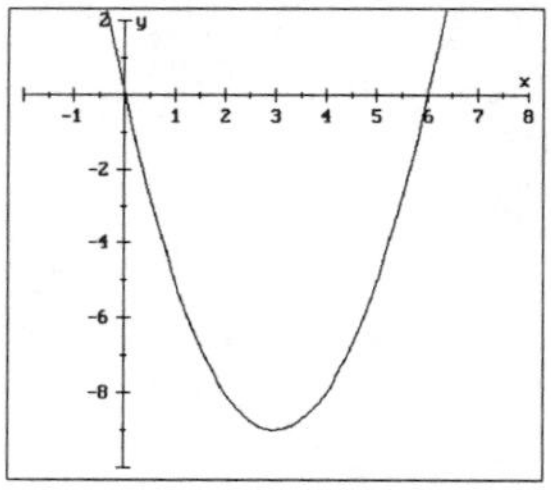

49. $y = x^3$
x-int: $(0, 0)$
y-int: $(0, 0)$
symmetry: origin

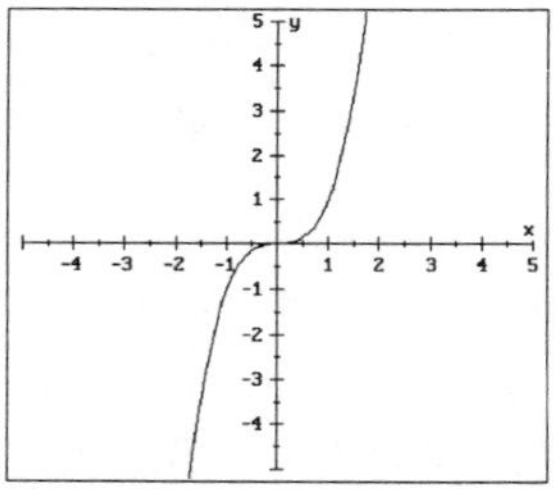

50. $y = x^3 + x$
x-int: $(0, 0)$
y-int: $(0, 0)$
symmetry: origin

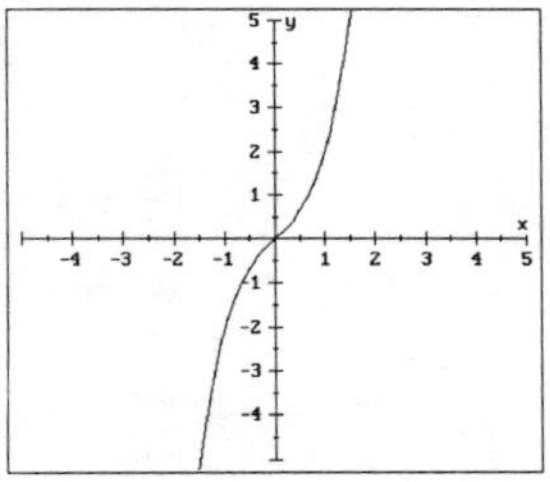

51. $y = |x - 2|$
x-int: $(2, 0)$
y-int: $(0, 2)$
symmetry: none

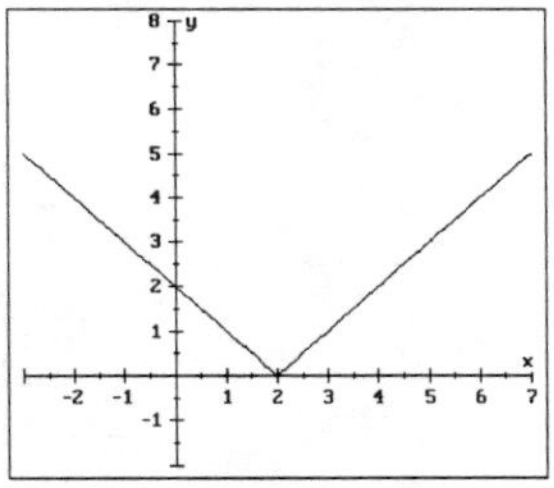

52. $y = |x| - 2$
x-int: $(-2, 0), (2, 0)$
y-int: $(0, -2)$
symmetry: y-axis

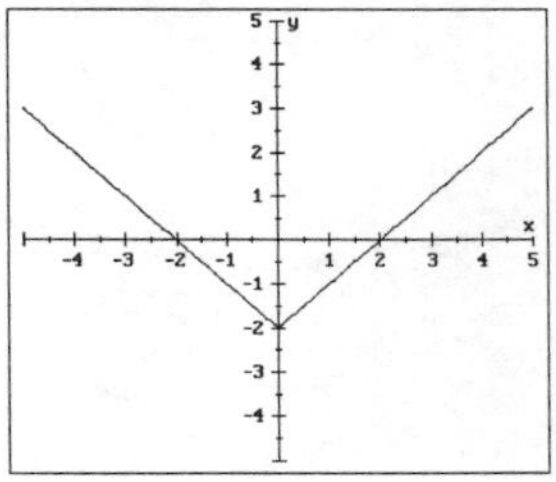

53. $y = 3 - |x|$
x-int: $(-3, 0), (3, 0)$
y-int: $(0, 3)$
symmetry: y-axis

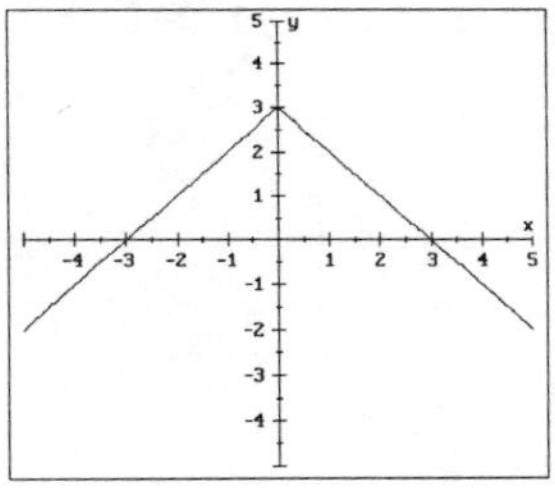

54. $y = 3|x|$
x-int: $(0, 0)$
y-int: $(0, 0)$
symmetry: y-axis

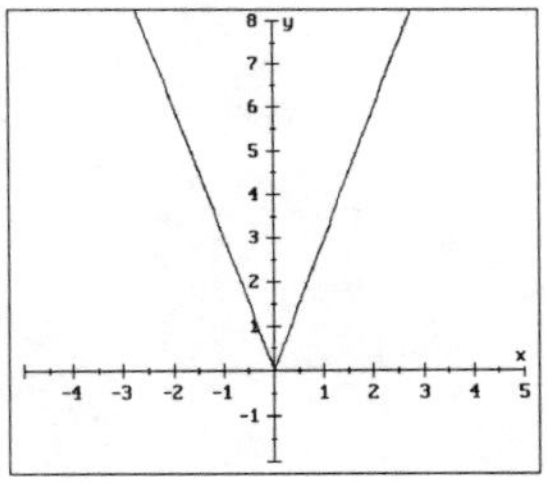

55. $y^2 = -x$
x-int: $(0, 0)$
y-int: $(0, 0)$
symmetry: x-axis

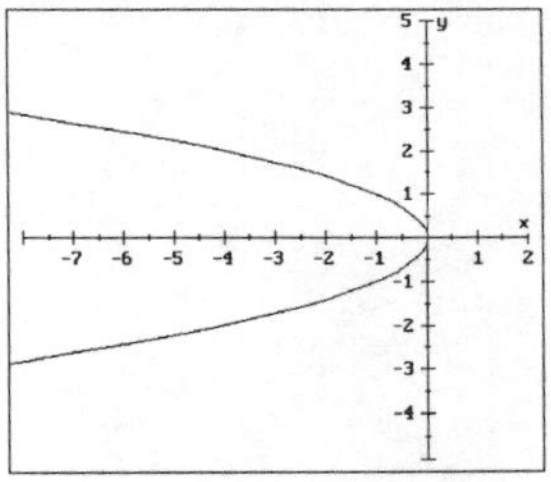

56. $y^2 = 4x$
x-int: $(0, 0)$
y-int: $(0, 0)$
symmetry: x-axis

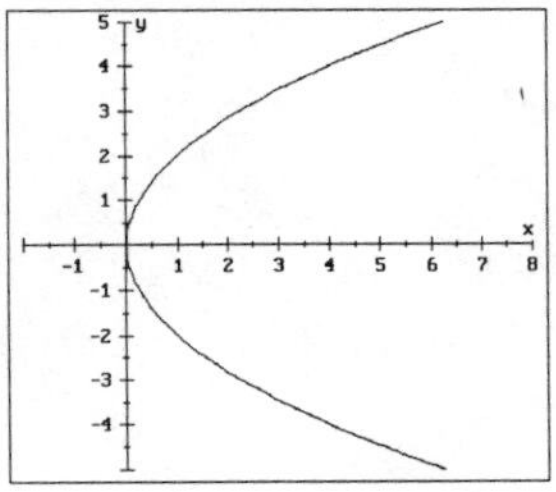

57. $y^2 = 9x$
x-int: $(0, 0)$
y-int: $(0, 0)$
symmetry: x-axis

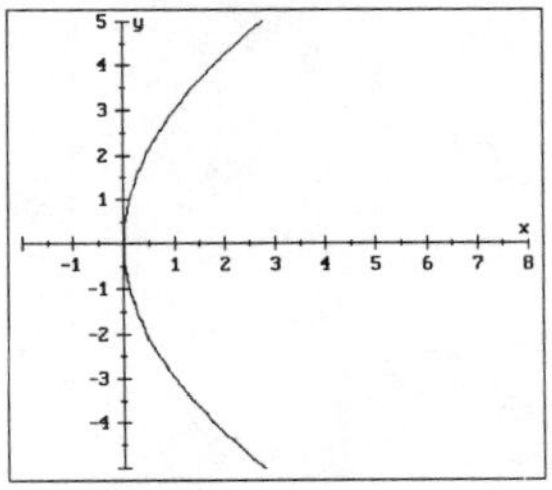

58. $y^2 = -4x$
x-int: $(0, 0)$
y-int: $(0, 0)$
symmetry: x-axis

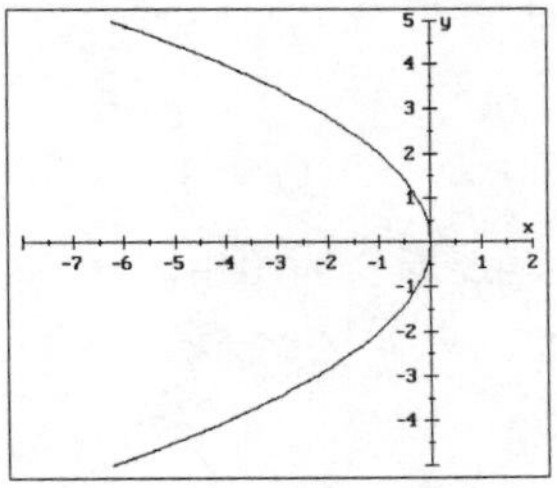

59. $y = \sqrt{x} - 1$
x-int: $(1, 0)$
y-int: $(0, -1)$
symmetry: none

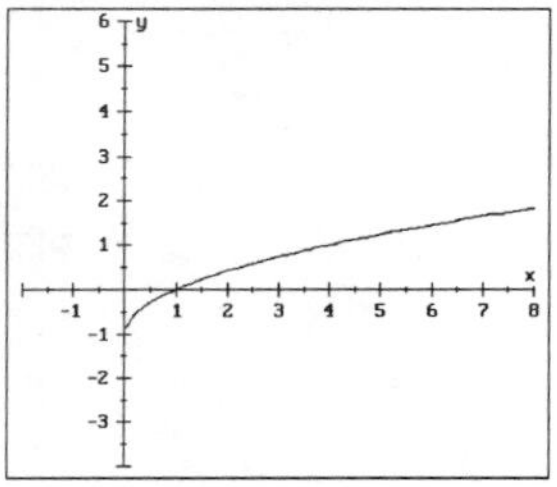

60. $y = 1 - \sqrt{x}$
x-int: $(1, 0)$
y-int: $(0, 1)$
symmetry: none

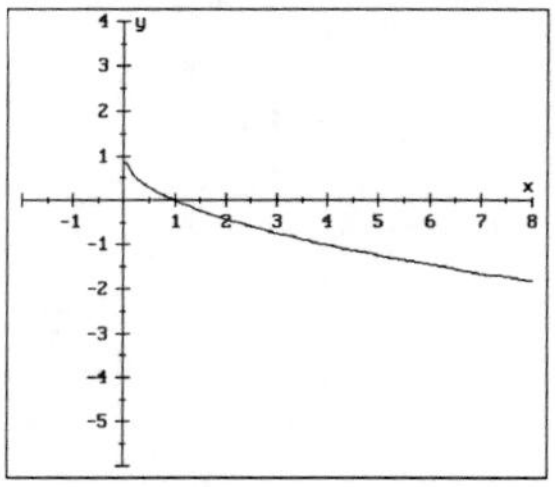

61. $xy = 4$
x-int: none
y-int: none
symmetry: origin

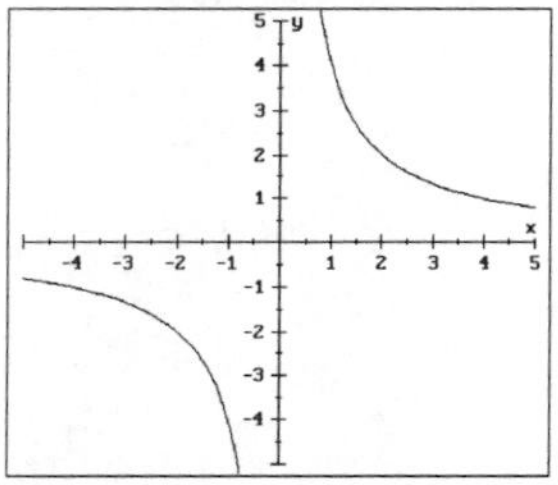

62. $xy = -9$
x-int: none
y-int: none
symmetry: origin

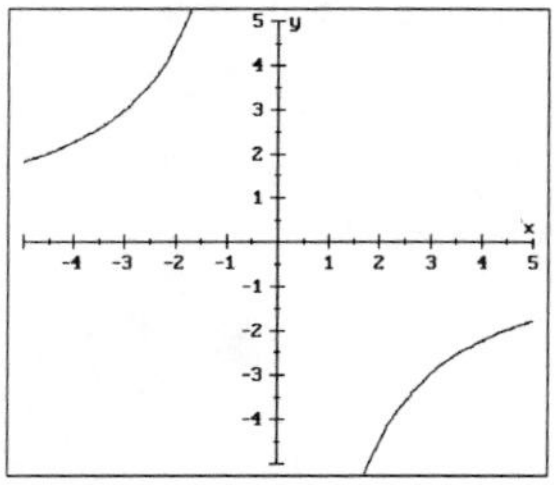

63. $x^2 + y^2 = 1^2 \Rightarrow x^2 + y^2 - 1 = 0$

64. $x^2 + y^2 = 4^2 \Rightarrow x^2 + y^2 - 16 = 0$

65.
$$\begin{aligned} (x-6)^2 + (y-8)^2 &= 4^2 \\ x^2 - 12x + 36 + y^2 - 16y + 64 &= 16 \\ x^2 + y^2 - 12x - 16y + 84 &= 0 \end{aligned}$$

66.
$$\begin{aligned} (x-5)^2 + (y-3)^2 &= 2^2 \\ x^2 - 10x + 25 + y^2 - 6y + 9 &= 4 \\ x^2 + y^2 - 10x - 6y + 30 &= 0 \end{aligned}$$

67.
$$\begin{aligned} (x-3)^2 + (y+4)^2 &= \left(\sqrt{2}\right)^2 \\ x^2 - 6x + 9 + y^2 + 8y + 16 &= 2 \\ x^2 + y^2 - 6x + 8y + 23 &= 0 \end{aligned}$$

68.
$$\begin{aligned} (x+9)^2 + (y-8)^2 &= \left(2\sqrt{3}\right)^2 \\ x^2 + 18x + 81 + y^2 - 16y + 64 &= 12 \\ x^2 + y^2 + 18x - 16y + 133 &= 0 \end{aligned}$$

69. Center: $x = \dfrac{3+3}{2} = 3,\ y = \dfrac{-2+8}{2} = 3$

$r =$ distance from center to endpoint

$$= \sqrt{(3-3)^2 + (3-8)^2} = 5$$

$$(x-3)^2 + (y-3)^2 = 5^2$$

$$x^2 - 6x + 9 + y^2 - 6y + 9 = 25$$

$$x^2 + y^2 - 6x - 6y - 7 = 0$$

70. Center: $x = \dfrac{-5+5}{2} = 0,\ y = \dfrac{-9+9}{2} = 0$

$r =$ distance from center to endpoint

$$= \sqrt{(0-5)^2 + (0-9)^2} = \sqrt{106}$$

$$(x-0)^2 + (y-0)^2 = \left(\sqrt{106}\right)^2$$

$$x^2 + y^2 = 106$$

$$x^2 + y^2 - 106 = 0$$

71. $r =$ distance from center to origin

$$= \sqrt{(0-(-3))^2 + (0-4)^2} = 5$$

$$(x+3)^2 + (y-4)^2 = 5^2$$

$$x^2 + 6x + 9 + y^2 - 8y + 16 = 25$$

$$x^2 + y^2 + 6x - 8y = 0$$

72. $r =$ distance from center to origin

$$= \sqrt{(0-(-2))^2 + (0-6)^2} = \sqrt{40}$$

$$(x+2)^2 + (y-6)^2 = \left(\sqrt{40}\right)^2$$

$$x^2 + 4x + 4 + y^2 - 12y + 36 = 40$$

$$x^2 + y^2 + 4x - 12y = 0$$

73. $x^2 + y^2 - 25 = 0$

$$x^2 + y^2 = 25$$

$C(0,0),\ r = 5$

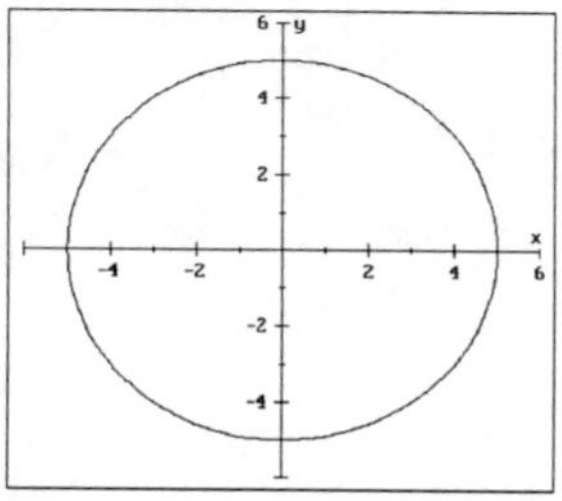

74. $x^2 + y^2 - 8 = 0$

$$x^2 + y^2 = 8$$

$C(0,0),\ r = \sqrt{8} = 2\sqrt{2}$

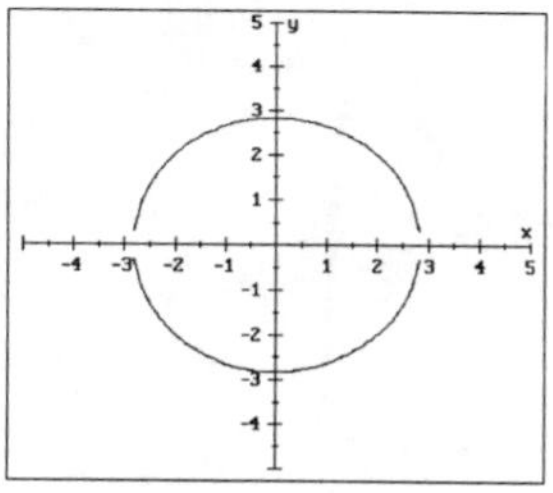

75. $(x-1)^2 + (y+2)^2 = 4$

$C(1,-2),\ r = 2$

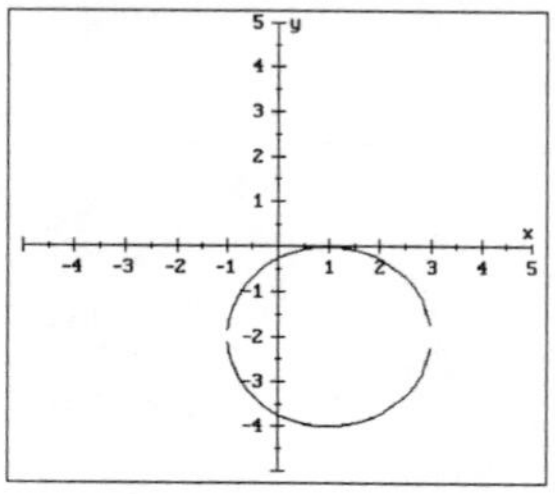

76. $(x+1)^2 + (y-2)^2 = 9$

$C(-1,2),\ r = 3$

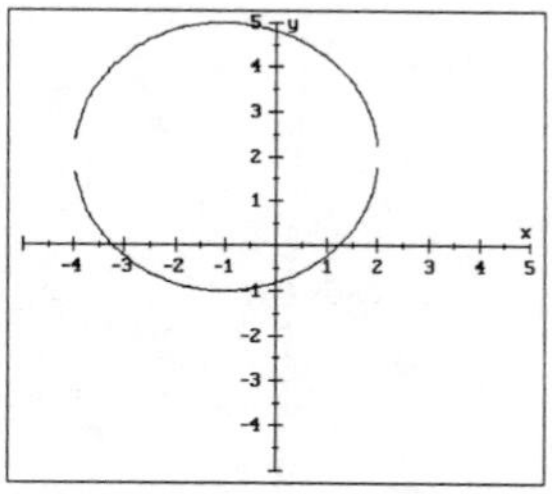

77.
$$\begin{aligned} x^2 + y^2 + 2x - 24 &= 0 \\ x^2 + 2x + y^2 &= 24 \\ x^2 + 2x + 1 + y^2 &= 24 + 1 \\ (x+1)^2 + y^2 &= 25 \end{aligned}$$
$C(-1, 0), r = 5$

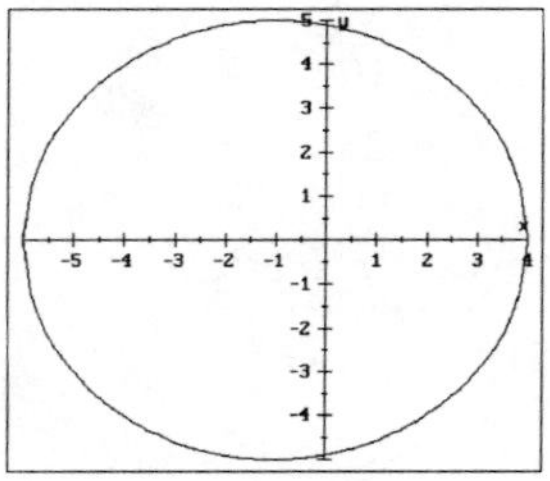

78.
$$\begin{aligned} x^2 + y^2 - 4y &= 12 \\ x^2 + y^2 - 4y + 4 &= 12 + 4 \\ x^2 + (y-2)^2 &= 16 \end{aligned}$$
$C(0, 2), r = 4$

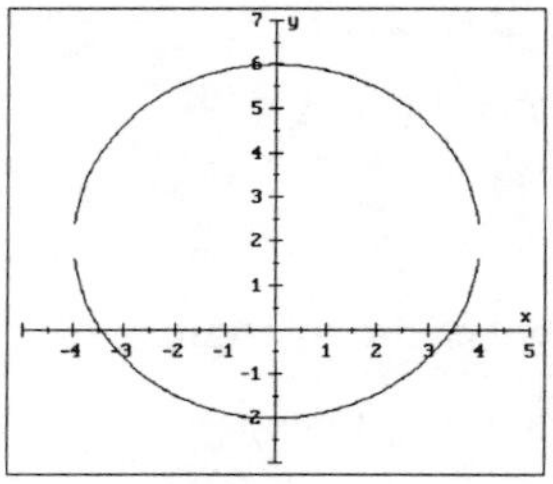

79.
$$\begin{aligned} 9x^2 + 9y^2 - 12y &= 5 \\ x^2 + y^2 - \frac{4}{3}y &= \frac{5}{9} \\ x^2 + y^2 - \frac{4}{3}y + \frac{4}{9} &= \frac{5}{9} + \frac{4}{9} \\ x^2 + \left(y - \frac{2}{3}\right)^2 &= 1 \end{aligned}$$
$C\left(0, \frac{2}{3}\right), r = 1$

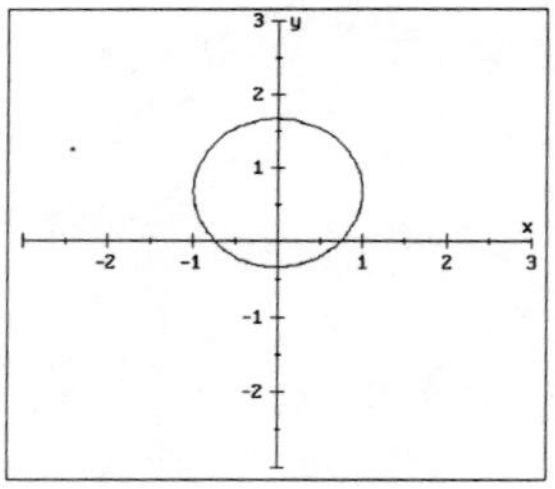

80.
$$\begin{aligned} 4x^2 + 4y^2 + 4y &= 15 \\ x^2 + y^2 + y &= \frac{15}{4} \\ x^2 + y^2 + y + \frac{1}{4} &= \frac{15}{4} + \frac{1}{4} \\ x^2 + \left(y + \frac{1}{2}\right)^2 &= 4 \end{aligned}$$
$C\left(0, -\frac{1}{2}\right), r = 2$

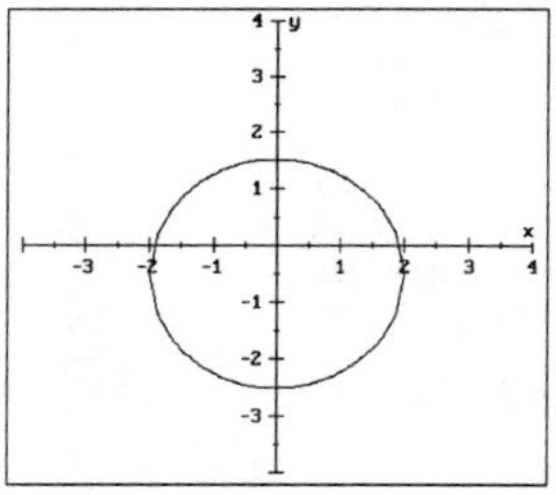

81. $4x^2 + 4y^2 - 4x + 8y + 1 = 0$

$$x^2 + y^2 - x + 2y = -\frac{1}{4}$$

$$x^2 - x + \frac{1}{4} + y^2 + 2y + 1 = -\frac{1}{4} + \frac{1}{4} + 1$$

$$\left(x - \frac{1}{2}\right)^2 + (y+1)^2 = 1$$

$$C\left(\frac{1}{2}, -1\right), r = 1$$

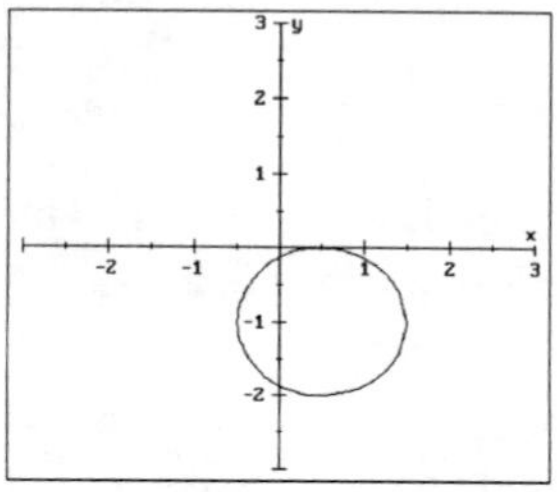

82. $9x^2 + 9y^2 - 6x + 18y + 1 = 0$

$$x^2 + y^2 - \frac{2}{3}x + 2y = -\frac{1}{9}$$

$$x^2 - \frac{2}{3}x + \frac{1}{9} + y^2 + 2y + 1 = -\frac{1}{9} + \frac{1}{9} + 1$$

$$\left(x - \frac{1}{3}\right)^2 + (y+1)^2 = 1$$

$$C\left(\frac{1}{3}, -1\right), r = 1$$

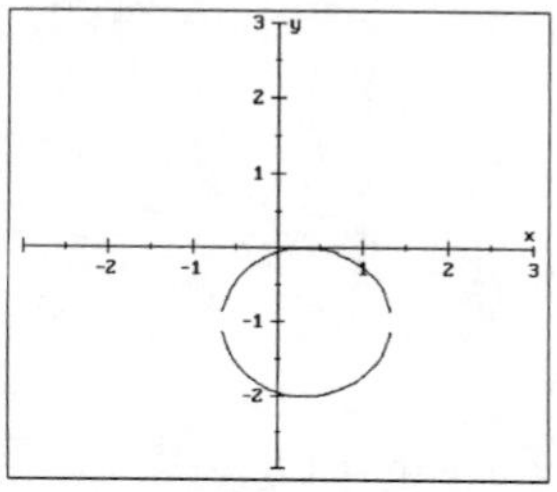

83. $y = 2x^2 - x + 1$
Vertex: (0.25, 0.88)

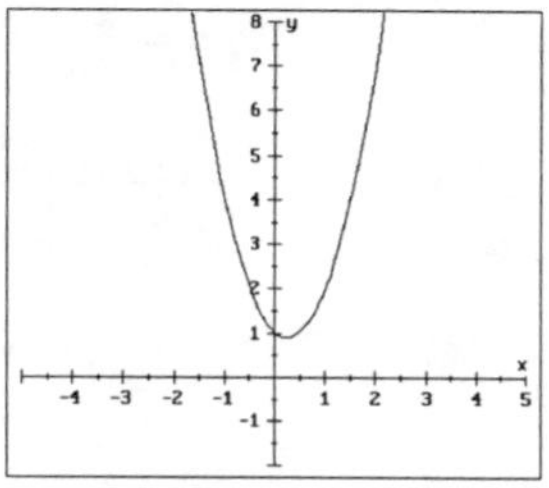

84. $y = x^2 + 5x - 6$
Vertex: (−2.50, −12.25)

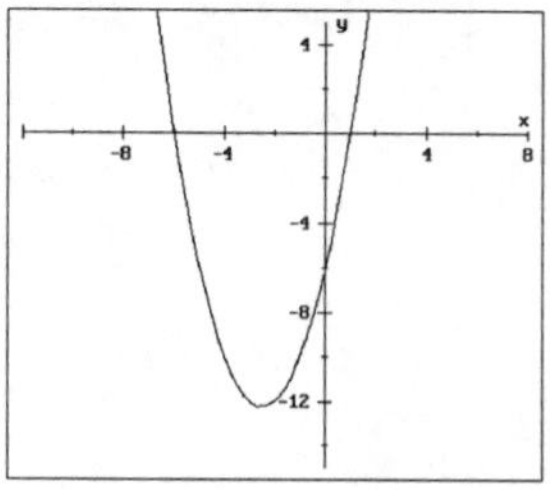

85. $y = 7 + x - x^2$
Vertex: (0.50, 7.25)

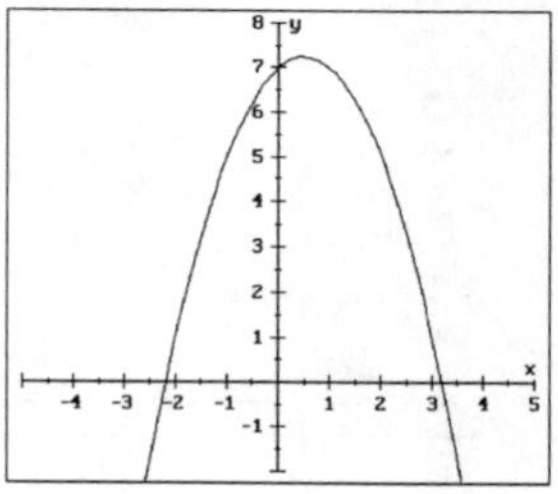

86. $y = 2x^2 - 3x + 2$
Vertex: (0.75, 0.88)

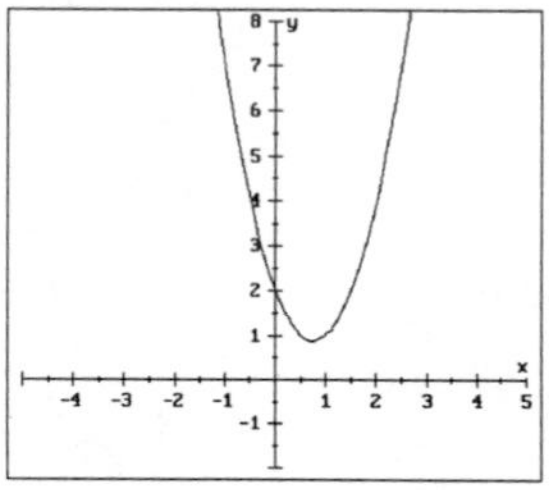

87. Graph $y = x^2 - 7$.
Find the x-intercepts.
$x = -2.65,\ x = 2.65$

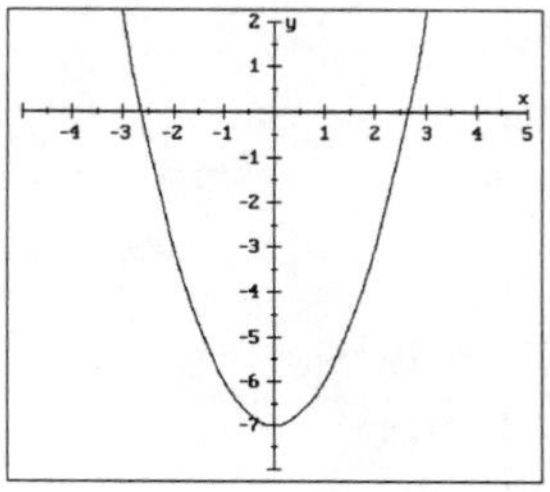

88. Graph $y = x^2 - 3x + 2$.
Find the x-intercepts.
$x = 1.00,\ x = 2.00$

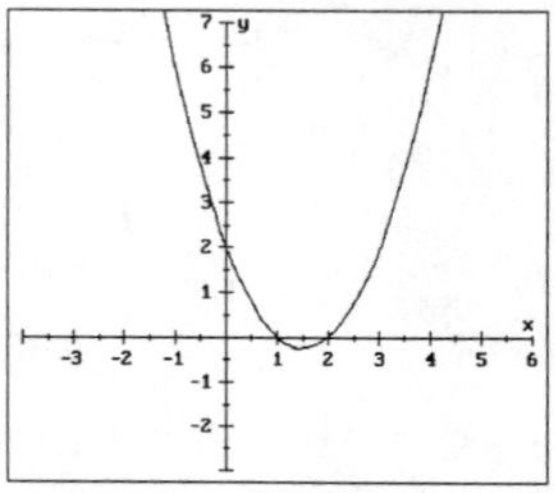

89. Graph $y = x^3 - 3$.
Find the x-intercepts.
$x = 1.44$

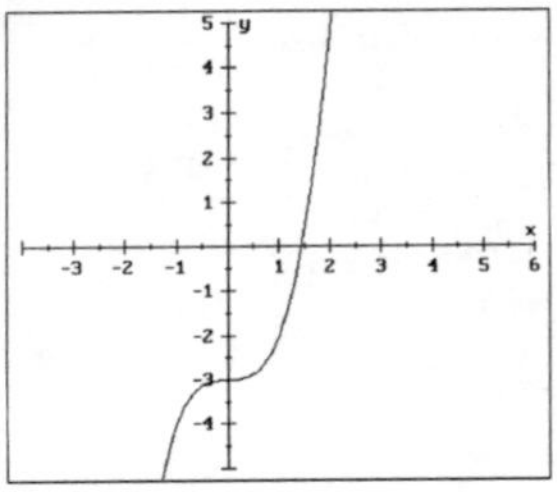

90. Graph $y = 3x^3 - x^2 - x$.
Find the x-intercepts.
$x = -0.44,\ x = 0,\ x = 0.77$

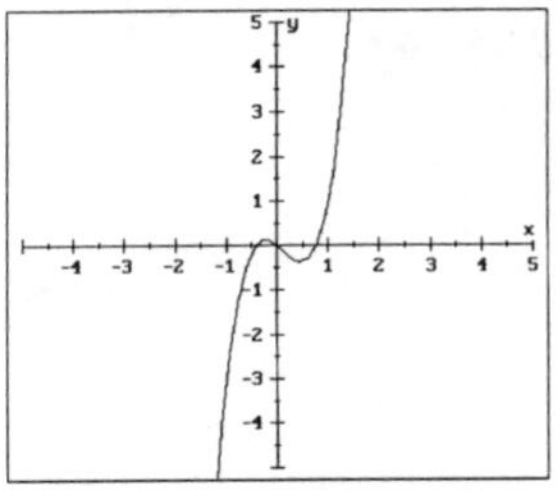

91. Let $y = 0$:
$y = 64t - 16t^2$
$0 = 16t(4 - t)$
$t = 0$ or $t = 4$
It strikes the ground after 4 seconds.

92. From **#91**, the flight lasts 4 seconds. Thus, half the flight is 2 seconds. Let $t = 2$:
$y = 64t - 16t^2$
$y = 64(2) - 16(2)^2 = 128 - 64 = 64$
The highest point is 64 feet above ground.

93. $y = 0.08x^2 + 0.9x$

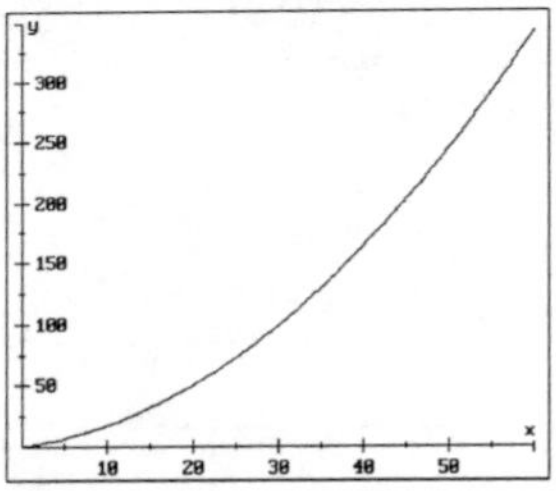

94. Refer to the graph for **#93**.
The y-coordinate for $x = 30$ is $y = 99$.
The y-coordinate for $x = 60$ is $y = 342$.
$342 - 99 = 243$
At 60 mph, 243 more feet is required to stop than at 30 mph.

95.
$$r = \sqrt{(10-7)^2 + (0-4)^2} = 5$$
$$(x-7)^2 + (y-4)^2 = 5^2$$
$$x^2 - 14x + 49 + y^2 - 8y + 16 = 25$$
$$x^2 + y^2 - 14x - 8y + 40 = 0$$

96.

First tire
$$C(12, 12),\ r = 12$$
$$(x-12)^2 + (y-12)^2 = 12^2$$
$$x^2 - 24x + 144 + y^2 - 24y + 144 = 144$$
$$x^2 + y^2 - 24x - 24y + 144 = 0$$

Second tire
$$C(36, 12),\ r = 12$$
$$(x-36)^2 + (y-12)^2 = 12^2$$
$$x^2 - 72x + 1296 + y^2 - 24y + 144 = 144$$
$$x^2 + y^2 - 72x - 24y + 1296 = 0$$

97. Graph $y = x^2 + x - 6$. Find the x-coordinates where the graph is below the x-axis.
Solution: $(-3, 2)$

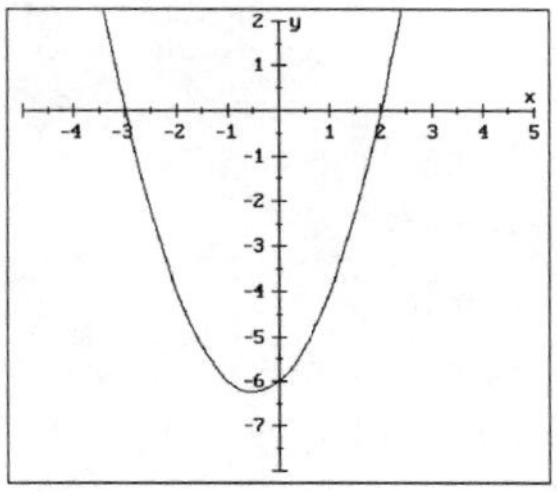

98. Graph $y = x^2 - 3x - 10$. Find the x-coordinates where the graph is above the x-axis.
Solution: $(-\infty, -2) \cup (5, \infty)$

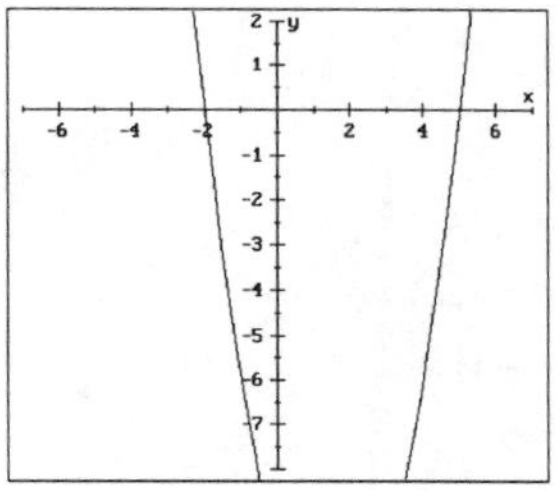

99.
$$\begin{aligned} 3(x+2) + x &= 5x \\ 3x + 6 + x &= 5x \\ 4x + 6 &= 5x \\ 6 &= x \end{aligned}$$

100.
$$\begin{aligned} 12b + 6(3 - b) &= b + 3 \\ 12b + 18 - 6b &= b + 3 \\ 6b + 18 &= b + 3 \\ 5b &= -15 \\ b &= -3 \end{aligned}$$

101.
$$\begin{aligned} \frac{5(2-x)}{3} - 1 &= x + 5 \\ 3\left[\frac{10-5x}{3} - 1\right] &= 3(x+5) \\ 10 - 5x - 3 &= 3x + 15 \\ -5x + 7 &= 3x + 15 \\ -8x &= 8 \\ x &= -1 \end{aligned}$$

102.
$$\begin{aligned} \frac{r-1}{3} &= \frac{r+2}{6} + 2 \\ 6 \cdot \frac{r-1}{3} &= 6\left(\frac{r+2}{6} + 2\right) \\ 2(r-1) &= r + 2 + 12 \\ 2r - 2 &= r + 14 \\ r &= 16 \end{aligned}$$

103. Let x = the ounces of copper added. Since 1 ounce out of 4 ounces are to be gold, the final result should be 25% gold.

$$\boxed{\text{Ounces of gold at start}} + \boxed{\text{Ounces of gold added}} = \boxed{\text{Ounces of gold at end}}$$

$$\begin{aligned} 20 + 0 &= 0.25(60 + x) \\ 20 &= 15 + 0.25x \\ 5 &= 0.25x \\ 20 &= x \end{aligned}$$

20 ounces of copper should be added.

104. Let x = pounds of cheaper coffee. Then $80 - x$ = pounds of other coffee

$$\boxed{\text{Value of cheaper}} + \boxed{\text{Value of other}} = \boxed{\text{Total value}}$$

$$\begin{aligned} 3.25x + 3.85(80 - x) &= 272 \\ 3.25x + 308 - 3.85x &= 272 \\ -0.60x &= -36 \\ x &= 60 \end{aligned}$$

60 pounds of the cheaper coffee should be used.

Exercise 2.5 (page 223)

1. quotient **2.** ratios **3.** means **4.** extremes

5. extremes, means **6.** $y = kx$ **7.** inverse **8.** constant

9. joint

10. x^2, z^3

11.
$$\frac{4}{x}=\frac{2}{7}$$
$$4\cdot 7=2\cdot x$$
$$28=2x$$
$$14=x$$

12.
$$\frac{5}{2}=\frac{x}{6}$$
$$5\cdot 6=x\cdot 2$$
$$30=2x$$
$$15=x$$

13.
$$\frac{x}{2}=\frac{3}{x+1}$$
$$x(x+1)=3\cdot 2$$
$$x^2+x=6$$
$$x^2+x-6=0$$
$$(x+3)(x-2)=0$$
$x=-3$ or $x=2$

14.
$$\frac{x+5}{6}=\frac{7}{8-x}$$
$$(x+5)(8-x)=7\cdot 6$$
$$-x^2+3x+40=42$$
$$0=x^2-3x+2$$
$$0=(x-2)(x-1)$$
$x=1$ or $x=2$

15. Let $x=$ the number of women.
$$\tfrac{3}{5}=\tfrac{x}{30}$$
$$3\cdot 30=5\cdot x$$
$$90=5x$$
$18=x\Rightarrow$ There are 18 women.

16. Let $x=$ the number of bags of lime.
$$\tfrac{3}{7}=\tfrac{x}{21}$$
$$3\cdot 21=x\cdot 7$$
$$63=7x$$
$9=x\Rightarrow$ 9 bags of lime should be used.

17.
$$y=kx$$
$$15=k(30)$$
$$\tfrac{1}{2}=k$$

18.
$$z=kt$$
$$21=k(7)$$
$$3=k$$

19.
$$I=\frac{k}{R}$$
$$50=\frac{k}{20}$$
$$1000=k$$

20.
$$R=\frac{k}{I^2}$$
$$100=\frac{k}{25^2}$$
$$100=\frac{k}{625}$$
$$62500=k$$

21.
$$E=kIR$$
$$125=k(5)(25)$$
$$125=125k$$
$$1=k$$

22.
$$z=k(x+y)$$
$$28=k(2+5)$$
$$28=7k$$
$$4=k$$

23.
$$y=kx \qquad y=\tfrac{15}{4}x$$
$$15=k(4) \qquad y=\tfrac{15}{4}\cdot\tfrac{7}{5}$$
$$\tfrac{15}{4}=k \qquad y=\tfrac{21}{4}$$

24.
$$w=kz \qquad w=-3z$$
$$-6=k(2) \qquad w=-3(-3)$$
$$-3=k \qquad w=9$$

25.
$$P=krs \qquad P=-\tfrac{2}{5}rs$$
$$16=k(5)(-8) \qquad P=-\tfrac{2}{5}(2)(10)$$
$$16=-40k \qquad P=-8$$
$$-\tfrac{16}{40}=k$$
$$-\tfrac{2}{5}=k$$

26.
$$m=kn^2\sqrt{q} \qquad m=3n^2\sqrt{q}$$
$$24=k(2)^2\sqrt{4} \qquad m=3(5)^2\sqrt{9}$$
$$24=k(4)(2) \qquad m=3(25)(3)$$
$$24=8k \qquad m=225$$
$$3=k$$

27. direct **28.** neither **29.** neither **30.** inverse

31.
$$V=\frac{kT}{P} \qquad V=\frac{\frac{80}{33}T}{P}$$
$$20=\frac{k(330)}{40} \qquad V=\frac{\frac{80}{33}(300)}{50}$$
$$800=330k \qquad V=\frac{\frac{8000}{11}}{50}$$
$$\frac{800}{330}=k \qquad V=\frac{160}{11}=14\frac{6}{11}\text{ ft}^3$$
$$\frac{80}{33}=k$$

32.
$$f=kd \qquad f=25d$$
$$5=k(0.2) \qquad f=25(0.35)$$
$$25=k \qquad f=8.75\text{ Newtons}$$

33.
$$d=kt^2 \qquad d=16t^2$$
$$16=k(1)^2 \qquad 144=16t^2$$
$$16=k \qquad 9=t^2$$
$$3=t\Rightarrow 3\text{ seconds}$$

34.
$$P=kRC^2 \qquad P=RC^2$$
$$10=k(10)(1)^2 \qquad P=5(3)^2$$
$$10=10k \qquad P=5(9)$$
$$1=k \qquad P=45\text{ watts}$$

35.
$$P=\frac{kV^2}{R} \qquad P=\frac{V^2}{R}$$
$$20=\frac{k(20)^2}{20} \qquad 40=\frac{V^2}{10}$$
$$400=400k \qquad 400=V^2$$
$$1=k \qquad 20=V\Rightarrow 20\text{ volts}$$

36.
$$t=kl^2 \qquad t=l^2$$
$$1=k(1)^2 \qquad 2=l^2$$
$$1=k \qquad \sqrt{2}=l\Rightarrow\sqrt{2}\text{ meters}$$

37.
$$f=k\sqrt{T} \qquad f=\frac{144}{\sqrt{2}}\sqrt{T}$$
$$144=k\sqrt{2} \qquad f=\frac{144}{\sqrt{2}}\sqrt{18}$$
$$\frac{144}{\sqrt{2}}=k \qquad f=144\sqrt{9}$$
$$f=144(3)=432\text{ hertz}$$

38.
$$G=\frac{km_1m_2}{d^2}=\frac{k(3m_1)(3m_2)}{(2d)^2}$$
$$=\frac{k(3m_1)(3m_2)}{(2d)^2}$$
$$=\frac{9km_1m_2}{4d^2}=\frac{9}{4}\cdot\frac{km_1m_2}{d^2}$$

The force is multiplied by $\frac{9}{4}$.

39. Consider this figure:

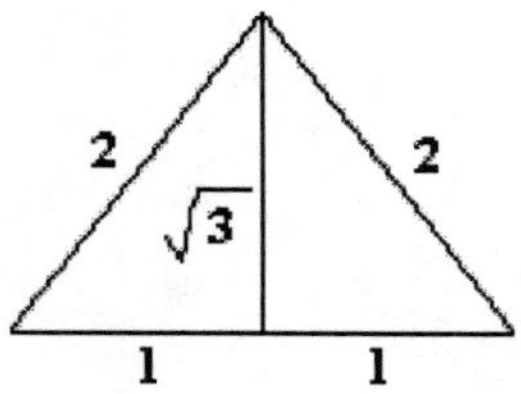

$h=\sqrt{3}$ can be computed using the Pythagorean Theorem.

$$A=\frac{1}{2}bh=\frac{1}{2}(2)\sqrt{3}=\sqrt{3}$$
$$A=ks^2$$
$$\sqrt{3}=k(2)^2$$
$$\sqrt{3}=4k$$
$$\frac{\sqrt{3}}{4}=k$$

40. Consider this figure:

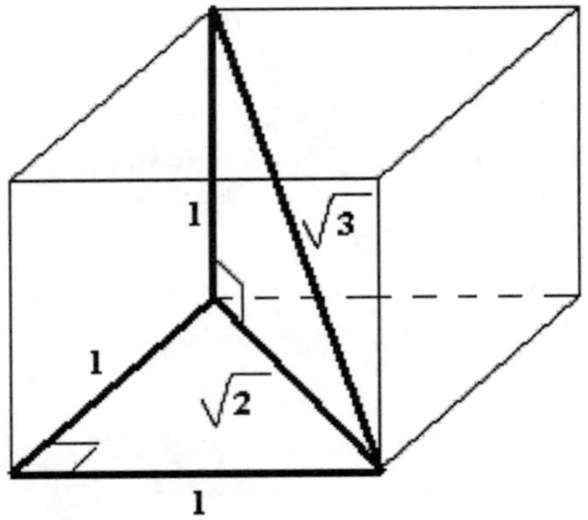

The diagonal is obtained by repeatedly using the Pythagorean Theorem.

$$d = ks$$
$$\sqrt{3} = k(1)$$
$$\sqrt{3} = k$$

41. **Answers may vary.** **42.** **Answers may vary.** **43.** **Answers may vary.**

44. **Answers may vary.** **45.** **Answers may vary.** **46.** **Answers may vary.**

47. $\dfrac{1}{x+2} + \dfrac{2}{x+1} = \dfrac{1(x+1)}{(x+2)(x+1)} + \dfrac{2(x+2)}{(x+1)(x+2)} = \dfrac{x+1+2x+4}{(x+1)(x+2)} = \dfrac{3x+5}{(x+1)(x+2)}$

48. $\dfrac{x^2-1}{x+1} \cdot \dfrac{x-1}{x^2-2x+1} = \dfrac{(x+1)(x-1)}{x+1} \cdot \dfrac{x-1}{(x-1)(x-1)} = 1$

49. $\dfrac{x^2+3x-4}{x^2-5x+4} \div \dfrac{x-1}{x^2-3x-4} = \dfrac{x^2+3x-4}{x^2-5x+4} \cdot \dfrac{x^2-3x-4}{x-1} = \dfrac{(x+4)(x-1)}{(x-4)(x-1)} \cdot \dfrac{(x-4)(x+1)}{x-1}$
$= \dfrac{(x+4)(x+1)}{x-1}$

50. $\dfrac{x+2}{3x-3} \div (2x+4) = \dfrac{x+2}{3x-3} \cdot \dfrac{1}{2x+4} = \dfrac{x+2}{3(x-1)} \cdot \dfrac{1}{2(x+2)} = \dfrac{1}{6(x-1)}$

51. $\dfrac{x^2+4-(x+2)^2}{4x^2} = \dfrac{x^2+4-(x^2+4x+4)}{4x^2} = \dfrac{x^2+4-x^2-4x-4}{4x^2} = \dfrac{-4x}{4x^2} = -\dfrac{1}{x}$

52. $\dfrac{\frac{1}{x}-\frac{1}{3}}{\frac{1}{x}-1} = \dfrac{3x\left(\frac{1}{x}-\frac{1}{3}\right)}{3x\left(\frac{1}{x}-1\right)} = \dfrac{3-x}{3-3x}$

Chapter 2 Summary (page 226)

1. **a.** $A(2, 0)$ **b.** $B(-2, 1)$ **c.** $C(0, -1)$ **d.** $D(3, -1)$

2. **a.** $A(-3, 5)$: QII

b. $B(5, -3)$: QIV

c. $C(0, -7)$: negative y-axis

d. $D\left(-\frac{1}{2}, 0\right)$: negative x-axis

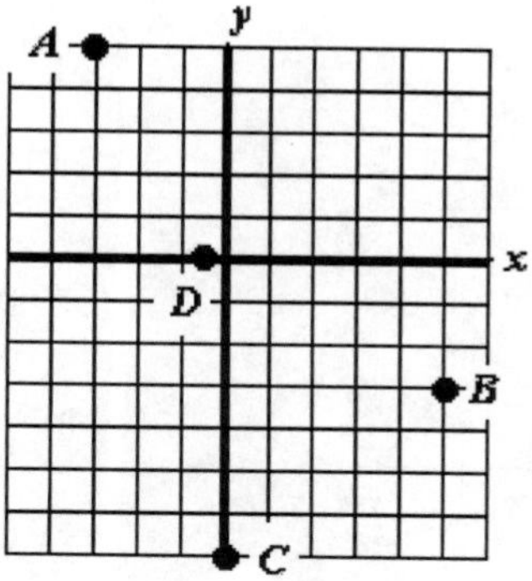

3. **a.**

$$\begin{aligned} 3x - 5y &= 15 \\ 3x - 5(0) &= 15 \\ 3x &= 15 \\ x &= 5 \end{aligned} \qquad \begin{aligned} 3x - 5y &= 15 \\ 3(0) - 5y &= 15 \\ -5y &= 15 \\ y &= -3 \end{aligned}$$

$(5, 0)$ $(0, -3)$

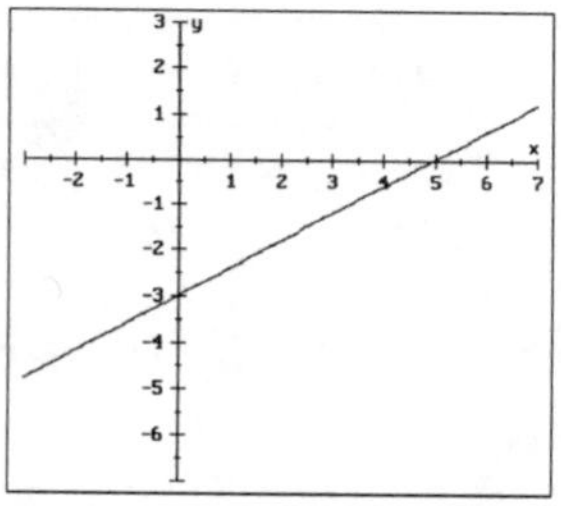

b.

$$\begin{aligned} x + y &= 7 \\ x + 0 &= 7 \\ x &= 7 \end{aligned} \qquad \begin{aligned} x + y &= 7 \\ 0 + y &= 7 \\ y &= 7 \end{aligned}$$

$(7, 0)$ $(0, 7)$

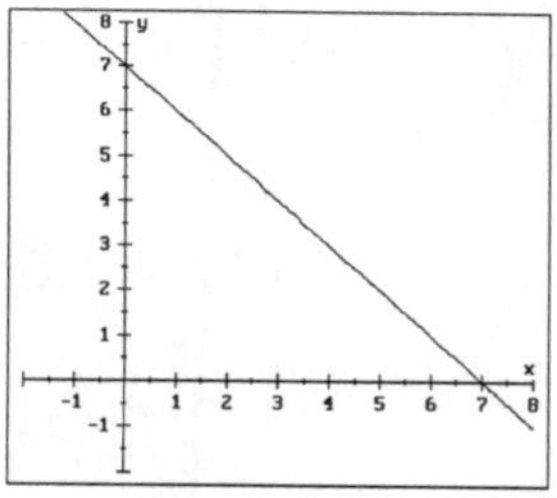

c.

$$\begin{aligned} x + y &= -7 \\ x + 0 &= -7 \\ x &= -7 \end{aligned} \qquad \begin{aligned} x + y &= -7 \\ 0 + y &= -7 \\ y &= -7 \end{aligned}$$

$(-7, 0)$ $(0, -7)$

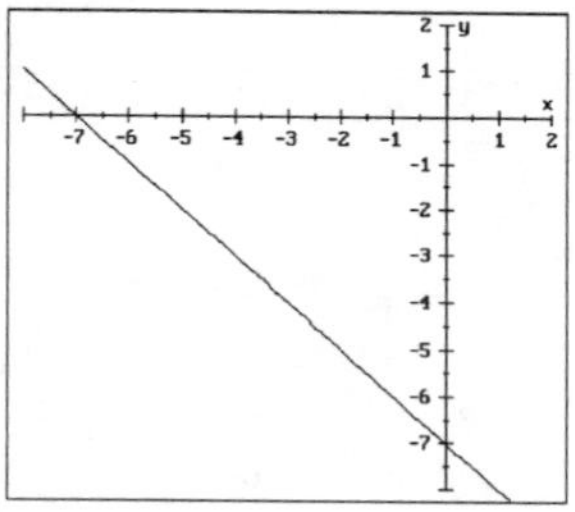

d.

$$\begin{aligned} x - 5y &= 5 \\ x - 5(0) &= 5 \\ x &= 5 \end{aligned} \qquad \begin{aligned} x - 5y &= 5 \\ 0 - 5y &= 5 \\ -5y &= 5 \\ y &= -1 \end{aligned}$$

$(5, 0)$ $(0, -1)$

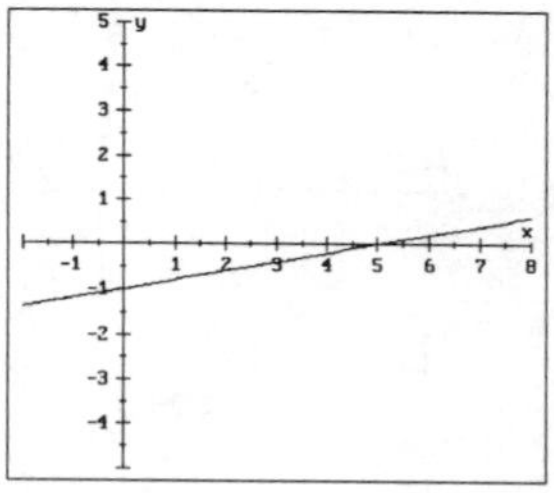

4. **a.** $y = 4 \Rightarrow$ horizontal

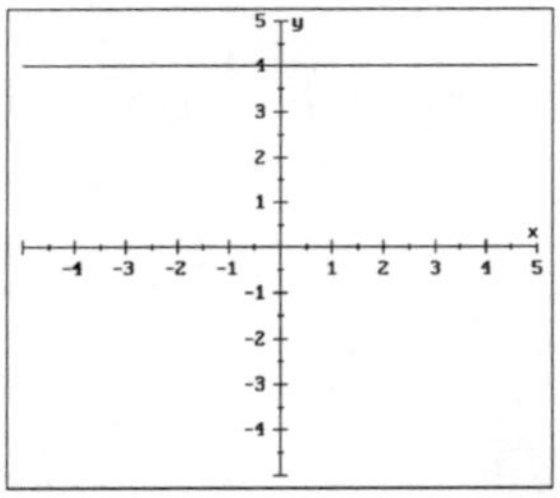

b. $x = -2 \Rightarrow$ vertical

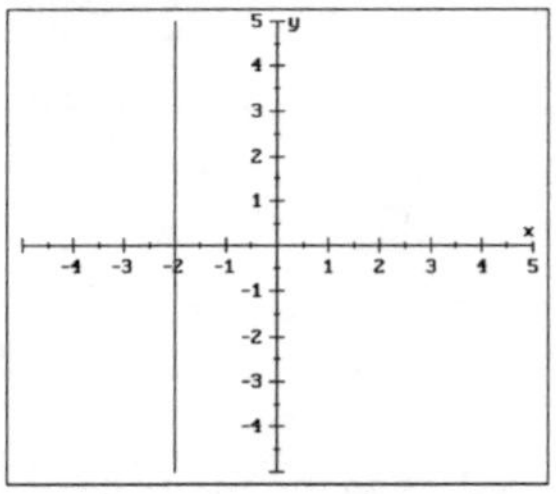

5. Let $x = 3$: $y = -2200x + 18{,}750 = -2200(3) + 18{,}750 = -6600 + 18{,}750 = \$12{,}150$

6. **a.**
$$\begin{aligned} d &= \sqrt{(x_2 - x_1)^2 + (y_2 - y_1)^2} \\ &= \sqrt{(-3-3)^2 + (7-(-1))^2} \\ &= \sqrt{(-6)^2 + (8)^2} \\ &= \sqrt{36+64} = \sqrt{100} = 10 \end{aligned}$$

b.
$$\begin{aligned} d &= \sqrt{(x_2 - x_1)^2 + (y_2 - y_1)^2} \\ &= \sqrt{(0-(-12))^2 + (5-10)^2} \\ &= \sqrt{12^2 + (-5)^2} \\ &= \sqrt{144+25} = \sqrt{169} = 13 \end{aligned}$$

c.
$$\begin{aligned} d &= \sqrt{(x_2 - x_1)^2 + (y_2 - y_1)^2} \\ &= \sqrt{\left(\sqrt{3}-\sqrt{3}\right)^2 + (9-7)^2} \\ &= \sqrt{0^2 + (2)^2} \\ &= \sqrt{0+4} = \sqrt{4} = 2 \end{aligned}$$

d.
$$\begin{aligned} d &= \sqrt{(x_2 - x_1)^2 + (y_2 - y_1)^2} \\ &= \sqrt{(a-(-a))^2 + (-a-a)^2} \\ &= \sqrt{(2a)^2 + (-2a)^2} \\ &= \sqrt{4a^2+4a^2} = \sqrt{8a^2} = 2\sqrt{2}|a| \end{aligned}$$

7. **a.** $M\left(\frac{x_1+x_2}{2}, \frac{y_1+y_2}{2}\right) = M\left(\frac{-3+3}{2}, \frac{7+(-1)}{2}\right) = M\left(\frac{0}{2}, \frac{6}{2}\right) = M(0,3)$

b. $M\left(\frac{x_1+x_2}{2}, \frac{y_1+y_2}{2}\right) = M\left(\frac{0+(-12)}{2}, \frac{5+10}{2}\right) = M\left(\frac{-12}{2}, \frac{15}{2}\right) = M\left(-6, \frac{15}{2}\right)$

c. $M\left(\frac{x_1+x_2}{2}, \frac{y_1+y_2}{2}\right) = M\left(\frac{\sqrt{3}+\sqrt{3}}{2}, \frac{9+7}{2}\right) = M\left(\frac{2\sqrt{3}}{2}, \frac{16}{2}\right) = M\left(\sqrt{3}, 8\right)$

d. $M\left(\frac{x_1+x_2}{2}, \frac{y_1+y_2}{2}\right) = M\left(\frac{a+(-a)}{2}, \frac{-a+a}{2}\right) = M\left(\frac{0}{2}, \frac{0}{2}\right) = M(0,0)$

8. **a.** $m = \frac{y_2-y_1}{x_2-x_1} = \frac{7-(-5)}{1-3} = \frac{12}{-2} = -6$

b. $m = \frac{y_2-y_1}{x_2-x_1} = \frac{-7-7}{-5-2} = \frac{-14}{-7} = 2$

c. $m = \frac{y_2-y_1}{x_2-x_1} = \frac{b-a}{a-b} = -1$

d. $m = \frac{y_2-y_1}{x_2-x_1} = \frac{(b-a)-b}{b-(a+b)} = \frac{-a}{-a} = 1$

9. $m = \dfrac{\Delta y}{\Delta x} = \dfrac{3000}{15} = 200$ ft. per minute

10. **a.** The slope is zero.

b. The slope is undefined.

11. **a.** The slope is negative.

b. The slope is positive.

12.
$$m = \frac{y_2 - y_1}{x_2 - x_1} = \frac{10-5}{6-(-2)} = \frac{5}{8}$$
$$m = \frac{y_2 - y_1}{x_2 - x_1} = \frac{y-2}{10-2} = \frac{5}{8}$$
$$8(y-2) = 5(8)$$
$$8y - 16 = 40$$
$$8y = 56$$
$$y = 7$$

13.
$$m = \frac{y_2 - y_1}{x_2 - x_1} = \frac{10-5}{6-(-2)} = \frac{5}{8}$$
$$m = \frac{y_2 - y_1}{x_2 - x_1} = \frac{-3-5}{x-(-2)} = \frac{-8}{5}$$
$$5(-8) = -8(x+2)$$
$$-40 = -8x - 16$$
$$8x = 24$$
$$x = 3$$

14. **a.**
$$m = \frac{y_2 - y_1}{x_2 - x_1} = \frac{7-0}{-5-0} = -\frac{7}{5}$$
$$y - y_1 = m(x - x_1)$$
$$y - 0 = -\frac{7}{5}(x-0)$$
$$y = -\frac{7}{5}x$$

b.
$$y - y_1 = m(x - x_1)$$
$$y - 1 = -4(x+2)$$

c.
$$m = \frac{y_2 - y_1}{x_2 - x_1} = \frac{1-(-5)}{4-7} = \frac{6}{-3} = -2$$
$y - y_1 = m(x - x_1)$ **or** $y - y_1 = m(x - x_1)$

$y + 5 = -2(x-7)$ $\quad\quad$ $y - 1 = -2(x-4)$

15. **a.**
$$y = mx + b$$
$$y = \frac{2}{3}x + 3$$

b.
$$y = mx + b$$
$$y = -\frac{3}{2}x - 5$$

16. **a.**
$$y = \frac{3}{5}x - 2$$
$$m = \frac{3}{5},\ b = -2$$

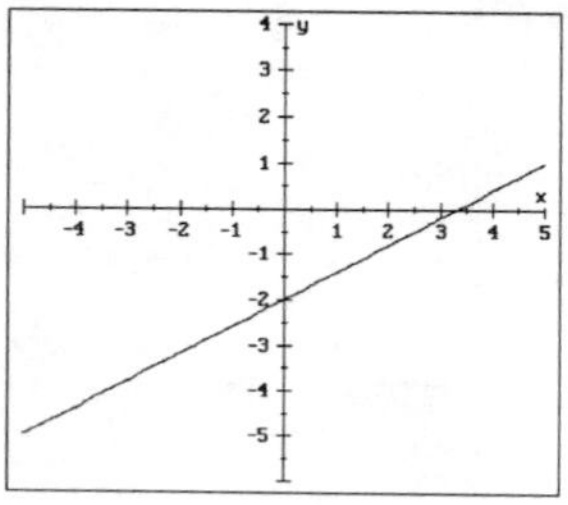

b.
$$y = -\frac{4}{3}x + 3$$
$$m = -\frac{4}{3},\ b = 3$$

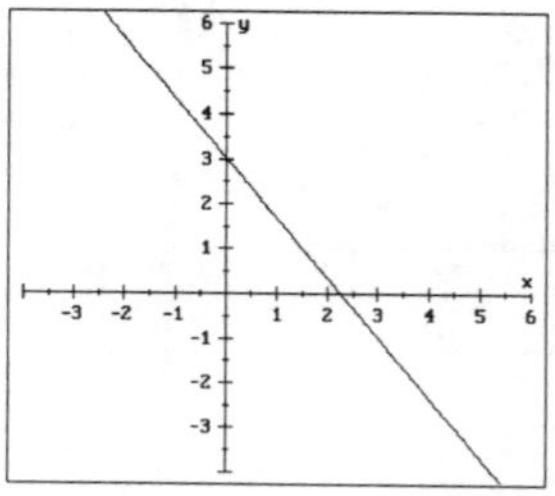

17. **a.** $m = \dfrac{y_2 - y_1}{x_2 - x_1} = \dfrac{-10-4}{4-2} = -7$

$y - y_1 = m(x - x_1)$
$y + 2 = -7(x - 7)$
$y + 2 = -7x + 49$
$y = -7x + 47$

b. $m = \dfrac{y_2 - y_1}{x_2 - x_1} = \dfrac{-10-4}{4-2} = -7$

$y - y_1 = m(x - x_1)$
$y + 2 = \frac{1}{7}(x - 7)$
$y + 2 = \frac{1}{7}x - 1$
$y = \frac{1}{7}x - 3$

c. $3x - 4y = 7$
$-4y = -3x + 7$
$y = \dfrac{3}{4}x - \dfrac{7}{4}$
$m = \dfrac{3}{4}$
Use $m = \dfrac{3}{4}$.
$y - y_1 = m(x - x_1)$
$y - 0 = \dfrac{3}{4}(x - 2)$
$\boxed{y = \frac{3}{4}x - \frac{3}{2}}$

d. $3y + x - 4 = 0$
$3y = -x + 4$
$y = -\dfrac{1}{3}x + \dfrac{4}{3}$
$m = -\dfrac{1}{3}$
Use $m = 3$.
$y - y_1 = m(x - x_1)$
$y - 5 = 3(x - 0)$
$y - 5 = 3x$
$\boxed{y = 3x + 5}$

18. **a.** $5x + 2y = 7$
$2y = -5x + 7$
$y = -\dfrac{5}{2}x + \dfrac{7}{2}$
$m = -\dfrac{5}{2}, \left(0, \dfrac{7}{2}\right)$

b. $3x - 4y = 14$
$-4y = -3x + 14$
$y = \dfrac{3}{4}x - \dfrac{7}{2}$
$m = \dfrac{3}{4}, \left(0, -\dfrac{7}{2}\right)$

19 **a.** If the slope is 0, then the line is horizontal: $y = 17$

b. If the slope is undefined, then the line is vertical: $x = -5$

20. **a.** $y = x^2 + 2$
x-int: none, y-int: $(0, 2)$
symmetry: y-axis

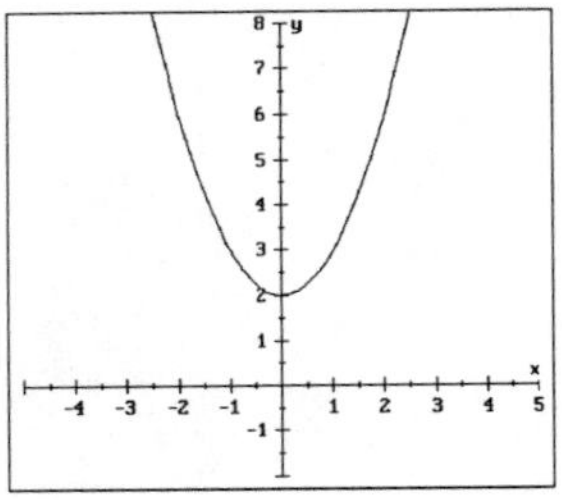

b. $y = x^3 - 2$
x-int: $\left(\sqrt[3]{2}, 0\right)$, y-int: $(0, -2)$
symmetry: none

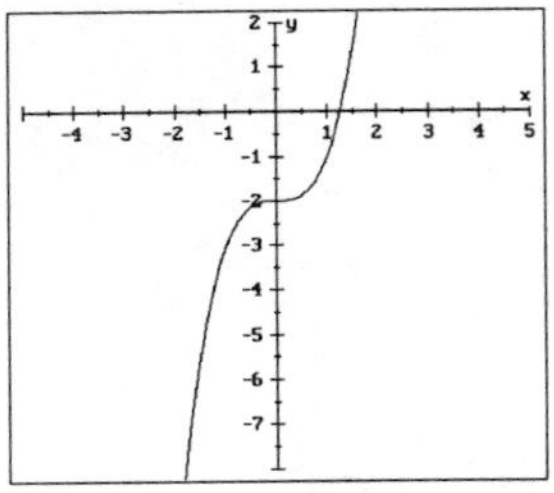

c. $y = \frac{1}{2}|x|$

x-int: $(0, 0)$, y-int: $(0, 0)$

symmetry: y-axis

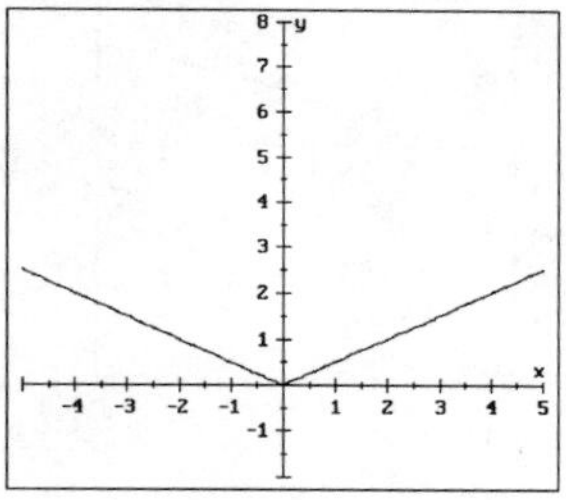

d. $y = -\sqrt{x-4}$

x-int: $(4, 0)$, y-int: none

symmetry: none

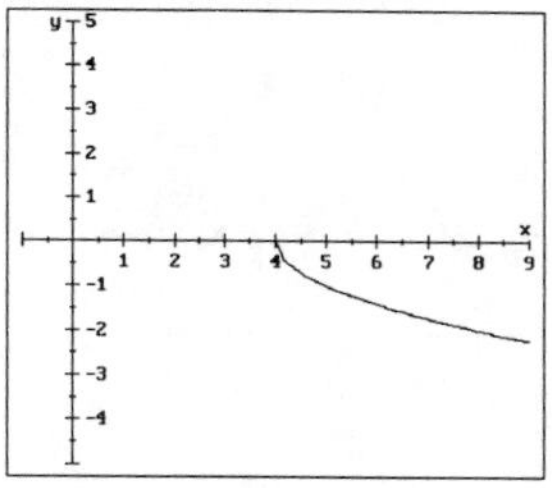

e. $y = \sqrt{x} + 2$

x-int: none, y-int: $(0, 2)$

symmetry: none

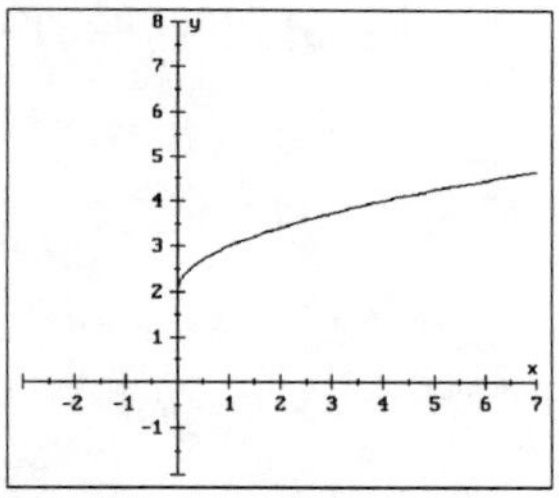

f. $y = |x+1| + 2$

x-int: none, y-int: $(0, 3)$

symmetry: none

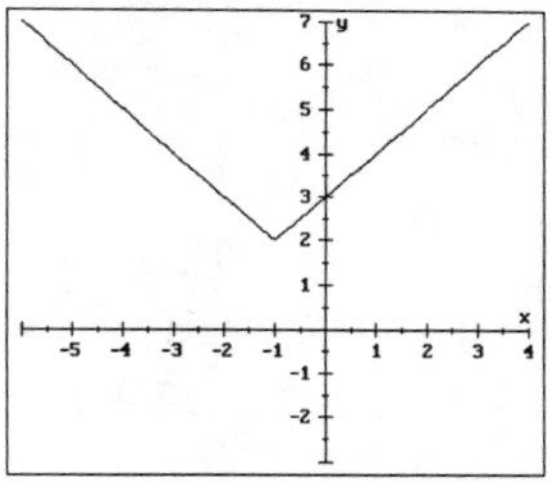

21. a. $y = |x-4| + 2$

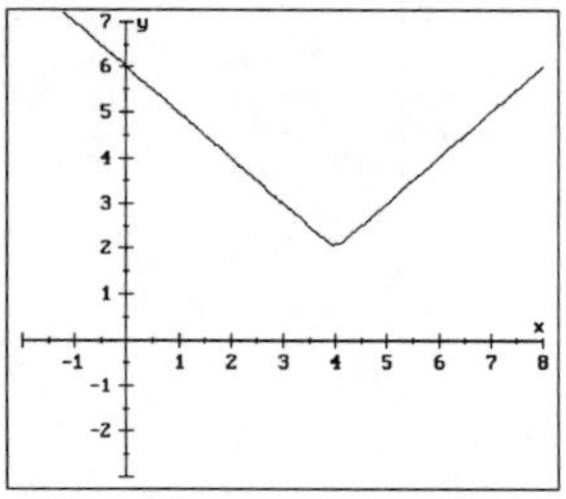

b. $y = -\sqrt{x+2} + 3$

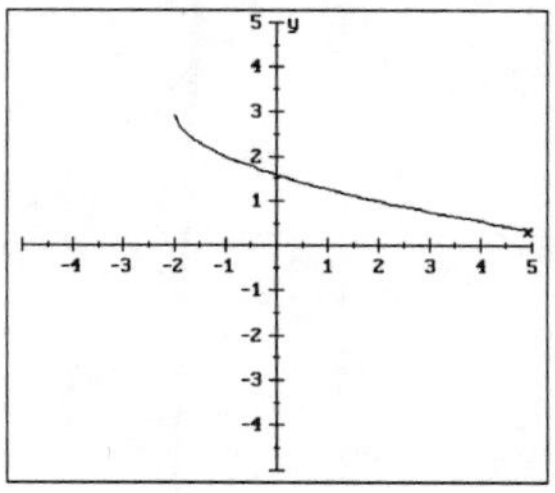

c. $y = x + 2|x|$

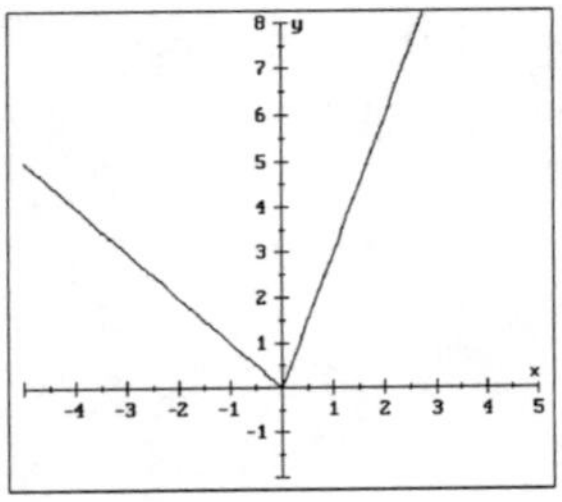

d. $y^2 = x - 3$

Graph $y = \pm\sqrt{x-3}$.

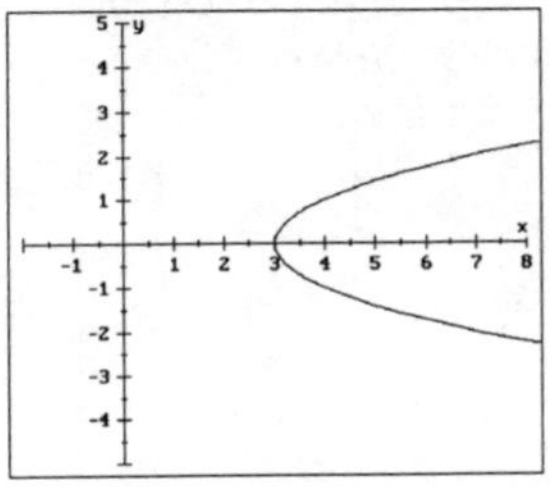

22 a. $C(-3, 4);\ r = 12$

$(x-h)^2 + (y-k)^2 = r^2$

$(x+3)^2 + (y-4)^2 = 144$

or $x^2 + y^2 + 6x - 8y - 119 = 0$

b. Center: $x = \dfrac{-6+5}{2} = -\dfrac{1}{2}$

$y = \dfrac{-3+8}{2} = \dfrac{5}{2}$

$r =$ distance from center to endpoint

$= \sqrt{\left(-\frac{1}{2}-5\right)^2 + \left(\frac{5}{2}-8\right)^2} = \sqrt{\frac{121}{2}}$

$\left(x+\frac{1}{2}\right)^2 + \left(y-\frac{5}{2}\right)^2 = \frac{121}{2}$, or

$x^2 + y^2 + x - 5y - 54 = 0$

23. a. $x^2 + y^2 - 2y = 15$

$x^2 + y^2 - 2y + 1 = 15 + 1$

$x^2 + (y-1)^2 = 16$

$C(0, 1),\ r = 4$

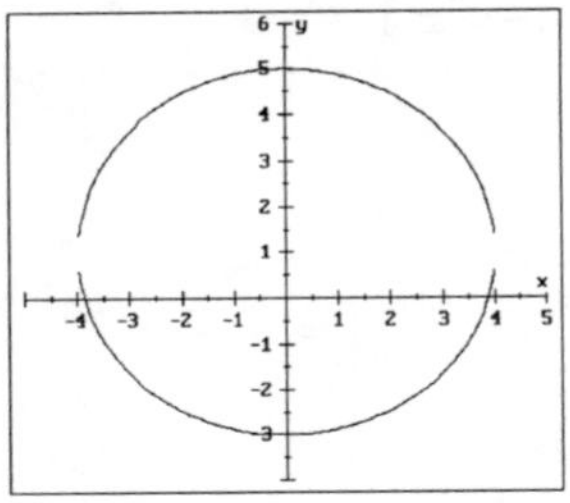

b. $x^2 + y^2 - 4x + 2y = 4$

$x^2 - 4x + 4 + y^2 + 2y + 1 = 4 + 4 + 1$

$(x-2)^2 + (y+1)^2 = 9$

$C(2, -1),\ r = 3$

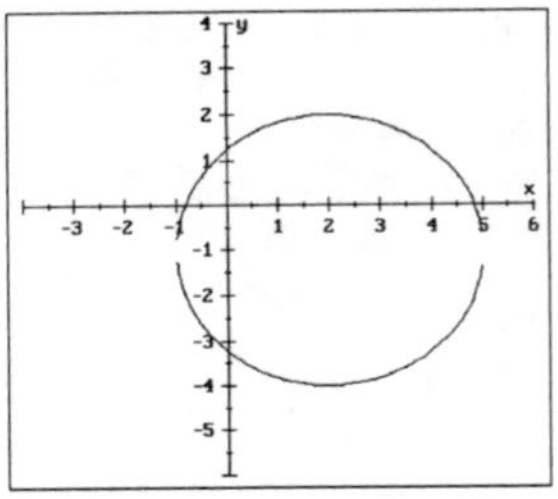

24. **a.** Graph $y = x^2 - 11$.
Find the x-intercepts.
$x = -3.32, \; x = 3.32$

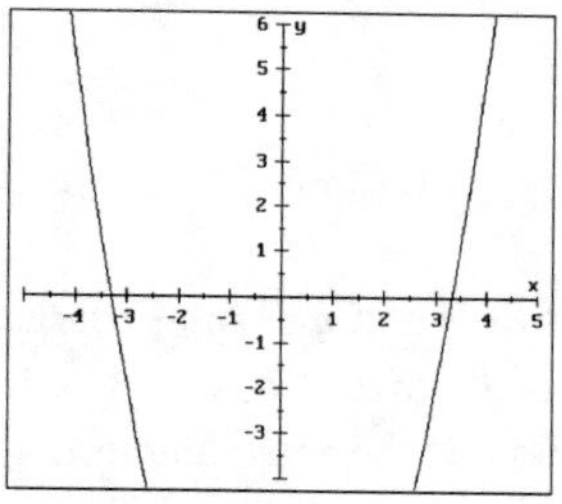

b. Graph $y = x^3 - x$.
Find the x-intercepts.
$x = -1, \; x = 0, x = 1$

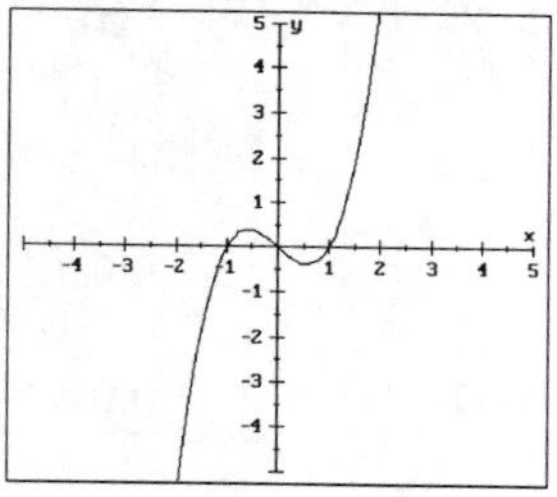

c. Graph $y = \left|x^2 - 2\right| - 1$.
Find the x-intercepts.
$x = -1.73, \; x = -1, x = 1, x = 1.73$

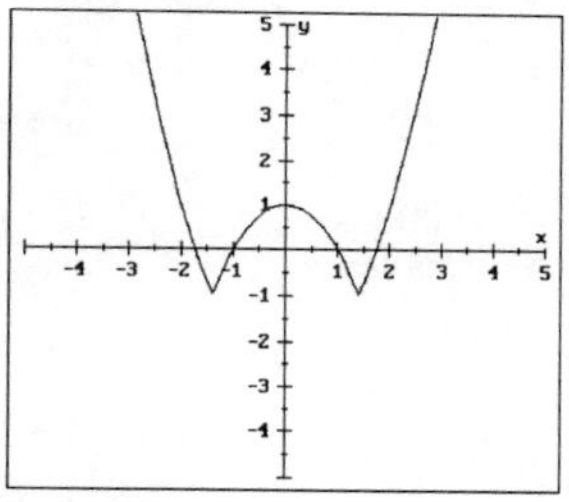

d. Graph $y = x^2 - 3x - 5$.
Find the x-intercepts.
$x = -1.19, \; x = 4.19$

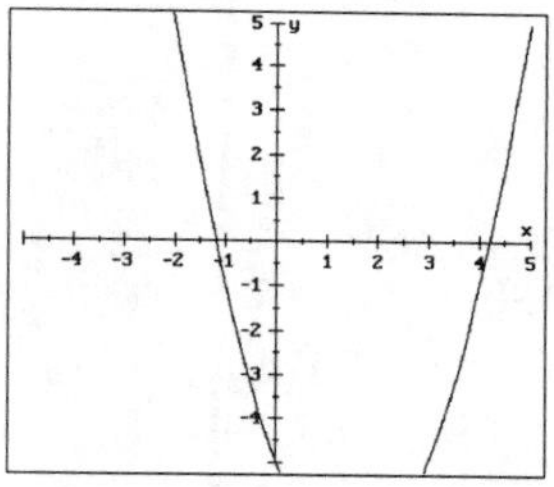

25. **a.**

$$\frac{x+3}{10} = \frac{x-1}{x}$$
$$x(x+3) = 10(x-1)$$
$$x^2 + 3x = 10x - 10$$
$$x^2 - 7x + 10 = 0$$
$$(x-5)(x-2) = 0$$
$$x = 5 \text{ or } x = 2$$

b.

$$\frac{x-1}{2} = \frac{12}{x+1}$$
$$(x+1)(x-1) = 2(12)$$
$$x^2 - 1 = 24$$
$$x^2 = 25$$
$$x = \pm 5$$

26.

$$f = ks$$
$$3 = k(5)$$
$$\frac{3}{5} = k$$

$$f = \frac{3}{5}s$$
$$f = \frac{3}{5}(3)$$
$$f = \frac{9}{5} \text{ pounds}$$

27.

$$E = kv^2$$

30 mph	50 mph
$E = k(30)^2$	$E = k(50)^2$
$E = 900k$	$E = 2500k$

$$\text{Factor of increase} = \frac{2500k}{900k} = \frac{25}{9}$$

28.
$$V = \frac{kT}{P} \qquad V = \frac{\frac{100}{3}T}{P}$$
$$400 = \frac{k(300)}{25} \qquad V = \frac{\frac{100}{3}(200)}{20}$$
$$10000 = 300k \qquad V = \frac{1000}{3}$$
$$\frac{100}{3} = k \qquad V = 333\tfrac{1}{3}\text{ cm}^3$$

29. $A = klw$
$A = 1lw \Rightarrow k = 1$

30.
$$R = \frac{kL}{D^2} \qquad R = \frac{0.0005L}{D^2}$$
$$200 = \frac{k(1000)}{(.05)^2} \qquad V = \frac{0.0005(1500)}{(0.08)^2}$$
$$200 = \frac{1000k}{.0025} \qquad V \approx 117\text{ ohms}$$
$$0.0005 = k$$

31. Let x = # rolls and y = total charge. Then the equation is $y = mx + b$, where m is the charge per roll and b is the fixed amount.
Given points: $(11, 177)$ and $(20, 294)$
$$m = \frac{y_2 - y_1}{x_2 - x_1} = \frac{294 - 177}{20 - 11} = \frac{117}{9} = 13$$
$$y - y_1 = m(x - x_1) \qquad \text{Let } x = 27:$$
$$y - 177 = 13(x - 11) \qquad y = 13x + 34$$
$$y = 13x + 34 \qquad y = 13(27) + 34$$
$$y = \$385$$

32. $14x + 18y = 5040$
Let $x = 180$:
$14(180) + 18y = 5040$
$2520 + 18y = 5040$
$18y = 2520$
$y = 140$ hours of tutoring Spanish.

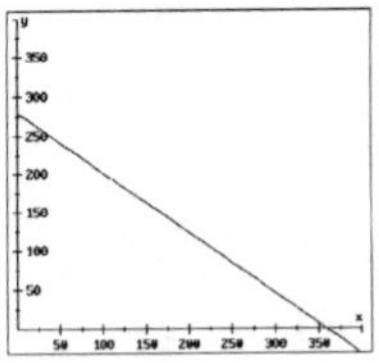

Chapter 2 Test (page 232)

1. $(-3, \pi) \Rightarrow$ QII

2. $(0, -8) \Rightarrow$ negative y-axis

3.
$$x + 3y = 6 \qquad x + 3y = 6$$
$$x + 3(0) = 6 \qquad 0 + 3y = 6$$
$$x = 6 \qquad y = 2$$
$$(6, 0) \qquad (0, 2)$$

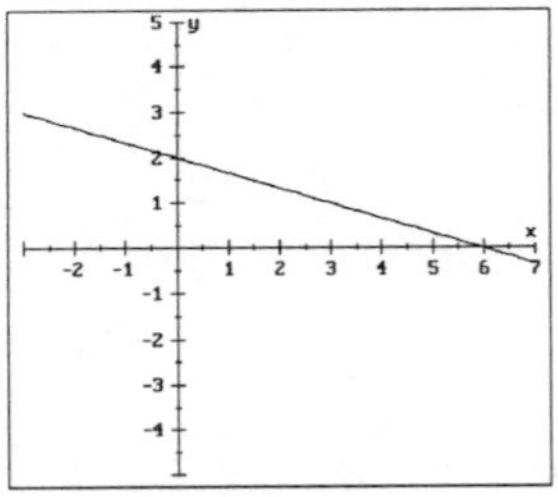

4.
$$2x - 5y = 10 \qquad 2x - 5y = 10$$
$$2x - 5(0) = 10 \qquad 2(0) - 5y = 10$$
$$x = 5 \qquad y = -2$$
$$(5, 0) \qquad (0, -2)$$

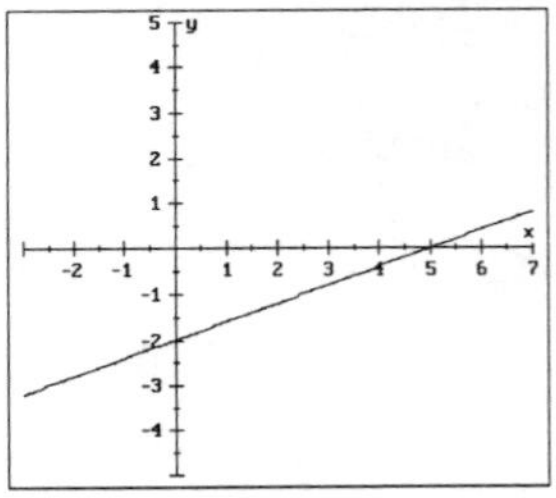

5.

$$\begin{aligned} 2(x+y) &= 3x+5 \\ 2x+2y &= 3x+5 \\ 2y &= x+5 \\ y &= \tfrac{1}{2}x+\tfrac{5}{2} \end{aligned}$$

x	y
0	$\frac{5}{2}$
1	3

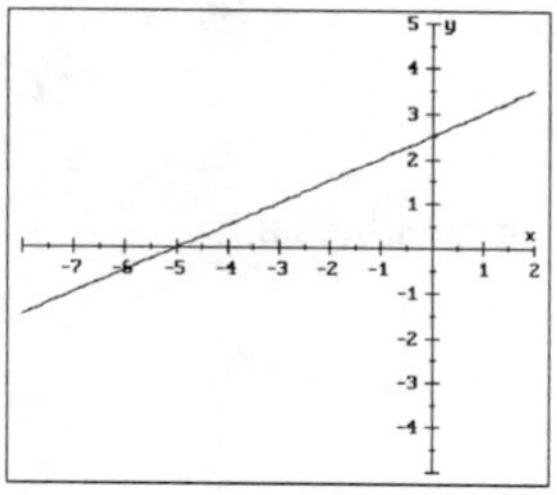

6.

$$\begin{aligned} 3x-5y &= 3(x-5) \\ 3x-5y &= 3x-15 \\ -5y &= -15 \\ y &= 3 \end{aligned}$$

x	y
0	3
-2	3

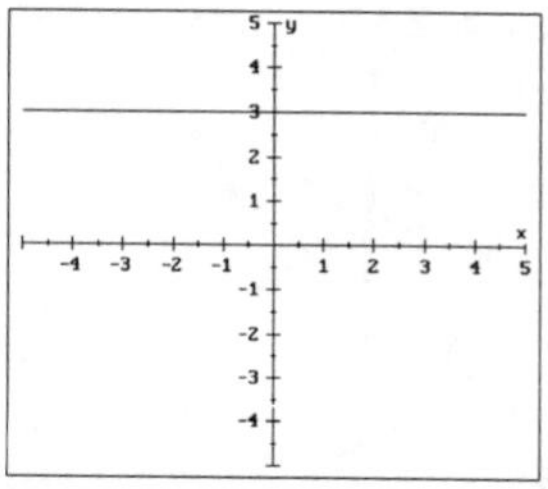

7.

$$\begin{aligned} \tfrac{1}{2}(x-2y) &= y-1 \\ \tfrac{1}{2}x-y &= y-1 \\ x-2y &= 2y-2 \\ -4y &= -x-2 \\ y &= \tfrac{1}{4}x+\tfrac{1}{2} \end{aligned}$$

x	y
0	$\frac{1}{2}$
2	1

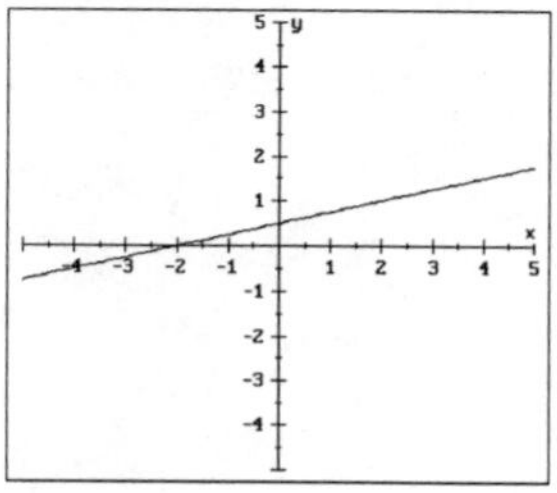

8.

$$\begin{aligned} \frac{x+y-5}{7} &= 3x \\ x+y-5 &= 21x \\ y &= 20x+5 \end{aligned}$$

x	y
0	5
$-\frac{1}{4}$	0

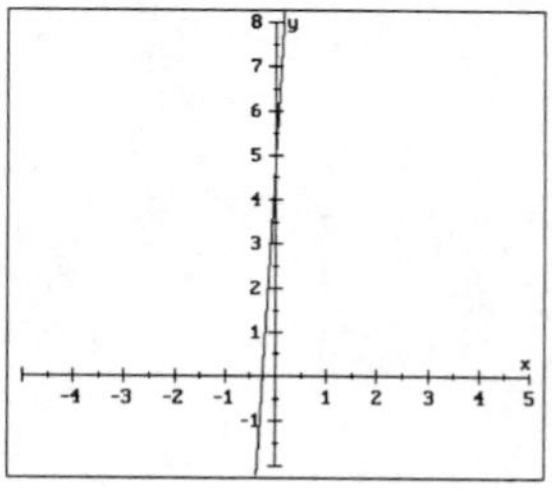

9.

$$\begin{aligned} d &= \sqrt{(x_2-x_1)^2+(y_2-y_1)^2} \\ &= \sqrt{(1-(-3))^2+(-1-4)^2} \\ &= \sqrt{(4)^2+(-5)^2} \\ &= \sqrt{16+25} = \sqrt{41} \end{aligned}$$

10.

$$\begin{aligned} d &= \sqrt{(x_2-x_1)^2+(y_2-y_1)^2} \\ &= \sqrt{(0-(-\pi))^2+(\pi-0)^2} \\ &= \sqrt{\pi^2+\pi^2} \\ &= \sqrt{2\pi^2} = \pi\sqrt{2} \approx 4.44 \end{aligned}$$

11. $M\left(\frac{x_1+x_2}{2}, \frac{y_1+y_2}{2}\right) = M\left(\frac{3+(-3)}{2}, \frac{-7+7}{2}\right) = M\left(\frac{0}{2}, \frac{0}{2}\right) = M(0,0)$

12. $M\left(\frac{x_1+x_2}{2}, \frac{y_1+y_2}{2}\right) = M\left(\frac{0+\sqrt{8}}{2}, \frac{\sqrt{2}+\sqrt{18}}{2}\right) = M\left(\frac{2\sqrt{2}}{2}, \frac{4\sqrt{2}}{2}\right) = M\left(\sqrt{2}, 2\sqrt{2}\right)$

13. $m = \frac{y_2-y_1}{x_2-x_1} = \frac{1-(-9)}{-5-3} = \frac{10}{-8} = -\frac{5}{4}$

14. $m = \dfrac{y_2 - y_1}{x_2 - x_1} = \dfrac{0-3}{-\sqrt{12}-\sqrt{3}} = \dfrac{-3}{-3\sqrt{3}} = \dfrac{1}{\sqrt{3}} = \dfrac{\sqrt{3}}{3}$

15. $y = 3x - 2 \quad y = 2x - 3$

$m = 3 \quad m = 2$

neither

16. $2x - 3y = 5 \qquad 3x + 2y = 7$

$-3y = -2x + 5 \qquad 2y = -3x + 7$

$y = \frac{2}{3}x - \frac{5}{3} \qquad y = -\frac{3}{2}x + \frac{7}{2}$

$m = \frac{2}{3} \qquad m = -\frac{3}{2}$

perpendicular

17.
$$\begin{aligned} y - y_1 &= m(x - x_1) \\ y + 5 &= 2(x - 3) \\ y + 5 &= 2x - 6 \\ y &= 2x - 11 \end{aligned}$$

18.
$$\begin{aligned} y &= mx + b \\ y &= 3x + \frac{1}{2} \end{aligned}$$

19.
$$\begin{aligned} 2x - y &= 3 \\ -y &= -2x + 3 \\ y &= 2x - 3 \\ m &= 2 \end{aligned}$$
$y = 2x + 5$

20.
$$\begin{aligned} 2x - y &= 3 \\ -y &= -2x + 3 \\ y &= 2x - 3 \\ m &= 2 \end{aligned}$$
$y = -\frac{1}{2}x + 5$

21. $m = \dfrac{y_2 - y_1}{x_2 - x_1} = \dfrac{\frac{1}{2} - \left(-\frac{3}{2}\right)}{3 - 2} = \dfrac{\frac{4}{2}}{1} = 2$
$$\begin{aligned} y - y_1 &= m(x - x_1) \\ y - \frac{1}{2} &= 2(x - 3) \\ y - \frac{1}{2} &= 2x - 6 \\ y &= 2x - \frac{11}{2} \end{aligned}$$

22. If the line is parallel to the y-axis, then it is a vertical line: $x = 3$

23.
$$\begin{aligned} y &= x^3 - 16x \\ 0 &= x\left(x^2 - 16\right) \\ 0 &= x(x + 4)(x - 4) \end{aligned}$$
$x = 0,\ x = -4,\ x = 4$

x-int: $(0, 0)$, $(-4, 0)$, $(4, 0)$

$$\begin{aligned} y &= x^3 - 16x \\ y &= 0^3 - 16(0) \\ y &= 0 \end{aligned}$$
y-int: $(0, 0)$

24.
$$\begin{aligned} y &= |x - 4| \\ 0 &= |x - 4| \\ 0 &= x - 4 \\ 4 &= x \end{aligned}$$
x-int: $(4, 0)$

$$\begin{aligned} y &= |x - 4| \\ y &= |0 - 4| \\ y &= |-4| \\ y &= 4 \end{aligned}$$
y-int: $(0, 4)$

25. $y^2 = x - 1$

x-axis	y-axis	origin
$(-y)^2 = x - 1$	$y^2 = -x - 1$	$(-y)^2 = -x - 1$
$y^2 = x - 1$	not equivalent: no symmetry	$y^2 = -x - 1$
equivalent: symmetry		not equivalent: no symmetry

26. $y = x^4 + 1$

x-axis	y-axis	origin
$-y = x^4 + 1$	$y = (-x)^4 + 1$	$-y = (-x)^4 + 1$
not equivalent: no symmetry	$y = x^4 + 1$	$-y = x^4 + 1$
	equivalent: symmetry	not equivalent: no symmetry

27. $y = x^2 - 9$
x-int: $(3, 0)$, $(-3, 0)$
y-int: $(0, -9)$
symmetry: y-axis

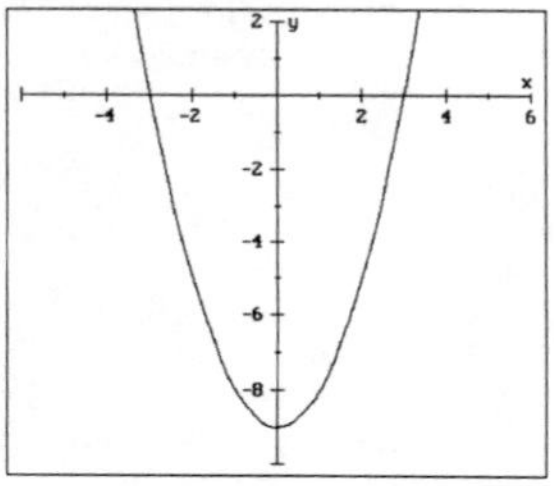

28. $x = |y|$
x-int: $(0, 0)$
y-int: $(0, 0)$
symmetry: x-axis

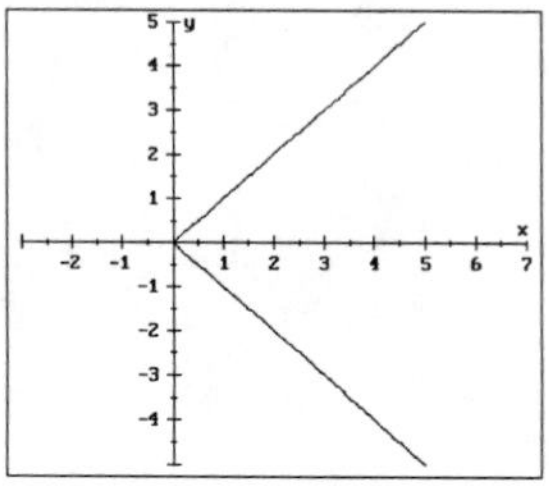

29. $y = 2\sqrt{x}$
x-int: $(0, 0)$
y-int: $(0, 0)$
symmetry: none

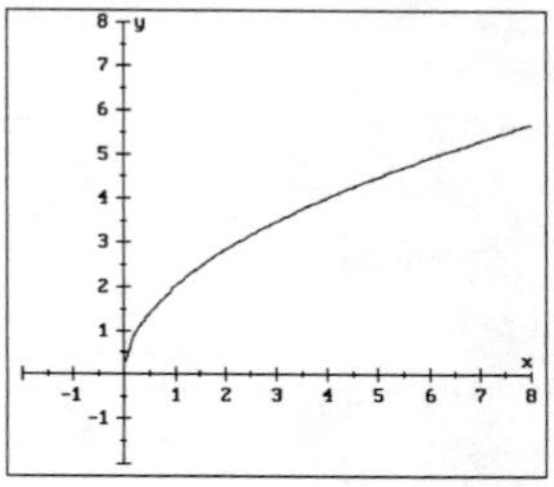

30. $x = y^3$
x-int: $(0, 0)$
y-int: $(0, 0)$
symmetry: origin

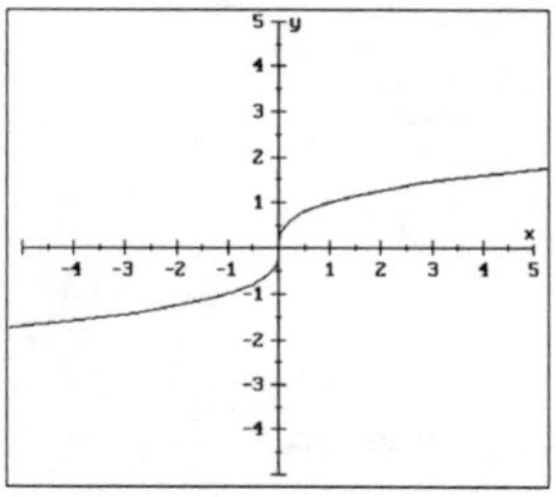

31. $C(5, 7)$; $r = 8$
$(x - h)^2 + (y - k)^2 = r^2$
$(x - 5)^2 + (y - 7)^2 = 64$

32. $r = \sqrt{(2-6)^2 + (4-8)^2}$
$= \sqrt{32}$
$(x - h)^2 + (y - k)^2 = r^2$
$(x - 2)^2 + (y - 4)^2 = 32$

33. $x^2 + y^2 = 9$

$C(0, 0),\ r = 3$

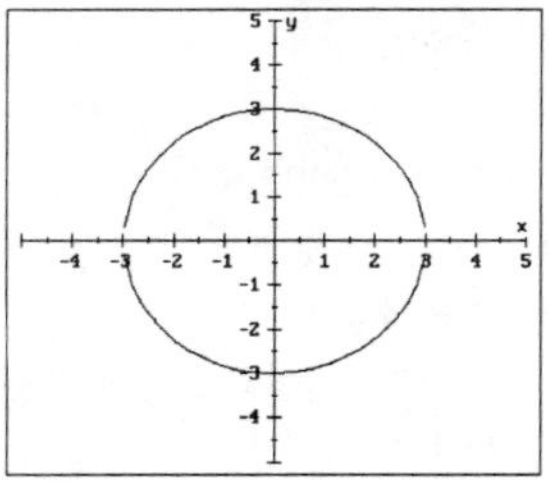

34. $x^2 - 4x + y^2 + 3 = 0$

$x^2 - 4x + y^2 = -3$

$x^2 - 4x + 4 + y^2 = -3 + 4$

$(x - 2)^2 + y^2 = 1$

$C(2, 0),\ r = 1$

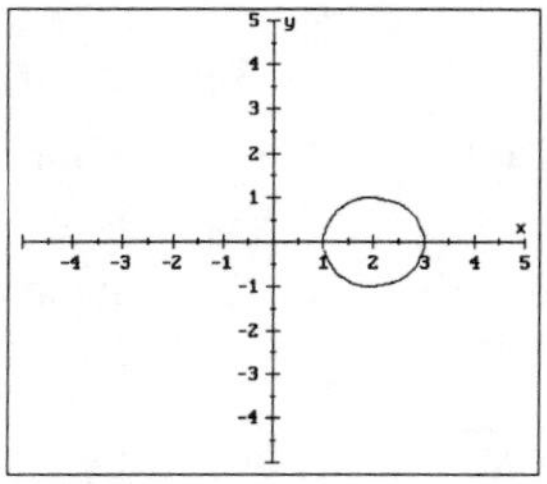

35. $y = kz^2$

36. $w = krs^2$

37.

$$P = kQ \qquad 7 = k(2) \qquad \frac{7}{2} = k$$

$$P = \frac{7}{2}Q \qquad P = \frac{7}{2}(5) \qquad P = \frac{35}{2}$$

38.

$$y = \frac{kx}{z^2} \qquad 16 = \frac{k(3)}{2^2} \qquad 16 = \frac{3k}{4} \qquad 64 = 3k \qquad \frac{64}{3} = k$$

$$y = \frac{\frac{64}{3}x}{z^2} \qquad 2 = \frac{\frac{64}{3}x}{3^2} \qquad 2 = \frac{\frac{64}{3}x}{9} \qquad 18 = \frac{64}{3}x \qquad 54 = 64x \qquad \frac{54}{64} = x \qquad \frac{27}{32} = x$$

39. Graph $y = x^2 - 7$.

Find any positive x-intercepts.

$x = 2.65$

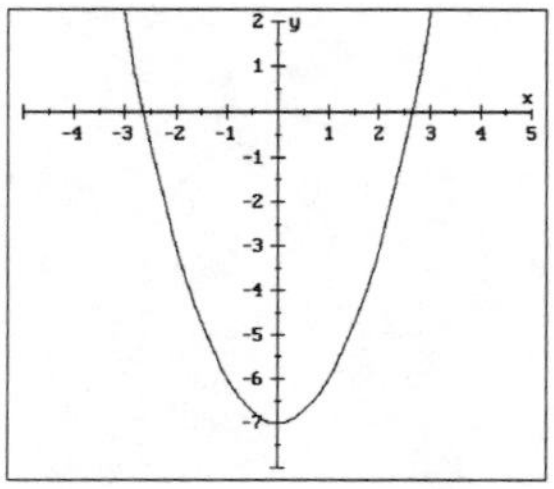

40. Graph $y = x^2 - 5x - 5$.

Find any positive x-intercepts.

$x = 5.85$

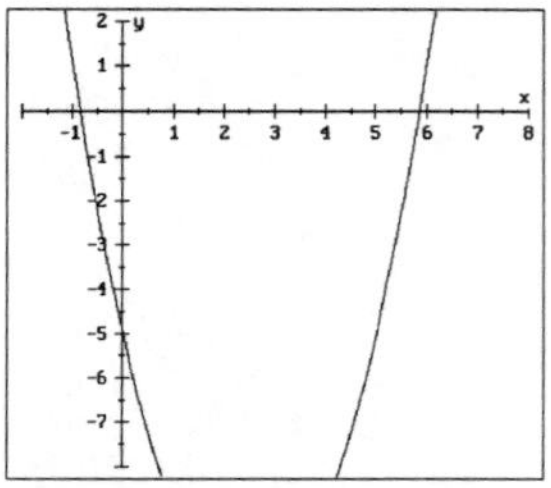

Exercise 3.1 (page 245)

1. function

2. relation

3. domain

4. range

5. $y = f(x)$

6. (x, y), domain, range

7. x

8. dependent

9. vertical, once

10. linear

11. $y = x$
Each value of x is paired with only one value of y.
function

12. $y - 2x = 0$
$y = 2x$
Each value of x is paired with only one value of y.
function

13. $y^2 = x$
$y = \pm\sqrt{x}$
At least one value of x is paired with more than one value of y. **not a function**

14. $|y| = x$
$y = \pm x$
At least one value of x is paired with more than one value of y. **not a function**

15. $y = x^2$
Each value of x is paired with only one value of y.
function

16. $y - 7 = 7$
$y = 14$
Each value of x is paired with only one value of y.
function

17. $y^2 - 4x = 1$
$y^2 = 4x + 1$
$y = \pm\sqrt{4x+1}$
At least one value of x is paired with more than one value of y. **not a function**

18. $|x - 2| = y$
$y = |x - 2|$
Each value of x is paired with only one value of y.
function

19. $|x| = |y|$
$|y| = |x|$
$y = \pm|x|$
At least one value of x is paired with more than one value of y. **not a function**

20. $x = 7$
At least one value of x is paired with more than one value of y. **not a function**

21. $y = 7$
Each value of x is paired with only one value of y.
function

22. $|x + y| = 7$
$x + y = \pm 7$
$y = -x \pm 7$
At least one value of x is paired with more than one value of y. **not a function**

23. $f(x) = y = 3x + 5 \Rightarrow$ domain $= (-\infty, \infty)$
$x = \dfrac{y-5}{3} \Rightarrow$ range $= (-\infty, \infty)$

24. $f(x) = y = -5x + 2 \Rightarrow$ domain $= (-\infty, \infty)$
$x = \dfrac{-y+2}{5} \Rightarrow$ range $= (-\infty, \infty)$

25. $f(x) = y = x^2 \Rightarrow$ domain $= (-\infty, \infty)$
$x = \pm\sqrt{y} \Rightarrow$ range $= [0, \infty)$

26. $f(x) = y = x^3 \Rightarrow$ domain $= (-\infty, \infty)$
$x = \sqrt[3]{y} \Rightarrow$ range $= (-\infty, \infty)$

27. $f(x) = y = \dfrac{3}{x+1}$

$x \neq -1$

domain $= (-\infty, -1) \cup (-1, \infty)$

$$\begin{aligned} y &= \frac{3}{x+1} \\ (x+1)y &= 3 \\ x+1 &= \frac{3}{y} \\ x &= \frac{3}{y} - 1 \Rightarrow \text{range} = (-\infty, 0) \cup (0, \infty) \end{aligned}$$

28. $f(x) = y = \dfrac{-7}{x+3}$

$x \neq -3$

domain $= (-\infty, -3) \cup (-3, \infty)$

$$\begin{aligned} y &= \frac{-7}{x+3} \\ (x+3)y &= -7 \\ x+3 &= -\frac{7}{y} \\ x &= -\frac{7}{y} - 3 \Rightarrow \text{range} = (-\infty, 0) \cup (0, \infty) \end{aligned}$$

29. $f(x) = y = \sqrt{x} \Rightarrow x \geq 0 \Rightarrow$ domain $= [0, \infty)$

note: $\sqrt{x} \geq 0$, so $y \geq 0 \Rightarrow$ range $= [0, \infty)$

30. $f(x) = y = \sqrt{x^2 - 1} \Rightarrow x^2 - 1 \geq 0 \Rightarrow$ domain $= (-\infty, -1] \cup [1, \infty)$

note: $\sqrt{x^2 - 1} \geq 0$, so $y \geq 0 \Rightarrow$ range $= [0, \infty)$

31. $f(x) = y = \dfrac{x}{x+3}$

$x \neq -3$

domain $= (-\infty, -3) \cup (-3, \infty)$

$$\begin{aligned} y &= \frac{x}{x+3} \\ (x+3)y &= x \\ xy + 3y &= x \\ xy - x &= -3y \\ x(y-1) &= -3y \\ x &= \frac{-3y}{y-1} \Rightarrow y \neq 1 \end{aligned}$$

range $= (-\infty, 1) \cup (1, \infty)$

32. $f(x) = y = \dfrac{x}{x-3}$

$x \neq 3$

domain $= (-\infty, 3) \cup (3, \infty)$

$$\begin{aligned} y &= \frac{x}{x-3} \\ (x-3)y &= x \\ xy - 3y &= x \\ xy - x &= 3y \\ x(y-1) &= 3y \\ x &= \frac{3y}{y-1} \Rightarrow y \neq 1 \end{aligned}$$

range $= (-\infty, 1) \cup (1, \infty)$

33. $f(x) = y = \dfrac{x-2}{x+3}$

$x \neq -3$

domain $= (-\infty, -3) \cup (-3, \infty)$

$$\begin{aligned} y &= \frac{x-2}{x+3} \\ (x+3)y &= x-2 \\ xy + 3y &= x-2 \\ xy - x &= -3y-2 \\ x(y-1) &= -3y-2 \\ x &= \frac{-3y-2}{y-1} \Rightarrow y \neq 1 \end{aligned}$$

range $= (-\infty, 1) \cup (1, \infty)$

34. $f(x) = y = \dfrac{x+2}{x-1}$

$x \neq 1$

domain $= (-\infty, 1) \cup (1, \infty)$

$$\begin{aligned} y &= \frac{x+2}{x-1} \\ (x-1)y &= x+2 \\ xy - y &= x+2 \\ xy - x &= y+2 \\ x(y-1) &= y+2 \\ x &= \frac{y+2}{y-1} \Rightarrow y \neq 1 \end{aligned}$$

range $= (-\infty, 1) \cup (1, \infty)$

35. $f(x) = 3x - 2$

$f(2) = 3(2) - 2$ $= 6 - 2$ $= 4$	$f(-3) = 3(-3) - 2$ $= -9 - 2$ $= -11$	$f(k) = 3k - 2$	$f(k^2-1) = 3(k^2-1) - 2$ $= 3k^2 - 3 - 2$ $= 3k^2 - 5$

36. $f(x) = 5x + 7$

$f(2) = 5(2) + 7$ $= 10 + 7$ $= 17$	$f(-3) = 5(-3) + 7$ $= -15 + 7$ $= -8$	$f(k) = 5k + 7$	$f(k^2-1) = 5(k^2-1) + 7$ $= 5k^2 - 5 + 7$ $= 5k^2 + 2$

37. $f(x) = \frac{1}{2}x + 3$

$f(2) = \frac{1}{2}(2) + 3$ $= 1 + 3$ $= 4$	$f(-3) = \frac{1}{2}(-3) + 3$ $= -\frac{3}{2} + 3$ $= \frac{3}{2}$	$f(k) = \frac{1}{2}k + 3$	$f(k^2-1) = \frac{1}{2}(k^2-1) + 3$ $= \frac{1}{2}k^2 - \frac{1}{2} + 3$ $= \frac{1}{2}k^2 + \frac{5}{2}$

38. $f(x) = \frac{2}{3}x + 5$

$f(2) = \frac{2}{3}(2) + 5$ $= \frac{4}{3} + 5$ $= \frac{19}{3}$	$f(-3) = \frac{2}{3}(-3) + 5$ $= -2 + 5$ $= 3$	$f(k) = \frac{2}{3}k + 5$	$f(k^2-1) = \frac{2}{3}(k^2-1) + 5$ $= \frac{2}{3}k^2 - \frac{2}{3} + 5$ $= \frac{2}{3}k^2 + \frac{13}{3}$

39. $f(x) = x^2$

$f(2) = 2^2$ $= 4$	$f(-3) = (-3)^2$ $= 9$	$f(k) = k^2$	$f(k^2-1) = (k^2-1)^2$ $= (k^2-1)(k^2-1)$ $= k^4 - 2k^2 + 1$

40. $f(x) = 3 - x^2$

$f(2) = 3 - 2^2$ $= 3 - 4$ $= -1$	$f(-3) = 3 - (-3)^2$ $= 3 - 9$ $= -6$	$f(k) = 3 - k^2$	$f(k^2-1) = 3 - (k^2-1)^2$ $= 3 - (k^2-1)(k^2-1)$ $= 3 - (k^4 - 2k^2 + 1)$ $= -k^4 + 2k^2 + 2$

41. $f(x) = \lvert x^2 + 1 \rvert$

$f(2) = \lvert 2^2 + 1 \rvert$ $= \lvert 5 \rvert$ $= 5$	$f(-3) = \lvert (-3)^2 + 1 \rvert$ $= \lvert 10 \rvert$ $= 10$	$f(k) = \lvert k^2 + 1 \rvert$ $= k^2 + 1$ $[k^2 + 1 \geq 0]$	$f(k^2-1) = \left\lvert (k^2-1)^2 + 1 \right\rvert$ $= (k^2-1)^2 + 1$ $= k^4 - 2k^2 + 1 + 1$ $= k^4 - 2k^2 + 2$ $\left[(k^2-1)^2 + 1 \geq 0\right]$

42. $f(x) = \lvert x^2 + x + 4 \rvert$

$f(2) = \lvert 2^2 + 2 + 4 \rvert$ $= \lvert 4 + 2 + 4 \rvert$ $= \lvert 10 \rvert$ $= 10$	$f(-3) = \lvert (-3)^2 + (-3) + 4 \rvert$ $= \lvert 9 - 3 + 4 \rvert$ $= \lvert 10 \rvert$ $= 10$	$f(k) = \lvert k^2 + k + 4 \rvert$ $= k^2 + k + 4$ $[k^2 + k + 4 \geq 0]$

$f(k^2-1) = \left\lvert (k^2-1)^2 + (k^2-1) + 4 \right\rvert$ $= \left\lvert (k^2-1)^2 + k^2 + 3 \right\rvert$ $= (k^2-1)^2 + k^2 + 3$ $= k^4 - 2k^2 + 1 + k^2 + 3$ $= k^4 - k^2 + 4$ $\left[(k^2-1)^2 + k^2 + 3 \geq 0\right]$

43.

$$f(x)=\frac{2}{x+4}$$

$f(2)=\frac{2}{2+4}$ $=\frac{2}{6}=\frac{1}{3}$	$f(-3)=\frac{2}{-3+4}$ $=\frac{2}{1}=2$	$f(k)=\frac{2}{k+4}$	$f(k^2-1)=\frac{2}{k^2-1+4}$ $=\frac{2}{k^2+3}$

44.

$$f(x)=\frac{3}{x-5}$$

$f(2)=\frac{3}{2-5}$ $=\frac{3}{-3}=-1$	$f(-3)=\frac{3}{-3-5}$ $=\frac{3}{-8}=-\frac{3}{8}$	$f(k)=\frac{3}{k-5}$	$f(k^2-1)=\frac{3}{k^2-1-5}$ $=\frac{3}{k^2-6}$

45.

$$f(x)=\frac{1}{x^2-1}$$

$f(2)=\frac{1}{2^2-1}$ $=\frac{1}{4-1}$ $=\frac{1}{3}$	$f(-3)=\frac{1}{(-3)^2-1}$ $=\frac{1}{9-1}$ $=\frac{1}{8}$	$f(k)=\frac{1}{k^2-1}$	$f(k^2-1)=\frac{1}{(k^2-1)^2-1}$ $=\frac{1}{k^4-2k^2+1-1}$ $=\frac{1}{k^4-2k^2}$

46.

$$f(x)=\frac{3}{x^2+3}$$

$f(2)=\frac{3}{2^2+3}$ $=\frac{3}{4+3}$ $=\frac{3}{7}$	$f(-3)=\frac{3}{(-3)^2+3}$ $=\frac{3}{9+3}$ $=\frac{3}{12}=\frac{1}{4}$	$f(k)=\frac{3}{k^2+3}$	$f(k^2-1)=\frac{3}{(k^2-1)^2+3}$ $=\frac{3}{k^4-2k^2+1+3}$ $=\frac{3}{k^4-2k^2+4}$

47.

$$f(x)=\sqrt{x^2+1}$$

$f(2)=\sqrt{2^2+1}$ $=\sqrt{4+1}$ $=\sqrt{5}$	$f(-3)=\sqrt{(-3)^2+1}$ $=\sqrt{9+1}$ $=\sqrt{10}$	$f(k)=\sqrt{k^2+1}$	$f(k^2-1)=\sqrt{(k^2-1)^2+1}$ $=\sqrt{k^4-2k^2+1+1}$ $=\sqrt{k^4-2k^2+2}$

48. $$f(x)=\sqrt{x^2-1}$$

$f(2)=\sqrt{2^2-1}$ $=\sqrt{4-1}$ $=\sqrt{3}$	$f(-3)=\sqrt{(-3)^2-1}$ $=\sqrt{9-1}$ $=\sqrt{8}=2\sqrt{2}$	$f(k)=\sqrt{k^2-1}$	$f(k^2-1)=\sqrt{(k^2-1)^2-1}$ $=\sqrt{k^4-2k^2+1-1}$ $=\sqrt{k^4-2k^2}$ $=\sqrt{k^2(k^2-2)}$ $=\lvert k\rvert\sqrt{k^2-2}$

49. $$\frac{f(x+h)-f(x)}{h}=\frac{[3(x+h)+1]-[3x+1]}{h}=\frac{[3x+3h+1]-[3x+1]}{h}=\frac{3x+3h+1-3x-1}{h}=\frac{3h}{h}=3$$

50. $$\frac{f(x+h)-f(x)}{h}=\frac{[5(x+h)-1]-[5x-1]}{h}=\frac{[5x+5h-1]-[5x-1]}{h}=\frac{5x+5h-1-5x+1}{h}=\frac{5h}{h}=5$$

51. $$\frac{f(x+h)-f(x)}{h}=\frac{\left[(x+h)^2+1\right]-[x^2+1]}{h}=\frac{[x^2+2xh+h^2+1]-[x^2+1]}{h}=\frac{x^2+2xh+h^2+1-x^2-1}{h}=\frac{2xh+h^2}{h}=\frac{h(2x+h)}{h}=2x+h$$

52. $$\frac{f(x+h)-f(x)}{h}=\frac{\left[(x+h)^2-3\right]-[x^2-3]}{h}=\frac{[x^2+2xh+h^2-3]-[x^2-3]}{h}=\frac{x^2+2xh+h^2-3-x^2+3}{h}=\frac{2xh+h^2}{h}=\frac{h(2x+h)}{h}=2x+h$$

53.

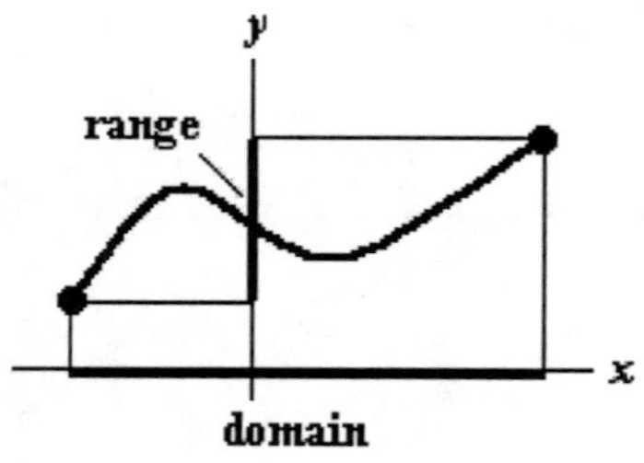

54.

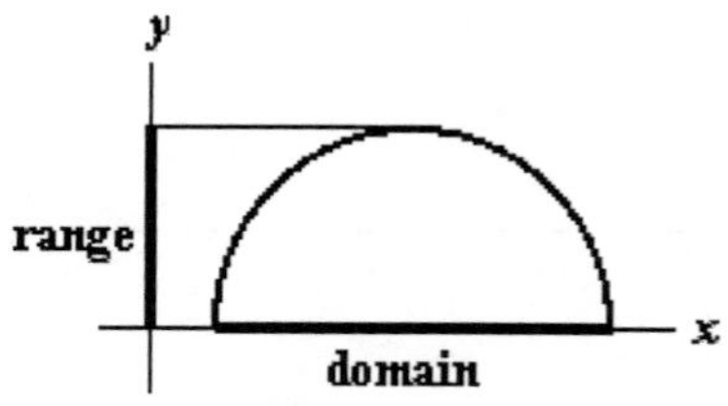

55. function

56. not a function

57. function

58. not a function

59. function

60. function

61. $f(x) = 2x + 3$

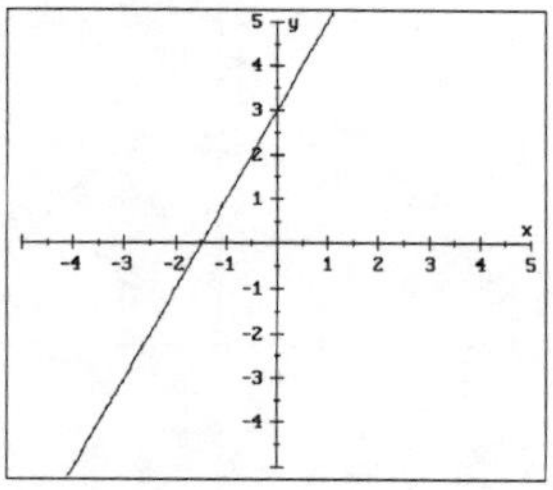

62. $f(x) = 3x + 2$

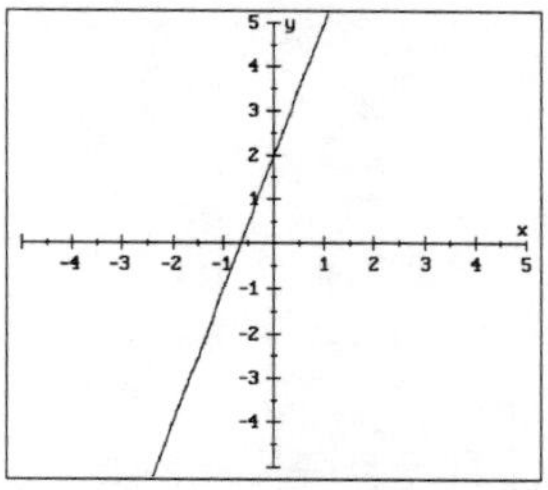

63. $f(x) = \frac{1}{2}x - 3$

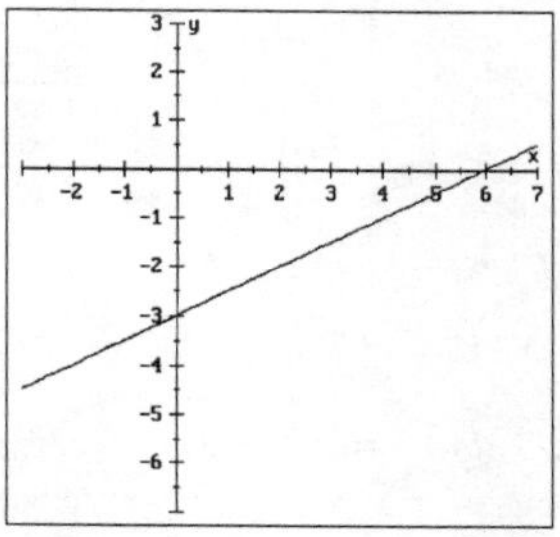

64. $f(x) = -\frac{3}{4}x + 4$

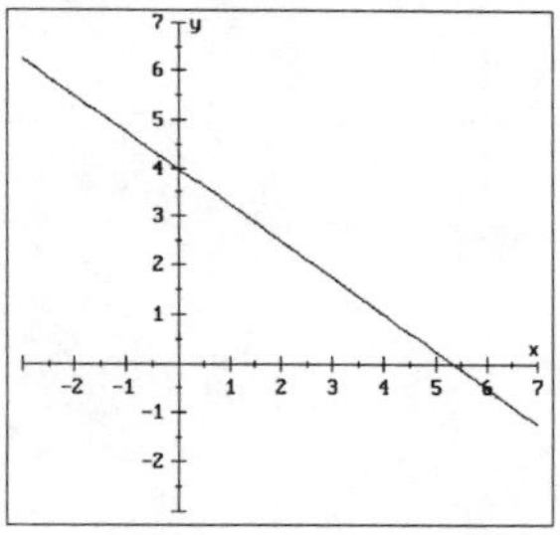

65.
$$\begin{aligned} 2x &= 3y - 3 \\ -3y &= -2x - 3 \\ y &= \frac{2}{3}x + 1 \end{aligned}$$

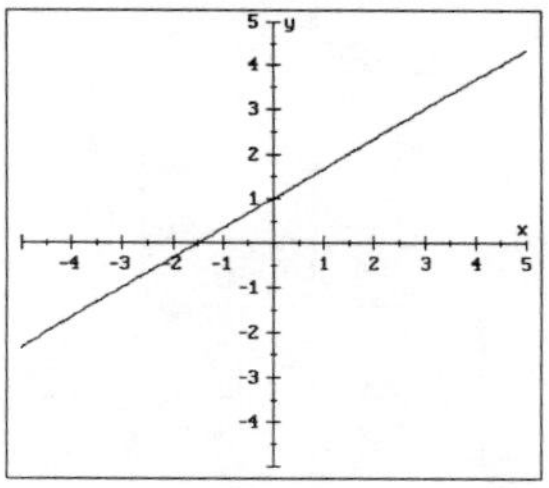

66.
$$\begin{aligned} 3x &= 2(y + 1) \\ 3x &= 2y + 2 \\ y &= \frac{3}{2}x - 1 \end{aligned}$$

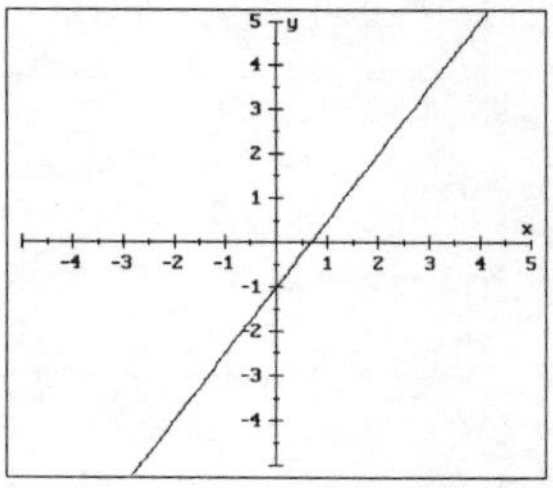

67. $f(x) = -\sqrt{x}$

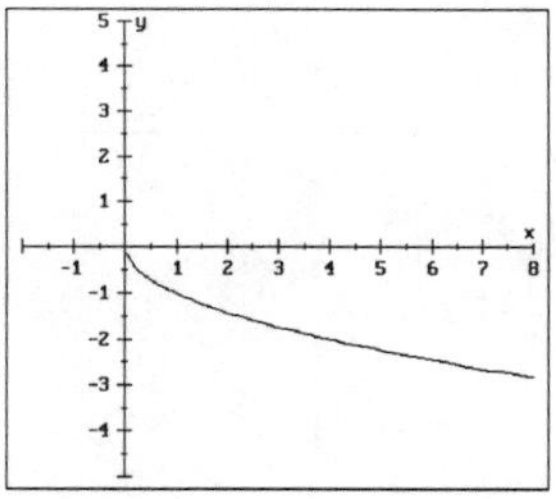

68. $f(x) = \sqrt{x + 1}$

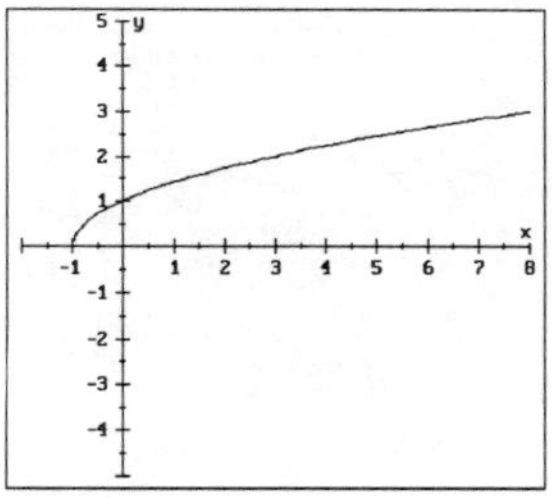

69. $f(x) = -\sqrt{x + 1}$

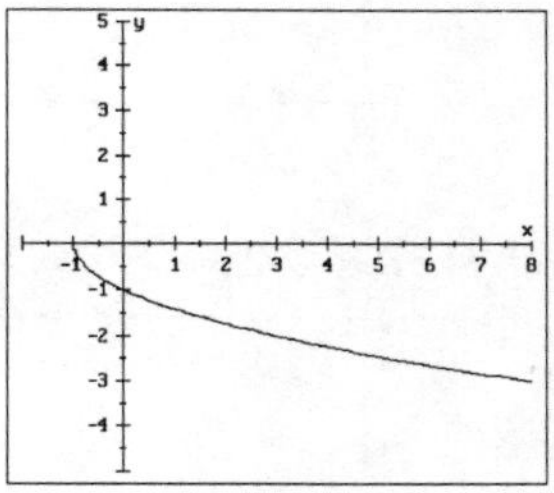

70. $f(x) = \sqrt{x} + 2$

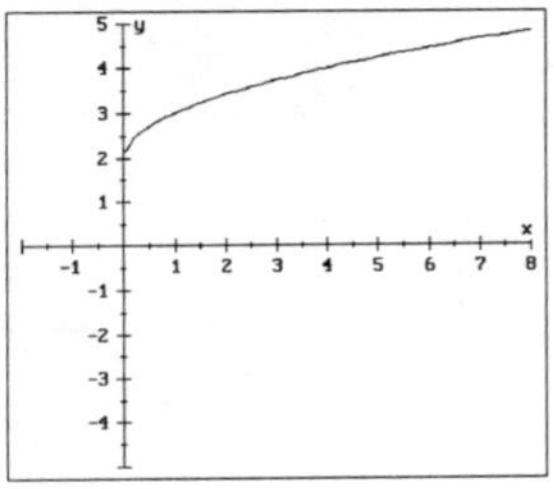

71. $f(x) = -|x|$

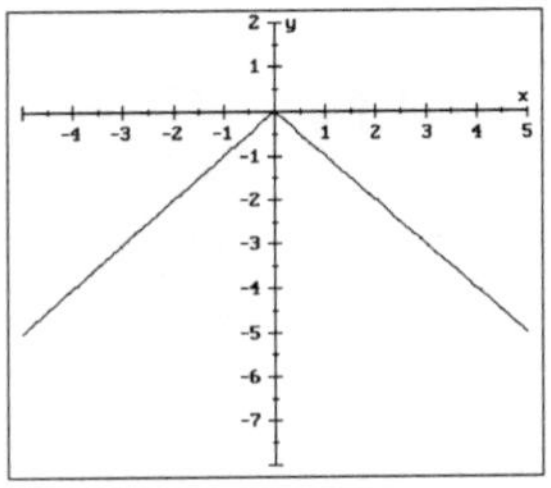

72. $f(x) = -|x| - 3$

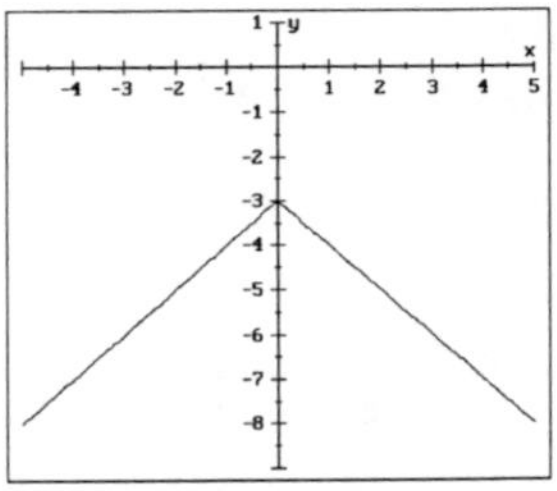

73. $f(x) = |x - 2|$

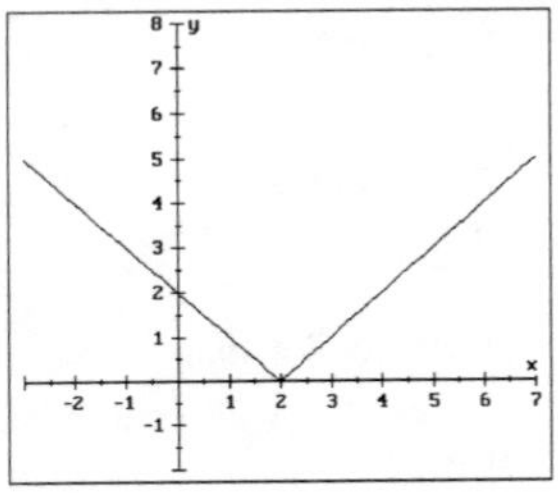

74. $f(x) = -|x - 2|$

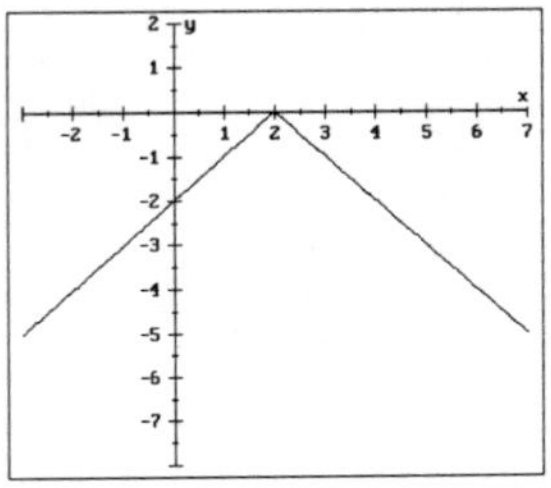

75. $f(x) = \sqrt{2x - 4}$

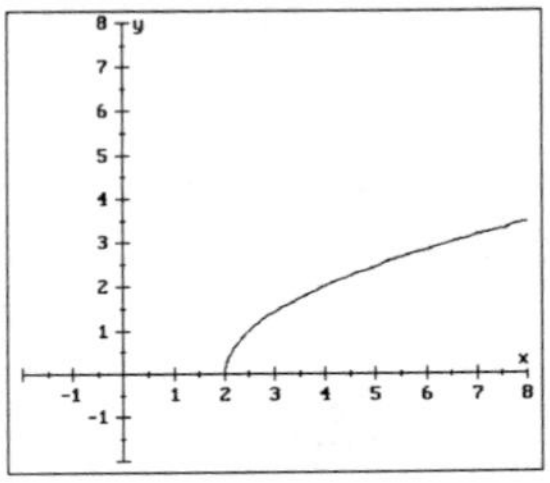

76. $f(x) = -\sqrt{2x - 4}$

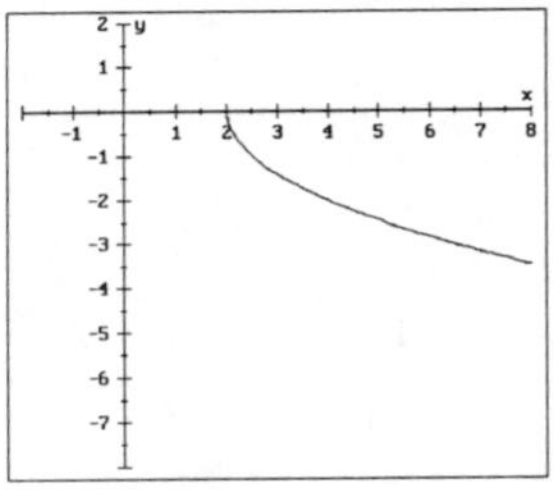

77. $f(x) = \left|\frac{1}{2}x + 3\right|$

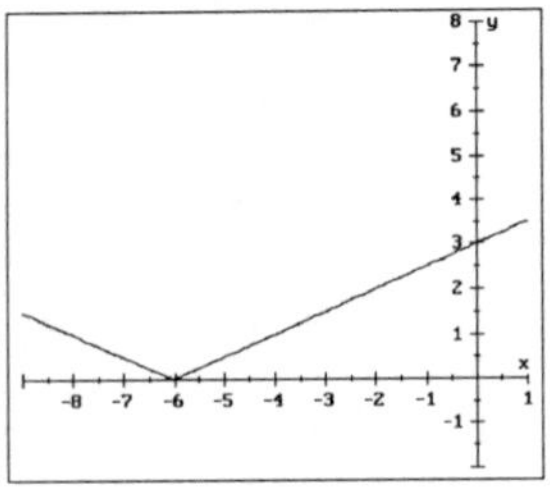

78. $f(x) = -\left|\frac{1}{2}x + 3\right|$

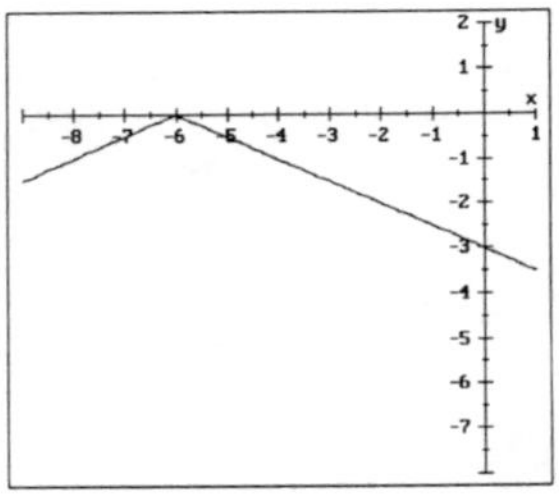

79. $f(x) = \sqrt{2x - 5}$

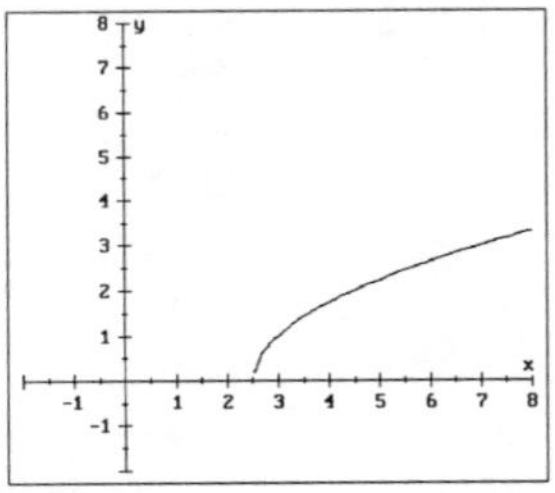

domain: $\left[\frac{5}{2}, \infty\right)$; range: $[0, \infty)$

80. $f(x) = |3x + 2|$

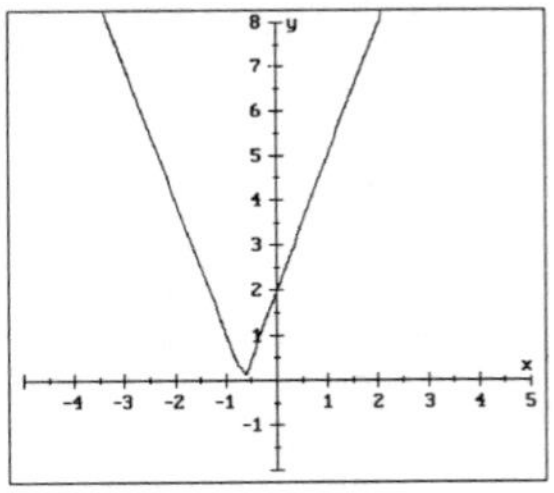

domain: $(-\infty, \infty)$; range: $[0, \infty)$

81. $f(x) = \sqrt[3]{5x-1}$

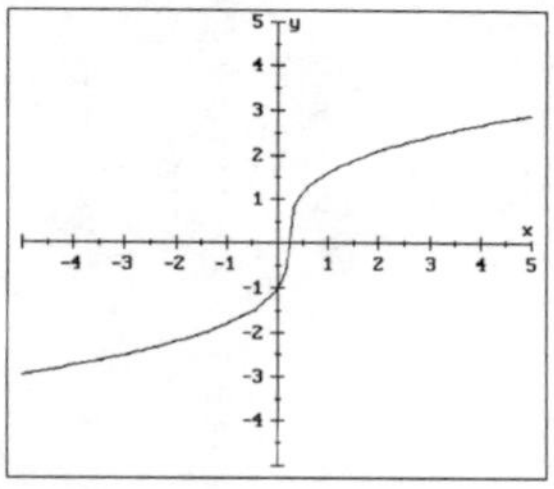

domain: $(-\infty, \infty)$; range: $(-\infty, \infty)$

82. $f(x) = -\sqrt[3]{3x+2}$

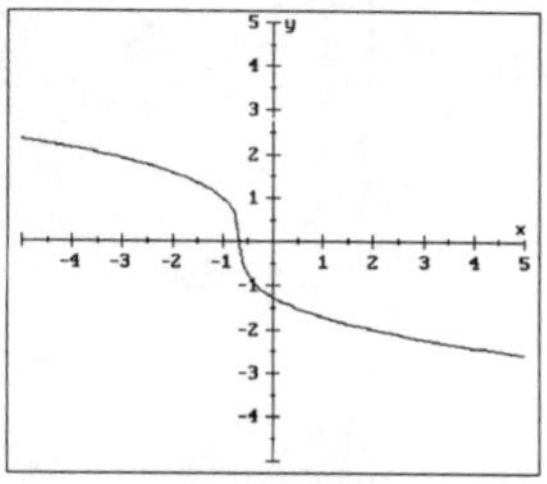

domain: $(-\infty, \infty)$; range: $(-\infty, \infty)$

83.
$$\begin{aligned} F &= mC + b \\ 32 &= m(0) + b \\ 32 &= b \end{aligned} \qquad \begin{aligned} F &= mC + 32 \\ -40 &= m(-40) + 32 \\ -72 &= -40m \\ \tfrac{9}{5} &= m \end{aligned} \qquad F = \tfrac{9}{5}C + 32$$

84.
$$\begin{aligned} v &= mt + b \\ 15 &= m(0) + b \\ 15 &= b \end{aligned} \qquad \begin{aligned} v &= mt + 15 \\ 79 &= m(2) + 15 \\ 32 &= m \end{aligned} \qquad v = 32t + 15$$

85.
$$c = mn + b \qquad m = \frac{14.30 - 4.70}{9000 - 1000} = \frac{9.60}{8000} = 0.0012$$
$$\begin{aligned} c &= 0.0012n + b \\ 4.70 &= 0.0012(1000) + b \\ 3.50 &= b \end{aligned} \qquad c = 0.0012n + 3.50$$

86.
$$A = mt + b \qquad m = \frac{320 - 272}{5 - 3} = \frac{48}{2} = 24$$
$$\begin{aligned} A &= 24t + b \\ 272 &= 24(3) + b \\ 200 &= b \end{aligned} \qquad A = 24t + 200$$

87. **a.** The \$14,000 cost is fixed regardless of the number of square feet. Thus, the cost is \$14,000 when the house has an area of 0 square feet ($c = 14{,}000$ when $f = 0$). If the house has an area of 1 square foot, the cost is $14{,}000 + 95 = 14{,}095$. Thus,

$$\begin{aligned} c &= mf + b \\ 14000 &= m(0) + b \\ 14000 &= b \end{aligned} \qquad \begin{aligned} c &= mf + 14000 \\ 14095 &= m(1) + 14000 \\ 95 &= m \end{aligned} \qquad \boxed{c = 95f + 14000}$$

b. $c = 95f + 14000 = 95(2600) + 14000 = 261000 \Rightarrow$ It will cost \$261,000.

88. **a.** The concessionaire must spend \$40 to hire the vendor regardless of whether the vendor sells any hot dogs. Thus, when 0 hot dogs are sold, the concessionaire loses \$40. Therefore, when $h = 0$, $I = -40$. When 1 hot dog is sold, the vendor "makes" $-40 + 2.50 = -37.50$.

$$\begin{aligned} I &= mh + b \\ -40 &= m(0) + b \\ -40 &= b \end{aligned} \qquad \begin{aligned} I &= mh - 40 \\ -37.50 &= m(1) - 40 \\ 2.50 &= m \end{aligned} \qquad \boxed{I = 2.50h - 40}$$

b. $I = 2.50h - 40 = 2.50(175) - 40 = 397.50 \Rightarrow$ The concessionaire will make \$397.50.

89. **Answers may vary.**

90. **Answers may vary.**

91. **Answers may vary.**

92. **Answers may vary.**

93. natural: $1, 7, 8$

94. rational: $-3, -1, 0, 0.5, \frac{3}{4}, 1, 7, 8$

95. prime: 7

96. even: $0, 8$

97. $(-4, 7]$

98. $(-\infty, -3) \cup [5, \infty)$

99. $(-3, 5) \cup [6, \infty)$: 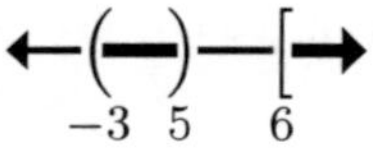

100. $(-\infty, 0) \cup (0, \infty)$: 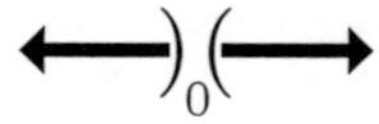

Exercise 3.2 (page 254)

1. $y = ax^2 + bx + c$ **2.** $(3, 5)$

3. $-\dfrac{b}{2a}$

4. $c - \dfrac{b^2}{4a}$

5. $y = x^2 - x;\ a = 1, b = -1, c = 0$

vertex: $x = -\dfrac{b}{2a} = -\dfrac{-1}{2(1)} = \dfrac{1}{2}$

$y = x^2 - x = \left(\dfrac{1}{2}\right)^2 - \dfrac{1}{2} = -\dfrac{1}{4}$

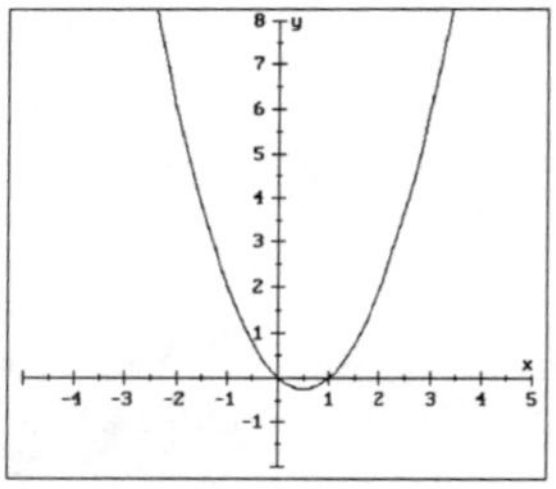

6. $y = x^2 + 2x;\ a = 1, b = 2, c = 0$

vertex: $x = -\dfrac{b}{2a} = -\dfrac{2}{2(1)} = -1$

$y = x^2 + 2x = (-1)^2 + 2(-1) = -1$

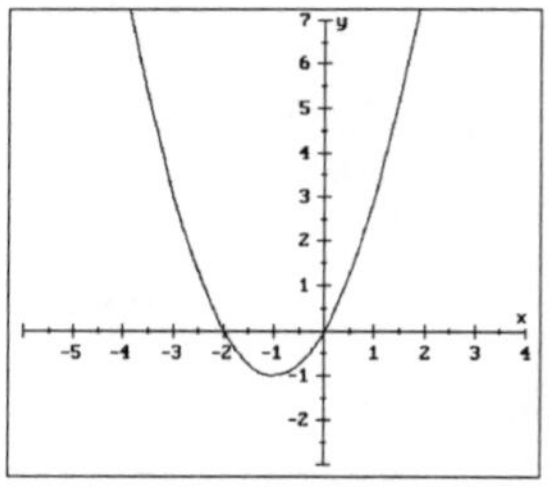

7. $y = -3x^2 + 2;\ a = -3, b = 0, c = 2$

vertex: $x = -\dfrac{b}{2a} = -\dfrac{0}{2(-3)} = 0$

$y = -3x^2 + 2 = -3(0)^2 + 2 = 2$

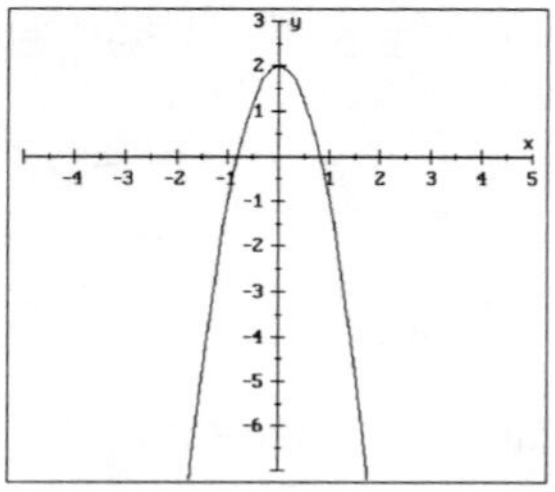

8. $y = -3x^2 + 4;\ a = -3, b = 0, c = 4$

vertex: $x = -\dfrac{b}{2a} = -\dfrac{0}{2(-3)} = 0$

$y = -3x^2 + 4 = -3(0)^2 + 4 = 4$

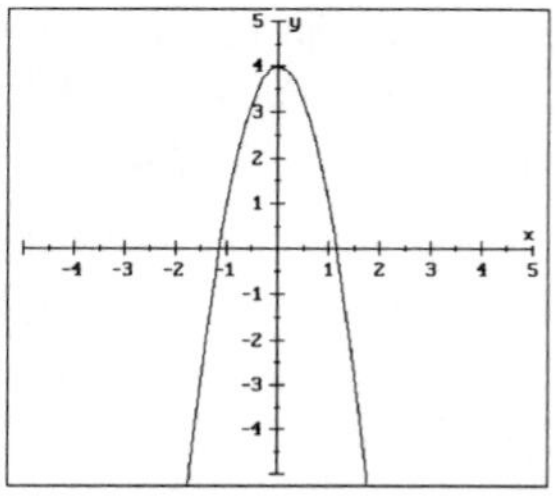

9. $y = -\frac{1}{2}x^2 + 3$; $a = -\frac{1}{2}, b = 0, c = 3$

vertex: $x = -\frac{b}{2a} = -\frac{0}{2(-\frac{1}{2})} = 0$

$y = -\frac{1}{2}x^2 + 3 = -\frac{1}{2}(0)^2 + 3 = 3$

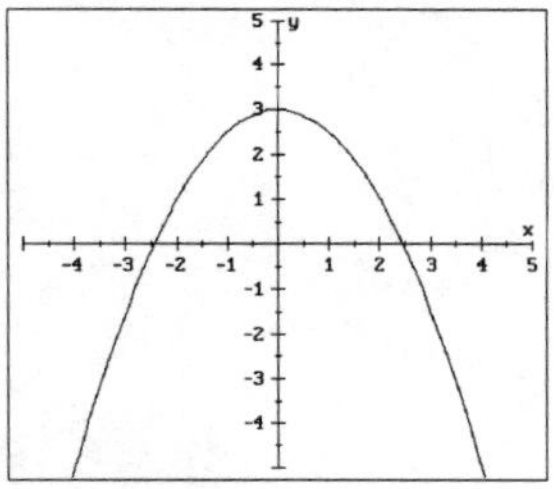

10. $y = \frac{1}{2}x^2 - 2$; $a = \frac{1}{2}, b = 0, c = -2$

vertex: $x = -\frac{b}{2a} = -\frac{0}{2(\frac{1}{2})} = 0$

$y = \frac{1}{2}x^2 - 2 = \frac{1}{2}(0)^2 - 2 = -2$

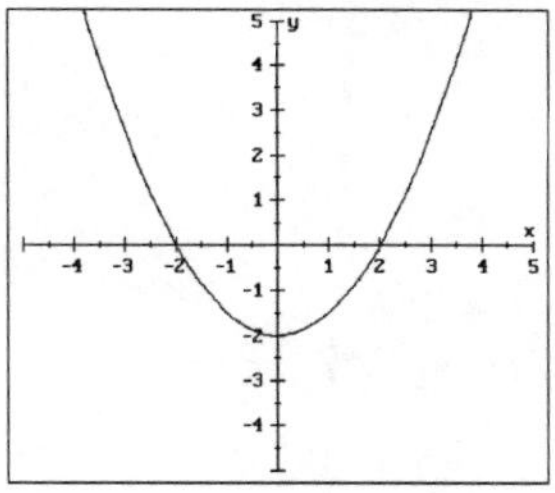

11. $y = x^2 - 4x + 1$; $a = 1, b = -4, c = 1$

vertex: $x = -\frac{b}{2a} = -\frac{-4}{2(1)} = 2$

$y = x^2 - 4x + 1 = 2^2 - 4(2) + 1 = -3$

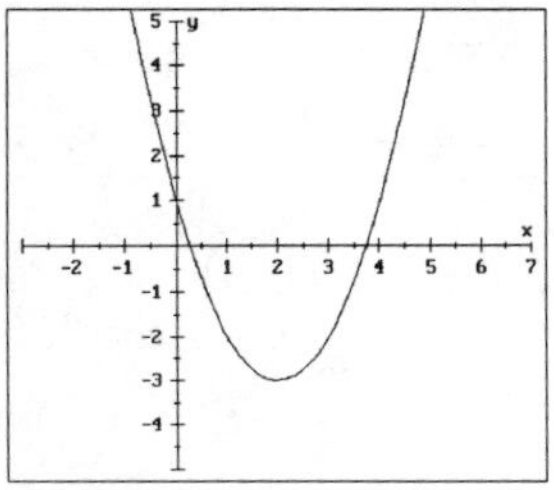

12. $y = -x^2 - 4x + 1$; $a = -1, b = -4, c = 1$

vertex: $x = -\frac{b}{2a} = -\frac{-4}{2(-1)} = -2$

$y = -x^2 - 4x + 1 = -(-2)^2 - 4(-2) + 1$
$= 5$

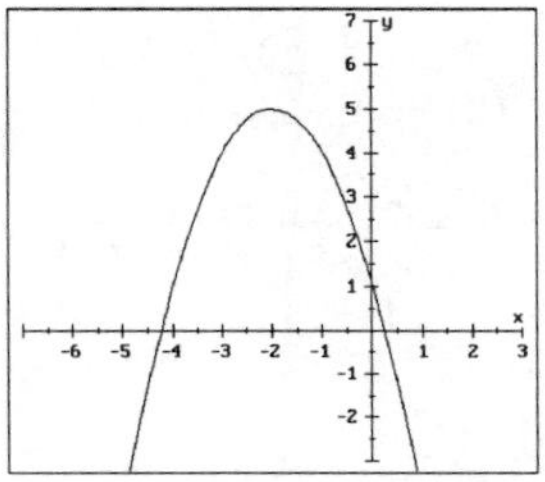

13. $y = x^2 - 1$; $a = 1, b = 0, c = -1$

$x = -\frac{b}{2a} = -\frac{0}{2(1)} = 0$

$y = x^2 - 1 = 0^2 - 1 = -1$

Vertex: $(0, -1)$

14. $y = -x^2 + 2$; $a = -1, b = 0, c = 2$

$x = -\frac{b}{2a} = -\frac{0}{2(-1)} = 0$

$y = -x^2 + 2 = -(0)^2 + 2 = 2$

Vertex: $(0, 2)$

15. $y = x^2 - 4x + 4$; $a = 1, b = -4, c = 4$

$x = -\frac{b}{2a} = -\frac{-4}{2(1)} = 2$

$y = x^2 - 4x + 4 = 2^2 - 4(2) + 4 = 0$

Vertex: $(2, 0)$

16. $y = x^2 - 10x + 25$; $a = 1, b = -10, c = 25$

$x = -\frac{b}{2a} = -\frac{-10}{2(1)} = 5$

$y = x^2 - 10x + 25 = 5^2 - 10(5) + 25 = 0$

Vertex: $(5, 0)$

17. $y = x^2 + 6x - 3;\ a = 1, b = 6, c = -3$

$$x = -\frac{b}{2a} = -\frac{6}{2(1)} = -3$$

$$y = x^2 + 6x - 3 = (-3)^2 + 6(-3) - 3 = -12$$

Vertex: $(-3, -12)$

18. $y = -x^2 + 9x - 2;\ a = -1, b = 9, c = -2$

$$x = -\frac{b}{2a} = -\frac{9}{2(-1)} = \frac{9}{2}$$

$$y = -x^2 + 9x - 2 = -\left(\frac{9}{2}\right)^2 + 9\left(\frac{9}{2}\right) - 2 = \frac{73}{4}$$

Vertex: $\left(\frac{9}{2}, \frac{73}{4}\right)$

19. $y = -2x^2 + 12x - 17;$

$a = -2, b = 12, c = -17$

$$x = -\frac{b}{2a} = -\frac{12}{2(-2)} = 3$$

$$y = -2x^2 + 12x - 17 = -2(3)^2 + 12(3) - 17 = 1$$

Vertex: $(3, 1)$

20. $y = 2x^2 + 16x + 33;$

$a = 2, b = 16, c = 33$

$$x = -\frac{b}{2a} = -\frac{16}{2(2)} = -4$$

$$y = 2x^2 + 16x + 33 = 2(-4)^2 + 16(-4) + 33 = 1$$

Vertex: $(-4, 1)$

21. $y = 3x^2 - 4x + 5;$

$a = 3, b = -4, c = 5$

$$x = -\frac{b}{2a} = -\frac{-4}{2(3)} = \frac{4}{6} = \frac{2}{3}$$

$$y = 3x^2 - 4x + 5 = 3\left(\frac{2}{3}\right)^2 - 4\left(\frac{2}{3}\right) + 5 = \frac{11}{3}$$

Vertex: $\left(\frac{2}{3}, \frac{11}{3}\right)$

22. $y = -4x^2 + 3x + 4;$

$a = -4, b = 3, c = 4$

$$x = -\frac{b}{2a} = -\frac{3}{2(-4)} = \frac{3}{8}$$

$$y = -4x^2 + 3x + 4 = -4\left(\frac{3}{8}\right)^2 + 3\left(\frac{3}{8}\right) + 4 = \frac{73}{16}$$

Vertex: $\left(\frac{3}{8}, \frac{73}{16}\right)$

23. $y = \frac{1}{2}x^2 + 4x - 3;$

$a = \frac{1}{2}, b = 4, c = -3$

$$x = -\frac{b}{2a} = -\frac{4}{2(\frac{1}{2})} = -4$$

$$y = \frac{1}{2}x^2 + 4x - 3 = \frac{1}{2}(-4)^2 + 4(-4) - 3 = -11$$

Vertex: $(-4, -11)$

24. $y = -\frac{2}{3}x^2 + 3x - 5;$

$a = -\frac{2}{3}, b = 3, c = -5$

$$x = -\frac{b}{2a} = -\frac{3}{2(-\frac{2}{3})} = \frac{3}{\frac{4}{3}} = \frac{9}{4}$$

$$y = -\frac{2}{3}x^2 + 3x - 5 = -\frac{2}{3}\left(\frac{9}{4}\right)^2 + 3\left(\frac{9}{4}\right) - 5 = -\frac{13}{8}$$

Vertex: $\left(\frac{9}{4}, -\frac{13}{8}\right)$

25. $x^2 + 20y - 400 = 0$

$$20y = -x^2 + 400$$

$$y = -\frac{1}{20}x^2 + 20$$

$a = -\frac{1}{20}, b = 0, c = 20$

$x = -\frac{b}{2a} = -\frac{0}{2\left(-\frac{1}{20}\right)} = 0$

$y = -\frac{1}{20}x^2 + 20 = -\frac{1}{20}(0)^2 + 20 = 20$

The maximum height is 20 feet.

26. $y = 400x - 16x^2$

$y = -16x^2 + 400x$

$a = -16, b = 400, c = 0$

$x = -\frac{b}{2a} = -\frac{400}{2(-16)} = \frac{25}{2}$

$y = 400x - 16x^2 = 400\left(\frac{25}{2}\right) - 16\left(\frac{25}{2}\right)^2$

$= 2500$

The maximum height is 2500 units.

27. Since the triangle is a 45°-45°-90° triangle, we get the figure below:

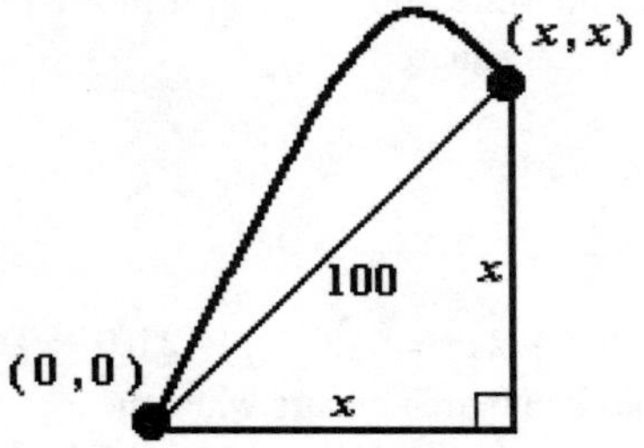

Use the Pythagorean Theorem to find x:

$x^2 + x^2 = 100^2$

$2x^2 = 100^2$

$x^2 = \frac{100^2}{2}$

$x = \pm\sqrt{\frac{100^2}{2}} = \pm\frac{100}{\sqrt{2}}$

Use the positive value for x.

The point $\left(\frac{100}{\sqrt{2}}, \frac{100}{\sqrt{2}}\right)$ must be on the graph: $y = -x^2 + ax$

$$\frac{100}{\sqrt{2}} = -\left(\frac{100}{\sqrt{2}}\right)^2 + a\left(\frac{100}{\sqrt{2}}\right)$$

$$\frac{100\sqrt{2}}{2} = -\frac{100^2}{2} + a\left(\frac{100\sqrt{2}}{2}\right)$$

$$100\sqrt{2} = -100^2 + \left(100\sqrt{2}\right)a$$

$$100\sqrt{2} + 100^2 = \left(100\sqrt{2}\right)a$$

$$\frac{100\sqrt{2} + 100^2}{100\sqrt{2}} = a \Rightarrow a = 1 + \frac{100}{\sqrt{2}} \Rightarrow a = 1 + 50\sqrt{2}$$

28. Perimeter $= 100$

$2l + 2w = 100$

$2l + 2x = 100$

$2l = 100 - 2x$

$l = \frac{100 - 2x}{2}$

$l = 50 - x$

Area $= lw$

$y = (50 - x)x$

$y = 50x - x^2$

$y = -x^2 + 50x$

$a = -1, b = 50, c = 0$

Find the vertex:

$x = -\frac{b}{2a} = -\frac{50}{2(-1)} = 25$

$y = -x^2 + 50x = -(25^2) + 50(25) = 625$

The maximum area occurs when $x = 25$.

29. Let x = the width.
Then $50 - x$ = the length.

$$\text{Area} = lw$$
$$y = (50 - x)x$$
$$y = 50x - x^2$$
$$y = -x^2 + 50x$$
$$a = -1,\ b = 50,\ c = 0$$

Find the vertex:

$$x = -\frac{b}{2a} = -\frac{50}{2(-1)} = 25$$
$$y = -x^2 + 50x = -\left(25^2\right) + 50(25) = 625$$

The maximum area occurs when the dimensions are 25 ft by 25 ft.

30. Set up the variables as indicated in the figure:

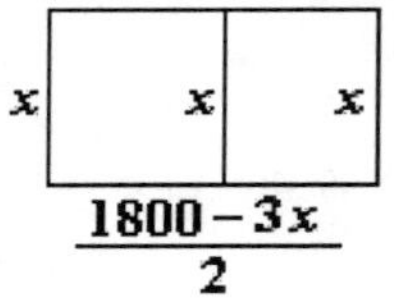

$$\text{Area} = lw$$
$$y = x\left(\frac{1800 - 3x}{2}\right)$$
$$y = 900x - \frac{3}{2}x^2$$
$$y = -\frac{3}{2}x^2 + 900x$$
$$a = -\frac{3}{2},\ b = 900,\ c = 0$$

Find the vertex:

$$x = -\frac{b}{2a} = -\frac{900}{2\left(-\frac{3}{2}\right)} = 300$$
$$y = -\tfrac{3}{2}x^2 + 900x = -\tfrac{3}{2}(300^2) + 900(300) = 135{,}000$$

The maximum area occurs when the dimensions are 300 ft by 450 ft, for an area of 135,000 square feet.

31. Set up the variables as indicated in the figure:

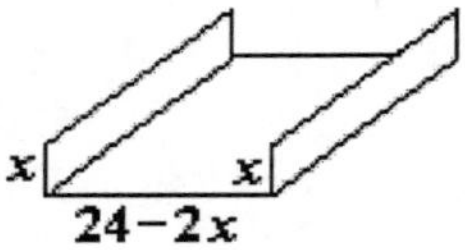

$$\text{Area} = lw$$
$$y = x(24 - 2x)$$
$$y = 24x - 2x^2$$
$$y = -2x^2 + 24x$$
$$a = -2,\ b = 24,\ c = 0$$

Find the vertex:

$$x = -\frac{b}{2a} = -\frac{24}{2(-2)} = 6$$
$$y = -2x^2 + 24x = -2\left(6^2\right) + 24(6) = 72$$

The maximum area occurs when the depth is 6 inches and the width is 12 inches.

32. Set up the variables as indicated in the figure:

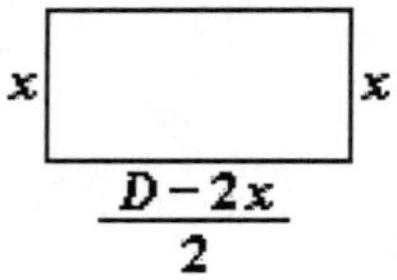

$$\text{Area} = lw$$
$$y = x\left(\frac{D - 2x}{2}\right)$$
$$y = \frac{D}{2}x - x^2$$
$$y = -x^2 + \frac{D}{2}x$$
$$a = -1,\ b = \frac{D}{2},\ c = 0$$

Find the vertex:

$$x = -\frac{b}{2a} = -\frac{\frac{D}{2}}{2(-1)} = \frac{D}{4}$$

The maximum area occurs when the width is $\frac{D}{4}$ inches. Thus, the maximum area results when the rectangle is a square.

33. Revenue = Price · # Sold

$$y = p(1200 - p)$$
$$y = 1200p - p^2$$
$$y = -p^2 + 1200p$$
$$a = -1,\ b = 1200,\ c = 0$$

Find the vertex:

$$p = -\frac{b}{2a} = -\frac{1200}{2(-1)} = 600$$

The maximum revenue occurs when the price is \$600.

34. Let $x = \#$ of penny decreases.
Then Fare $= 180 - x$ (cents)
$\#$ Riders $= 150{,}000 + 1000x$
Revenue $=$ Fare $\cdot$ $\#$ Riders

$$y = (180 - x)(150{,}000 + 1000x)$$
$$y = 27{,}000{,}000 + 30{,}000x - 1000x^2$$
$$a = -1000,\ b = 30{,}000,\ c = 27{,}000{,}000$$

Find the vertex:

$$x = -\frac{b}{2a} = -\frac{30{,}000}{2(-1000)} = 15$$

The maximum revenue occurs when the fare is decreased by 15 pennies, or when the fare is decreased to \$1.65.

35. Let $x = \#$ of \$5 increases.
Then Rate $= 90 + 5x$
$\#$ Rooms $= 200 - 10x$
Revenue $=$ Rate $\cdot$ $\#$ Rooms

$$y = (90 + 5x)(200 - 10x)$$
$$y = 18{,}000 + 100x - 50x^2$$
$$a = -50,\ b = 100,\ c = 18{,}000$$

Find the vertex:

$$x = -\frac{b}{2a} = -\frac{100}{2(-50)} = 1$$

The maximum revenue occurs when the room rate increases by 1 five-dollar increment, or when the rate is \$95.

36. Let $x = \#$ of blocks of tickets sold (over one).
Then Charge $= 10 - 0.50x$ (cents)
$\#$ Tickets $= 100 + 100x$
Revenue $=$ Charge $\cdot$ $\#$ Tickets

$$y = (10 - 0.50x)(100 + 100x)$$
$$y = 1000 + 950x - 50x^2$$
$$a = -50,\ b = 950,\ c = 1000$$

Find the vertex:

$$x = -\frac{b}{2a} = -\frac{950}{2(-50)} = 9.5$$

The maximum revenue occurs when 9 or 10 additional blocks are sold, or when there are a total of 10 or 11 blocks sold.

37. $s = 80t - 16t^2$
$a = -16,\ b = 80,\ c = 0$
Find the x-coord. of the vertex:

$$x = t = -\frac{b}{2a} = -\frac{80}{2(-16)} = \frac{5}{2} = 2.5$$

The max. height occurs after 2.5 seconds.

38. Let $s = 0$:
$s = 80t - 16t^2$
$0 = 80t - 16t^2$
$0 = 16t(5 - t)$
$t = 0$ or $t = 5$: The object returns after 5 sec.

39. $s = 80t - 16t^2$
$a = -16,\ b = 80,\ c = 0$
Find the y-coord. of the vertex.
Note: The x-coord. was found in **#37**.

$$y = s = 80t - 16t^2 = 80(2.5) - 16(2.5)^2 = 100$$

The max. height is 100 ft.

40. Refer to **#37** and **#38** to answer the question.

41. $y = 2x^2 + 9x - 56$

Vertex: $(-2.25, 66.13)$

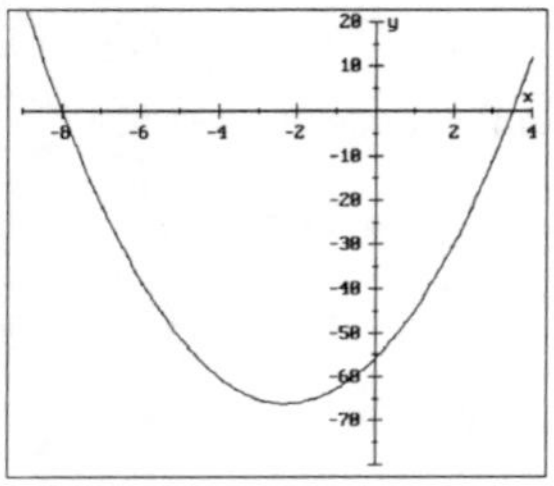

42. $y = 14x - \dfrac{x^2}{5}$

Vertex: $(35, 245)$

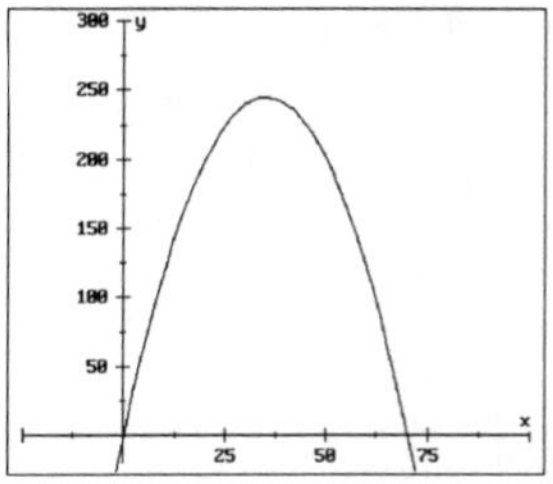

43. $y = (x - 7)(5x + 2)$

Vertex: $(3.3, -68.5)$

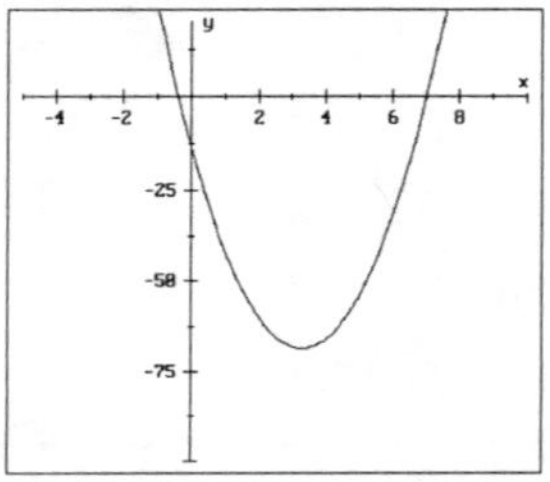

44. $y = -x(0.2 + 0.1x)$

Vertex: $(-1, 0.1)$

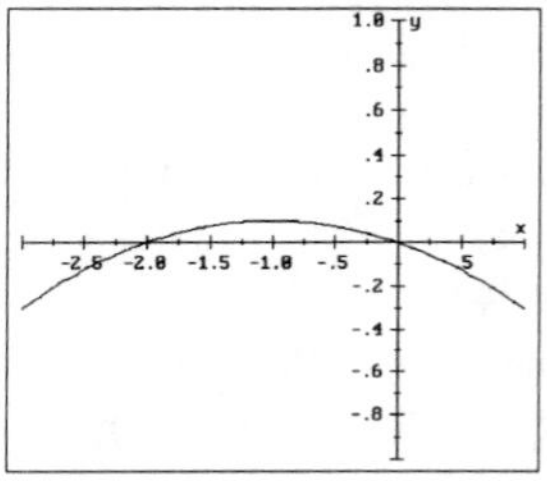

45. The equation of the line is $y = -\frac{3}{4}x + 9$.

Thus the point $(x, y) = \left(x, -\frac{3}{4}x + 9\right)$.

Area $= x\left(-\frac{3}{4}x + 9\right)$

$y = -\frac{3}{4}x^2 + 9x$

$a = -\frac{3}{4}, b = 9, c = 0$

Find the x-coord. of the vertex:

$$x = -\frac{b}{2a} = -\frac{9}{2\left(-\frac{3}{4}\right)} = 6$$

Thus, the dimensions are 6 by $4\frac{1}{2}$ units.

46. The point $(x, y) = (x, 1 - x)$.

Area $= \frac{1}{2}bh$

$y = \frac{1}{2}x(1 - x)$

$y = \frac{1}{2}x - \frac{1}{2}x^2$

$a = -\frac{1}{2}, b = \frac{1}{2}, c = 0$

Find the x-coord. of the vertex:

$$x = -\frac{b}{2a} = -\frac{\frac{1}{2}}{2\left(-\frac{1}{2}\right)} = \frac{1}{2}$$

Thus, point P has coordinates $\left(\frac{1}{2}, \frac{1}{2}\right)$.

47. Let $x =$ one number.

Then $6 - x =$ the other number.

Sum of squares $= x^2 + (6 - x)^2$

$y = x^2 + 36 - 12x + x^2$

$y = 2x^2 - 12x + 36$

$a = 2, b = -12, c = 36$

Find the x-coord. of the vertex:

$$x = -\frac{b}{2a} = -\frac{-12}{2(2)} = 3$$

Thus, the numbers are both 3.

48. Let $x =$ the number.
Then $x^2 =$ its square.
Amt. by which it exceeds square $= x - x^2$

$$y = x - x^2$$

$a = -1, b = 1, c = 0$
Find the x-coord. of the vertex:

$$x = -\frac{b}{2a} = -\frac{1}{2(-1)} = \frac{1}{2}$$

The number $\frac{1}{2}$ is the number which most exceeds its square.

49. $f(a) = a^2 - 3a$
$f(-a) = (-a)^2 - 3(-a)$
$= a^2 + 3a$

50. $f(a) = a^3 - 3a$
$f(-a) = (-a)^3 - 3(-a)$
$= -a^3 + 3a$

51. $f(a) = (5 - a)^2$
$f(-a) = [5 - (-a)]^2$
$= (5 + a)^2$

52. $f(a) = \frac{1}{a^2-4}$
$f(-a) = \frac{1}{(-a)^2-4}$
$= \frac{1}{a^2-4}$

53. $f(a) = 7$
$f(-a) = 7$

54. $f(a) = -|a|$
$f(-a) = -|-a|$
$= -|-1||a| = -|a|$

Exercise 3.3 (page 265)

1. 4

2. turning

3. $n - 1$

4. y-axis

5. odd

6. increasing

7. piecewise-defined

8. decreasing

9. 3

10. constant

11. $f(x) = x^3 - x$
$f(-x) = (-x)^3 - (-x)$
$= -x^3 + x$
$= -f(x) \Rightarrow$ odd

x-int.	y-int.
$x^3 - x = 0$	$f(0) = 0^3 - 0$
$x(x^2 - 1) = 0$	$y = 0$
$x(x + 1)(x - 1) = 0$	$(0, 0)$
$x = 0, x = -1, x = 1$	
$(0, 0), (-1, 0), (1, 0)$	

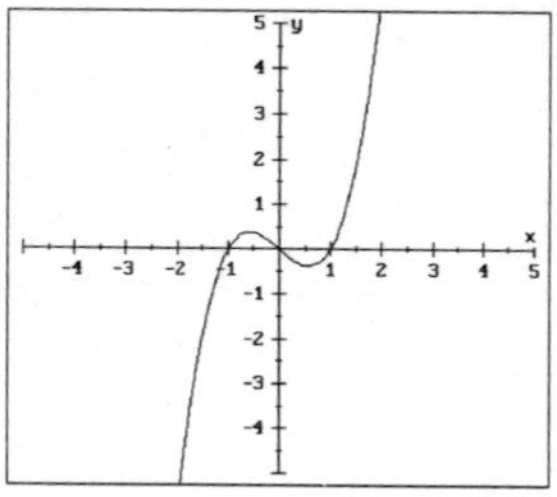

12. $f(x) = x^3 + x^2$
$f(-x) = (-x)^3 + (-x)^2$
$= -x^3 + x^2 \Rightarrow$ neither even nor odd

x-int.	y-int.
$x^3 + x^2 = 0$	$f(0) = 0^3 + 0^2$
$x^2(x + 1) = 0$	$y = 0$
$x = 0, x = -1$	$(0, 0)$
$(0, 0), (-1, 0)$	

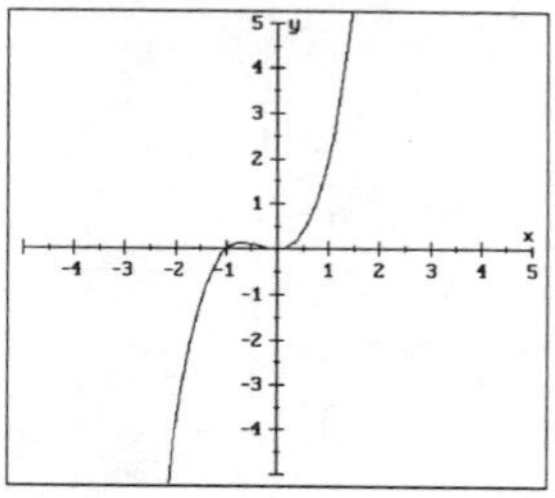

13. $f(x) = -x^3$

$f(-x) = -(-x)^3$

$= -(-x^3)$

$= x^3 = -f(x) \Rightarrow$ odd

x-int.	y-int.
$-x^3 = 0$	$f(0) = -0^3$
$x^3 = 0$	$y = 0$
$x = 0$	$(0, 0)$
$(0, 0)$	

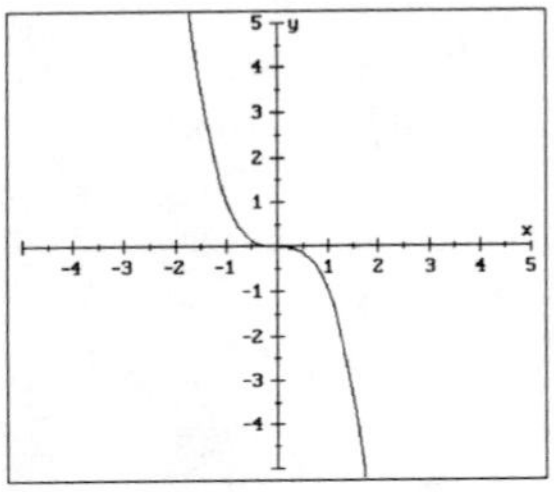

14. $f(x) = -x^3 + 1$

$f(-x) = -(-x)^3 + 1$

$= -(-x^3) + 1$

$= x^3 + 1 \Rightarrow$ neither even nor odd

x-int.	y-int.
$-x^3 + 1 = 0$	$f(0) = -0^3 + 1$
$1 = x^3$	$y = 1$
$1 = x$	$(0, 1)$
$(1, 0)$	

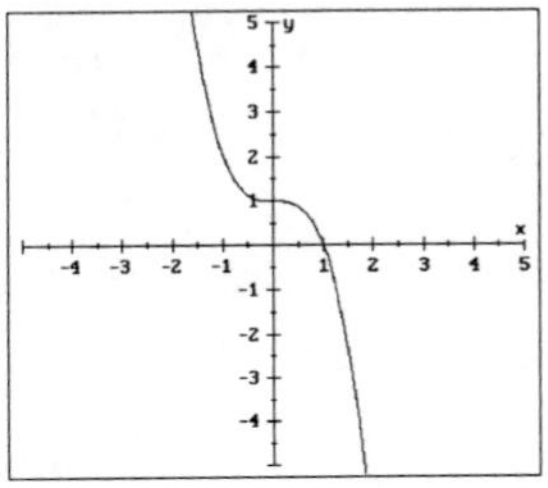

15. $f(x) = x^4 - 2x^2 + 1$

$f(-x) = (-x)^4 - 2(-x)^2 + 1$

$= x^4 + 2x^2 + 1 \Rightarrow$ even

x-int.	y-int.
$x^4 - 2x^2 + 1 = 0$	$f(0) = 1$
$(x^2 - 1)(x^2 - 1) = 0$	$y = 1$
$x^2 = 1$	$(0, 1)$
$x = 1, x = -1$	
$(1, 0), (-1, 0)$	

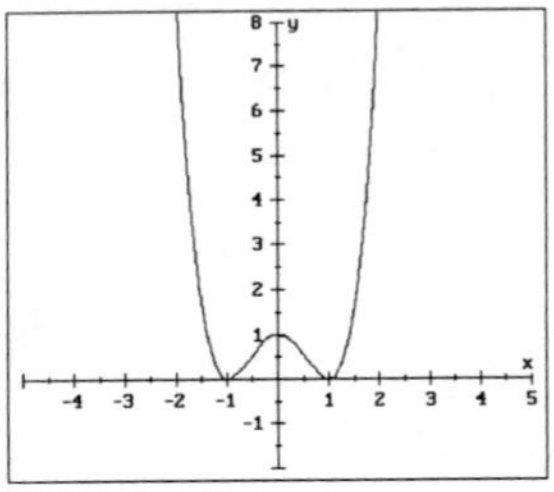

16. $f(x) = x^4 - 5x^2 + 4$

$f(-x) = (-x)^4 - 5(-x)^2 + 4$

$= x^4 - 5x^2 + 4 \Rightarrow$ even

x-int.	y-int.
$x^4 - 5x^2 + 4 = 0$	$f(0) = 4$
$(x^2 - 1)(x^2 - 4) = 0$	$y = 4$
$x^2 = 1$ or $x^2 = 4$	$(0, 4)$
$x = 1, x = -1, x = 2, x = -2$	
$(1, 0), (-1, 0), (2, 0), (-2, 0)$	

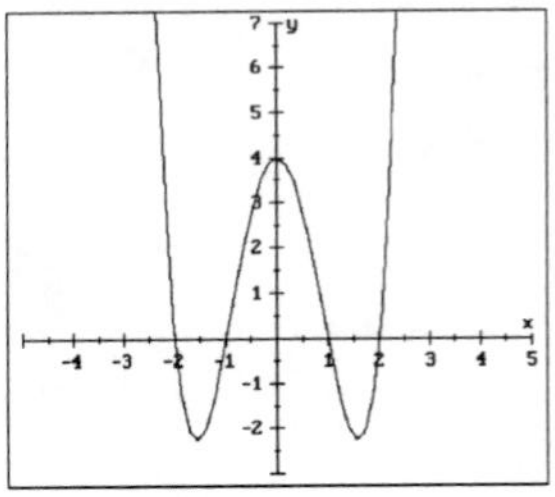

17. $f(x) = x^3 - x^2 - 4x + 4$

$f(-x) = (-x)^3 - (-x)^2 - 4(-x) + 4$

$= -x^3 - x^2 + 4x + 4$

$\Rightarrow$ neither even nor odd

x-int.	y-int.
$x^3 - x^2 - 4x + 4 = 0$	$f(0) = 4$
$x^2(x - 1) - 4(x - 1) = 0$	$y = 4$
$(x - 1)(x^2 - 4) = 0$	$(0, 4)$
$x = 1$ or $x^2 = 4$	
$x = 1, x = 2, x = -2$	
$(1, 0), (2, 0), (-2, 0)$	

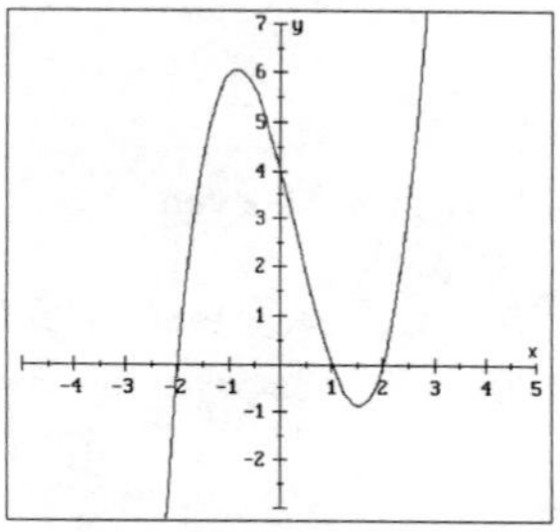

18. $f(x) = 4x^3 - 4x^2 - x + 1$

$f(-x) = 4(-x)^3 - 4(-x)^2 - (-x) + 1$

$= -4x^3 - 4x^2 + x + 1$

$\Rightarrow$ neither even nor odd

x-int.	y-int.
$4x^3 - 4x^2 - x + 1 = 0$	$f(0) = 1$
$4x^2(x - 1) - (x - 1) = 0$	$y = 1$
$(x - 1)(4x^2 - 1) = 0$	$(0, 1)$
$x = 1$ or $x^2 = \frac{1}{4}$	
$x = 1, x = \frac{1}{2}, x = -\frac{1}{2}$	
$(1, 0), (\frac{1}{2}, 0), (-\frac{1}{2}, 0)$	

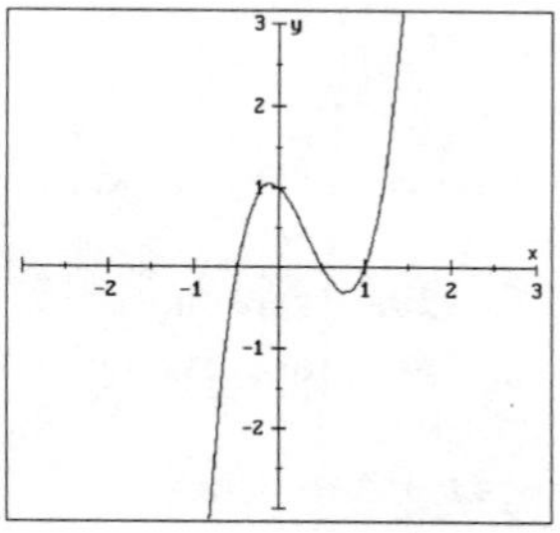

19. $f(x) = -x^4 + 5x^2 - 4$

$f(-x) = -(-x)^4 + 5(-x)^2 - 4$

$= -x^4 + 5x^2 - 4 \Rightarrow$ even

x-int.	y-int.
$-x^4 + 5x^2 - 4 = 0$	$f(0) = -4$
$-(x^4 - 5x^2 + 4) = 0$	$y = -4$
$(x^2 - 1)(x^2 - 4) = 0$	$(0, -4)$
$x^2 = 1$ or $x^2 = 4$	
$x = \pm 1, x = \pm 2$	
$(\pm 1, 0), (\pm 2, 0)$	

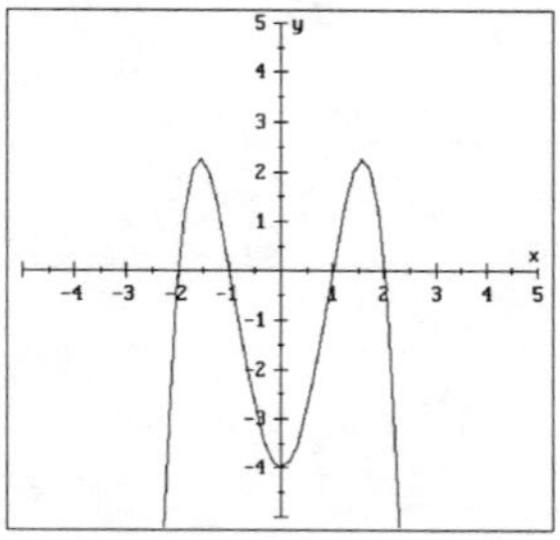

20. $f(x) = x^4 - 4x^3 + x^2 + 6x$

$f(-x) = (-x)^4 - 4(-x)^3 + (-x)^2 + 6(-x)$

$= x^4 + 4x^3 + x^2 - 6x$

$\Rightarrow$ neither even nor odd

x-int.	y-int.
$x^4 - 4x^3 + x^2 + 6x = 0$	$f(0) = 0$
$(x - 3)(x^3 - x^2 - 2x) = 0$	$y = 0$
$x(x - 3)(x^2 - x - 2) = 0$	$(0, 0)$
$x(x - 3)(x - 2)(x + 1) = 0$	
$x = 0, x = 3, x = 2, x = -1$	
$(0, 0), (3, 0), (2, 0), (-1, 0)$	

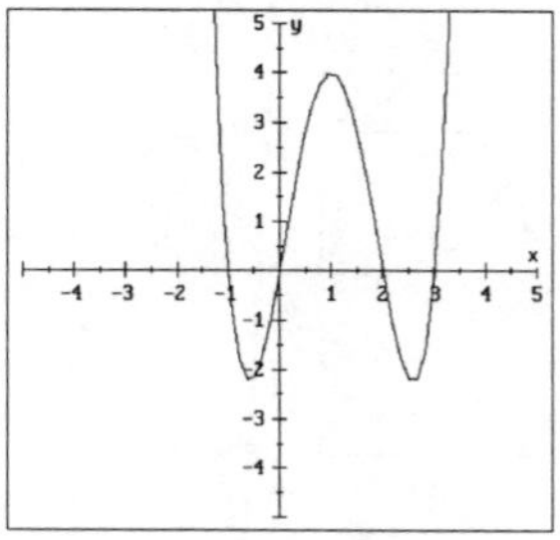

21. $y = f(x) = x^4 + x^2$
$f(-x) = (-x)^4 + (-x)^2$
$= x^4 + x^2 = f(x) \Rightarrow$ even

22. $y = f(x) = x^3 - 2x$
$f(-x) = (-x)^3 - 2(-x)$
$= -x^3 + 2x = -f(x) \Rightarrow$ odd

23. $y = f(x) = x^3 + x^2$
$f(-x) = (-x)^3 + (-x)^2$
$= -x^3 + x^2 \Rightarrow$ neither

24. $y = f(x) = x^6 - x^2$
$f(-x) = (-x)^6 - (-x)^2$
$= x^6 - x^2 = f(x) \Rightarrow$ even

25. $y = f(x) = x^5 + x^3$
$f(-x) = (-x)^5 + (-x)^3$
$= -x^5 - x^3 = -f(x) \Rightarrow$ odd

26. $y = f(x) = x^3 - x^2$
$f(-x) = (-x)^3 - (-x)^2$
$= -x^3 - x^2 \Rightarrow$ neither

27. $y = f(x) = 2x^3 - 3x$
$f(-x) = 2(-x)^3 - 3(-x)$
$= -2x^3 + 3x = -f(x) \Rightarrow$ odd

28. $y = f(x) = 4x^2 - 5$
$f(-x) = 4(-x)^2 - 5$
$= 4x^2 - 5 = f(x) \Rightarrow$ even

29. increasing: $x > 0$
decreasing: $x < 0$

30. constant: $x < 0$
decreasing: $x > 0$

31. increasing: $x < 0$
decreasing: $x > 0$

32. constant: $x > 0$
decreasing: $x < 0$

33. $y = f(x) = x^2 - 4x + 4$

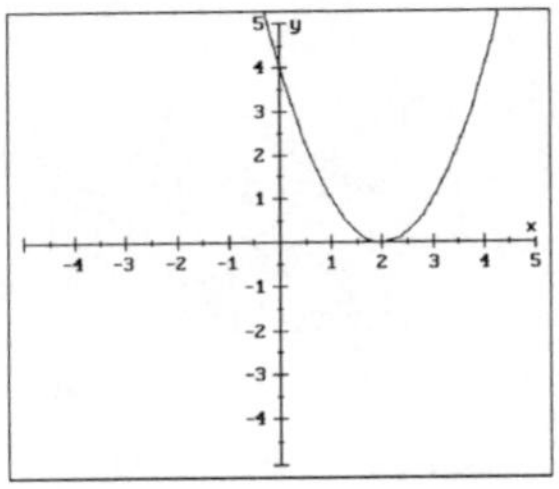

increasing: $x > 2$
decreasing: $x < 2$

34. $y = f(x) = 4 - x^2$

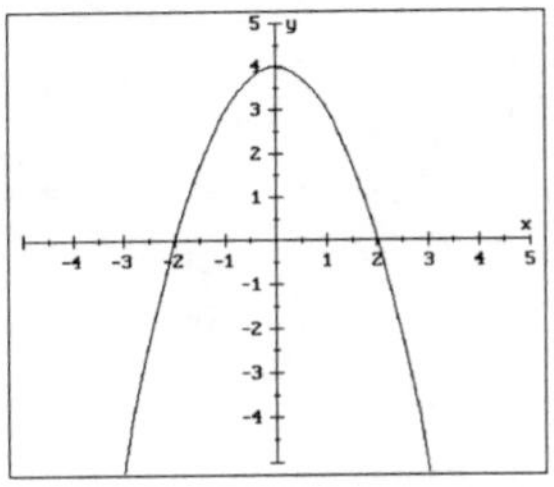

increasing: $x < 0$
decreasing: $x > 0$

35. $y = f(x) = \begin{cases} x + 2 & \text{if } x < 0 \\ 2 & \text{if } x \geq 0 \end{cases}$

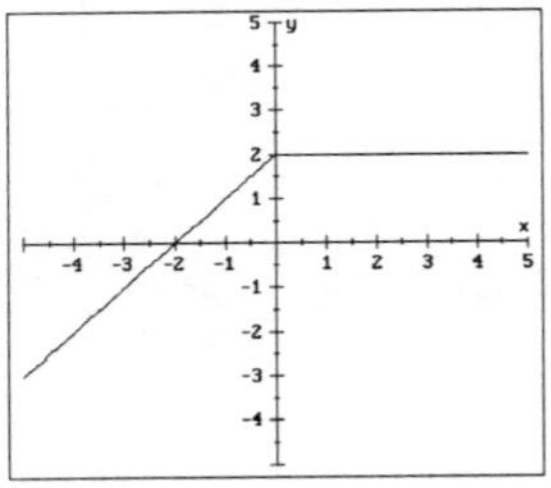

36. $y = f(x) = \begin{cases} 2x & \text{if } x < 0 \\ -2x & \text{if } x \geq 0 \end{cases}$

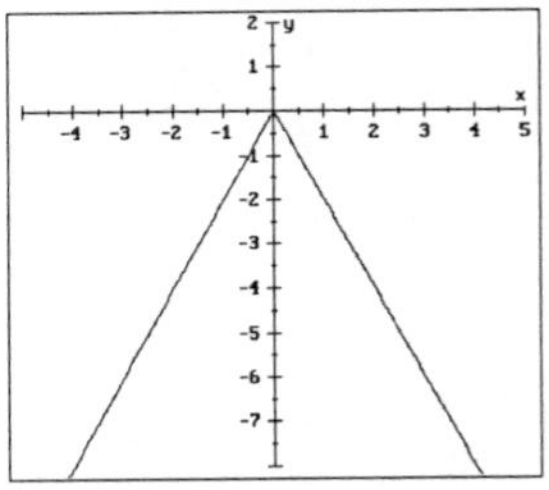

37. $y = f(x) = \begin{cases} -x & \text{if } x < 0 \\ x^2 & \text{if } x \geq 0 \end{cases}$

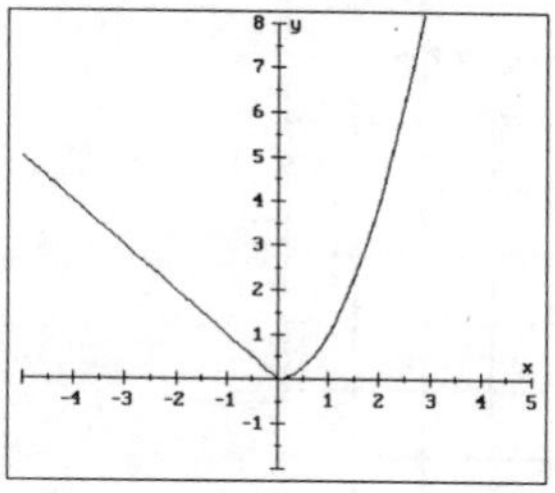

38. $y = f(x) = \begin{cases} |x| & \text{if } x < 0 \\ \sqrt{x} & \text{if } x \geq 0 \end{cases}$

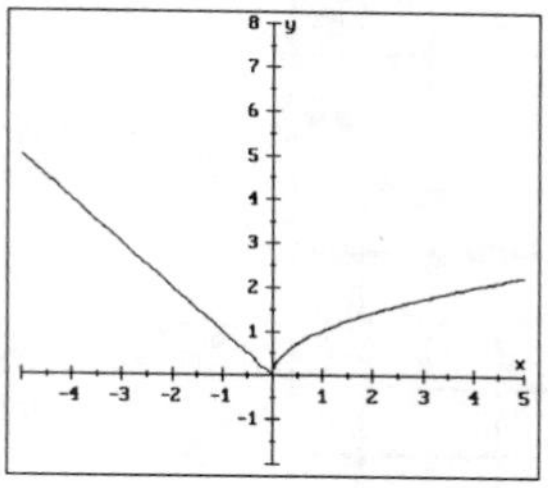

39. $y = f(x) = \begin{cases} 0 & \text{if } x < 0 \\ x^2 & \text{if } 0 \leq x \leq 2 \\ 4 - 2x & \text{if } x > 2 \end{cases}$

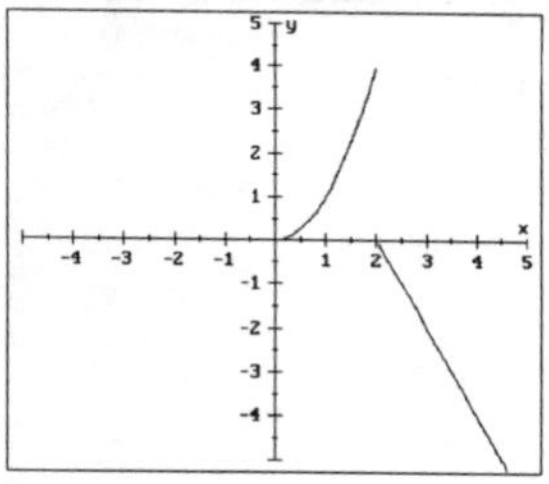

40. $y = f(x) = \begin{cases} 2 & \text{if } x < 0 \\ 2 - x & \text{if } 0 \leq x < 2 \\ x & \text{if } x \geq 2 \end{cases}$

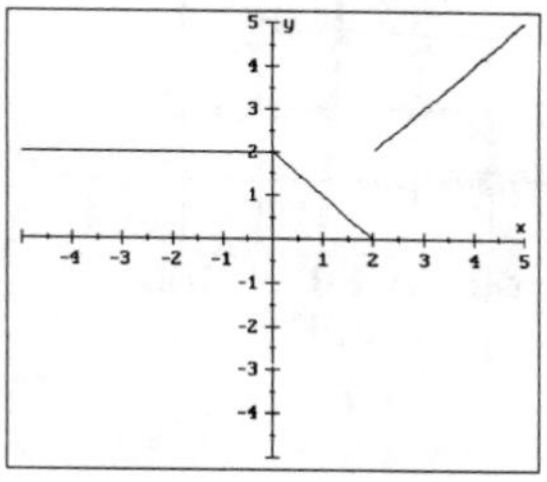

41. $y = [[2x]]$

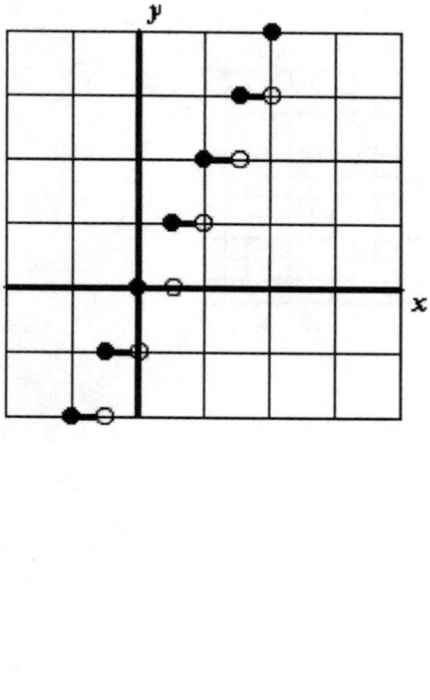

42. $y = \left[\left[\frac{1}{3}x + 3\right]\right]$

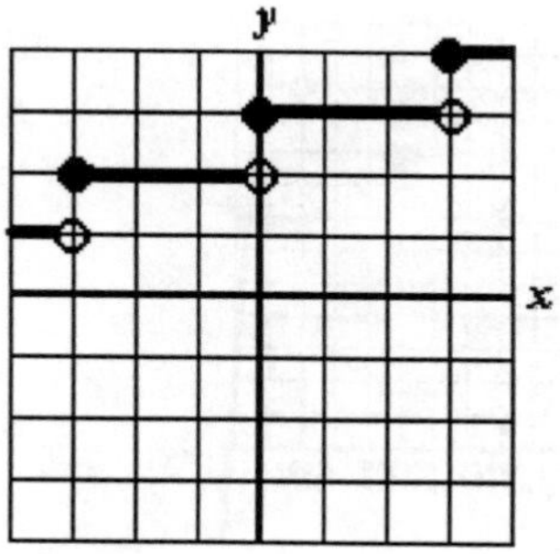

43. $y = [[x]] - 1$

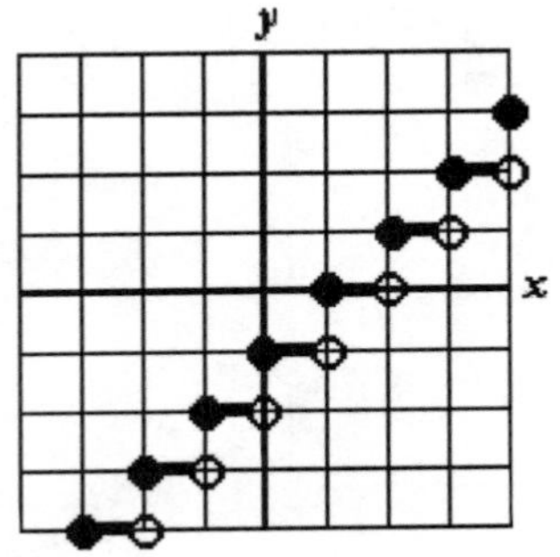

44. $y = [[x + 2]]$

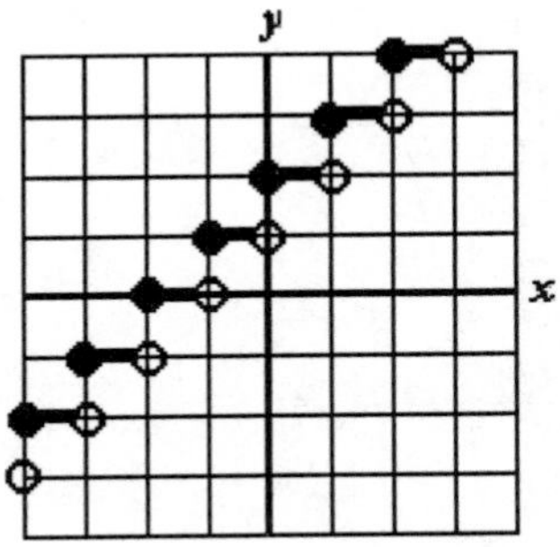

45.

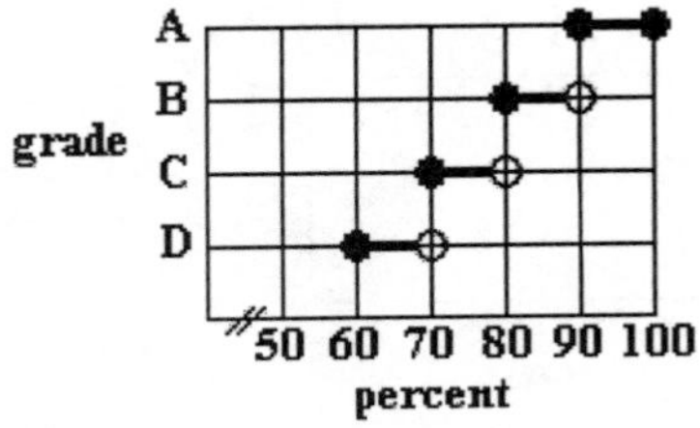

$$\frac{67 + 73 + 84 + 87 + 93}{5} = \frac{404}{5} = 80.8$$

The student's grade is B.

46. Refer to **#45**.

$$\frac{53 + 65 + 64 + 73 + 89 + 82}{6} = \frac{426}{6} = 71$$

The student's grade is C.

47. \$26 for 275 miles

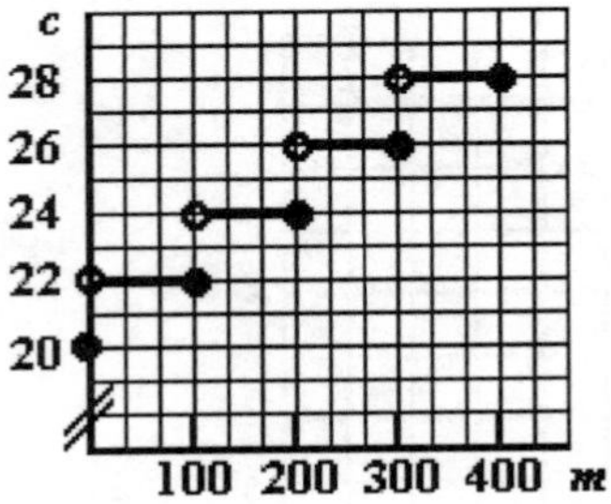

48. \$23 for $10\frac{1}{4}$ miles

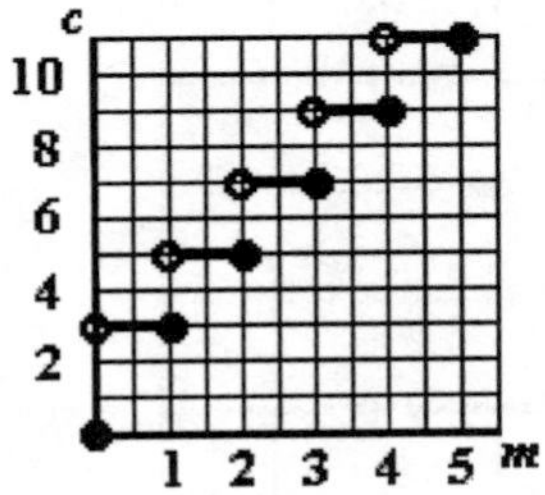

49. \$12 per hour $\Rightarrow$ \$0.20 per minute
\$1.60 for $7\frac{1}{2}$ minutes

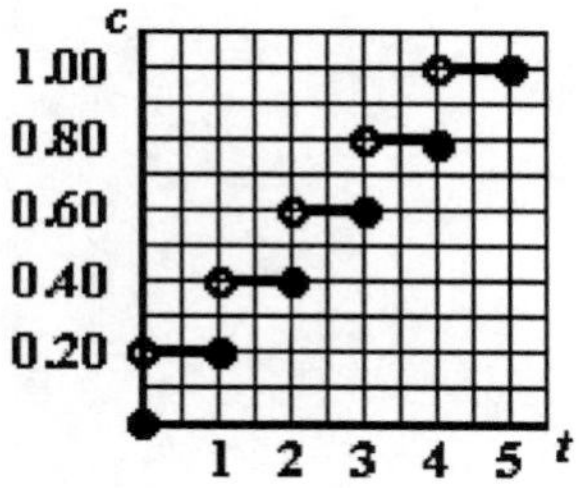

50. \$190 for 4 hours

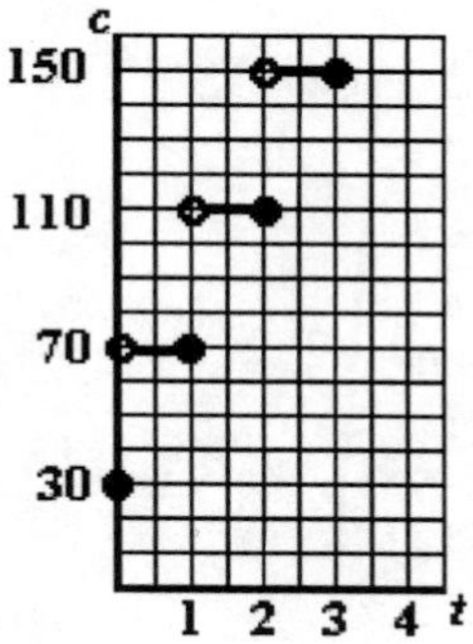

51.

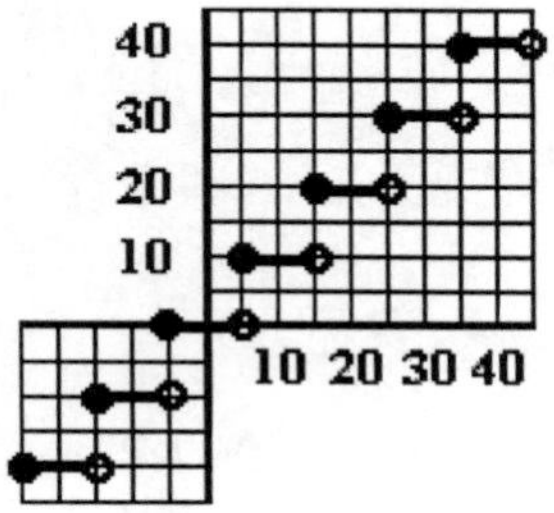

52. $y = \text{sgn } x$

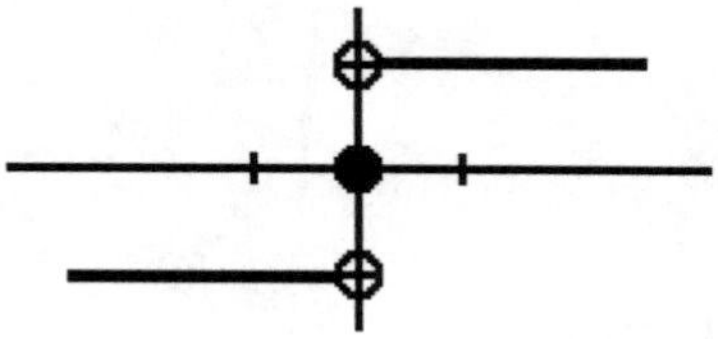

53. $y = \dfrac{|x|}{x}$; NO $\Rightarrow$ not defined at $x = 0$

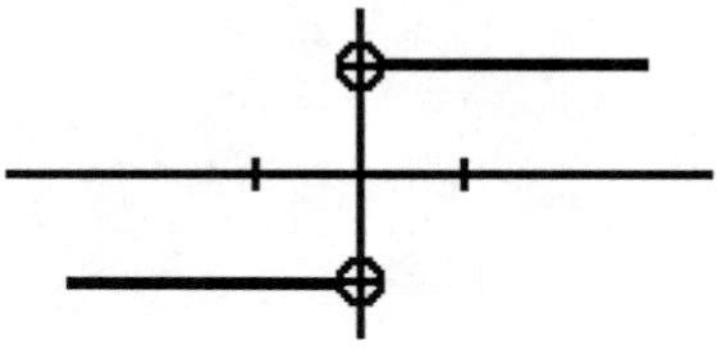

54. $y = x + |x|$

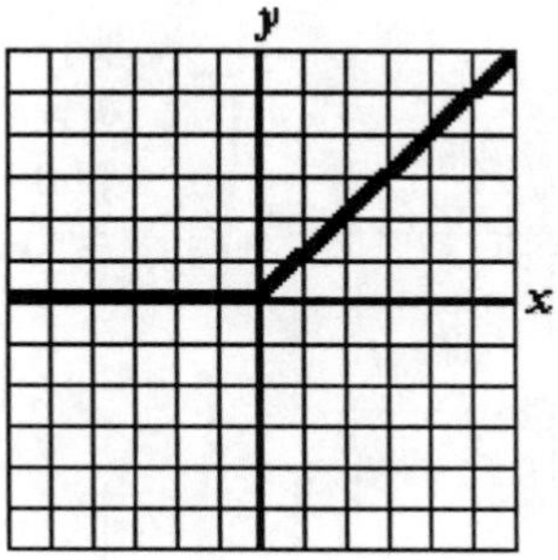

55. **Answers may vary.**

56. **Answers may vary.**

57. **Answers may vary.**

58. **Answers may vary.**

59. $f(x+1) = 3(x+1) + 2 = 3x + 5$
$f(x) + 1 = (3x + 2) + 1 = 3x + 3$

60. $f(x-2) = (x-2)^2 = x^2 - 4x + 4$
$f(x) - 2 = (x^2) - 2 = x^2 - 2$

61. $f(x-3) = \dfrac{3(x-3)+1}{5} = \dfrac{3x-8}{5}$

$f(x) - 3 = \dfrac{3x+1}{5} - 3 = \dfrac{3x-14}{5}$

62. $f(x+8) = 8$

$f(x) + 8 = 8 + 8 = 16$

63.
$$2x^2 - 3 = x$$
$$2x^2 - x - 3 = 0$$
$$(2x-3)(x+1) = 0$$
$$2x = 3 \text{ or } x = -1$$
$$x = \tfrac{3}{2},\ x = -1$$

64. $4x^2 = 24x - 37 \Rightarrow 4x^2 - 24x + 37 = 0 \Rightarrow a = 4,\ b = -24,\ c = 37$

$$x = \frac{-b \pm \sqrt{b^2 - 4ac}}{2a} = \frac{-(-24) \pm \sqrt{(-24)^2 - 4(4)(37)}}{2(4)} = \frac{24 \pm \sqrt{576 - 592}}{8} = \frac{24 \pm \sqrt{-16}}{8}$$
$$= \frac{24 \pm 4i}{8}$$
$$= 3 \pm \tfrac{1}{2}i$$

Exercise 3.4 (page 276)

1. up

2. $f(x) - 7$

3. to the right

4. to the left

5. 2, down

6. right, up

7. y-axis

8. $y = -f(x)$

9. horizontally

10. vertically

11. $y = x^2 - 2$

Shift $y = x^2$ D 2

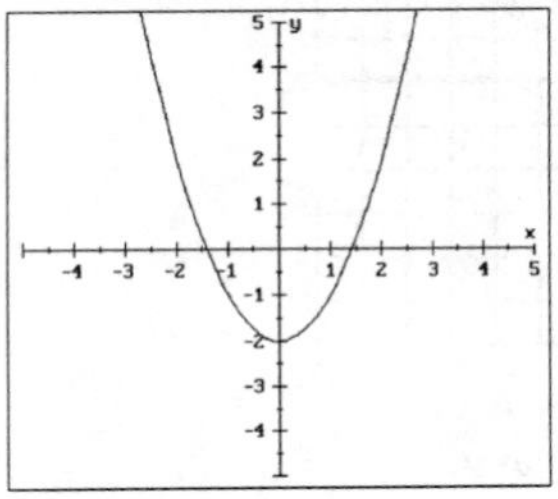

12. $y = (x-2)^2$

Shift $y = x^2$ R 2

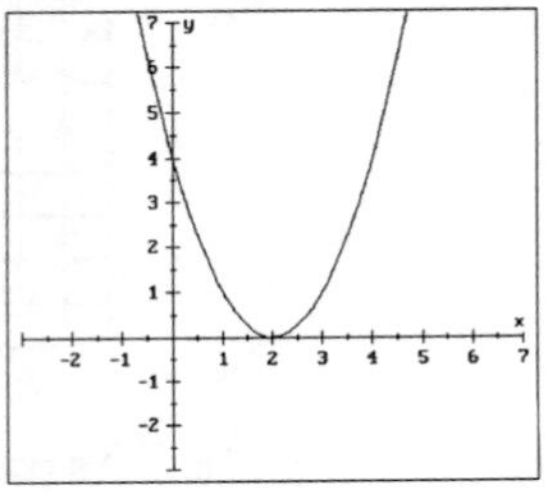

13. $y = (x+3)^2$

Shift $y = x^2$ L 3

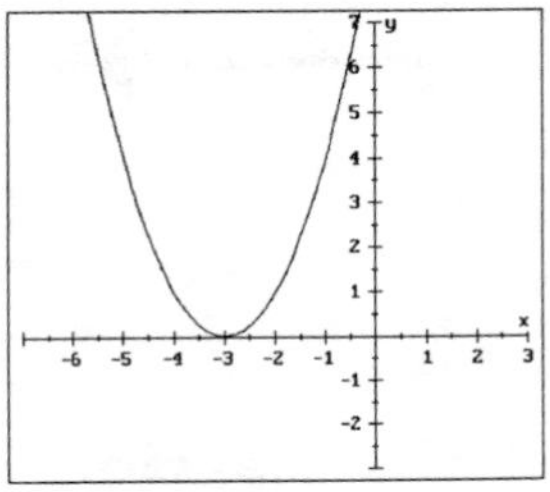

14. $y = x^2 + 3$
Shift $y = x^2$ U 3

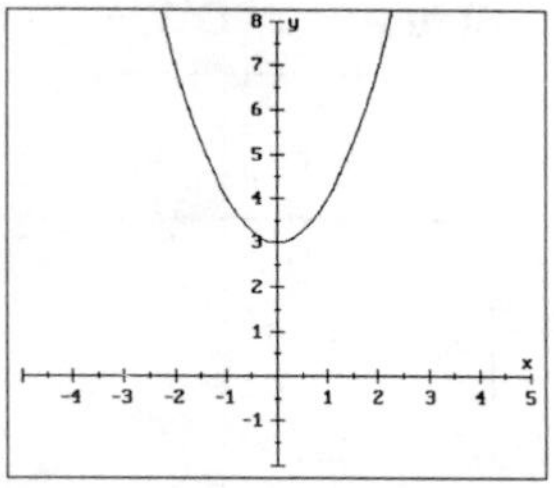

15. $y = (x + 1)^2 + 2$
Shift $y = x^2$ U 2, L 1

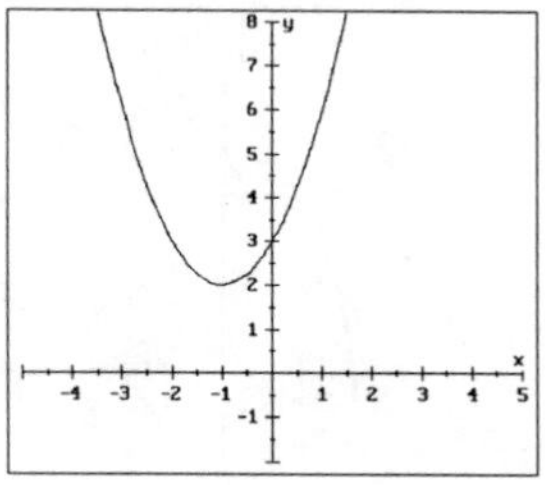

16. $y = (x - 3)^2 - 1$
Shift $y = x^2$ D 1, R 3

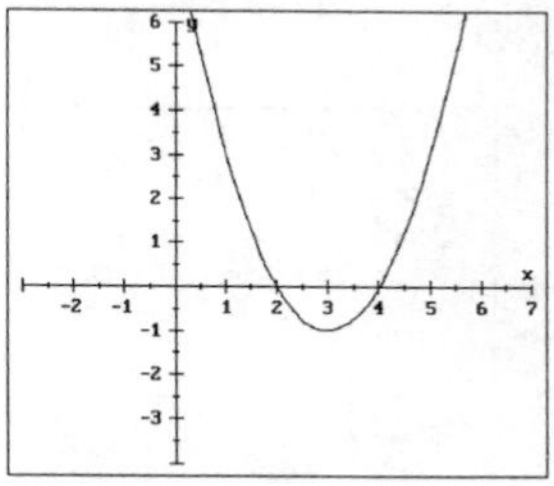

17. $y = \left(x + \frac{1}{2}\right)^2 - \frac{1}{2}$
Shift $y = x^2$ D $\frac{1}{2}$, L $\frac{1}{2}$

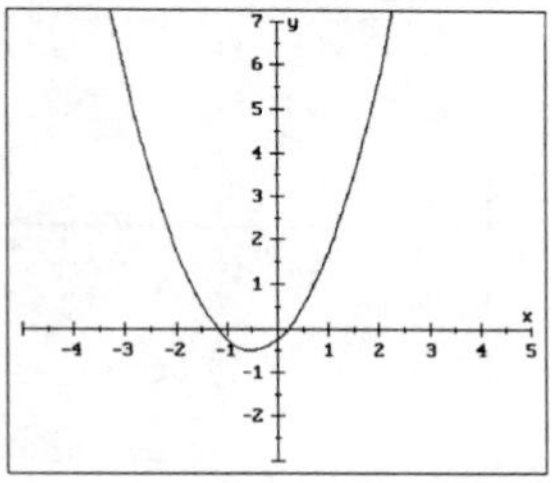

18. $y = \left(x - \frac{3}{2}\right)^2 + \frac{5}{2}$
Shift $y = x^2$ U $\frac{5}{2}$, R $\frac{3}{2}$

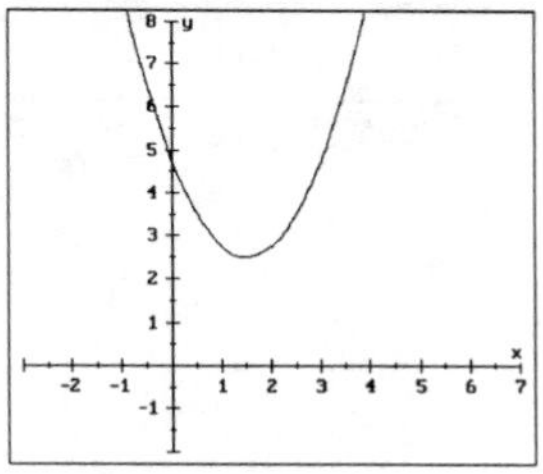

19. $y = x^3 + 1$
Shift $y = x^3$ U 1

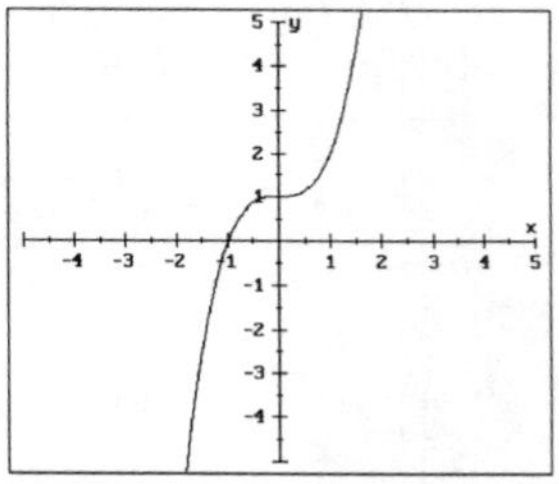

20. $y = x^3 - 3$
Shift $y = x^3$ D 3

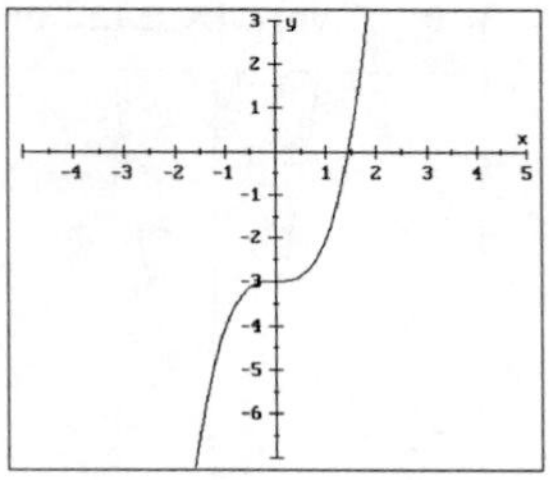

21. $y = (x - 2)^3$
Shift $y = x^3$ R 2

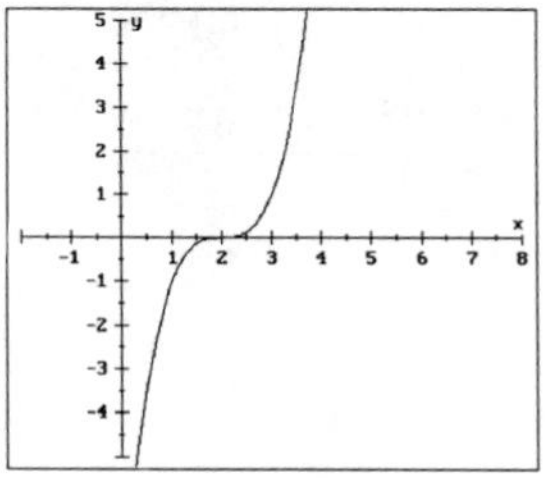

22. $y = (x + 3)^3$
Shift $y = x^3$ L 3

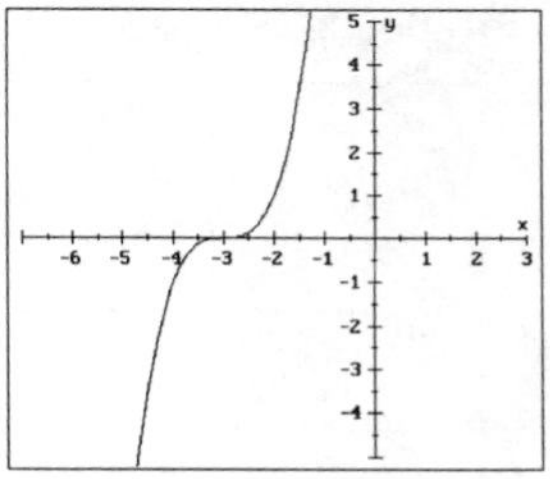

SECTION 3.4

23. $y = (x-2)^3 - 3$
Shift $y = x^3$ D 3, R 2

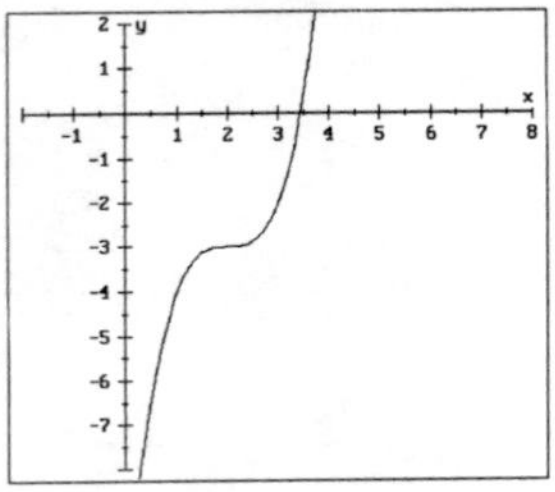

24. $y = (x+1)^3 + 4$
Shift $y = x^3$ U 4, L 1

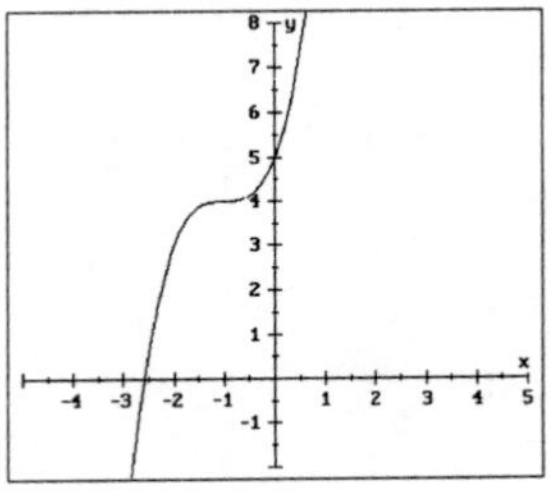

25. $y + 2 = x^3$
$y = x^3 - 2$
Shift $y = x^3$ D 2

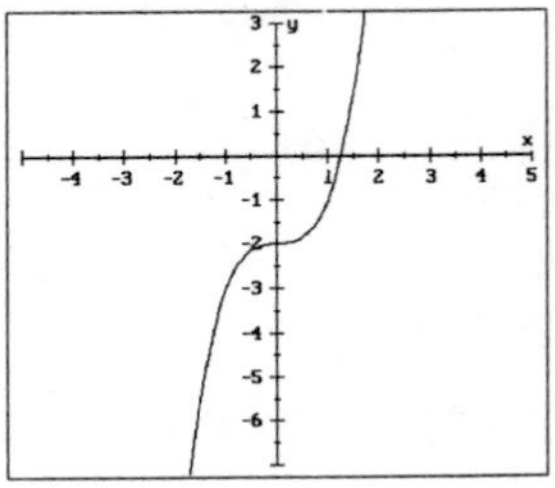

26. $y - 7 = (x-5)^3$
$y = (x-5)^3 + 7$
Shift $y = x^3$ U 7, R 5

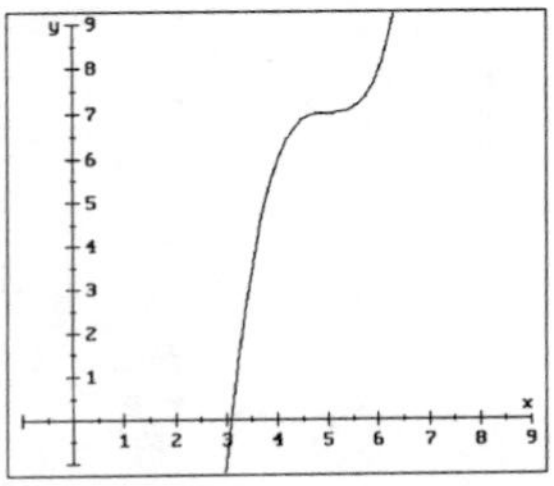

27. $y = -x^2$
Reflect $y = x^2$ about x

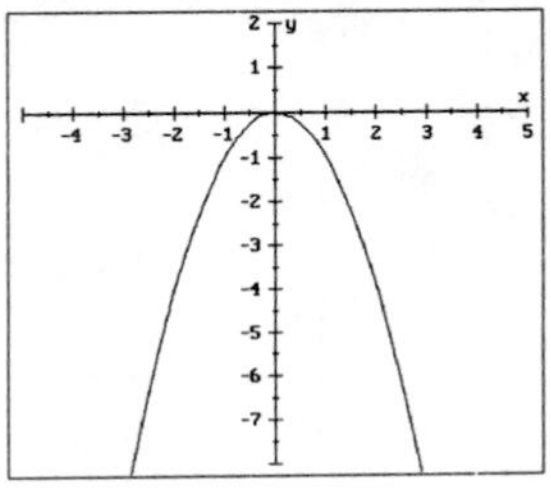

28. $y = (-x)^3$
Reflect $y = x^3$ about y

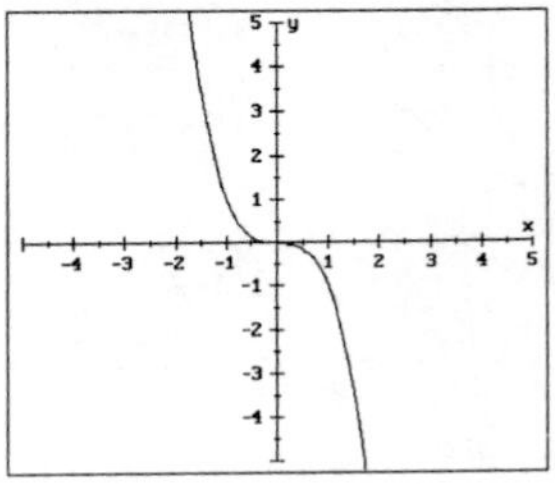

29. $y = -x^3$
Reflect $y = x^3$ about x

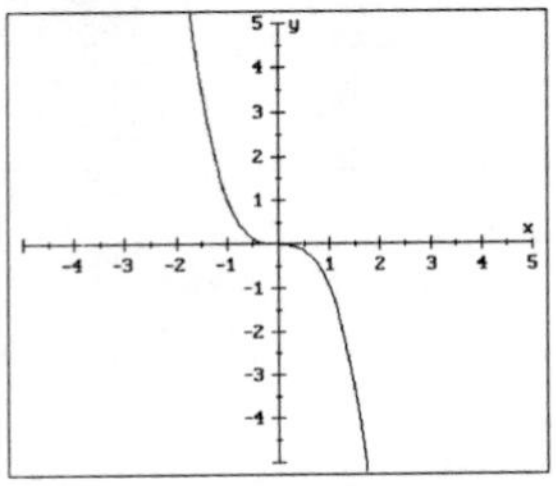

30. $y = (-x-1)^2$
$y = [(-x)-1]^2$
Reflect $y = (x-1)^2$ about y

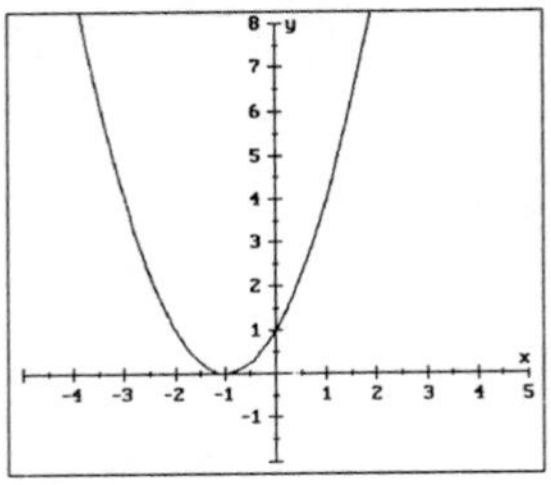

31. $y = 2x^2$: Stretch
$y = x^2$ vert. by a factor of 2

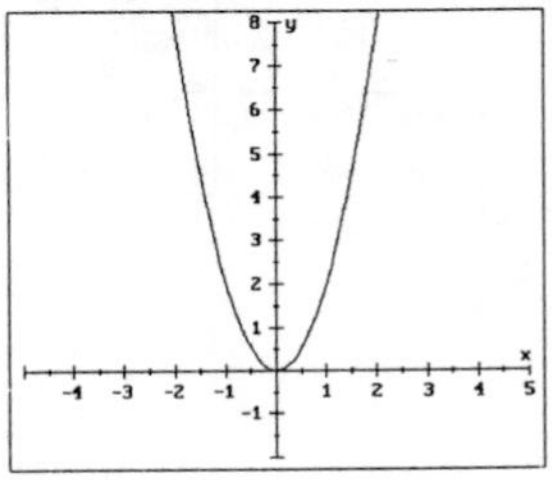

32. $y = \frac{1}{2}x^2$: Stretch
$y = x^2$ vert. by a factor of $\frac{1}{2}$

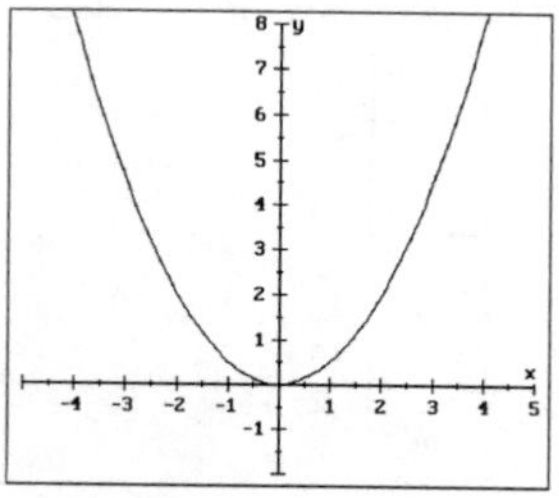

33. $y = -3x^2$: Stretch
$y = x^2$ vert. by a factor of 3
Reflect about x

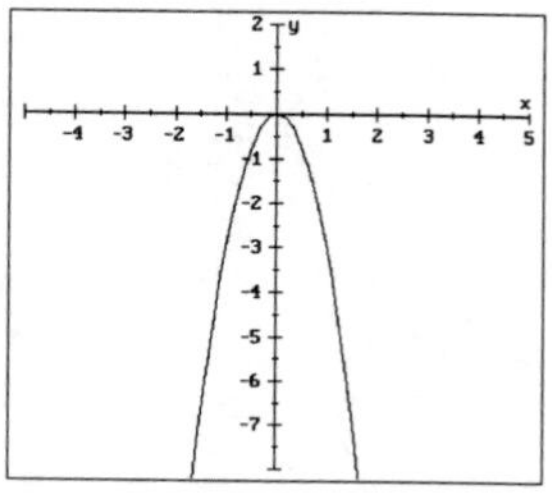

34. $y = -\frac{1}{3}x^2$: Stretch
$y = x^2$ vert. by a factor of $\frac{1}{3}$
Reflect about x

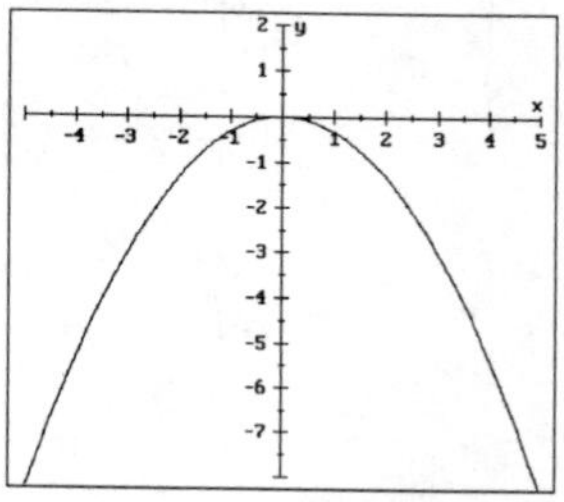

35. $y = \left(\frac{1}{2}x\right)^3$: Stretch
$y = x^3$ hor. by a factor of 2

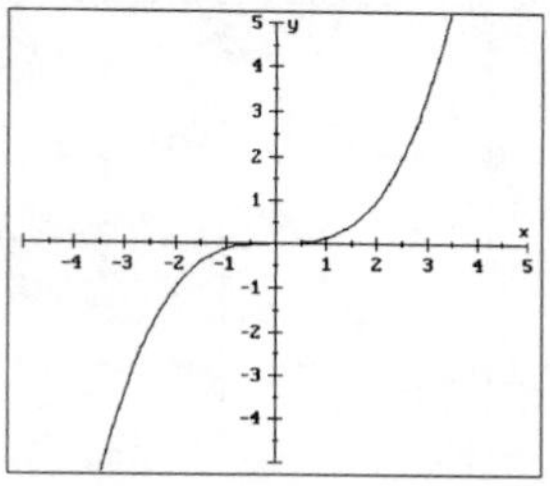

36. $y = \frac{1}{8}x^3$: Stretch
$y = x^3$ vert. by a factor of $\frac{1}{8}$

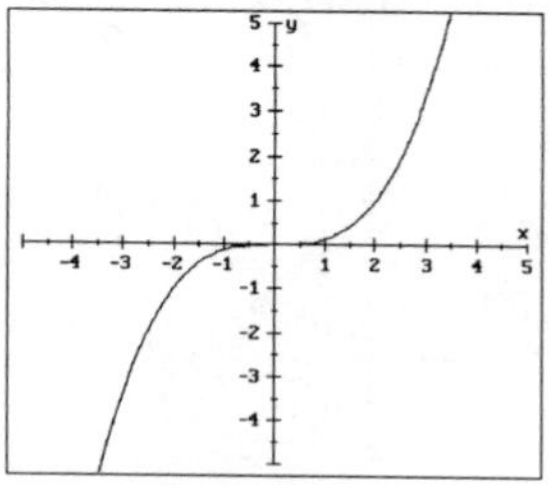

37. $y = -8x^3$: Stretch
$y = x^3$ vert. by a factor of 8
Reflect about x

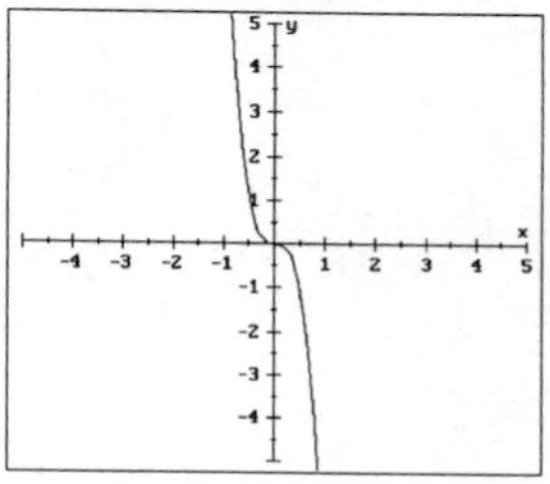

38. $y = (-2x)^3$: Stretch
$y = x^3$ hor. by a factor of $\frac{1}{2}$
Reflect about y

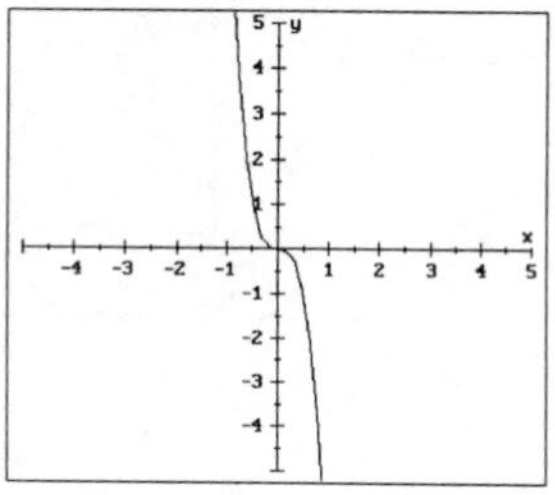

39. $y = |x - 2| + 1$
Shift $y = |x|$ U 1, R 2

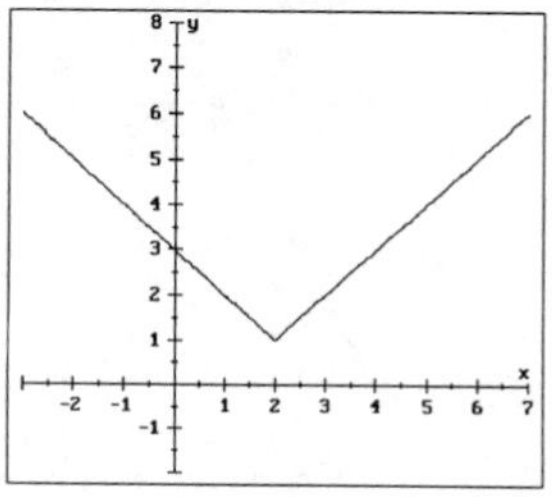

40. $y = |x + 5| - 2$
Shift $y = |x|$ D 2, L 5

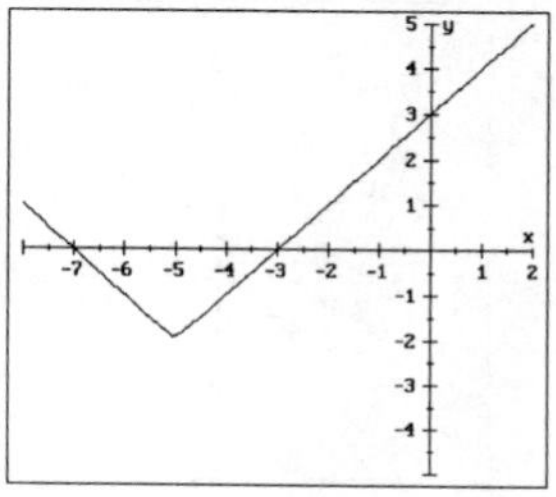

41. $y = |3x|$: Stretch $y = |x|$ hor. by a factor of $\frac{1}{3}$

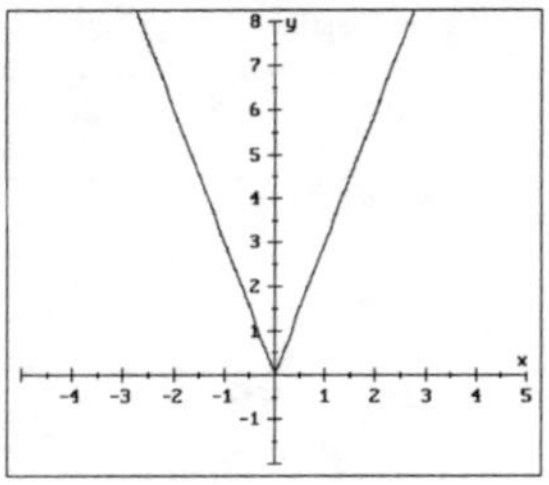

42. $y = 3|x|$: Stretch $y = |x|$ vert. by a factor of 3

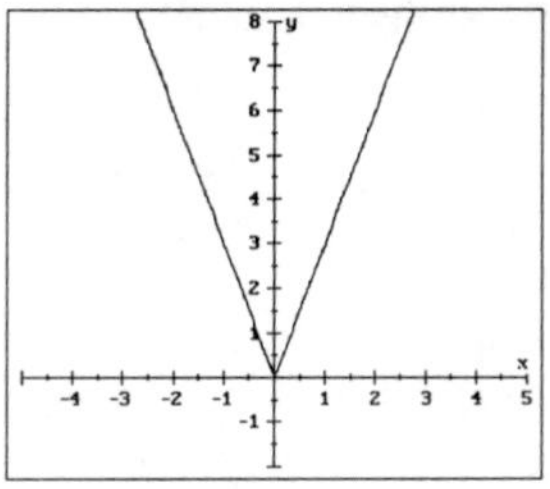

43. $y = \sqrt{x-2} + 1$ Shift $y = \sqrt{x}$ U 1, R 2

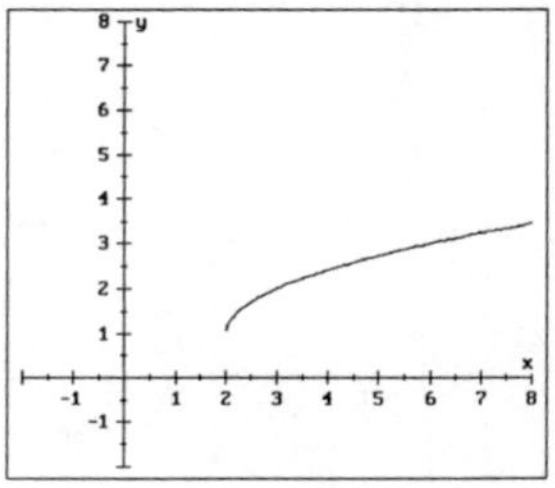

44. $y = \sqrt{x+5} - 2$ Shift $y = \sqrt{x}$ D 2, L 5

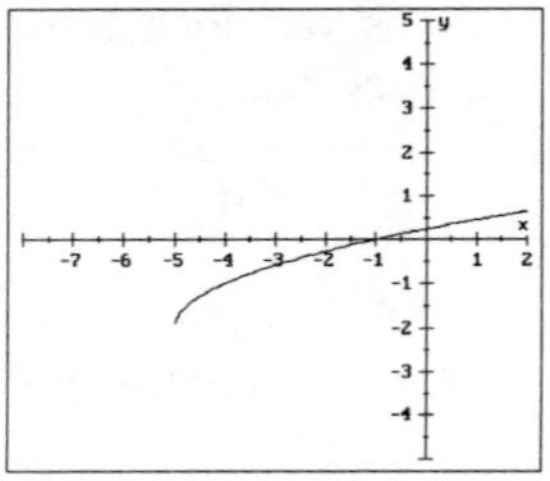

45. $y = 2\sqrt{x} + 3$: Stretch $y = \sqrt{x}$ vert. by a factor of 2; Shift U 3

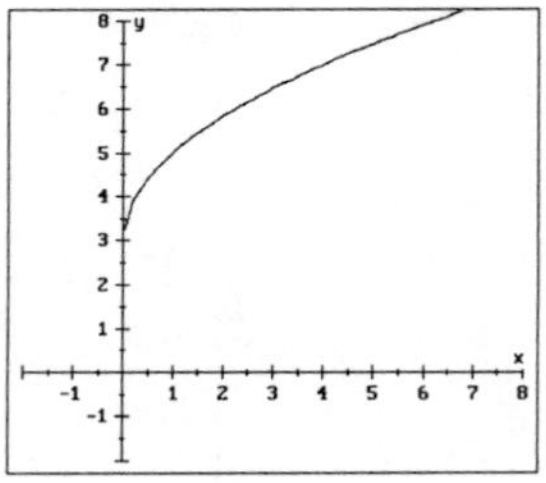

46. $y = 2\sqrt{x+3}$: Stretch $y = \sqrt{x}$ vert. by a factor of 2; Shift L 3

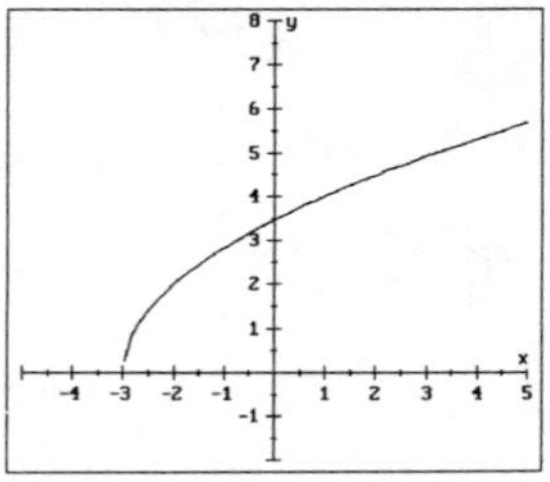

47. $y = -2|x| + 3$: Stretch $y = |x|$ vert. by a factor of 2; Reflect x; Shift U 3

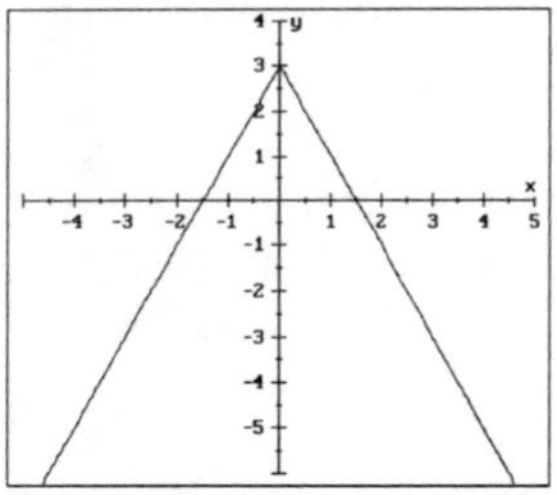

48. $y = -2|x+3|$: Stretch $y = |x|$ vert. by a factor of 2; Reflect x; Shift L 3

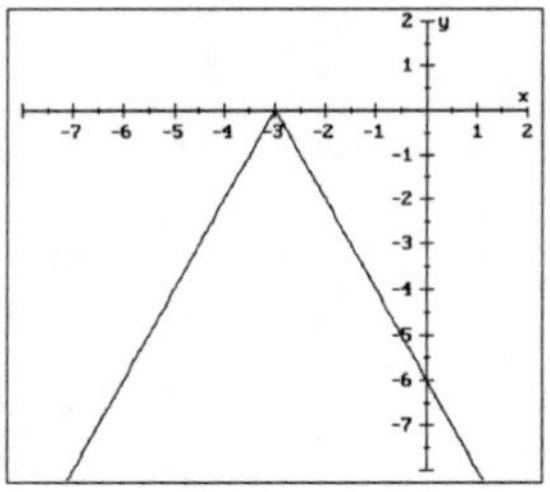

49. Shift $y = f(x)$ U 1

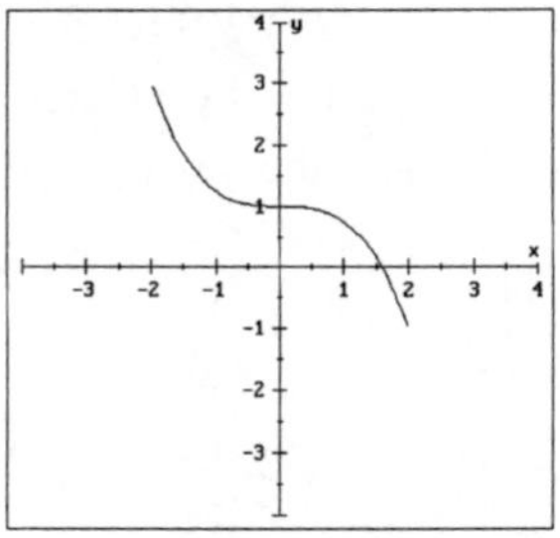

50. Shift $y = f(x)$ L 1

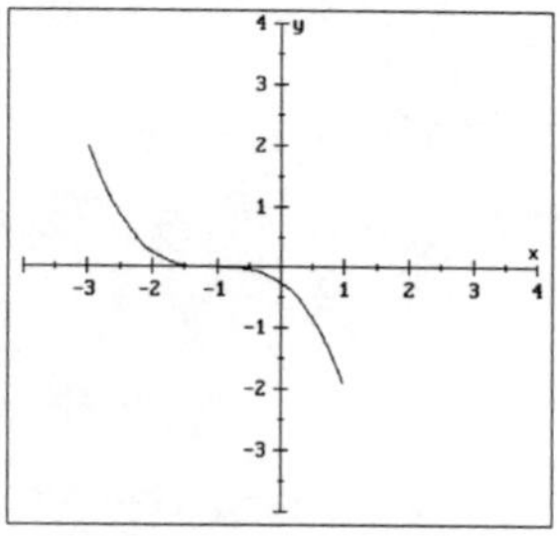

51. Stretch $y = f(x)$ vert. by a factor of 2

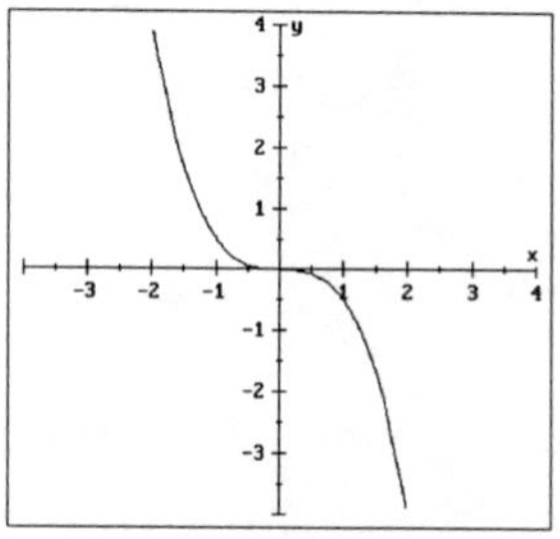

52. Stretch $y = f(x)$ hor. by a factor of 2

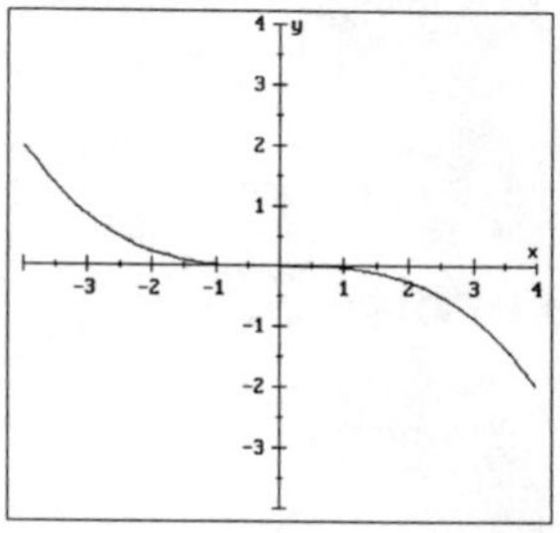

53. Shift $y = f(x)$ U 1, 2 R

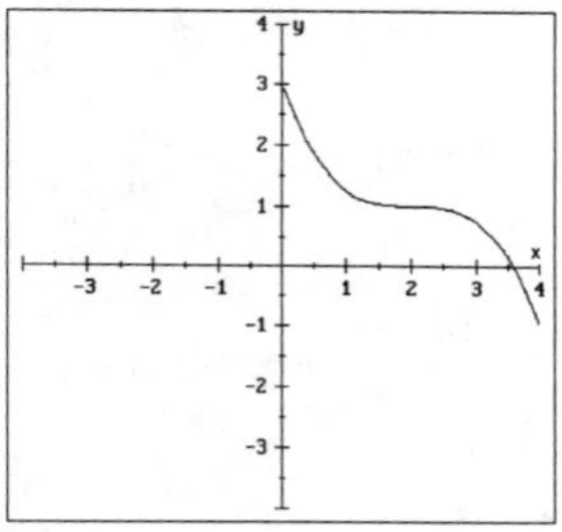

54. Reflect $y = f(x)$ about x

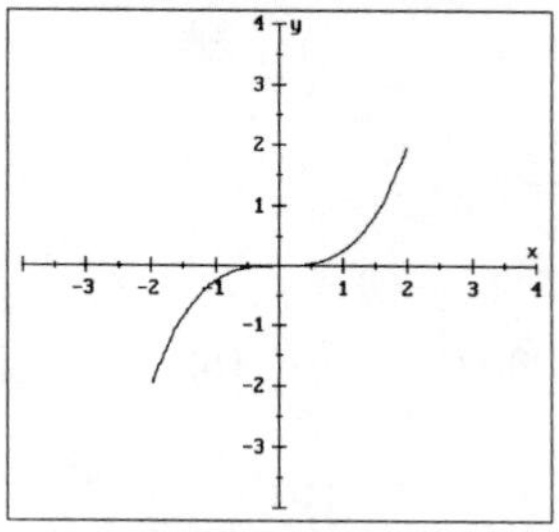

55. Stretch $y = f(x)$ vert. by a factor of 2, reflect about y

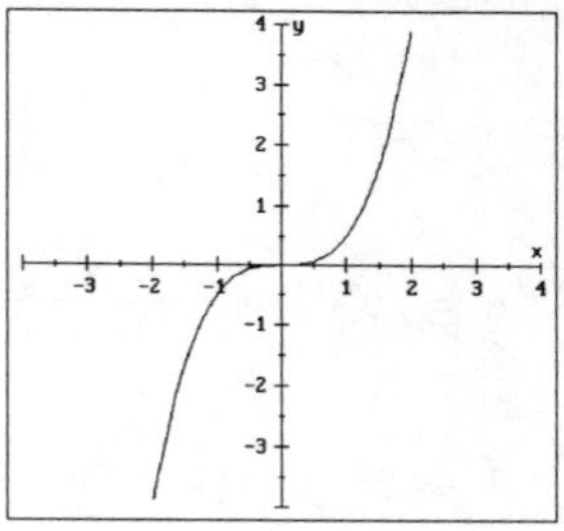

56. Shift $y = f(x)$ D 2, L 1

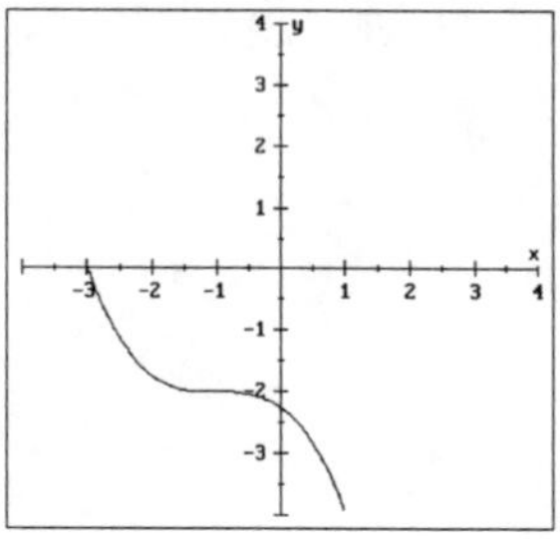

57. **Answers may vary.**

58. **Answers may vary.**

59. **Answers may vary.**

60. **Answers may vary.**

61. **Answers may vary.**

62. **Answers may vary.**

63. $\dfrac{x^2+x-6}{x^2+5x+6} = \dfrac{(x+3)(x-2)}{(x+2)(x+3)} = \dfrac{x-2}{x+2}$

64. $\dfrac{2x^2+3x}{2x^2+x-3} = \dfrac{x(2x+3)}{(2x+3)(x-1)} = \dfrac{x}{x-1}$

65. $f(x) = \dfrac{x+7}{x-3}$; domain $= (-\infty, 3) \cup (3, \infty)$

66. $f(x) = \dfrac{x^2+1}{x^2+3x+2} = \dfrac{x^2+1}{(x+2)(x+1)}$
domain $= (-\infty, -2) \cup (-2, -1) \cup (-1, \infty)$

67.
$$\begin{array}{r|l} & x + \ 2 + \frac{-2}{x+1} \\ \hline x+1 & x^2+3x+\ \ 0 \\ & \underline{x^2+\ x} \\ & \quad 2x+\ \ 0 \\ & \quad \underline{2x+\ \ 2} \\ & \qquad -2 \end{array}$$

68.
$$\begin{array}{r|l} & x - \ 1 + \frac{4}{x+1} \\ \hline x+1 & x^2+0x+\ \ 3 \\ & \underline{x^2+\ x} \\ & \quad -x+\ \ 3 \\ & \quad \underline{-x-\ \ 1} \\ & \qquad\quad 4 \end{array}$$

Exercise 3.5 (page 290)

1. asymptote **2.** nonzero **3.** vertical **4.** y-intercept

5. x-intercept **6.** $y = 0$ **7.** the same **8.** slant asymptote

9. horizontal **10.** missing **11.** $t = f(30) = \frac{600}{30} = 20$ hr

12. $t = f(40) = \frac{600}{40} = 15$ hr **13.** $t = f(50) = \frac{600}{50} = 12$ hr **14.** $t = f(60) = \frac{600}{60} = 10$ hr

15. $c = f(10) = \dfrac{50{,}000(10)}{100 - 10} \approx \$5555.56$

16. $c = f(30) = \dfrac{50{,}000(30)}{100 - 30} \approx \$21{,}428.57$

17. $c = f(50) = \dfrac{50{,}000(50)}{100 - 50} = \$50{,}000.00$

18. $c = f(80) = \dfrac{50{,}000(80)}{100 - 80} = \$200{,}000.00$

19. $f(x) = \dfrac{x^2}{x - 2}$; domain $= (-\infty, 2) \cup (2, \infty)$

20. $f(x) = \dfrac{x^3 - 3x^2 + 1}{x + 3}$
domain $= (-\infty, -3) \cup (-3, \infty)$

21. $f(x) = \dfrac{2x^2 + 7x - 2}{x^2 - 25} = \dfrac{2x^2 + 7x - 2}{(x + 5)(x - 5)}$
domain $= (-\infty, -5) \cup (-5, 5) \cup (5, \infty)$

22. $\dfrac{5x^2 + 1}{x^2 + 5}$; domain $= (-\infty, \infty)$

23. $f(x) = \dfrac{x - 1}{x^3 - x} = \dfrac{x - 1}{x(x + 1)(x - 1)}$; domain $= (-\infty, -1) \cup (-1, 0) \cup (0, 1) \cup (1, \infty)$

24. $f(x) = \dfrac{x + 2}{2x^2 - 9x + 9} = \dfrac{x + 2}{(2x - 3)(x - 3)}$; domain $= \left(-\infty, \dfrac{3}{2}\right) \cup \left(\dfrac{3}{2}, 3\right) \cup (3, \infty)$

25. $\dfrac{3x^2 + 5}{x^2 + 1}$; domain $= (-\infty, \infty)$

26. $\dfrac{7x^2 - x + 2}{x^4 + 4}$; domain $= (-\infty, \infty)$

27. $y = \dfrac{1}{x-2}$
Vertical: $x = 2$; Horizontal: $y = 0$
Slant: none; x-intercepts: none
y-intercepts: $\left(0, -\frac{1}{2}\right)$; Symmetry: none

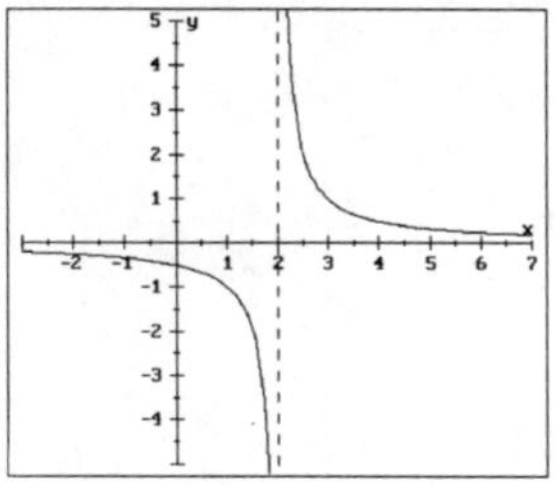

28. $y = \dfrac{3}{x+3}$
Vertical: $x = -3$; Horizontal: $y = 0$
Slant: none; x-intercepts: none
y-intercepts: $(0, 1)$; Symmetry: none

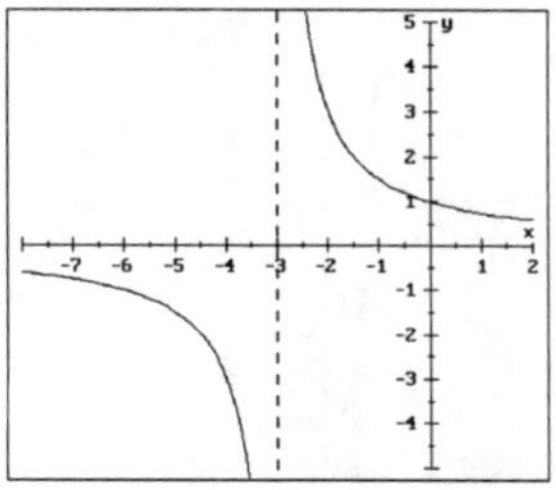

29. $y = \dfrac{x}{x-1} = 1 + \dfrac{1}{x-1}$
Vertical: $x = 1$; Horizontal: $y = 1$
Slant: none; x-intercepts: $(0, 0)$
y-intercepts: $(0, 0)$; Symmetry: none

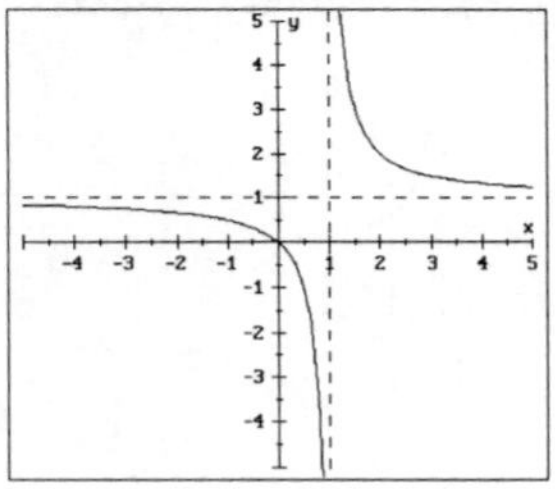

30. $y = \dfrac{x}{x+2} = 1 + \dfrac{-2}{x+2}$
Vertical: $x = -2$; Horizontal: $y = 1$
Slant: none; x-intercepts: $(0, 0)$
y-intercepts: $(0, 0)$; Symmetry: none

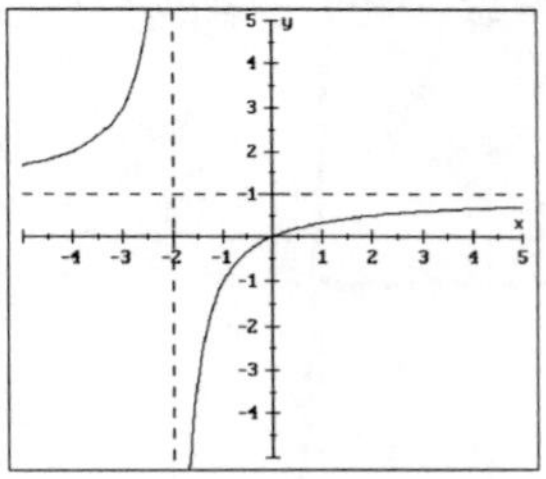

31. $y = \dfrac{x+1}{x+2} = 1 + \dfrac{-1}{x+2}$
Vertical: $x = -2$; Horizontal: $y = 1$
Slant: none; x-intercepts: $(-1, 0)$
y-intercepts: $\left(0, \frac{1}{2}\right)$; Symmetry: none

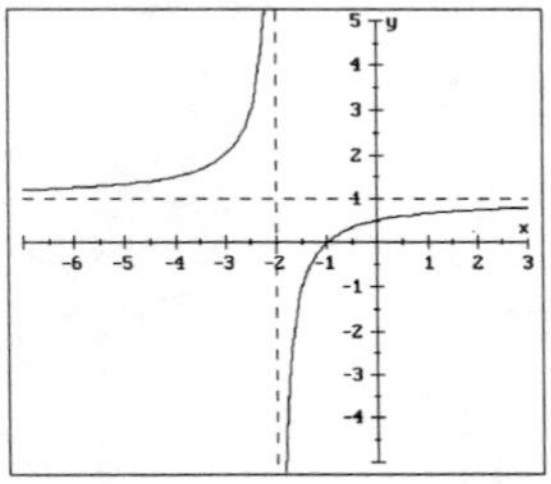

32. $y = \dfrac{x-1}{x-2} = 1 + \dfrac{1}{x-2}$
Vertical: $x = 2$; Horizontal: $y = 1$
Slant: none; x-intercepts: $(1, 0)$
y-intercepts: $\left(0, \frac{1}{2}\right)$; Symmetry: none

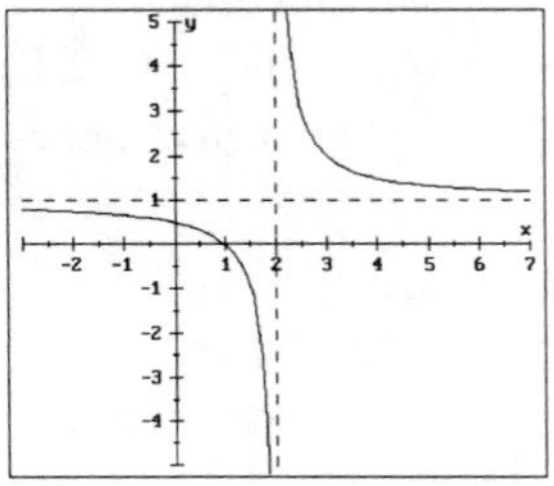

33. $y = \dfrac{2x-1}{x-1} = 2 + \dfrac{1}{x-1}$
Vertical: $x = 1$; Horizontal: $y = 2$
Slant: none; x-intercepts: $\left(\frac{1}{2}, 0\right)$
y-intercepts: $(0, 1)$; Symmetry: none

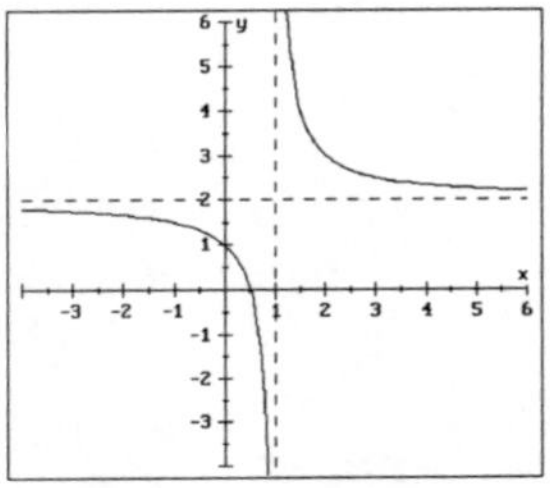

34. $y = \dfrac{3x+2}{x^2-4} = \dfrac{3x+2}{(x+2)(x-2)}$
Vertical: $x = -2$, $x = 2$; Horizontal: $y = 0$
Slant: none; x-intercepts: $\left(-\frac{2}{3}, 0\right)$
y-intercepts: $\left(0, -\frac{1}{2}\right)$; Symmetry: none

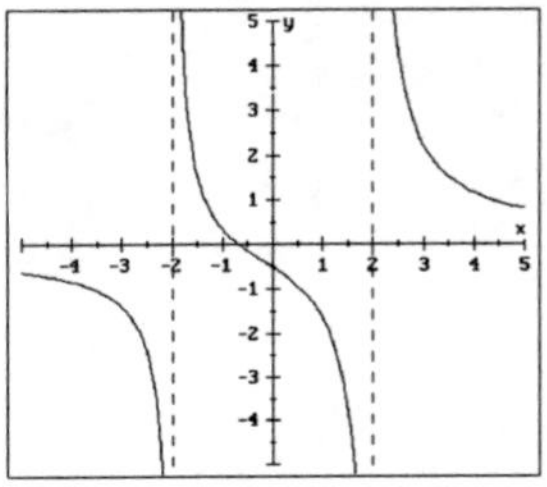

35. $y = \dfrac{x^2-9}{x^2-4} = \dfrac{(x+3)(x-3)}{(x+2)(x-2)} = 1 + \frac{-5}{x^2-4}$
Vertical: $x = -2$, $x = 2$; Horizontal: $y = 1$
Slant: none; x-intercepts: $(-3, 0)$, $(3, 0)$
y-intercepts: $\left(0, \frac{9}{4}\right)$; Symmetry: y-axis

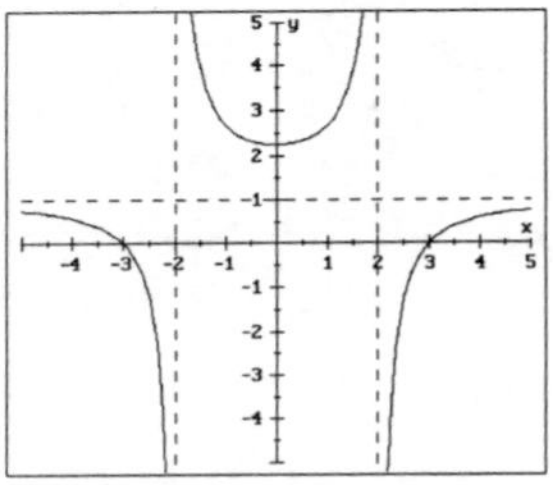

36. $y = \dfrac{x^2-4}{x^2-9} = \dfrac{(x+2)(x-2)}{(x+3)(x-3)} = 1 + \frac{5}{x^2-9}$
Vertical: $x = -3$, $x = 3$; Horizontal: $y = 1$
Slant: none; x-intercepts: $(-2, 0)$, $(2, 0)$
y-intercepts: $\left(0, \frac{4}{9}\right)$; Symmetry: y-axis

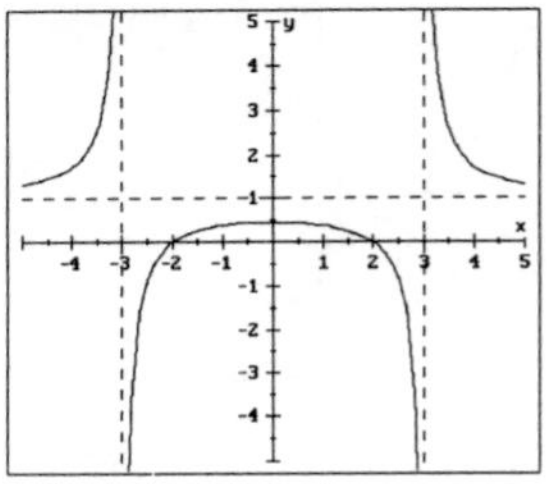

37. $y = \dfrac{x^2-x-2}{x^2-4x+3} = \dfrac{(x+1)(x-2)}{(x-3)(x-1)}$
$= 1 + \dfrac{3x-5}{x^2-4x+3}$
Vertical: $x = 3$, $x = 1$; Horizontal: $y = 1$
Slant: none; x-intercepts: $(-1, 0)$, $(2, 0)$
y-intercepts: $\left(0, -\frac{2}{3}\right)$; Symmetry: none

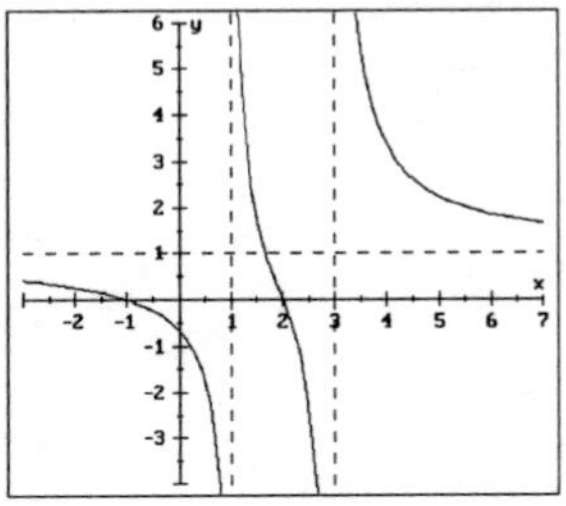

38. $y = \dfrac{x^2+7x+12}{x^2-7x+12} = \dfrac{(x+3)(x+4)}{(x-3)(x-4)}$
$= 1 + \dfrac{14x}{x^2-7x+12}$

Vertical: $x = 3$, $x = 4$; Horizontal: $y = 1$
Slant: none; x-intercepts: $(-3, 0)$, $(-4, 0)$
y-intercepts: $(0, 1)$; Symmetry: none

Because of the differences in scale, 3 different views of the graph are needed to see all of the characteristic parts of the graph:

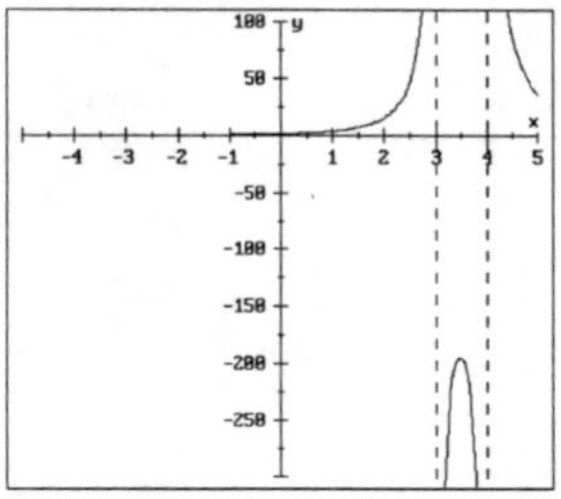

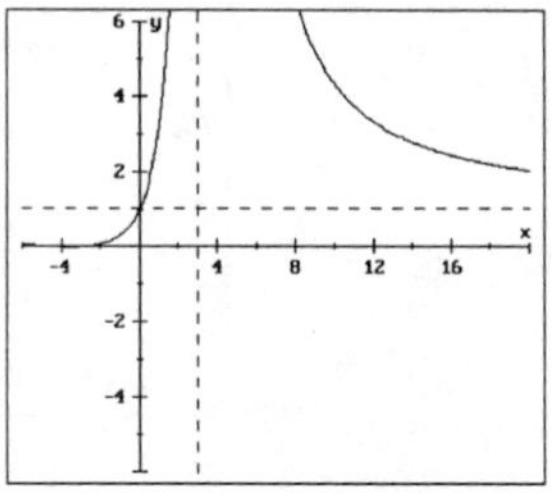

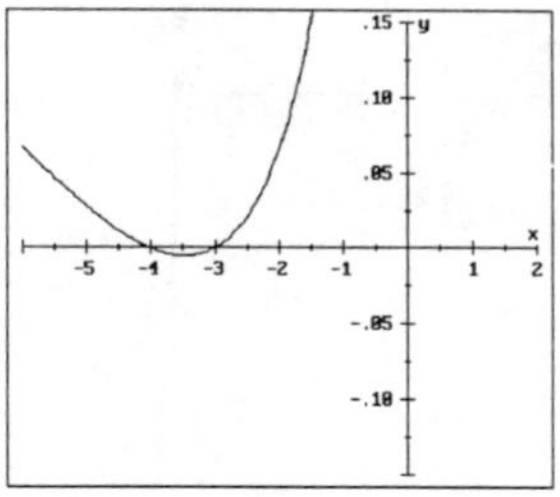

39. $y = \dfrac{x^2+2x-3}{x^3-4x} = \dfrac{(x-1)(x+3)}{x(x+2)(x-2)}$

Vert: $x = 0$, $x = -2$, $x = 2$; Horiz: $y = 0$
Slant: none; x-intercepts: $(1, 0)$, $(-3, 0)$
y-intercepts: none; Symmetry: none

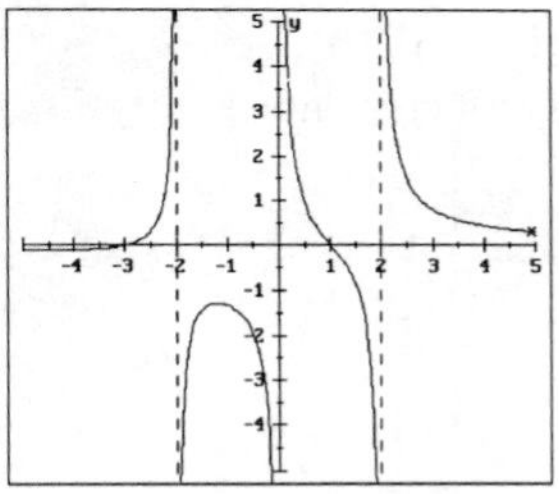

40. $y = \dfrac{3x^2-4x+1}{2x^3+3x^2+x} = \dfrac{(3x-1)(x-1)}{x(2x+1)(x+1)}$

Vert: $x = 0$, $x = -\frac{1}{2}$, $x = -1$; Horiz: $y = 0$
y-intercepts: none; Symmetry: none
Slant: none; x-intercepts: $\left(\frac{1}{3}, 0\right)$, $(1, 0)$

Because of the differences in scale, 2 different views of the graph are needed to see all of the characteristic parts of the graph:

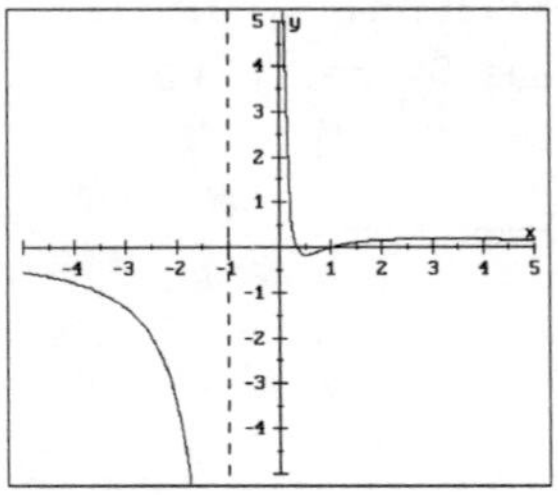

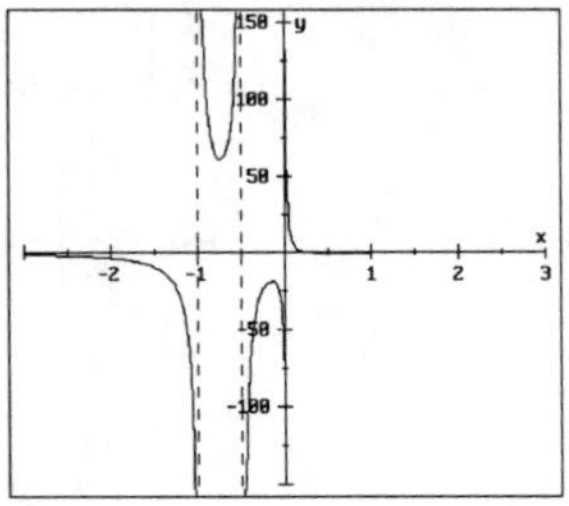

41. $y = \dfrac{x^2 - 9}{x^2} = \dfrac{(x+3)(x-3)}{x^2} = 1 + \frac{-9}{x^2}$

Vert: $x = 0$; Horiz: $y = 1$
Slant: none; x-intercepts: $(3, 0)$, $(-3, 0)$
y-intercepts: none; Symmetry: y-axis

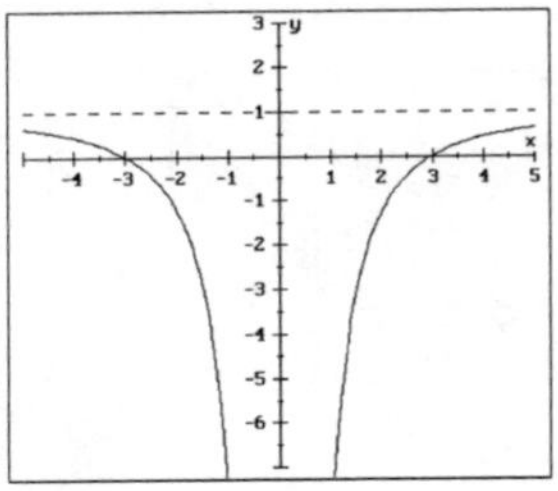

42. $y = \dfrac{3x^2 - 12}{x^2} = \dfrac{3(x+2)(x-2)}{x^2} = 3 + \frac{-12}{x^2}$

Vert: $x = 0$; Horiz: $y = 3$
Slant: none; x-intercepts: $(2, 0)$, $(-2, 0)$
y-intercepts: none; Symmetry: y-axis

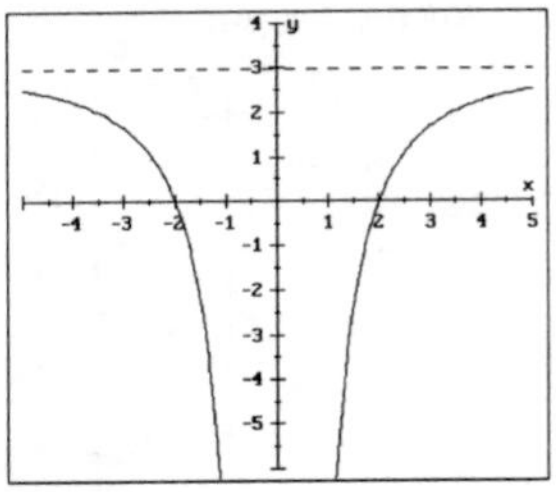

43. $y = \dfrac{x}{(x+3)^2}$

Vert: $x = -3$; Horiz: $y = 0$
Slant: none; x-intercepts: $(0, 0)$
y-intercepts: $(0, 0)$; Symmetry: none

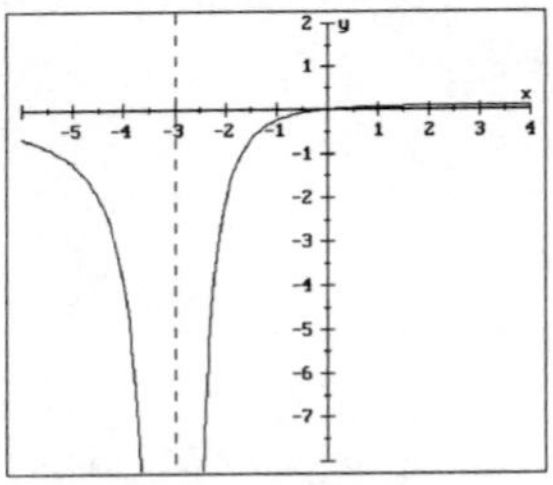

44. $y = \dfrac{x}{(x-1)^2}$

Vert: $x = 1$; Horiz: $y = 0$
Slant: none; x-intercepts: $(0, 0)$
y-intercepts: $(0, 0)$; Symmetry: none

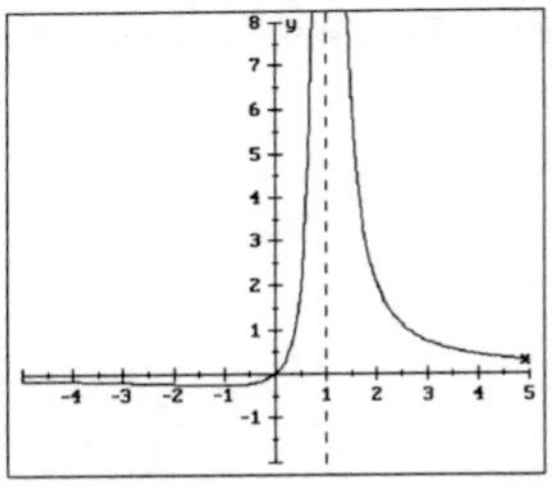

45. $y = \dfrac{x+1}{x^2(x-2)}$

Vert: $x = 0$, $x = 2$; Horiz: $y = 0$
Slant: none; x-intercepts: $(-1, 0)$
y-intercepts: none; Symmetry: none

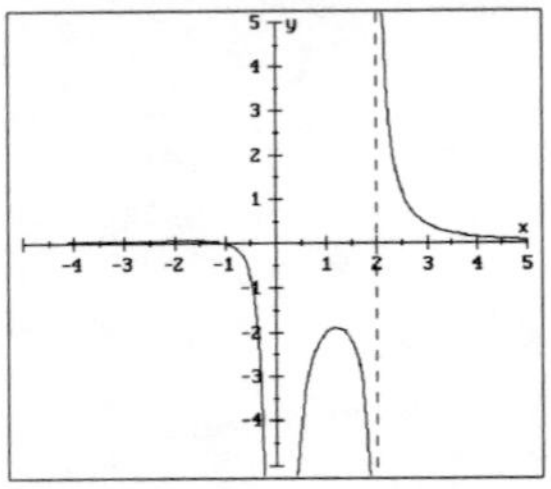

46. $y = \dfrac{x-1}{x^2(x+2)^2}$

Vert: $x = 0$, $x = -2$; Horiz: $y = 0$
Slant: none; x-intercepts: $(1, 0)$
y-intercepts: none; Symmetry: none

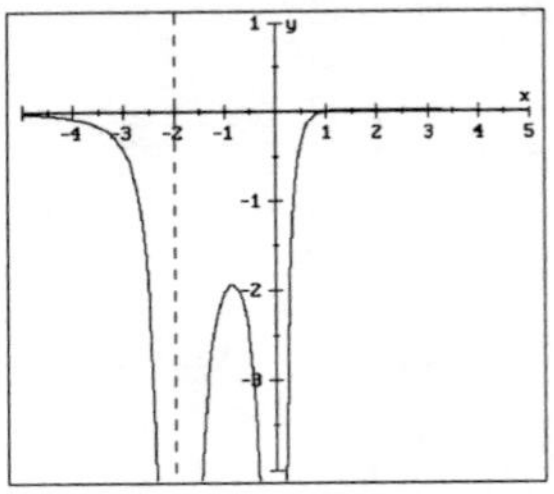

47. $y = \dfrac{x}{x^2+1}$

Vert: none; Horiz: $y = 0$

Slant: none; x-intercepts: $(0, 0)$

y-intercepts: $(0, 0)$; Symmetry: origin

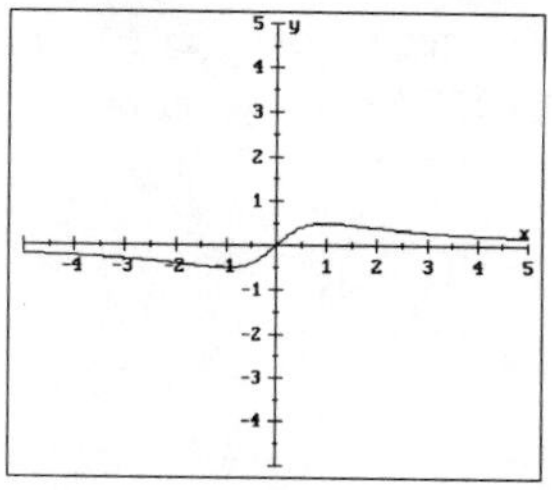

48. $y = \dfrac{x-1}{x^2+2}$

Vert: none; Horiz: $y = 0$

Slant: none; x-intercepts: $(1, 0)$

y-intercepts: $\left(0, -\frac{1}{2}\right)$; Symmetry: none

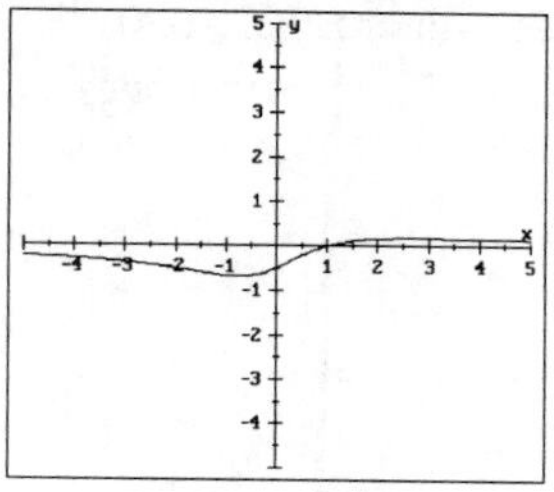

49. $y = \dfrac{3x^2}{x^2+1} = 3 + \dfrac{-3}{x^2+1}$

Vert: none; Horiz: $y = 3$

Slant: none; x-intercepts: $(0, 0)$

y-intercepts: $(0, 0)$; Symmetry: y-axis

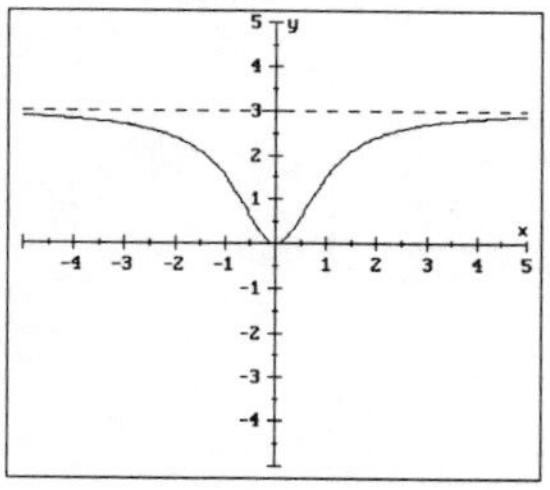

50. $y = \dfrac{x^2-9}{2x^2+1} = \dfrac{(x+3)(x-3)}{2x^2+1} = \frac{1}{2} + \frac{-19/2}{2x^2+1}$

Vert: none; Horiz: $y = \frac{1}{2}$

Slant: none; x-intercepts: $(3, 0)$, $(-3, 0)$

y-intercepts: $(0, -9)$; Symmetry: y-axis

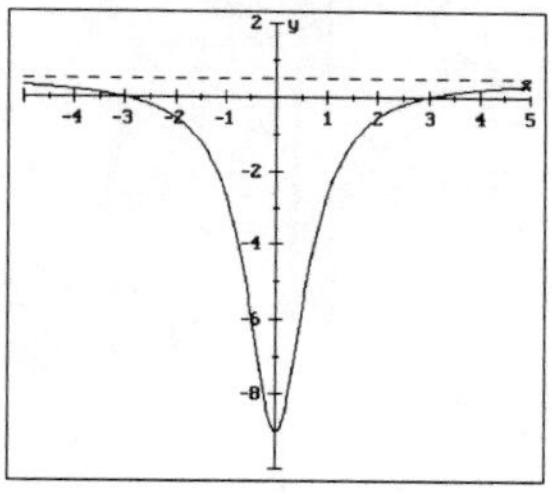

51. $y = \dfrac{x^2-2x-8}{x-1} = \dfrac{(x+2)(x-4)}{x-1}$

$= x - 1 + \dfrac{-9}{x-1}$

Vert: $x = 1$; Horiz: none; Slant: $y = x - 1$

x-intercepts: $(4, 0)$, $(-2, 0)$

y-intercepts: $(0, 8)$; Symmetry: none

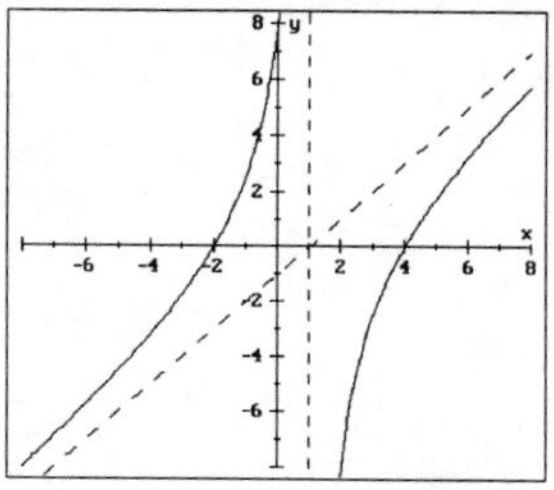

52. $y = \dfrac{x^2+x-6}{x+2} = \dfrac{(x+3)(x-2)}{x+2}$

$= x - 1 + \dfrac{-4}{x+2}$

Vert: $x = -2$; Horiz: none; Slant: $y = x - 1$

x-intercepts: $(2, 0)$, $(-3, 0)$

y-intercepts: $(0, -3)$; Symmetry: none

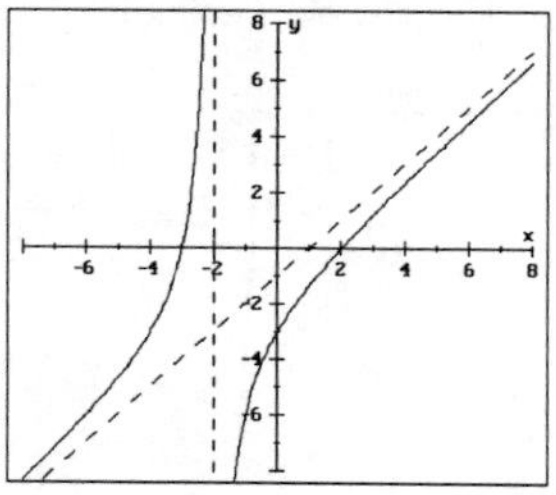

53. $y = \dfrac{x^3 + x^2 + 6x}{x^2 - 1} = \dfrac{x(x^2 + x + 6)}{(x+1)(x-1)} = x + 1 + \dfrac{7x + 1}{x^2 - 1}$

Vert: $x = -1$, $x = 1$; Horiz: none
Slant: $y = x + 1$; x-intercepts: $(0, 0)$
y-intercepts: $(0, 0)$; Symmetry: none

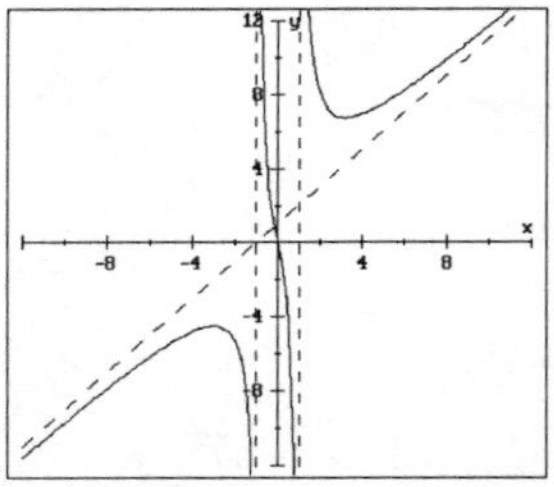

54. $y = \dfrac{x^3 - 2x^2 + x}{x^2 - 4} = \dfrac{x(x-1)^2}{(x+2)(x-2)} = x - 2 + \dfrac{5x - 8}{x^2 - 4}$

Vert: $x = -2$, $x = 2$; Horiz: none
Slant: $y = x - 2$; x-intercepts: $(0, 0)$, $(1, 0)$
y-intercepts: $(0, 0)$; Symmetry: none

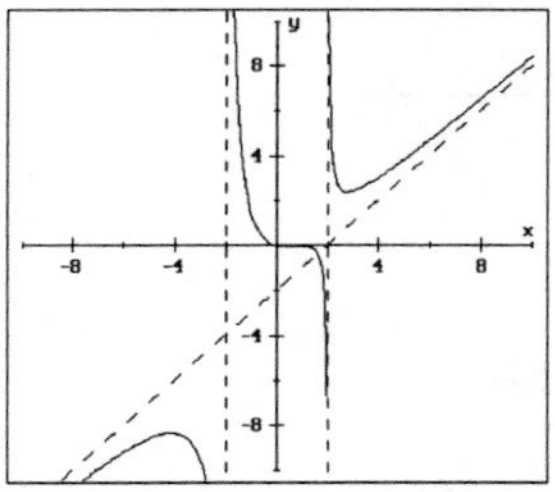

55. $y = \dfrac{x^2}{x} = x$ (if $x \neq 0$)

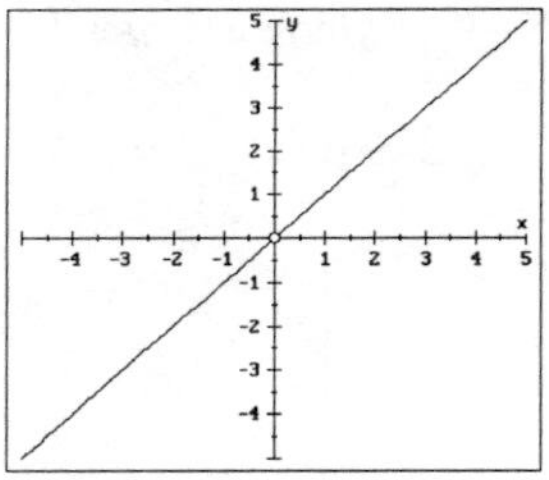

56. $y = \dfrac{x^2 - 1}{x - 1} = \dfrac{(x+1)(x-1)}{x - 1} = x + 1$
(if $x \neq 1$)

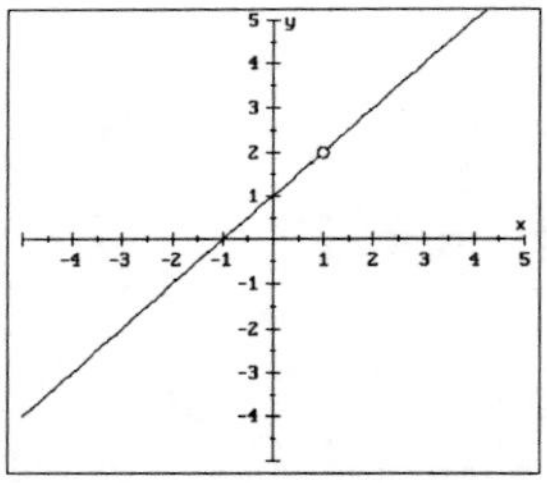

57. $y = \dfrac{x^3 + x}{x} = \dfrac{x(x^2 + 1)}{x} = x^2 + 1$
(if $x \neq 0$)

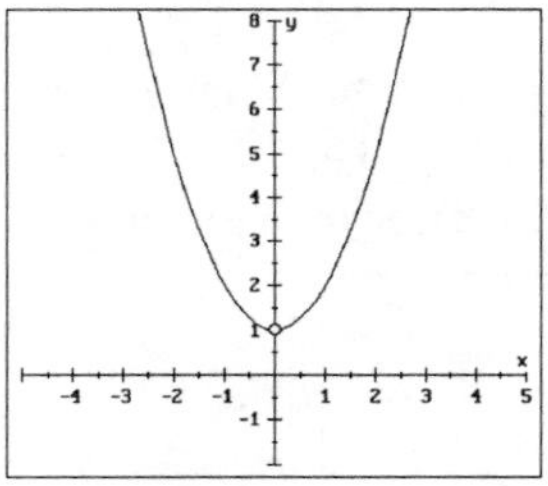

58. $y = \dfrac{x^3 - x^2}{x - 1} = \dfrac{x^2(x - 1)}{x - 1} = x^2$
(if $x \neq 1$)

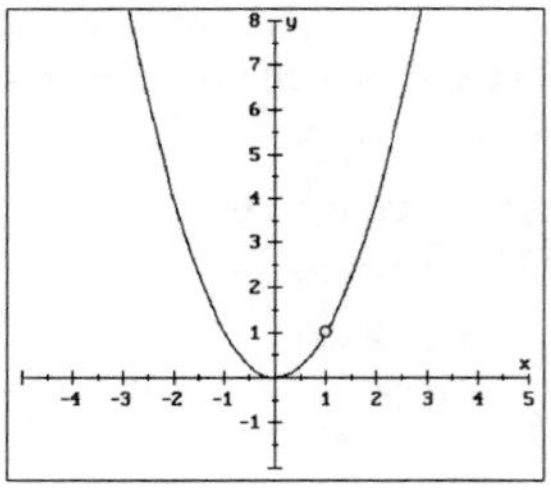

59. $y = \dfrac{x^2 - 2x + 1}{x - 1} = \dfrac{(x-1)(x-1)}{x-1}$
$= x - 1 \text{ (if } x \neq 1)$

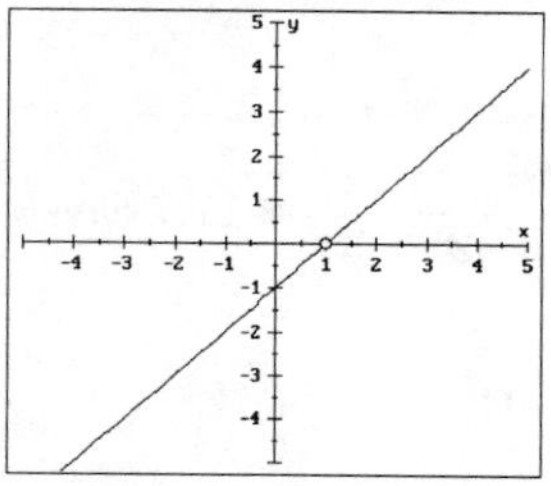

60. $y = \dfrac{2x^2 + 3x - 2}{x + 2} = \dfrac{(2x-1)(x+2)}{x+2}$
$= 2x - 1 \text{ (if } x \neq -2)$

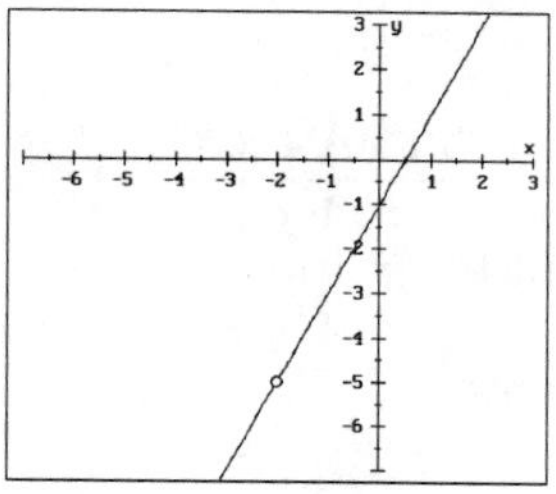

61. $y = \dfrac{x^3 - 1}{x - 1} = \dfrac{(x-1)(x^2+x+1)}{x-1}$
$= x^2 + x + 1 \text{ (if } x \neq 1)$

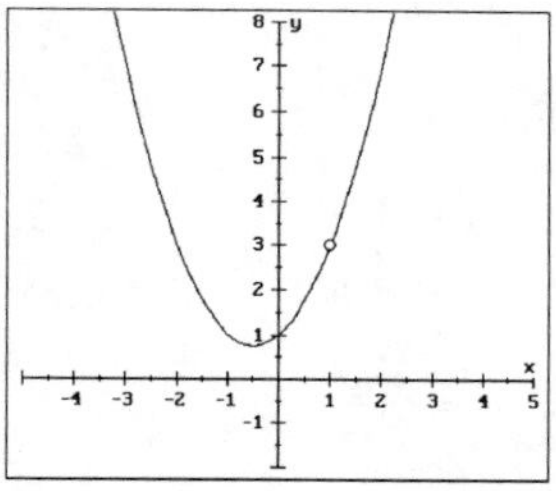

62. $y = \dfrac{x^2 - x}{x^2} = \dfrac{x(x-1)}{x^2} = \dfrac{x-1}{x} \text{ (if } x \neq 0)$

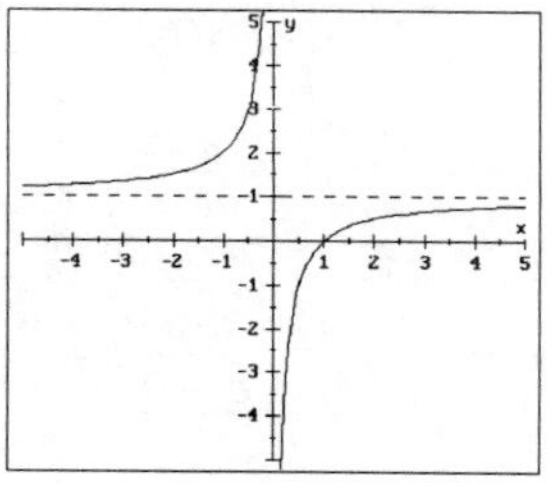

63. $c = f(x) = 1.25x + 700$

64. $\overline{c} = \dfrac{1.25(500) + 700}{500} = \$2.65$

65. $\overline{c} = f(x) = \dfrac{1.25x + 700}{x}$

66. $\overline{c} = \dfrac{1.25(1000) + 700}{1000} = \$1.95$

67. $c = 1.25(500) + 700 = \$1325$

68. $\overline{c} = \dfrac{1.25(2000) + 700}{2000} = \$1.60$

69. $c = f(n) = 0.09n + 7.50$

70. $\overline{c} = \dfrac{0.09n + 7.50}{n}$

71. $c = 0.09(775) + 7.50 = \$77.25$

72. $\overline{c} = \dfrac{0.09(775) + 7.50}{775} \approx \$0.0997 = 9.97¢$

73. $\overline{c} = \dfrac{0.09(1000) + 7.50}{1000} = \$0.0975$
$= 9.75¢$

74. $\overline{c} = \dfrac{0.09(1200) + 7.50}{1200} = \$0.09625$
$= 9.625¢$

75. **a.** $c(n) = 0.095n + 8.50$

b. $\bar{c}(n) = \dfrac{0.095n + 8.50}{n}$

c. $\bar{c}(850) = \dfrac{0.095(850) + 8.50}{850}$
$= \$0.105 = 10.5¢$

76. **a.** Let $t = 21$:
$f(21) = \dfrac{21^2 + 3(21)}{2(21) + 3} = 11.2$ days

b. Let $t + 3 = 25$, so $t = 22$:
$f(22) = \dfrac{22^2 + 3(22)}{2(22) + 3} \approx 11.7$ days

77. **Answers may vary.**

78. **Answers may vary.**

79. $y = \dfrac{ax + b}{cx^2 + d} = \dfrac{\frac{ax+b}{x^2}}{\frac{cx^2+d}{x^2}} = \dfrac{\frac{ax}{x^2} + \frac{b}{x^2}}{\frac{cx^2}{x^2} + \frac{d}{x^2}} = \dfrac{\frac{a}{x} + \frac{b}{x^2}}{c + \frac{d}{x^2}}$

As x approaches $\pm\infty$, $y \approx \dfrac{0+0}{c+0} = 0$. Thus the horizontal asymptote is $y = 0$.

80. $y = \dfrac{ax^3 + b}{cx^2 + d} = \dfrac{\frac{ax^3+b}{x^2}}{\frac{cx^2+d}{x^2}} = \dfrac{\frac{ax^3}{x^2} + \frac{b}{x^2}}{\frac{cx^2}{x^2} + \frac{d}{x^2}} = \dfrac{ax + \frac{b}{x^2}}{c + \frac{d}{x^2}}$

As x approaches $\pm\infty$, $y \approx \dfrac{ax+0}{c+0} = \dfrac{a}{c}x$. Thus the slant asymptote is $y = \dfrac{a}{c}x$.

81. $y = \dfrac{ax^2 + b}{cx^2 + d} = \dfrac{\frac{ax^2+b}{x^2}}{\frac{cx^2+d}{x^2}} = \dfrac{\frac{ax^2}{x^2} + \frac{b}{x^2}}{\frac{cx^2}{x^2} + \frac{d}{x^2}} = \dfrac{a + \frac{b}{x^2}}{c + \frac{d}{x^2}}$

As x approaches $\pm\infty$, $y \approx \dfrac{a+0}{c+0} = \dfrac{a}{c}$. Thus the horizontal asymptote is $y = \dfrac{a}{c}$.

82. $y = \dfrac{x^3 + 1}{x} = \dfrac{\frac{x^3}{x} + \frac{1}{x}}{\frac{x}{x}} = \dfrac{x^2 + \frac{1}{x}}{1}$. As x approaches $\pm\infty$, $y \approx \dfrac{x^2 + 0}{1} = x^2$.

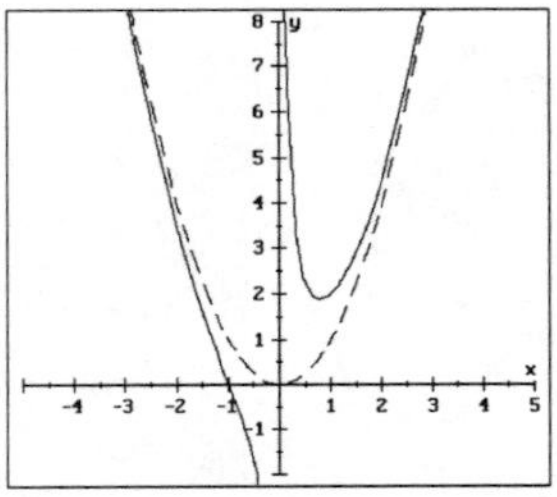

The dotted graph to the left is the graph of the equation $y = x^2$.
The solid graph is the graph of the equation $y = \dfrac{x^3 + 1}{x}$.
Notice that for x-coordinates more than 2 units away from $x = 0$, the two graphs are very similar. Thus $y = x^2$ is called a parabolic **asymptote** of the function $f(x) = \dfrac{x^3 + 1}{x}$.

83. **Answers may vary.**

84. **Answers may vary.**

85. **Answers may vary.**

86. **Answers may vary.**

87. $(2x^2 + 3x) + (x^2 - 2x) = 2x^2 + 3x + x^2 - 2x = 3x^2 + x$

88. $(3x + 2) - (x^2 + 2) = 3x + 2 - x^2 - 2 = -x^2 + 3x$

89. $(5x + 2)(2x + 5) = 10x^2 + 25x + 4x + 10 = 10x^2 + 29x + 10$

90. $\dfrac{2x^2 + 3x + 1}{x + 1} = \dfrac{(2x + 1)(x + 1)}{x + 1} = 2x + 1$

91. $f(x + 1) = 3(x + 1) + 2 = 3x + 3 + 2 = 3x + 5$

92. $f(2x + 1) = (2x + 1)^2 + (2x + 1) = 4x^2 + 4x + 1 + 2x + 1 = 4x^2 + 6x + 2$

Exercise 3.6 (page 303)

1. $f(x) + g(x)$ **2.** $f(x) - g(x)$ **3.** $f(x)g(x)$ **4.** $\dfrac{f(x)}{g(x)}$

5. $(-\infty, \infty)$ **6.** $f(g(x))$ **7.** $g(f(x))$ **8.** $g(x)$

9. identity **10.** $f(x)$

11. $(f + g)(x) = f(x) + g(x) = (2x + 1) + (3x - 2) = 5x - 1$; domain $= (-\infty, \infty)$

12. $(f - g)(x) = f(x) - g(x) = (2x + 1) - (3x - 2) = -x + 3$; domain $= (-\infty, \infty)$

13. $(f \cdot g)(x) = f(x)g(x) = (2x + 1)(3x - 2) = 6x^2 - x - 2$; domain $= (-\infty, \infty)$

14. $(f/g)(x) = \dfrac{f(x)}{g(x)} = \dfrac{2x + 1}{3x - 2}$; domain $= \left(-\infty, \frac{2}{3}\right) \cup \left(\frac{2}{3}, \infty\right)$

15. $(f - g)(x) = f(x) - g(x) = (x^2 + x) - (x^2 - 1) = x + 1$; domain $= (-\infty, \infty)$

16. $(f + g)(x) = f(x) + g(x) = (x^2 + x) + (x^2 - 1) = 2x^2 + x - 1$; domain $= (-\infty, \infty)$

17. $(f/g)(x) = \dfrac{f(x)}{g(x)} = \dfrac{x^2 + x}{x^2 - 1} = \dfrac{x(x + 1)}{(x + 1)(x - 1)} = \dfrac{x}{x - 1}$; domain $= (-\infty, -1) \cup (-1, 1) \cup (1, \infty)$

18. $(f \cdot g)(x) = f(x)g(x) = (x^2 + x)(x^2 - 1) = x^4 + x^3 - x^2 - x$; domain $= (-\infty, \infty)$

19. $(f + g)(2) = f(2) + g(2) = \left[(2)^2 - 1\right] + [3(2) - 2] = 3 + 4 = 7$

20. $(f + g)(-3) = f(-3) + g(-3) = \left[(-3)^2 - 1\right] + [3(-3) - 2] = 8 + (-11) = -3$

21. $(f - g)(0) = f(0) - g(0) = \left[(0)^2 - 1\right] - [3(0) - 2] = -1 - (-2) = 1$

22. $(f-g)(-5) = f(-5) - g(-5) = \left[(-5)^2 - 1\right] - [3(-5) - 2] = 24 - (-17) = 41$

23. $(f \cdot g)(2) = f(2) \cdot g(2) = \left[(2)^2 - 1\right] \cdot [3(2) - 2] = (3)(4) = 12$

24. $(f \cdot g)(-1) = f(-1) \cdot g(-1) = \left[(-1)^2 - 1\right] \cdot [3(-1) - 2] = (0)(-5) = 0$

25. $(f/g)\left(\frac{2}{3}\right) = \dfrac{f\left(\frac{2}{3}\right)}{g\left(\frac{2}{3}\right)} = \dfrac{\left[\left(\frac{2}{3}\right)^2 - 1\right]}{\left[3\left(\frac{2}{3}\right) - 2\right]} = \dfrac{-\frac{5}{9}}{0} \Rightarrow$ undefined

26. $(f/g)(t) = \dfrac{f(t)}{g(t)} = \dfrac{t^2 - 1}{3t - 2}$

27. Let $f(x) = 3x^2$ and $g(x) = 2x$.
Then $(f+g)(x) = 3x^2 + 2x = h(x)$.

28. Let $f(x) = 3$ and $g(x) = x^2$.
Then $(f \cdot g)(x) = 3x^2 = h(x)$.

29. Let $f(x) = 3x^2$ and $g(x) = x^2 - 1$.
Then $(f/g)(x) = \dfrac{3x^2}{x^2 - 1} = h(x)$.

30. Let $f(x) = 5x$ and $g(x) = -x^2$.
Then $(f-g)(x) = 5x + x^2 = h(x)$.

31. Let $f(x) = 3x^3$ and $g(x) = -x$.
Then $(f-g)(x) = 3x^3 + x$
$= x\left(3x^2 + 1\right) = h(x)$.

32. Let $f(x) = 9x^2$ and $g(x) = -4$.
Then $(f+g)(x) = 9x^2 - 4$
$= (3x-2)(3x+2) = h(x)$.

33. Let $f(x) = x + 9$ and $g(x) = x - 2$.
Then $(f \cdot g)(x) = (x+9)(x-2)$
$= x^2 + 7x - 18 = h(x)$.

34. Let $f(x) = 5x^6$ and $g(x) = x$.
Then $(f/g)(x) = \dfrac{5x^6}{x} = 5x^5 = h(x)$.

35. $(f \circ g)(2) = f(g(2)) = f(5(2) - 2) = f(8) = 2(8) - 5 = 11$

36. $(g \circ f)(-3) = g(f(-3)) = g(2(-3) - 5) = g(-11) = 5(-11) - 2 = -57$

37. $(f \circ f)\left(-\frac{1}{2}\right) = f\left(f\left(-\frac{1}{2}\right)\right) = f\left(2\left(-\frac{1}{2}\right) - 5\right) = f(-6) = 2(-6) - 5 = -17$

38. $(g \circ g)\left(\frac{3}{5}\right) = g\left(g\left(\frac{3}{5}\right)\right) = g\left(5\left(\frac{3}{5}\right) - 2\right) = g(1) = 5(1) - 2 = 3$

39. $(f \circ g)(-3) = f(g(-3)) = f(4(-3) + 4) = f(-8) = 3(-8)^2 - 2 = 190$

40. $(g \circ f)(3) = g(f(3)) = g\left(3(3)^2 - 2\right) = g(25) = 4(25) + 4 = 104$

41. $(f \circ f)\left(\sqrt{3}\right) = f\left(f\left(\sqrt{3}\right)\right) = f\left(3\left(\sqrt{3}\right)^2 - 2\right) = f(7) = 3(7)^2 - 2 = 145$

42. $(g \circ g)(-4) = g(g(-4)) = g(4(-4) + 4) = g(-12) = 4(-12) + 4 = -44$

43. The domain of $f \circ g$ is the set of all real numbers in the domain of $g(x)$ such that $g(x)$ is in the domain of $f(x)$. Domain of $g(x)$: $(-\infty, \infty)$. Domain of $f(x) = (-\infty, \infty)$. Thus, all values of $g(x)$ are in the domain of $f(x)$. $\boxed{\text{Domain of } f \circ g\text{: } (-\infty, \infty)}$
$(f \circ g)(x) = f(g(x)) = f(x+1) = 3(x+1) = 3x+3$

44. The domain of $g \circ f$ is the set of all real numbers in the domain of $f(x)$ such that $f(x)$ is in the domain of $g(x)$. Domain of $f(x)$: $(-\infty, \infty)$. Domain of $g(x) = (-\infty, \infty)$. Thus, all values of $f(x)$ are in the domain of $g(x)$. $\boxed{\text{Domain of } g \circ f\text{: } (-\infty, \infty)}$
$(g \circ f)(x) = g(f(x)) = g(3x) = 3x+1$

45. The domain of $f \circ f$ is the set of all real numbers in the domain of $f(x)$ such that $f(x)$ is in the domain of $f(x)$. Domain of $f(x)$: $(-\infty, \infty)$. Thus, all values of $f(x)$ are in the domain of $f(x)$.
$\boxed{\text{Domain of } f \circ f\text{: } (-\infty, \infty)}$ $(f \circ f)(x) = f(f(x)) = f(3x) = 3(3x) = 9x$

46. The domain of $g \circ g$ is the set of all real numbers in the domain of $g(x)$ such that $g(x)$ is in the domain of $g(x)$. Domain of $g(x)$: $(-\infty, \infty)$. Thus, all values of $g(x)$ are in the domain of $g(x)$.
$\boxed{\text{Domain of } g \circ g\text{: } (-\infty, \infty)}$ $(g \circ g)(x) = g(g(x)) = g(x+1) = x+1+1 = x+2$

47. The domain of $g \circ f$ is the set of all real numbers in the domain of $f(x)$ such that $f(x)$ is in the domain of $g(x)$. Domain of $f(x)$: $(-\infty, \infty)$. Domain of $g(x) = (-\infty, \infty)$. Thus, all values of $f(x)$ are in the domain of $g(x)$. $\boxed{\text{Domain of } g \circ f\text{: } (-\infty, \infty)}$
$(g \circ f)(x) = g(f(x)) = g(x^2) = 2x^2$

48. The domain of $f \circ g$ is the set of all real numbers in the domain of $g(x)$ such that $g(x)$ is in the domain of $f(x)$. Domain of $g(x)$: $(-\infty, \infty)$. Domain of $f(x) = (-\infty, \infty)$. Thus, all values of $g(x)$ are in the domain of $f(x)$. $\boxed{\text{Domain of } f \circ g\text{: } (-\infty, \infty)}$
$(f \circ g)(x) = f(g(x)) = f(2x) = (2x)^2 = 4x^2$

49. The domain of $g \circ g$ is the set of all real numbers in the domain of $g(x)$ such that $g(x)$ is in the domain of $g(x)$. Domain of $g(x)$: $(-\infty, \infty)$. Thus, all values of $g(x)$ are in the domain of $g(x)$.
$\boxed{\text{Domain of } g \circ g\text{: } (-\infty, \infty)}$ $(g \circ g)(x) = g(g(x)) = g(2x) = 2(2x) = 4x$

50. The domain of $f \circ f$ is the set of all real numbers in the domain of $f(x)$ such that $f(x)$ is in the domain of $f(x)$. Domain of $f(x)$: $(-\infty, \infty)$. Thus, all values of $f(x)$ are in the domain of $f(x)$.
$\boxed{\text{Domain of } f \circ f\text{: } (-\infty, \infty)}$ $(f \circ f)(x) = f(f(x)) = f(x^2) = (x^2)^2 = x^4$

51. The domain of $f \circ g$ is the set of all real numbers in the domain of $g(x)$ such that $g(x)$ is in the domain of $f(x)$. Domain of $g(x)$: $(-\infty, \infty)$. Domain of $f(x) = [0, \infty)$. Thus, we must have $g(x) \geq 0 \Rightarrow x+1 \geq 0 \Rightarrow x \geq -1$. $\boxed{\text{Domain of } f \circ g\text{: } [-1, \infty)}$
$(f \circ g)(x) = f(g(x)) = f(x+1) = \sqrt{x+1}$

52. The domain of $g \circ f$ is the set of all real numbers in the domain of $f(x)$ such that $f(x)$ is in the domain of $g(x)$. Domain of $f(x)$: $[0, \infty)$. Domain of $g(x) = (-\infty, \infty)$. Thus, all values of $f(x)$ are in the domain of $g(x)$. $\boxed{\text{Domain of } g \circ f\text{: } [0, \infty)}$
$(g \circ f)(x) = g(f(x)) = g(\sqrt{x}) = \sqrt{x} + 1$

53. The domain of $f \circ f$ is the set of all real numbers in the domain of $f(x)$ such that $f(x)$ is in the domain of $f(x)$. Domain of $f(x)$: $[0, \infty)$. Thus, we must have $f(x) \geq 0 \Rightarrow \sqrt{x} \geq 0$. This is true for all real values of x. $\boxed{\text{Domain of } f \circ f\text{: } [0, \infty)}$
$(f \circ f)(x) = f(f(x)) = f(\sqrt{x}) = \sqrt{\sqrt{x}} = \left((x)^{1/2}\right)^{1/2} = x^{1/4} = \sqrt[4]{x}$

54. The domain of $g \circ g$ is the set of all real numbers in the domain of $g(x)$ such that $g(x)$ is in the domain of $g(x)$. Domain of $g(x)$: $(-\infty, \infty)$. Thus, all values of $g(x)$ are in the domain of $g(x)$.
$\boxed{\text{Domain of } g \circ g\text{: } (-\infty, \infty)}$ $(g \circ g)(x) = g(g(x)) = g(x+1) = (x+1) + 1 = x + 2$

55. The domain of $g \circ f$ is the set of all real numbers in the domain of $f(x)$ such that $f(x)$ is in the domain of $g(x)$. Domain of $f(x)$: $[-1, \infty)$. Domain of $g(x) = (-\infty, \infty)$. Thus, all values of $f(x)$ are in the domain of $g(x)$. $\boxed{\text{Domain of } g \circ f\text{: } [-1, \infty)}$
$(g \circ f)(x) = g(f(x)) = g\left(\sqrt{x+1}\right) = \left(\sqrt{x+1}\right)^2 - 1 = x$

56. The domain of $f \circ g$ is the set of all real numbers in the domain of $g(x)$ such that $g(x)$ is in the domain of $f(x)$. Domain of $g(x)$: $(-\infty, \infty)$. Domain of $f(x) = [-1, \infty)$. Thus, we must have $g(x) \geq -1 \Rightarrow x^2 - 1 \geq -1 \Rightarrow x^2 \geq 0$. This is true for all real values of x.
$\boxed{\text{Domain of } f \circ g\text{: } (-\infty, \infty)}$ $(f \circ g)(x) = f(g(x)) = f(x^2 - 1) = \sqrt{x^2 - 1 + 1} = \sqrt{x^2} = |x|$

57. The domain of $g \circ g$ is the set of all real numbers in the domain of $g(x)$ such that $g(x)$ is in the domain of $g(x)$. Domain of $g(x)$: $(-\infty, \infty)$. Thus, all values of $g(x)$ are in the domain of $g(x)$.
$\boxed{\text{Domain of } g \circ g\text{: } (-\infty, \infty)}$ $(g \circ g)(x) = g(g(x)) = g(x^2 - 1) = (x^2 - 1)^2 - 1 = x^4 - 2x^2$

58. The domain of $f \circ f$ is the set of all real numbers in the domain of $f(x)$ such that $f(x)$ is in the domain of $f(x)$. Domain of $f(x)$: $[-1, \infty)$. Thus, we must have $f(x) \geq -1 \Rightarrow \sqrt{x+1} \geq -1$. This is true for all real values of x. $\boxed{\text{Domain of } f \circ f\text{: } [-1, \infty)}$
$(f \circ f)(x) = f(f(x)) = f\left(\sqrt{x+1}\right) = \sqrt{\sqrt{x+1} + 1}$

59. The domain of $f \circ g$ is the set of all real numbers in the domain of $g(x)$ such that $g(x)$ is in the domain of $f(x)$. Domain of $g(x)$: $(-\infty, 2) \cup (2, \infty)$. Domain of $f(x) = (-\infty, 1) \cup (1, \infty)$. Thus, we must have $g(x) \neq 1 \Rightarrow \dfrac{1}{x-2} \neq 1 \Rightarrow 1 \neq x - 2 \Rightarrow x \neq 3$

Domain of $f \circ g$: $(-\infty, 2) \cup (2, 3) \cup (3, \infty)$

$$(f \circ g)(x) = f(g(x)) = f\left(\frac{1}{x-2}\right) = \frac{1}{\frac{1}{x-2} - 1} = \frac{1}{\frac{1}{x-2} - 1} \cdot \frac{x-2}{x-2} = \frac{x-2}{1-(x-2)} = \frac{x-2}{3-x}$$

60. The domain of $g \circ f$ is the set of all real numbers in the domain of $f(x)$ such that $f(x)$ is in the domain of $g(x)$. Domain of $f(x)$: $(-\infty, 1) \cup (1, \infty)$. Domain of $g(x) = (-\infty, 2) \cup (2, \infty)$. Thus, we must have $f(x) \neq 2 \Rightarrow \dfrac{1}{x-1} \neq 2 \Rightarrow 1 \neq 2(x-1) \Rightarrow 1 \neq 2x - 2 \Rightarrow 2x \neq 3 \Rightarrow x \neq \frac{3}{2}$

Domain of $f \circ g$: $(-\infty, 1) \cup \left(1, \frac{3}{2}\right) \cup \left(\frac{3}{2}, \infty\right)$

$$(g \circ f)(x) = g(f(x)) = g\left(\frac{1}{x-1}\right) = \frac{1}{\frac{1}{x-1} - 2} = \frac{1}{\frac{1}{x-1} - 2} \cdot \frac{x-1}{x-1} = \frac{x-1}{1-2(x-1)} = \frac{x-1}{3-2x}$$

61. The domain of $f \circ f$ is the set of all real numbers in the domain of $f(x)$ such that $f(x)$ is in the domain of $f(x)$. Domain of $f(x)$: $(-\infty, 1) \cup (1, \infty)$. Thus, we must have $f(x) \neq 1 \Rightarrow \dfrac{1}{x-1} \neq 1 \Rightarrow 1 \neq x - 1 \Rightarrow x \neq 2$ Domain of $f \circ f$: $(-\infty, 1) \cup (1, 2) \cup (2, \infty)$

$$(f \circ f)(x) = f(f(x)) = f\left(\frac{1}{x-1}\right) = \frac{1}{\frac{1}{x-1} - 1} = \frac{1}{\frac{1}{x-1} - 1} \cdot \frac{x-1}{x-1} = \frac{x-1}{1-(x-1)} = \frac{x-1}{2-x}$$

62. The domain of $g \circ g$ is the set of all real numbers in the domain of $g(x)$ such that $g(x)$ is in the domain of $g(x)$. Domain of $g(x)$: $(-\infty, 2) \cup (2, \infty)$. Thus, we must have $g(x) \neq 2 \Rightarrow \dfrac{1}{x-2} \neq 2 \Rightarrow 1 \neq 2x - 4 \Rightarrow x \neq \frac{5}{2}$ Domain of $g \circ g$: $(-\infty, 2) \cup \left(2, \frac{5}{2}\right) \cup \left(\frac{5}{2}, \infty\right)$

$$(g \circ g)(x) = g(g(x)) = g\left(\frac{1}{x-2}\right) = \frac{1}{\frac{1}{x-2} - 2} = \frac{1}{\frac{1}{x-2} - 2} \cdot \frac{x-2}{x-2} = \frac{x-2}{1-2(x-2)} = \frac{x-2}{5-2x}$$

63. Let $f(x) = x - 2$ and $g(x) = 3x$.
Then $(f \circ g)(x) = f(g(x))$
$= f(3x) = 3x - 2.$

64. Let $f(x) = x - 5$ and $g(x) = 7x$.
Then $(f \circ g)(x) = f(g(x))$
$= f(7x) = 7x - 5.$

65. Let $f(x) = x - 2$ and $g(x) = x^2$.
Then $(f \circ g)(x) = f(g(x))$
$= f\left(x^2\right) = x^2 - 2.$

66. Let $f(x) = x - 3$ and $g(x) = x^3$.
Then $(f \circ g)(x) = f(g(x))$
$= f\left(x^3\right) = x^3 - 3.$

67. Let $f(x) = x^2$ and $g(x) = x - 2$.
Then $(f \circ g)(x) = f(g(x))$
$= f(x-2) = (x-2)^2.$

68. Let $f(x) = x^3$ and $g(x) = x - 3$.
Then $(f \circ g)(x) = f(g(x))$
$= f(x-3) = (x-3)^3.$

69. Let $f(x) = \sqrt{x}$ and $g(x) = x + 2$.
Then $(f \circ g)(x) = f(g(x))$
$= f(x+2) = \sqrt{x+2}$.

70. Let $f(x) = \dfrac{1}{x}$ and $g(x) = x - 5$.
Then $(f \circ g)(x) = f(g(x))$
$= f(x-5) = \dfrac{1}{x-5}$.

71. Let $f(x) = x + 2$ and $g(x) = \sqrt{x}$.
Then $(f \circ g)(x) = f(g(x))$
$= f(\sqrt{x}) = \sqrt{x} + 2$.

72. Let $f(x) = x - 5$ and $g(x) = \dfrac{1}{x}$.
Then $(f \circ g)(x) = f(g(x))$
$= f\left(\dfrac{1}{x}\right) = \dfrac{1}{x} - 5$.

73. Let $f(x) = x$ and $g(x) = x$.
Then $(f \circ g)(x) = f(g(x))$
$= f(x) = x$.

74. Let $f(x) = 3$ and $g(x) = x$.
Then $(f \circ g)(x) = f(g(x))$
$= f(x) = 3$.

75. **a.** $A = 17w$

b.
$$\begin{aligned} w^2 + 17^2 &= d^2 \\ w^2 &= d^2 - 17^2 \\ w &= \sqrt{d^2 - 289} \end{aligned}$$

c.
$$\begin{aligned} A &= 17w \\ &= 17\sqrt{d^2 - 289} \end{aligned}$$

76. If the perimeter is P, then each side is $s = \dfrac{P}{4}$. Area $= s^2 = \left(\dfrac{P}{4}\right)^2 = \dfrac{P^2}{16}$.

77. If the area is A and the length of a side is s, then $s^2 = A \Rightarrow s = \sqrt{A}$. Then $P = 4s = 4\sqrt{A}$.

78. Use the relationship $C = \frac{5}{9}(F - 32)$.

$F = mt + b$
$F = -81t + 1200$

$$\begin{aligned} C \circ F = C(F) &= \tfrac{5}{9}((-81t + 1200) - 32) \\ &= \tfrac{5}{9}(-81t + 1168) \\ &= -45t + \tfrac{5840}{9} \end{aligned}$$

79. $(f + f)(x) = f(x) + f(x) = 3x + 3x = 6x$
$f(x + x) = f(2x) = 3(2x) = 6x$

80. $(g + g)(x) = g(x) + g(x) = x^2 + x^2 = 2x^2$
$g(x + x) = g(2x) = (2x)^2 = 4x^2$

81.
$$\begin{aligned} (f \circ f)(x) = f(f(x)) = f\left(\frac{x-1}{x+1}\right) = \frac{\frac{x-1}{x+1} - 1}{\frac{x-1}{x+1} + 1} = \frac{(x+1)\left(\frac{x-1}{x+1} - 1\right)}{(x+1)\left(\frac{x-1}{x+1} + 1\right)} &= \frac{x - 1 - (x+1)}{x - 1 + x + 1} \\ &= \frac{-2}{2x} = -\frac{1}{x} \end{aligned}$$

82.
$$(g \circ g)(x) = g(g(x)) = g\left(\frac{x}{x-1}\right) = \frac{\frac{x}{x-1}}{\frac{x}{x-1} - 1} = \frac{(x-1)\frac{x}{x-1}}{(x-1)\left(\frac{x}{x-1} - 1\right)} = \frac{x}{x - (x-1)} = \frac{x}{1} = x$$

83-86. **Answers may vary.**

87.
$$x = 3y - 7$$
$$x + 7 = 3y$$
$$\frac{x+7}{3} = y$$

88.
$$x = \frac{7}{y}$$
$$xy = 7$$
$$y = \frac{7}{x}$$

89.
$$x = \frac{y}{y+3}$$
$$x(y+3) = y$$
$$xy + 3x = y$$
$$xy - y = -3x$$
$$y(x-1) = -3x$$
$$y = \frac{-3x}{x-1} = \frac{3x}{1-x}$$

90.
$$x = \frac{y-1}{y}$$
$$xy = y - 1$$
$$xy - y = -1$$
$$y(x-1) = -1$$
$$y = \frac{-1}{x-1} = \frac{1}{1-x}$$

Exercise 3.7 (page 311)

1. one-to-one

2. horizontal

3. interchange

4. $y = x$

5. $y = 3x$
one-to-one

6. $y = \frac{1}{2}x$
one-to-one

7. $y = x^2 + 3$
$x = 1$ and $x = -1$ both correspond to $y = 4$.
not one-to-one

8. $y = x^4 - x^2$
$x = 1$ and $x = -1$ both correspond to $y = 0$.
not one-to-one

9. $y = x^3 - x$
$x = 1$ and $x = -1$ both correspond to $y = 0$.
not one-to-one

10. $y = x^2 - x$
$x = 0$ and $x = 1$ both correspond to $y = 0$.
not one-to-one

11. $y = |x|$
$x = 1$ and $x = -1$ both correspond to $y = 1$.
not one-to-one

12. $y = |x - 3|$
$x = 4$ and $x = 2$ both correspond to $y = 1$.
not one-to-one

13. $y = 5$
$x = 1$ and $x = 2$ both correspond to $y = 5$.
not one-to-one

14. $y = \sqrt{x-5}; x \geq 5$
one-to-one

15. $y = (x-2)^2,\ x \geq 2$
one-to-one

16. $y = \frac{1}{x}$
one-to-one

17. one-to-one

18. not one-to-one

19. not one-to-one (not a function)

20. one-to-one

21. $(f \circ g)(x) = f(g(x)) = f\left(\frac{1}{5}x\right) = 5\left(\frac{1}{5}x\right) = x$

$(g \circ f)(x) = g(f(x)) = g(5x) = \frac{1}{5}(5x) = x$

22. $(f \circ g)(x) = f(g(x)) = f\left(\dfrac{x-2}{3}\right) = 3\left(\dfrac{x-2}{3}\right) + 2 = x - 2 + 2 = x$

$(g \circ f)(x) = g(f(x)) = g(3x+2) = \dfrac{(3x+2)-2}{3} = \dfrac{3x}{3} = x$

23. $(f \circ g)(x) = f(g(x)) = f\left(\dfrac{1}{x-1}\right) = \dfrac{\frac{1}{x-1}+1}{\frac{1}{x-1}} = \dfrac{(x-1)\left(\frac{1}{x-1}+1\right)}{(x-1)\frac{1}{x-1}} = \dfrac{1+x-1}{1} = x$

$(g \circ f)(x) = g(f(x)) = g\left(\dfrac{x+1}{x}\right) = \dfrac{1}{\frac{x+1}{x}-1} = \dfrac{x(1)}{x\left(\frac{x+1}{x}-1\right)} = \dfrac{x}{x+1-x} = \dfrac{x}{1} = x$

24. $(f \circ g)(x) = f(g(x)) = f\left(\dfrac{x+1}{x-1}\right) = \dfrac{\frac{x+1}{x-1}+1}{\frac{x+1}{x-1}-1} = \dfrac{(x-1)\left(\frac{x+1}{x-1}+1\right)}{(x-1)\left(\frac{x+1}{x-1}-1\right)} = \dfrac{x+1+x-1}{x+1-(x-1)} = x$

Note that $(g \circ f)(x)$ will involve the same calculations.

25.
$$\begin{aligned} y = f(x) &= 3x \\ x &= 3y \\ \frac{x}{3} &= y \\ f^{-1}(x) &= \frac{x}{3} \end{aligned}$$
$$\begin{aligned} (f \circ f^{-1})(x) &= f(f^{-1}(x)) \\ &= f\left(\frac{x}{3}\right) \\ &= 3\left(\frac{x}{3}\right) \\ &= x \end{aligned}$$
$$\begin{aligned} (f^{-1} \circ f)(x) &= f^{-1}(f(x)) \\ &= f^{-1}(3x) \\ &= \frac{3x}{3} \\ &= x \end{aligned}$$

26.
$$\begin{aligned} y = f(x) &= \frac{1}{3}x \\ x &= \frac{1}{3}y \\ 3x &= y \\ f^{-1}(x) &= 3x \end{aligned}$$
$$\begin{aligned} (f \circ f^{-1})(x) &= f(f^{-1}(x)) \\ &= f(3x) \\ &= \frac{1}{3}(3x) \\ &= x \end{aligned}$$
$$\begin{aligned} (f^{-1} \circ f)(x) &= f^{-1}(f(x)) \\ &= f^{-1}\left(\frac{1}{3}x\right) \\ &= 3\left(\frac{1}{3}x\right) \\ &= x \end{aligned}$$

27.
$$\begin{aligned} y = f(x) &= 3x+2 \\ x &= 3y+2 \\ x-2 &= 3y \\ \frac{x-2}{3} &= y \\ f^{-1}(x) &= \frac{x-2}{3} \end{aligned}$$
$$\begin{aligned} (f \circ f^{-1})(x) &= f(f^{-1}(x)) \\ &= f\left(\frac{x-2}{3}\right) \\ &= 3\left(\frac{x-2}{3}\right) + 2 \\ &= x - 2 + 2 = x \end{aligned}$$
$$\begin{aligned} (f^{-1} \circ f)(x) &= f^{-1}(f(x)) \\ &= f^{-1}(3x+2) \\ &= \frac{(3x+2)-2}{3} \\ &= \frac{3x}{3} = x \end{aligned}$$

28.
$$\begin{aligned} y = f(x) &= 2x-5 \\ x &= 2y-5 \\ x+5 &= 2y \\ \frac{x+5}{2} &= y \\ f^{-1}(x) &= \frac{x+5}{2} \end{aligned}$$
$$\begin{aligned} (f \circ f^{-1})(x) &= f(f^{-1}(x)) \\ &= f\left(\frac{x+5}{2}\right) \\ &= 2\left(\frac{x+5}{2}\right) - 5 \\ &= x + 5 - 5 = x \end{aligned}$$
$$\begin{aligned} (f^{-1} \circ f)(x) &= f^{-1}(f(x)) \\ &= f^{-1}(2x-5) \\ &= \frac{(2x-5)+5}{2} \\ &= \frac{2x}{2} = x \end{aligned}$$

29.

$$\begin{aligned} y = f(x) &= \frac{1}{x+3} \\ x &= \frac{1}{y+3} \\ x(y+3) &= 1 \\ y+3 &= \frac{1}{x} \\ f^{-1}(x) &= \frac{1}{x} - 3 \end{aligned}$$

$$\begin{aligned} (f \circ f^{-1})(x) &= f\big(f^{-1}(x)\big) \\ &= f\left(\frac{1}{x} - 3\right) \\ &= \frac{1}{\frac{1}{x} - 3 + 3} \\ &= \frac{1}{\frac{1}{x}} \\ &= x \end{aligned}$$

$$\begin{aligned} (f^{-1} \circ f)(x) &= f^{-1}(f(x)) \\ &= f^{-1}\left(\frac{1}{x+3}\right) \\ &= \frac{1}{\frac{1}{x+3}} - 3 \\ &= x + 3 - 3 \\ &= x \end{aligned}$$

30.

$$\begin{aligned} y = f(x) &= \frac{1}{x-2} \\ x &= \frac{1}{y-2} \\ x(y-2) &= 1 \\ y-2 &= \frac{1}{x} \\ f^{-1}(x) &= \frac{1}{x} + 2 \end{aligned}$$

$$\begin{aligned} (f \circ f^{-1})(x) &= f\big(f^{-1}(x)\big) \\ &= f\left(\frac{1}{x} + 2\right) \\ &= \frac{1}{\frac{1}{x} + 2 - 2} \\ &= \frac{1}{\frac{1}{x}} \\ &= x \end{aligned}$$

$$\begin{aligned} (f^{-1} \circ f)(x) &= f^{-1}(f(x)) \\ &= f^{-1}\left(\frac{1}{x-2}\right) \\ &= \frac{1}{\frac{1}{x-2}} + 2 \\ &= x - 2 + 2 \\ &= x \end{aligned}$$

31.

$$\begin{aligned} y = f(x) &= \frac{1}{2x} \\ x &= \frac{1}{2y} \\ x(2y) &= 1 \\ 2xy &= 1 \\ y &= \frac{1}{2x} \\ f^{-1}(x) &= \frac{1}{2x} \end{aligned}$$

$$\begin{aligned} (f \circ f^{-1})(x) &= f\big(f^{-1}(x)\big) \\ &= f\left(\frac{1}{2x}\right) \\ &= \frac{1}{2\left(\frac{1}{2x}\right)} \\ &= \frac{1}{\frac{1}{x}} \\ &= x \end{aligned}$$

$$\begin{aligned} (f^{-1} \circ f)(x) &= f^{-1}(f(x)) \\ &= f^{-1}\left(\frac{1}{2x}\right) \\ &= \frac{1}{2\left(\frac{1}{2x}\right)} \\ &= \frac{1}{\frac{1}{x}} \\ &= x \end{aligned}$$

32.

$$\begin{aligned} y = f(x) &= \frac{1}{x^3} \\ x &= \frac{1}{y^3} \\ xy^3 &= 1 \\ y^3 &= \frac{1}{x} \\ y &= \sqrt[3]{\frac{1}{x}} \\ f^{-1}(x) &= \sqrt[3]{\frac{1}{x}} \end{aligned}$$

$$\begin{aligned} (f \circ f^{-1})(x) &= f\big(f^{-1}(x)\big) \\ &= f\left(\sqrt[3]{\frac{1}{x}}\right) \\ &= \frac{1}{\left(\sqrt[3]{\frac{1}{x}}\right)^3} \\ &= \frac{1}{\frac{1}{x}} \\ &= x \end{aligned}$$

$$\begin{aligned} (f^{-1} \circ f)(x) &= f^{-1}(f(x)) \\ &= f^{-1}\left(\frac{1}{x^3}\right) \\ &= \sqrt[3]{\frac{1}{\frac{1}{x^3}}} \\ &= \sqrt[3]{\frac{x^3}{1}} \\ &= x \end{aligned}$$

33.
$$y = f(x) = 5x$$
$$x = 5y$$
$$\frac{x}{5} = y$$
$$f^{-1}(x) = \frac{1}{5}x$$

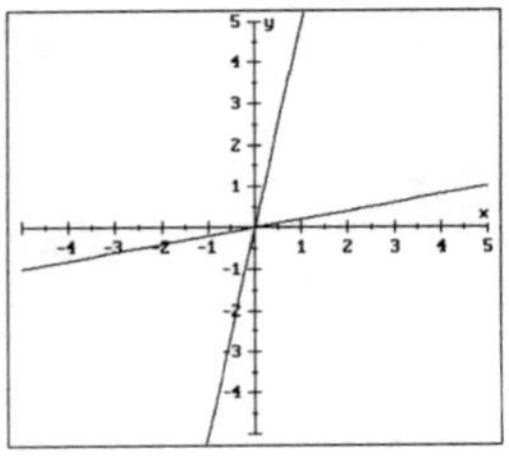

34.
$$y = f(x) = \frac{3}{2}x$$
$$x = \frac{3}{2}y$$
$$\frac{2}{3}x = y$$
$$f^{-1}(x) = \frac{2}{3}x$$

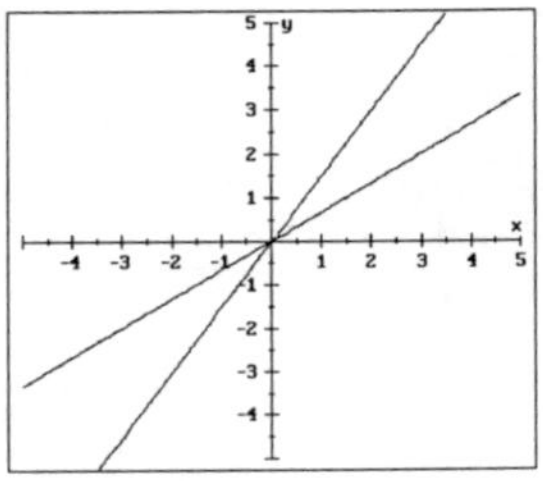

35.
$$y = f(x) = 2x - 4$$
$$x = 2y - 4$$
$$x + 4 = 2y$$
$$\frac{x+4}{2} = y$$
$$f^{-1}(x) = \frac{x+4}{2}$$

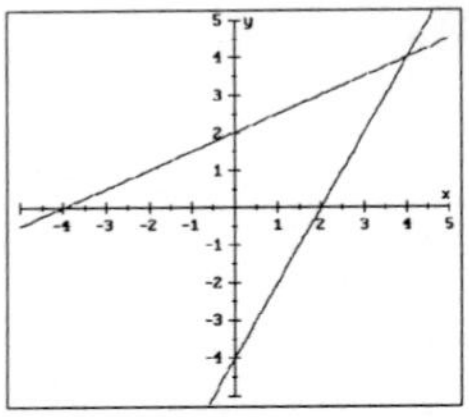

36.
$$y = f(x) = \tfrac{3}{2}x - 2$$
$$x = \tfrac{3}{2}y - 2$$
$$x + 2 = \tfrac{3}{2}y$$
$$\tfrac{2}{3}(x+2) = y$$
$$f^{-1}(x) = \tfrac{2}{3}(x+2)$$

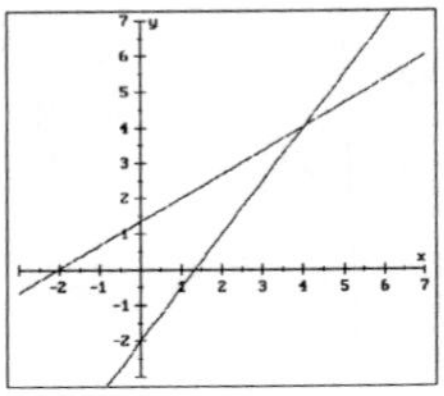

37.
$$x - y = 2$$
$$y - x = 2$$
$$y = x + 2$$
$$f^{-1}(x) = x + 2$$

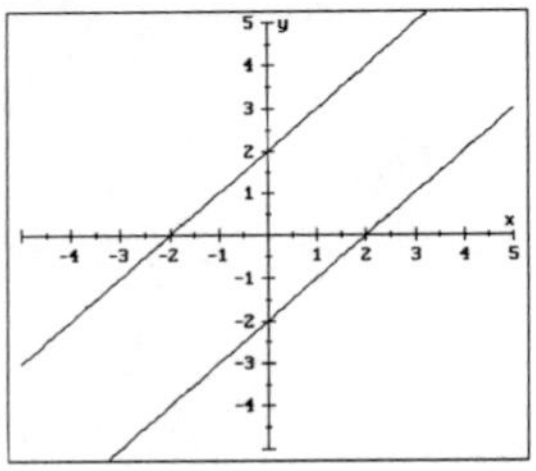

38.
$$x + y = 0$$
$$y + x = 0$$
$$y = -x$$
$$f^{-1}(x) = -x$$

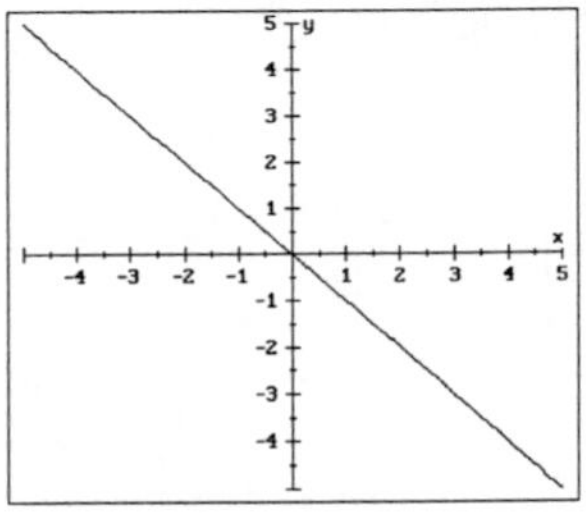

39.
$$2x + y = 4$$
$$2y + x = 4$$
$$2y = 4 - x$$
$$y = \frac{4-x}{2}$$
$$f^{-1}(x) = \frac{4-x}{2}$$

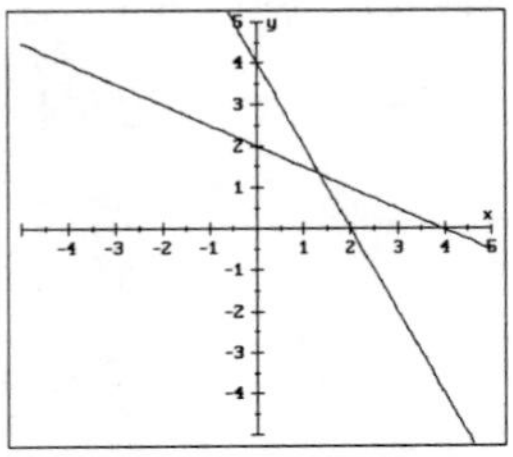

40.
$$3x + 2y = 6$$
$$3y + 2x = 6$$
$$3y = 6 - 2x$$
$$y = \frac{6-2x}{3}$$
$$f^{-1}(x) = \frac{6-2x}{3}$$

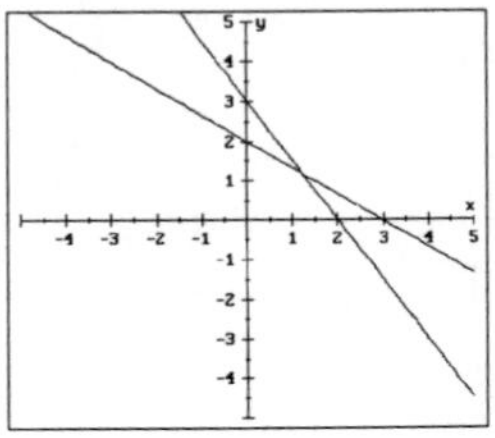

41.

$$\begin{aligned} y &= \frac{1}{2x} \\ x &= \frac{1}{2y} \\ 2xy &= 1 \\ y &= \frac{1}{2x} \\ f^{-1}(x) &= \frac{1}{2x} \end{aligned}$$

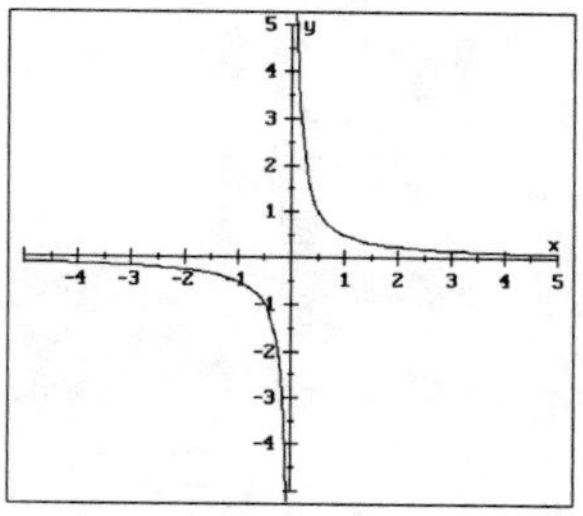

42.

$$\begin{aligned} y &= \frac{1}{x-3} \\ x &= \frac{1}{y-3} \\ x(y-3) &= 1 \\ y-3 &= \frac{1}{x} \\ f^{-1}(x) &= \frac{1}{x}+3 \end{aligned}$$

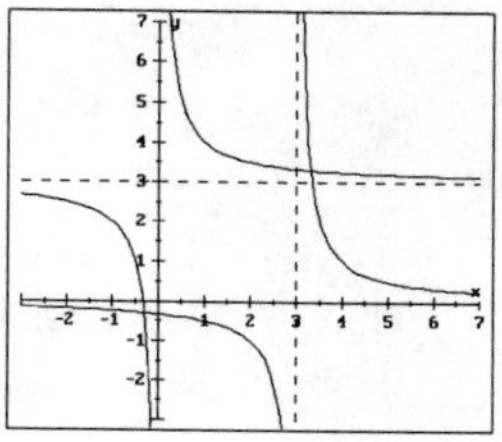

43.

$$\begin{aligned} y &= \frac{x+1}{x-1} \\ x &= \frac{y+1}{y-1} \\ x(y-1) &= y+1 \\ xy-x &= y+1 \\ xy-y &= x+1 \\ y(x-1) &= x+1 \\ f^{-1}(x) &= \frac{x+1}{x-1} \end{aligned}$$

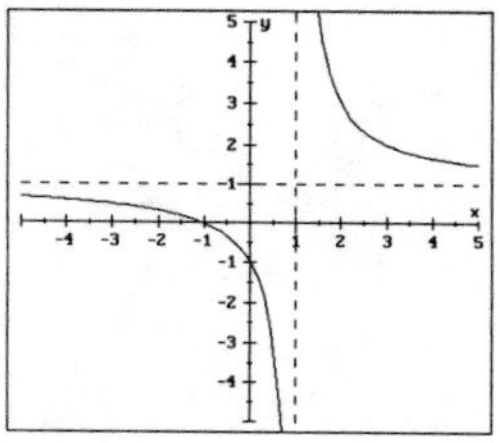

44.

$$\begin{aligned} y &= \frac{x-1}{x} \\ x &= \frac{y-1}{y} \\ xy &= y-1 \\ xy-y &= -1 \\ y(x-1) &= -1 \\ f^{-1}(x) &= \frac{-1}{x-1} \\ &= \frac{1}{1-x} \end{aligned}$$

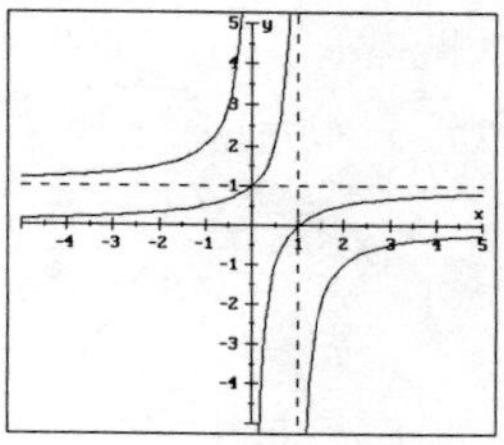

45.

$$\begin{aligned} f(x) &= x^2-3 & x &\le 0 \\ y &= x^2-3 & x &\le 0 \\ x &= y^2-3 & y &\le 0 \\ x+3 &= y^2 & y &\le 0 \\ \pm\sqrt{x+3} &= y & y &\le 0 \end{aligned}$$

Thus, $f^{-1}(x) = -\sqrt{x+3}$ $(x \ge -3)$.

46.

$$\begin{aligned} f(x) &= \frac{1}{x^2} & x &> 0 \\ y &= \frac{1}{x^2} & x &> 0 \\ x &= \frac{1}{y^2} & y &> 0 \\ xy^2 &= 1 & y &> 0 \\ y^2 &= \frac{1}{x} & y &> 0 \\ y &= \pm\sqrt{\frac{1}{x}} & y &> 0 \end{aligned}$$

Thus, $f^{-1}(x) = \sqrt{\frac{1}{x}}$ $(x > 0)$.

47.
$$\begin{aligned} f(x) &= x^4 - 8 \quad & x \geq 0 \\ y &= x^4 - 8 & x \geq 0 \\ x &= y^4 - 8 & y \geq 0 \\ x + 8 &= y^4 & y \geq 0 \\ \pm\sqrt[4]{x+8} &= y & y \geq 0 \end{aligned}$$
Thus, $f^{-1}(x) = \sqrt[4]{x+8}$ $(x \geq -8)$.

48.
$$\begin{aligned} f(x) &= \frac{-1}{x^4} \quad & x < 0 \\ y &= \frac{-1}{x^4} & x < 0 \\ x &= \frac{-1}{y^4} & y < 0 \\ xy^4 &= -1 & y < 0 \\ y^4 &= \frac{-1}{x} & y < 0 \\ y &= \pm\sqrt[4]{\frac{-1}{x}} & y < 0 \end{aligned}$$
Thus, $f^{-1}(x) = -\sqrt[4]{\frac{-1}{x}}$ $(x < 0)$.

49.
$$\begin{aligned} f(x) &= \sqrt{4-x^2} \quad & 0 \leq x \leq 2 \\ y &= \sqrt{4-x^2} & 0 \leq x \leq 2 \\ x &= \sqrt{4-y^2} & 0 \leq y \leq 2 \\ x^2 &= 4 - y^2 & 0 \leq y \leq 2 \\ y^2 &= 4 - x^2 & 0 \leq y \leq 2 \\ y &= \pm\sqrt{4-x^2} & 0 \leq y \leq 2 \end{aligned}$$
Thus, $f^{-1}(x) = \sqrt{4-x^2}$ $(0 \leq x \leq 2)$.

50.
$$\begin{aligned} f(x) &= \sqrt{x^2-1} \quad & x \leq -1 \\ y &= \sqrt{x^2-1} & x \leq -1 \\ x &= \sqrt{y^2-1} & y \leq -1 \\ x^2 &= y^2 - 1 & y \leq -1 \\ y^2 &= x^2 + 1 & y \leq -1 \\ y &= \pm\sqrt{x^2+1} & y \leq -1 \end{aligned}$$
Thus, $f^{-1}(x) = -\sqrt{x^2+1}$ $(x \geq 0)$.

51. $f(x) = \dfrac{x}{x-1}$

Domain of $f = \boxed{(-\infty, 1) \cup (1, \infty)}$

$f^{-1}(x) = \dfrac{x}{x-1}$

Range of f = Domain of f^{-1}

$= \boxed{(-\infty, 1) \cup (1, \infty)}$

52. $f(x) = \dfrac{x-2}{x+3}$

Domain of $f = \boxed{(-\infty, -3) \cup (-3, \infty)}$

$f^{-1}(x) = \dfrac{3x+2}{1-x}$

Range of f = Domain of f^{-1}

$= \boxed{(-\infty, 1) \cup (1, \infty)}$

53. $f(x) = \dfrac{1}{x} - 2$

Domain of $f = \boxed{(-\infty, 0) \cup (0, \infty)}$

$f^{-1}(x) = \dfrac{1}{x+2}$

Range of f = Domain of f^{-1}

$= \boxed{(-\infty, -2) \cup (-2, \infty)}$

54. $f(x) = \dfrac{3}{x} - \dfrac{1}{2}$

Domain of $f = \boxed{(-\infty, 0) \cup (0, \infty)}$

$f^{-1}(x) = \dfrac{3}{x + \frac{1}{2}}$

Range of f = Domain of f^{-1}

$= \boxed{(-\infty, -\frac{1}{2}) \cup (-\frac{1}{2}, \infty)}$

55. **a.** $y = 0.75x + 8.50$

b. $y = 0.75(4) + 8.50$
$= \$11.50$

c.
$$\begin{aligned} y &= 0.75x + 8.50 \\ x &= 0.75y + 8.50 \\ x - 8.50 &= 0.75y \\ \frac{x - 8.50}{0.75} &= y \end{aligned}$$

d.
$$\begin{aligned} y &= \frac{x - 8.50}{0.75} \\ &= \frac{10 - 8.50}{0.75} \\ &= \frac{1.50}{0.75} = 2 \end{aligned}$$

56. **a.** $y = \dfrac{0.05x + 11}{x}$

b. $y = \dfrac{0.05(68) + 11}{68}$
$\approx \$0.212 = 21.2¢$

c.
$$\begin{aligned} y &= \frac{0.05x + 11}{x} \\ x &= \frac{0.05y + 11}{y} \\ xy &= 0.05y + 11 \\ xy - 0.05y &= 11 \\ y(x - 0.05) &= 11 \\ y &= \frac{11}{x - 0.05} \end{aligned}$$

d.
$$\begin{aligned} y &= \frac{11}{x - 0.05} \\ &= \frac{11}{0.15 - 0.05} \\ &= \frac{11}{0.10} = 110 \end{aligned}$$

57. **Answers may vary.**

58. **Answers may vary.**

59. $a \geq 0$

60. $a = 0$

61. $16^{3/4} = \left(16^{1/4}\right)^3 = 8$

62. $25^{-1/2} = \dfrac{1}{25^{1/2}} = \dfrac{1}{5}$

63. $(-8)^{2/3} = \left((-8)^{1/3}\right)^2 = 4$

64. $-8^{2/3} = -1 \cdot 8^{2/3} = -1\left(\left(8^{1/3}\right)^2\right) = -4$

65. $\left(\dfrac{64}{125}\right)^{-1/3} = \left(\dfrac{125}{64}\right)^{1/3} = \dfrac{5}{4}$

66. $49^{3/2} = \left(49^{1/2}\right)^3 = 343$

67. $49^{-1/2} = \dfrac{1}{49^{1/2}} = \dfrac{1}{7}$

68.
$$\begin{aligned} \left(\frac{9}{25}\right)^{-3/2} &= \left(\frac{25}{9}\right)^{3/2} = \left(\left(\frac{25}{9}\right)^{1/2}\right)^3 \\ &= \frac{125}{27} \end{aligned}$$

Chapter 3 Summary (page 315)

1. **a.** $y = 3$
Each value of x is paired with only one value of y.
function

b. $y + 5x^2 = 2$
$y = -5x^2 + 2$
Each value of x is paired with only one value of y.
function

c. $y^2 - x = 5$

$y^2 = x + 5$

$y = \pm\sqrt{x+5}$

Each value of x is paired with more than one value of y.

not a function

d. $y = |x| + x$

Each value of x is paired with only one value of y.

function

2. a. $f(x) = y = 3x^2 - 5$: domain $= (-\infty, \infty)$

$x = \pm\sqrt{\dfrac{y+5}{3}}$: range $= [-5, \infty)$

b. $f(x) = y = \dfrac{3x}{x-5}$: domain $= (-\infty, 5) \cup (5, \infty)$

$x = \dfrac{5y}{y-3}$: range $= (-\infty, 3) \cup (3, \infty)$

c. $f(x) = y = \sqrt{x-1} \Rightarrow$ domain $= [1, \infty)$

note: $\sqrt{x-1} \geq 0$, so $y \geq 0 \Rightarrow$ range $= [0, \infty)$

d. $f(x) = y = \sqrt{x^2+1} \Rightarrow x^2 + 1 \geq 0 \Rightarrow$ domain $= (-\infty, \infty)$

note: $\sqrt{x^2+1} \geq 1$, so $y \geq 1 \Rightarrow$ range $= [1, \infty)$

3. a. $f(x) = 5x - 2$

$f(2) = 5(2) - 2 = 8$

$f(-3) = 5(-3) - 2 = -17$

$f(0) = 5(0) - 2 = -2$

b. $f(x) = \dfrac{6}{x-5}$

$f(2) = \dfrac{6}{2-5} = \dfrac{6}{-3} = -2$

$f(-3) = \dfrac{6}{-3-5} = \dfrac{6}{-8} = -\dfrac{3}{4}$

$f(0) = \dfrac{6}{0-5} = \dfrac{6}{-5} = -\dfrac{6}{5}$

c. $f(x) = |x - 2|$

$f(2) = |2 - 2| = |0| = 0$

$f(-3) = |-3 - 2| = |-5| = 5$

$f(0) = |0 - 2| = |-2| = 2$

d. $f(x) = \dfrac{x^2-3}{x^2+3}$

$f(2) = \dfrac{2^2-3}{2^2+3} = \dfrac{1}{7}$

$f(-3) = \dfrac{(-3)^2-3}{(-3)^2+3} = \dfrac{6}{12} = \dfrac{1}{2}$

$f(0) = \dfrac{0^2-3}{0^2+3} = \dfrac{-3}{3} = -1$

4. **a.** $y = x^2 - x;\ a = 1, b = -1, c = 0$

vertex: $x = -\frac{b}{2a} = -\frac{-1}{2(1)} = \frac{1}{2}$

$y = x^2 - x = \left(\frac{1}{2}\right)^2 - \frac{1}{2} = -\frac{1}{4}$

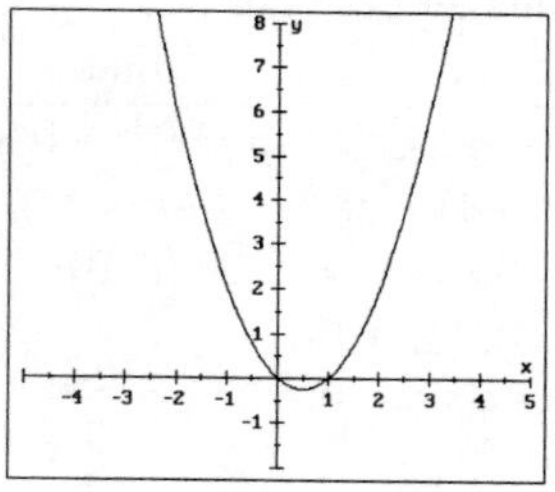

b. $y = x - x^2;\ a = -1, b = 1, c = 0$

vertex: $x = -\frac{b}{2a} = -\frac{1}{2(-1)} = \frac{1}{2}$

$y = x - x^2 = \frac{1}{2} - \left(\frac{1}{2}\right)^2 = \frac{1}{4}$

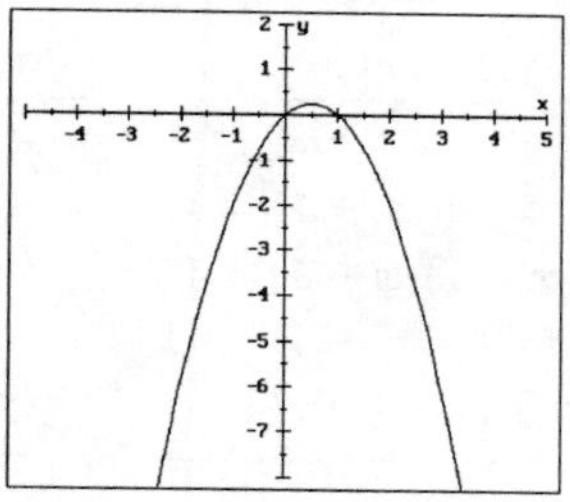

c. $y = x^2 - 3x - 4;\ a = 1, b = -3, c = -4$

vertex: $x = -\frac{b}{2a} = -\frac{-3}{2(1)} = \frac{3}{2}$

$y = x^2 - 3x - 4 = \left(\frac{3}{2}\right)^2 - 3\left(\frac{3}{2}\right) - 4$

$= -\frac{25}{4}$

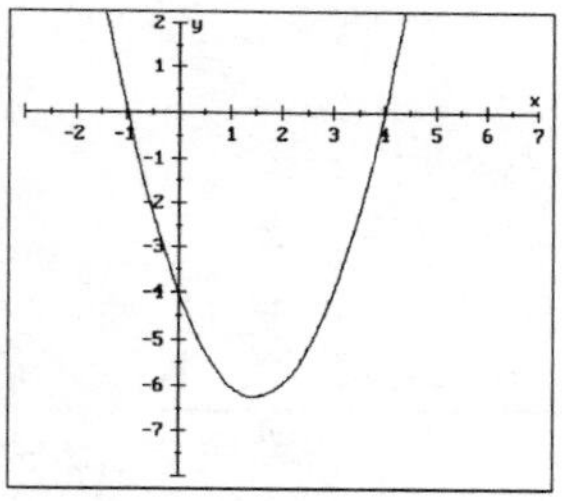

d. $y = 3x^2 - 8x - 3$

$a = 3, b = -8, c = -3$

vertex: $x = -\frac{b}{2a} = -\frac{-8}{2(3)} = \frac{4}{3}$

$y = 3x^2 - 8x - 3 = 3\left(\frac{4}{3}\right)^2 - 8\left(\frac{4}{3}\right) - 3$

$= -\frac{25}{3}$

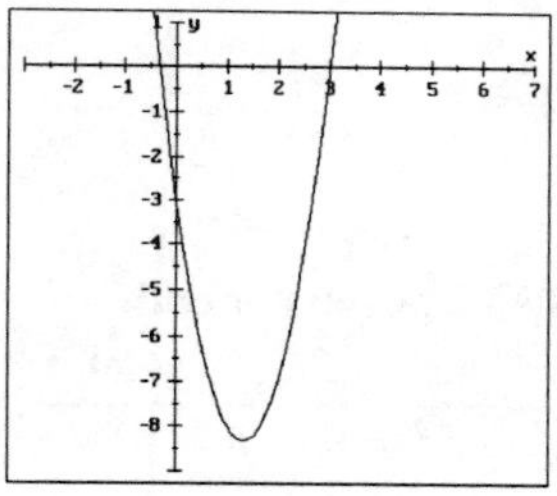

5. **a.** $3x^2 + y - 300 = 0$

$y = -3x^2 + 300$

$a = -3, b = 0, c = 300$

$x = -\frac{b}{2a} = -\frac{0}{2(-3)} = 0$

$y = -3(0)^2 + 300 = 300$

The maximum height is 300 units.

6. Let the numbers be x and $1 - x$.

Product $= x(1 - x)$

$y = x - x^2$: $a = -1, b = 1, c = 0$

vertex: $x = -\frac{b}{2a} = -\frac{1}{2(-1)} = \frac{1}{2}$

Both numbers are $\frac{1}{2}$.

7. **a.** $y = f(x) = x^3 - x$

$f(-x) = (-x)^3 - (-x)$

$= -x^3 + x$

$= -f(x) \Rightarrow$ odd

x-int.	y-int.
$x^3 - x = 0$	$y = 0^3 - 0$
$x(x^2 - 1) = 0$	$y = 0$
$x(x+1)(x-1) = 0$	$(0, 0)$
$x = 0, x = -1, x = 1$	
$(0, 0), (-1, 0), (1, 0)$	

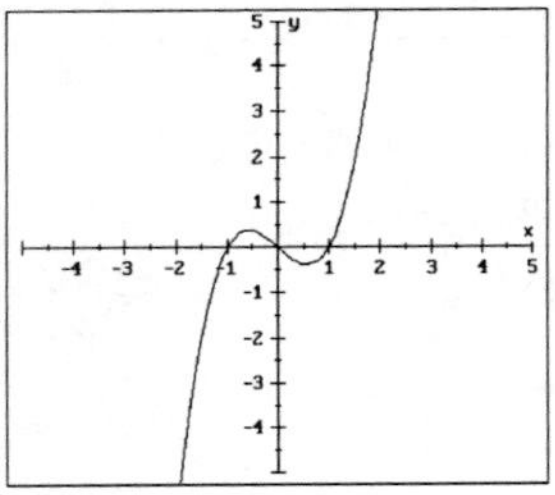

b. $f(x) = x^2 - 4x$

$f(-x) = (-x)^2 - 4(-x)$

$= x^2 + 4x$

$\Rightarrow$ neither even nor odd

x-int.	y-int.
$x^2 - 4x = 0$	$y = 0^2 - 4(0)$
$x(x-4) = 0$	$y = 0$
$x = 0, x = 4$	$(0, 0)$
$(0, 0), (4, 0)$	

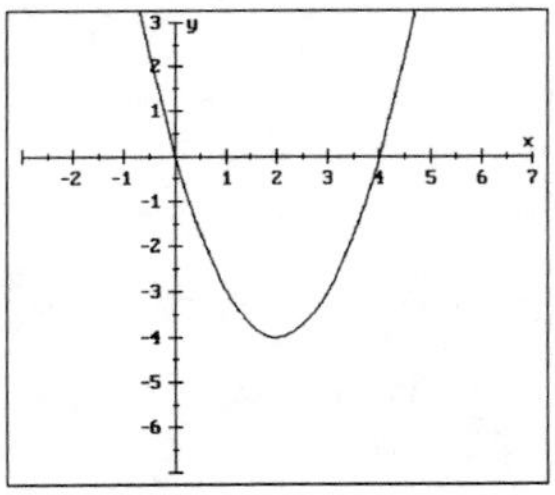

c. $f(x) = x^3 - x^2$

$f(-x) = (-x)^3 - (-x)^2$

$= -x^3 - x^2$

$\Rightarrow$ neither even nor odd

x-int.	y-int.
$x^3 - x^2 = 0$	$y = 0^3 - 0^2$
$x^2(x-1) = 0$	$y = 0$
$x = 0, x = 1$	$(0, 0)$
$(0, 0), (1, 0)$	

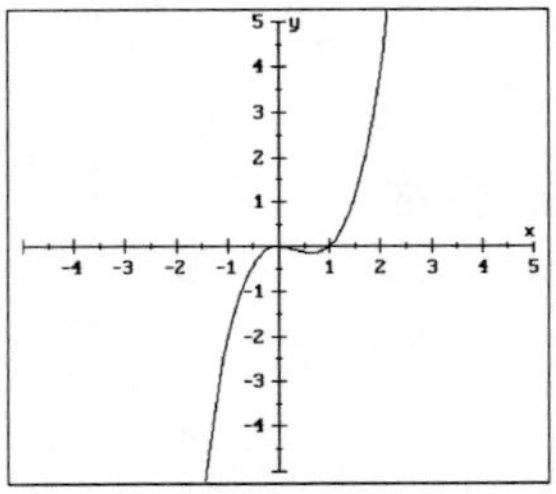

d. $y = f(x) = 1 - x^4$

$f(-x) = 1 - (-x)^4$

$= 1 - x^4 = f(x) \Rightarrow$ even

x-int.	y-int.
$1 - x^4 = 0$	$y = 1 - 0^4$
$(1 + x^2)(1 - x^2) = 0$	$y = 1$
$x^2 = -1, x^2 = 1$	$(0, 1)$
$x = -1, x = 1$	
$(-1, 0), (1, 0)$	

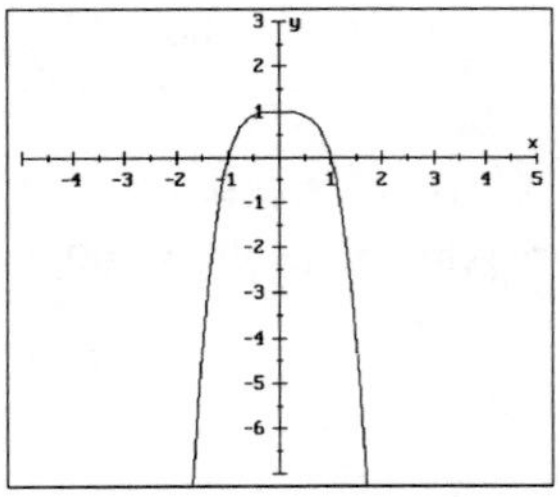

8. **a.** inc: $(-\infty, 0)$; dec: $(0, \infty)$

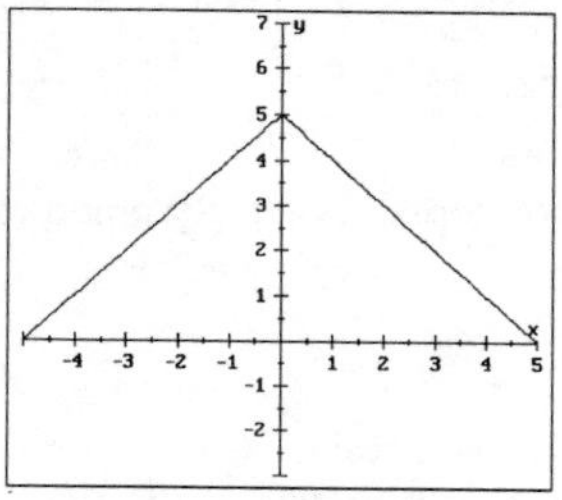

b. inc: $(-\infty, 0)$; const: $(0, \infty)$

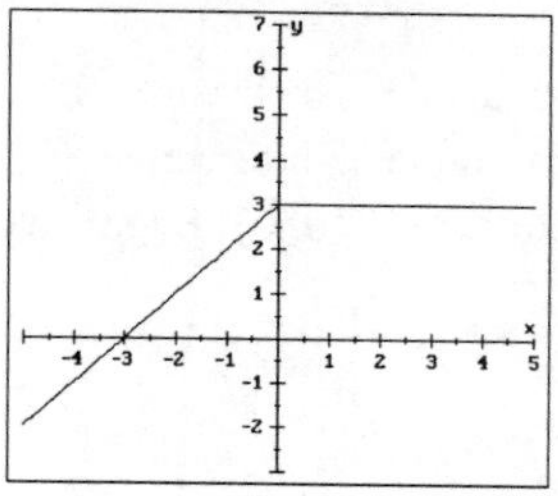

9. **a.** $y = \sqrt{x+2} + 3$
Shift $y = \sqrt{x}$ U 3, L 2

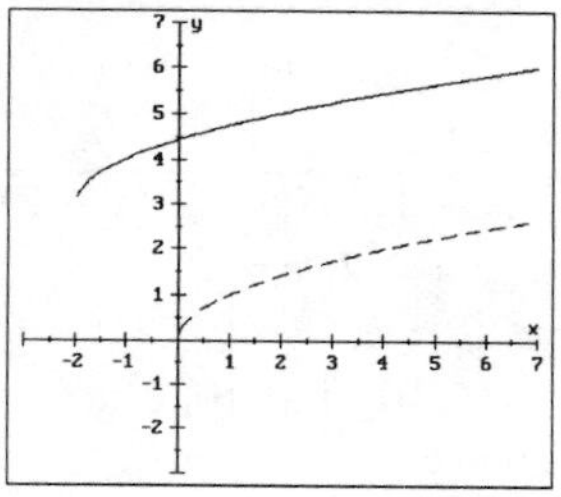

b. $y = |x-4| + 2$
Shift $y = |x|$ U 2, R 4

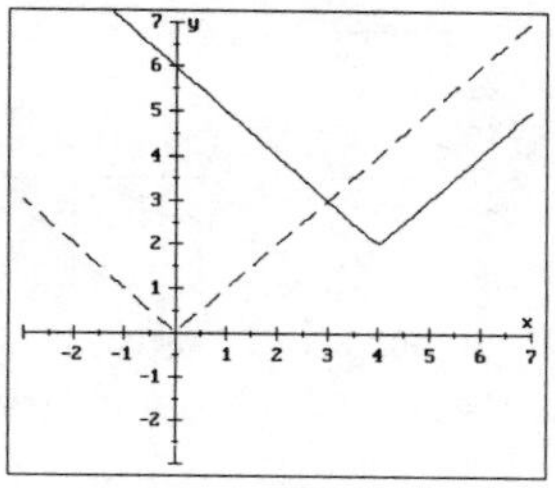

10. **a.** $y = \dfrac{1}{3}x^3$: Stretch
$y = x^3$ vert. by a factor of $\frac{1}{3}$

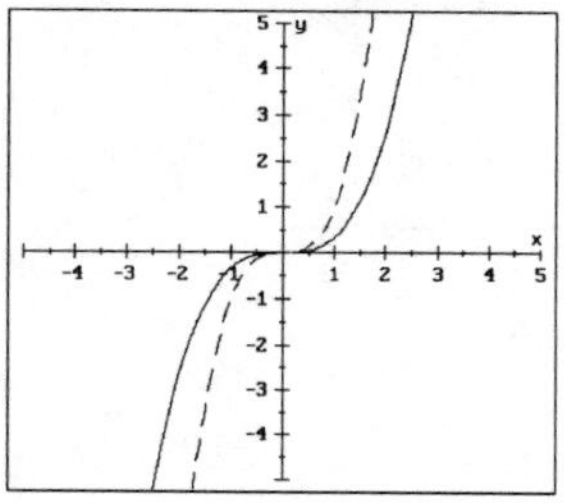

b. $y = (-5x)^3$: Stretch $y = x^3$ hor. by a factor of $\frac{1}{5}$. Reflect about y.

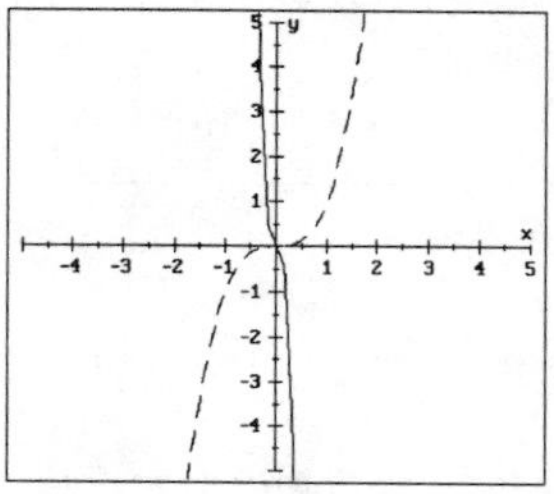

11. **a.** $y = \dfrac{x}{(x-1)^2}$

Vert: $x = 1$; Horiz: $y = 0$
Slant: none; x-intercepts: $(0, 0)$
y-intercepts: $(0, 0)$; Symmetry: none

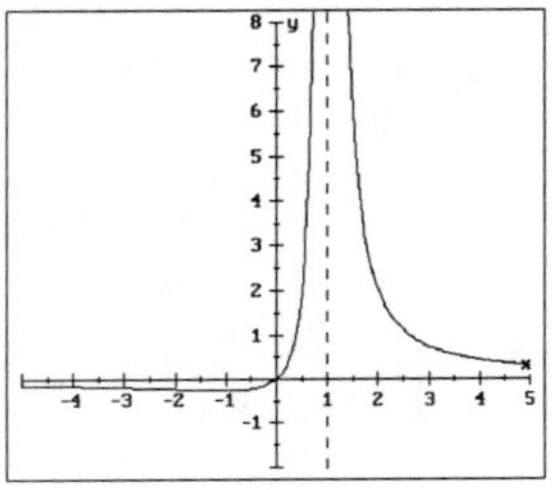

b. $y = \dfrac{(x-1)^2}{x}$: Vert: $x = 0$

Horiz: none; Slant: $y = x - 2$
x-intercepts: $(1, 0)$
y-intercepts: none; Symmetry: none

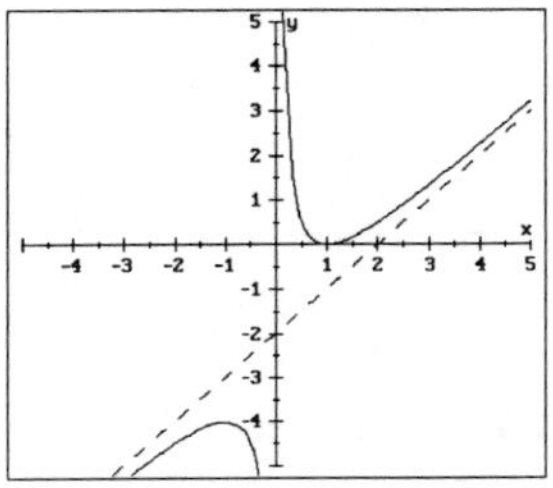

c. $y = \dfrac{x^2 - x - 2}{x^2 + x - 2} = \dfrac{(x+1)(x-2)}{(x+2)(x-1)}$

Vert: $x = -2$, $x = 1$; Horiz: $y = 1$
Slant: none; x-intercepts: $(-1, 0)$, $(2, 0)$
y-intercepts: $(0, 1)$; Symmetry: none

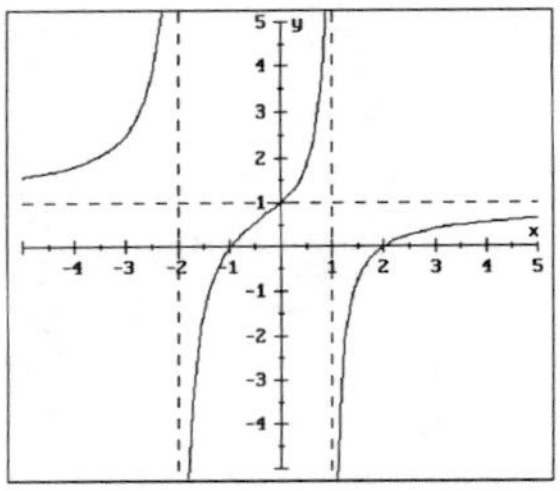

d. $y = \dfrac{x^3 + x}{x^2 - 4} = \dfrac{x(x^2+1)}{(x+2)(x-2)}$

Vert: $x = -2$, $x = 2$;
Slant: $y = x$;
x-int: $(0, 0)$$y$-int: $(0, 0)$;
Symmetry: none

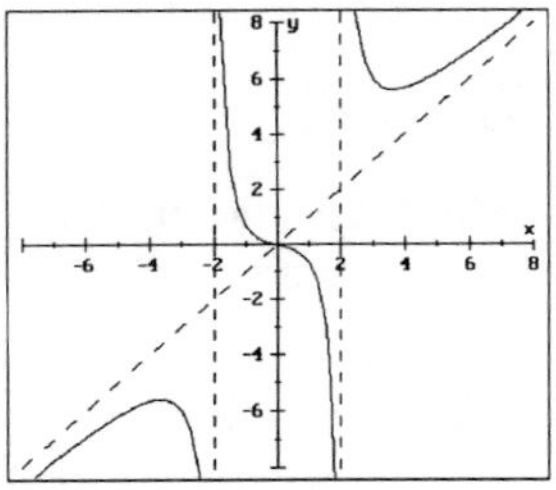

12. **a.** $(f+g)(x) = f(x) + g(x) = (x^2 - 1) + (2x + 1) = x^2 + 2x$

b. $(f \cdot g)(x) = f(x)g(x) = (x^2 - 1)(2x + 1) = 2x^3 + x^2 - 2x - 1$

c. $(f - g)(x) = f(x) - g(x) = (x^2 - 1) - (2x + 1) = x^2 - 2x - 2$

d. $(f/g)(x) = \dfrac{f(x)}{g(x)} = \dfrac{x^2 - 1}{2x + 1}$

e. $(f \circ g)(x) = f(g(x)) = f(2x + 1) = (2x + 1)^2 - 1 = 4x^2 + 4x + 1 - 1 = 4x^2 + 4x$

f. $(g \circ f)(x) = g(f(x)) = g(x^2 - 1) = 2(x^2 - 1) + 1 = 2x^2 - 2 + 1 = 2x^2 - 1$

13. **a.**
$$\begin{aligned} y = f(x) &= 7x - 1 \\ x &= 7y - 1 \\ x + 1 &= 7y \\ \frac{x+1}{7} &= y \\ f^{-1}(x) &= \frac{x+1}{7} \end{aligned}$$

b.
$$\begin{aligned} y = f(x) &= \frac{1}{2-x} \\ x &= \frac{1}{2-y} \\ x(2-y) &= 1 \\ 2 - y &= \frac{1}{x} \\ 2 - \frac{1}{x} &= y \\ f^{-1}(x) &= 2 - \frac{1}{x} \end{aligned}$$

c.
$$\begin{aligned} y = f(x) &= \frac{x}{1-x} \\ x &= \frac{y}{1-y} \\ x(1-y) &= y \\ x - xy &= y \\ x &= xy + y \\ x &= y(x+1) \\ \frac{x}{x+1} &= y \\ f^{-1}(x) &= \frac{x}{x+1} \end{aligned}$$

d.
$$\begin{aligned} y = f(x) &= \frac{3}{x^3} \\ x &= \frac{3}{y^3} \\ xy^3 &= 3 \\ y^3 &= \frac{3}{x} \\ y &= \sqrt[3]{\frac{3}{x}} \\ f^{-1}(x) &= \sqrt[3]{\frac{3}{x}} \end{aligned}$$

14.
$$\begin{aligned} y &= \frac{2x+3}{5x-10} \\ x &= \frac{2y+3}{5y-10} \\ x(5y-10) &= 2y+3 \\ 5xy - 10x &= 2y + 3 \\ 5xy - 2y &= 10x + 3 \\ y(5x-2) &= 10x + 3 \\ y &= \frac{10x+3}{5x-2} \end{aligned}$$

Range of f = Domain of f^{-1}
$= \boxed{\left(-\infty, \frac{2}{5}\right) \cup \left(\frac{2}{5}, \infty\right)}$

Chapter 3 Test (page 319)

1. $f(x) = \dfrac{3}{x-5}$: domain $= (-\infty, 5) \cup (5, \infty)$
$x = \dfrac{3}{x} + 5$: range $= (-\infty, 0) \cup (0, \infty)$

2. $f(x) = \sqrt{x+3}$: domain $= [-3, \infty)$
Since $\sqrt{x+3} \geq 0$, range $= [0, \infty)$.

3. $f(-1) = \dfrac{-1}{-1-1} = \dfrac{-1}{-2} = \dfrac{1}{2}$
$f(2) = \dfrac{2}{2-1} = \dfrac{2}{1} = 2$

4. $f(-1) = \sqrt{-1+7} = \sqrt{6}$
$f(2) = \sqrt{2+7} = \sqrt{9} = 3$

5. $y = 3(x-7)^2 - 3$
Vertex: $(7, -3)$

6. $y = x^2 - 2x - 3$; $a = 1, b = -2, c = -3$
vertex: $x = -\frac{b}{2a} = -\frac{-2}{2(1)} = 1$
$y = x^2 - 2x - 3 = 1^2 - 2(1) - 3 = -4$

7. $y = 3x^2 - 24x + 38$
$a = 3, b = -24, c = 38$
vertex: $x = -\frac{b}{2a} = -\frac{-24}{2(3)} = 4$
$y = 3x^2 - 24x + 38 = 3(4)^2 - 24(4) + 38$
$= -10$

8. $y = 5 - 4x - x^2$; $a = -1, b = -4, c = 5$
vertex: $x = -\frac{b}{2a} = -\frac{-4}{2(-1)} = -2$
$y = 5 - 4x - x^2 = 5 - 4(-2) - (-2)^2$
$= 9$

9. $y = f(x) = x^4 - x^2$
$f(-x) = (-x)^4 - (-x)^2$
$= x^4 - x^2 = f(x) \Rightarrow$ even

x-int.	y-int.
$x^4 - x^2 = 0$	$y = 0^4 - 0^2$
$x^2(x^2 - 1) = 0$	$y = 0$
$x^2 = 0, x^2 = 1$	$(0, 0)$
$x = 0, x = -1, x = 1$	
$(0, 0), (-1, 0), (1, 0)$	

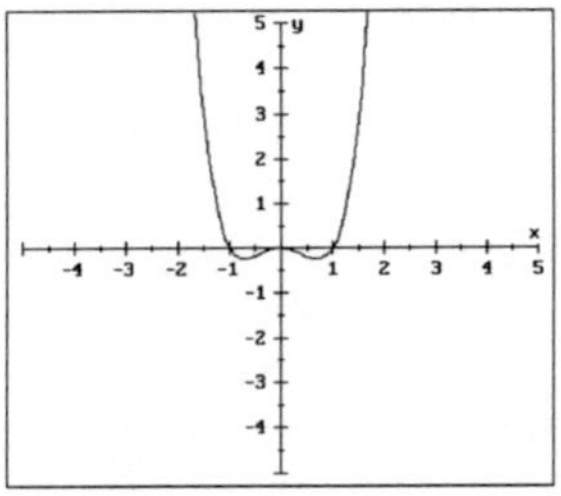

10. $y = f(x) = x^5 - x^3$
$f(-x) = (-x)^5 - (-x)^3$
$= -x^5 - (-x)^3$
$= -x^5 + x^3 = -f(x) \Rightarrow$ odd

x-int.	y-int.
$x^5 - x^3 = 0$	$y = 0^5 - 0^3$
$x^3(x^2 - 1) = 0$	$y = 0$
$x^3 = 0, x^2 = 1$	$(0, 0)$
$x = 0, x = -1, x = 1$	
$(0, 0), (-1, 0), (1, 0)$	

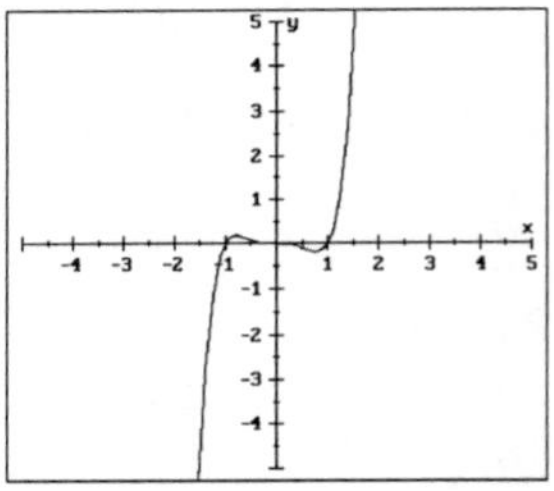

11. $h = 100t - 16t^2$: $a = -16, b = 100, c = 0$
$$x = -\frac{b}{2a} = -\frac{100}{2(-16)} = \frac{25}{8} \text{ seconds}$$

12. $h = 100t - 16t^2$: $a = -16, b = 100, c = 0$
From **#11**, $x = \frac{25}{8}$.
$y = 100\left(\frac{25}{8}\right) - 16\left(\frac{25}{8}\right)^2 = \frac{625}{4}$ feet

13. The roadway is at $y=0$, so the distance to the lowest point will be the y-coord. of the vertex:

$$x^2 - 2500y + 25000 = 0$$
$$x^2 + 25000 = 2500y$$
$$\frac{1}{2500}x^2 + 10 = y$$
$$y = c - \frac{b^2}{4a} = 10 - \frac{0^2}{4\left(\frac{1}{2500}\right)} = 10$$

The lowest point is 10 ft above.

14. Let $x = \pm 500$:

$$x^2 - 2500y + 25000 = 0$$
$$(\pm 500)^2 - 2500y + 25000 = 0$$
$$250{,}000 - 2500y + 25{,}000 = 0$$
$$275{,}000 = 2500y$$
$$110 = y$$

The cable attaches to the vertical pillars 110 feet above the roadway.

15. $y = (x-3)^2 + 1$

Shift $y = x^2$ U 1, R 3

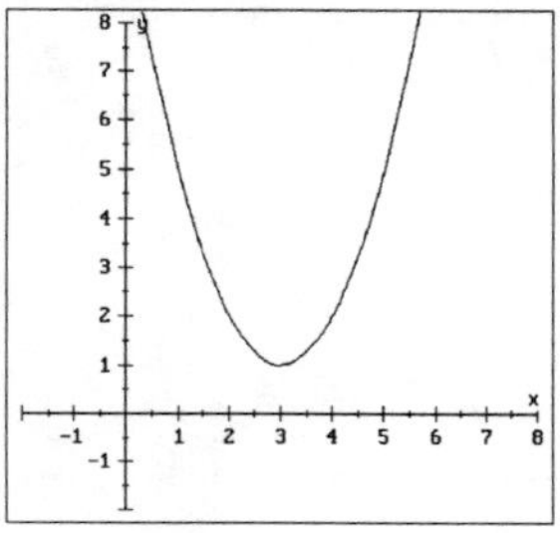

16. $y = \sqrt{x-1} + 5$

Shift $y = \sqrt{x}$ U 5, R 1

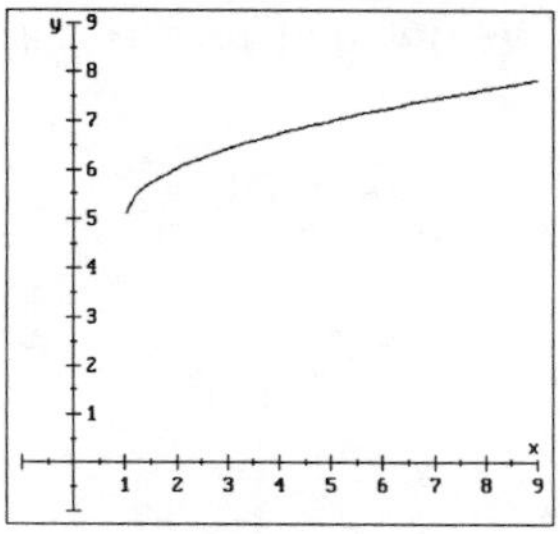

17. $y = \dfrac{x-1}{x^2-9} = \dfrac{x-1}{(x+3)(x-3)}$

Vert: $x=-3$, $x=3$; Horiz: $y=0$

18. $y = \dfrac{x^2-5x-14}{x-3} = \dfrac{(x-7)(x+2)}{(x-3)}$

$= x - 2 + \frac{-20}{x-3}$

Vert: $x=3$; Slant: $y = x-2$

19. $y = \dfrac{x^2}{x^2-9} = \dfrac{x^2}{(x+3)(x-3)}$

Vert: $x=-3$, $x=3$; Horiz: $y=1$

Slant: none; x-intercepts: $(0,0)$

y-intercepts: $(0,0)$; Symmetry: y-axis

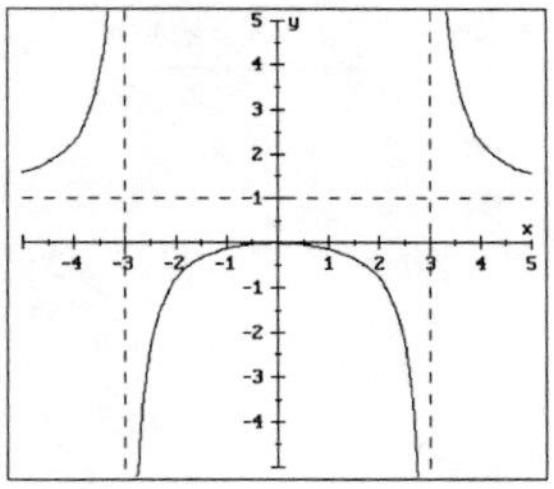

20. $y = \dfrac{x}{x^2+1}$

Vert: none; Horiz: $y=0$

Slant: none; x-intercepts: $(0,0)$

y-intercepts: $(0,0)$; Symmetry: origin

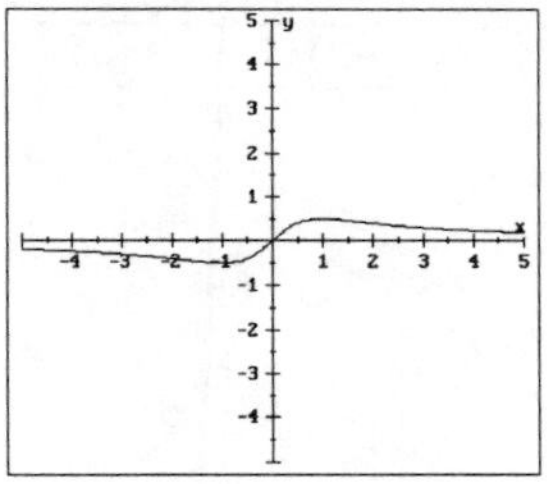

21. $y = \dfrac{2x^2 - 3x - 2}{x - 2} = \dfrac{(2x+1)(x-2)}{x-2}$
$= 2x + 1$ (if $x \neq 2$)

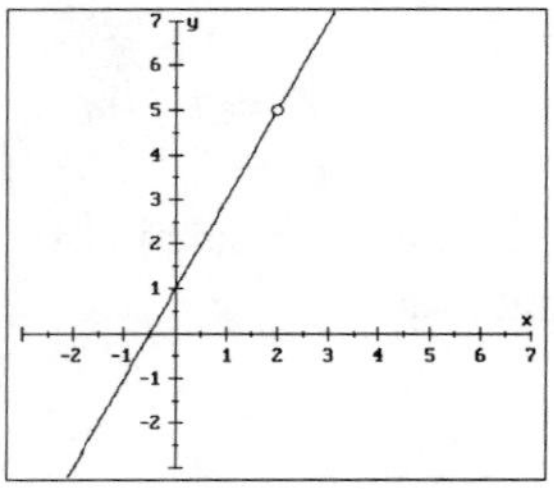

22. $y = \dfrac{x}{x^2 - x} = \dfrac{x}{x(x-1)} = \dfrac{1}{x-1}$ (if $x \neq 0$)

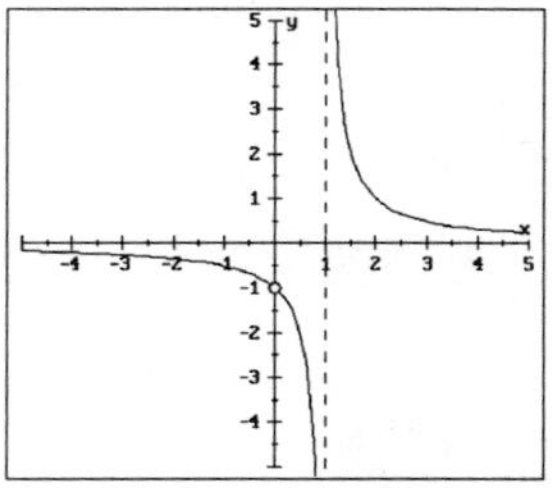

23. $(f+g)(x) = f(x) + g(x) = (3x) + (x^2 + 2) = x^2 + 3x + 2$

24. $(g \circ f)(x) = g(f(x)) = g(3x) = (3x)^2 + 2 = 9x^2 + 2$

25. $(f/g)(x) = \dfrac{f(x)}{g(x)} = \dfrac{3x}{x^2+2}$

26. $(f \circ g)(x) = f(g(x)) = f(x^2+2) = 3(x^2+2) = 3x^2 + 6$

27.
$$\begin{aligned} y &= \frac{x+1}{x-1} \\ x &= \frac{y+1}{y-1} \\ x(y-1) &= y+1 \\ xy - x &= y+1 \\ xy - y &= x+1 \\ y(x-1) &= x+1 \\ f^{-1}(x) &= \frac{x+1}{x-1} \end{aligned}$$

28.
$$\begin{aligned} y &= x^3 - 3 \\ x &= y^3 - 3 \\ x + 3 &= y^3 \\ \sqrt[3]{x+3} &= y \\ f^{-1}(x) &= \sqrt[3]{x+3} \end{aligned}$$

29. $f(x) = \dfrac{3}{x} - 2$; $f^{-1}(x) = \dfrac{3}{x+2}$
Range of f = Domain of f^{-1}
$= \boxed{(-\infty, -2) \cup (-2, \infty)}$

30. $f(x) = \dfrac{3x-1}{x-3}$; $f^{-1}(x) = \dfrac{3x-1}{x-3}$
Range of f = Domain of f^{-1}
$= \boxed{(-\infty, 3) \cup (3, \infty)}$

Cumulative Review Exercises (page 320)

1.
$$\begin{aligned} 5x - 3y &= 15 \\ 5x - 3(0) &= 15 \\ 5x &= 15 \\ x &= 3 \end{aligned} \qquad \begin{aligned} 5x - 3y &= 15 \\ 5(0) - 3y &= 15 \\ -3y &= 15 \\ y &= -5 \end{aligned}$$
(3, 0) (0, −5)

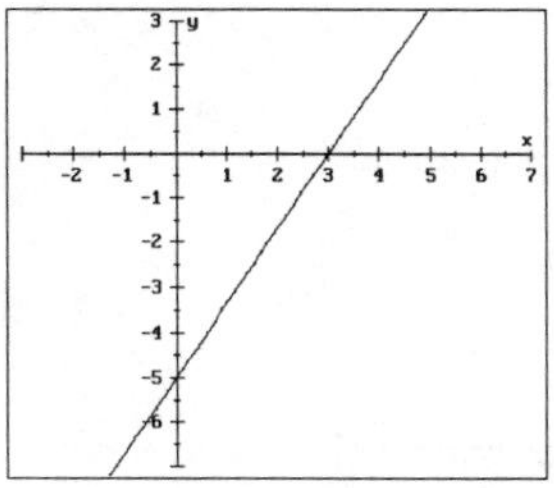

2.
$$\begin{aligned} 3x + 2y &= 12 \\ 3x + 2(0) &= 12 \\ 3x &= 12 \\ x &= 4 \end{aligned} \qquad \begin{aligned} 3x + 2y &= 12 \\ 3(0) + 2y &= 12 \\ 2y &= 12 \\ y &= 6 \end{aligned}$$
(4, 0) (0, 6)

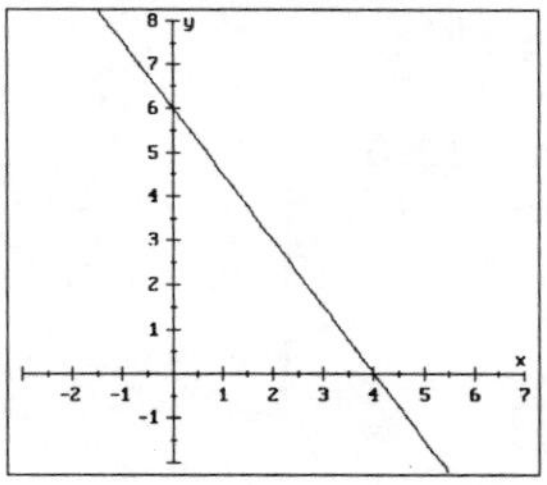

3. **a.** $d = \sqrt{(x_2 - x_1)^2 + (y_2 - y_1)^2} = \sqrt{(-2-3)^2 + \left(\frac{7}{2} - \left(-\frac{1}{2}\right)\right)^2} = \sqrt{25+16} = \sqrt{41}$

b. $x = \dfrac{x_1 + x_2}{2} = \dfrac{-2+3}{2} = \dfrac{1}{2}; y = \dfrac{\frac{7}{2} + \left(-\frac{1}{2}\right)}{2} = \dfrac{\frac{6}{2}}{2} = \dfrac{3}{2} \quad \left(\dfrac{1}{2}, \dfrac{3}{2}\right)$

c. $m = \dfrac{-\frac{1}{2} - \frac{7}{2}}{3 - (-2)} = \dfrac{-\frac{8}{2}}{5} = -\dfrac{4}{5}$

4. **a.** $d = \sqrt{(x_2 - x_1)^2 + (y_2 - y_1)^2} = \sqrt{(3 - (-7))^2 + (7-3)^2} = \sqrt{100+16} = \sqrt{116} = 2\sqrt{29}$

b. $x = \dfrac{x_1 + x_2}{2} = \dfrac{3 + (-7)}{2} = \dfrac{-4}{2} = -2; y = \dfrac{7+3}{2} = \dfrac{10}{2} = 5 \quad (-2, 5)$

c. $m = \dfrac{3-7}{-7-3} = \dfrac{-4}{-10} = \dfrac{2}{5}$

5.
$$\begin{aligned} m &= \frac{y_2 - y_1}{x_2 - x_1} = \frac{-7-5}{3-(-3)} = \frac{-12}{6} = -2 \\ y - y_1 &= m(x - x_1) \\ y - 5 &= -2(x+3) \\ y &= -2x - 1 \end{aligned}$$

6.
$$\begin{aligned} y - y_1 &= m(x - x_1) \\ y - \tfrac{5}{2} &= \tfrac{7}{2}\left(x - \tfrac{3}{2}\right) \\ y &= \tfrac{7}{2}x - \tfrac{21}{4} + \tfrac{5}{2} \\ y &= \tfrac{7}{2}x - \tfrac{11}{4} \end{aligned}$$

7.

$3x - 5y = 7$

$-5y = -3x + 7$

$y = \frac{3}{5}x - \frac{7}{5}$

$m = \frac{3}{5}$

Use $m = \frac{3}{5}$.

$y - y_1 = m(x - x_1)$

$y - 3 = \frac{3}{5}(x + 5)$

$y - 3 = \frac{3}{5}x + 3$

$\boxed{y = \frac{3}{5}x + 6}$

8.

$x - 4y = 12$

$-4y = -x + 12$

$y = \dfrac{1}{4}x - 3$

$m = \dfrac{1}{4}$

Use $m = -4$.

$y - y_1 = m(x - x_1)$

$y - 0 = -4(x - 0)$

$\boxed{y = -4x}$

9. $x^2 = y - 2$

symmetry: y-axis

x-int: none, y-int: $(2, 0)$

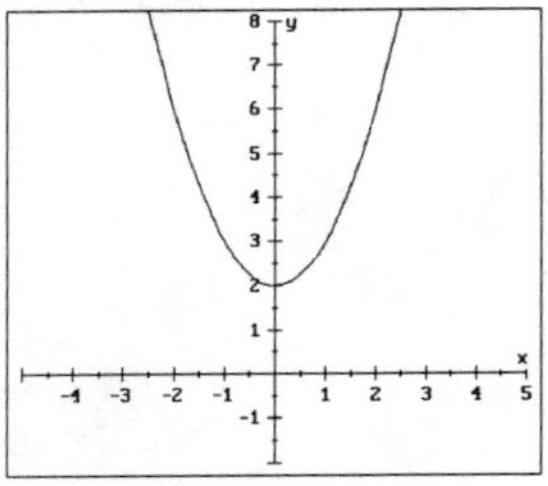

10. $y^2 = x - 2$

symmetry: x-axis

x-int: $(2, 0)$, y-int: none

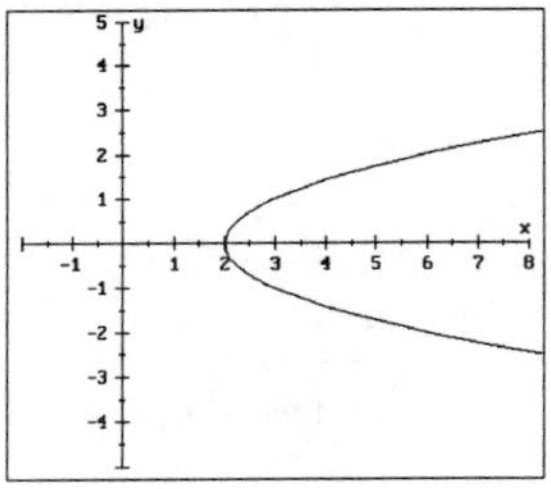

11. $x^2 + y^2 = 100$

Circle: $C(0, 0)$; $r = 10$

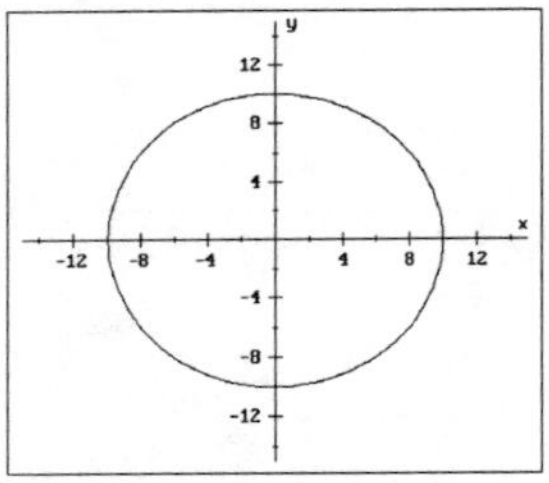

12. $x^2 - 2x + y^2 = 8$

$(x - 1)^2 + y^2 = 9$

Circle: $C(1, 0)$; $r = 3$

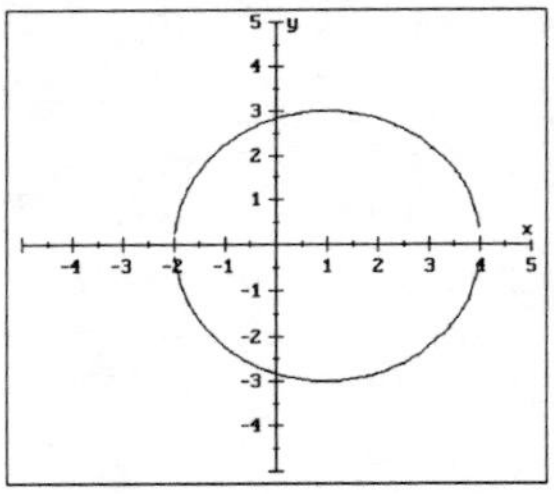

13.

$$\frac{x-2}{x} = \frac{x-6}{5}$$

$5(x - 2) = x(x - 6)$

$5x - 10 = x^2 - 6x$

$0 = x^2 - 11x + 10$

$0 = (x - 10)(x - 1)$

$x = 10$ or $x = 1$

14.

$$\frac{x+2}{x-6} = \frac{3x+1}{2x-11}$$

$(x + 2)(2x - 11) = (3x + 1)(x - 6)$

$2x^2 - 7x - 22 = 3x^2 - 17x - 6$

$0 = x^2 - 10x + 16$

$0 = (x - 8)(x - 2)$

$x = 8$ or $x = 2$

15. $m = \dfrac{54-37}{4-2} = \dfrac{17}{2} = 8.5$

$y = mx + b$
$y = 8.5x + b$
$37 = 8.5(2) + b$
$37 = 17 + b$
$20 = b$

$y = 8.5x + 20$
$y = 8.5(5) + 20$
$y = 62.50$
It will cost \$62.50.

16. $E = ks^2$

$E = k(50)^2 \qquad E = k(20)^2$
$E = 2500k \qquad E = 400k$
$\dfrac{50 \text{ mph } E}{20 \text{ mph } E} = \dfrac{2500k}{400k} = \dfrac{25}{4}$

17. $y = 3x - 1$: Each value of x is paired with only one value of y. $\Rightarrow$ **function**

18. $y = x^2 + 3$: Each value of x is paired with only one value of y. $\Rightarrow$ **function**

19. $y = \dfrac{1}{x-2}$: Each value of x is paired with only one value of y. $\Rightarrow$ **function**

20. $y^2 = 4x$
$y = \pm\sqrt{4x}$: Each value of x is paired with more than one value of y. $\Rightarrow$ **not a function**

21. $y = f(x) = x^2 + 5$: domain $= (-\infty, \infty)$; $x = \pm\sqrt{y-5}$: range $= [5, \infty)$

22. $y = f(x) = \dfrac{7}{x+2}$: domain $= (-\infty, -2) \cup (-2, \infty)$; $x = \dfrac{7}{y} - 2$: range $= (-\infty, 0) \cup (0, \infty)$

23. $y = f(x) = -\sqrt{x-2} \Rightarrow$ domain $= [2, \infty)$; $\sqrt{x-2} \geq 0$, so $-\sqrt{x-2} \leq 0 \Rightarrow$ range $= (-\infty, 0]$

24. $y = f(x) = \sqrt{x+4} \Rightarrow$ domain $= [-4, \infty)$; $\sqrt{x+4} \geq 0$, so $y \geq 0 \Rightarrow$ range $= [0, \infty)$

25. $y = x^2 + 5x - 6$; $a = 1, b = 5, c = -6$
vertex: $x = -\frac{b}{2a} = -\frac{5}{2(1)} = -\frac{5}{2}$
$y = x^2 + 5x - 6 = \left(-\frac{5}{2}\right)^2 + 5\left(-\frac{5}{2}\right) - 6$
$= -\frac{49}{4}$

26. $y = -x^2 + 5x + 6$; $a = -1, b = 5, c = 6$
vertex: $x = -\frac{b}{2a} = -\frac{5}{2(-1)} = \frac{5}{2}$
$y = -x^2 + 5x + 6 = -\left(\frac{5}{2}\right)^2 + 5\left(\frac{5}{2}\right) + 6$
$= \frac{49}{4}$

27. $y = x^2 - 4$: Shift $y = x^2$ D 4.

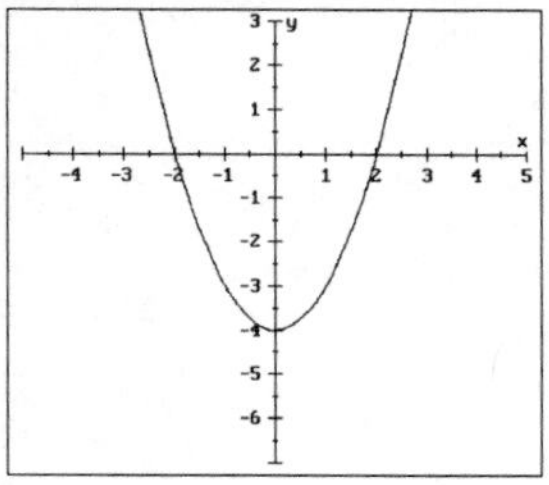

28. $y = -x^2 + 4$: Reflect $y = x^2$ about x and shift U 4.

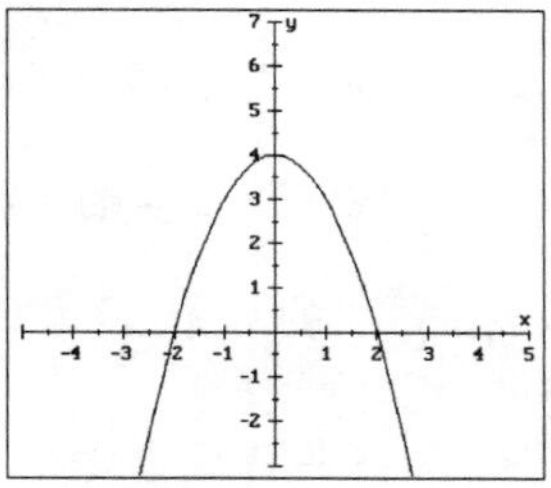

29. $y = f(x) = x^3 + x$

$$f(-x) = (-x)^3 + (-x) = -x^3 - x = -f(x) \Rightarrow \text{odd}$$

x-int.	y-int.
$x^3 + x = 0$	$y = 0^3 + 0$
$x(x^2+1) = 0$	$y = 0$
$x = 0$	$(0, 0)$
$(0, 0)$	

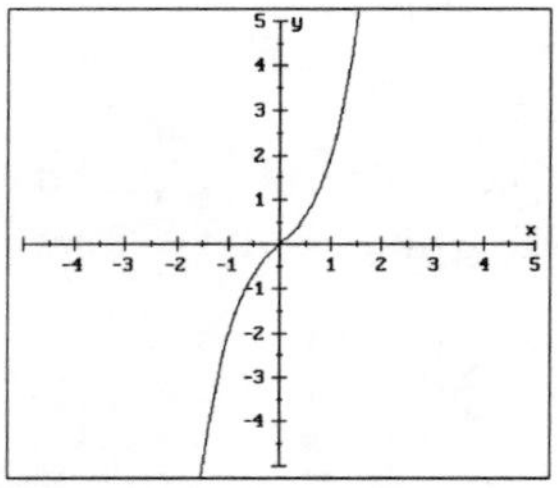

30. $f(x) = -x^4 + 2x^2 + 1$

$$f(-x) = -(-x)^4 + 2(-x)^2 + 1 = -x^4 + 2x^2 + 1 \Rightarrow \text{even}$$

x-int.	y-int.
$-x^4 + 2x^2 + 1 = 0$	$f(0) = 1$
$x^4 - 2x^2 - 1 = 0$	$y = 1$
not rational numbers	$(0, 1)$

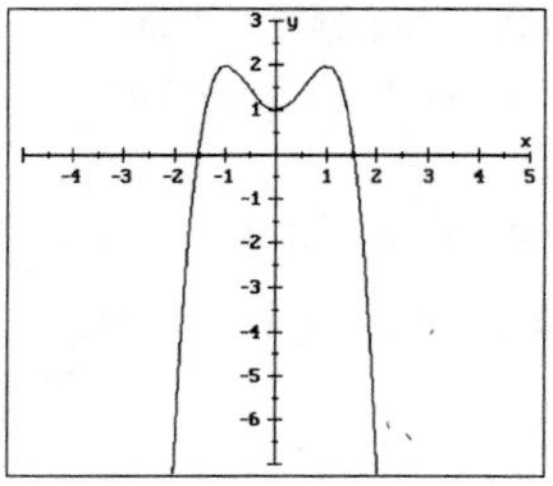

31. $y = \dfrac{x}{x-3} = 1 + \dfrac{3}{x-3}$

Vertical: $x = 3$; Horizontal: $y = 1$
Slant: none; x-intercepts: $(0, 0)$
y-intercepts: $(0, 0)$; Symmetry: none

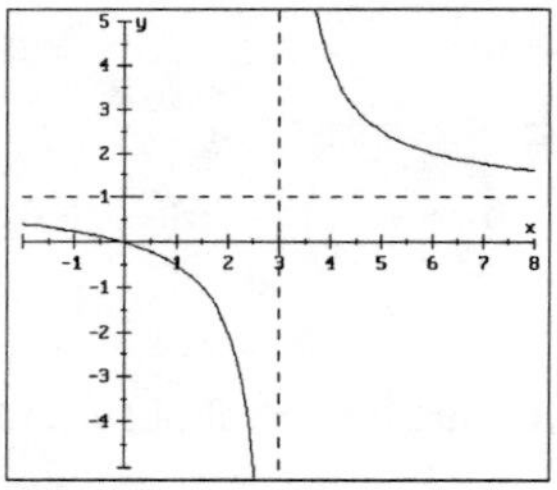

32. $y = \dfrac{x^2-1}{x^2-9} = \dfrac{(x+1)(x-1)}{(x+3)(x-3)} = 1 + \frac{8}{x^2-9}$

Vertical: $x = -3$, $x = 3$; Horizontal: $y = 1$
Slant: none; x-intercepts: $(-1, 0)$, $(1, 0)$
y-intercepts: $\left(0, \frac{1}{9}\right)$; Symmetry: y-axis

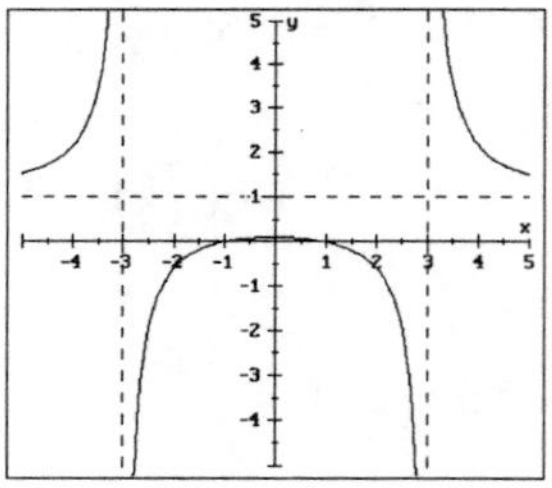

33. $(f+g)(x) = f(x) + g(x) = (3x-4) + (x^2+1) = x^2 + 3x - 3$; domain $= (-\infty, \infty)$

34. $(f-g)(x) = f(x) - g(x) = (3x-4) - (x^2+1) = -x^2 + 3x - 5$; domain $= (-\infty, \infty)$

35. $(f \cdot g)(x) = f(x)g(x) = (3x-4)(x^2+1) = 3x^3 - 4x^2 + 3x - 4$; domain $= (-\infty, \infty)$

36. $(f/g)(x) = \frac{f(x)}{g(x)} = \frac{3x-4}{x^2+1}$; domain $= (-\infty, \infty)$

37. $(f \circ g)(2) = f(g(2)) = f((2^2+1)) = f(5) = 3(5) - 4 = 11$

38. $(g \circ f)(2) = g(f(2)) = g(3(2) - 4) = g(2) = 2^2 + 1 = 5$

39. $(f \circ g)(x) = f(g(x)) = f(x^2+1) = 3(x^2+1) - 4 = 3x^2 - 1$

40. $(g \circ f)(x) = g(f(x)) = g(3x-4) = (3x-4)^2 + 1 = 9x^2 - 24x + 16 + 1 = 9x^2 - 24x + 17$

41.
$$\begin{aligned} y &= 3x+2 \\ x &= 3y+2 \\ x-2 &= 3y \\ \tfrac{x-2}{3} &= y \\ f^{-1}(x) &= \tfrac{x-2}{3} \end{aligned}$$

42.
$$\begin{aligned} y &= \tfrac{1}{x-3} \\ x &= \tfrac{1}{y-3} \\ x(y-3) &= 1 \\ y-3 &= \tfrac{1}{x} \\ y &= \tfrac{1}{x}+3 \\ f^{-1}(x) &= \tfrac{1}{x}+3 \end{aligned}$$

43.
$$\begin{aligned} y &= x^2+5 \\ x &= y^2+5 \\ x-5 &= y^2 \\ \pm\sqrt{x-5} &= y \\ \sqrt{x-5} &= y \ (y \geq 0) \\ f^{-1}(x) &= \sqrt{x-5} \end{aligned}$$

44.
$$\begin{aligned} 3x - y &= 1 \\ 3y - x &= 1 \\ 3y &= x+1 \\ y &= \tfrac{x+1}{3} \\ f^{-1}(x) &= \tfrac{x+1}{3} \end{aligned}$$

45. $y = kwz$

46. $y = \dfrac{kx}{t^2}$

Exercise 4.1 (page 333)

1. exponential

2. 1

3. $(-\infty, \infty)$

4. base

5. $(0, \infty)$

6. y, $(0, 1)$

7. asymptote

8. $0 < b < 1$

9. increasing

10. $(1, b)$

11. 2.72

12. Pe^{rt}

13. increasing

14. $(1, e)$

15. $4^{\sqrt{3}} \approx 11.0357$

16. $5^{\sqrt{2}} \approx 9.7385$

17. $7^{\pi} \approx 451.8079$

18. $3^{-\pi} \approx 0.0317$

19. $5^{\sqrt{2}}5^{\sqrt{2}} = 5^{\sqrt{2}+\sqrt{2}} = 5^{2\sqrt{2}} = \left(5^2\right)^{\sqrt{2}} = 25^{\sqrt{2}}$

20. $\left(5^{\sqrt{2}}\right)^{\sqrt{2}} = 5^{\sqrt{2}\cdot\sqrt{2}} = 5^2 = 25$

21. $\left(a^{\sqrt{8}}\right)^{\sqrt{2}} = a^{\sqrt{8}\cdot\sqrt{2}} = a^{\sqrt{16}} = a^4$

22. $a^{\sqrt{12}}a^{\sqrt{3}} = a^{\sqrt{12}+\sqrt{3}} = a^{2\sqrt{3}+\sqrt{3}} = a^{3\sqrt{3}}$

23. $y = 3^x$

points: $(0, 1)$, $(1, 3)$

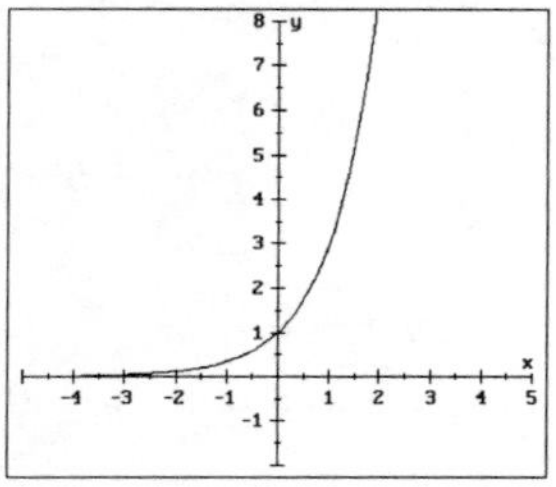

24. $y = 5^x$

points: $(0, 1)$, $(1, 5)$

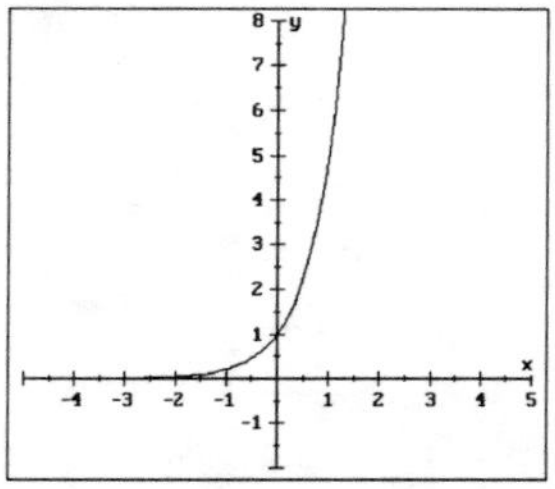

25. $y = \left(\frac{1}{5}\right)^x$

points: $(0, 1)$, $\left(1, \frac{1}{5}\right)$

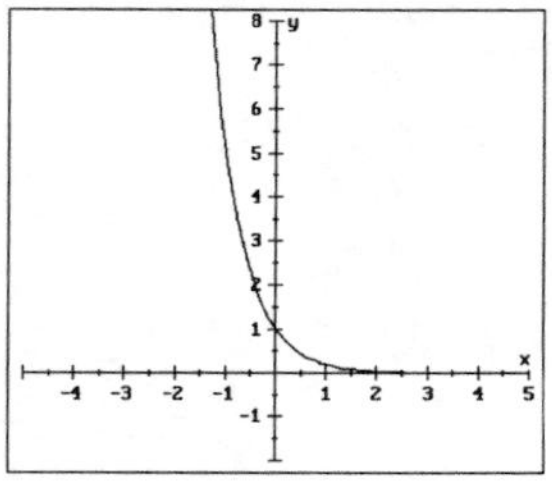

26. $y = \left(\frac{1}{3}\right)^x$

points: $(0, 1)$, $\left(1, \frac{1}{3}\right)$

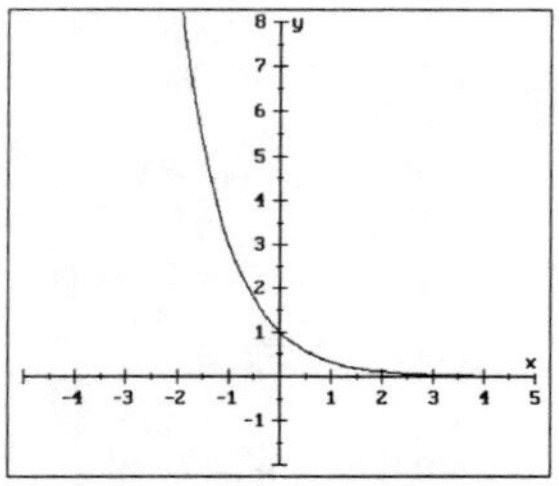

27. $y = \left(\frac{3}{4}\right)^x$

points: $(0, 1)$, $\left(1, \frac{3}{4}\right)$

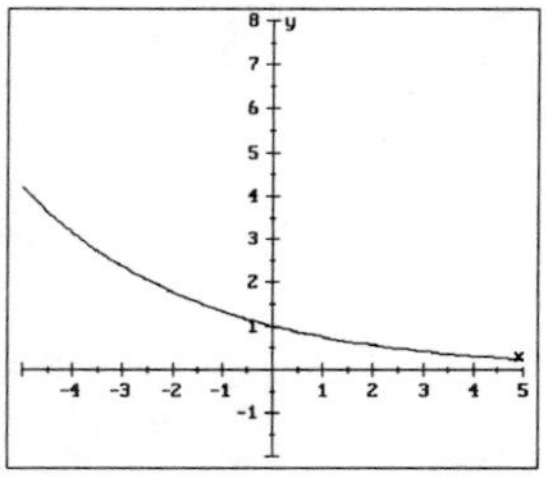

28. $y = \left(\frac{4}{3}\right)^x$

points: $(0, 1)$, $\left(1, \frac{4}{3}\right)$

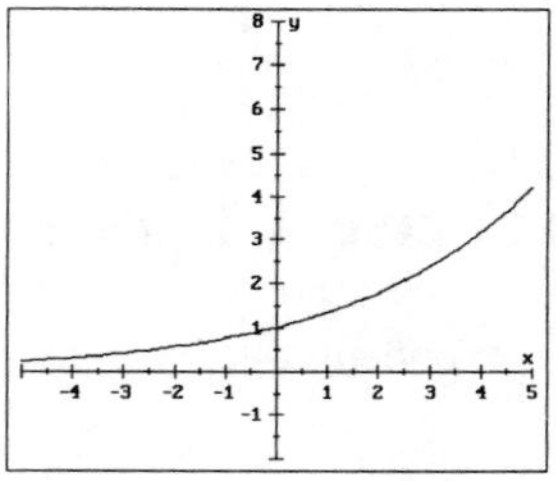

29. $y = (1.5)^x$

points: $(0, 1)$, $(1, 1.5)$

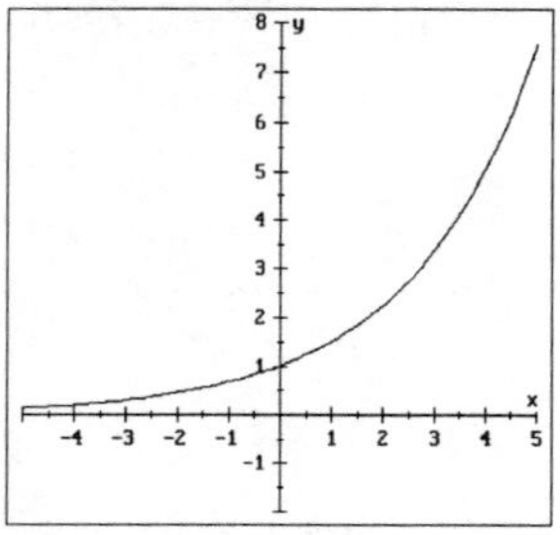

30. $y = (0.3)^x$

points: $(0, 1)$, $(1, 0.3)$

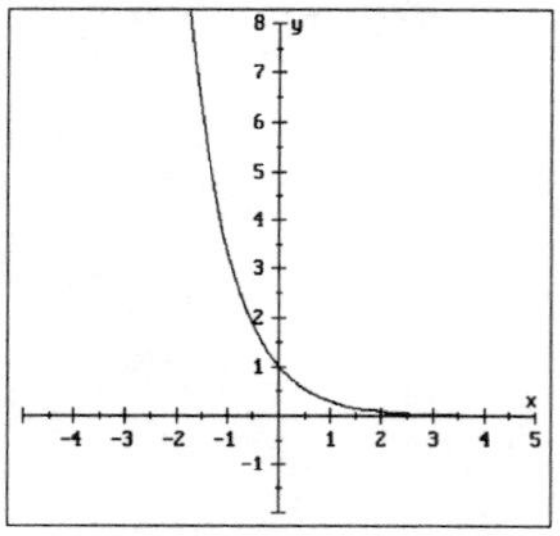

31. The graph passes through $(0, 1)$ and has the x-axis as an asymptote. YES

32. The graph does not pass through $(0, 1)$. NO

33. The graph does not pass through $(0, 1)$. NO

34. The graph passes through $(0, 1)$ and has the x-axis as an asymptote. YES

35. The graph passes through $(0, 1)$ and has the x-axis as an asymptote, so it could be an exponential function. It passes through the point $\left(1, \frac{1}{2}\right) = (1, b)$. $b = \frac{1}{2}$

36. The graph passes through $(0, 1)$ and has the x-axis as an asymptote, so it could be an exponential function. It passes through the point $(1, 7) = (1, b)$. $b = 7$

37. The graph does not pass through $(0, 1)$. It is not an exponential function.

38. The graph passes through $(0, 1)$ and has the x-axis as an asymptote, so it could be an exponential function. It passes through the point $(1, 3) = (1, b)$. $b = 3$

39. The graph passes through $(0, 1)$ and has the x-axis as an asymptote, so it could be an exponential function. It passes through the point $(1, 2) = (1, b)$. $b = 2$

40. The graph passes through $(0, 1)$ and has the x-axis as an asymptote, so it could be an exponential function.

$$y = b^x$$
$$\frac{1}{3} = b^{-1}$$
$$\left(\frac{1}{3}\right)^{-1} = \left(b^{-1}\right)^{-1}$$
$$3 = b$$

41. The graph passes through $(0, 1)$ and has the x-axis as an asymptote, so it could be an exponential function.

$$y = b^x$$
$$e^2 = b^2$$
$$e = b$$

42. The graph does not pass through $(0, 1)$. It is not an exponential function.

43. $y = 3^x - 1$
Shift $y = 3^x$ D1.

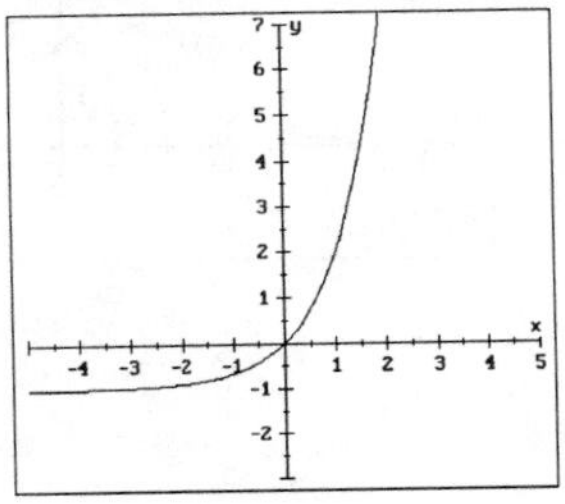

44. $y = 2^x + 3$
Shift $y = 2^x$ U3.

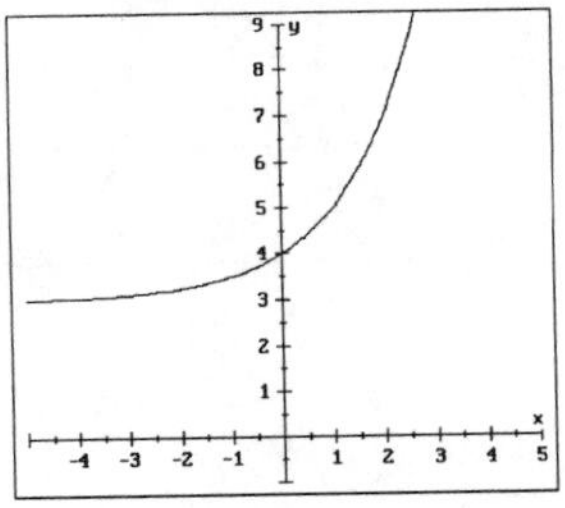

45. $y = 2^x + 1$
Shift $y = 2^x$ U1.

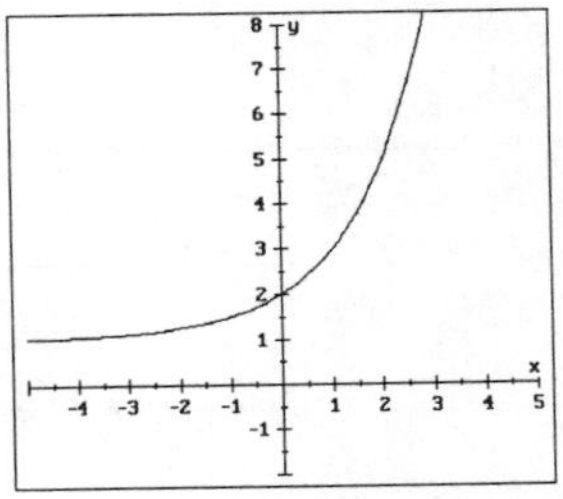

SECTION 4.1

46. $y = 4^x - 4$

Shift $y = 4^x$ D4.

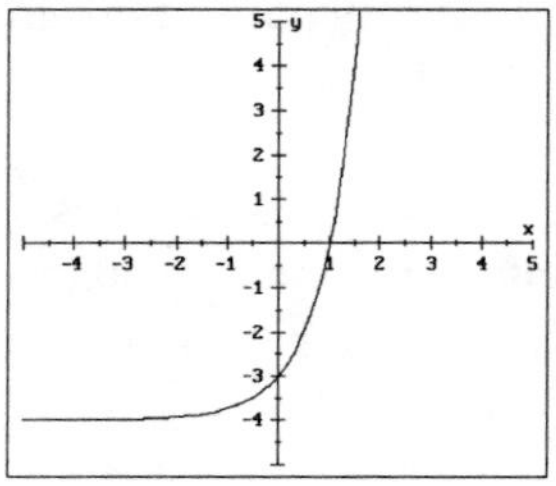

47. $y = 3^{x-1}$

Shift $y = 3^x$ R1.

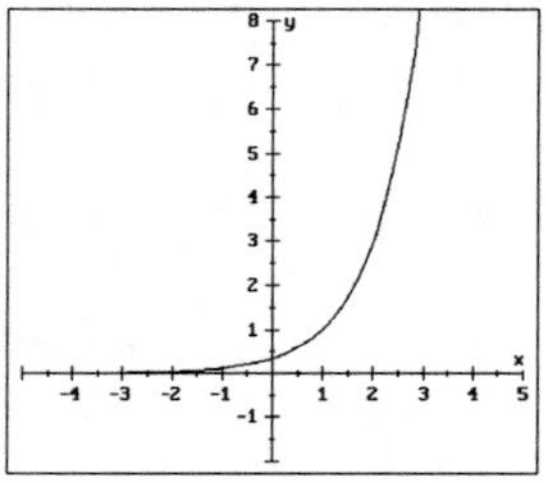

48. $y = 2^{x+3}$

Shift $y = 2^x$ L3.

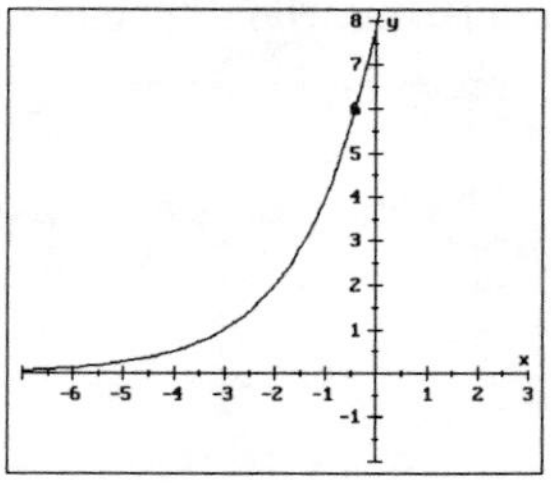

49. $y = 3^{x+1}$

Shift $y = 3^x$ L1.

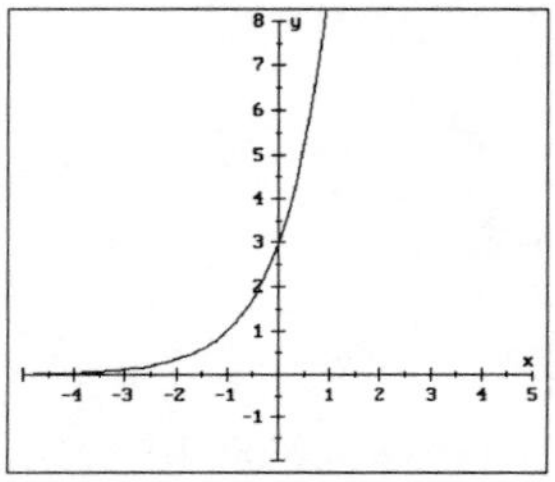

50. $y = 2^{x-3}$

Shift $y = 2^x$ R3.

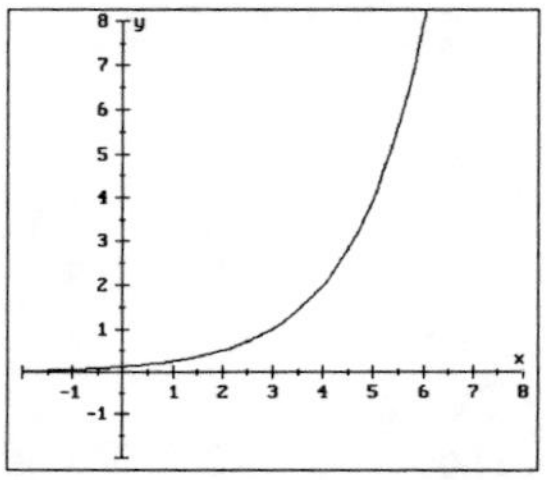

51. $y = e^x - 4$

Shift $y = e^x$ D4.

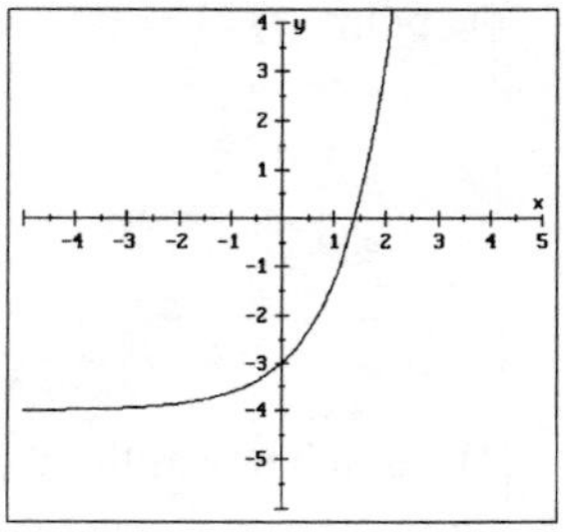

52. $y = e^x + 2$

Shift $y = e^x$ U2.

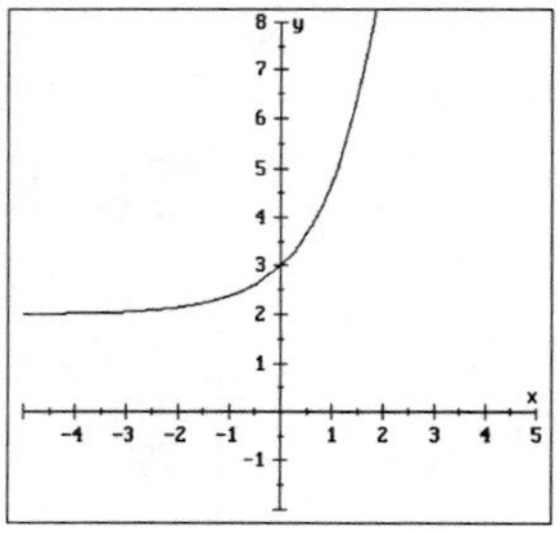

53. $y = e^{x-2}$

Shift $y = e^x$ R2.

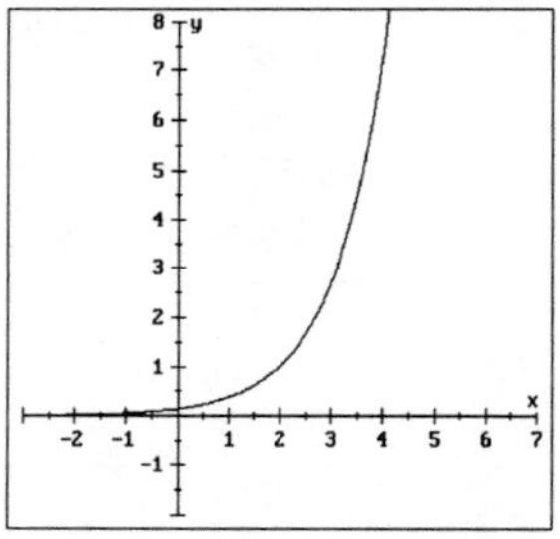

54. $y = e^{x+3}$

Shift $y = e^x$ L3.

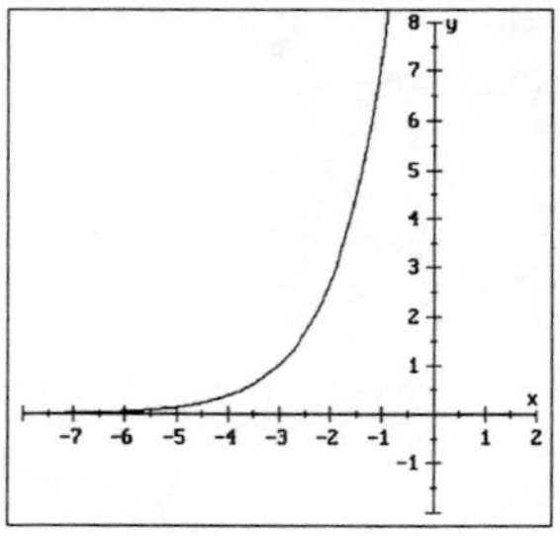

55. $y = 2^{x+1} - 2$
Shift $y = 2^x$ L1, D2.

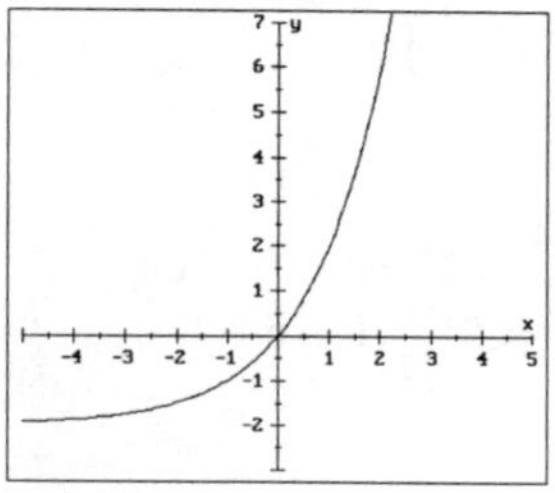

56. $y = 3^{x-1} + 2$
Shift $y = 3^x$ R1, U2.

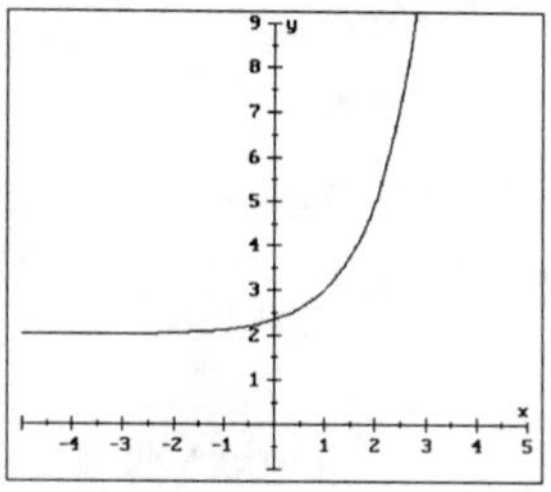

57. $y = 3^{x-2} + 1$
Shift $y = 3^x$ R2, U1.

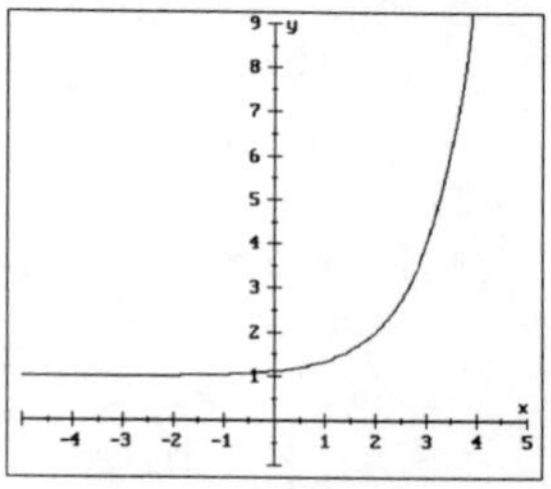

58. $y = 3^{x+2} - 1$
Shift $y = 3^x$ L2, D1.

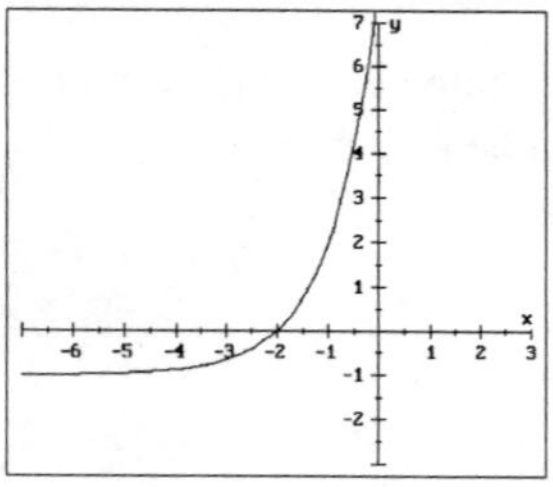

59. $y = 5(2^x)$

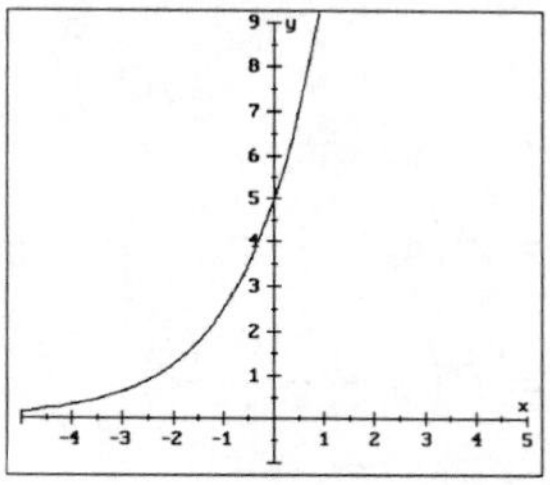

60. $y = 2(5^x)$

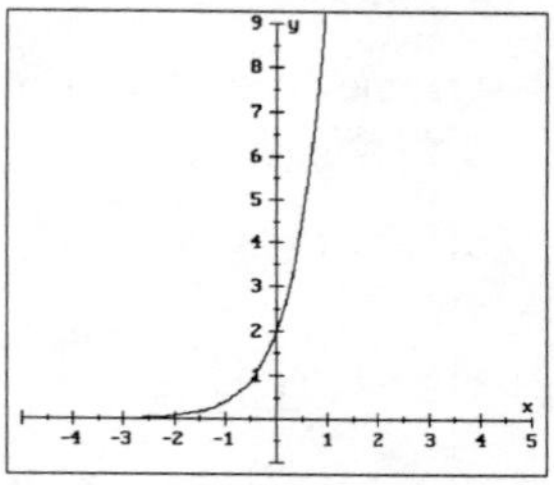

61. $y = 3^{-x}$

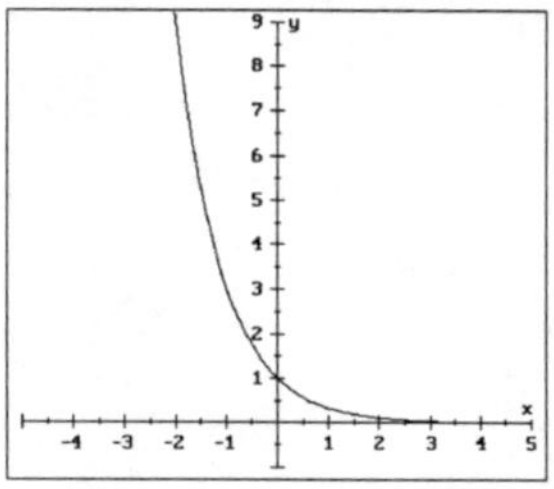

62. $y = 2^{-x}$

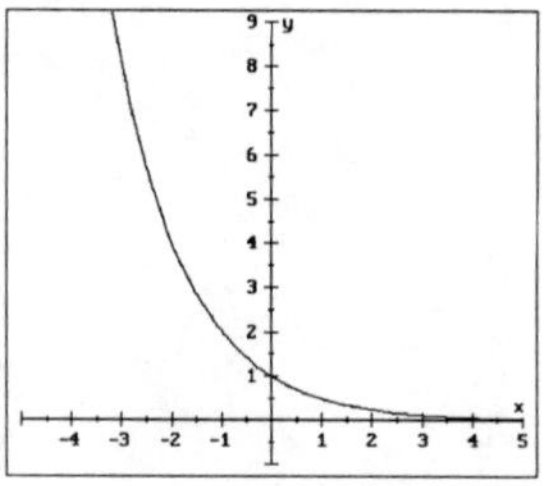

63. $y = 2e^x$

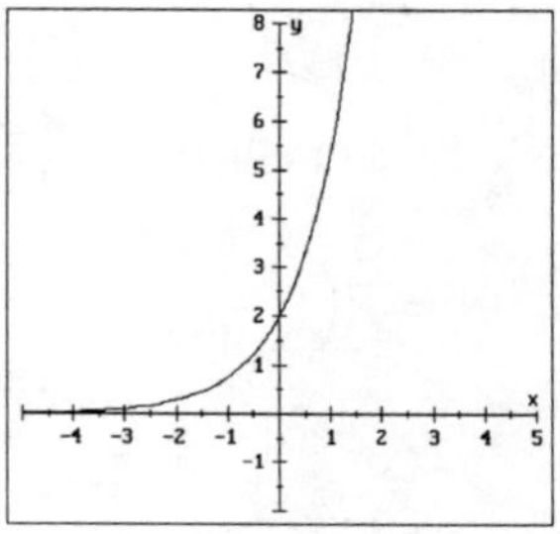

64. $y = 3e^{-x}$

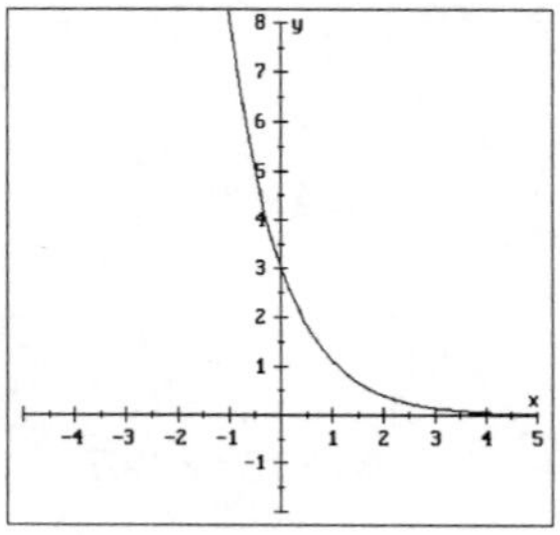

65. $y = 5e^{-0.5x}$

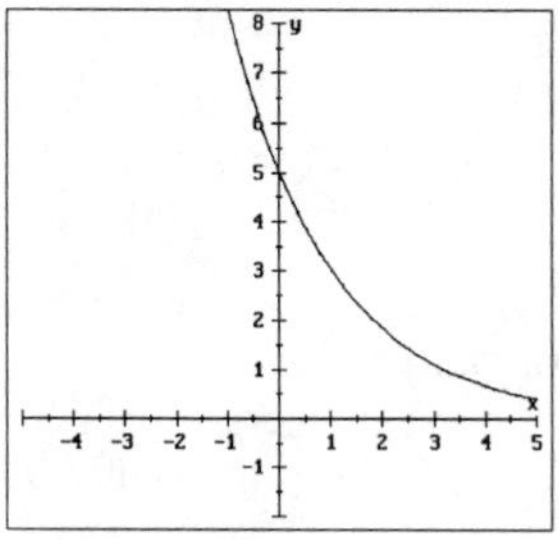

66. $y = -3e^{2x}$

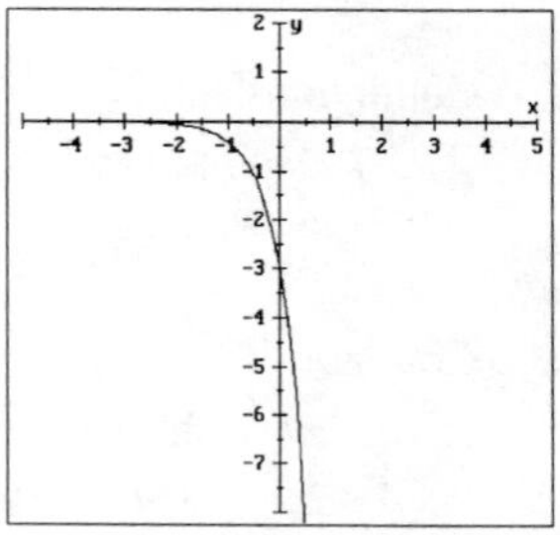

67. $A = P\left(1+\frac{r}{k}\right)^{kt}$
$= 500\left(1+\frac{0.08}{4}\right)^{4(10)}$
$\approx \$1104.02$

68. $A = P\left(1+\frac{r}{k}\right)^{kt}$
$= 1000\left(1+\frac{0.09}{12}\right)^{12(4.5)}$
$\approx \$1497.04$

69. 5% interest:
$A = P\left(1+\frac{r}{k}\right)^{kt}$
$= 500\left(1+\frac{0.05}{2}\right)^{2(5)}$
$\approx \$640.04$

$5\frac{1}{2}$% interest:
$A = P\left(1+\frac{r}{k}\right)^{kt}$
$= 500\left(1+\frac{0.055}{2}\right)^{2(5)}$
$\approx \$655.83$

Difference = 655.83 – 640.04
= $15.79 more

70. Assume 1 year for each account:

7.25% interest:
$A = P\left(1+\frac{r}{k}\right)^{kt}$
$= P\left(1+\frac{0.0725}{12}\right)^{12(1)}$
$\approx P(1.0750)$

7.35% interest:
$A = P\left(1+\frac{r}{k}\right)^{kt}$
$= P\left(1+\frac{0.0735}{1}\right)^{1(1)}$
$\approx P(1.0735)$

The 7.25% rate compounded monthly provides a better return.

71. $A = A_0\left(1+\frac{r}{360}\right)^{365t}$
$= 1000\left(1+\frac{0.07}{360}\right)^{365(5)}$
$\approx \$1425.93$

72. $A = P\left(1+\frac{r}{k}\right)^{kt}$
$= 1100\left(1+\frac{0.0175}{1}\right)^{1(8)}$
$\approx \$1263.77$

73. $A = P\left(1+\frac{r}{k}\right)^{kt}$
$= 1500\left(1+\frac{0.21}{12}\right)^{12(1)}$
$\approx \$1847.16$

74. $A = Pe^{rt}$
$= 5000e^{0.082(12)}$
$\approx \$13{,}375.68$

75. $A = Pe^{rt} = 2000e^{0.08(15)} \approx \$6640.23$

76. Continuous:
$A = Pe^{rt} = 5000e^{0.085(5)}$
$\approx \$7647.95$

Annually:
$A = P\left(1+\frac{r}{k}\right)^{kt} = 5000\left(1+\frac{0.085}{1}\right)^{1(5)} \approx \$7518.28$

77. Continuous:
$A = Pe^{rt} = 30{,}000e^{0.08(20)}$
$\approx \$148{,}590.97$

Annually:
$A = P\left(1+\frac{r}{k}\right)^{kt} = 30{,}000\left(1+\frac{0.08}{1}\right)^{1(20)} \approx \$139{,}828.71$

78.

$$\begin{aligned} A &= Pe^{rt} \\ 11{,}180 &= Pe^{0.07(7)} \\ 11{,}180 &= P(1.632316) \\ \$6849.16 &\approx P \end{aligned}$$

79.

$$\begin{aligned} A &= P\left(1+\frac{r}{k}\right)^{kt} \\ P &= A(1+r)^n \\ \frac{P}{(1+r)^n} &= A \\ P(1+r)^{-n} &= A \end{aligned}$$

80.

$$\begin{aligned} 2^{t+4} &= k2^t \\ 2^t \cdot 2^4 &= 2^t \cdot k \\ 2^4 &= k \\ 16 &= k \end{aligned}$$

81.

$$\begin{aligned} 5^{3t} &= k^t \\ \left(5^3\right)^t &= k^t \\ 125^t &= k^t \\ 125 &= k \end{aligned}$$

82. **a.**

$$\begin{aligned} e^{t+3} &= ke^t \\ e^t \cdot e^3 &= e^t \cdot k \\ e^3 &= k \end{aligned}$$

b.

$$\begin{aligned} e^{3t} &= k^t \\ \left(e^3\right)^t &= k^t \\ e^3 &= k \end{aligned}$$

83. $x^2 + 9x^4 = x^2(1+9x^2)$

84.

$$\begin{aligned} x^2 - 9x^4 &= x^2(1-9x^2) \\ &= x^2(1+3x)(1-3x) \end{aligned}$$

85. $x^2 + x - 12 = (x+4)(x-3)$

86. $x^3 + 27 = (x+3)(x^2 - 3x + 9)$

Exercise 4.2 (page 340)

1. birth, death

2. population, linearly

3.

$$\begin{aligned} A &= A_0 2^{-t/h} \\ &= 50 \cdot 2^{-100/(12.4)} \\ &\approx 0.1868 \text{ grams} \end{aligned}$$

4.

$$\begin{aligned} A &= A_0 2^{-t/h} \\ &= 1000 \cdot 2^{-100/(30.17)} \\ &\approx 101 \text{ kg} \end{aligned}$$

5.

$$\begin{aligned} A &= A_0 2^{-t/h} \\ &= 1000 \cdot 2^{-200/(30.17)} \\ &\approx 10 \text{ kg} \end{aligned}$$

6.

$$\begin{aligned} A &= A_0 2^{-t/h} \\ &= A_0 \cdot 2^{-3000/5700} \\ &\approx A_0(0.694) \end{aligned}$$

About 69.4% will remain.

7. $A = A_0 2^{-t/h} = A_0 \cdot 2^{-60/40} \approx A_0(0.354) \Rightarrow$ About 35.4% will remain.

8. ^{162}Ho:

$$\begin{aligned} A &= A_0 2^{-t/h} \\ &= A_0 \cdot 2^{-60/22} \\ &\approx A_0(0.151) \end{aligned}$$

About 15.1% will remain.

^{164}Ho:

$$\begin{aligned} A &= A_0 2^{-t/h} \\ &= A_0 \cdot 2^{-60/37} \\ &\approx A_0(0.325) \end{aligned}$$

About 32.5% will remain.

$$\frac{\text{amt. of } ^{162}\text{Ho}}{\text{amt. of } ^{164}\text{Ho}} = \frac{0.151}{0.325} = 0.465$$

9. $A = A_0 2^{-t/h}$
$= 1 \cdot 2^{-12/(4.5)}$
≈ 0.1575 unit

10. $A = A_0 2^{-t/h}$
$= 1 \cdot 2^{-12/8}$
≈ 0.3536 unit

11. $P = P_0 2^{t/2}$
$= 10{,}000 \cdot 2^{5/2}$
$\approx 56{,}570$ fish

12. $P = 375(1.3)^t$
$= 375(1.3)^3$
≈ 824 people

13. $I = I_0 k^x$
$= 8(0.5)^2$
$= 2$ lumens

14. $I = I_0 k^x$
$= 12(0.6)^5$
≈ 0.933 lumens

15. $T = 40 + 60(0.75)^t$
$= 40 + 60(0.75)^{3.5}$
$\approx 61.9°$ C

16. $P = (6 \times 10^6)(2.3)^t$
$= (6 \times 10^6)(2.3)^4$
$\approx 167{,}904{,}600$

17. $P = 173e^{0.03t}$
$= 173e^{0.03(20)}$
≈ 315

18. $P = 1.2 \times 10^6 e^{-0.008t}$
$= 1.2 \times 10^6 e^{-0.008(30)}$
$\approx 9.44 \times 10^5$

19. $P = P_0 e^{0.27t}$
$= 2e^{0.27(12)}$
≈ 51 cases

20. $P = 0.3\left(1 - e^{-0.05t}\right)$
$= 0.3\left(1 - e^{-0.05(20)}\right)$
≈ 0.19

21. $P = P_0 e^{kt}$
$= 6e^{0.019(30)}$
≈ 10.6 billion

22. $P = P_0 e^{kt}$
$= 6e^{0.019(40)}$
≈ 12.8 billion

23. $P = P_0 e^{kt}$
$= 6e^{0.019(50)}$
≈ 15.5 billion
$\frac{15.5}{6} \approx$ a factor of 2.6

24. $P = P_0 e^{kt}$
$= 6e^{0.019(100)}$
≈ 40.1 billion
$\frac{40.1}{6} \approx$ a factor of 6.7

25. $P = e^{-0.3t}$
$= e^{-0.3(24)}$
≈ 0.0007
$= 0.07\%$

26. $x = 0.08\left(1 - e^{-0.1t}\right)$
$= 0.08\left(1 - e^{-0.1(30)}\right)$
≈ 0.076

27. Let $t = 0$:
$x = 0.08\left(1 - e^{-0.1t}\right)$
$= 0.08\left(1 - e^{-0.1(0)}\right)$
$= 0.08\left(1 - e^0\right) = 0.08(1 - 1) = 0$

28. $P = \dfrac{1{,}200{,}000}{1 + (1200 - 1)e^{-0.4t}}$
$= \dfrac{1{,}200{,}000}{1 + (1200 - 1)e^{-0.4(5)}}$
≈ 7350 people

29. $P = \dfrac{1{,}200{,}000}{1 + (1200 - 1)e^{-0.4t}}$
$= \dfrac{1{,}200{,}000}{1 + (1200 - 1)e^{-0.4(8)}}$
$\approx 24{,}060$ people

30. $I = 78.5(1.001)^x$
$= 78.5(1.001)^{50}$
≈ 82.5 years

31. $w = 1.54e^{0.503n}$
$= 1.54e^{0.503(5)}$
≈ 19.0 mm

32. $v = 50(1 - e^{-0.2t})$
$= 50(1 - e^{-0.2(0)})$
$= 50(1 - e^{0})$
$= 0$ meters/second

33. $v = 50(1 - e^{-0.2t})$
$= 50(1 - e^{-0.2(20)})$
≈ 49 meters/second

34. $v = 50(1 - e^{-0.2t})$
$= 50(1 - e^{-0.2(2)})$
$\approx$ 16.5 meters/second

$v = 50(1 - e^{-0.3t})$
$= 50(1 - e^{-0.3(2)})$
$\approx$ 22.6 meters/second

This object will be falling faster.

35.

Males	Females
$P = P_0e^{kt}$	$P = P_0e^{kt}$
$= 133e^{0.01t}$	$= 139e^{0.01t}$
$= 133e^{0.01(20)}$	$= 139e^{0.01(20)}$
≈ 162.4 million	≈ 169.8 million

There will be about 7 million more females.

36.

Males	Females
$P = P_0e^{kt}$	$P = P_0e^{kt}$
$= 133e^{0.01t}$	$= 139e^{0.01t}$
$= 133e^{0.01(50)}$	$= 139e^{0.01(20)}$
≈ 219.3 million	≈ 229.2 million

There will be about 10 million more females.

37. Find where these graphs meet:
$y = 1000e^{0.02t}$, $y = 31x + 2000$

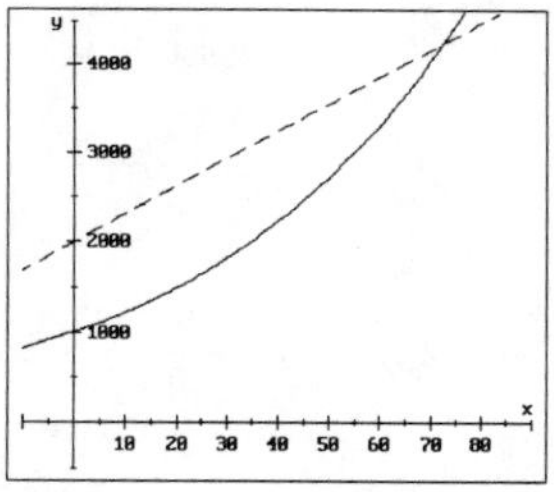

It will take about 72.2 years.

38. Find where these graphs meet:
$y = 1000e^{0.01t}$, $y = 30.624x + 2000$

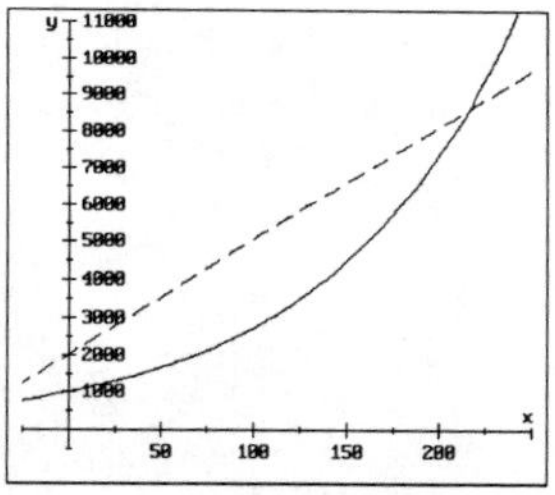

It will take about 215 years.

39. $1 + 1 + \frac{1}{2} + \frac{1}{2\cdot3} + \frac{1}{2\cdot3\cdot4} + \frac{1}{2\cdot3\cdot4\cdot5} \approx 2.71\overline{6}$; $e \approx 2.718$: accurate to 2 places

40. $y = \dfrac{e^x + e^{-x}}{2}$

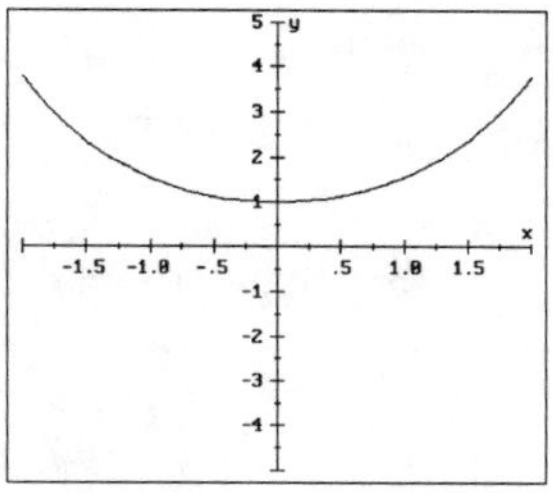

41. $P = \dfrac{1{,}200{,}000}{1 + 1199e^{-0.4t}}$

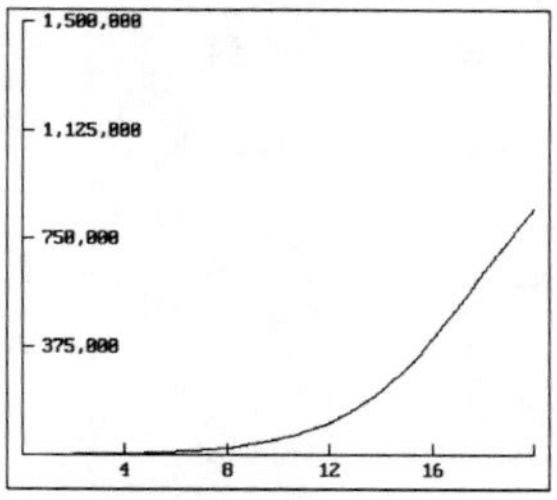

42. **Answers may vary.**

43. $2^3 = x$
$8 = x$

44. $3^x = 9$
$x = 2$

45. $x^3 = 27$
$x = 3$

46. $3^{-2} = x$
$\frac{1}{9} = x$

47. $x^{-3} = \frac{1}{8}$
$\frac{1}{x^3} = \frac{1}{8}$
$x = 2$

48. $3^x = \frac{1}{3}$
$3^x = 3^{-1}$
$x = -1$

49. $9^{1/2} = x$
$3 = x$

50. $x^{1/3} = 3$
$\left(x^{1/3}\right)^3 = 3^3$
$x = 27$

Exercise 4.3 (page 350)

1. $x = b^y$

2. $(0, \infty)$

3. range

4. x

5. inverse

6. logarithmic

7. exponent

8. asymptote

9. $(b, 1)$, $(1, 0)$

10. x

11. $\log_e x$

12. $(0, \infty)$

13. $(-\infty, \infty)$

14. y-axis

15. 10

16. e

17. $\log_3 81 = 4$
$3^4 = 81$

18. $\log_7 7 = 1$
$7^1 = 7$

19. $\log_{1/2} \frac{1}{8} = 3$
$\left(\frac{1}{2}\right)^3 = \frac{1}{8}$

20. $\log_{1/5} 1 = 0$
$\left(\frac{1}{5}\right)^0 = 1$

21. $\log_4 \frac{1}{64} = -3$
$4^{-3} = \frac{1}{64}$

22. $\log_6 \frac{1}{36} = -2$
$6^{-2} = \frac{1}{36}$

23. $\log_\pi \pi = 1$
$\pi^1 = \pi$

24. $\log_7 \frac{1}{49} = -2$
$7^{-2} = \frac{1}{49}$

25. $8^2 = 64$
$\log_8 64 = 2$

26. $10^3 = 1000$
$\log_{10} 1000 = 3$

27. $4^{-2} = \frac{1}{16}$
$\log_4 \frac{1}{16} = -2$

28. $3^{-4} = \frac{1}{81}$
$\log_3 \frac{1}{81} = -4$

29. $\left(\frac{1}{2}\right)^{-5} = 32$
$\log_{1/2} 32 = -5$

30. $\left(\frac{1}{3}\right)^{-3} = 27$
$\log_{1/3} 27 = -3$

31. $x^y = z$
$\log_x z = y$

32. $m^n = p$
$\log_m p = n$

33. $\log_2 8 = x$
$2^x = 8$
$x = 3$

34. $\log_3 9 = x$
$3^x = 9$
$x = 2$

35. $\log_4 64 = x$
$4^x = 64$
$x = 3$

36. $\log_6 216 = x$
$6^x = 216$
$x = 3$

37. $\log_{1/2} \frac{1}{8} = x$

$\left(\frac{1}{2}\right)^x = \frac{1}{8}$

$x = 3$

38. $\log_{1/3} \frac{1}{81} = x$

$\left(\frac{1}{3}\right)^x = \frac{1}{81}$

$x = 4$

39. $\log_9 3 = x$

$9^x = 3$

$x = \frac{1}{2}$

40. $\log_{125} 5 = x$

$125^x = 5$

$x = \frac{1}{3}$

41. $\log_{1/2} 8 = x$

$\left(\frac{1}{2}\right)^x = 8$

$x = -3$

42. $\log_{1/2} 16 = x$

$\left(\frac{1}{2}\right)^x = 16$

$x = -4$

43. $\log_8 x = 2$

$8^2 = x$

$64 = x$

44. $\log_7 x = 0$

$7^0 = x$

$1 = x$

45. $\log_7 x = 1$

$7^1 = x$

$7 = x$

46. $\log_2 x = 8$

$2^8 = x$

$256 = x$

47. $\log_{25} x = \frac{1}{2}$

$25^{1/2} = x$

$5 = x$

48. $\log_4 x = \frac{1}{2}$

$4^{1/2} = x$

$2 = x$

49. $\log_5 x = -2$

$5^{-2} = x$

$\frac{1}{5^2} = x$

$\frac{1}{25} = x$

50. $\log_3 x = -4$

$3^{-4} = x$

$\frac{1}{3^4} = x$

$\frac{1}{81} = x$

51. $\log_{36} x = -\frac{1}{2}$

$36^{-1/2} = x$

$\frac{1}{36^{1/2}} = x$

$\frac{1}{6} = x$

52. $\log_{27} x = -\frac{1}{3}$

$27^{-1/3} = x$

$\frac{1}{27^{1/3}} = x$

$\frac{1}{3} = x$

53. $\log_x 5^3 = 3$

$x^3 = 5^3$

$x = 5$

54. $\log_x 5 = 1$

$x^1 = 5$

$x = 5$

55. $\log_x \frac{9}{4} = 2$

$x^2 = \frac{9}{4}$

$x = \frac{3}{2}$

56. $\log_x \frac{\sqrt{3}}{3} = \frac{1}{2}$

$x^{1/2} = \frac{\sqrt{3}}{3}$

$\left(x^{1/2}\right)^2 = \left(\frac{\sqrt{3}}{3}\right)^2$

$x = \frac{3}{9} = \frac{1}{3}$

57. $\log_x \frac{1}{64} = -3$

$x^{-3} = \frac{1}{64}$

$\frac{1}{x^3} = \frac{1}{4^3}$

$x = 4$

58. $\log_x \frac{1}{100} = -2$

$x^{-2} = \frac{1}{100}$

$\frac{1}{x^2} = \frac{1}{10^2}$

$x = 10$

59.
$$\log_x \frac{9}{4} = -2$$
$$x^{-2} = \frac{9}{4}$$
$$\left(x^{-2}\right)^{-1} = \left(\frac{9}{4}\right)^{-1}$$
$$x^2 = \frac{4}{9}$$
$$x = \frac{2}{3}$$

60.
$$\log_x \frac{\sqrt{3}}{3} = -\frac{1}{2}$$
$$x^{-1/2} = \frac{\sqrt{3}}{3}$$
$$\left(x^{-1/2}\right)^{-2} = \left(\frac{\sqrt{3}}{3}\right)^{-2}$$
$$x = \left(\frac{3}{\sqrt{3}}\right)^2$$
$$x = \frac{9}{3} = 3$$

61. From the definition: $2^{\log_2 5} = 5$

62. From the definition: $3^{\log_3 4} = 4$

63. From the definition: $x^{\log_4 6} = 6 \Rightarrow x = 4$

64. From the definition: $x^{\log_3 8} = 8 \Rightarrow x = 3$

65. $\log 3.25 \approx 0.5119$

66. $\log 0.57 \approx -0.2441$

67. $\log 0.00467 \approx -2.3307$

68. $\log 375.876 \approx 2.5750$

69. $\ln 45.7 \approx 3.8221$

70. $\ln 0.005 \approx -5.2983$

71. $\ln \frac{2}{3} \approx -0.4055$

72. $\ln \frac{12}{7} \approx 0.5390$

73. $\ln 35.15 \approx 3.5596$

74. $\ln 0.675 \approx -0.3930$

75. $\ln 7.896 \approx 2.0664$

76. $\ln 0.00465 \approx -5.3709$

77. $\log(\ln 1.7) \approx -0.2752$

78. $\ln(\log 9.8) \approx -0.0088$

79. $\ln(\log 0.1)$: undefined

80. $\log(\ln 0.01)$: undefined

81. $\log y = 1.4023$
$y \approx 25.2522$

82. $\log y = 0.926$
$y \approx 8.4333$

83. $\log y = -3.71$
$y \approx 1.9498 \times 10^{-4}$

84. $\log y = \log \pi$
$y \approx 3.1416$

85. $\ln y = 1.4023$
$y \approx 4.0645$

86. $\ln y = 2.6490$
$y \approx 14.1399$

87. $\ln y = 4.24$
$y \approx 69.4079$

88. $\ln y = 0.926$
$y \approx 2.5244$

89. $\ln y = -3.71$
$y \approx 0.0245$

90. $\ln y = -0.28$
$y \approx 0.7558$

91. $\log y = \ln 8$
$y \approx 120.0719$

92. $\ln y = \log 7$
$y \approx 2.3282$

93. The graph passes through the point $(b, 1) = (2, 1)$. $\Rightarrow b = 2$

94. The graph passes through the point $(b, 1) = \left(\frac{1}{2}, 1\right)$. $\Rightarrow b = \frac{1}{2}$

SECTION 4.3

95.
$$\begin{aligned} y &= \log_b x \\ b^y &= x \\ b^{-1} &= \tfrac{1}{2} \\ \left(b^{-1}\right)^{-1} &= \left(\tfrac{1}{2}\right)^{-1} \\ b &= 2 \end{aligned}$$

96.
$$\begin{aligned} y &= \log_b x \\ b^y &= x \\ b^{-1} &= 2 \\ \left(b^{-1}\right)^{-1} &= (2)^{-1} \\ b &= \tfrac{1}{2} \end{aligned}$$

97. $y = \log_3 x$
points: $(1, 0)$, $(3, 1)$

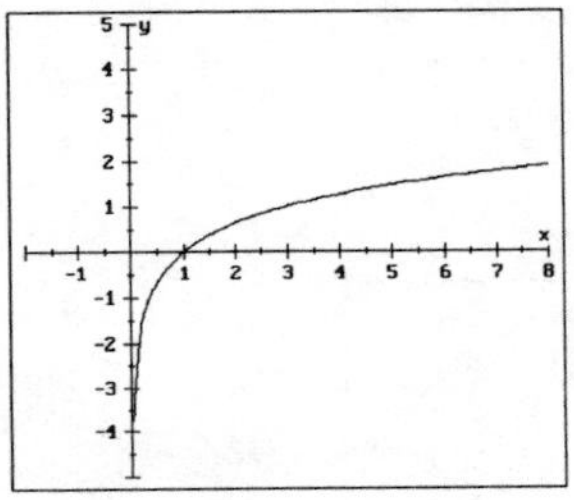

98. $y = \log_4 x$
points: $(1, 0)$, $(4, 1)$

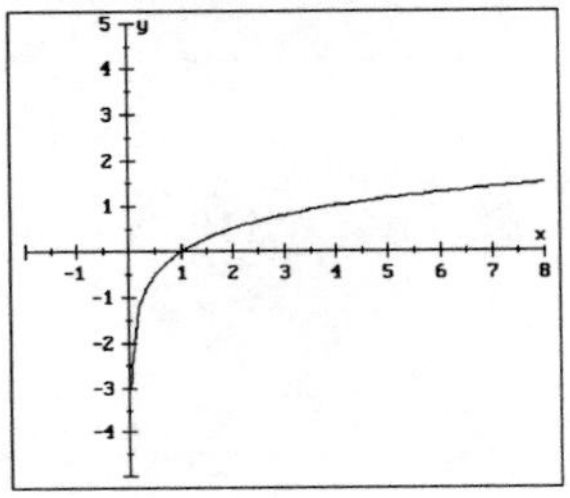

99. $y = \log_{1/3} x$
points: $(1, 0)$, $\left(\frac{1}{3}, 1\right)$

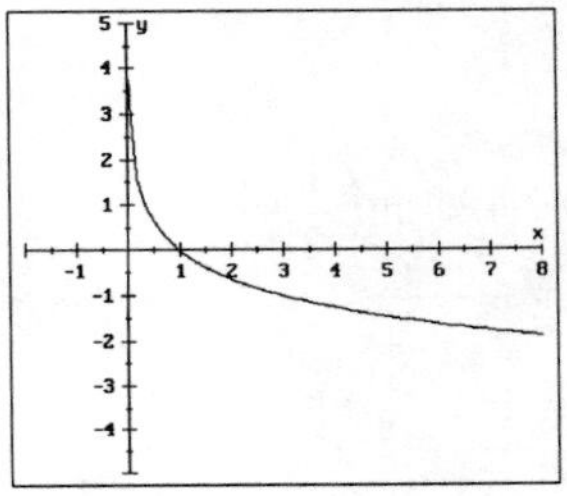

100. $y = \log_{1/4} x$
points: $(1, 0)$, $\left(\frac{1}{4}, 1\right)$

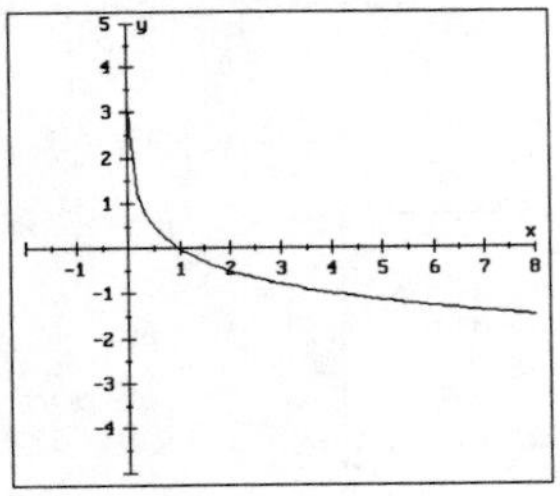

101. $y = 2 + \log_2 x$
Shift $y = \log_2 x$ U2.

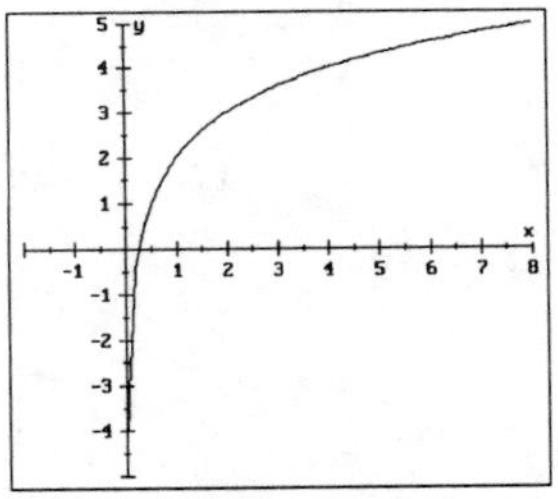

102. $y = \log_2 (x - 1)$
Shift $y = \log_2 x$ R1.

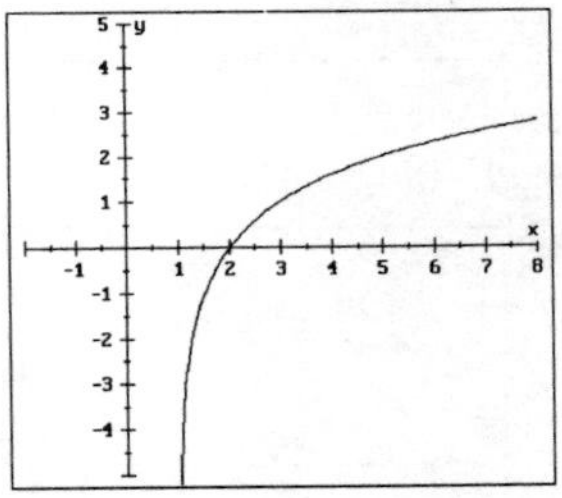

103. $y = \log_3 (x + 2)$
Shift $y = \log_3 x$ L2.

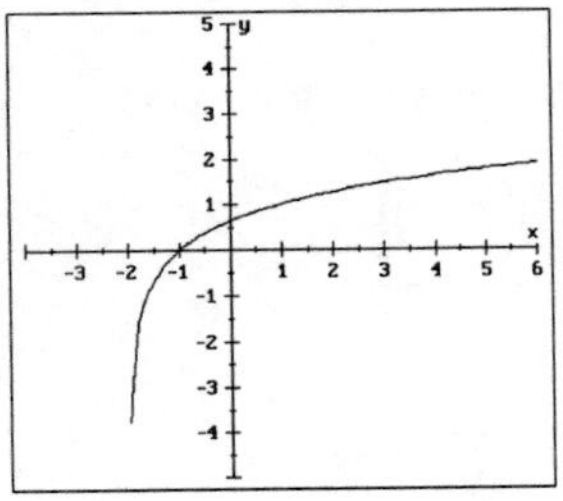

104. $y = -3 + \log_3 x$
Shift $y = \log_3 x$ D3.

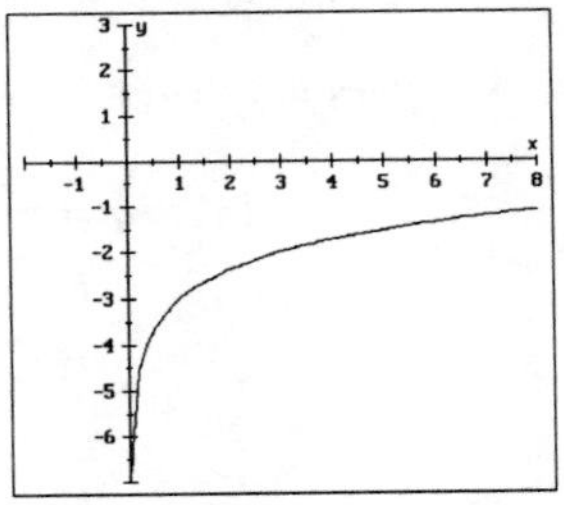

105. $y = \log (3x)$

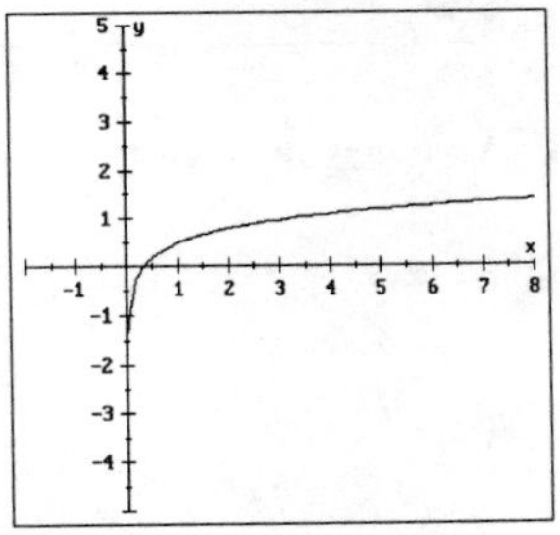

SECTION 4.3

106. $y = \log\left(\frac{x}{3}\right)$

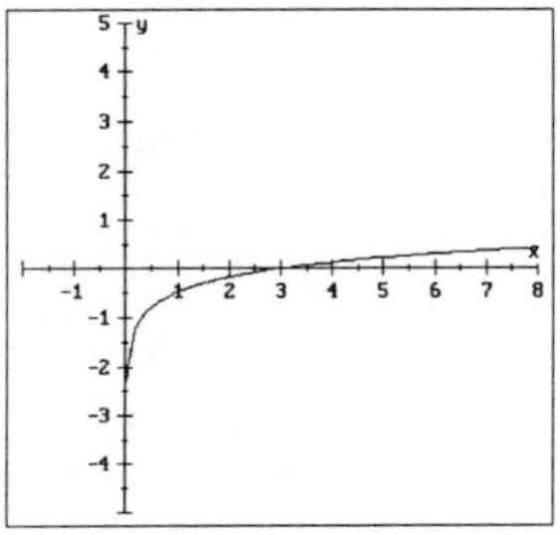

107. $y = \log(-x)$

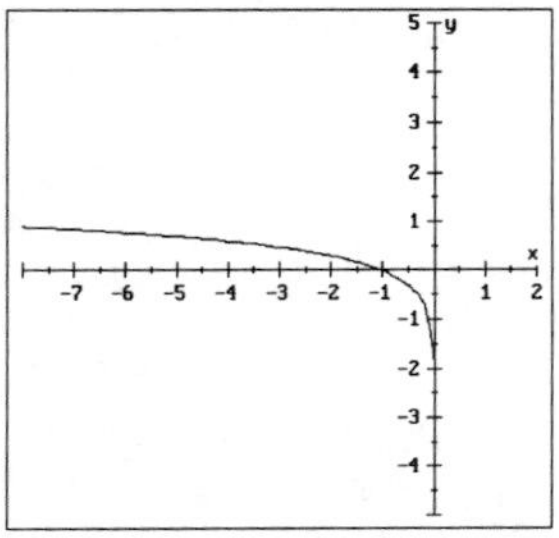

108. $y = -\log x$

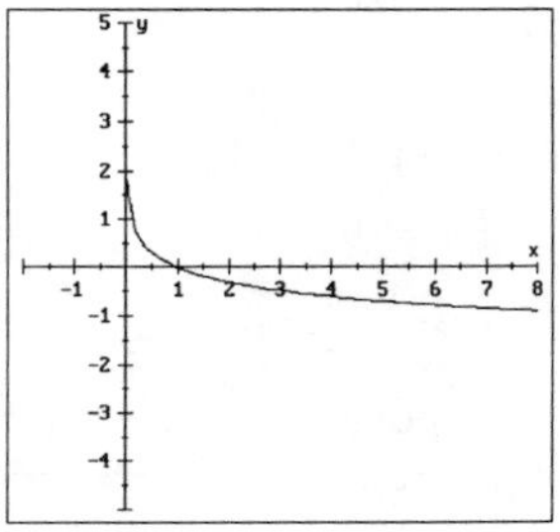

109. $y = \ln\left(\frac{1}{2}x\right)$

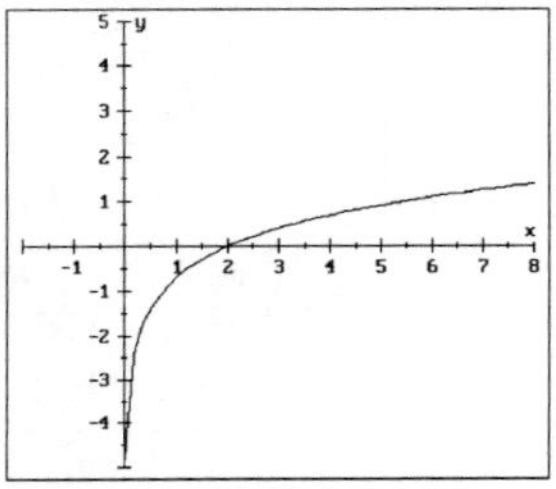

110. $y = \ln x^2$

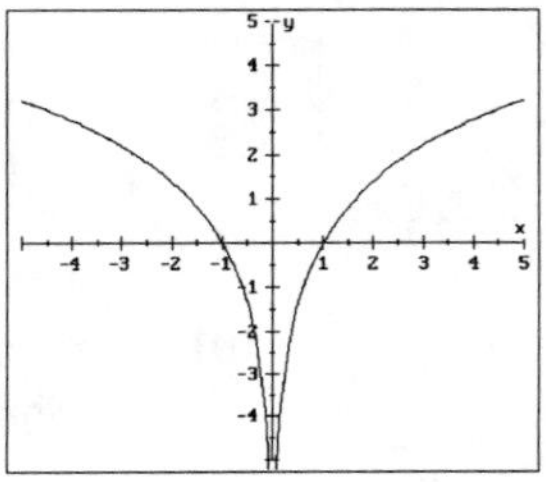

111. $y = \ln(-x)$

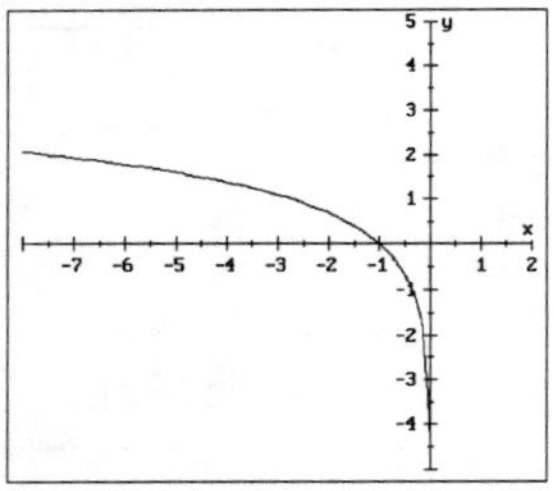

112. $y = \ln(3x)$

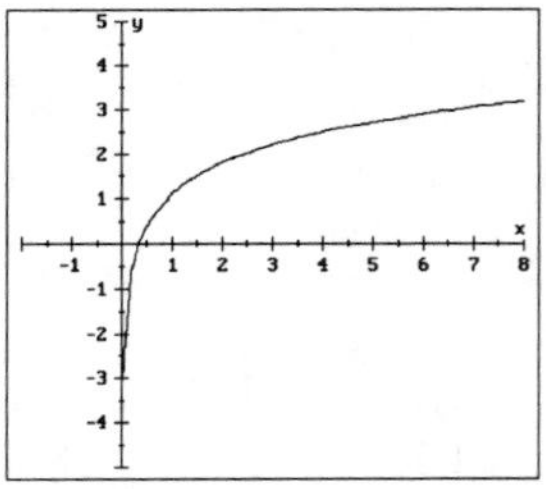

113. Answers may vary.

114. Answers may vary.

115. Answers may vary.

116.
$$\log_a b = 7$$
$$a^7 = b$$
$$\left(a^7\right)^{1/7} = b^{1/7}$$
$$a = b^{1/7}$$
$$\log_b a = \frac{1}{7}$$

117. $y = x^2 + 7x + 3;\ a = 1, b = 7, c = 3$

$x = -\frac{b}{2a} = -\frac{7}{2(1)} = -\frac{7}{2}$

$y = x^2 + 7x + 3$

$= \left(-\frac{7}{2}\right)^2 + 7\left(-\frac{7}{2}\right) + 3 = -\frac{37}{4}$

Vertex: $\left(-\frac{7}{2}, -\frac{37}{4}\right)$

118. $y = 3x^2 - 8x - 1;\ a = 3, b = -8, c = -1$

$x = -\frac{b}{2a} = -\frac{-8}{2(3)} = \frac{4}{3}$

$y = 3x^2 - 8x - 1$

$= 3\left(\frac{4}{3}\right)^2 - 8\left(\frac{4}{3}\right) - 1 = -\frac{19}{3}$

Vertex: $\left(\frac{4}{3}, -\frac{19}{3}\right)$

119. Let $x =$ width. Then $\dfrac{3400 - 4x}{2} =$ length.

$$A = x\left(\frac{3400 - 4x}{2}\right) = x(1700 - 2x)$$
$$= 1700x - 2x^2$$
$$= -2x^2 + 1700x$$
$$x = -\frac{b}{2a} = -\frac{1700}{2(-2)} = 425$$

The dimensions are 425 feet by 850 feet.

120. Revenue = price · # sold

$= p(2200 - p)$

$= 2200p - p^2$

$= -p^2 + 2200p$

$$x = -\frac{b}{2a} = -\frac{2200}{2(-1)} = 1100$$

A price of \$1100 will maximize revenue.

121. $y = 5x - 8:\ m = 5$

Use $m = 5$:

$y - y_1 = m(x - x_1)$

$y - 0 = 5(x - 0)$

$y = 5x$

122. $y = \frac{2}{3}x - 12$

$m = \frac{2}{3}$

Use $m = -\frac{3}{2}$.

$y - y_1 = m(x - x_1)$

$y - 2 = -\frac{3}{2}(x - 3)$

$y - 2 = -\frac{3}{2}x + \frac{9}{2}$

$\boxed{y = -\frac{3}{2}x + \frac{13}{2}}$

Exercise 4.4 (page 356)

1. $20 \log \dfrac{E_O}{E_I}$

2. $\log \dfrac{A}{P}$

3. $t = -\dfrac{1}{k} \ln\left(1 - \dfrac{C}{M}\right)$

4. $\dfrac{\ln 2}{r}$

5. $E = RT \ln\left(\dfrac{V_f}{V_i}\right)$

6. undefined

7. $\text{db gain} = 20 \log \dfrac{E_0}{E_I}$

$= 20 \log \dfrac{17}{0.03}$

≈ 55 db

8. $\text{db gain} = 20 \log \dfrac{E_0}{E_I}$

$= 20 \log \dfrac{4.7}{4.9}$

≈ -0.36 db gain

≈ 0.36 db loss

9. $\text{db gain} = 20 \log \dfrac{E_0}{E_I}$

$= 20 \log \dfrac{20}{0.71}$

≈ 29 db

10. $\text{db gain} = 20 \log \dfrac{E_0}{E_I}$

$= 20 \log \dfrac{2.8}{0.05}$

≈ 35 db

11. $R = \log \dfrac{A}{P}$

$= \log \dfrac{5000}{0.2}$

≈ 4.4

12. $R = \log \dfrac{A}{P}$

$= \log \dfrac{8000}{0.008}$

$= 6$

13. $R = \log \frac{A}{P} = \log \frac{2500}{\frac{1}{4}} = 4$

14. $R = \log \frac{A}{P} = \log \frac{50{,}000}{\frac{1}{2}} = 5$

15. $t = -\frac{1}{k} \ln\left(1 - \frac{C}{M}\right)$

$t = -\frac{1}{0.116} \ln\left(1 - \frac{0.9M}{M}\right)$

$t = -\frac{1}{0.116} \ln(1 - 0.9) \approx 19.8$ hours

16. $t = -\frac{1}{k} \ln\left(1 - \frac{C}{M}\right)$

$t = -\frac{1}{0.201} \ln\left(1 - \frac{0.4M}{M}\right)$

$t = -\frac{1}{0.201} \ln(1 - 0.4) \approx 2.5$ hours

17. $t = \frac{\ln 2}{r} = \frac{\ln 2}{0.12} \approx 5.8$ years

18. $t = \frac{\ln 2}{r} = \frac{\ln 2}{0.25} \approx 2.8$ years

19. $t = \frac{\ln 3}{r} = \frac{\ln 3}{0.12} \approx 9.2$ years

20. $t = \frac{\ln 3}{r} = \frac{\ln 3}{0.25} \approx 4.4$ years

21. $E = RT \ln\left(\frac{V_f}{V_i}\right)$

$E = (8.314)(400) \ln\left(\frac{3V_i}{V_i}\right)$

$E = (8.314)(400) \ln(3)$

$E \approx 3654$ joules

22. $E = RT \ln\left(\frac{V_f}{V_i}\right)$

$E = (8.314)(300) \ln\left(\frac{2V_i}{V_i}\right)$

$E = (8.314)(300) \ln(2)$

$E \approx 1729$ joules

23. $r = \frac{1}{t} \ln \frac{P}{P_0} = \frac{1}{7} \ln \frac{10{,}400{,}000}{10{,}400} \approx 0.99 \Rightarrow$ about 99% per year

24. $r = \frac{1}{t} \ln \frac{P}{P_0} = \frac{1}{4} \ln \frac{237{,}000}{5{,}000} \approx 0.96 \Rightarrow$ about 96% per year

25. $n = \frac{\log V - \log C}{\log\left(1 - \frac{2}{N}\right)} = \frac{\log 8000 - \log 37{,}000}{\log\left(1 - \frac{2}{5}\right)} \approx 3$ years old

26. $n = \frac{\log V - \log C}{\log\left(1 - \frac{2}{N}\right)} = \frac{\log 189 - \log 470}{\log\left(1 - \frac{2}{12}\right)} \approx 5$ years old

27. $n = \frac{\log\left[\frac{Ar}{P} + 1\right]}{\log(1 + r)} = \frac{\log\left[\frac{20000(0.12)}{1000} + 1\right]}{\log(1 + 0.12)} \approx 10.8$ years

28. $n = \frac{\log\left[\frac{Ar}{P} + 1\right]}{\log(1 + r)} = \frac{\log\left[\frac{50000(0.08)}{5000} + 1\right]}{\log(1 + 0.08)} \approx 7.6$ years

29. $V = ER_1 \ln \frac{R_2}{R_1}$

$V = (400{,}000)(0.25) \ln\left(\frac{2}{0.25}\right)$

$V \approx 208{,}000$ V

30. $V = ER_1 \ln \frac{R_2}{R_1}$

$V = (400{,}000)(0.25) \ln\left(\frac{4}{0.25}\right)$

$V \approx 277{,}000$ V

31. $f(x) = 12 \Rightarrow \ln x = 12 \Rightarrow x \approx 162755 \Rightarrow$ You would go out 162,755 cm.

$162{,}755 \text{ cm} = \frac{162{,}755 \text{ cm}}{1} \cdot \frac{1 \text{ in}}{2.54 \text{ cm}} \cdot \frac{1 \text{ ft}}{12 \text{ in}} \cdot \frac{1 \text{ mi}}{5280 \text{ ft}} \approx 1$ mile

32. $f(x) = 12 \Rightarrow \log x = 12 \Rightarrow x = 10^{12}$ cm $\Rightarrow$ You would go out 10^{12} cm.

$10^{12} \text{ cm} = \frac{10^{12} \text{ cm}}{1} \cdot \frac{1 \text{ in}}{2.54 \text{ cm}} \cdot \frac{1 \text{ ft}}{12 \text{ in}} \cdot \frac{1 \text{ mi}}{5280 \text{ ft}} \approx 6{,}214{,}000$ mile

It is bigger because ln has a base of $e \approx 2.72$ while log has a base of 10.

33. Set $x = 0$:

$y = \frac{1}{1 + e^{-2(0)}}$

$= \frac{1}{1 + e^0}$

$= \frac{1}{1+1} = \frac{1}{2}$

y-intercept: $\left(0, \frac{1}{2}\right)$

34. **Explanations may vary.**

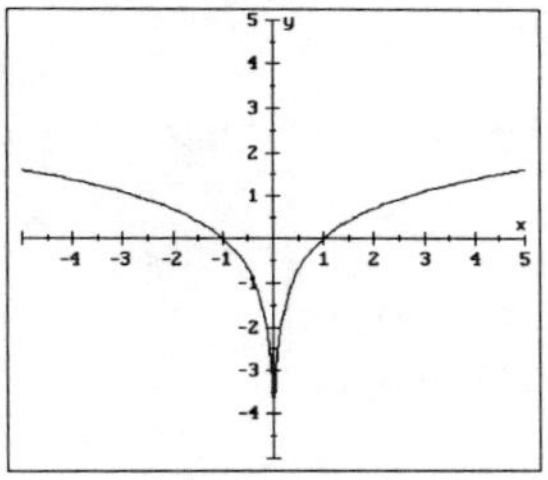

35. $y = mx + b$

$y = 7x + 3$

36. $3x + 2y = 9$

$y = -\frac{3}{2}x + \frac{9}{2}$

$m = -\frac{3}{2}$

Use $m = -\frac{3}{2}$.

$y - y_1 = m(x - x_1)$

$y - 5 = -\frac{3}{2}(x + 3)$

$y - 5 = -\frac{3}{2}x - \frac{9}{2}$

$y = -\frac{3}{2}x + \frac{1}{2}$

or $3x + 2y = 1$

37. Vertical through (2, 3): $x = 2$

38. Horizontal through (2, 3): $y = 3$

39. $\frac{2(x+2)-1}{4x^2-9} = \frac{2x+4-1}{(2x+3)(2x-3)} = \frac{2x+3}{(2x+3)(2x-3)} = \frac{1}{2x-3}$

40. $\frac{x+1}{x} + \frac{x-1}{x+1} = \frac{(x+1)(x+1)}{x(x+1)} + \frac{(x-1)\cdot x}{(x+1)\cdot x} = \frac{x^2+2x+1+x^2-x}{x(x+1)} = \frac{2x^2+x+1}{x(x+1)}$

41. $\frac{x^2+3x+2}{3x+9} \cdot \frac{x+3}{x^2-4} = \frac{(x+2)(x+1)}{3(x+3)} \cdot \frac{x+3}{(x+2)(x-2)} = \frac{x+1}{3(x-2)}$

42. $\frac{1+\frac{y}{x}}{\frac{y}{x}-1} = \frac{1+\frac{y}{x}}{\frac{y}{x}-1} \cdot \frac{x}{x} = \frac{x+y}{y-x}$

Exercise 4.5 (page 365)

1. 0

2. 1

3. M, N

4. x

5. x, y

6. $-$

7. x

8. x

9. $\neq$

10. $=$

11. $\log_4 1 = 0$

12. $\log_4 4 = 1$

13. $\log_4 4^7 = 7\log_4 4 = 7$

14. $4^{\log_4 8} = 8$

15. $5^{\log_5 10} = 10$

16. $\log_5 5^2 = 2\log_5 5 = 2$

17. $\log_5 5 = 1$

18. $\log_5 1 = 0$

19-24. Answers may vary.

25. $\log_b 2xy = \log_b 2 + \log_b x + \log_b y$

26. $\log_b 3xz = \log_b 3 + \log_b x + \log_b z$

27.
$$\begin{aligned}\log_b \frac{2x}{y} &= \log_b 2x - \log_b y\\ &= \log_b 2 + \log_b x - \log_b y\end{aligned}$$

28.
$$\begin{aligned}\log_b \frac{x}{yz} &= \log_b x - \log_b yz\\ &= \log_b x - (\log_b y + \log_b z)\\ &= \log_b x - \log_b y - \log_b z\end{aligned}$$

29.
$$\begin{aligned}\log_b x^2y^3 &= \log_b x^2 + \log_b y^3\\ &= 2\log_b x + 3\log_b y\end{aligned}$$

30.
$$\begin{aligned}\log_b x^3y^2z &= \log_b x^3 + \log_b y^2 + \log_b z\\ &= 3\log_b x + 2\log_b y + \log_b z\end{aligned}$$

31.
$$\begin{aligned}\log_b (xy)^{1/3} &= \frac{1}{3}\log_b xy\\ &= \frac{1}{3}(\log_b x + \log_b y)\end{aligned}$$

32.
$$\begin{aligned}\log_b x^{1/2}y^3 &= \log_b x^{1/2} + \log_b y^3\\ &= \frac{1}{2}\log_b x + 3\log_b y\end{aligned}$$

33.
$$\begin{aligned}\log_b x\sqrt{z} &= \log_b xz^{1/2}\\ &= \log_b x + \log_b z^{1/2}\\ &= \log_b x + \frac{1}{2}\log_b z\end{aligned}$$

34.
$$\begin{aligned}\log_b \sqrt{xy} &= \log_b (xy)^{1/2}\\ &= \frac{1}{2}\log_b xy\\ &= \frac{1}{2}(\log_b x + \log_b y)\end{aligned}$$

35.
$$\begin{aligned}\log_b \frac{\sqrt[3]{x}}{\sqrt[3]{yz}} = \log_b \sqrt[3]{x} - \log_b \sqrt[3]{yz} = \log_b x^{1/3} - \log_b (yz)^{1/3} &= \frac{1}{3}\log_b x - \frac{1}{3}\log_b yz\\ &= \frac{1}{3}\log_b x - \frac{1}{3}(\log_b y + \log_b z)\\ &= \frac{1}{3}\log_b x - \frac{1}{3}\log_b y - \frac{1}{3}\log_b z\end{aligned}$$

36. $\log_b \sqrt[4]{\frac{x^3y^2}{z^4}} = \log_b \left(\frac{x^3y^2}{z^4}\right)^{1/4} = \frac{1}{4}\log_b \frac{x^3y^2}{z^4} = \frac{1}{4}\left(\log_b x^3y^2 - \log_b z^4\right)$

$= \frac{1}{4}\left(\log_b x^3 + \log_b y^2 - \log_b z^4\right)$

$= \frac{1}{4}(3\log_b x + 2\log_b y - 4\log_b z)$

$= \frac{3}{4}\log_b x + \frac{1}{2}\log_b y - \log_b z$

37. $\log_b (x+1) - \log_b x = \log_b \frac{x+1}{x}$

38. $\log_b x + \log_b (x+2) - \log_b 8 = \log_b x(x+2) - \log_b 8 = \log_b \frac{x(x+2)}{8}$

39. $2\log_b x + \frac{1}{3}\log_b y = \log_b x^2 + \log_b y^{1/3} = \log_b x^2y^{1/3} = \log_b x^2\sqrt[3]{y}$

40. $-2\log_b x - 3\log_b y + \log_b z = \log_b x^{-2} + \log_b y^{-3} + \log_b z = \log_b x^{-2}y^{-3}z = \log_b \frac{z}{x^2y^3}$

41. $-3\log_b x - 2\log_b y + \frac{1}{2}\log_b z = \log_b x^{-3} + \log_b y^{-2} + \log_b z^{1/2} = \log_b x^{-3}y^{-2}\sqrt{z} = \log_b \frac{\sqrt{z}}{x^3y^2}$

42. $3\log_b (x+1) - 2\log_b (x+2) + \log_b x = \log_b (x+1)^3 + \log_b (x+2)^{-2} + \log_b x = \log_b \frac{x(x+1)^3}{(x+2)^2}$

43. $\log_b\left(\frac{x}{z} + x\right) - \log_b\left(\frac{y}{z} + y\right) = \log_b \frac{\frac{x}{z}+x}{\frac{y}{z}+y} = \log_b \frac{z\left(\frac{x}{z}+x\right)}{z\left(\frac{y}{z}+y\right)} = \log_b \frac{x+xz}{y+yz} = \log_b \frac{x}{y}$

44. $\log_b(xy + y^2) - \log_b(xz + yz) + \log_b z = \log_b \frac{(xy+y^2)z}{xz+yz} = \log_b \frac{(x+y)yz}{z(x+y)} = \log_b y$

45. $\log_b ab = \log_b a + \log_b b = \log_b a + 1$
TRUE

46. $\log_b \frac{1}{a} = \log_b a^{-1} = -\log_b a$
TRUE

47. $\log_b 0$ is undefined.
FALSE

48. $\log_b 2 = \log_2 b$
FALSE (except for $b = 2$)

49. $\log_b (x \cdot y) = \log_b x + \log_b y$, so
$\log_b (x+y) \neq \log_b x + \log_b y$
TRUE (unless $x \cdot y = x + y$)

50. $\log_b (x \cdot y) = \log_b x + \log_b y$, so
$\log_b (xy) \neq (\log_b x)(\log_b y)$
FALSE

51. If $\log_a b = c$, then $\log_b a = c$
FALSE

52. If $\log_a b = c$, then $\log_b a = \frac{1}{c}$

$$\log_a b = c \Rightarrow a^c = b$$
$$(a^c)^{1/c} = b^{1/c}$$
$$a = b^{1/c} \Rightarrow \log_b a = \frac{1}{c}$$
TRUE

53. $\log_7 7^7 = 7 \Rightarrow 7^7 = 7^7$
TRUE

54. $7^{\log_7 7} = 7$
TRUE

55. $-\log_b x = \log_b x^{-1} = \log_b \frac{1}{x}$
FALSE

56. $\log_b a^p = p \log_b a = pc$
TRUE

57. $\log_b \left(\frac{A}{B}\right) = \log_b A - \log_b B$, so

$$\frac{\log_b (A)}{\log_b (B)} \neq \log_b A - \log_b B$$
FALSE

58. $\log_b (A - B) = \frac{\log_b (A)}{\log_b (B)}$
FALSE

59. $\log_b \frac{1}{5} = \log_b 5^{-1} = -\log_b 5$
TRUE

60. $3 \log_b \sqrt[3]{a} = 3 \log_b a^{1/3} = 3 \cdot \frac{1}{3} \log_b a$
$= \log_b a$
TRUE

61. $\frac{1}{3} \log_b a^3 = \frac{1}{3} \cdot 3 \log_b a = \log_b a$
TRUE

62. Let $\log_{4/3} y = c$.
Then $\left(\frac{4}{3}\right)^c = y$.
$$\left(\left(\tfrac{3}{4}\right)^{-1}\right)^c = y$$
$$\left(\tfrac{3}{4}\right)^{-c} = y \Rightarrow \log_{3/4} y = -c.$$
Thus, $\log_{4/3} y = c = -\log_{3/4} y. \Rightarrow$ TRUE

63. Let $\log_{1/b} y = c$.
Then $\left(\frac{1}{b}\right)^c = y$.
$$\left(\left(\tfrac{b}{1}\right)^{-1}\right)^c = y$$
$$(b)^{-c} = y \Rightarrow \log_b y = -c.$$
$\log_{1/b} y + \log_b y = c + (-c) = 0.$
TRUE

64. $\log_{10} 10^3 = 3$
$3\left(10^{\log_{10} 3}\right) = 3(3) = 9$
$\log_{10} 10^3 \neq 3\left(10^{\log_{10} 3}\right)$
FALSE

65. $\log_{10} 28 = \log_{10} (4 \cdot 7)$
$= \log_{10} 4 + \log_{10} 7$
$= 0.6021 + 0.8451 = 1.4472$

66. $\log_{10} \left(\frac{7}{4}\right) = \log_{10} 7 - \log_{10} 4$
$= 0.8451 - 0.6021 = 0.2430$

67. $$\log_{10} 2.25 = \log_{10}\left(\frac{9}{4}\right) = \log_{10} 9 - \log_{10} 4 = 0.9542 - 0.6021 = 0.3521$$

68. $$\log_{10} 36 = \log_{10}(4 \cdot 9) = \log_{10} 4 + \log_{10} 9 = 0.6021 + 0.9542 = 1.5563$$

69. $$\log_{10}\left(\frac{63}{4}\right) = \log_{10} 63 - \log_{10} 4 = \log_{10}(7 \cdot 9) - \log_{10} 4 = \log_{10} 7 + \log_{10} 9 - \log_{10} 4 = 0.8451 + 0.9542 - 0.6021 = 1.1972$$

70. $$\log_{10}\left(\frac{4}{63}\right) = \log_{10} 4 - \log_{10} 63 = \log_{10} 4 - \log_{10}(7 \cdot 9) = \log_{10} 4 - \log_{10} 7 - \log_{10} 9 = 0.6021 - 0.8451 - 0.9542 = -1.1972$$

71. $$\log_{10} 252 = \log_{10}(4 \cdot 63) = \log_{10}(4 \cdot 7 \cdot 9) = \log_{10} 4 + \log_{10} 7 + \log_{10} 9 = 0.6021 + 0.8451 + 0.9542 = 2.4014$$

72. $$\log_{10} 49 = \log_{10} 7^2 = 2\log_{10} 7 = 2(0.8451) = 1.6902$$

73. $$\log_{10} 112 = \log_{10}(4 \cdot 28) = \log_{10}(4 \cdot 7 \cdot 4) = \log_{10} 4 + \log_{10} 7 + \log_{10} 4 = 0.6021 + 0.8451 + 0.6021 = 2.0493$$

74. $$\log_{10} 324 = \log_{10}(4 \cdot 81) = \log_{10}(4 \cdot 9 \cdot 9) = \log_{10} 4 + \log_{10} 9 + \log_{10} 9 = 0.6021 + 0.9542 + 0.9542 = 2.5105$$

75. $$\log_{10}\left(\frac{144}{49}\right) = \log_{10} 144 - \log_{10} 49 = \log_{10}(4 \cdot 4 \cdot 9) - \log_{10}(7 \cdot 7) = \log_{10} 4 + \log_{10} 4 + \log_{10} 9 - \log_{10} 7 - \log_{10} 7 = 0.6021 + 0.6021 + 0.9542 - 0.8451 - 0.8451 = 0.4682$$

76. $$\log_{10}\left(\frac{324}{63}\right) = \log_{10} 324 - \log_{10} 63 = \log_{10}(4 \cdot 9 \cdot 9) - \log_{10}(7 \cdot 9) = \log_{10} 4 + \log_{10} 9 + \log_{10} 9 - \log_{10} 7 - \log_{10} 9 = 0.6021 + 0.9542 + 0.9542 - 0.8451 - 0.9542 = 0.7112$$

77. $$\log_3 7 = \frac{\log_{10} 7}{\log_{10} 3} \approx 1.7712$$

78. $$\log_7 3 = \frac{\log_{10} 3}{\log_{10} 7} \approx 0.5646$$

79. $$\log_\pi 3 = \frac{\log_{10} 3}{\log_{10} \pi} \approx 0.9597$$

80. $$\log_3 \pi = \frac{\log_{10} \pi}{\log_{10} 3} \approx 1.0420$$

81. $\log_3 8 = \dfrac{\log_e 8}{\log_e 3} \approx 1.8928$

82. $\log_5 10 = \dfrac{\log_e 10}{\log_e 5} \approx 1.4307$

83. $\log_{\sqrt{2}} \sqrt{5} = \dfrac{\log_e \sqrt{5}}{\log_e \sqrt{2}} \approx 2.3219$

84. $\log_\pi e = \dfrac{\log_e e}{\log_e \pi} \approx 0.8736$

85.
$$\begin{aligned} \text{pH} &= -\log\,[\text{H}^+] \\ &= -\log\left(1.7 \times 10^{-5}\right) \\ &\approx 4.77 \end{aligned}$$

86.
$$\begin{aligned} \text{pH} &= -\log\,[\text{H}^+] \\ 13.2 &= -\log\,[\text{H}^+] \\ -13.2 &= \log\,[\text{H}^+] \\ 6.3 \times 10^{-14} &\approx [\text{H}^+] \end{aligned}$$

87.
$$\begin{aligned} \text{pH} &= -\log\,[\text{H}^+] \\ 2.9 &= -\log\,[\text{H}^+] \\ -2.9 &= \log\,[\text{H}^+] \\ 1.26 \times 10^{-3} &\approx [\text{H}^+] \end{aligned} \qquad \begin{aligned} \text{pH} &= -\log\,[\text{H}^+] \\ 3.3 &= -\log\,[\text{H}^+] \\ -3.3 &= \log\,[\text{H}^+] \\ 5.01 \times 10^{-4} &\approx [\text{H}^+] \end{aligned}$$

The hydrogen ion concentration can range from 5.01×10^{-4} to 1.26×10^{-3}.

88.
$$\begin{aligned} \text{pH} &= -\log\,[\text{H}^+] \\ &= -\log\left(6.31 \times 10^{-4}\right) \\ &\approx 3.2 \end{aligned}$$

89.
$$\begin{aligned} \text{db gain} &= 10 \log \frac{P_O}{P_I} \\ &= 10 \log \frac{40}{\frac{1}{2}} \\ &\approx 19 \text{ db} \end{aligned}$$

90.
$$\begin{aligned} \text{db gain} &= 10 \log \frac{P_O}{P_I} \\ &= 10 \log \frac{3}{12} \\ &\approx -6 \text{ db} \end{aligned}$$

91. $L = k \ln I$

$4L = 4k \ln I = k \cdot 4 \ln I = k \ln I^4$

The original intensity must be raised to the fourth power.

92. $L = k \ln I$

$\frac{1}{2}L = \frac{1}{2}k \ln I = k \cdot \frac{1}{2} \ln I = k \ln I^{1/2}$

The original intensity must be raised to the one-half power (the square root).

93. $E = 8300 \ln V$

$2E = 2 \cdot 8300 \ln V = 8300 \ln V^2$

The original volume is squared.

94. $R = \log \frac{A}{P}$

$R + 1 = \log \frac{A}{P} + 1 = \log \frac{A}{P} + \log 10 = \log\left(\frac{A}{P} \cdot 10\right) = \log \frac{10A}{P}$

The amplitude must be multiplied by a factor of 10.

95. Let $\log_b M = x$ and $\log_b N = y$.
Then $b^x = M$ and $b^y = N$.
$\frac{M}{N} = \frac{b^x}{b^y} = b^{x-y}$.
So $\log_b \frac{M}{N} = x - y$, or
$\log_b \frac{M}{N} = \log_b M - \log_b N$.

96. $-\log_b x = Q \Rightarrow b^Q = x^{-1}$
$\log_b x^{-1} = Q \quad (b^Q)^{-1} = (x^{-1})^{-1}$
$b^{-Q} = x$
$(b^{-1})^Q = x$
$\left(\frac{1}{b}\right)^Q = x$
$\log_{1/b} x = Q$
Thus, $-\log_b x = Q = \log_{1/b} x$.

97. $e^{x \ln a} = e^{\ln a^x} = a^x$

98. $\ln x = M \Rightarrow e^M = x$, by definition.
Thus, $e^{\ln x} = e^M = x$.

99. $\ln(e^x) = x \ln e = x(1) = x$

100. $\log_b 3x = 1 + \log_b x$
$\log_b 3 + \log_b x = 1 + \log_b x$
$\log_b 3 = 1$
$b^1 = 3 \Rightarrow b = 3$

101. $\log(0.9) < 0$, so $\ln(\log(0.9))$ is undefined.

102. $\ln 1 = 0$, so $\log_b(\ln 1)$ is undefined.

103. Answers may vary.

104. Answers may vary.

105. $y = 3x - 1 \Rightarrow$ function

106. $y = \frac{x+3}{x-1} \Rightarrow$ function

107. $y^2 = 4x$
$y = \pm\sqrt{4x} \Rightarrow$ not a function

108. $y = 4x^2 \Rightarrow$ function

109. $f(x) = x^2 - 4$; domain $= (-\infty, \infty)$

110. $f(x) = \frac{1}{x^2 - 4} = \frac{1}{(x+2)(x-2)}$
domain $= (-\infty, -2) \cup (-2, 2) \cup (2, \infty)$

111. $f(x) = \sqrt{x^2 + 4}$; domain $= (-\infty, \infty)$

112. $f(x) = \sqrt{x^2 - 4}$
$x^2 - 4 \geq 0 \Rightarrow x \leq -2$ or $x \geq 2$
domain $= (-\infty, -2] \cup [2, \infty)$

Exercise 4.6 (page 373)

1. exponential

2. logarithmic

3. $A_0 2^{-t/h}$

4. $P_0 e^{kt}$

5.
$$\begin{aligned} 4^x &= 5 \\ \log 4^x &= \log 5 \\ x\log 4 &= \log 5 \\ x &= \frac{\log 5}{\log 4} \\ x &\approx 1.1610 \end{aligned}$$

6.
$$\begin{aligned} 7^x &= 12 \\ \log 7^x &= \log 12 \\ x\log 7 &= \log 12 \\ x &= \frac{\log 12}{\log 7} \\ x &\approx 1.2770 \end{aligned}$$

7.
$$\begin{aligned} 13^{x-1} &= 2 \\ \log 13^{x-1} &= \log 2 \\ (x-1)\log 13 &= \log 2 \\ x\log 13 - \log 13 &= \log 2 \\ x\log 13 &= \log 2 + \log 13 \\ x &= \frac{\log 2 + \log 13}{\log 13} \\ x &\approx 1.2702 \end{aligned}$$

8.
$$\begin{aligned} 5^{x+1} &= 3 \\ \log 5^{x+1} &= \log 3 \\ (x+1)\log 5 &= \log 3 \\ x\log 5 + \log 5 &= \log 3 \\ x\log 5 &= \log 3 - \log 5 \\ x &= \frac{\log 3 - \log 5}{\log 5} \\ x &\approx -0.3174 \end{aligned}$$

9.
$$\begin{aligned} 2^{x+1} &= 3^x \\ \log 2^{x+1} &= \log 3^x \\ (x+1)\log 2 &= x\log 3 \\ x\log 2 + \log 2 &= x\log 3 \\ x\log 2 - x\log 3 &= -\log 2 \\ x(\log 2 - \log 3) &= -\log 2 \\ x &= \frac{-\log 2}{\log 2 - \log 3} \\ x &\approx 1.7095 \end{aligned}$$

10.
$$\begin{aligned} 5^{x-3} &= 3^{2x} \\ \log 5^{x-3} &= \log 3^{2x} \\ (x-3)\log 5 &= 2x\log 3 \\ x\log 5 - 3\log 5 &= 2x\log 3 \\ x\log 5 - 2x\log 3 &= 3\log 5 \\ x(\log 5 - 2\log 3) &= 3\log 5 \\ x &= \frac{3\log 5}{\log 5 - 2\log 3} \\ x &\approx -8.2144 \end{aligned}$$

11.
$$\begin{aligned} 2^x &= 3^x \\ \log 2^x &= \log 3^x \\ x\log 2 &= x\log 3 \\ x\log 2 - x\log 3 &= 0 \\ x(\log 2 - \log 3) &= 0 \\ x &= \frac{0}{\log 2 - \log 3} = 0 \end{aligned}$$

12.
$$\begin{aligned} 3^{2x} &= 4^x \\ \log 3^{2x} &= \log 4^x \\ 2x\log 3 &= x\log 4 \\ 2x\log 3 - x\log 4 &= 0 \\ x(2\log 3 - \log 4) &= 0 \\ x &= \frac{0}{2\log 3 - \log 4} = 0 \end{aligned}$$

13.
$$\begin{aligned} 7^{x^2} &= 10 \\ \log 7^{x^2} &= \log 10 \\ x^2\log 7 &= \log 10 \\ x^2 &= \frac{\log 10}{\log 7} \\ x &= \pm\sqrt{\frac{\log 10}{\log 7}} \\ x &\approx \pm 1.0878 \end{aligned}$$

14.
$$\begin{aligned} 8^{x^2} &= 11 \\ \log 8^{x^2} &= \log 11 \\ x^2\log 8 &= \log 11 \\ x^2 &= \frac{\log 11}{\log 8} \\ x &= \pm\sqrt{\frac{\log 11}{\log 8}} \\ x &\approx \pm 1.0738 \end{aligned}$$

15.

$$
\begin{aligned}
8^{x^2} &= 9^x \\
\log 8^{x^2} &= \log 9^x \\
x^2 \log 8 &= x \log 9 \\
x^2 \log 8 - x \log 9 &= 0 \\
x(x \log 8 - \log 9) &= 0
\end{aligned}
$$

$$
\begin{array}{lcl}
x = 0 & \textbf{or} & x \log 8 - \log 9 = 0 \\
x = 0 & & x \log 8 = \log 9 \\
x = 0 & & x = \dfrac{\log 9}{\log 8} \\
x = 0 & & x \approx 1.0566
\end{array}
$$

16.

$$
\begin{aligned}
5^{x^2} &= 2^{5x} \\
\log 5^{x^2} &= \log 2^{5x} \\
x^2 \log 5 &= 5x \log 2 \\
x^2 \log 5 - 5x \log 2 &= 0 \\
x(x \log 5 - 5 \log 2) &= 0
\end{aligned}
$$

$$
\begin{array}{lcl}
x = 0 & \textbf{or} & x \log 5 - 5 \log 2 = 0 \\
x = 0 & & x \log 5 = 5 \log 2 \\
x = 0 & & x = \dfrac{5 \log 2}{\log 5} \\
x = 0 & & x \approx 2.1534
\end{array}
$$

17.

$$
\begin{aligned}
2^{x^2-2x} &= 8 \\
2^{x^2-2x} &= 2^3 \\
x^2 - 2x &= 3 \\
x^2 - 2x - 3 &= 0 \\
(x-3)(x+1) &= 0
\end{aligned}
$$

$$
\begin{array}{lcl}
x - 3 = 0 & \textbf{or} & x + 1 = 0 \\
x = 3 & & x = -1
\end{array}
$$

18.

$$
\begin{aligned}
5^{x^2-3x} &= 625 \\
5^{x^2-3x} &= 5^4 \\
x^2 - 3x &= 4 \\
x^2 - 3x - 4 &= 0 \\
(x-4)(x+1) &= 0
\end{aligned}
$$

$$
\begin{array}{lcl}
x - 4 = 0 & \textbf{or} & x + 1 = 0 \\
x = 4 & & x = -1
\end{array}
$$

19.

$$
\begin{aligned}
3^{x^2+4x} &= \frac{1}{81} \\
3^{x^2+4x} &= 3^{-4} \\
x^2 + 4x &= -4 \\
x^2 + 4x + 4 &= 0 \\
(x+2)(x+2) &= 0
\end{aligned}
$$

$$
\begin{array}{lcl}
x + 2 = 0 & \textbf{or} & x + 2 = 0 \\
x = -2 & & x = -2
\end{array}
$$

20.

$$
\begin{aligned}
7^{x^2+3x} &= \frac{1}{49} \\
7^{x^2+3x} &= 7^{-2} \\
x^2 + 3x &= -2 \\
x^2 + 3x + 2 &= 0 \\
(x+2)(x+1) &= 0
\end{aligned}
$$

$$
\begin{array}{lcl}
x + 2 = 0 & \textbf{or} & x + 1 = 0 \\
x = -2 & & x = -1
\end{array}
$$

21.

$$
\begin{aligned}
4^{x+2} - 4^x &= 15 \\
4^x 4^2 - 4^x &= 15 \\
16 \cdot 4^x - 4^x &= 15 \\
15 \cdot 4^x &= 15 \\
4^x &= 1 \\
x &= 0
\end{aligned}
$$

22.

$$
\begin{aligned}
3^{x+3} + 3^x &= 84 \\
3^x 3^3 + 3^x &= 84 \\
27 \cdot 3^x + 3^x &= 84 \\
28 \cdot 3^x &= 84 \\
3^x &= 3 \\
x &= 1
\end{aligned}
$$

23.
$$\begin{aligned} 2(3^x) &= 6^{2x} \\ \log[2(3^x)] &= \log 6^{2x} \\ \log 2 + \log 3^x &= 2x\log 6 \\ \log 2 + x\log 3 &= 2x\log 6 \\ x\log 3 - 2x\log 6 &= -\log 2 \\ x(\log 3 - 2\log 6) &= -\log 2 \\ x &= \frac{-\log 2}{\log 3 - 2\log 6} \\ x &\approx 0.2789 \end{aligned}$$

24.
$$\begin{aligned} 2\left(3^{x+1}\right) &= 3\left(2^{x-1}\right) \\ \log\left[2\left(3^{x+1}\right)\right] &= \log\left[3\left(2^{x-1}\right)\right] \\ \log 2 + \log 3^{x+1} &= \log 3 + \log 2^{x-1} \\ \log 2 + (x+1)\log 3 &= \log 3 + (x-1)\log 2 \\ \log 2 + x\log 3 + \log 3 &= \log 3 + x\log 2 - \log 2 \\ x\log 3 - x\log 2 &= -2\log 2 \\ x(\log 3 - \log 2) &= -2\log 2 \\ x &= \frac{-2\log 2}{\log 3 - \log 2} \\ x &\approx -3.4190 \end{aligned}$$

25.
$$\begin{aligned} 2^{2x} - 10(2^x) + 16 &= 0 \\ (2^x - 2)(2^x - 8) &= 0 \end{aligned}$$
$2^x - 2 = 0$ **or** $2^x - 8 = 0$
$2^x = 2$ $\qquad 2^x = 8$
$x = 1$ $\qquad x = 3$

26.
$$\begin{aligned} 3^{2x} - 10(3^x) + 9 &= 0 \\ (3^x - 1)(3^x - 9) &= 0 \end{aligned}$$
$3^x - 1 = 0$ **or** $3^x - 9 = 0$
$3^x = 1$ $\qquad 3^x = 9$
$x = 0$ $\qquad x = 2$

27.
$$\begin{aligned} 2^{2x+1} - 2^x &= 1 \\ 2^{2x}2^1 - 2^x - 1 &= 0 \\ 2\left(2^{2x}\right) - 2^x - 1 &= 0 \\ (2(2^x) + 1)(2^x - 1) &= 0 \end{aligned}$$
$2(2^x) + 1 = 0$ **or** $2^x - 1 = 0$
$2(2^x) = -1$ $\qquad 2^x = 1$
$2^x = -\frac{1}{2}$ $\qquad x = 0$
impossible

28.
$$\begin{aligned} 3^{2x+1} - 10(3^x) + 3 &= 0 \\ 3^{2x}3^1 - 10(3^x) + 3 &= 0 \\ 3\left(3^{2x}\right) - 10(3^x) + 3 &= 0 \\ (3(3^x) - 1)(3^x - 3) &= 0 \end{aligned}$$
$3(3^x) - 1 = 0$ **or** $3^x - 3 = 0$
$3(3^x) = 1$ $\qquad 3^x = 3$
$3^x = \frac{1}{3}$ $\qquad x = 1$
$x = -1$

29.
$$\begin{aligned} \log(2x - 3) &= \log(x + 4) \\ 2x - 3 &= x + 4 \\ x &= 7 \end{aligned}$$

30.
$$\begin{aligned} \log(3x + 5) - \log(2x + 6) &= 0 \\ \log(3x + 5) &= \log(2x + 6) \\ 3x + 5 &= 2x + 6 \\ x &= 1 \end{aligned}$$

31.
$$\begin{aligned}\log\frac{4x+1}{2x+9} &= 0\\ 10^0 &= \frac{4x+1}{2x+9}\\ 1 &= \frac{4x+1}{2x+9}\\ 2x+9 &= 4x+1\\ 8 &= 2x\\ 4 &= x\end{aligned}$$

32.
$$\begin{aligned}\log\frac{5x+2}{2(x+7)} &= 0\\ 10^0 &= \frac{5x+2}{2(x+7)}\\ 1 &= \frac{5x+2}{2x+14}\\ 2x+14 &= 5x+2\\ -3x &= -12\\ x &= 4\end{aligned}$$

33.
$$\begin{aligned}\log x^2 &= 2\\ 10^2 &= x^2\\ 100 &= x^2\\ \pm\sqrt{100} &= x\\ \pm 10 &= x\end{aligned}$$

34.
$$\begin{aligned}\log x^3 &= 3\\ 10^3 &= x^3\\ 1000 &= x^3\\ \sqrt[3]{1000} &= x\\ 10 &= x\end{aligned}$$

35.
$$\begin{aligned}\log x + \log(x-48) &= 2\\ \log x(x-48) &= 2\\ x(x-48) &= 10^2\\ x^2-48x-100 &= 0\\ (x-50)(x+2) &= 0\end{aligned}$$
$x-50=0$ **or** $x+2=0$

$x=50$ $\quad x=-2$: extraneous

36.
$$\begin{aligned}\log x + \log(x+9) &= 1\\ \log x(x+9) &= 1\\ x(x+9) &= 10^1\\ x^2+9x-10 &= 0\\ (x-1)(x+10) &= 0\end{aligned}$$
$x-1=0$ **or** $x+10=0$

$x=1$ $\quad x=-10$: extraneous

37.
$$\begin{aligned}\log x + \log(x-15) &= 2\\ \log x(x-15) &= 2\\ x(x-15) &= 10^2\\ x^2-15x-100 &= 0\\ (x-20)(x+5) &= 0\end{aligned}$$
$x-20=0$ **or** $x+5=0$

$x=20$ $\quad x=-5$: extraneous

38.
$$\begin{aligned}\log x + \log(x+21) &= 2\\ \log x(x+21) &= 2\\ x(x+21) &= 10^2\\ x^2+21x-100 &= 0\\ (x-4)(x+25) &= 0\end{aligned}$$
$x-4=0$ **or** $x+25=0$

$x=4$ $\quad x=-25$: extraneous

39.

$$\begin{aligned} \log(x+90) &= 3-\log x \\ \log x + \log(x+90) &= 3 \\ \log x(x+90) &= 3 \\ x(x+90) &= 10^3 \\ x^2+90x-1000 &= 0 \\ (x-10)(x+100) &= 0 \end{aligned}$$

$x-10=0$ **or** $x+100=0$

$x=10$ $\quad$ $x=-100$

extraneous

40.

$$\begin{aligned} \log(x-6)-\log(x-2) &= \log\frac{5}{x} \\ \log\frac{x-6}{x-2} &= \log\frac{5}{x} \\ \frac{x-6}{x-2} &= \frac{5}{x} \\ x(x-6) &= 5(x-2) \\ x^2-6x &= 5x-10 \\ x^2-11x+10 &= 0 \\ (x-1)(x-10) &= 0 \end{aligned}$$

$x-1=0$ **or** $x-10=0$

$x=1$ $\quad$ $x=10$

extraneous

41.

$$\begin{aligned} \log(x-1)-\log 6 &= \log(x-2)-\log x \\ \log\tfrac{x-1}{6} &= \log\tfrac{x-2}{x} \\ \tfrac{x-1}{6} &= \tfrac{x-2}{x} \\ x(x-1) &= 6(x-2) \\ x^2-x &= 6x-12 \\ x^2-7x+12 &= 0 \\ (x-3)(x-4) &= 0 \end{aligned}$$

$x-3=0$ **or** $x-4=0$

$x=3$ $\quad$ $x=4$

42.

$$\begin{aligned} \log(2x-3)-\log(x-1) &= 0 \\ \log(2x-3) &= \log(x-1) \\ 2x-3 &= x-1 \\ x &= 2 \end{aligned}$$

43.

$$\begin{aligned} \log x^2 &= (\log x)^2 \\ 2\log x &= (\log x)^2 \\ 0 &= (\log x)^2 - 2\log x \\ 0 &= \log x\,(\log x - 2) \end{aligned}$$

$\log x = 0$ **or** $\log x - 2 = 0$

$x=1$ $\quad$ $\log x = 2$

$x=1$ $\quad$ $x=100$

44.

$$\begin{aligned} \log(\log x) &= 1 \\ \log x &= 10^1 \\ \log x &= 10 \\ x &= 10^{10} \end{aligned}$$

45.

$$\begin{aligned} \frac{\log(3x-4)}{\log x} &= 2 \\ \log(3x-4) &= 2\log x \\ \log(3x-4) &= \log x^2 \\ 3x-4 &= x^2 \\ 0 &= x^2-3x+4 \end{aligned}$$

No real solutions

46.

$$\begin{aligned} \frac{\log(8x-7)}{\log x} &= 2 \\ \log(8x-7) &= 2\log x \\ \log(8x-7) &= \log x^2 \\ 8x-7 &= x^2 \\ 0 &= x^2-8x+7 \\ 0 &= (x-7)(x-1) \end{aligned}$$

$x-7=0$ **or** $x-1=0$

$x=7$ $\quad$ $x=1$

extraneous

47.
$$\begin{aligned}\tfrac{\log(5x+6)}{2} &= \log x\\ \log(5x+6) &= 2\log x\\ \log(5x+6) &= \log x^2\\ 5x+6 &= x^2\\ 0 &= x^2-5x-6\\ 0 &= (x-6)(x+1)\end{aligned}$$
$x-6=0$ **or** $x+1=0$
$x=6$ $\quad$ $x=-1$
extraneous

48.
$$\begin{aligned}\tfrac{1}{2}\log(4x+5) &= \log x\\ \log(4x+5) &= 2\log x\\ \log(4x+5) &= \log x^2\\ 4x+5 &= x^2\\ 0 &= x^2-4x-5\\ 0 &= (x-5)(x+1)\end{aligned}$$
$x-5=0$ **or** $x+1=0$
$x=5$ $\quad$ $x=-1$
extraneous

49.
$$\begin{aligned}\log_3 x &= \log_3\left(\frac{1}{x}\right)+4\\ \log_3 x &= \log_3 x^{-1}+4\\ \log_3 x &= -\log_3 x+4\\ 2\log_3 x &= 4\\ \log_3 x &= 2\\ x &= 9\end{aligned}$$

50.
$$\begin{aligned}\log_5(7+x)+\log_5(8-x)-\log_5 2 &= 2\\ \log_5\tfrac{(7+x)(8-x)}{2} &= 2\\ \tfrac{(7+x)(8-x)}{2} &= 5^2\\ (7+x)(8-x) &= 50\\ -x^2+x+56 &= 50\\ x^2-x-6 &= 0\\ (x-3)(x+2) &= 0\end{aligned}$$
$x-3=0$ **or** $x+2=0$
$x=3$ $\quad$ $x=-2$

51.
$$\begin{aligned}2\log_2 x &= 3+\log_2(x-2)\\ \log_2 x^2-\log_2(x-2) &= 3\\ \log_2\tfrac{x^2}{x-2} &= 3\\ \tfrac{x^2}{x-2} &= 2^3\\ x^2 &= 8(x-2)\\ x^2-8x+16 &= 0\\ (x-4)(x-4) &= 0\end{aligned}$$
$x-4=0$ **or** $x-4=0$
$x=4$ $\quad$ $x=4$

52.
$$\begin{aligned}2\log_3 x-\log_3(x-4) &= 2+\log_3 2\\ \log_3 x^2-\log_3(x-4)-\log_3 2 &= 2\\ \log_3\tfrac{x^2}{2(x-4)} &= 2\\ \tfrac{x^2}{2x-8} &= 3^2\\ x^2 &= 9(2x-8)\\ x^2-18x+72 &= 0\\ (x-12)(x-6) &= 0\end{aligned}$$
$x-12=0$ **or** $x-6=0$
$x=12$ $\quad$ $x=6$

53.
$$\begin{aligned}\log(7y+1) &= 2\log(y+3)-\log 2\\ \log(7y+1) &= \log\tfrac{(y+3)^2}{2}\\ 7y+1 &= \tfrac{y^2+6y+9}{2}\\ 14y+2 &= y^2+6y+9\\ 0 &= y^2-8y+7\\ 0 &= (y-7)(y-1)\end{aligned}$$
$y-7=0$ **or** $y-1=0$
$y=7$ $\quad$ $y=1$

54.
$$\begin{aligned}2\log(y+2) &= \log(y+2)-\log 12\\ \log(y+2)^2 &= \log\tfrac{(y+2)}{12}\\ y^2+4y+4 &= \tfrac{y+2}{12}\\ 12y^2+48y+48 &= y+2\\ 12y^2+47y+46 &= 0\\ (12y+23)(y+2) &= 0\end{aligned}$$
$12y+23=0$ **or** $y+2=0$
$12y=-23$ $\quad$ $y=-2$
$y=-\frac{23}{12}$ $\quad$ extraneous

55. Graph $y = \log x + \log(x - 15)$ and $y = 2$ and find the x-coordinate of the point(s) of intersection: $x = 20$

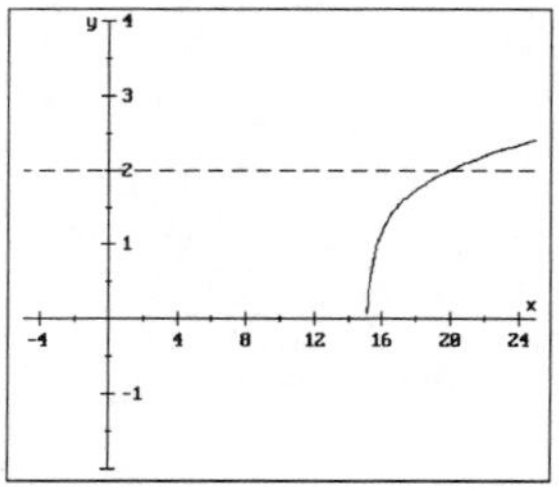

56. Graph $y = \log x + \log(x + 3)$ and $y = 1$ and find the x-coordinate of the point(s) of intersection: $x = 2$

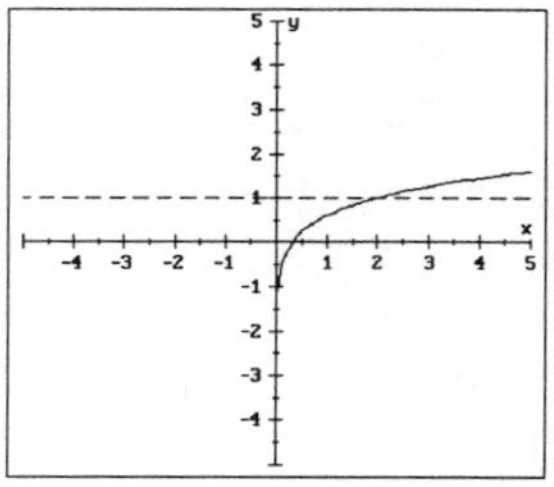

57. Graph $y = 2^{x+1}$ and $y = 7$ and find the x-coordinate of the point(s) of intersection: $x \approx 1.81$

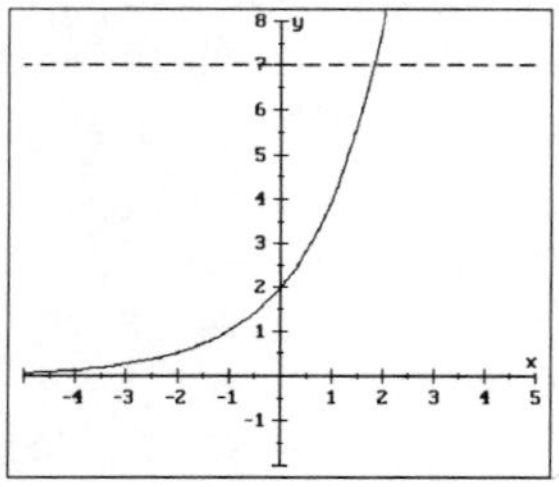

58. Graph $y = \ln(2x + 5) - \ln 3$ and $y = \ln(x - 1)$ and find the x-coordinate of the point(s) of intersection: $x = 8$

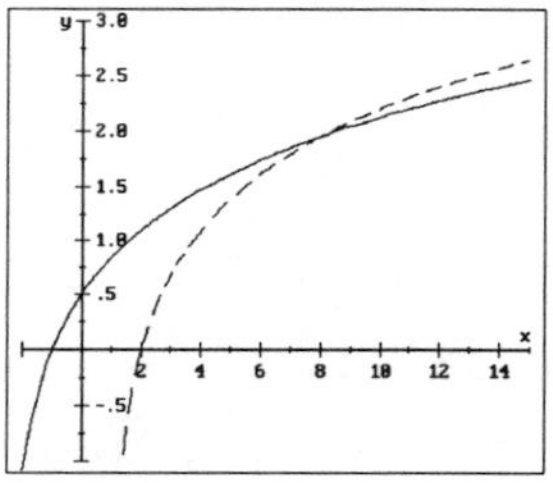

59.

$$\begin{aligned} A &= A_0 2^{-t/h} \\ 0.75A_0 &= A_0 \cdot 2^{-t/(12.4)} \\ 0.75 &= 2^{-t/12.4} \\ \log(0.75) &= \log\left(2^{-t/12.4}\right) \\ \log(0.75) &= -\frac{t}{12.4}\log 2 \\ -\frac{12.4\log(0.75)}{\log 2} &= t \\ 5.1 \text{ years} &\approx t \end{aligned}$$

60.

$$\begin{aligned} A &= A_0 2^{-t/h} \\ 0.80A_0 &= A_0 \cdot 2^{-2/h} \\ 0.80 &= 2^{-2/h} \\ \log(0.80) &= \log\left(2^{-2/h}\right) \\ \log(0.80) &= -\frac{2}{h}\log 2 \\ h\log(0.80) &= -2\log 2 \\ h &= \frac{-2\log 2}{\log(0.80)} \\ h &\approx 6.2 \text{ years} \end{aligned}$$

61.
$$\begin{aligned} A &= A_0 2^{-t/h} \\ 0.20A_0 &= A_0 \cdot 2^{-t/(18.4)} \\ 0.20 &= 2^{-t/18.4} \\ \log(0.20) &= \log\left(2^{-t/18.4}\right) \\ \log(0.20) &= -\frac{t}{18.4}\log 2 \\ -\frac{18.4\log(0.20)}{\log 2} &= t \\ 42.7 \text{ days} &\approx t \end{aligned}$$

62.
$$\begin{aligned} A &= A_0 2^{-t/h} \\ 1.3A_0 &= A_0 \cdot 2^{-t/(8.4)} \\ 1.3 &= 2^{-t/8.4} \\ \log(1.3) &= \log\left(2^{-t/8.4}\right) \\ \log(1.3) &= -\frac{t}{8.4}\log 2 \\ -\frac{8.4\log(1.3)}{\log 2} &= t \\ -3.2 \text{ hours} &\approx t \Rightarrow \text{About 3.2 hours ago} \end{aligned}$$

63.
$$\begin{aligned} A &= A_0 2^{-t/h} \\ 0.70A_0 &= A_0 \cdot 2^{-t/5700} \\ 0.70 &= 2^{-t/5700} \\ \log(0.70) &= \log\left(2^{-t/5700}\right) \\ \log(0.70) &= -\frac{t}{5700}\log 2 \\ -\frac{5700\log(0.70)}{\log 2} &= t \\ 2900 \text{ years} &\approx t \end{aligned}$$

64.
$$\begin{aligned} A &= A_0 2^{-t/h} \\ 0.25A_0 &= A_0 \cdot 2^{-t/5700} \\ 0.25 &= 2^{-t/5700} \\ \log(0.25) &= \log\left(2^{-t/5700}\right) \\ \log(0.25) &= -\frac{t}{5700}\log 2 \\ -\frac{5700\log(0.25)}{\log 2} &= t \\ 11{,}000 \text{ years} &\approx t \end{aligned}$$

65.
$$\begin{aligned} A &= P\left(1+\frac{r}{k}\right)^{kt} \\ 800 &= 500\left(1+\frac{0.085}{2}\right)^{2t} \\ \frac{8}{5} &= (1.0425)^{2t} \\ \log\left(\frac{8}{5}\right) &= \log(1.0425)^{2t} \\ \log 8 - \log 5 &= 2t\log(1.0425) \\ \frac{\log 8 - \log 5}{2\log(1.0425)} &= t \\ 5.6 \text{ years} &\approx t \end{aligned}$$

66.
$$\begin{aligned} A &= Pe^{rt} \\ 800 &= 500e^{0.085t} \\ \frac{8}{5} &= e^{0.085t} \\ \ln\left(\frac{8}{5}\right) &= \ln e^{0.085t} \\ \ln 8 - \ln 5 &= 0.085t \\ \frac{\ln 8 - \ln 5}{0.085} &= t \\ 5.5 \text{ years} &\approx t \end{aligned}$$

67.

$$A = P\left(1+\frac{r}{k}\right)^{kt}$$
$$2100 = 1300\left(1+\frac{0.09}{4}\right)^{4t}$$
$$\frac{21}{13} = (1.0225)^{4t}$$
$$\log\left(\frac{21}{13}\right) = \log(1.0225)^{4t}$$
$$\log 21 - \log 13 = 4t\log(1.0225)$$
$$\frac{\log 21 - \log 13}{4\log(1.0225)} = t$$
$$5.4 \text{ years} \approx t$$

68.

$$A = P\left(1+\frac{r}{k}\right)^{kt}$$
$$7000 = 5000\left(1+\frac{r}{1}\right)^{1(5)}$$
$$\frac{7}{5} = (1+r)^5$$
$$\sqrt[5]{\frac{7}{5}} = \sqrt[5]{(1+r)^5}$$
$$\sqrt[5]{\frac{7}{5}} = 1+r$$
$$\sqrt[5]{\frac{7}{5}} - 1 = r \Rightarrow r \approx 0.696 = 6.96\%$$

69.

$$A = Pe^{rt}$$
$$2P = Pe^{rt}$$
$$2 = e^{rt}$$
$$\ln 2 = \ln e^{rt}$$
$$\ln 2 = rt$$
$$\frac{\ln 2}{r} = t$$
$$\frac{0.70}{r} \approx t$$
$$\frac{70}{(100\cdot r)\%} \approx t$$

70.

$$P = P_0a^t$$
$$3P_0 = P_0a^5$$
$$3 = a^5$$
$$3^{1/5} = \left(a^5\right)^{1/5}$$
$$3^{1/5} = a$$

$$P = P_0a^t$$
$$2P_0 = P_0\left(3^{1/5}\right)^t$$
$$2 = 3^{t/5}$$
$$\log 2 = \log 3^{t/5}$$
$$\log 2 = \frac{t}{5}\log 3$$
$$\frac{5\log 2}{\log 3} = t$$
$$3.2 \text{ days} \approx t$$

71.

$$I = I_0e^{kd}$$
$$0.70I_0 = I_0e^{k(6)}$$
$$0.70 = e^{6k}$$
$$\ln 0.70 = \ln e^{6k}$$
$$\ln 0.70 = 6k$$
$$\frac{\ln 0.70}{6} = k$$

$$I = I_0e^{kd}$$
$$0.20I_0 = I_0e^{\frac{\ln 0.70}{6}d}$$
$$0.20 = e^{\frac{\ln 0.70}{6}d}$$
$$\ln 0.20 = \ln e^{\frac{\ln 0.70}{6}d}$$
$$\ln 0.20 = \frac{\ln 0.70}{6}d$$
$$\frac{6\ln 0.20}{\ln 0.70} = d \Rightarrow d \approx 27 \text{ meters}$$

72.

$$P = P_0e^{kt}$$
$$60{,}000 = 30{,}000e^{k(5)}$$
$$2 = e^{5k}$$
$$\ln 2 = \ln e^{5k}$$
$$\ln 2 = 5k$$
$$\frac{\ln 2}{5} = k$$

$$P = P_0e^{kt}$$
$$1{,}000{,}000 = 30{,}000e^{\frac{\ln 2}{5}t}$$
$$\frac{100}{3} = e^{\frac{\ln 2}{5}t}$$
$$\ln\frac{100}{3} = \ln e^{\frac{\ln 2}{5}t}$$
$$\ln 100 - \ln 3 = \frac{\ln 2}{5}t$$
$$\frac{5(\ln 100 - \ln 3)}{\ln 2} = t \Rightarrow t \approx 25.3 \text{ years}$$

73.

$$\begin{aligned} T &= 60 + 40e^{kt} \\ 90 &= 60 + 40e^{k(3)} \\ 30 &= 40e^{3k} \\ 0.75 &= e^{3k} \\ \ln(0.75) &= \ln e^{3k} \\ \ln(0.75) &= 3k \\ \frac{\ln(0.75)}{3} &= k \end{aligned}$$

74. From **#73**, $k = \frac{\ln(0.75)}{3}$.

$$\begin{aligned} T &= 60 + 40e^{\frac{\ln 0.75}{3}t} \\ 70 &= 60 + 40e^{\frac{\ln 0.75}{3}t} \\ 10 &= 40e^{\frac{\ln 0.75}{3}t} \\ 0.25 &= e^{\frac{\ln 0.75}{3}t} \\ \ln 0.25 &= \ln e^{\frac{\ln 0.75}{3}t} \\ \ln 0.25 &= \frac{\ln 0.75}{3}t \\ \frac{3\ln 0.25}{\ln 0.75} &= t \Rightarrow t \approx 14.5 \text{ minutes} \end{aligned}$$

75.

$$\begin{aligned} T &= 300 - 300e^{kt} \\ 100 &= 300 - 300e^{k(5)} \\ -200 &= -300e^{5k} \\ \frac{2}{3} &= e^{5k} \\ \ln\left(\frac{2}{3}\right) &= \ln e^{5k} \\ \ln\left(\frac{2}{3}\right) &= 5k \\ \frac{\ln\left(\frac{2}{3}\right)}{5} &= k \end{aligned}$$

76. From **#75**, $k = \frac{\ln\left(\frac{2}{3}\right)}{5}$.

$$\begin{aligned} T &= 300 - 300e^{\frac{\ln(2/3)}{5}t} \\ 200 &= 300 - 300e^{\frac{\ln(2/3)}{5}t} \\ -100 &= -300e^{\frac{\ln(2/3)}{5}t} \\ \frac{1}{3} &= e^{\frac{\ln(2/3)}{5}t} \\ \ln(1/3) &= \ln e^{\frac{\ln(2/3)}{5}t} \\ \ln(1/3) &= \frac{\ln(2/3)}{5}t \\ \frac{5\ln(1/3)}{\ln(2/3)} &= t \Rightarrow t \approx 13.5 \text{ minutes} \end{aligned}$$

77. **Answers may vary.**

78.

$$\begin{aligned} P &= P_0e^{rt} \\ 2P_0 &= P_0e^{rt} \\ 2 &= e^{rt} \\ \ln 2 &= \ln e^{rt} \\ \ln 2 &= rt \\ \frac{\ln 2}{r} &= t \end{aligned}$$

79.

$$\begin{aligned} P &= P_0e^{rt} \\ 3P_0 &= P_0e^{rt} \\ 3 &= e^{rt} \\ \ln 3 &= \ln e^{rt} \\ \ln 3 &= rt \\ \frac{\ln 3}{r} &= t \end{aligned}$$

80. **Answers may vary.**

81.

$$\begin{aligned} y &= 3x + 2 \\ x &= 3y + 2 \\ x - 2 &= 3y \\ \frac{x-2}{3} &= y \end{aligned}$$

82.

$$\begin{aligned} y &= \frac{1}{x-3} \\ x &= \frac{1}{y-3} \\ x(y-3) &= 1 \\ xy - 3x &= 1 \\ xy &= 3x + 1 \\ y &= \frac{3x+1}{x} = \frac{1}{x} + 3 \end{aligned}$$

83. $(f \circ g)(2) = f(g(2)) = f(2^2) = f(4) = 5(4) - 1 = 19$

84. $(g \circ f)(2) = g(f(2)) = g(5(2) - 1) = g(9) = 9^2 = 81$

85. $(f \circ g)(x) = f(g(x)) = f(x^2) = 5x^2 - 1$

86. $(g \circ f)(2) = g(f(x)) = g(5x - 1) = (5x - 1)^2$

Chapter 4 Summary (page 377)

1. **a.** $5^{\sqrt{2}}5^{\sqrt{2}} = 5^{\sqrt{2}+\sqrt{2}} = 5^{2\sqrt{2}}$

b. $\left(2^{\sqrt{5}}\right)^{\sqrt{2}} = 2^{\sqrt{5}\cdot\sqrt{2}} = 2^{\sqrt{10}}$

2. **a.** $y = 3^x$: (0, 1), (1, 3)

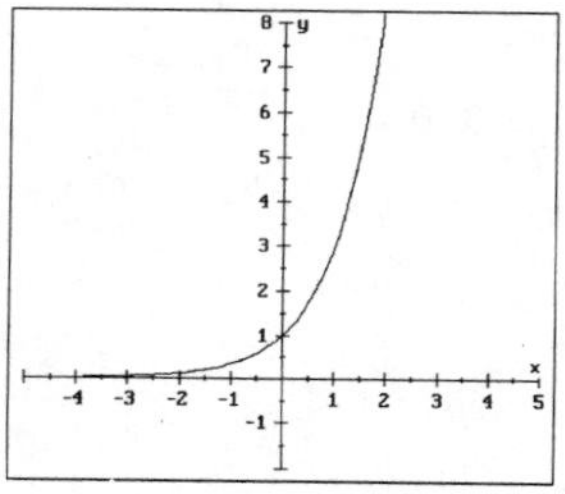

b. $y = \left(\frac{1}{3}\right)^x$: (0, 1), $\left(1, \frac{1}{3}\right)$

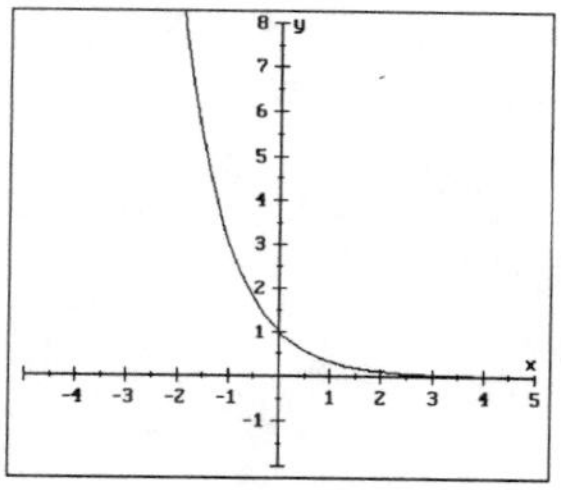

3. $f(x) = 6^x$: goes through $(0, 1)$ and $(1, 6)$
$p = 1, q = 6$

4. $y = b^x$: domain $= (-\infty, \infty)$; range $= (0, \infty)$

5. **a.** $y = \left(\frac{1}{2}\right)^x - 2$

Shift $y = \left(\frac{1}{2}\right)^x$ down 2:

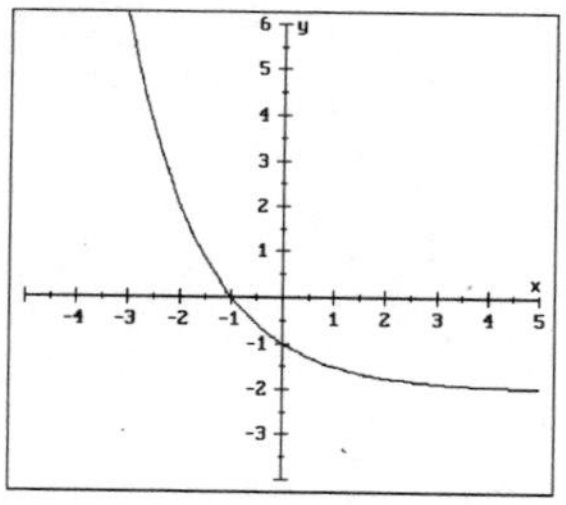

b. $y = \left(\frac{1}{2}\right)^{x+2}$

Shift $y = \left(\frac{1}{2}\right)^x$ left 2:

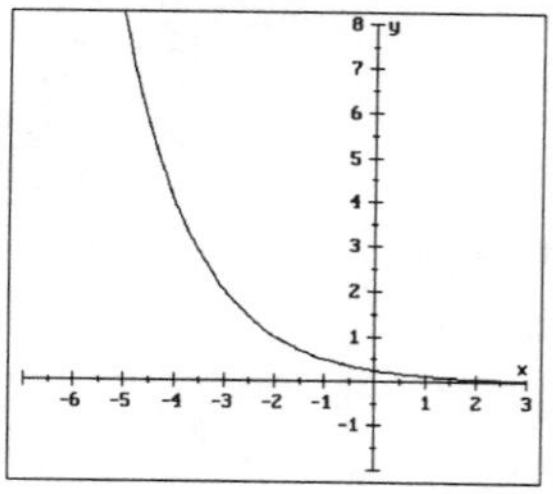

6. **a.** $y = e^x + 1$

Shift $y = e^x$ up 1:

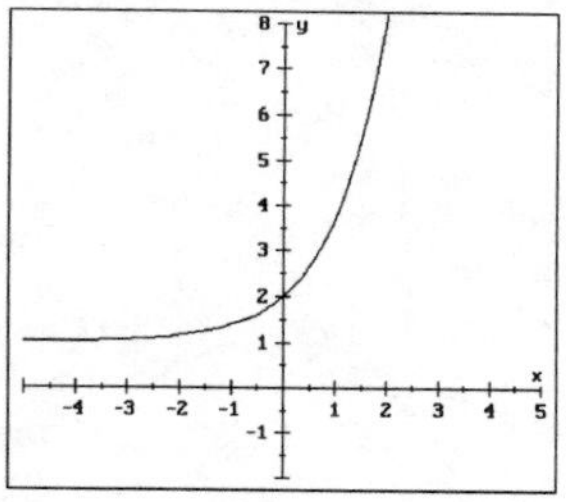

b. $y = e^{x-3}$

Shift $y = e^x$ right 3:

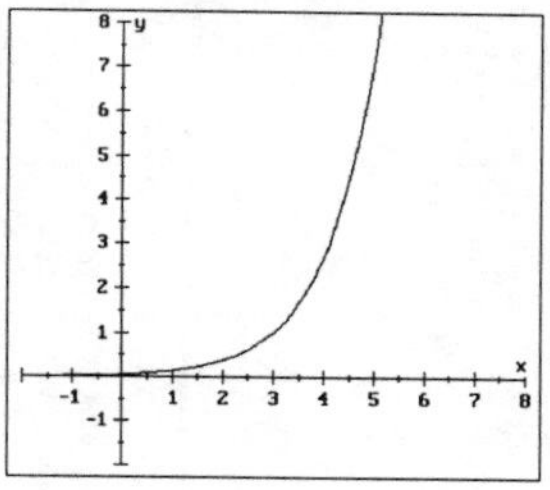

7. If $\frac{1}{3}$ decays in 20 years, $\frac{2}{3}$ is left.

$$\begin{aligned} A &= A_0 2^{-t/h} \\ \tfrac{2}{3} A_0 &= A_0 \cdot 2^{-20/h} \\ \tfrac{2}{3} &= 2^{-20/h} \\ \log\left(\tfrac{2}{3}\right) &= \log\left(2^{-20/h}\right) \\ \log\left(\tfrac{2}{3}\right) &= -\tfrac{20}{h} \log 2 \\ h \log\left(\tfrac{2}{3}\right) &= -20 \log 2 \\ h &= \frac{-20 \log 2}{\log(2/3)} \\ h &\approx 34.2 \text{ years} \end{aligned}$$

8.

$$\begin{aligned} A &= P\left(1 + \frac{r}{k}\right)^{kt} \\ &= 10{,}500\left(1 + \frac{0.09}{4}\right)^{4(60)} \\ &\approx \$2{,}189{,}703.45 \end{aligned}$$

9.

$$\begin{aligned} I &= I_0 k^x \\ &= 14(0.7)^{12} \\ &\approx 0.19 \text{ lumens} \end{aligned}$$

10.

$$\begin{aligned} A &= Pe^{rt} \\ &= 10{,}500e^{0.09(60)} \\ &\approx \$2{,}324{,}767.37 \end{aligned}$$

11.

$$\begin{aligned} P &= P_0 e^{kt} \\ P &= 275{,}000{,}000e^{0.015(50)} \\ P &\approx 582{,}000{,}000 \text{ people} \end{aligned}$$

12. domain $= (0, \infty)$

range $= (-\infty, \infty)$

13. **a.**

$$\begin{aligned} \log_3 9 &= ? \\ 3^? &= 9 \\ \log_3 9 &= 2 \end{aligned}$$

b.

$$\begin{aligned} \log_9 \frac{1}{3} &= ? \\ 9^? &= \frac{1}{3} \\ \log_9 \frac{1}{3} &= -\frac{1}{2} \end{aligned}$$

c.

$$\begin{aligned} \log_x 1 &= ? \\ x^? &= 1 \\ \log_x 1 &= 0 \end{aligned}$$

d.

$$\begin{aligned} \log_5 0.04 &= ? \\ 5^? &= 0.04 = \frac{1}{25} \\ \log_5 0.04 &= -2 \end{aligned}$$

e. $\log_a \sqrt{a} = ?$

$$a^? = \sqrt{a}$$

$$\log_a \sqrt{a} = \frac{1}{2}$$

f. $\log_a \sqrt[3]{a} = ?$

$$a^? = \sqrt[3]{a}$$

$$\log_a \sqrt[3]{a} = \frac{1}{3}$$

14. **a.** $\log_2 x = 5$

$$2^5 = x$$

$$32 = x$$

b. $\log_{\sqrt{3}} x = 4$

$$\left(\sqrt{3}\right)^4 = x$$

$$9 = x$$

c. $\log_{\sqrt{2}} x = 6$

$$\left(\sqrt{2}\right)^6 = x$$

$$8 = x$$

d. $\log_{0.1} 10 = x$

$$(0.1)^x = 10$$

$$\left(\frac{1}{10}\right)^x = 10$$

$$x = -1$$

e. $\log_x 2 = -\frac{1}{3}$

$$x^{-1/3} = 2$$

$$\left(x^{-1/3}\right)^{-3} = 2^{-3}$$

$$x = \frac{1}{8}$$

f. $\log_x 32 = 5$

$$x^5 = 32$$

$$x = 2$$

g. $\log_{0.25} x = -1$

$$(0.25)^{-1} = x$$

$$\left(\tfrac{1}{4}\right)^{-1} = x$$

$$4 = x$$

h. $\log_{0.125} x = -\frac{1}{3}$

$$(0.125)^{-1/3} = x$$

$$\left(\tfrac{1}{8}\right)^{-1/3} = x$$

$$2 = x$$

i. $\log_{\sqrt{2}} 32 = x$

$$\left(\sqrt{2}\right)^x = 32$$

$$\left(2^{1/2}\right)^x = 2^5$$

$$\frac{1}{2}x = 5$$

$$x = 10$$

j. $\log_{\sqrt{5}} x = -4$

$$\left(\sqrt{5}\right)^{-4} = x$$

$$\frac{1}{25} = x$$

k. $\log_{\sqrt{3}} 9\sqrt{3} = x$

$$\left(\sqrt{3}\right)^x = 9\sqrt{3}$$

$$\left(3^{1/2}\right)^x = 3^{5/2}$$

$$\frac{1}{2}x = \frac{5}{2}$$

$$x = 5$$

l. $\log_{\sqrt{5}} 5\sqrt{5} = x$

$$\left(\sqrt{5}\right)^x = 5\sqrt{5}$$

$$\left(5^{1/2}\right)^x = 5^{3/2}$$

$$\frac{1}{2}x = \frac{3}{2}$$

$$x = 3$$

15. **a.** $y = \log(x - 2)$

Shift $y = \log x$ right 2:

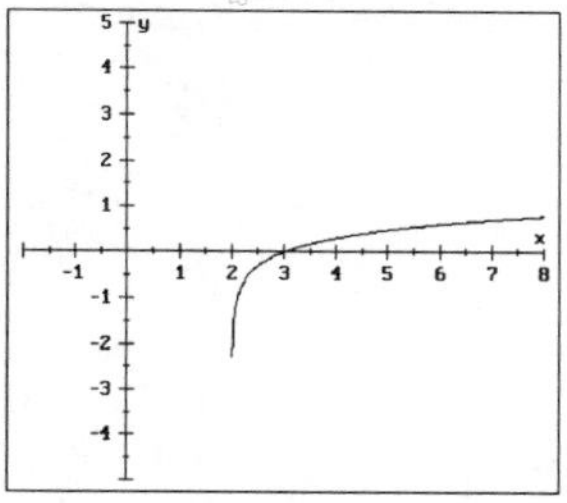

b. $y = 3 + \log x$

Shift $y = \log x$ up 3:

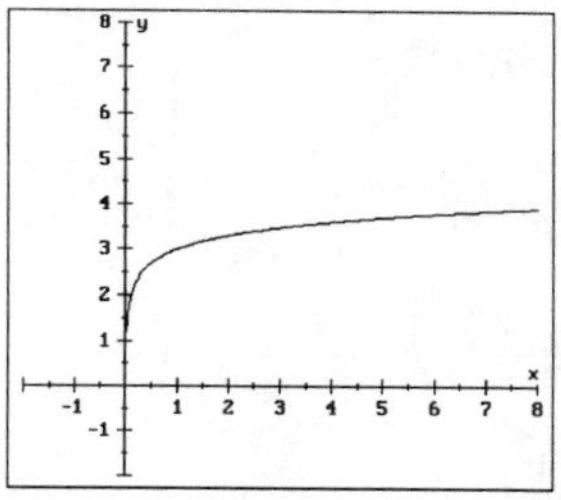

16. **a.** $y = 4^x;\ y = \log_4 x$

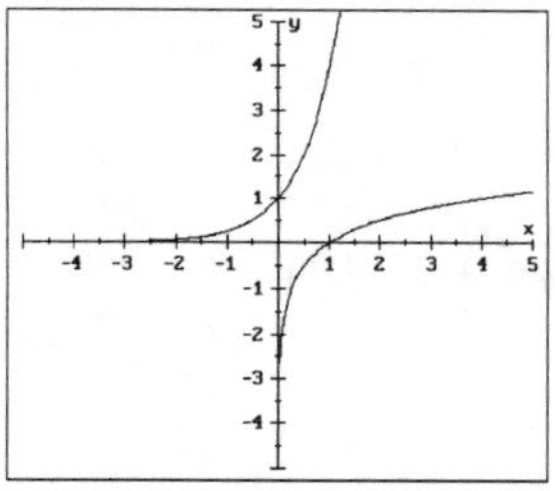

b. $y = \left(\dfrac{1}{3}\right)^x;\ y = \log_{1/3} x$

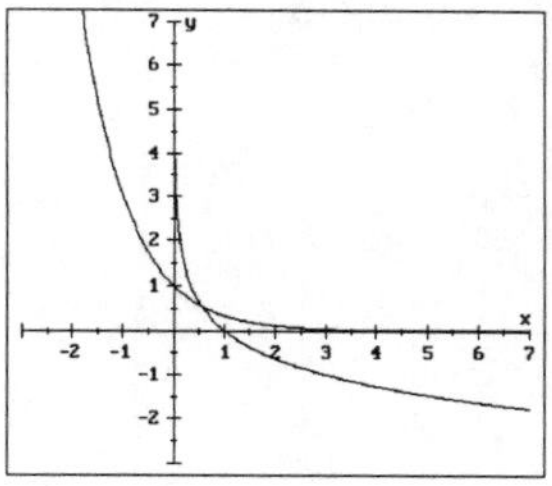

17. **a.** $\ln 452 \approx 6.1137$

b. $\ln(\log 7.85) \approx -0.1111$

18. **a.** $\ln x = 2.336$

$x \approx 10.3398$

b. $\ln x = \log 8.8$

$x \approx 2.5715$

19. **a.** $y = 1 + \ln x$

Shift $y = \ln x$ up 1:

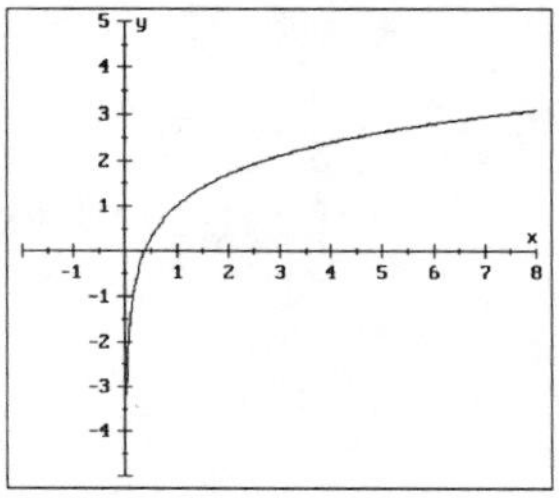

b. $y = \ln(x + 1)$

Shift $y = \ln x$ left 1:

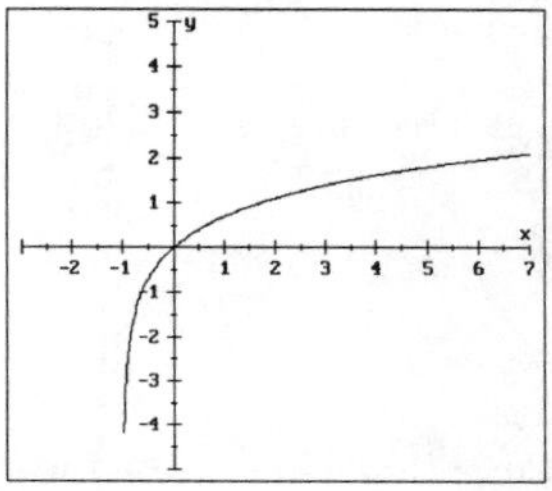

20.

$$\begin{aligned} \text{db gain} &= 20 \log \frac{E_0}{E_I} \\ &= 20 \log \frac{18}{0.04} \\ &\approx 53 \text{ db gain} \end{aligned}$$

21.

$$\begin{aligned} R &= \log \frac{A}{P} \\ &= \log \frac{7500}{0.3} \\ &\approx 4.4 \end{aligned}$$

22. $t = -\frac{1}{k}\ln\left(1 - \frac{C}{M}\right)$

$t = -\frac{1}{0.17}\ln\left(1 - \frac{0.8M}{M}\right)$

$t = -\frac{1}{0.17}\ln(1 - 0.8) \approx 9.5$ hours

23. $t = \frac{\ln 2}{r} = \frac{\ln 2}{0.03} \approx 23$ years

24. $E = RT\ln\left(\frac{V_f}{V_i}\right) = (8.314)(350)\ln\left(\frac{2V_i}{V_i}\right) = (8.314)(350)\ln(2) \approx 2017$ joules

25. **a.** $\log_7 1 = 0$ **b.** $\log_7 7 = 1$

c. $\log_7 7^3 = 3$ **d.** $7^{\log_7 4} = 4$

26. **a.** $\ln e^4 = 4\ln e = 4$ **b.** $\ln 1 = 0$

c. $10^{\log_{10} 7} = 7$ **d.** $e^{\log_e 3} = 3$

e. $\log_b b^4 = 4\log_b b = 4$ **f.** $\ln e^9 = 9\ln e = 9$

27. **a.** $\log_b \frac{x^2y^3}{z^4} = \log_b(x^2y^3) - \log_b(z^4) = \log_b x^2 + \log_b y^3 - \log_b z^4$
$= 2\log_b x + 3\log_b y - 4\log_b z$

b. $\log_b \sqrt{\frac{x}{yz^2}} = \log_b\left(\frac{x}{yz^2}\right)^{1/2} = \frac{1}{2}\log_b\left(\frac{x}{yz^2}\right) = \frac{1}{2}(\log_b x - \log_b yz^2)$
$= \frac{1}{2}(\log_b x - \log_b y - 2\log_b z)$

28. **a.** $3\log_b x - 5\log_b y + 7\log_b z = \log_b x^3 + \log_b y^{-5} + \log_b z^7 = \log_b \frac{x^3z^7}{y^5}$

b. $\frac{1}{2}(\log_b x + 3\log_b y) - 7\log_b z = \frac{1}{2}(\log_b x + \log_b y^3) + \log_b z^{-7} = \frac{1}{2}\log_b xy^3 + \log_b z^{-7}$
$= \log_b \sqrt{xy^3} + \log_b z^{-7}$
$= \log_b \frac{\sqrt{xy^3}}{z^7}$

29. **a.** $\log abc = \log a + \log b + \log c = 0.6 + 0.36 + 2.4 = 3.36$

b. $\log a^2b = \log a^2 + \log b = 2\log a + \log b = 2(0.6) + 0.36 = 1.56$

c. $\log \frac{ac}{b} = \log a + \log c - \log b = 0.6 + 2.4 - 0.36 = 2.64$

d. $\log \dfrac{a^2}{c^3b^2} = \log a^2 - \log c^3b^2 = \log a^2 - \log c^3 - \log b^2$

$= 2\log a - 3\log c - 2\log b$

$= 2(0.6) - 3(2.4) - 2(0.36) = -6.72$

30. $\log_5 17 = \dfrac{\log 17}{\log 5} \approx 1.7604$

31.
$$\begin{aligned} \text{pH} &= -\log[\text{H}^+] \\ 3.1 &= -\log[\text{H}^+] \\ -3.1 &= \log[\text{H}^+] \\ 7.94 \times 10^{-4} &\approx [\text{H}^+] \end{aligned}$$

32. $L = k \ln I$

$k \ln \dfrac{I}{2} = k(\ln I - \ln 2) = k \ln I - k \ln 2 \Rightarrow$ The loudness decreases by $k \ln 2$.

33. **a.**
$$\begin{aligned} 3^x &= 7 \\ \log 3^x &= \log 7 \\ x\log 3 &= \log 7 \\ x &= \frac{\log 7}{\log 3} \\ x &\approx 1.7712 \end{aligned}$$

b.
$$\begin{aligned} 5^{x+2} &= 625 \\ \log 5^{x+2} &= \log 625 \\ (x+2)\log 5 &= \log 625 \\ x\log 5 + 2\log 5 &= \log 625 \\ x\log 5 &= \log 625 - 2\log 5 \\ x &= \frac{\log 625 - 2\log 5}{\log 5} \\ x &= 2 \end{aligned}$$

c.
$$\begin{aligned} 2^x &= 3^{x-1} \\ \log 2^x &= \log 3^{x-1} \\ x\log 2 &= (x-1)\log 3 \\ x\log 2 &= x\log 3 - \log 3 \\ x\log 2 - x\log 3 &= -\log 3 \\ x(\log 2 - \log 3) &= -\log 3 \\ x &= \frac{-\log 3}{\log 2 - \log 3} \\ x &\approx 2.7095 \end{aligned}$$

d.
$$\begin{aligned} 2^{x^2+4x} &= \frac{1}{8} \\ 2^{x^2+4x} &= 2^{-3} \\ x^2 + 4x &= -3 \\ x^2 + 4x + 3 &= 0 \\ (x+1)(x+3) &= 0 \end{aligned}$$

$x + 1 = 0$ **or** $x + 3 = 0$

$x = -1$ $\quad$ $x = -3$

34. **a.**
$$\begin{aligned} \log x + \log(29 - x) &= 2 \\ \log x(29 - x) &= 2 \\ x(29 - x) &= 10^2 \\ -x^2 + 29x - 100 &= 0 \\ x^2 - 29x + 100 &= 0 \\ (x - 25)(x - 4) &= 0 \end{aligned}$$

$x - 25 = 0$ **or** $x - 4 = 0$

$x = 25$ $\quad$ $x = 4$

b.
$$\begin{aligned} \log_2 x + \log_2(x - 2) &= 3 \\ \log_2 x(x - 2) &= 3 \\ x(x - 2) &= 2^3 \\ x^2 - 2x - 8 &= 0 \\ (x - 4)(x + 2) &= 0 \end{aligned}$$

$x - 4 = 0$ **or** $x + 2 = 0$

$x = 4$ $\quad$ $x = -2$

extraneous

c.

$$\begin{aligned}
\log_2(x+2) + \log_2(x-1) &= 2\\
\log_2(x+2)(x-1) &= 2\\
(x+2)(x-1) &= 2^2\\
x^2 + x - 2 &= 4\\
x^2 + x - 6 &= 0\\
(x-2)(x+3) &= 0\\
x - 2 = 0 \quad \textbf{or} \quad x + 3 &= 0\\
x = 2 \qquad\qquad x &= -3
\end{aligned}$$

extraneous

d.

$$\begin{aligned}
\frac{\log(7x-12)}{\log x} &= 2\\
\log(7x-12) &= 2\log x\\
\log(7x-12) &= \log x^2\\
7x - 12 &= x^2\\
0 &= x^2 - 7x + 12\\
0 &= (x-3)(x-4)\\
x = 3&,\ x = 4
\end{aligned}$$

e.

$$\begin{aligned}
\log x + \log(x-5) &= \log 6\\
\log x(x-5) &= \log 6\\
x(x-5) &= 6\\
x^2 - 5x &= 6\\
x^2 - 5x - 6 &= 0\\
(x-6)(x+1) &= 0\\
x - 6 = 0 \quad \textbf{or} \quad x + 1 &= 0\\
x = 6 \qquad\qquad x &= -1
\end{aligned}$$

extraneous

f.

$$\begin{aligned}
\log 3 - \log(x-1) &= -1\\
\log\frac{3}{x-1} &= -1\\
\frac{3}{x-1} &= 10^{-1}\\
\frac{3}{x-1} &= \frac{1}{10}\\
30 &= x - 1\\
31 &= x
\end{aligned}$$

g.

$$\begin{aligned}
e^{x\ln 2} &= 9\\
\ln e^{x\ln 2} &= \ln 9\\
x\ln 2\ln e &= \ln 9\\
x\ln 2 &= \ln 9\\
x &= \frac{\ln 9}{\ln 2} \approx 3.1699
\end{aligned}$$

h.

$$\begin{aligned}
\ln x &= \ln(x-1)\\
x &= x - 1
\end{aligned}$$

no solution

i.

$$\begin{aligned}
\ln x &= \ln(x-1) + 1\\
\ln x - \ln(x-1) &= 1\\
\ln\frac{x}{x-1} &= 1\\
\frac{x}{x-1} &= e^1\\
\frac{x}{x-1} &= \frac{e}{1}\\
x &= e(x-1)\\
\frac{e}{e-1} &= x, \text{ or } x \approx 1.5820
\end{aligned}$$

j. Note: $\log_{10} x = \dfrac{\ln x}{\ln 10}$

$$\begin{aligned}
\ln x &= \log_{10} x\\
\ln x &= \frac{\ln x}{\ln 10}\\
\ln x\ln 10 &= \ln x\\
\ln x\ln 10 - \ln x &= 0\\
\ln x(\ln 10 - 1) &= 0\\
\ln x = 0 &\Rightarrow x = 1
\end{aligned}$$

35.
$$\begin{aligned} A &= A_0 2^{-t/h} \\ \frac{2}{3}A_0 &= A_0 \cdot 2^{-t/5700} \\ \frac{2}{3} &= 2^{-t/5700} \\ \log(2/3) &= \log\left(2^{-t/5700}\right) \\ \log(2/3) &= -\frac{t}{5700}\log 2 \\ -\frac{5700\log(2/3)}{\log 2} &= t \Rightarrow t \approx 3300 \text{ years} \end{aligned}$$

Chapter 4 Test (page 382)

1. $y = 2^x + 1 \Rightarrow$ Shift $y = 2^x$ up 1.

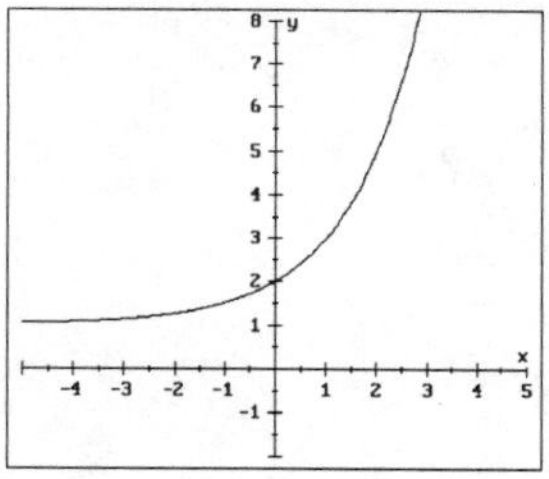

2. $y = e^{x-2} \Rightarrow$ Shift $y = e^x$ right 2.

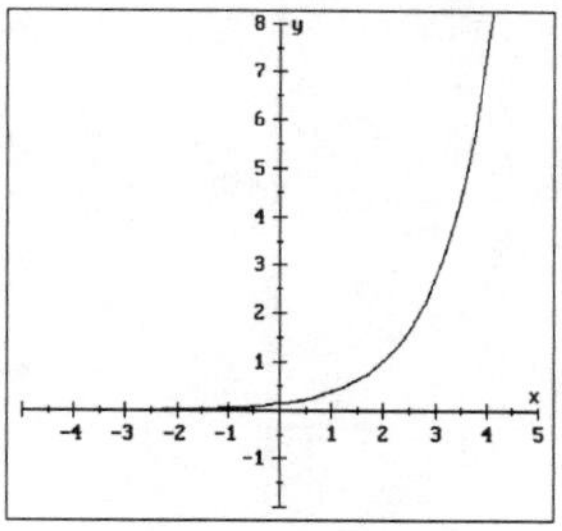

3. $A = 3(2)^{-6} = 3 \cdot \frac{1}{64} = \frac{3}{64}$ gram

4. $A = 1000\left(1 + \frac{0.06}{2}\right)^{2(1)} \approx \$1060.90$

5. $A = 2000e^{0.08(10)} \approx \$4451.08$

6. $\log_7 343 = \log_7 7^3 = 3$

7. $\log_3 \frac{1}{27} = \log_3 3^{-3} = -3$

8. $\log_{10} 10^{12} + 10^{\log_{10} 5} = 12 + 5 = 17$

9. $\log_{3/2} \frac{9}{4} = \log_{3/2}\left(\frac{3}{2}\right)^2 = 2$

10. $\log_{2/3} \frac{27}{8} = \log_{2/3}\left(\frac{2}{3}\right)^{-3} = -3$

11. $y = \log(x-1) \Rightarrow$ Shift $y = \log x$ right 1.

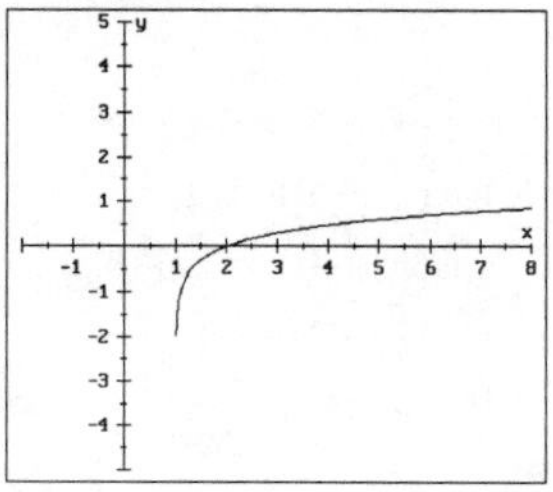

12. $y = 2 + \ln x \Rightarrow$ Shift $y = \ln x$ up 2.

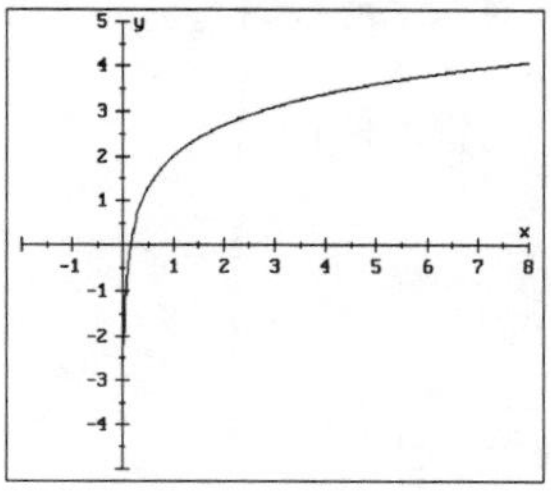

13. $\log a^2bc^3 = \log a^2 + \log b + \log c^3 = 2\log a + \log b + 3\log c$

14. $\ln\sqrt{\dfrac{a}{b^2c}} = \ln\left(\dfrac{a}{b^2c}\right)^{1/2} = \dfrac{1}{2}\ln\dfrac{a}{b^2c} = \dfrac{1}{2}\left(\ln a - \ln b^2 - \ln c\right) = \dfrac{1}{2}(\ln a - 2\ln b - \ln c)$

15. $\dfrac{1}{2}\log(a+2) + \log b - 2\log c = \log\sqrt{a+2} + \log b - \log c^2 = \log\dfrac{b\sqrt{a+2}}{c^2}$

16. $\dfrac{1}{3}(\log a - 2\log b) - \log c = \dfrac{1}{3}\log\dfrac{a}{b^2} - \log c = \log\sqrt[3]{\dfrac{a}{b^2}} - \log c = \log\dfrac{\sqrt[3]{\frac{a}{b^2}}}{c}$

17. $\log 24 = \log 8\cdot 3 = \log 2^3\cdot 3 = 3\log 2 + \log 3 = 3(0.3010) + 0.4771 = 1.3801$

18. $\log\dfrac{8}{3} = \log\dfrac{2^3}{3} = 3\log 2 - \log 3 = 3(0.3010) - 0.4771 = 0.4259$

19. $\log_7 3 = \dfrac{\log 3}{\log 7}$ or $\dfrac{\ln 3}{\ln 7}$

20. $\log_\pi e = \dfrac{\log e}{\log \pi}$ or $\dfrac{\ln e}{\ln \pi}$

21. $\log_a ab = \log_a a + \log_a b = 1 + \log_a b$
TRUE

22. $\log\dfrac{a}{b} = \log a - \log b$
FALSE

23.
$$\begin{aligned} \text{pH} &= -\log\,[\text{H}^+] \\ &= -\log\left(3.7\times 10^{-7}\right) \\ &\approx 6.4 \end{aligned}$$

24.
$$\begin{aligned} \text{db gain} &= 20\log\frac{E_O}{E_I} \\ &= 20\log\frac{60}{0.3} \\ &\approx 46 \text{ db gain} \end{aligned}$$

25.
$$\begin{aligned} 3^{x-1} &= 100^x \\ \log 3^{x-1} &= \log 100^x \\ (x-1)\log 3 &= x\log 100 \\ x\log 3 - \log 3 &= x\log 100 \\ x\log 3 - x\log 100 &= \log 3 \\ x(\log 3 - \log 100) &= \log 3 \\ x &= \frac{\log 3}{\log 3 - \log 100} \\ x &\approx -0.3133 \end{aligned}$$

26.
$$\begin{aligned} 3^{x^2-2x} &= 27 \\ 3^{x^2-2x} &= 3^3 \\ x^2 - 2x &= 3 \\ x^2 - 2x - 3 &= 0 \\ (x-3)(x+1) &= 0 \end{aligned}$$
$x - 3 = 0$ **or** $x + 1 = 0$
$x = 3$ $\qquad x = -1$

27.
$$\begin{aligned} \log(5x+2) &= \log(2x+5) \\ 5x+2 &= 2x+5 \\ 3x &= 3 \\ x &= 1 \end{aligned}$$

28.
$$\begin{aligned} \log x + \log(x-9) &= 1 \\ \log x(x-9) &= 1 \\ x(x-9) &= 10^1 \\ x^2 - 9x - 10 &= 0 \\ (x-10)(x+1) &= 0 \end{aligned}$$
$x - 10 = 0$ **or** $x + 1 = 0$
$x = 10$ $\qquad x = -1$: extraneous

Exercise 5.1 (page 393)

1. whole **2.** $P(r) = 0$ **3.** any

4. $x - r$ **5.** factor **6.** synthetic

7.
$$
\begin{aligned}
P(1) &= 2(1)^4 - 2(1)^3 + 5(1)^2 - 1 \\
&= 2(1) - 2(1) + 5(1) - 1 \\
&= 2 - 2 + 5 - 1 = \boxed{4}
\end{aligned}
$$
$$
\begin{array}{r}
2x^3 + 5x + 5 \\
x - 1\,\overline{)\,2x^4 - 2x^3 + 5x^2 + 0x - 1} \\
\underline{2x^4 - 2x^3} \\
0 + 5x^2 \\
\underline{5x^2 - 5x} \\
5x - 1 \\
\underline{5x - 5} \\
\boxed{4}
\end{array}
$$

8.
$$
\begin{aligned}
P(2) &= 2(2)^4 - 2(2)^3 + 5(2)^2 - 1 \\
&= 2(16) - 2(8) + 5(4) - 1 \\
&= 32 - 16 + 20 - 1 = \boxed{35}
\end{aligned}
$$
$$
\begin{array}{r}
2x^3 + 2x^2 + 9x + 18 \\
x - 2\,\overline{)\,2x^4 - 2x^3 + 5x^2 + 0x - 1} \\
\underline{2x^4 - 4x^3} \\
2x^3 + 5x^2 \\
\underline{2x^3 - 4x^2} \\
9x^2 + 0x \\
\underline{9x^2 - 18x} \\
18x - 1 \\
\underline{18x - 36} \\
\boxed{35}
\end{array}
$$

9.
$$
\begin{aligned}
P(-2) &= 2(-2)^4 - 2(-2)^3 + 5(-2)^2 - 1 \\
&= 2(16) - 2(-8) + 5(4) - 1 \\
&= 32 + 16 + 20 - 1 = \boxed{67}
\end{aligned}
$$
$$
\begin{array}{r}
2x^3 - 6x^2 + 17x - 34 \\
x + 2\,\overline{)\,2x^4 - 2x^3 + 5x^2 + 0x - 1} \\
\underline{2x^4 + 4x^3} \\
-6x^3 + 5x^2 \\
\underline{-6x^3 - 12x^2} \\
17x^2 + 0x \\
\underline{17x^2 + 34x} \\
-34x - 1 \\
\underline{-34x - 68} \\
\boxed{67}
\end{array}
$$

10.
$$
\begin{aligned}
P(-1) &= 2(-1)^4 - 2(-1)^3 + 5(-1)^2 - 1 \\
&= 2(1) - 2(-1) + 5(1) - 1 \\
&= 2 + 2 + 5 - 1 = \boxed{8}
\end{aligned}
$$
$$
\begin{array}{r}
2x^3 - 4x^2 + 9x - 9 \\
x + 1\,\overline{)\,2x^4 - 2x^3 + 5x^2 + 0x - 1} \\
\underline{2x^4 + 2x^3} \\
-4x^3 + 5x^2 \\
\underline{-4x^3 - 4x^2} \\
9x^2 + 0x \\
\underline{9x^2 + 9x} \\
-9x - 1 \\
\underline{-9x - 9} \\
\boxed{8}
\end{array}
$$

11.
$$
\begin{aligned}
\text{remainder} = P(12) &= 3(12)^4 + 5(12)^3 - 4(12)^2 - 2(12) + 1 \\
&= 3(20{,}736) + 5(1728) - 4(144) - 2(12) + 1 \\
&= 62{,}208 + 8640 - 576 - 24 + 1 = 70{,}249
\end{aligned}
$$

12.
$$
\begin{aligned}
\text{remainder} = P(-15) &= 3(-15)^4 + 5(-15)^3 - 4(-15)^2 - 2(-15) + 1 \\
&= 3(50{,}625) + 5(-3375) - 4(225) - 2(-15) + 1 \\
&= 151{,}875 - 16{,}875 - 900 + 30 + 1 = 134{,}131
\end{aligned}
$$

13.
$$
\begin{aligned}
\text{remainder} = P(-3.25) &= 3(-3.25)^4 + 5(-3.25)^3 - 4(-3.25)^2 - 2(-3.25) + 1 \\
&= 3(111.56640625) + 5(-34.328125) - 4(10.5625) - 2(-3.25) + 1 \\
&= 334.69921875 - 171.640625 - 42.25 + 6.5 + 1 = 128.3085938
\end{aligned}
$$

14. remainder $= P(7.12) = 3(7.12)^4 + 5(7.12)^3 - 4(7.12)^2 - 2(7.12) + 1$
$= 3(2569.92219136) + 5(360.944128) - 4(50.6944) - 2(7.12) + 1$
$= 7709.76657408 + 1804.72064 - 202.7776 - 14.24 + 1 = 9298.469614$

15. $(x-1)$ is a factor if $P(1) = 0$.
$P(1) = 1^7 - 1 = 0$: true

16. $(x-2)$ is a factor if $P(2) = 0$.
$P(2) = 2^3 - 2^2 + 2(2) - 8 = 0$: true

17. $(x-1)$ is a factor if $P(1) = 0$.
$P(1) = 3(1)^5 + 4(1)^2 - 7 = 0$: true

18. $(x+1)$ is a factor if $P(-1) = 0$.
$P(-1) = 3(-1)^5 + 4(-1)^2 - 7 = -6$: false

19. $(x+3)$ is a factor if $P(-3) = 0$.
$P(-3) = 2(-3)^3 - 2(-3)^2 + 1$
$= -71$: false

20. $(x-3)$ is a factor if $P(3) = 0$.
$P(3) = 3(3)^5 - 3(3)^4 + 5(3)^2 - 13(3) - 6$
$= 486$: false

21. $(x-1)$ is a factor if $P(1) = 0$. $P(1) = (1)^{1984} - (1)^{1776} + (1)^{1492} - (1)^{1066} = 0$: true

22. $(x+1)$ is a factor if $P(-1) = 0$. $P(1) = (-1)^{1984} + (-1)^{1776} - (-1)^{1492} - (-1)^{1066} = 0$: true

23. $x = -1$ is a solution, so $(x+1)$ is a factor.
Use synthetic division to divide by $(x+1)$.

$$\begin{array}{r|rrrr} -1 & 1 & 3 & -13 & -15 \\ & & -1 & -2 & 15 \\ \hline & 1 & 2 & -15 & 0 \end{array}$$

$x^3 + 3x^2 - 13x - 15 = 0$
$(x+1)(x^2 + 2x - 15) = 0$
$(x+1)(x+5)(x-3) = 0$
Solution set: $\{-1, -5, 3\}$

24. $x = 1$ is a solution, so $(x-1)$ is a factor.
Use synthetic division to divide by $(x-1)$.

$$\begin{array}{r|rrrr} 1 & 1 & 6 & 5 & -12 \\ & & 1 & 7 & 12 \\ \hline & 1 & 7 & 12 & 0 \end{array}$$

$x^3 + 6x^2 + 5x - 12 = 0$
$(x-1)(x^2 + 7x + 12) = 0$
$(x-1)(x+3)(x+4) = 0$
Solution set: $\{1, -3, -4\}$

25. $x = 1$ is a solution, so $(x-1)$ is a factor.
Use synthetic division to divide by $(x-1)$.

$$\begin{array}{r|rrrrr} 1 & 1 & -2 & -2 & 6 & -3 \\ & & 1 & -1 & -3 & 3 \\ \hline & 1 & -1 & -3 & 3 & 0 \end{array}$$

$x^4 - 2x^3 - 2x^2 + 6x - 3 = 0$
$(x-1)(x^3 - x^2 - 3x + 3) = 0$

Use the fact that $x = 1$ is a double root and divide the depressed polynomial by $(x-1)$:

$$\begin{array}{r|rrrr} 1 & 1 & -1 & -3 & 3 \\ & & 1 & 0 & -3 \\ \hline & 1 & 0 & -3 & 0 \end{array}$$

$(x-1)(x^3 - x^2 - 3x + 3) = 0$
$(x-1)(x-1)(x^2 - 3) = 0$
Solution set: $\left\{1, 1, \sqrt{3}, -\sqrt{3}\right\}$

26. $x = -2$ is a solution, so $(x+2)$ is a factor.
Use synthetic division to divide by $(x+2)$.

-2	1	4	4	-1	-4	-4
		-2	-4	0	2	4
	1	2	0	-1	-2	0

$$x^5 + 4x^4 + 4x^3 - x^2 - 4x - 4 = 0$$
$$(x+2)\left(x^4 + 2x^3 - x - 2\right) = 0$$

Use the fact that $x = -2$ is a double root and divide the depressed polynomial by $(x+2)$:

-2	1	2	0	-1	-2
		-2	0	0	2
	1	0	0	-1	0

$$(x+2)\left(x^4 + 2x^3 - x - 2\right) = 0$$
$$(x+2)(x+2)\left(x^3 - 1\right) = 0$$

Use the fact that $x = 1$ is a solution and divide the depressed polynomial by $(x-1)$:

1	1	0	0	-1
		1	1	1
	1	1	1	0

$$(x+2)(x+2)\left(x^3 - 1\right) = 0$$
$$(x+2)(x+2)(x-1)\left(x^2 + x + 1\right) = 0$$

[Use the quadratic formula to finish...]

Solution set: $\left\{-2, -2, 1, -\frac{1}{2} \pm \frac{\sqrt{3}}{2}i\right\}$

27. $x = 2$ is a solution, so $(x-2)$ is a factor.
Use synthetic division to divide by $(x-2)$.

2	1	-5	7	-5	6
		2	-6	2	-6
	1	-3	1	-3	0

$$x^4 - 5x^3 + 7x^2 - 5x + 6 = 0$$
$$(x-2)\left(x^3 - 3x^2 + x - 3\right) = 0$$

$x = 3$ is a root, so $(x-3)$ is a factor.
Use synthetic division to divide by $(x-3)$.

3	1	-3	1	-3
		3	0	3
	1	0	1	0

$$(x-2)\left(x^3 - 3x^2 + x - 3\right) = 0$$
$$(x-2)(x-3)\left(x^2 + 1\right) = 0$$
$$x^2 + 1 = 0 \Rightarrow x^2 = -1 \Rightarrow x = \pm i$$

Solution set: $\{2, 3, \pm i\}$

28. $x = 1$ is a solution, so $(x-1)$ is a factor.
Use synthetic division to divide by $(x-1)$.

1	1	2	-3	-4	4
		1	3	0	-4
	1	3	0	-4	0

$$x^4 + 2x^3 - 3x^2 - 4x + 4 = 0$$
$$(x-1)\left(x^3 + 3x^2 - 4\right) = 0$$

$x = -2$ is a root, so $(x+2)$ is a factor.
Use synthetic division to divide by $(x+2)$.

-2	1	3	0	-4
		-2	-2	4
	1	1	-2	0

$$(x-1)\left(x^3 + 3x^2 - 4\right) = 0$$
$$(x-1)(x+2)\left(x^2 + x - 2\right) = 0$$
$$(x-1)(x+2)(x+2)(x-1) = 0$$

Solution set: $\{1, -2, 1, -2\}$

29. $(x-4)(x-5) = x^2 - 9x + 20$

30. $(x+3)(x-5) = x^2 - 2x - 15$

31. $(x-1)(x-1)(x-1) = (x^2 - 2x + 1)(x-1) = x^3 - 3x^2 + 3x - 1$

32. $(x-1)(x-0)(x+1) = (x^2 - x)(x+1) = x^3 - x$

33. $(x-2)(x-4)(x-5) = (x^2 - 6x + 8)(x-5) = x^3 - 11x^2 + 38x - 40$

34. $(x-7)(x-6)(x-3) = (x^2 - 13x + 42)(x-3) = x^3 - 16x^2 + 81x - 126$

35. $(x-1)(x+1)\left(x - \sqrt{2}\right)\left(x + \sqrt{2}\right) = (x^2 - 1)(x^2 - 2) = x^4 - 3x^2 + 2$

36. $(x-0)(x-0)(x-0)\left(x-\sqrt{3}\right)\left(x+\sqrt{3}\right)=x^3(x^2-3)=x^5-3x^3$

37. $\left(x-\sqrt{2}\right)(x-i)(x+i)=\left(x-\sqrt{2}\right)(x^2-i^2)=\left(x-\sqrt{2}\right)(x^2+1)=x^3-\sqrt{2}x^2+x-\sqrt{2}$

38. $$\begin{aligned}(x-i)(x-i)(x-2)=(x^2-2ix+i^2)(x-2)&=(x^2-2ix-1)(x-2)\\&=x^3-2x^2-2ix^2+4ix-x+2\\&=x^3-(2+2i)x^2-(1-4i)x+2\end{aligned}$$

39. $$\begin{aligned}(x-0)[x-(1+i)][x-(1-i)]&=x\left[x^2-(1-i)x-(1+i)x+(1+i)(1-i)\right]\\&=x\left[x^2-x+ix-x-ix+1-i^2\right]\\&=x\left[x^2-2x+2\right]=x^3-2x^2+2x\end{aligned}$$

40. $$\begin{aligned}(x-i)[x-(2+i)][x-(2-i)]&=(x-i)\left[x^2-(2-i)x-(2+i)x+(2+i)(2-i)\right]\\&=(x-i)\left[x^2-2x+ix-2x-ix+4-i^2\right]\\&=(x-i)\left[x^2-4x+5\right]\\&=x^3-4x^2+5x-ix^2+4ix-5i\\&=x^3-(4+i)x^2+(5+4i)x-5i\end{aligned}$$

41. $$\begin{array}{r|rrrr}1 & 3 & -2 & -6 & -4\\ & & 3 & 1 & -5\\ \hline & 3 & 1 & -5 & -9\end{array}$$

$$\begin{aligned}P(x)&=3x^3-2x^2-6x-4\\&=(x-1)\left(3x^2+x-5\right)-9\end{aligned}$$

42. $$\begin{array}{r|rrrr}2 & 3 & -2 & -6 & -4\\ & & 6 & 8 & 4\\ \hline & 3 & 4 & 2 & 0\end{array}$$

$$\begin{aligned}P(x)&=3x^3-2x^2-6x-4\\&=(x-2)\left(3x^2+4x+2\right)+0\end{aligned}$$

43. $$\begin{array}{r|rrrr}3 & 3 & -2 & -6 & -4\\ & & 9 & 21 & 45\\ \hline & 3 & 7 & 15 & 41\end{array}$$

$$\begin{aligned}P(x)&=3x^3-2x^2-6x-4\\&=(x-3)\left(3x^2+7x+15\right)+41\end{aligned}$$

44. $$\begin{array}{r|rrrr}4 & 3 & -2 & -6 & -4\\ & & 12 & 40 & 136\\ \hline & 3 & 10 & 34 & 132\end{array}$$

$$\begin{aligned}P(x)&=3x^3-2x^2-6x-4\\&=(x-4)\left(3x^2+10x+34\right)+132\end{aligned}$$

45. $$\begin{array}{r|rrrr}-1 & 3 & -2 & -6 & -4\\ & & -3 & 5 & 1\\ \hline & 3 & -5 & -1 & -3\end{array}$$

$$\begin{aligned}P(x)&=3x^3-2x^2-6x-4\\&=(x+1)\left(3x^2-5x-1\right)-3\end{aligned}$$

46. $$\begin{array}{r|rrrr}-2 & 3 & -2 & -6 & -4\\ & & -6 & 16 & -20\\ \hline & 3 & -8 & 10 & -24\end{array}$$

$$\begin{aligned}P(x)&=3x^3-2x^2-6x-4\\&=(x+2)\left(3x^2-8x+10\right)-24\end{aligned}$$

47. $$\begin{array}{r|rrrr}-3 & 3 & -2 & -6 & -4\\ & & -9 & 33 & -81\\ \hline & 3 & -11 & 27 & -85\end{array}$$

$$\begin{aligned}P(x)&=3x^3-2x^2-6x-4\\&=(x+3)\left(3x^2-11x+27\right)-85\end{aligned}$$

48. $$\begin{array}{r|rrrr}-4 & 3 & -2 & -6 & -4\\ & & -12 & 56 & -200\\ \hline & 3 & -14 & 50 & -204\end{array}$$

$$\begin{aligned}P(x)&=3x^3-2x^2-6x-4\\&=(x+4)\left(3x^2-14x+50\right)-204\end{aligned}$$

49.
$$\begin{array}{r|rrrr} 1 & 1 & 1 & 1 & -3 \\ & & 1 & 2 & 3 \\ \hline & 1 & 2 & 3 & 0 \end{array}$$
$x^2 + 2x + 3$

50.
$$\begin{array}{r|rrrr} 2 & 1 & -1 & -5 & 6 \\ & & 2 & 2 & -6 \\ \hline & 1 & 1 & -3 & 0 \end{array}$$
$x^2 + x - 3$

51.
$$\begin{array}{r|rrrr} -1 & 7 & -3 & -5 & 1 \\ & & -7 & 10 & -5 \\ \hline & 7 & -10 & 5 & -4 \end{array}$$
$7x^2 - 10x + 5 + \dfrac{-4}{x+1}$

52.
$$\begin{array}{r|rrrr} 3 & 2 & 4 & -3 & 8 \\ & & 6 & 30 & 81 \\ \hline & 2 & 10 & 27 & 89 \end{array}$$
$2x^2 + 10x + 27 + \dfrac{89}{x-3}$

53.
$$\begin{array}{r|rrrrr} 3 & 4 & -3 & 0 & -1 & 5 \\ & & 12 & 27 & 81 & 240 \\ \hline & 4 & 9 & 27 & 80 & 245 \end{array}$$
$4x^3 + 9x^2 + 27x + 80 + \dfrac{245}{x-3}$

54.
$$\begin{array}{r|rrrrr} -1 & 1 & 5 & -2 & 1 & -1 \\ & & -1 & -4 & 6 & -7 \\ \hline & 1 & 4 & -6 & 7 & -8 \end{array}$$
$x^3 + 4x^2 - 6x + 7 + \dfrac{-8}{x+1}$

55.
$$\begin{array}{r|rrrrrr} 4 & 3 & 0 & 0 & 0 & -768 & 0 \\ & & 12 & 48 & 192 & 768 & 0 \\ \hline & 3 & 12 & 48 & 192 & 0 & 0 \end{array}$$
$3x^4 + 12x^3 + 48x^2 + 192x$

56.
$$\begin{array}{r|rrrrrr} -3 & 1 & 0 & 0 & -4 & 4 & 4 \\ & & -3 & 9 & -27 & 93 & -291 \\ \hline & 1 & -3 & 9 & -31 & 97 & -287 \end{array}$$
$x^4 - 3x^3 + 9x^2 - 31x + 97 + \dfrac{-287}{x+3}$

57.
$$\begin{array}{r|rrrr} 2 & 5 & 2 & -1 & 1 \\ & & 10 & 24 & 46 \\ \hline & 5 & 12 & 23 & 47 \end{array}$$
$\boxed{P(2) = 47}$

58.
$$\begin{array}{r|rrrr} -2 & 5 & 2 & -1 & 1 \\ & & -10 & 16 & -30 \\ \hline & 5 & -8 & 15 & -29 \end{array}$$
$\boxed{P(2) = -29}$

59.
$$\begin{array}{r|rrrr} -5 & 5 & 2 & -1 & 1 \\ & & -25 & 115 & -570 \\ \hline & 5 & -23 & 114 & -569 \end{array}$$
$\boxed{P(-5) = -569}$

60.
$$\begin{array}{r|rrrr} 3 & 5 & 2 & -1 & 1 \\ & & 15 & 51 & 150 \\ \hline & 5 & 17 & 50 & 151 \end{array}$$
$\boxed{P(3) = 151}$

61.
$$\begin{array}{r|rrrrr} \frac{1}{2} & 2 & 0 & -1 & 0 & 2 \\ & & 1 & \frac{1}{2} & -\frac{1}{4} & -\frac{1}{8} \\ \hline & 2 & 1 & -\frac{1}{2} & -\frac{1}{4} & \frac{15}{8} \end{array}$$
$\boxed{P\left(\frac{1}{2}\right) = \frac{15}{8}}$

62.
$$\begin{array}{r|rrrrr} \frac{1}{3} & 2 & 0 & -1 & 0 & 2 \\ & & \frac{2}{3} & \frac{2}{9} & -\frac{7}{27} & -\frac{7}{81} \\ \hline & 2 & \frac{2}{3} & -\frac{7}{9} & -\frac{7}{27} & \frac{155}{81} \end{array}$$
$\boxed{P\left(\frac{1}{3}\right) = \frac{155}{81}}$

63.
$$\begin{array}{r|rrrrr} i & 2 & 0 & -1 & 0 & 2 \\ & & 2i & -2 & -3i & 3 \\ \hline & 2 & 2i & -3 & -3i & 5 \end{array}$$
$\boxed{P(i) = 5}$

64.
$$\begin{array}{r|rrrrr} -i & 2 & 0 & -1 & 0 & 2 \\ & & -2i & -2 & 3i & 3 \\ \hline & 2 & -2i & -3 & 3i & 5 \end{array}$$
$\boxed{P(-i) = 5}$

65.
$$\begin{array}{r|rrrrr} 1 & 1 & -8 & 14 & 8 & -15 \\ & & 1 & -7 & 7 & 15 \\ \hline & 1 & -7 & 7 & 15 & 0 \end{array}$$
$$\boxed{P(1) = 0}$$

66.
$$\begin{array}{r|rrrrr} 0 & 1 & -8 & 14 & 8 & -15 \\ & & 0 & 0 & 0 & 0 \\ \hline & 1 & -8 & 14 & 8 & -15 \end{array}$$
$$\boxed{P(0) = -15}$$

67.
$$\begin{array}{r|rrrrr} -3 & 1 & -8 & 14 & 8 & -15 \\ & & -3 & 33 & -141 & 399 \\ \hline & 1 & -11 & 47 & -133 & 384 \end{array}$$
$$\boxed{P(-3) = 384}$$

68.
$$\begin{array}{r|rrrrr} -1 & 1 & -8 & 14 & 8 & -15 \\ & & -1 & 9 & -23 & 15 \\ \hline & 1 & -9 & 23 & -15 & 0 \end{array}$$
$$\boxed{P(-1) = 0}$$

69.
$$\begin{array}{r|rrrrrr} i & 1 & 0 & -1 & -8 & 0 & 8 \\ & & i & -1 & -2i & 2-8i & 8+2i \\ \hline & 1 & i & -2 & -8-2i & 2-8i & 16+2i \end{array} \quad \boxed{P(i) = 16+2i}$$

70.
$$\begin{array}{r|rrrrrr} -i & 1 & 0 & -1 & -8 & 0 & 8 \\ & & -i & -1 & 2i & 2+8i & 8-2i \\ \hline & 1 & -i & -2 & -8+2i & 2+8i & 16-2i \end{array} \quad \boxed{P(-i) = 16-2i}$$

71.
$$\begin{array}{r|rrrrrr} -2i & 1 & 0 & -1 & -8 & 0 & 8 \\ & & -2i & -4 & 10i & 20+16i & 32-40i \\ \hline & 1 & -2i & -5 & -8+10i & 20+16i & 40-40i \end{array} \quad \boxed{P(-2i) = 40-40i}$$

72.
$$\begin{array}{r|rrrrrr} 2i & 1 & 0 & -1 & -8 & 0 & 8 \\ & & 2i & -4 & -10i & 20-16i & 32+40i \\ \hline & 1 & 2i & -5 & -8-10i & 20-16i & 40+40i \end{array} \quad \boxed{P(2i) = 40+40i}$$

73.
$$\begin{aligned} P(0) &= 0 \\ a_n(0)^n + a_{n-1}(0)^{n-1} + \cdots + a_1(0) + a_0 &= 0 \\ 0 + 0 + \cdots + 0 + a_0 &= 0 \\ a_0 &= 0 \end{aligned}$$

74. From **#73**, $a_0 = 0$. Then,
$P(x) = a_n x^n + a_{n-1}x^{n-1} + \cdots + a_1 x = x\left(a_n x^{n-1} + a_{n-1}x^{n-2} + \cdots + a_2 x + a_1\right)$.
If 0 is a double root, then it is a root of the depressed polynomial, so
$a_n(0)^{n-1} + a_{n-1}(0)^{n-2} + \cdots + a_2(0) + a_1 = 0 \Rightarrow a_1 = 0$ (as in **#73**).

75. $P(2) = 0 \Rightarrow (x-2)$ is a factor.
$P(-2) = 0 \Rightarrow (x+2)$ is a factor. The product of two factors will also be a factor, so $(x-2)(x+2) = x^2 - 4$ is a factor of the polynomial $P(x)$.

76.
$$\begin{aligned} P(2) &= 11 \\ 2^4 - 3(2)^3 + k(2)^2 + 4(2) - 1 &= 11 \\ 16 - 3(8) + 4k + 8 - 1 &= 11 \\ 4k - 1 &= 11 \\ 4k &= 12 \\ k &= 3 \end{aligned}$$

77. $P(3, -2)$: QIV

78. $Q(-2, -5)$: QIII

79. $R(8, \pi)$: QI

80. $S(-9, 9)$: QII

81. $d = \sqrt{(3-(-5))^2 + (-3-3)^2} = \sqrt{(8)^2 + (-6)^2} = \sqrt{64+36} = \sqrt{100} = 10$

82. $d = \sqrt{(-8-2)^2 + (2-(-22))^2} = \sqrt{(-10)^2 + (24)^2} = \sqrt{100+576} = \sqrt{676} = 26$

83. $m = \dfrac{-3-5}{-5-3} = \dfrac{-8}{-8} = 1$

84. $m = \dfrac{1-\frac{3}{5}}{-\frac{3}{5}-3} = \dfrac{\frac{2}{5}}{-\frac{18}{5}} = -\dfrac{1}{9}$

Exercise 5.2 (page 400)

1. zero

2. fundamental theorem of algebra

3. conjugate

4. 2

5. $(-x)^3 - (-x)^2 - 4$
$= -x^3 - x^2 - 4$
0 variations

6. 2 variations $\Rightarrow$ at most 2 positive roots

7. $7x^4 + 5x^3 - 2x + 1 \Rightarrow 7(-x)^4 + 5(-x)^3 - 2(-x) + 1$
$\Rightarrow 7x^4 - 5x^3 + 2x + 1 \Rightarrow$ 2 variations $\Rightarrow$ at most 2 negative roots

8. conjugate

9. lower bound

10. upper bound

11. $x^{10} = 1$
$x^{10} - 1 = 0 \Rightarrow$ 10 roots

12. $x^{40} = 1$
$x^{40} - 1 = 0 \Rightarrow$ 40 roots

13. $3x^4 - 4x^2 - 2x = -7$
$3x^4 - 4x^2 - 2x + 7 = 0 \Rightarrow$ 4 roots

14. $-32x^{111} - x^5 = 1$
$-32x^{111} - x^5 - 1 = 0 \Rightarrow$ 111 roots

15. $x(3x^4 - 2) = 12x$
$3x^5 - 14x = 0$
5 total roots $\Rightarrow$ **4 other roots**

16. $3x^2(x^7 - 14x + 3) = 0$
$3x^9 - 42x^3 + 9x^2 = 0$
9 total roots $\Rightarrow$ **7 other roots**

17. If $-i$ is a root, then i is a root also:
$(x-3)(x+i)(x-i) = 0$
$(x-3)(x^2 - i^2) = 0$
$(x-3)(x^2+1) = 0$
$x^3 - 3x^2 + x - 3 = 0$

18. If i is a root, then $-i$ is a root also:
$(x-1)(x-i)(x+i) = 0$
$(x-1)(x^2 - i^2) = 0$
$(x-1)(x^2+1) = 0$
$x^3 - x^2 + x - 1 = 0$

19. If $2+i$ is a root, then $2-i$ is a root also:

$$\begin{aligned}(x-2)[x-(2+i)][x-(2-i)]&=0\\(x-2)\left[x^2-(2-i)x-(2+i)x+(2+i)(2-i)\right]&=0\\(x-2)\left[x^2-2x+ix-2x-ix+4-i^2\right]&=0\\(x-2)\left[x^2-4x+5\right]&=0\\x^3-6x^2+13x-10&=0\end{aligned}$$

20. If $3-i$ is a root, then $3+i$ is a root also:

$$\begin{aligned}(x+2)[x-(3-i)][x-(3+i)]&=0\\(x+2)\left[x^2-(3+i)x-(3-i)x+(3-i)(3+i)\right]&=0\\(x+2)\left[x^2-3x-ix-3x+ix+9-i^2\right]&=0\\(x+2)\left[x^2-6x+10\right]&=0\\x^3-4x^2-2x+20&=0\end{aligned}$$

21. If i is a root, then $-i$ is a root also:

$$\begin{aligned}(x-3)(x-2)(x-i)(x+i)&=0\\\left(x^2-5x+6\right)\left(x^2-i^2\right)&=0\\\left(x^2-5x+6\right)\left(x^2+1\right)&=0\\x^4-5x^3+7x^2-5x+6&=0\end{aligned}$$

22. If $1+i$ is a root, then $1-i$ is a root also:

$$\begin{aligned}(x-1)(x-2)[x-(1+i)][x-(1-i)]&=0\\\left(x^2-3x+2\right)\left[x^2-(1-i)x-(1+i)x+(1+i)(1-i)\right]&=0\\\left(x^2-3x+2\right)\left[x^2-x+ix-x-ix+1-i^2\right]&=0\\\left(x^2-3x+2\right)\left[x^2-2x+2\right]&=0\\x^4-5x^3+10x^2-10x+4&=0\end{aligned}$$

23. If i and $1-i$ are roots, then $-i$ and $1+i$ are roots also:

$$\begin{aligned}(x-i)(x+i)[x-(1-i)][x-(1+i)]&=0\\\left(x^2-i^2\right)\left[x^2-(1+i)x-(1-i)x+(1-i)(1+i)\right]&=0\\\left(x^2+1\right)\left[x^2-x-ix-x+ix+1-i^2\right]&=0\\\left(x^2+1\right)\left[x^2-2x+2\right]&=0\\x^4-2x^3+3x^2-2x+2&=0\end{aligned}$$

24. If i and $2-i$ are roots, then $-i$ and $2+i$ are roots also:

$$\begin{aligned}(x-i)(x+i)[x-(2-i)][x-(2+i)]&=0\\\left(x^2-i^2\right)\left[x^2-(2+i)x-(2-i)x+(2-i)(2+i)\right]&=0\\\left(x^2+1\right)\left[x^2-2x-ix-2x+ix+4-i^2\right]&=0\\\left(x^2+1\right)\left[x^2-4x+5\right]&=0\\x^4-4x^3+6x^2-4x+5&=0\end{aligned}$$

25. $P(x) = 3x^3 + 5x^2 - 4x + 3$

2 sign variations $\Rightarrow$ 2 or 0 positive roots

$P(-x) = 3(-x)^3 + 5(-x)^2 - 4(-x) + 3$
$= -3x^3 + 5x^2 + 4x + 3$

1 sign variation $\Rightarrow$ 1 negative root

# pos	# neg	# nonreal
2	1	0
0	1	2

26. $P(x) = 3x^3 - 5x^2 - 4x - 3$

1 sign variation $\Rightarrow$ 1 positive root

$P(-x) = 3(-x)^3 - 5(-x)^2 - 4(-x) - 3$
$= -3x^3 - 5x^2 + 4x - 3$

2 sign variations $\Rightarrow$ 2 or 0 negative roots

# pos	# neg	# nonreal
1	2	0
1	0	2

27. $P(x) = 2x^3 + 7x^2 + 5x + 5$

0 sign variations $\Rightarrow$ 0 positive roots

$P(-x) = 2(-x)^3 + 7(-x)^2 + 5(-x) + 3$
$= -2x^3 + 7x^2 - 5x + 3$

3 sign variations $\Rightarrow$ 3 or 1 negative roots

# pos	# neg	# nonreal
0	3	0
0	1	2

28. $P(x) = -2x^3 - 7x^2 - 5x - 4$

0 sign variations $\Rightarrow$ 0 positive roots

$P(-x) = -2(-x)^3 - 7(-x)^2 - 5(-x) - 4$
$= 2x^3 - 7x^2 + 5x - 4$

3 sign variations $\Rightarrow$ 3 or 1 negative roots

# pos	# neg	# nonreal
0	3	0
0	1	2

29. $P(x) = 8x^4 + 5$

0 sign variations $\Rightarrow$ 0 positive roots

$P(-x) = 8(-x)^4 + 5$
$= 8x^4 + 5$

0 sign variations $\Rightarrow$ 0 negative roots

# pos	# neg	# nonreal
0	0	4

30. $P(x) = -3x^3 + 5$

1 sign variation $\Rightarrow$ 1 positive root

$P(-x) = -3(-x)^3 + 5$
$= 3x^3 + 5$

0 sign variations $\Rightarrow$ 0 negative roots

# pos	# neg	# nonreal
1	0	2

31. $P(x) = x^4 + 8x^2 - 5x - 10$: 1 sign variation $\Rightarrow$ 1 positive root

$P(-x) = (-x)^4 + 8(-x)^2 - 5(-x) - 10$
$= x^4 + 8x^2 + 5x - 10$: 1 sign variation $\Rightarrow$ 1 negative root

# pos	# neg	# nonreal
1	1	2

32. $P(x) = 5x^7 + 3x^6 - 2x^5 + 3x^4 + 9x^3 + x^2 + 1$: 2 sign variations $\Rightarrow$ 2 or 0 positive roots

$P(-x) = 5(-x)^7 + 3(-x)^6 - 2(-x)^5 + 3(-x)^4 + 9(-x)^3 + (-x)^2 + 1$
$= -5x^7 + 3x^6 + 2x^5 + 3x^4 - 9x^3 + x^2 + 1$: 3 sign variations $\Rightarrow$ 3 or 1 negative roots

# pos	# neg	# nonreal
2	3	2
2	1	4
0	3	4
0	1	6

33. $P(x) = -x^{10} - x^8 - x^6 - x^4 - x^2 - 1$: 0 sign variations $\Rightarrow$ 0 positive roots
$P(-x) = -(-x)^{10} - (-x)^8 - (-x)^6 - (-x)^4 - (-x)^2 - 1$
$= -x^{10} - x^8 - x^6 - x^4 - x^2 - 1$: 0 sign variations $\Rightarrow$ 0 negative roots

# pos	# neg	# nonreal
0	0	10

34. $P(x) = x^{10} + x^8 + x^6 + x^4 + x^2 + 1$: 0 sign variations $\Rightarrow$ 0 positive roots
$P(-x) = (-x)^{10} + (-x)^8 + (-x)^6 + (-x)^4 + (-x)^2 + 1$
$= x^{10} + x^8 + x^6 + x^4 + x^2 + 1$: 0 sign variations $\Rightarrow$ 0 negative roots

# pos	# neg	# nonreal
0	0	10

35. $P(x) = x^9 + x^7 + x^5 + x^3 + x = x\left(x^8 + x^6 + x^4 + x^2 + 1\right)$: 0 sign variations $\Rightarrow$ 0 positive roots
$P(-x) = (-x)\left[(-x)^8 + (-x)^6 + (-x)^4 + (-x)^2 + 1\right]$
$= -x\left[x^8 + x^6 + x^4 + x^2 + 1\right]$: 0 sign variations $\Rightarrow$ 0 negative roots

# pos	# neg	# zero	# nonreal
0	0	1	8

36. $P(x) = -x^9 - x^7 - x^5 - x^3 - x = -x\left(x^8 + x^6 + x^4 + x^2 + 1\right)$: 0 sign var $\Rightarrow$ 0 positive roots
$P(-x) = -(-x)\left[(-x)^8 + (-x)^6 + (-x)^4 + (-x)^2 + 1\right]$
$= x\left[x^8 + x^6 + x^4 + x^2 + 1\right]$: 0 sign variations $\Rightarrow$ 0 negative roots

# pos	# neg	# zero	# nonreal
0	0	1	8

37. $P(x) = -2x^4 - 3x^2 + 2x + 3$: 1 sign variation $\Rightarrow$ 1 positive root
$P(-x) = -2(-x)^4 - 3(-x)^2 + 2(-x) + 3$
$= -2x^4 - 3x^2 - 2x + 3$: 1 sign variation $\Rightarrow$ 1 negative root

# pos	# neg	# nonreal
1	1	2

38. $P(x) = -7x^5 - 6x^4 + 3x^3 - 2x^2 + 7x - 4$: 4 sign variations $\Rightarrow$ 4 or 2 or 0 positive roots
$P(-x) = -7(-x)^5 - 6(-x)^4 + 3(-x)^3 - 2(-x)^2 + 7(-x) - 4$
$= 7x^5 - 6x^4 - 3x^3 - 2x^2 - 7x - 4$: 1 sign variation $\Rightarrow$ 1 negative root

# pos	# neg	# nonreal
4	1	0
2	1	2
0	1	4

39. $P(x) = x^2 - 2x - 4$

$$\begin{array}{r|rrr} 4 & 1 & -2 & -4 \\ & & 4 & 8 \\ \hline & 1 & 2 & 4 \end{array} \qquad \begin{array}{r|rrr} -2 & 1 & -2 & -4 \\ & & -2 & 8 \\ \hline & 1 & -4 & 4 \end{array}$$

Upper bound: 4 Lower bound: -2

40. $P(x) = 9x^2 - 6x - 1$

$$\begin{array}{r|rrr} 1 & 9 & -6 & -1 \\ & & 9 & 3 \\ \hline & 9 & 3 & 2 \end{array} \qquad \begin{array}{r|rrr} -1 & 9 & -6 & -1 \\ & & -9 & 15 \\ \hline & 9 & -15 & 14 \end{array}$$

Upper bound: 1 Lower bound: -1

41. $P(x) = 18x^2 - 6x - 1$

$$\begin{array}{r|rrr} 1 & 18 & -6 & -1 \\ & & 18 & 12 \\ \hline & 18 & 12 & 11 \end{array}$$

Upper bound: 1

$$\begin{array}{r|rrr} -1 & 18 & -6 & -1 \\ & & -18 & 24 \\ \hline & 18 & -24 & 23 \end{array}$$

Lower bound: -1

42. $P(x) = 2x^2 - 10x - 9$

$$\begin{array}{r|rrr} 6 & 2 & -10 & -9 \\ & & 12 & 12 \\ \hline & 2 & 2 & 3 \end{array}$$

Upper bound: 6

$$\begin{array}{r|rrr} -1 & 2 & -10 & -9 \\ & & -2 & 12 \\ \hline & 2 & -12 & 3 \end{array}$$

Lower bound: -1

43. $P(x) = 6x^3 - 13x^2 - 110x$

$$\begin{array}{r|rrrr} 6 & 6 & -13 & -110 & 0 \\ & & 36 & 138 & 168 \\ \hline & 6 & 23 & 28 & 168 \end{array}$$

Upper bound: 6

$$\begin{array}{r|rrrr} -4 & 6 & -13 & -110 & 0 \\ & & -24 & 148 & -152 \\ \hline & 6 & -37 & 38 & -152 \end{array}$$

Lower bound: -4

44. $P(x) = 12x^3 + 20x^2 - x - 6$

$$\begin{array}{r|rrrr} 1 & 12 & 20 & -1 & -6 \\ & & 12 & 32 & 31 \\ \hline & 12 & 32 & 31 & 25 \end{array}$$

Upper bound: 1

$$\begin{array}{r|rrrr} -2 & 12 & 20 & -1 & -6 \\ & & -24 & 8 & -14 \\ \hline & 12 & -4 & 7 & -20 \end{array}$$

Lower bound: -2

45. $P(x) = x^5 + x^4 - 8x^3 - 8x^2 + 15x + 15$

$$\begin{array}{r|rrrrrr} 3 & 1 & 1 & -8 & -8 & 15 & 15 \\ & & 3 & 12 & 12 & 12 & 81 \\ \hline & 1 & 4 & 4 & 4 & 27 & 96 \end{array}$$

Upper bound: 3

$$\begin{array}{r|rrrrrr} -4 & 1 & 1 & -8 & -8 & 15 & 15 \\ & & -4 & 12 & -16 & 96 & -444 \\ \hline & 1 & -3 & 4 & -24 & 111 & -429 \end{array}$$

Lower bound: -4

46. $P(x) = 3x^4 - 5x^3 - 9x^2 + 15x$

$$\begin{array}{r|rrrrr} 3 & 3 & -5 & -9 & 15 & 0 \\ & & 9 & 12 & 9 & 72 \\ \hline & 3 & 4 & 3 & 24 & 72 \end{array}$$

Upper bound: 3

$$\begin{array}{r|rrrrr} -2 & 3 & -5 & -9 & 15 & 0 \\ & & -6 & 22 & -26 & 22 \\ \hline & 3 & -11 & 13 & -11 & 22 \end{array}$$

Lower bound: -2

47. $P(x) = 3x^5 - 11x^4 - 2x^3 + 38x^2 - 21x - 15$

$$\begin{array}{r|rrrrrr} 4 & 3 & -11 & -2 & 38 & -21 & -15 \\ & & 12 & 4 & 8 & 184 & 652 \\ \hline & 3 & 1 & 2 & 46 & 163 & 637 \end{array} \qquad \begin{array}{r|rrrrrr} -2 & 3 & -11 & -2 & 38 & -21 & -15 \\ & & -6 & 34 & -64 & 52 & -62 \\ \hline & 3 & -17 & 32 & -26 & 31 & -77 \end{array}$$

Upper bound: 4 Lower bound: -2

48. $P(x) = 3x^6 - 4x^5 - 21x^4 + 4x^3 + 8x^2 + 8x + 32$

$$\begin{array}{r|rrrrrrr} 4 & 3 & -4 & -21 & 4 & 8 & 8 & 32 \\ & & 12 & 32 & 44 & 192 & 800 & 3232 \\ \hline & 3 & 8 & 11 & 48 & 200 & 808 & 3264 \end{array}$$

Upper bound: 4

$$\begin{array}{r|rrrrrrr} -3 & 3 & -4 & -21 & 4 & 8 & 8 & 32 \\ & & -9 & 39 & -54 & 150 & -474 & 1398 \\ \hline & 3 & -13 & 18 & -50 & 158 & -466 & 1430 \end{array}$$

Lower bound: -3

49. **Answers may vary.**

50. **Answers may vary.**

51. The number of nonreal roots must occur in conjugate pairs, so the number of nonreal roots will always be even. Since a polynomial of odd degree has an odd number of roots, at least one root must not be nonreal. Thus, at least one root of such a polynomial will be real.

52. According to Descartes' Rule of Signs, the polynomial will have 1 positive root and 1 negative root. Since the polynomial has a total of 4 roots, the other 2 roots must be nonreal (and conjugates).

53. k units to the right

54. k units down

55. reflected about the y-axis

56. reflected about the x-axis

57. stretched vertically by a factor of k

58. stretched horizontally by a factor of $\frac{1}{k}$

Exercise 5.3 (page 408)

1. -7

2. 5

3. root

4. $5x^2 + 8x + 21 = 0$

5. $x^3 - 5x^2 - x + 5 = 0$

Possible rational roots: $\pm 1, \pm 5$

Descartes' Rule of Signs:

# pos	# neg	# nonreal
2	1	0
0	1	2

Test $x = -1$:

$$\begin{array}{r|rrrr} -1 & 1 & -5 & -1 & 5 \\ & & -1 & 6 & -5 \\ \hline & 1 & -6 & 5 & 0 \end{array}$$

Factor out $(x + 1)$:

$$x^3 - 5x^2 - x + 5 = 0$$
$$(x + 1)(x^2 - 6x + 5) = 0$$
$$(x + 1)(x - 5)(x - 1) = 0$$

Solution set: $\{-1, 5, 1\}$

6. $x^3 + 7x^2 - x - 7 = 0$

Possible rational roots: $\pm 1, \ \pm 7$

Descartes' Rule of Signs:

# pos	# neg	# nonreal
1	2	0
1	0	2

Test $x = 1$:

$$\begin{array}{r|rrrr} 1 & 1 & 7 & -1 & -7 \\ & & 1 & 8 & 7 \\ \hline & 1 & 8 & 7 & 0 \end{array}$$

Factor out $(x-1)$:

$$x^3 + 7x^2 - x - 7 = 0$$
$$(x-1)(x^2 + 8x + 7) = 0$$
$$(x-1)(x+1)(x+7) = 0$$

Solution set: $\{1, -1, -7\}$

7. $x^3 - 2x^2 - 9x + 18 = 0$

Possible rational roots:

$\pm 1, \ \pm 2, \ \pm 3, \ \pm 6, \ \pm 9, \ \pm 18$

Descartes' Rule of Signs:

# pos	# neg	# nonreal
2	1	0
0	1	2

Test $x = 2$:

$$\begin{array}{r|rrrr} 2 & 1 & -2 & -9 & 18 \\ & & 2 & 0 & -18 \\ \hline & 1 & 0 & -9 & 0 \end{array}$$

Factor out $(x-2)$:

$$x^3 - 2x^2 - 9x + 18 = 0$$
$$(x-2)(x^2 - 9) = 0$$
$$(x-2)(x+3)(x-3) = 0$$

Solution set: $\{2, -3, 3\}$

8. $x^3 + 3x^2 - 4x - 12 = 0$

Possible rational roots:

$\pm 1, \ \pm 2, \ \pm 3, \ \pm 4, \ \pm 6, \ \pm 12$

Descartes' Rule of Signs:

# pos	# neg	# nonreal
1	2	0
1	0	2

Test $x = 2$:

$$\begin{array}{r|rrrr} 2 & 1 & 3 & -4 & -12 \\ & & 2 & 10 & 12 \\ \hline & 1 & 5 & 6 & 0 \end{array}$$

Factor out $(x-2)$:

$$x^3 + 3x^2 - 4x - 12 = 0$$
$$(x-2)(x^2 + 5x + 6) = 0$$
$$(x-2)(x+3)(x+2) = 0$$

Solution set: $\{2, -3, -2\}$

9. $x^3 - 2x^2 - x + 2 = 0$

Possible rational roots

$\pm 1, \ \pm 2$

Descartes' Rule of Signs

# pos	# neg	# nonreal
2	1	0
0	1	2

Test $x = -1$:

$$\begin{array}{r|rrrr} -1 & 1 & -2 & -1 & 2 \\ & & -1 & 3 & -2 \\ \hline & 1 & -3 & 2 & 0 \end{array}$$

$$x^3 - 2x^2 - x + 2 = 0$$
$$(x+1)(x^2 - 3x + 2) = 0$$
$$(x+1)(x-1)(x-2) = 0$$

Solution set: $\{-1, 1, 2\}$

10. Possible rational roots

$\pm 1, \ \pm 2$

Descartes' Rule of Signs

# pos	# neg	# nonreal
1	2	0
1	0	2

Test $x = 1$:

$$\begin{array}{r|rrrr} 1 & 1 & 2 & -1 & -2 \\ & & 1 & 3 & 2 \\ \hline & 1 & 3 & 2 & 0 \end{array}$$

$$x^3 + 2x^2 - x - 2 = 0$$
$$(x-1)(x^2 + 3x + 2) = 0$$
$$(x-1)(x+1)(x+2) = 0$$

Solution set: $\{1, -1, -2\}$

11. Possible rational roots

$\pm 1,\ \pm 2,\ \pm 3,\ \pm 4,$
$\pm 6,\ \pm 8,\ \pm 12,\ \pm 24$

Descartes' Rule of Signs

# pos	# neg	# nonreal
4	0	0
2	0	2
0	0	4

$$x^4 - 10x^3 + 35x^2 - 50x + 24 = 0$$
$$(x-1)(x^3 - 9x^2 + 26x - 24) = 0$$
$$(x-1)(x-2)(x^2 - 7x + 12) = 0$$
$$(x-1)(x-2)(x-3)(x-4) = 0$$
Solution set: $\{1, 2, 3, 4\}$

Test $x = 1$:

$$\begin{array}{r|rrrrr} 1 & 1 & -10 & 35 & -50 & 24 \\ & & 1 & -9 & 26 & -24 \\ \hline & 1 & -9 & 26 & -24 & 0 \end{array}$$

Test $x = 2$:

$$\begin{array}{r|rrrr} 2 & 1 & -9 & 26 & -24 \\ & & 2 & -14 & 24 \\ \hline & 1 & -7 & 12 & 0 \end{array}$$

12. Possible rational roots

± 1

Descartes' Rule of Signs

# pos	# neg	# nonreal
0	4	0
0	2	2
0	0	4

$$x^4 + 4x^3 + 6x^2 + 4x + 1 = 0$$
$$(x+1)(x^3 + 3x^2 + 3x + 1) = 0$$
$$(x+1)(x+1)(x^2 + 2x + 1) = 0$$
$$(x+1)(x+1)(x+1)(x+1) = 0$$
Solution set: $\{-1, -1, -1, -1\}$

Test $x = -1$:

$$\begin{array}{r|rrrrr} -1 & 1 & 4 & 6 & 4 & 1 \\ & & -1 & -3 & -3 & -1 \\ \hline & 1 & 3 & 3 & 1 & 0 \end{array}$$

Test $x = -1$:

$$\begin{array}{r|rrrr} -1 & 1 & 3 & 3 & 1 \\ & & -1 & -2 & -1 \\ \hline & 1 & 2 & 1 & 0 \end{array}$$

13. Possible rational roots

$\pm 1,\ \pm 2,\ \pm 3,\ \pm 5,$
$\pm 6,\ \pm 10,\ \pm 15,$
± 30

Descartes' Rule of Signs

# pos	# neg	# nonreal
2	2	0
2	0	2
0	2	2
0	0	4

$$x^4 + 3x^3 - 13x^2 - 9x + 30 = 0$$
$$(x-2)(x^3 + 5x^2 - 3x - 15) = 0$$
$$(x-2)(x+5)(x^2 - 3) = 0$$
$x^2 - 3$ does not factor rationally.
Rational solutions: $\{2, -5\}$

Test $x = 2$:

$$\begin{array}{r|rrrrr} 2 & 1 & 3 & -13 & -9 & 30 \\ & & 2 & 10 & -6 & -30 \\ \hline & 1 & 5 & -3 & -15 & 0 \end{array}$$

Test $x = -5$:

$$\begin{array}{r|rrrr} -5 & 1 & 5 & -3 & -15 \\ & & -5 & 0 & 15 \\ \hline & 1 & 0 & -3 & 0 \end{array}$$

14. Possible rational roots

$\pm 1,\ \pm 3,\ \pm 5,\ \pm 15$

Descartes' Rule of Signs

# pos	# neg	# nonreal
3	1	0
1	1	2

$$x^4 - 8x^3 + 14x^2 + 8x - 15 = 0$$
$$(x+1)(x^3 - 9x^2 + 23x - 15) = 0$$
$$(x+1)(x-1)(x^2 - 8x + 15) = 0$$
$$(x+1)(x-1)(x-3)(x-5) = 0$$
Solution set: $\{-1, 1, 3, 5\}$

Test $x = -1$:

$$\begin{array}{r|rrrrr} -1 & 1 & -8 & 14 & 8 & -15 \\ & & -1 & 9 & -23 & 15 \\ \hline & 1 & -9 & 23 & -15 & 0 \end{array}$$

Test $x = 1$:

$$\begin{array}{r|rrrr} 1 & 1 & -9 & 23 & -15 \\ & & 1 & -8 & 15 \\ \hline & 1 & -8 & 15 & 0 \end{array}$$

15. Possible rat. roots: $\pm 1, \pm 2, \pm 3, \pm 4, \pm 6, \pm 12$

Descartes' Rule of Signs

# pos	# neg	# nonreal
2	3	0
2	1	2
0	3	2
0	1	4

$$x^5 + 3x^4 - 5x^3 - 15x^2 + 4x + 12 = 0$$
$$(x+1)\left(x^4 + 2x^3 - 7x^2 - 8x + 12\right) = 0$$
$$(x+1)(x-1)\left(x^3 + 3x^2 - 4x - 12\right) = 0$$
$$(x+1)(x-1)(x-2)\left(x^2 + 5x + 6\right) = 0$$
$$(x+1)(x-1)(x-2)(x+2)(x+3) = 0$$

Solution set: $\{-1, 1, 2, -2, -3\}$

Test $x = -1$:
$$\begin{array}{r|rrrrrr} -1 & 1 & 3 & -5 & -15 & 4 & 12 \\ & & -1 & -2 & 7 & 8 & -12 \\ \hline & 1 & 2 & -7 & -8 & 12 & 0 \end{array}$$

Test $x = 1$:
$$\begin{array}{r|rrrrr} 1 & 1 & 2 & -7 & -8 & 12 \\ & & 1 & 3 & -4 & -12 \\ \hline & 1 & 3 & -4 & -12 & 0 \end{array}$$

Test $x = 2$:
$$\begin{array}{r|rrrr} 2 & 1 & 3 & -4 & -12 \\ & & 2 & 10 & 12 \\ \hline & 1 & 5 & 6 & 0 \end{array}$$

16. Possible rat. roots: $\pm 1, \pm 2, \pm 3, \pm 4, \pm 6, \pm 12$

Descartes' Rule of Signs

# pos	# neg	# nonreal
3	2	0
3	0	2
1	2	2
1	0	4

$$x^5 - 3x^4 - 5x^3 + 15x^2 + 4x - 12 = 0$$
$$(x-1)\left(x^4 - 2x^3 - 7x^2 + 8x + 12\right) = 0$$
$$(x-1)(x+1)\left(x^3 - 3x^2 - 4x + 12\right) = 0$$
$$(x-1)(x+1)(x-2)\left(x^2 - x - 6\right) = 0$$
$$(x-1)(x+1)(x-2)(x+2)(x-3) = 0$$

Solution set: $\{1, -1, 2, -2, 3\}$

Test $x = 1$:
$$\begin{array}{r|rrrrrr} 1 & 1 & -3 & -5 & 15 & 4 & -12 \\ & & 1 & -2 & -7 & 8 & 12 \\ \hline & 1 & -2 & -7 & 8 & 12 & 0 \end{array}$$

Test $x = -1$:
$$\begin{array}{r|rrrrr} -1 & 1 & -2 & -7 & 8 & 12 \\ & & -1 & 3 & 4 & -12 \\ \hline & 1 & -3 & -4 & 12 & 0 \end{array}$$

Test $x = 2$:
$$\begin{array}{r|rrrr} 2 & 1 & -3 & -4 & 12 \\ & & 2 & -2 & -12 \\ \hline & 1 & -1 & -6 & 0 \end{array}$$

17. First, factor out the common factor of x: $x^7 - 12x^5 + 48x^3 - 64x = x\left(x^6 - 12x^4 + 48x^2 - 64\right)$

Possible rat. roots: $\pm 1, \pm 2, \pm 4, \pm 8, \pm 16, \pm 32, \pm 64$

Descartes' Rule of Signs

# pos	# neg	# zero	# nonreal
3	3	1	0
3	1	1	2
1	3	1	2
1	1	1	4

Test $x = 2$:
$$\begin{array}{r|rrrrrrr} 2 & 1 & 0 & -12 & 0 & 48 & 0 & -64 \\ & & 2 & 4 & -16 & -32 & 32 & 64 \\ \hline & 1 & 2 & -8 & -16 & 16 & 32 & 0 \end{array}$$

Test $x = 2$:
$$\begin{array}{r|rrrrrr} 2 & 1 & 2 & -8 & -16 & 16 & 32 \\ & & 2 & 8 & 0 & -32 & -32 \\ \hline & 1 & 4 & 0 & -16 & -16 & 0 \end{array}$$

Test $x = 2$:
$$\begin{array}{r|rrrrr} 2 & 1 & 4 & 0 & -16 & -16 \\ & & 2 & 12 & 24 & 16 \\ \hline & 1 & 6 & 12 & 8 & 0 \end{array}$$

Test $x = -2$:
$$\begin{array}{r|rrrr} -2 & 1 & 6 & 12 & 8 \\ & & -2 & -8 & -8 \\ \hline & 1 & 4 & 4 & 0 \end{array}$$

continued on next page...

17. continued

$$
\begin{aligned}
x^7 - 12x^5 + 48x^3 - 64x &= 0 \\
x(x^6 - 12x^4 + 48x^2 - 64) &= 0 \\
x(x-2)(x^5 + 2x^4 - 8x^3 - 16x^2 + 16x + 32) &= 0 \\
x(x-2)(x-2)(x^4 + 4x^3 - 16x - 16) &= 0 \\
x(x-2)(x-2)(x-2)(x^3 + 6x^2 + 12x + 8) &= 0 \\
x(x-2)(x-2)(x-2)(x+2)(x^2 + 4x + 4) &= 0 \\
x(x-2)(x-2)(x-2)(x+2)(x+2)(x+2) &= 0 \Rightarrow \text{Sol. set} = \{0, 2, 2, 2, -2, -2, -2\}
\end{aligned}
$$

18. Possible rat. roots: ± 1

Descartes' Rule of Signs

# pos	# neg	# nonreal
0	7	0
0	5	2
0	3	4
0	1	6

Test $x = -1$:

$$
\begin{array}{r|rrrrrrrr}
-1 & 1 & 7 & 21 & 35 & 35 & 21 & 7 & 1 \\
 & & -1 & -6 & -15 & -20 & -15 & -6 & -1 \\
\hline
 & 1 & 6 & 15 & 20 & 15 & 6 & 1 & 0
\end{array}
$$

Test $x = -1$:

$$
\begin{array}{r|rrrrrrr}
-1 & 1 & 6 & 15 & 20 & 15 & 6 & 1 \\
 & & -1 & -5 & -10 & -10 & -5 & -1 \\
\hline
 & 1 & 5 & 10 & 10 & 5 & 1 & 0
\end{array}
$$

Test $x = -1$:

$$
\begin{array}{r|rrrrrr}
-1 & 1 & 5 & 10 & 10 & 5 & 1 \\
 & & -1 & -4 & -6 & -4 & -1 \\
\hline
 & 1 & 4 & 6 & 4 & 1 & 0
\end{array}
$$

Test $x = -1$:

$$
\begin{array}{r|rrrrr}
-1 & 1 & 4 & 6 & 4 & 1 \\
 & & -1 & -3 & -3 & -1 \\
\hline
 & 1 & 3 & 3 & 1 & 0
\end{array}
$$

Test $x = -1$:

$$
\begin{array}{r|rrrr}
-1 & 1 & 3 & 3 & 1 \\
 & & -1 & -2 & -1 \\
\hline
 & 1 & 2 & 1 & 0
\end{array}
$$

$$
\begin{aligned}
x^7 + 7x^6 + 21x^5 + 35x^4 + 35x^3 + 21x^2 + 7x + 1 &= 0 \\
(x+1)(x^6 + 6x^5 + 15x^4 + 20x^3 + 15x^2 + 6x + 1) &= 0 \\
(x+1)(x+1)(x^5 + 5x^4 + 10x^3 + 10x^2 + 5x + 1) &= 0 \\
(x+1)(x+1)(x+1)(x^4 + 4x^3 + 6x^2 + 4x + 1) &= 0 \\
(x+1)(x+1)(x+1)(x+1)(x^3 + 3x^2 + 3x + 1) &= 0 \\
(x+1)(x+1)(x+1)(x+1)(x+1)(x^2 + 2x + 1) &= 0 \\
(x+1)(x+1)(x+1)(x+1)(x+1)(x+1)(x+1) &= 0
\end{aligned}
$$

Solution set $= \{-1, -1, -1, -1, -1, -1, -1\}$

19. Possible rational roots

$\pm 1,\ \pm 2,\ \pm 4,\ \pm 8$

$\pm \frac{1}{3},\ \pm \frac{2}{3},\ \pm \frac{4}{3},\ \pm \frac{8}{3}$

Descartes' Rule of Signs

# pos	# neg	# nonreal
3	0	0
1	0	2

$3x^3 - 2x^2 + 12x - 8 = 0$

$\left(x - \frac{2}{3}\right)\left(3x^2 + 12\right) = 0$

$3x^2 + 12$ does not factor rationally.

Rational solutions: $\left\{\frac{2}{3}\right\}$

Test $x = \frac{2}{3}$:

$$\begin{array}{r|rrrr} \frac{2}{3} & 3 & -2 & 12 & -8 \\ & & 2 & 0 & 8 \\ \hline & 3 & 0 & 12 & 0 \end{array}$$

20. Possible rational roots

$\pm 1,\ \pm 3,\ \pm \frac{1}{4},\ \pm \frac{3}{4}$

$\pm \frac{1}{2},\ \pm \frac{3}{2}$

Descartes' Rule of Signs

# pos	# neg	# nonreal
3	1	0
1	1	2

$4x^4 - 8x^3 - x^2 + 8x - 3 = 0$

$(x+1)\left(4x^3 - 12x^2 + 11x - 3\right) = 0$

$(x+1)(x-1)\left(4x^2 - 8x + 3\right) = 0$

$(x+1)(x-1)(2x-1)(2x-3) = 0$

Solution set: $\left\{-1,\ 1,\ \frac{1}{2},\ \frac{3}{2}\right\}$

Test $x = -1$:

$$\begin{array}{r|rrrrr} -1 & 4 & -8 & -1 & 8 & -3 \\ & & -4 & 12 & -11 & 3 \\ \hline & 4 & -12 & 11 & -3 & 0 \end{array}$$

Test $x = 1$:

$$\begin{array}{r|rrrr} 1 & 4 & -12 & 11 & -3 \\ & & 4 & -8 & 3 \\ \hline & 4 & -8 & 3 & 0 \end{array}$$

21. Possible rational roots

$\pm 1,\ \pm 2,\ \pm 3,\ \pm 4,$

$\pm 6,\ \pm 12,\ \pm \frac{1}{3},$

$\pm \frac{2}{3},\ \pm \frac{4}{3}$

Descartes' Rule of Signs

# pos	# neg	# nonreal
3	1	0
1	1	2

$3x^4 - 14x^3 + 11x^2 + 16x - 12 = 0$

$(x+1)\left(3x^3 - 17x^2 + 28x - 12\right) = 0$

$(x+1)(x-2)\left(3x^2 - 11x + 6\right) = 0$

$(x+1)(x-2)(3x-2)(x-3) = 0$

Solution set: $\left\{-1,\ 2,\ \frac{2}{3},\ 3\right\}$

Test $x = -1$:

$$\begin{array}{r|rrrrr} -1 & 3 & -14 & 11 & 16 & -12 \\ & & -3 & 17 & -28 & 12 \\ \hline & 3 & -17 & 28 & -12 & 0 \end{array}$$

Test $x = 2$:

$$\begin{array}{r|rrrr} 2 & 3 & -17 & 28 & -12 \\ & & 6 & -22 & 12 \\ \hline & 3 & -11 & 6 & 0 \end{array}$$

22. Possible rational roots

$\pm 1,\ \pm 2,\ \pm 4,\ \pm 5,$

$\pm 8,\ \pm 10,\ \pm 20,$

$\pm 40,\ \pm \frac{1}{2},\ \pm \frac{5}{2}$

Descartes' Rule of Signs

# pos	# neg	# nonreal
1	3	0
1	1	2

$2x^4 - x^3 - 2x^2 - 4x - 40 = 0$

$(x+2)\left(2x^3 - 5x^2 + 8x - 20\right) = 0$

$(x+2)\left(x - \frac{5}{2}\right)\left(2x^2 + 8\right) = 0$

$2x^2 + 8$ does not factor rationally.

Rational solutions: $\left\{-2,\ \dfrac{5}{2}\right\}$

Test $x = -2$:

$$\begin{array}{r|rrrrr} -2 & 2 & -1 & -2 & -4 & -40 \\ & & -4 & 10 & -16 & 40 \\ \hline & 2 & -5 & 8 & -20 & 0 \end{array}$$

Test $x = \frac{5}{2}$:

$$\begin{array}{r|rrrr} \frac{5}{2} & 2 & -5 & 8 & -20 \\ & & 5 & 0 & 20 \\ \hline & 2 & 0 & 8 & 0 \end{array}$$

23. Possible rational roots

$\pm 1,\ \pm 3,\ \pm \frac{1}{2},\ \pm \frac{3}{2},$
$\pm \frac{1}{3},\ \pm \frac{1}{4},\ \pm \frac{3}{4},\ \pm \frac{1}{6}$
$\pm \frac{1}{12}$

Descartes' Rule of Signs

# pos	# neg	# nonreal
3	1	0
1	1	2

$$12x^4 + 20x^3 - 41x^2 + 20x - 3 = 0$$
$$(x+3)(12x^3 - 16x^2 + 7x - 1) = 0$$
$$(x+3)(x - \tfrac{1}{2})(12x^2 - 10x + 2) = 0$$
$$(x+3)(x - \tfrac{1}{2})(2x - 1)(6x - 2) = 0$$

Solution set: $\{-3, \frac{1}{2}, \frac{1}{2}, \frac{1}{3}\}$

Test $x = -3$:

−3	12	20	−41	20	−3
		−36	48	−21	3
	12	−16	7	−1	0

Test $x = \frac{1}{2}$:

$\frac{1}{2}$	12	−16	7	−1
		6	−5	1
	12	−10	2	0

24. Possible rat. roots

$\pm 1,\ \pm 2,\ \pm 3,$
$\pm 4,\ \pm 6,\ \pm 12,$
$\pm \frac{1}{2},\ \pm \frac{3}{2},\ \pm \frac{1}{4},$
$\pm \frac{3}{4}$

Descartes' Rule of Signs

# pos	# neg	# nonreal
4	1	0
2	1	2
0	1	4

$$4x^5 - 12x^4 + 15x^3 - 45x^2 - 4x + 12 = 0$$
$$(x-3)(4x^4 + 15x^2 - 4) = 0$$
$$(x-3)(x - \tfrac{1}{2})(4x^3 + 2x^2 + 16x + 8) = 0$$
$$(x-3)(x - \tfrac{1}{2})(x + \tfrac{1}{2})(4x^2 + 16) = 0$$

$4x^2 + 16$ does not factor rationally.

Rational solutions: $\{3, \frac{1}{2}, -\frac{1}{2}\}$

Test $x = 3$:

3	4	−12	15	−45	−4	12
		12	0	45	0	−12
	4	0	15	0	−4	0

Test $x = \frac{1}{2}$:

$\frac{1}{2}$	4	0	15	0	−4
		2	1	8	4
	4	2	16	8	0

Test $x = -\frac{1}{2}$:

$-\frac{1}{2}$	4	2	16	8
		−2	0	−8
	4	0	16	0

25. Possible rat. roots

$\pm 1,\ \pm 2,\ \pm 3,$
$\pm 4,\ \pm 6,\ \pm 12,$
$\pm \frac{1}{2},\ \pm \frac{3}{2},\ \pm \frac{1}{3},$
$\pm \frac{2}{3},\ \pm \frac{4}{3},\ \pm \frac{1}{6}$

Descartes' Rule of Signs

# pos	# neg	# nonreal
3	2	0
3	0	2
1	2	2
1	0	4

$$6x^5 - 7x^4 - 48x^3 + 81x^2 - 4x - 12 = 0$$
$$(x-2)(6x^4 + 5x^3 - 38x^2 + 5x + 6) = 0$$
$$(x-2)(x-2)(6x^3 + 17x^2 - 4x - 3) = 0$$
$$(x-2)(x-2)(x+3)(6x^2 - x - 1) = 0$$
$$(x-2)(x-2)(x+3)(2x-1)(3x+1) = 0$$

Solution set: $\{2, 2, -3, \frac{1}{2}, -\frac{1}{3}\}$

Test $x = 2$:

2	6	−7	−48	81	−4	−12
		12	10	−76	10	12
	6	5	−38	5	6	0

Test $x = 2$:

2	6	5	−38	5	6
		12	34	−8	−6
	6	17	−4	−3	0

Test $x = -3$:

−3	6	17	−4	−3
		−18	3	3
	6	−1	−1	0

26.

Possible rational roots

$\pm 1, \pm \frac{1}{2}, \pm \frac{1}{3}, \pm \frac{1}{4},$
$\pm \frac{1}{6}, \pm \frac{1}{9}, \pm \frac{1}{12}, \pm \frac{1}{18}$
$\pm \frac{1}{36}$

Descartes' Rule of Signs

# pos	# neg	# nonreal
3	1	0
1	1	2

$$36x^4 - x^2 + 2x - 1 = 0$$
$$\left(x + \tfrac{1}{2}\right)\left(36x^3 - 18x^2 + 8x - 2\right) = 0$$
$$\left(x + \tfrac{1}{2}\right)\left(x - \tfrac{1}{3}\right)\left(36x^2 - 6x + 6\right) = 0$$

$36x^2 - 6x + 6$ does not factor rationally

Rational solutions: $\left\{-\frac{1}{2}, \frac{1}{3}\right\}$

Test $x = -\frac{1}{2}$:

$$\begin{array}{r|rrrrr} -\frac{1}{2} & 36 & 0 & -1 & 2 & -1 \\ & & -18 & 9 & -4 & 1 \\ \hline & 36 & -18 & 8 & -2 & 0 \end{array}$$

Test $x = \frac{1}{3}$:

$$\begin{array}{r|rrrr} \frac{1}{3} & 36 & -18 & 8 & -2 \\ & & 12 & -2 & 2 \\ \hline & 36 & -6 & 6 & 0 \end{array}$$

27.

Possible rational roots

$\pm 1, \pm 2, \pm 3, \pm 6,$
$\pm 9, \pm 18, \pm \frac{1}{2}, \pm \frac{3}{2}$
$\pm \frac{9}{2}, \pm \frac{1}{3}, \pm \frac{2}{3}, \pm \frac{1}{5},$
$\pm \frac{2}{5}, \pm \frac{3}{5}, \pm \frac{6}{5}, \pm \frac{9}{5},$
$\pm \frac{18}{5}, \pm \frac{1}{6}, \pm \frac{1}{10}, \pm \frac{3}{10},$
$\pm \frac{9}{10}, \pm \frac{1}{15}, \pm \frac{2}{15}, \pm \frac{1}{30}$

Descartes' Rule of Signs

# pos	# neg	# nonreal
2	1	0
0	1	2

Test $x = -\frac{3}{5}$:

$$\begin{array}{r|rrrr} -\frac{3}{5} & 30 & -47 & -9 & 18 \\ & & -18 & 39 & -18 \\ \hline & 30 & -65 & 30 & 0 \end{array}$$

$$30x^3 - 47x^2 - 9x + 18 = 0$$
$$\left(x + \tfrac{3}{5}\right)\left(30x^2 - 65x + 30\right) = 0$$
$$\left(x + \tfrac{3}{5}\right)(3x - 2)(10x - 15) = 0$$

Solution set: $\left\{-\frac{3}{5}, \frac{2}{3}, \frac{3}{2}\right\}$

28.

Possible rational roots

$\pm 1, \pm 2, \pm 3, \pm 6,$
$\pm 9, \pm 18, \pm \frac{1}{2}, \pm \frac{3}{2}$
$\pm \frac{9}{2}, \pm \frac{1}{3}, \pm \frac{2}{3}, \pm \frac{1}{4},$
$\pm \frac{3}{4}, \pm \frac{9}{4}, \pm \frac{1}{5}, \pm \frac{2}{5},$
$\pm \frac{3}{5}, \pm \frac{6}{5}, \pm \frac{9}{5}, \pm \frac{18}{5},$
$\pm \frac{1}{10}, \pm \frac{3}{10}, \pm \frac{9}{10}, \pm \frac{1}{20}$

Descartes' Rule of Signs

# pos	# neg	# nonreal
2	1	0
0	1	2

Test $x = -\frac{3}{4}$:

$$\begin{array}{r|rrrr} -\frac{3}{4} & 20 & -53 & -27 & 18 \\ & & -15 & 51 & -18 \\ \hline & 20 & -68 & 24 & 0 \end{array}$$

$$20x^3 - 53x^2 - 27x + 18 = 0$$
$$\left(x + \tfrac{3}{4}\right)\left(20x^2 - 68x + 24\right) = 0$$
$$\left(x + \tfrac{3}{4}\right)(2x - 6)(10x - 4) = 0$$

Solution set: $\left\{-\frac{3}{4}, 3, \frac{2}{5}\right\}$

29.

Possible rational roots

$\pm 1, \pm 2, \pm 3, \pm 4,$
$\pm 6, \pm 8, \pm 12, \pm 24$
$\pm \frac{1}{3}, \pm \frac{2}{3}, \pm \frac{4}{3}, \pm \frac{8}{3},$
$\pm \frac{1}{5}, \pm \frac{2}{5}, \pm \frac{3}{5}, \pm \frac{4}{5},$
$\pm \frac{6}{5}, \pm \frac{8}{5}, \pm \frac{12}{5}, \pm \frac{24}{5},$
$\pm \frac{1}{15}, \pm \frac{2}{15}, \pm \frac{4}{15}, \pm \frac{8}{15}$

Descartes' Rule of Signs

# pos	# neg	# nonreal
2	1	0
0	1	2

Test $x = -\frac{3}{5}$:

$$\begin{array}{r|rrrr} -\frac{3}{5} & 15 & -61 & -2 & 24 \\ & & -9 & 42 & -24 \\ \hline & 15 & -70 & 40 & 0 \end{array}$$

$$15x^3 - 61x^2 - 2x + 24 = 0$$
$$\left(x + \tfrac{3}{5}\right)\left(15x^2 - 70x + 40\right) = 0$$
$$\left(x + \tfrac{3}{5}\right)(3x - 2)(5x - 20) = 0$$

Solution set: $\left\{-\frac{3}{5}, \frac{2}{3}, 4\right\}$

30. Possible rational roots

$\pm 1,\ \pm 2,\ \pm 3,\ \pm 4,$
$\pm 6,\ \pm 8,\ \pm 12,\ \pm 24$
$\pm \frac{1}{2},\ \pm \frac{3}{2}, \pm \frac{1}{3},\ \pm \frac{2}{3},$
$\pm \frac{4}{3},\ \pm \frac{8}{3},\ \pm \frac{1}{4},\ \pm \frac{3}{4},$
$\pm \frac{1}{6},\ \pm \frac{1}{12}$

Descartes' Rule of Signs

# pos	# neg	# nonreal
1	3	0
1	1	2

$$12x^4 + x^3 + 42x^2 + 4x - 24 = 0$$
$$\left(x - \tfrac{2}{3}\right)\left(12x^3 + 9x^2 + 48x + 36\right) = 0$$
$$\left(x - \tfrac{2}{3}\right)\left(x + \tfrac{3}{4}\right)\left(12x^2 + 48\right) = 0$$

$12x^2 + 48$ does not factor rationally.

Rational solutions: $\left\{\frac{2}{3}, -\frac{3}{4}\right\}$

Test $x = \frac{2}{3}$:

$$\begin{array}{r|rrrrr} \frac{2}{3} & 12 & 1 & 42 & 4 & -24 \\ & & 8 & 6 & 32 & 24 \\ \hline & 12 & 9 & 48 & 36 & 0 \end{array}$$

Test $x = -\frac{3}{4}$:

$$\begin{array}{r|rrrr} -\frac{3}{4} & 12 & 9 & 48 & 36 \\ & & -9 & 0 & -36 \\ \hline & 12 & 0 & 48 & 0 \end{array}$$

31. Possible rational roots

$\pm 1,\ \pm 2,\ \pm 3,\ \pm 6,$
$\pm 9,\ \pm 18,\ \pm \frac{1}{2},\ \pm \frac{3}{2}$
$\pm \frac{9}{2},\ \pm \frac{1}{3},\ \pm \frac{2}{3},\ \pm \frac{1}{4},$
$\pm \frac{3}{4},\ \pm \frac{9}{4},\ \pm \frac{1}{5},\ \pm \frac{2}{5},$
$\pm \frac{3}{5},\ \pm \frac{6}{5},\ \pm \frac{9}{5},\ \pm \frac{18}{5},$
$\pm \frac{1}{10},\ \pm \frac{3}{10},\ \pm \frac{9}{10},\ \pm \frac{1}{20}$

Descartes' Rule of Signs

# pos	# neg	# nonreal
2	1	0
0	1	2

Test $x = -\frac{1}{2}$:

$$\begin{array}{r|rrrr} -\frac{1}{2} & 20 & -44 & 9 & 18 \\ & & -10 & 27 & -18 \\ \hline & 20 & -54 & 36 & 0 \end{array}$$

$$20x^3 - 44x^2 + 9x + 18 = 0$$
$$\left(x + \tfrac{1}{2}\right)\left(20x^2 - 54x + 36\right) = 0$$
$$\left(x + \tfrac{1}{2}\right)(4x - 6)(5x - 6) = 0$$

Solution set: $\left\{-\frac{1}{2}, \frac{3}{2}, \frac{6}{5}\right\}$

32. Possible rational roots

$\pm 1,\ \pm 2,\ \pm 3,\ \pm 5,$
$\pm 6,\ \pm 10,\ \pm 15,\ \pm 30$
$\pm \frac{1}{2},\ \pm \frac{3}{2},\ \pm \frac{5}{2},\ \pm \frac{15}{2},$
$\pm \frac{1}{3},\ \pm \frac{2}{3},\ \pm \frac{5}{3},\ \pm \frac{10}{3},$
$\pm \frac{1}{4},\ \pm \frac{3}{4},\ \pm \frac{5}{4},\ \pm \frac{15}{4},$
$\pm \frac{1}{6},\ \pm \frac{5}{6},\ \pm \frac{1}{8},\ \pm \frac{3}{8},$
$\pm \frac{5}{8},\ \pm \frac{15}{8},\ \pm \frac{1}{12},\ \pm \frac{5}{12},$
$\pm \frac{1}{24},\ \pm \frac{5}{24}$

Descartes' Rule of Signs

# pos	# neg	# nonreal
3	0	0
1	0	2

Test $x = \frac{3}{2}$:

$$\begin{array}{r|rrrr} \frac{3}{2} & 24 & -82 & 89 & -30 \\ & & 36 & -69 & 30 \\ \hline & 24 & -46 & 20 & 0 \end{array}$$

$$24x^3 - 82x^2 + 89x - 30 = 0$$
$$\left(x - \tfrac{3}{2}\right)\left(24x^2 - 46x + 20\right) = 0$$
$$\left(x - \tfrac{3}{2}\right)(4x - 5)(6x - 4) = 0$$

Solution set: $\left\{\frac{3}{2}, \frac{5}{4}, \frac{2}{3}\right\}$

33. If $(1 + i)$ is a root, then so is $(1 - i)$, and $x - (1 + i)$ and $x - (1 - i)$ are factors. Then $[x - (1 + i)][x - (1 - i)] = x^2 - 2x + 2$ is a factor. Divide it out:

$$\begin{array}{r|l} & x - 3 \\ \hline x^2 - 2x + 2 & x^3 - 5x^2 + 8x - 6 \\ & \underline{x^3 - 2x^2 + 2x} \\ & - 3x^2 + 6x - 6 \\ & \underline{- 3x^2 + 6x - 6} \\ & \phantom{x^3 - 3x^2 + 6x - {}} 0 \end{array}$$

$$x^3 - 5x^2 + 8x - 6 = 0$$
$$\left(x^2 - 2x + 2\right)(x - 3) = 0$$

Solution set: $\{1 + i, 1 - i, 3\}$

34. If $(1+i)$ is a root, then so is $(1-i)$, and $x-(1+i)$ and $x-(1-i)$ are factors. Then $[x-(1+i)][x-(1-i)] = x^2-2x+2$ is a factor. Divide it out:

$$\begin{array}{r|l} & x + 2 \\ \hline x^2-2x+2 & x^3+0x^2-2x+4 \\ & x^3-2x^2+2x \\ \hline & 2x^2-4x+4 \\ & 2x^2-4x+4 \\ \hline & 0 \end{array}$$

$$x^3-2x+4=0$$
$$(x^2-2x+2)(x+2)=0$$
Solution set: $\{1+i, 1-i, -2\}$

35. If $(1+i)$ is a root, then so is $(1-i)$, and $x-(1+i)$ and $x-(1-i)$ are factors. Then $[x-(1+i)][x-(1-i)] = x^2-2x+2$ is a factor. Divide it out:

$$\begin{array}{r|l} & x^2 - 9 \\ \hline x^2-2x+2 & x^4-2x^3-7x^2+18x-18 \\ & x^4-2x^3+2x^2 \\ \hline & -9x^2+18x-18 \\ & -9x^2+18x-18 \\ \hline & 0 \end{array}$$

$$x^4-2x^3-7x^2+18x-18=0$$
$$(x^2-2x+2)(x^2-9)=0$$
$$(x^2-2x+2)(x+3)(x-3)=0$$
Solution set: $\{1+i, 1-i, -3, 3\}$

36. If $(1+i)$ is a root, then so is $(1-i)$, and $x-(1+i)$ and $x-(1-i)$ are factors. Then $[x-(1+i)][x-(1-i)] = x^2-2x+2$ is a factor. Divide it out:

$$\begin{array}{r|l} & x^2 - 4 \\ \hline x^2-2x+2 & x^4-2x^3-2x^2+8x-8 \\ & x^4-2x^3+2x^2 \\ \hline & -4x^2+8x-8 \\ & -4x^2+8x-8 \\ \hline & 0 \end{array}$$

$$x^4-2x^3-2x^2+8x-8=0$$
$$(x^2-2x+2)(x^2-4)=0$$
$$(x^2-2x+2)(x+2)(x-2)=0$$
Solution set: $\{1+i, 1-i, -2, 2\}$

37. Possible rational roots

$\pm 1, \pm 2, \pm 3, \pm 6,$
$\pm \frac{1}{3}, \pm \frac{2}{3}$

Descartes' Rule of Signs

# pos	# neg	# nonreal
1	2	0
1	0	2

Test $x=-1$:

$$\begin{array}{r|rrrr} -1 & 3 & -4 & -13 & -6 \\ & & -3 & 7 & 6 \\ \hline & 3 & -7 & -6 & 0 \end{array}$$

$$x^3-\frac{4}{3}x^2-\frac{13}{3}x-2=0$$
$$3x^3-4x^2-13x-6=0$$
$$(x+1)(3x^2-7x-6)=0$$
$$(x+1)(3x+2)(x-3)=0$$
Solution set: $\{-1, -\frac{2}{3}, 3\}$

38. Possible rational roots

$\pm 1, \pm 2, \pm 3, \pm 6,$
$\pm \frac{1}{2}, \pm \frac{3}{2}, \pm \frac{1}{3}, \pm \frac{2}{3},$
$\pm \frac{1}{6}$

Descartes' Rule of Signs

# pos	# neg	# nonreal
2	1	0
0	1	2

Test $x=3$:

$$\begin{array}{r|rrrr} 3 & 6 & -19 & 1 & 6 \\ & & 18 & -3 & -6 \\ \hline & 6 & -1 & -2 & 0 \end{array}$$

$$x^3-\frac{19}{6}x^2+\frac{1}{6}x+1=0$$
$$6x^3-19x^2+x+6=0$$
$$(x-3)(6x^2-x-2)=0$$
$$(x-3)(3x-2)(2x+1)=0$$
Solution set: $\{3, \frac{2}{3}, -\frac{1}{2}\}$

39.

$$x^{-5}-8x^{-4}+25x^{-3}-38x^{-2}+28x^{-1}-8=0$$
$$x^5\left(x^{-5}-8x^{-4}+25x^{-3}-38x^{-2}+28x^{-1}-8\right)=x^5(0)$$
$$1-8x+25x^2-38x^3+28x^4-8x^5=0$$

Possible rat. roots: $\pm 1,\ \pm\frac{1}{2},\ \pm\frac{1}{4},\ \pm\frac{1}{8}$

Descartes' Rule of Signs

# pos	# neg	# nonreal
5	0	0
3	0	2
1	0	4

$$8x^5-28x^4+38x^3-25x^2+8x-1=0$$
$$(x-1)\left(8x^4-20x^3+18x^2-7x+1\right)=0$$
$$(x-1)(x-1)\left(8x^3-12x^2+6x-1\right)=0$$
$$(x-1)(x-1)\left(x-\tfrac{1}{2}\right)\left(8x^2-8x+2\right)=0$$
$$(x-1)(x-1)\left(x-\tfrac{1}{2}\right)(4x-2)(2x-1)=0$$

Solution set: $\left\{1,1,\frac{1}{2},\frac{1}{2},\frac{1}{2}\right\}$

Test $x=1$:

1	8	−28	38	−25	8	−1
		8	−20	18	−7	1
	8	−20	18	−7	1	0

Test $x=1$:

1	8	−20	18	−7	1
		8	−12	6	−1
	8	−12	6	−1	0

Test $x=\frac{1}{2}$:

$\frac{1}{2}$	8	−12	6	−1
		4	−4	1
	8	−8	2	0

40.

$$1-x^{-1}-x^{-2}-2x^{-3}=0$$
$$x^3\left(1-x^{-1}-x^{-2}-2x^{-3}\right)=x^3(0)\Rightarrow x^3-x^2-x-2=0$$

Possible rat. roots: $\pm 1,\ \pm 2$

Descartes' Rule of Signs

# pos	# neg	# nonreal
1	2	0
1	0	2

Test $x=2$:

2	1	−1	−1	−2
		2	2	2
	1	1	1	0

$$x^3-x^2-x-2=0$$
$$(x-2)\left(x^2+x+1\right)=0$$

Use the quadratic formula on the second factor.

Sol. set: $\left\{2,-\frac{1}{2}+\frac{\sqrt{3}}{2}i,-\frac{1}{2}-\frac{\sqrt{3}}{2}i\right\}$

41. Let $x=R_1$. Then $x+10=R_2$ and $x+50=R_3$.

$$\frac{1}{R}=\frac{1}{R_1}+\frac{1}{R_2}+\frac{1}{R_3}$$
$$\frac{1}{6}=\frac{1}{x}+\frac{1}{x+10}+\frac{1}{x+50}$$
$$6x(x+10)(x+50)\cdot\frac{1}{6}=6x(x+10)(x+50)\left(\frac{1}{x}+\frac{1}{x+10}+\frac{1}{x+50}\right)$$
$$x(x+10)(x+50)=6(x+10)(x+50)+6x(x+50)+6x(x+10)$$
$$x^3+60x^2+500x=6x^2+360x+3000+6x^2+300x+6x^2+60x$$
$$x^3+42x^2-220x-3000=0$$
$$(x-10)\left(x^2+52x+300\right)=0$$

10	1	42	−220	−3000
		10	520	3000
	1	52	300	0

Use the quadratic formula on the second factor. The two solutions from that factor are negative. The only solution that makes sense is $x=10$. The resistances are 10, 20 and 60 ohms.

42. The volume is $(12-2x)(14-2x)x = 4x^3 - 52x^2 + 168x$.

$$4x^3 - 52x^2 + 168x = 160$$
$$4x^3 - 52x^2 + 168x - 160 = 0$$
$$4(x^3 - 13x^2 + 42x - 40) = 0$$
$$x^3 - 13x^2 + 42x - 40 = 0$$
$$(x-2)(x^2 - 11x + 20) = 0$$
$$(x-2)(x-2)(x-9) = 0$$

The only solution that makes sense is $x = 2$.
2 inch by 2 inch squares should be cut from the corners.

Test $x = 2$:

2	1	−13	42	−40
		2	−22	40
	1	−11	20	0

43. **Answers may vary.**

44. **Answers may vary.**

45. A coordinate of a point on the parabola has coordinates $(x, 16-x^2)$.
Thus, the area of the rectangle is $A = 2x(16-x^2) = 32x - 2x^3$.

$$32x - 2x^3 = 42$$
$$-2x^3 + 32x - 42 = 0$$
$$x^3 - 16x + 21 = 0$$
$$(x-3)(x^2 + 3x - 7) = 0$$

Using the quadratic formula on the second factor yields the solutions $x = \frac{-3 \pm \sqrt{37}}{2} \approx 1.54$ or -4.54.
The only solutions that make sense are $x = 3$ or $x = 1.54$.
Points: (3, 7) or (1.54, 13.63)

Test $x = 3$:

3	1	0	−16	21
		3	9	−21
	1	3	−7	0

46. A coordinate of a point on the curve has coordinates $(x, x^3 - 2x^2)$.
Thus, the area of the rectangle is $A = x(x^3 - 2x^2) = x^4 - 2x^3$.

$$x^4 - 2x^3 = 27$$
$$x^4 - 2x^3 - 27 = 0$$
$$(x-3)(x^3 + x^2 + 3x + 9) = 0$$

Since the coefficients of the second factor are all positive, Descartes' Rule of Signs indicates that there are no more positive solutions. Thus, $x = 3$: (3, 9).

Test $x = 3$:

3	1	−2	0	0	−27
		3	3	9	27
	1	1	3	9	0

47. $\sqrt{72a^3b^5c} = \sqrt{36a^2b^4}\sqrt{2abc} = 6ab^2\sqrt{2abc}$

48. $\frac{5a}{\sqrt{5a}} = \frac{5a\sqrt{5a}}{\sqrt{5a}\cdot\sqrt{5a}} = \frac{5a\sqrt{5a}}{5a} = \sqrt{5a}$

49. $\sqrt{18a^2b} + a\sqrt{50b} = \sqrt{9a^2}\sqrt{2b} + a\sqrt{25}\sqrt{2b} = 3a\sqrt{2b} + 5a\sqrt{2b} = 8a\sqrt{2b}$

50. $\left(\sqrt{3}+\sqrt{5b}\right)\left(\sqrt{12}-\sqrt{45b}\right) = \sqrt{36}-\sqrt{135b}+\sqrt{60b}-\sqrt{225b^2}$
$= 6-\sqrt{9}\sqrt{15b}+\sqrt{4}\sqrt{15b}-15b$
$= 6-3\sqrt{15b}+2\sqrt{15b}-15b = 6-\sqrt{15b}-15b$

51. $\dfrac{2}{\sqrt{3}-1} = \dfrac{2\left(\sqrt{3}+1\right)}{\left(\sqrt{3}-1\right)\left(\sqrt{3}+1\right)} = \dfrac{2\left(\sqrt{3}+1\right)}{\left(\sqrt{3}\right)^2-1^2} = \dfrac{2\left(\sqrt{3}+1\right)}{3-1} = \dfrac{2\left(\sqrt{3}+1\right)}{2} = \sqrt{3}+1$

52. $\dfrac{\sqrt{11}+\sqrt{x}}{\sqrt{11}-\sqrt{x}} = \dfrac{\left(\sqrt{11}+\sqrt{x}\right)\left(\sqrt{11}+\sqrt{x}\right)}{\left(\sqrt{11}-\sqrt{x}\right)\left(\sqrt{11}+\sqrt{x}\right)} = \dfrac{11+2\sqrt{11x}+x}{11-x}$

Exercise 5.4 (page 413)

1. $P(a)$ and $P(b)$

2. $P(r)=0$

3. x_l and x_r

4. continuous

5. $P(x)=2x^2+x-3$
$P(-2)=3;\ P(-1)=-2$
Thus, there is a root between -2 and -1.

6. $P(x)=2x^3+17x^2+31x-20$
$P(-1)=-36;\ P(2)=126$
Thus, there is a root between -1 and 2.

7. $P(x)=3x^3-11x^2-14x$
$P(4)=-40;\ P(5)=30$
Thus, there is a root between 4 and 5.

8. $P(x)=2x^3-3x^2+2x-3$
$P(1)=-2;\ P(2)=5$
Thus, there is a root between 1 and 2.

9. $P(x)=x^4-8x^2+15$
$P(1)=8;\ P(2)=-1$
Thus, there is a root between 1 and 2.

10. $P(x)=x^4-8x^2+15$
$P(2)=-1;\ P(3)=24$
Thus, there is a root between 2 and 3.

11. $30x^3+10=61x^2+39x$
$30x^3-61x^2-39x+10=0$
$P(x)=30x^3-61x^2-39x+10$
$P(2)=-72;\ P(3)=154$
Thus, there is a root between 2 and 3.

12. $30x^3+10=61x^2+39x$
$30x^3-61x^2-39x+10=0$
$P(x)=30x^3-61x^2-39x+10$
$P(-1)=-42;\ P(0)=10$
Thus, there is a root between -1 and 0.

13. $30x^3+10=61x^2+39x$
$30x^3-61x^2-39x+10=0$
$P(x)=30x^3-61x^2-39x+10$
$P(0)=10;\ P(1)=-60$
Thus, there is a root between 0 and 1.

14. $P(x)=5x^3-9x^2-4x+9$
$P(-1)=-1;\ P(2)=5$
Thus, there is a root between -1 and 2.

15. $P(x) = x^2 - 3$. Note that $P(1) = -2$ and $P(2) = 1$. There is a root between 1 and 2.

STEP	x_l	c	x_r	$P(x_l)$	$P(x_c)$	$P(x_r)$
0	1	1.5	2	−2.0	−0.75	1.0
1	1.5	1.75	2	−0.75	0.0625	1.0
2	1.5	1.625	1.75	−0.75	−0.3594	0.0625
3	1.625	1.6875	1.75	−0.3594	−0.1523	0.0625
4	1.6875	1.71875	1.75	−0.1523	−0.0459	0.0625
5	1.71875	1.734375	1.75			

To the nearest tenth, the solution is $x = 1.7$.

16. $P(x) = x^2 - 3$. Note that $P(-2) = 1$ and $P(-1) = -2$. There is a root between -2 and -1.

STEP	x_l	c	x_r	$P(x_l)$	$P(x_c)$	$P(x_r)$
0	−2	−1.5	−1	1.0	−0.75	−2.0
1	−2	−1.75	−1.5	1.0	0.0625	−0.75
2	−1.75	−1.625	−1.5	0.0625	−0.3594	−0.75
3	−1.75	−1.6875	−1.625	0.0625	−0.1523	−0.3594
4	−1.75	−1.71875	−1.6875	0.0625	−0.0459	−0.1523
5	−1.75	−1.734375	−1.71875			

To the nearest tenth, the solution is $x = -1.7$.

17. $P(x) = x^2 - 5$. Note that $P(-3) = 4$ and $P(-2) = -1$. There is a root between -3 and -2.

STEP	x_l	c	x_r	$P(x_l)$	$P(x_c)$	$P(x_r)$
0	−3	−2.5	−2	4.0	1.25	−1.0
1	−2.5	−2.25	−2	1.25	0.0625	−1.0
2	−2.25	−2.125	−2	0.0625	−0.4844	−1.0
3	−2.25	−2.1875	−2.125	0.0625	−0.2148	−0.4844
4	−2.25	−2.21875	−2.1875	0.0625	−0.0771	−0.2148
5	−2.25	−2.234375	−2.21875			

To the nearest tenth, the solution is $x = -2.2$.

18. $P(x) = x^2 - 5$. Note that $P(2) = -1$ and $P(3) = 4$. There is a root between 2 and 3.

STEP	x_l	c	x_r	$P(x_l)$	$P(x_c)$	$P(x_r)$
0	2	2.5	3	−1.0	1.25	4.0
1	2	2.25	2.5	−1.0	0.0625	1.25
2	2	2.125	2.25	−1.0	−0.4844	0.0625
3	2.125	2.1875	2.25	−0.4844	−0.2148	0.0625
4	2.1875	2.21875	2.25	−0.2148	−0.0771	0.0625
5	2.21875	2.234375	2.25			

To the nearest tenth, the solution is $x = 2.2$.

19. $P(x) = x^3 - x^2 - 2$. Note that $P(1) = -2$ and $P(2) = 2$. There is a root between 1 and 2.

STEP	x_l	c	x_r	$P(x_l)$	$P(x_c)$	$P(x_r)$
0	1	1.5	2	−2.0	−0.875	2.0
1	1.5	1.75	2	−0.875	0.2969	2.0
2	1.5	1.625	1.75	−0.875	−0.3496	0.2969
3	1.625	1.6875	1.75	−0.3496	−0.0422	0.2969
4	1.6875	1.71875	1.75	−0.0422	0.1233	0.2969
5	1.6875	1.703125	1.71875			

To the nearest tenth, the solution is $x = 1.7$.

20. $P(x) = x^3 - x + 2$. Note that $P(-2) = -4$ and $P(-1) = 2$. There is a root between -2 and -1.

STEP	x_l	c	x_r	$P(x_l)$	$P(x_c)$	$P(x_r)$
0	−2	−1.5	−1	−4.0	−0.125	2.0
1	−1.5	−1.25	−1	−0.125	1.2969	2.0
2	−1.5	−1.375	−1.25	−0.125	0.7754	1.2969
3	−1.5	−1.4375	−1.375	−0.125	0.4670	0.7754
4	−1.5	−1.46875	−1.4375	−0.125	0.3003	0.4670
5	−1.5	−1.484375	−1.46875			

To the nearest tenth, the solution is $x = -1.5$.

21. $P(x) = 3x^4 + 3x^3 - x^2 - 4x - 4$. Note that $P(-2) = 24$ and $P(-1) = -1$.
There is a root between -2 and -1.

STEP	x_l	c	x_r	$P(x_l)$	$P(x_c)$	$P(x_r)$
0	−2	−1.5	−1	24.0	4.8125	−1.0
1	−1.5	−1.25	−1	4.8125	0.9023	−1.0
2	−1.25	−1.125	−1	0.9023	−0.2317	−1.0
3	−1.25	−1.1875	−1.125	0.9023	0.2818	−0.2317
4	−1.1875	−1.15625	−1.125	0.2818	0.0127	−0.2317
5	−1.15625	−1.140625	−1.125	0.0127	−0.1125	−0.2317
6	−1.15625	−1.1484375	−1.140625	0.0127	−0.0507	−0.1125
7	−1.15625	−1.15234375	−1.1484375	0.0127	−0.0192	−0.0507
8	−1.15625	−1.154296875	−1.15234375			

To the nearest tenth, the solution is $x = -1.2$.

22. $P(x) = x^5 + x^4 - 4x^3 - 4x^2 - 5x - 5$. Note that $P(2) = -15$ and $P(3) = 160$. There is a root between 2 and 3.

STEP	x_l	c	x_r	$P(x_l)$	$P(x_c)$	$P(x_r)$
0	2	2.5	3	−15.0	31.7188	160.0
1	2	2.25	2.5	−15.0	1.2314	31.7188
2	2	2.125	2.25	−15.0	−8.3488	1.2314
3	2.125	2.1875	2.25	−8.3488	−3.9618	1.2314
4	2.1875	2.21875	2.25	−3.9618	−1.4708	1.2314
5	2.21875	2.234375	2.25	−1.4708	−0.1467	1.2314
6	2.234375	2.2421875	2.25	−0.1467	0.5355	1.2314
7	2.234275	2.23823125	2.2421875			

To the nearest tenth, the solution is $x = 2.2$.

23. Find the x-coordinates of any x-intercepts:

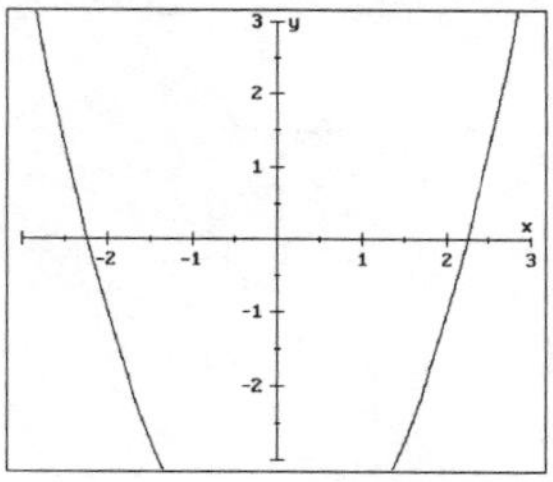

$\{-2.2, 2.2\}$

24. Find the x-coordinates of any x-intercepts:

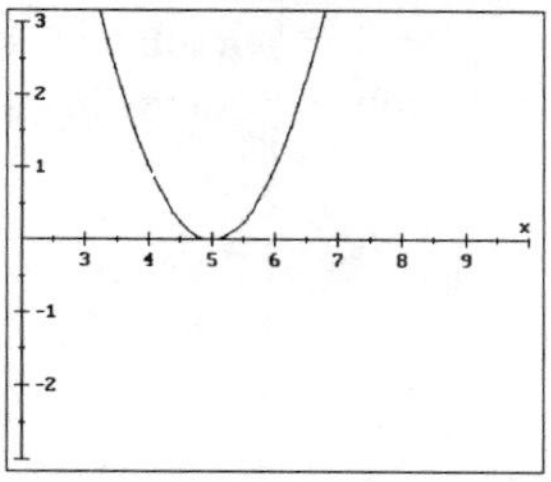

$\{5\}$: Bisection fails since the solution cannot be bracketed by a negative y-coordinate and a positive y-coordinate.

25. Find the x-coordinates of any x-intercepts:

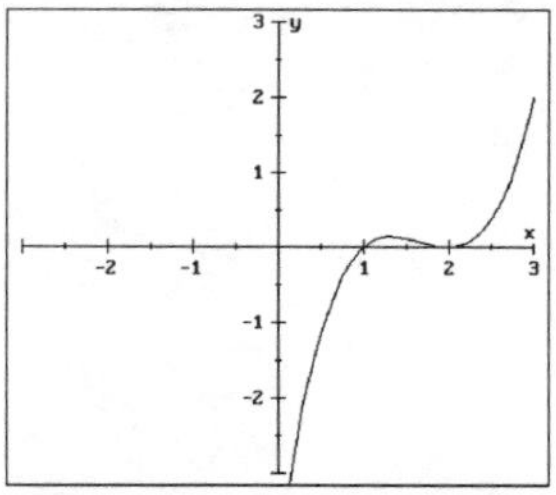

$\{1, 2\}$: Bisection fails for $x = 2$ since the solution cannot be bracketed by a negative y-coordinate and a positive y-coordinate.

26. Find the x-coordinates of any x-intercepts:

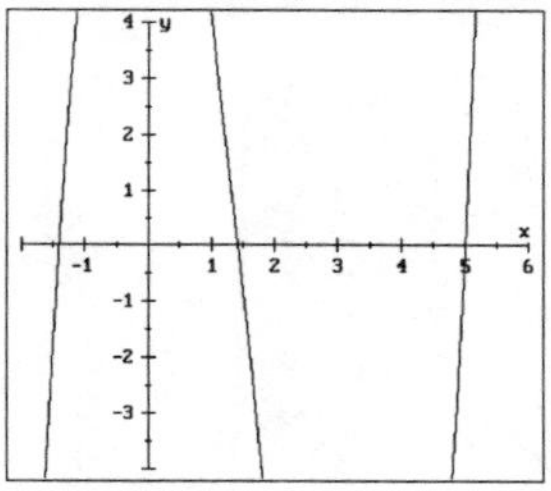

$\{-1.4, 1.4, 5\}$

27. A point on the graph has coordinates (x, x^3). Then the distance to the origin is found by the distance formula:

$$d = \sqrt{(x-0)^2 + (x^3-0)^2} = \sqrt{x^2 + x^6} = 1$$

$$\sqrt{x^2 + x^6} = 1$$

$$x^2 + x^6 = 1$$

$x^2 + x^6 - 1 = 0$: Graph and find intercepts.
The x-coordinates are about 0.83 and -0.83.
Find the y-coordinates using $y = x^3$.
The points are $(0.83, 0.56)$ and $(-0.83, -0.56)$.

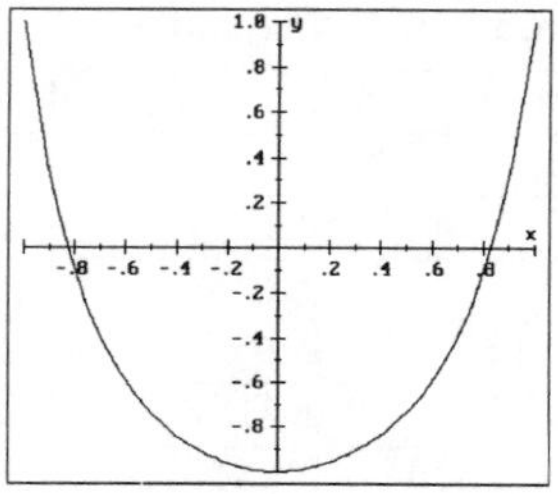

28. Let $x =$ the length. Then $x - 2 =$ the height and $x - 5 =$ the width.

$$x(x-2)(x-5) = 170$$

$x^3 - 7x^2 + 10x - 170 = 0$: Graph and find intercepts.
The x-coordinate is about 8.2, so the height is abut 3.2 feet.

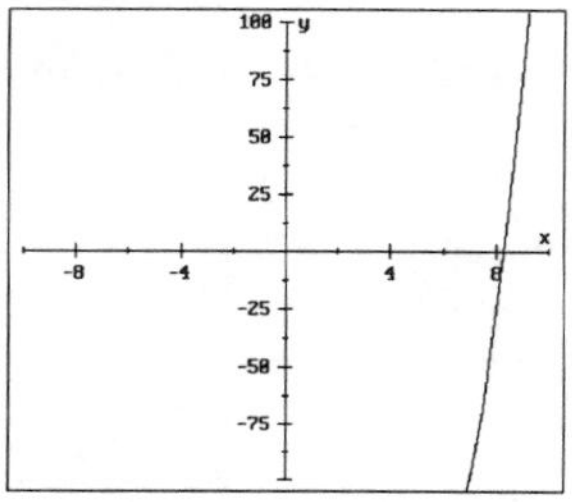

29. **Answers may vary.**

30. **Answers may vary.**

31. $y = \dfrac{5x-3}{x^2-4} = \dfrac{5x-3}{(x+2)(x-2)}$
vertical: $x = -2$, $x = 2$
horizontal: $y = 0$
slant: none

32. $y = \dfrac{5x^2-3}{x^2-25} = \dfrac{5x^2-3}{(x+5)(x-5)}$
vertical: $x = -5$, $x = 5$
horizontal: $y = \dfrac{5}{1} \Rightarrow y = 5$
slant: none

33. $y = \dfrac{x^2}{x-2} = x + 2 + \dfrac{4}{x-2}$
vertical: $x = 2$
horizontal: none
slant: $y = x + 2$

34. $y = \dfrac{x+1}{x^2+1}$
vertical: none
horizontal: $y = 0$
slant: none

Chapter 5 Summary (page 416)

1. **a.** $P(1) = 4(1)^4 + 2(1)^3 - 3(1)^2 - 2 = 1 \Rightarrow$ The remainder is 1.

b. $P(2) = 4(2)^4 + 2(2)^3 - 3(2)^2 - 2 = 66 \Rightarrow$ The remainder is 66.

c. $P(-3) = 4(-3)^4 + 2(-3)^3 - 3(-3)^2 - 2 = 241 \Rightarrow$ The remainder is 241.

d. $P(-2) = 4(-2)^4 + 2(-2)^3 - 3(-2)^2 - 2 = 34 \Rightarrow$ The remainder is 34.

2. **a.** $P(2) = (2)^3 + 4(2)^2 - 2(2) + 4 = 24 \Rightarrow$ The remainder is 24. $\Rightarrow$ not a factor

b. $P(-3) = 2(-3)^4 + 10(-3)^3 + 4(-3)^2 + 7(-3) + 21 = -83 \Rightarrow$ The remainder is -83. $\Rightarrow$ not a factor

c. $P(5) = (5)^5 - 3125 = 0 \Rightarrow$ The remainder is 0. $\Rightarrow$ factor

d. $P(6) = (6)^5 - 6(6)^4 - 4(6) + 24 = 0 \Rightarrow$ The remainder is 0. $\Rightarrow$ factor

3. **a.** $$2(x+1)(x-2)\left(x-\tfrac{3}{2}\right) = 2(x^2 - x - 2)\left(x - \tfrac{3}{2}\right) = 2\left(x^3 - \tfrac{5}{2}x^2 - \tfrac{1}{2}x + 3\right) = 2x^3 - 5x^2 - x + 6$$

b. $$2(x-1)(x+3)\left(x-\tfrac{1}{2}\right) = 2(x^2 + 2x - 3)\left(x - \tfrac{1}{2}\right) = 2\left(x^3 + \tfrac{3}{2}x^2 - 4x + \tfrac{3}{2}\right) = 2x^3 + 3x^2 - 8x + 3$$

c. $$(x-2)(x+5)(x-i)(x+i) = \left(x^2 + 3x - 10\right)\left(x^2 - i^2\right) = \left(x^2 + 3x - 10\right)\left(x^2 + 1\right) = x^4 + 3x^3 - 9x^2 + 3x - 10$$

d. $$(x+3)(x-2)(x-i)(x+i) = \left(x^2 + x - 6\right)\left(x^2 - i^2\right) = \left(x^2 + x - 6\right)\left(x^2 + 1\right) = x^4 + x^3 - 5x^2 + x - 6$$

4. **a.**

3	3	0	2	3	7
		9	27	87	270
	3	9	29	90	277

quotient: $3x^3 + 9x^2 + 29x + 90$
remainder: 277

b.

2	2	0	−3	3	−1
		4	8	10	26
	2	4	5	13	25

quotient: $2x^3 + 4x^2 + 5x + 13$
remainder: 25

c.

−2	5	−4	3	−2	1	−1
		−10	28	−62	128	−258
	5	−14	31	−64	129	−259

quotient: $5x^4 - 14x^3 + 31x^2 - 64x + 129$
remainder: -259

d.

−1	4	2	−1	3	2	1
		−4	2	−1	−2	0
	4	−2	1	2	0	1

quotient: $4x^4 - 2x^3 + x^2 + 2x$
remainder: 1

5. **a.** $3x^6 - 4x^5 + 3x + 2 = 0$
6 roots

b. $2x^6 - 5x^4 + 5x^3 - 4x + x - 12 = 0$
6 roots

c. $3x^{65} - 4x^{50} + 3x^{17} + 2x = 0$
65 roots

d. $x^{1984} - 12 = 0$
1984 roots

6. **a.** $2 - i$ is also a root.

b. $-i = 0 - i$, so $0 + i = i$ is also a root.

7. **a.** $P(x) = 3x^4 + 2x^3 - 4x + 2$: 2 sign variations $\Rightarrow$ 2 or 0 positive roots

$P(-x) = 3(-x)^4 + 2(-x)^3 - 4(-x) + 2$

$= 3x^4 - 2x^3 + 4x + 2$: 2 sign variations $\Rightarrow$ 2 or 0 negative roots

# pos	# neg	# nonreal
2	2	0
2	0	2
0	2	2
0	0	4

b. $P(x) = 2x^4 - 3x^3 + 5x^2 + x - 5$: 3 sign variations $\Rightarrow$ 3 or 1 positive roots

$P(-x) = 2(-x)^4 - 3(-x)^3 + 5(-x)^2 + (-x) - 5$

$= 2x^4 + 3x^3 + 5x^2 - x - 5$: 1 sign variation $\Rightarrow$ 1 negative root

# pos	# neg	# nonreal
3	1	0
1	1	2

c. $4x^5 + 3x^4 + 2x^3 + x^2 + x = 7$

$4x^5 + 3x^4 + 2x^3 + x^2 + x - 7 = 0$

$P(x) = 4x^5 + 3x^4 + 2x^3 + x^2 + x - 7$: 1 sign variation $\Rightarrow$ 1 positive root

$P(-x) = 4(-x)^5 + 3(-x)^4 + 2(-x)^3 + (-x)^2 + (-x) - 7$

$= -4x^5 + 3x^4 - 2x^3 + x^2 - x - 7$: 4 sign variations $\Rightarrow$ 4 or 2 or 0 negative roots

# pos	# neg	# nonreal
1	4	0
1	2	2
1	0	4

d. $P(x) = 3x^7 - 4x^5 + 3x^3 + x - 4$: 3 sign variations $\Rightarrow$ 3 or 1 positive roots

$P(-x) = 3(-x)^7 - 4(-x)^5 + 3(-x)^3 + (-x) - 4$

$= -3x^7 + 4x^5 - 3x^3 - x - 4$: 2 sign variations $\Rightarrow$ 2 or 0 negative roots

# pos	# neg	# nonreal
3	2	2
3	0	4
1	2	4
1	0	6

e. $P(x) = x^4 + x^2 + 24{,}567$: 0 sign variations $\Rightarrow$ 0 positive roots

$P(-x) = (-x)^4 + (-x)^2 + 24{,}567$

$= x^4 + x^2 + 24{,}567$: 0 sign variations $\Rightarrow$ 0 negative roots

# pos	# neg	# nonreal
0	0	4

f. $P(x) = -x^7 - 5$: 0 sign variations $\Rightarrow$ 0 positive roots

$P(-x) = -(-x)^7 - 5$

$= x^7 - 5$: 1 sign variation $\Rightarrow$ 1 negative root

# pos	# neg	# nonreal
0	1	6

8. a. $P(x) = 5x^3 - 4x^2 - 2x + 4$

$$\begin{array}{r|rrrr} 2 & 5 & -4 & -2 & 4 \\ & & 10 & 12 & 20 \\ \hline & 5 & 6 & 10 & 24 \end{array}$$

Upper bound: 2

$$\begin{array}{r|rrrr} -1 & 5 & -4 & -2 & 4 \\ & & -5 & 9 & -7 \\ \hline & 5 & -9 & 7 & -3 \end{array}$$

Lower bound: -1

b. $P(x) = x^4 + 3x^3 - 5x^2 - 9x + 1$

$$\begin{array}{r|rrrrr} 2 & 1 & 3 & -5 & -9 & 1 \\ & & 2 & 10 & 10 & 2 \\ \hline & 1 & 5 & 5 & 1 & 3 \end{array}$$

Upper bound: 2

$$\begin{array}{r|rrrrr} -5 & 1 & 3 & -5 & -9 & 1 \\ & & -5 & 10 & -25 & 170 \\ \hline & 1 & -2 & 5 & -34 & 171 \end{array}$$

Lower bound: -5

9. a. Possible rational roots

$\pm 1, \pm 2, \pm 3, \pm 5,$
$\pm 6, \pm 10, \pm 15, \pm 30,$
$\pm \frac{1}{2}, \pm \frac{3}{2}, \pm \frac{5}{2}, \pm \frac{15}{2}$

Test $x = -2$:

$$\begin{array}{r|rrrr} -2 & 2 & 17 & 41 & 30 \\ & & -4 & -26 & -30 \\ \hline & 2 & 13 & 15 & 0 \end{array}$$

Descartes' Rule of Signs

# pos	# neg	# nonreal
0	3	0
0	1	2

$2x^3 + 17x^2 + 41x + 30 = 0$

$(x+2)\left(2x^2 + 13x + 15\right) = 0$

$(x+2)(2x+3)(x+5) = 0$

Solution set: $\left\{-2, -\frac{3}{2}, -5\right\}$

b. Possible rational roots

$\pm 1, \pm \frac{1}{3}$

Test $x = \frac{1}{3}$:

$$\begin{array}{r|rrrr} \frac{1}{3} & 3 & 2 & 2 & -1 \\ & & 1 & 1 & 1 \\ \hline & 3 & 3 & 3 & 0 \end{array}$$

Descartes' Rule of Signs

# pos	# neg	# nonreal
1	2	0
1	0	2

$3x^3 + 2x^2 + 2x - 1 = 0$

$\left(x - \frac{1}{3}\right)\left(3x^2 + 3x + 3\right) = 0$

$3x^2 + 3x + 3$ does not factor rationally.

Rational solutions: $\left\{\frac{1}{3}\right\}$

c. Possible rat. roots

$\pm 1, \pm 2, \pm 3, \pm 4, \pm 6, \pm 9, \pm 12, \pm 18, \pm 36, \pm \frac{1}{2}, \pm \frac{3}{2}, \pm \frac{9}{2}, \pm \frac{1}{4}, \pm \frac{3}{4}, \pm \frac{9}{4}$

Descartes' Rule of Signs

# pos	# neg	# nonreal
2	2	0
2	0	2
0	2	2
0	0	4

$$4x^4 - 25x^2 + 36 = 0$$
$$(x-2)\left(4x^3 + 8x^2 - 9x - 18\right) = 0$$
$$(x-2)(x+2)\left(4x^2 - 9\right) = 0$$
$$(x-2)(x+2)(2x+3)(2x-3) = 0$$

Solution set: $\left\{2, -2, -\frac{3}{2}, \frac{3}{2}\right\}$

Test $x = 2$:

$$\begin{array}{r|rrrrr} 2 & 4 & 0 & -25 & 0 & 36 \\ & & 8 & 16 & -18 & -36 \\ \hline & 4 & 8 & -9 & -18 & 0 \end{array}$$

Test $x = -2$:

$$\begin{array}{r|rrrr} -2 & 4 & 8 & -9 & -18 \\ & & -8 & 0 & 18 \\ \hline & 4 & 0 & -9 & 0 \end{array}$$

d. Possible rat. roots

$\pm 1, \pm 2, \pm 4, \pm 8, \pm 16, \pm 32, \pm \frac{1}{2}$

Descartes' Rule of Signs

# pos	# neg	# nonreal
2	2	0
2	0	2
0	2	2
0	0	4

$$2x^4 - 11x^3 - 6x^2 + 64x + 32 = 0$$
$$(x-4)\left(2x^3 - 3x^2 - 18x - 8\right) = 0$$
$$(x-4)(x-4)\left(2x^2 + 5x + 2\right) = 0$$
$$(x-4)(x-4)(2x+1)(x+2) = 0$$

Solution set: $\left\{4, 4, -\frac{1}{2}, -2\right\}$

Test $x = 4$:

$$\begin{array}{r|rrrrr} 4 & 2 & -11 & -6 & 64 & 32 \\ & & 8 & -12 & -72 & -32 \\ \hline & 2 & -3 & -18 & -8 & 0 \end{array}$$

Test $x = 4$:

$$\begin{array}{r|rrrr} 4 & 2 & -3 & -18 & -8 \\ & & 8 & 20 & 8 \\ \hline & 2 & 5 & 2 & 0 \end{array}$$

10. **a.** $P(x) = 5x^3 + 37x^2 + 59x + 18$
$P(-1) = -9$; $P(0) = 18$

b. $P(x) = 6x^3 - x^2 - 10x - 3$
$P(1) = -8$; $P(2) = 21$

11. **a.** $P(x) = x^3 - 2x^2 - 9x - 2$. Note that $P(4) = -6$ and $P(5) = 28$.
There is a root between 4 and 5.

STEP	x_l	c	x_r	$P(x_l)$	$P(x_c)$	$P(x_r)$
0	4	4.5	5	−8.0	8.125	21.0
1	4	4.25	4.5	−8.0	0.3906	8.125
2	4	4.125	4.25	−8.0	−2.9668	0.3906
3	4.125	4.1875	4.25	−2.9668	−1.3293	0.3906
4	4.1875	4.21875	4.25	−1.3293	−0.4798	0.3906
5	4.21875	4.234375	4.25	−0.4798	−0.0472	0.3906
6	4.234375	4.2421875	2.25	−0.0472	0.1711	0.3906
7	4.234275	4.23823125	4.2421875			

To the nearest tenth, the solution is $x = 4.2$.

b. $P(x) = 6x^2 - 13x - 5$. Note that $P(2) = -7$ and $P(3) = 10$.
There is a root between 2 and 3.

STEP	x_l	c	x_r	$P(x_l)$	$P(x_c)$	$P(x_r)$
0	2	2.5	3	−7.0	0	10.0

The solution is exactly $x = 2.5$.

12. **a.** Find the x-coordinates of any positive x-intercepts:

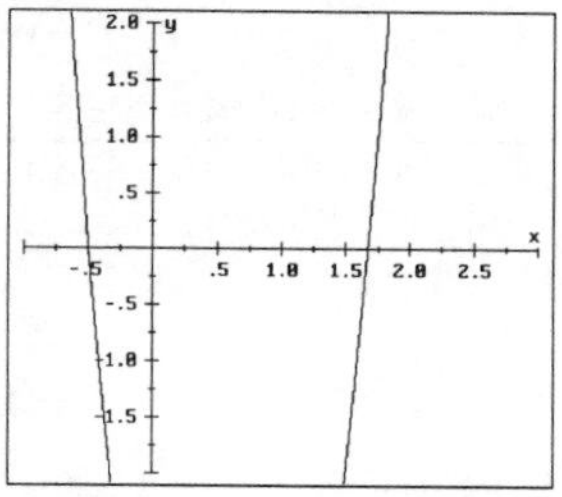

$x = 1.67$

b. Find the x-coordinates of any positive x-intercepts:

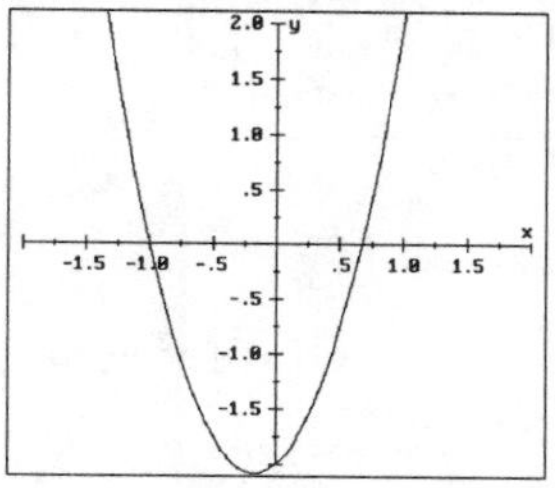

$x = 0.67$

13. Let $x =$ the length of the shortest panel. Then $x + 2$ and $x + 5$ are the lengths of the other panels. Since each panel has an area of 60, the widths are $\frac{60}{x}$, $\frac{60}{x+2}$ and $\frac{60}{x+5}$, respectively.

$$15 = \frac{60}{x} + \frac{60}{x+2} + \frac{60}{x+5}$$
$$x(x+2)(x+5)(15) = x(x+2)(x+5)\left(\frac{60}{x} + \frac{60}{x+2} + \frac{60}{x+5}\right)$$
$$15x(x+2)(x+5) = 60(x+2)(x+5) + 60x(x+5) + 60x(x+2)$$
$$15x^3 + 105x^2 + 150x = 60x^2 + 420x + 600 + 60x^2 + 300x + 60x^2 + 120x$$
$$15x^3 - 75x^2 - 690x - 600 = 0$$
$$15\left(x^3 - 5x^2 - 46x - 40\right) = 0$$
$$x^3 - 5x^2 - 46x - 40 = 0$$
$$(x-10)\left(x^2 + 5x + 4\right) = 0$$
$$(x-10)(x+4)(x+1) = 0$$

Test $x = 10$:

10	1	−5	−46	−40
		10	50	40
	1	5	4	0

The positive solution $x = 10$ is the only one that makes sense.
The dimensions are 10 m by 6 m, 12 m by 5 m, and 15 m by 4 m.

14. Let $x =$ the radius. Then $x + 3$ is the height.

$$\pi r^2 h = V$$
$$r^2 h = \frac{V}{\pi}$$
$$x^2(x+3) = \frac{19000}{\pi}$$
$$x^3 + 3x^2 = 6047.89$$
$$x^3 + 3x^2 - 6047.89 = 0$$

Graph $y = x^3 + 3x^2 - 6047.89$ and find the x-coordinates of any x-intercepts:

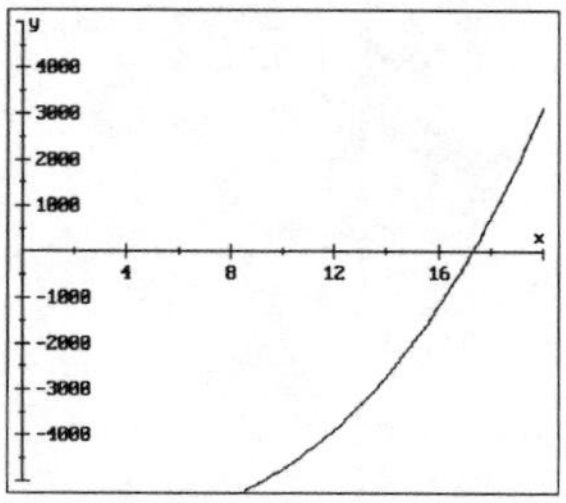

The radius should be about 17.27 feet.

Chapter 5 Test (page 419)

1.
$$\begin{array}{r|rrrr} 2 & 3 & 0 & -9 & -5 \\ & & 6 & 12 & 6 \\ \hline & 3 & 6 & 3 & 1 \end{array}$$
$P(2) = 1$

2.
$$\begin{array}{r|rrrrrr} -2 & 1 & 0 & 0 & 0 & 0 & 2 \\ & & -2 & 4 & -8 & 16 & -32 \\ \hline & 1 & -2 & 4 & -8 & 16 & -30 \end{array}$$
$P(-2) = -30$

3. $(x-5)(x+1)(x-0) = (x^2-4x-5)x = x^3 - 4x^2 - 5x$

4. $(x-i)(x+i)\left(x-\sqrt{3}\right)\left(x+\sqrt{3}\right) = (x^2-i^2)(x^2-3) = (x^2+1)(x^2-3) = x^4 - 2x^2 - 3$

5.
$$\begin{array}{r|rrrr} 1 & 3 & -2 & 0 & 4 \\ & & 3 & 1 & 1 \\ \hline & 3 & 1 & 1 & 5 \end{array}$$
$P(1) = 5$

6.
$$\begin{array}{r|rrrr} -2 & 3 & -2 & 0 & 4 \\ & & -6 & 16 & -32 \\ \hline & 3 & -8 & 16 & -28 \end{array}$$
$P(-2) = -28$

7.
$$\begin{array}{r|rrrr} -\frac{1}{3} & 3 & -2 & 0 & 4 \\ & & -1 & 1 & -\frac{1}{3} \\ \hline & 3 & 1 & 1 & \frac{11}{3} \end{array}$$
$P\left(-\frac{1}{3}\right) = \frac{11}{3}$

8.
$$\begin{array}{r|rrrr} i & 3 & -2 & 0 & 4 \\ & & 3i & -3-2i & 2-3i \\ \hline & 3 & -2+3i & -3-2i & 6-3i \end{array}$$
$P(i) = 6 - 3i$

9.
$$\begin{array}{r|rrrr} 2 & 2 & -3 & -4 & -1 \\ & & 4 & 2 & -4 \\ \hline & 2 & 1 & -2 & -5 \end{array}$$
$2x^3 - 3x^2 - 4x - 1 = (x-2)\left(2x^2 + x - 2\right) - 5$

10.
$$\begin{array}{r|rrrr} -1 & 2 & -3 & -4 & -1 \\ & & -2 & 5 & -1 \\ \hline & 2 & -5 & 1 & -2 \end{array}$$
$2x^3 - 3x^2 - 4x - 1 = (x+1)\left(2x^2 - 5x + 1\right) - 2$

11.
$$\begin{array}{r|rrr} 5 & 2 & -7 & -15 \\ & & 10 & 15 \\ \hline & 2 & 3 & 0 \end{array}$$
$2x + 3$

12.
$$\begin{array}{r|rrrr} -2 & 3 & 7 & 2 & 0 \\ & & -6 & -2 & 0 \\ \hline & 3 & 1 & 0 & 0 \end{array}$$
$3x^2 + x$

13. If i is a root, then $-i$ is a root also:
$$\begin{aligned} (x-2)(x-i)(x+i) &= 0 \\ (x-2)\left(x^2-i^2\right) &= 0 \\ (x-2)\left(x^2+1\right) &= 0 \\ x^3 - 2x^2 + x - 2 &= 0 \end{aligned}$$

14. If $2+i$ is a root, then $2-i$ is a root also:

$$(x-1)[x-(2+i)][x-(2-i)]=0$$
$$(x-1)\left[x^2-(2-i)x-(2+i)x+(2+i)(2-i)\right]=0$$
$$(x-1)\left[x^2-2x+ix-2x-ix+4-i^2\right]=0$$
$$(x-1)\left[x^2-4x+5\right]=0$$
$$x^3-5x^2+9x-5=0$$

15. $P(x)=3x^5-2x^4+2x^2-x-3$: 3 sign variations $\Rightarrow$ 3 or 1 positive roots

$P(-x)=3(-x)^5-2(-x)^4+2(-x)^2-(-x)-3$

$\quad =-3x^5-2x^4+2x^2+x-4$: 2 sign variations $\Rightarrow$ 2 or 0 negative roots

# pos	# neg	# nonreal
3	2	0
3	0	2
1	2	2
1	0	4

16. $P(x)=2x^3-5x^2-2x-1$: 1 sign variation $\Rightarrow$ 1 positive root

$P(-x)=2(-x)^3-5(-x)^2-2(-x)-1$

$\quad =-2x^3-5x^2+2x-1$: 2 sign variations $\Rightarrow$ 2 or 0 negative roots

# pos	# neg	# nonreal
1	2	0
1	0	2

17. $P(x)=x^5-x^4-5x^3+5x^2+4x-5$

3	1	−1	−5	5	4	−5
		3	6	3	24	84
	1	2	1	8	28	79

Upper bound: 3

−3	1	−1	−5	5	4	−5
		−3	12	−21	48	−156
	1	−4	7	−16	52	−161

Lower bound: -3

18. $P(x)=2x^3-11x^2+10x+3$

6	2	−11	10	3
		12	6	96
	2	1	16	99

Upper bound: 6

−1	2	−11	10	3
		−2	13	−23
	2	−13	23	−20

Lower bound: -1

19. Possible rational roots

$\pm 1,\ \pm 2,\ \pm 3,\ \pm 6,\ \pm\frac{1}{2},\ \pm\frac{3}{2}$

Descartes' Rule of Signs

# pos	# neg	# nonreal
1	2	0
1	0	2

Test $x=2$:

2	2	3	−11	−6
		4	14	6
	2	7	3	0

$$2x^3+3x^2-11x-6=0$$
$$(x-2)\left(2x^2+7x+3\right)=0$$
$$(x-2)(2x+1)(x+3)=0$$

Solution set: $\left\{2,\ -\frac{1}{2},\ -3\right\}$

20. $P(x) = x^2 - 11$. Note that $P(3) = -2$ and $P(4) = 5$. There is a root between 3 and 4.

STEP	x_l	c	x_r	$P(x_l)$	$P(x_c)$	$P(x_r)$
0	3	3.5	4	−2.0	1.25	5.0
1	3	3.25	3.5	−2.0	−0.4375	1.25
2	3.25	3.375	3.5	−0.4375	0.3906	1.25
3	3.25	3.3125	3.375	−0.4375	−0.0273	0.3906
4	3.3125	3.34375	3.375			

To the nearest tenth, the solution is $x = 3.3$.

Cumulative Review Exercises (page 420)

1. $y = 3^x - 2$

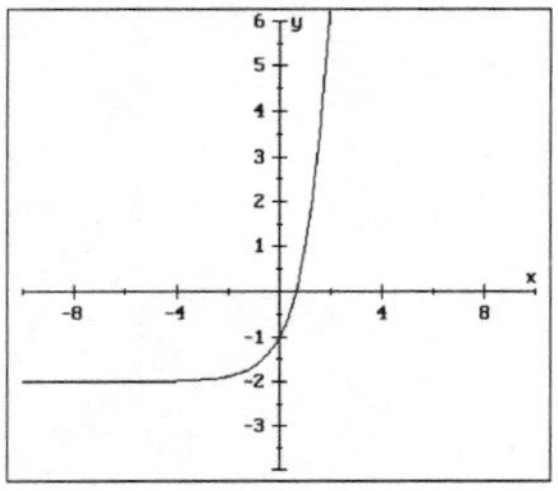

2. $y = 2e^x$

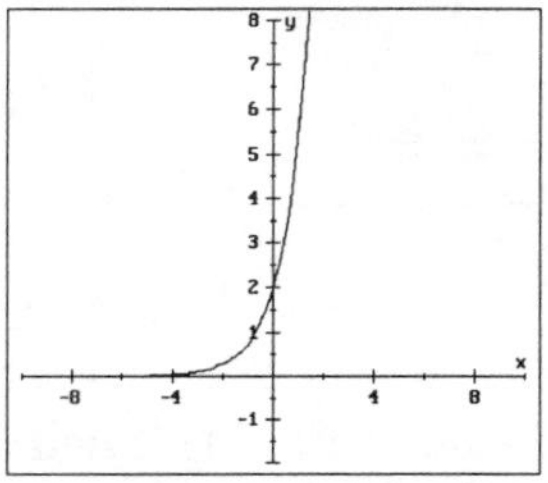

3. $y = \log_3 x$

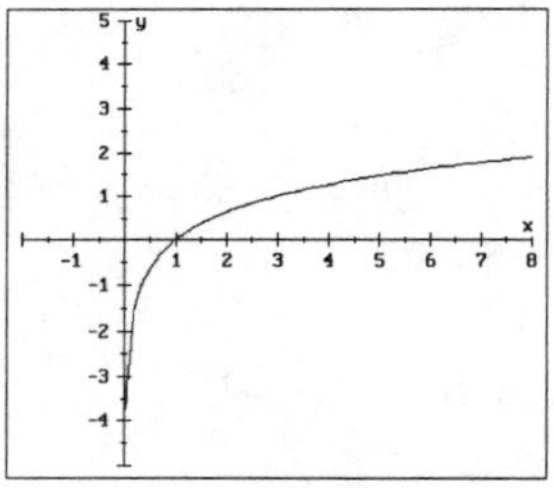

4. $y = \ln(x - 2)$

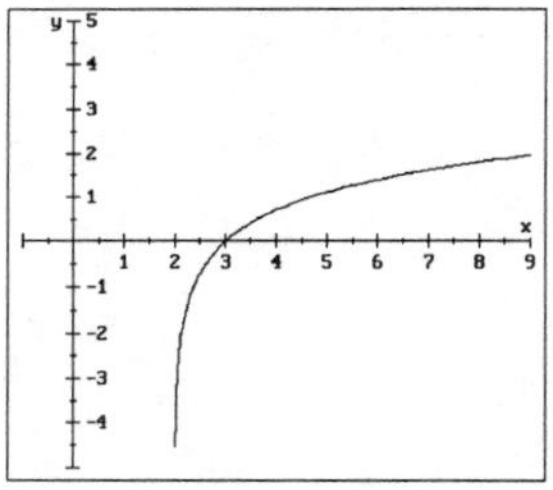

5. $\log_2 64 = 6$ (because $2^6 = 64$)

6. $\log_{1/2} 8 = -3$ $\left(\text{because } \left(\frac{1}{2}\right)^{-3} = 8\right)$

7. $\ln e^3 = 3 \ln e = 3$

8. $2^{\log_2 2} = 2$

9. $\log abc = \log a + \log b + \log c$

10. $$\begin{aligned}\log \frac{a^2b}{c} &= \log a^2b - \log c \\ &= \log a^2 + \log b - \log c \\ &= 2\log a + \log b - \log c\end{aligned}$$

11. $\log\sqrt{\dfrac{ab}{c^3}} = \log\left(\dfrac{ab}{c^3}\right)^{1/2}$
$= \frac{1}{2}\log\left(\dfrac{ab}{c^3}\right)$
$= \frac{1}{2}(\log ab - \log c^3)$
$= \frac{1}{2}(\log a + \log b - 3\log c)$

12. $\log\dfrac{\sqrt{ab^2}}{c} = \log\dfrac{(ab^2)^{1/2}}{c}$
$= \log(ab^2)^{1/2} - \log c$
$= \frac{1}{2}\log(ab^2) - \log c$
$= \frac{1}{2}(\log a + \log b^2) - \log c$
$= \frac{1}{2}(\log a + 2\log b) - \log c$
$= \frac{1}{2}\log a + \log b - \log c$

13. $3\log a - 3\log b = \log a^3 - \log b^3 = \log\dfrac{a^3}{b^3}$

14. $\dfrac{1}{2}\log a + 3\log b - \dfrac{2}{3}\log c = \log a^{1/2} + \log b^3 - \log c^{2/3} = \log\dfrac{a^{1/2}b^3}{c^{2/3}} = \log\dfrac{\sqrt{a}\,b^3}{\sqrt[3]{c^2}}$

15. $3^{x+1} = 8$
$\log 3^{x+1} = \log 8$
$(x+1)\log 3 = \log 8$
$x + 1 = \dfrac{\log 8}{\log 3}$
$x = \dfrac{\log 8}{\log 3} - 1$

16. $3^{x-1} = 3^{2x}$
$x - 1 = 2x$
$-1 = x$

17. $\log x + \log 2 = 3$
$\log 2x = 3$
$10^3 = 2x$
$1000 = 2x$
$500 = x$

18. $\log(x+1) + \log(x-1) = 1$
$\log(x+1)(x-1) = 1$
$\log(x^2 - 1) = 1$
$10^1 = x^2 - 1$
$10 = x^2 - 1$
$11 = x^2$
$\pm\sqrt{11} = x$
Only the positive answer, $x = \sqrt{11}$, checks.

19.

1 |	4	0	3	2
		4	4	7
	4	4	7	9

$P(1) = 9$

20.

−2 |	4	0	3	2
		−8	16	−38
	4	−8	19	−36

$P(-2) = -36$

21.

$\frac{1}{2}$ |	4	0	3	2
		2	1	2
	4	2	4	4

$P(\frac{1}{2}) = 4$

22.

i |	4	0	3	2
		$4i$	−4	$-i$
	4	$4i$	−1	$2-i$

$P(i) = 2 - i$

23.

−1 |	1	2	−1	−2
		−1	−1	2
	1	1	−2	0

factor

24.

2 |	1	2	−1	−2
		2	8	14
	1	4	7	12

not a factor

25. $\begin{array}{r|rrrr} 1 & 1 & 2 & -1 & -2 \\ & & 1 & 3 & 2 \\ \hline & 1 & 3 & 2 & 0 \end{array}$ factor

26. $\begin{array}{r|rrrr} -2 & 1 & 2 & -1 & -2 \\ & & -2 & 0 & 2 \\ \hline & 1 & 0 & -1 & 0 \end{array}$ factor

27. $x^{12} - 4x^8 + 2x^4 + 12 = 0 \Rightarrow$ 12 roots

28. $x^{2000} - 1 = 0 \Rightarrow$ 2000 roots

29. $P(x) = x^4 + 2x^3 - 3x^2 + x + 2$: 2 sign variations $\Rightarrow$ 2 or 0 positive roots

$P(-x) = (-x)^4 + 2(-x)^3 - 3(-x)^2 + (-x) + 2$

$= x^4 - 2x^3 - 3x^2 - x + 2$: 2 sign variations $\Rightarrow$ 2 or 0 negative roots

# pos	# neg	# nonreal
2	2	0
2	0	2
0	2	2
0	0	4

30. $P(x) = x^4 - 3x^3 - 2x^2 - 3x - 5$

1 sign variation $\Rightarrow$ 1 positive root

$P(-x) = (-x)^4 - 3(-x)^3 - 2(-x)^2 - 3(-x) - 5$

$= x^4 + 3x^3 - 2x^2 + 3x - 3$

3 sign variations $\Rightarrow$ 3 or 1 negative roots

# pos	# neg	# nonreal
1	3	0
1	1	2

31. Possible rational roots

$\pm 1,\ \pm 3,\ \pm 9$

Descartes' Rule of Signs

# pos	# neg	# nonreal
1	2	0
1	0	2

Test $x = -1$: $\begin{array}{r|rrrr} -1 & 1 & 1 & -9 & -9 \\ & & -1 & 0 & 9 \\ \hline & 1 & 0 & -9 & 0 \end{array}$

$x^3 + x^2 - 9x - 9 = 0$

$(x+1)(x^2 - 9) = 0$

$(x+1)(x+3)(x-3) = 0$

Solution set: $\{-1, -3, 3\}$

32. Possible rational roots

$\pm 1,\ \pm 2$

Descartes' Rule of Signs

# pos	# neg	# nonreal
2	1	0
0	1	2

Test $x = -1$: $\begin{array}{r|rrrr} -1 & 1 & -2 & -1 & 2 \\ & & -1 & 3 & -2 \\ \hline & 1 & -3 & 2 & 0 \end{array}$

$x^3 - 2x^2 - x + 2 = 0$

$(x+1)(x^2 - 3x + 2) = 0$

$(x+1)(x-1)(x-2) = 0$

Solution set: $\{-1, 1, 2\}$

Exercise 6.1 (page 432)

1. system **2.** solution **3.** consistent **4.** inconsistent

5. independent **6.** dependent **7.** consistent **8.** inconsistent

9. dependent **10.** independent **11.** is **12.** is

13. $\begin{cases} y = -3x + 5 \\ x - 2y = -3 \end{cases}$

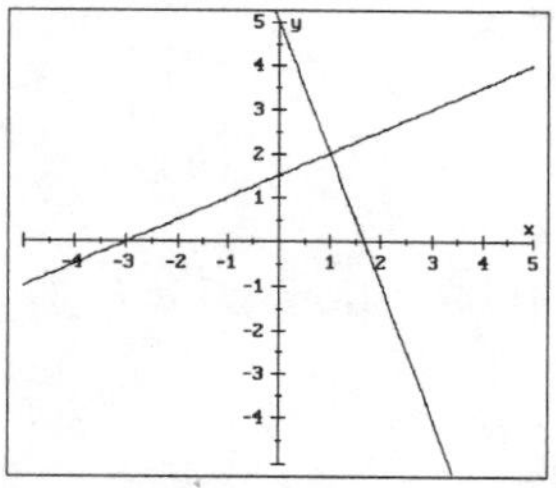

solution: $(1, 2)$

14. $\begin{cases} x - 2y = -3 \\ 3x + y = -9 \end{cases}$

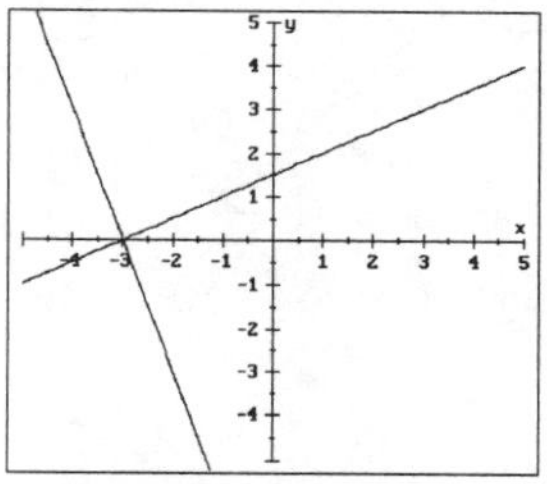

solution: $(-3, 0)$

15. $\begin{cases} 3x + 2y = 2 \\ -2x + 3y = 16 \end{cases}$

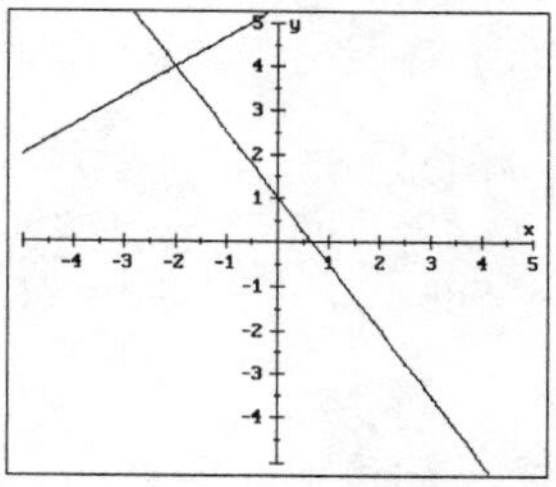

solution: $(-2, 4)$

16. $\begin{cases} x + y = 0 \\ 5x - 2y = 14 \end{cases}$

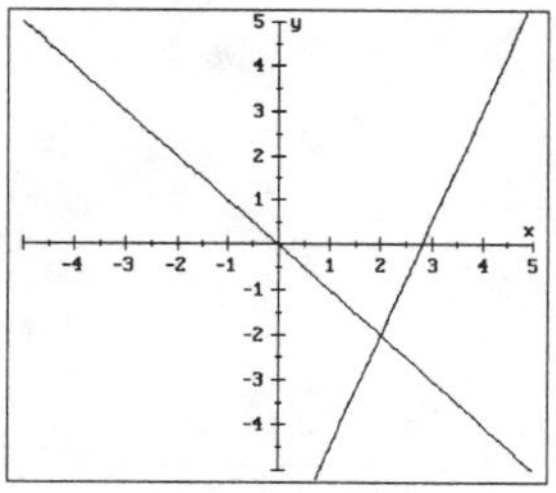

solution: $(2, -2)$

17. $\begin{cases} y = -5.7x + 7.8 \\ y = 37.2 - 19.1x \end{cases}$

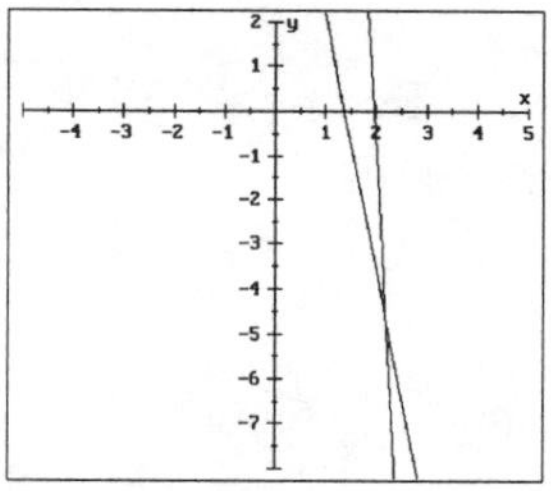

solution: $(2.2, -4.7)$

18. $\begin{cases} y = 3.4x - 1 \\ y = -7.1x + 3.1 \end{cases}$

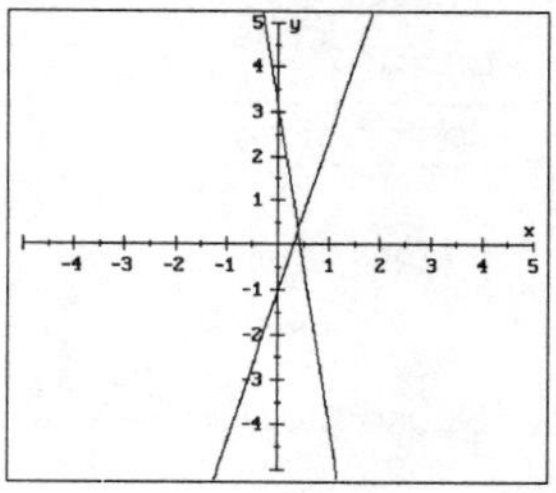

solution: $(0.4, 0.3)$

19. $\begin{cases} y = \dfrac{5.5 - 2.7x}{3.5} \\ 5.3x - 9.2y = 6.0 \end{cases}$

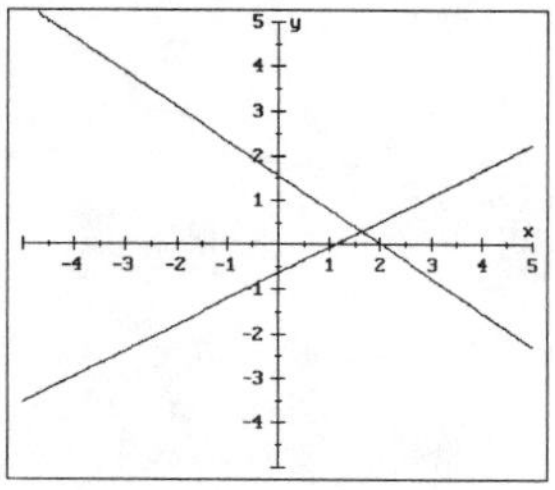

solution: $(1.7, 0.3)$

20. $\begin{cases} 29x + 17y = 7 \\ -17x + 23y = 19 \end{cases}$

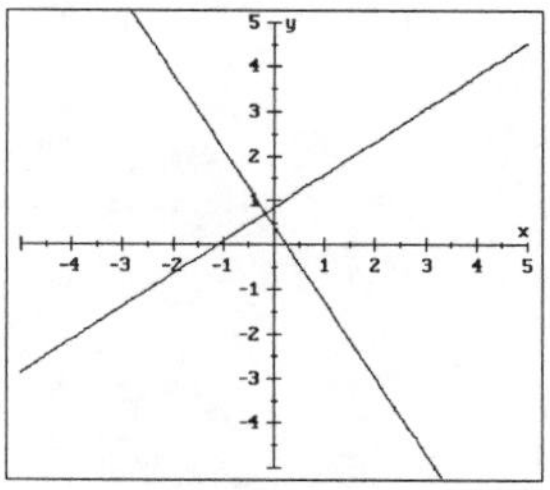

solution: $(-0.2, 0.7)$

21. $\begin{cases} (1) & y = x - 1 \\ (2) & y = 2x \end{cases}$

Substitute $y = x - 1$ from (1) into (2):

$$\begin{aligned} y &= 2x \\ x - 1 &= 2x \\ -1 &= x \end{aligned}$$

Substitute and solve for y:

$y = 2x$

$y = 2(-1) = -2$

$\boxed{x = -1, y = -2}$

22. $\begin{cases} (1) & y = 2x - 1 \\ (2) & x + y = 5 \end{cases}$

Substitute $y = 2x - 1$ from (1) into (2):

$$\begin{aligned} x + y &= 5 \\ x + 2x - 1 &= 5 \\ 3x &= 6 \\ x &= 2 \end{aligned}$$

Substitute and solve for y:

$y = 2x - 1$

$y = 2(2) - 1 = 3$

$\boxed{x = 2, y = 3}$

23. $\begin{cases} (1) & 2x + 3y = 0 \\ (2) & y = 3x - 11 \end{cases}$

Substitute $y = 3x - 11$ from (2) into (1):

$$\begin{aligned} 2x + 3y &= 0 \\ 2x + 3(3x - 11) &= 0 \\ 2x + 9x - 33 &= 0 \\ 11x &= 33 \\ x &= 3 \end{aligned}$$

Substitute and solve for y:

$y = 3x - 11$

$y = 3(3) - 11 = -2$

$\boxed{x = 3, y = -2}$

24. $\begin{cases} (1) & 2x + y = 3 \\ (2) & y = 5x - 11 \end{cases}$

Substitute $y = 5x - 11$ from (2) into (1):

$$\begin{aligned} 2x + y &= 3 \\ 2x + 5x - 11 &= 3 \\ 7x &= 14 \\ x &= 2 \end{aligned}$$

Substitute and solve for y:

$y = 5x - 11$

$y = 5(2) - 11 = -1$

$\boxed{x = 2, y = -1}$

25. $\begin{cases} (1) & 4x + 3y = 3 \\ (2) & 2x - 6y = -1 \end{cases}$

Substitute $y = \dfrac{3 - 4x}{3}$ from (1) into (2):

$$\begin{aligned} 2x - 6y &= -1 \\ 2x - 6 \cdot \frac{3 - 4x}{3} &= -1 \\ 2x - 2(3 - 4x) &= -1 \\ 2x - 6 + 8x &= -1 \\ 10x &= 5 \\ x &= \tfrac{1}{2} \end{aligned}$$

Substitute and solve for y:

$$\begin{aligned} 4x + 3y &= 3 \\ 4\left(\tfrac{1}{2}\right) + 3y &= 3 \\ 2 + 3y &= 3 \\ 3y &= 1 \\ y &= \tfrac{1}{3} \end{aligned}$$

Solution:

$\boxed{x = \tfrac{1}{2}, y = \tfrac{1}{3}}$

26. $\begin{cases} (1) & 4x+5y=4 \\ (2) & 8x-15y=3 \end{cases}$

Substitute $y=\dfrac{4-4x}{5}$ from (1) into (2):

$$\begin{aligned} 8x-15y&=3 \\ 8x-15\cdot\frac{4-4x}{5}&=3 \\ 8x-3(4-4x)&=3 \\ 8x-12+12x&=3 \\ 20x&=15 \\ x&=\tfrac{3}{4} \end{aligned}$$

Substitute and solve for y:

$$\begin{aligned} 4x+5y&=4 \\ 4\left(\tfrac{3}{4}\right)+5y&=4 \\ 3+5y&=4 \\ 5y&=1 \\ y&=\tfrac{1}{5} \end{aligned}$$

Solution: $\boxed{x=\tfrac{3}{4},\ y=\tfrac{1}{5}}$

27. $\begin{cases} (1) & x+3y=1 \\ (2) & 2x+6y=3 \end{cases}$

Substitute $x=1-3y$ from (1) into (2):

$$\begin{aligned} 2x+6y&=3 \\ 2(1-3y)+6y&=3 \\ 2-6y+6y&=3 \\ 2&\neq 3 \end{aligned}$$

$\boxed{\text{Inconsistent system} \Rightarrow \text{No solution}}$

28. $\begin{cases} (1) & x-3y=14 \\ (2) & 3(x-12)=9y \end{cases}$

Substitute $x=3y+14$ from (1) into (2):

$$\begin{aligned} 3(x-12)&=9y \\ 3(3y+14-12)&=9y \\ 3(3y+2)&=9y \\ 9y+6&=9y \\ 6&\neq 0 \end{aligned}$$

$\boxed{\text{Inconsistent system} \Rightarrow \text{No solution}}$

29. $5x-3y=12 \Rightarrow \times\ (-1)$ $\quad -5x+3y=-12$
$\underline{2x-3y=\ \ 3}$ $\quad \underline{2x-3y=\ \ 3}$
$-3x=-9$
$x=3$

$$\begin{aligned} 2x-3y&=3 \\ 2(3)-3y&=3 \\ 6-3y&=3 \\ -3y&=-3 \\ y&=1 \end{aligned}$$

Solution: $\boxed{x=3,\ y=1}$

30. $2x+3y=\ \ 8$ $\quad 2x+3y=\ \ 8$
$\underline{-5x+\ y=-3} \Rightarrow \times\ (-3)$ $\quad \underline{15x-3y=\ \ 9}$
$17x=17$
$x=1$

$$\begin{aligned} 2x+3y&=8 \\ 2(1)+3y&=8 \\ 2+3y&=8 \\ 3y&=6 \\ y&=2 \end{aligned}$$

Solution: $\boxed{x=1,\ y=2}$

31. $x-7y=-11 \Rightarrow \times\ (-8)$ $\quad -8x+56y=\ \ 88$
$\underline{8x+2y=\ \ 28}$ $\quad \underline{8x+\ 2y=\ \ 28}$
$58y=116$
$y=2$

$$\begin{aligned} x-7y&=-11 \\ x-7(2)&=-11 \\ x-14&=-11 \\ x&=3 \end{aligned}$$

Solution: $\boxed{x=3,\ y=2}$

32. $3x+9y=\ \ 9$ $\quad 3x+\ 9y=\ \ 9$
$\underline{-x+5y=-3} \Rightarrow \times\ (3)$ $\quad \underline{-3x+15y=-9}$
$24y=0$
$y=0$

$$\begin{aligned} 3x+9y&=9 \\ 3x+9(0)&=9 \\ 3x+0&=9 \\ 3x&=9 \\ x&=3 \end{aligned}$$

Solution: $\boxed{x=3,\ y=0}$

33.
$$\begin{aligned} 3(x-y) = y-9 &\Rightarrow 3x-3y = y-9 \Rightarrow 3x-4y = -9 \Rightarrow \times\ (5) & 15x-20y &= -45 \\ 5(x+y) = -15 &\Rightarrow 5x+5y = -15 \Rightarrow 5x+5y = -15 \Rightarrow \times\ (4) & 20x+20y &= -60 \\ & & 35x &= -105 \\ & & x &= -3 \end{aligned}$$

$$\begin{aligned} 5x+5y &= -15 \\ 5(-3)+5y &= -15 \\ -15+5y &= -15 \\ 5y &= 0 \\ y &= 0 \end{aligned}$$

Solution: $\boxed{x=-3,\ y=0}$

34.
$$\begin{aligned} 2(x+y) = y+1 &\Rightarrow 2x+2y = y+1 \Rightarrow 2x+y = 1 \\ 3(x+1) = y-3 &\Rightarrow 3x+3 = y-3 \Rightarrow 3x-y = -6 \\ & 5x = -5 \\ & x = -1 \end{aligned}$$

$$\begin{aligned} 2x+y &= 1 \\ 2(-1)+y &= 1 \\ -2+y &= 1 \\ y &= 3 \end{aligned}$$

Solution: $\boxed{x=-1,\ y=3}$

35.
$$\begin{aligned} 2 = \frac{1}{x+y} &\Rightarrow 2(x+y) = 1 \Rightarrow 2x+2y = 1 \\ 2 = \frac{3}{x-y} &\Rightarrow 2(x-y) = 3 \Rightarrow 2x-2y = 3 \\ & 4x = 4 \\ & x = 1 \end{aligned}$$

$$\begin{aligned} 2x+2y &= 1 \\ 2(1)+2y &= 1 \\ 2+2y &= 1 \\ 2y &= -1 \\ y &= -\tfrac{1}{2} \end{aligned}$$

Solution: $\boxed{x=1,\ y=-\tfrac{1}{2}}$

36.
$$\begin{aligned} \frac{1}{x+y} = 12 &\Rightarrow 1 = 12(x+y) \Rightarrow -12x-12y = -1 & -12x-12y &= -1 \\ \frac{3x}{y} = -4 &\Rightarrow 3x = -4y \Rightarrow 3x+4y = 0 \Rightarrow \times\ (4) & 12x+16y &= 0 \\ & & 4y &= -1 \\ & & y &= -\tfrac{1}{4} \end{aligned}$$

$$\begin{aligned} 3x &= -4y \\ 3x &= -4\left(-\tfrac{1}{4}\right) \\ 3x &= 1 \\ x &= \tfrac{1}{3} \end{aligned}$$

Solution: $\boxed{x=\tfrac{1}{3},\ y=-\tfrac{1}{4}}$

37.
$$\begin{aligned} y+2x = 5 &\Rightarrow 2x+y = 5 & 2x+y &= 5 \\ 0.5y = 2.5-x &\Rightarrow x+0.5y = 2.5 \Rightarrow \times\ (-2) & -2x-y &= -5 \\ & & 0 &= 0 \end{aligned}$$

Dependent Equations

$$\begin{aligned} 2x+y &= 5 \\ y &= -2x+5 \end{aligned}$$

Gen. sol.: $(x, -2x+5)$

38.
$$\begin{aligned} -0.3x+0.1y = -0.1 &\Rightarrow \times\ (20) & -6x+2y &= -2 \\ 6x-2y = 2 & & 6x-2y &= 2 \\ & & 0 &= 0 \end{aligned}$$

Dependent Equations

$$\begin{aligned} 6x-2y &= 2 \\ -2y &= 2-6x \\ y &= -1+3x = 3x-1 \end{aligned}$$

General solution: $(x, 3x-1)$

39. $$\begin{array}{l} x+2(x-y)=2 \Rightarrow x+2x-2y=2 \Rightarrow \quad 3x-2y=2 \\ \underline{3(y-x)-y=5} \Rightarrow \underline{3y-3x-y=5} \Rightarrow \underline{-3x+2y=5} \\ \qquad\qquad\qquad\qquad\qquad\qquad\qquad\qquad 0 \neq 7 \end{array}$$

No Solution

Inconsistent system

40. $$\begin{array}{l} x+\frac{y}{3}=\frac{5}{3} \Rightarrow \times (3)\ \ 3x+y=5 \Rightarrow 3x+y=5 \qquad 3x+y=5 \\ \underline{\frac{x+y}{3}=3-x} \Rightarrow \times (3)\ \ \underline{x+y=9-3x} \Rightarrow \underline{4x+y=9} \Rightarrow \times (-1)\ \ \underline{-4x-y=-9} \\ \qquad -x=-4 \\ \qquad x=4 \end{array}$$

$$\begin{aligned} 3x+y&=5 \\ 3(4)+y&=5 \\ 12+y&=5 \\ y&=-7 \end{aligned}$$

Solution: $x=4,\ y=-7$

41. $$\begin{array}{l} \frac{3}{2}x+\frac{1}{3}y=2 \Rightarrow \times (6)\ \ 9x+2y=12 \Rightarrow \qquad 9x+2y=12 \\ \underline{\frac{2}{3}x+\frac{1}{9}y=1} \Rightarrow \times (9)\ \ \underline{6x+\ y=\ 9} \Rightarrow \times (-2)\ \ \underline{-12x-2y=-18} \\ \qquad -3x=-6 \\ \qquad x=2 \end{array}$$

$$\begin{aligned} 6x+y&=9 \\ 6(2)+y&=9 \\ 12+y&=9 \\ y&=-3 \end{aligned}$$

Solution: $x=2,\ y=-3$

42. $$\begin{array}{l} \frac{x+y}{2}+\frac{x-y}{5}=2 \Rightarrow \times (10)\ \ 5(x+y)+2(x-y)=20 \Rightarrow 5x+5y+2x-2y=20 \\ \underline{x=\frac{y}{2}+1} \Rightarrow \times (2)\ \ \underline{2x=y+2} \Rightarrow \underline{2x-y=2} \end{array}$$

$$\begin{array}{l} 7x+3y=20 \\ \underline{2x-\ y=\ 2} \Rightarrow \times (3) \end{array} \qquad \begin{array}{l} 7x+3y=20 \\ \underline{6x-3y=\ 6} \\ 13x=26 \\ x=2 \end{array} \qquad \begin{aligned} 7x+3y&=20 \\ 7(2)+3y&=20 \\ 14+3y&=20 \\ 3y&=6 \\ y&=2 \end{aligned}$$

Solution: $x=2,\ y=2$

43. $$\begin{array}{l} \frac{x-y}{5}+\frac{x+y}{2}=6 \Rightarrow \times (10)\ \ 2(x-y)+5(x+y)=60 \Rightarrow 2x-2y+5x+5y=60 \\ \underline{\frac{x-y}{2}-\frac{x+y}{4}=3} \Rightarrow \times (8)\ \ \underline{4(x-y)-2(x+y)=24} \Rightarrow \underline{4x-4y-2x-2y=24} \end{array}$$

$$\begin{array}{l} 7x+3y=60 \Rightarrow \times (2) \\ \underline{2x-6y=24} \end{array} \qquad \begin{array}{l} 14x+6y=120 \\ \underline{2x-6y=\ 24} \\ 16x=144 \\ x=9 \end{array} \qquad \begin{aligned} 7x+3y&=60 \\ 7(9)+3y&=60 \\ 63+3y&=60 \\ 3y&=-3 \\ y&=-1 \end{aligned}$$

Solution: $x=9,\ y=-1$

44. $\frac{x-2}{5}+\frac{y+3}{2}=5 \Rightarrow \times(10)\ \ 2(x-2)+5(y+3)=50 \Rightarrow 2x-4+5y+15=50$

$\frac{x+3}{2}+\frac{y-2}{3}=6 \Rightarrow \times(6)\ \ 3(x+3)+2(y-2)=36 \Rightarrow 3x+9+2y-4=36$

$$\begin{array}{lll} 2x+5y=39 \Rightarrow \times(-2) & -4x-10y=-78 & 3x+2y=31 \\ 3x+2y=31 \Rightarrow \times(5) & \underline{15x+10y=155} & 3(7)+2y=31 \\ & 11x = 77 & 2y=10 \\ & x = 7 & y=5 \end{array}$$

Solution: $\boxed{x=7,\ y=5}$

45. $$\begin{array}{lll} (1)\ x+y+z=3 & \text{Add (1) and (3):} & \text{Add equations (2) and (3):} \\ (2)\ 2x+y+z=4 & (1)\ \ x+y+z=3 & (2)\ \ 2x+y+z=4 \\ (3)\ 3x+y-z=5 & (3)\ \ \underline{3x+y-z=5} & (3)\ \ \underline{3x+y-z=5} \\ & (4)\ \ 4x+2y=8 & (5)\ \ 5x+2y=9 \end{array}$$

Solve the system of two equations and two unknowns formed by equations (4) and (5):

$$\begin{array}{llll} 4x+2y=8 \Rightarrow \times(-1) & -4x-2y=-8 & 4x+2y=8 & x+y+z=3 \\ 5x+2y=9 \Rightarrow & \underline{5x+2y=9} & 4(1)+2y=8 & 1+2+z=3 \\ & x=1 & 2y=4 & 3+z=3 \\ & & y=2 & z=0 \end{array}$$

Solution: $\boxed{x=1,\ y=2,\ z=0}$

46. $$\begin{array}{lll} (1)\ x-y-z=0 & \text{Add (1) and (3):} & \text{Add equations (2) and (3):} \\ (2)\ x+y-z=0 & (1)\ \ x-y-z=0 & (2)\ \ x+y-z=0 \\ (3)\ x-y+z=2 & (3)\ \ \underline{x-y+z=2} & (3)\ \ \underline{x-y+z=2} \\ & (4)\ \ 2x-2y=2 & (5)\ \ 2x=2 \\ & & \qquad x=1 \end{array}$$

Solve the system of two equations and two unknowns formed by equations (4) and (5):

$$\begin{array}{ll} 2x-2y=2 & x-y+z=2 \\ 2(1)-2y=2 & 1-0+z=2 \\ -2y=0 & 1+z=2 \\ y=0 & z=1 \end{array}$$

Solution: $\boxed{x=1,\ y=0,\ z=1}$

47. $$\begin{array}{lll} (1)\ x-y+z=0 & \text{Add (1) and (2):} & \text{Add equations (2) and (3):} \\ (2)\ x+y+2z=-1 & (1)\ \ x-y+z=0 & (2)\ \ x+y+2z=-1 \\ (3)\ -x-y+z=0 & (2)\ \ \underline{x+y+2z=-1} & (3)\ \ \underline{-x-y+z=0} \\ & (4)\ \ 2x+3z=-1 & (5)\ \ 3z=-1 \\ & & \qquad z=-\tfrac{1}{3} \end{array}$$

Solve the system of two equations and two unknowns formed by equations (4) and (5):

$$\begin{array}{ll} 2x+3z=-1 & x-y+z=0 \\ 2x+3(-\tfrac{1}{3})=-1 & 0-y+(-\tfrac{1}{3})=0 \\ 2x=0 & -y=\tfrac{1}{3} \\ x=0 & y=-\tfrac{1}{3} \end{array}$$

Solution: $\boxed{x=0,\ y=-\tfrac{1}{3},\ z=-\tfrac{1}{3}}$

48.
(1) $2x + y - z = 7$
(2) $x - y + z = 2$
(3) $x + y - 3z = 2$

Add (1) and (2):

$$\begin{array}{rl} (1) & 2x + y - z = 7 \\ (3) & \underline{x - y + z = 2} \\ (4) & 3x \qquad\quad = 9 \\ & x \qquad\quad = 3 \end{array}$$

Add equations (2) and (3):

$$\begin{array}{rl} (2) & x - y + z = 2 \\ (3) & \underline{x + y - 3z = 2} \\ (5) & 2x \qquad - 2z = 4 \end{array}$$

Solve the system of two equations and two unknowns formed by equations (4) and (5):

$$\begin{aligned} 2x - 2z &= 4 \\ 2(3) - 2z &= 4 \\ -2z &= -2 \\ z &= 1 \end{aligned} \qquad \begin{aligned} x + y - 3z &= 2 \\ 3 + y - 3(1) &= 2 \\ y &= 2 \end{aligned}$$

Solution: $\boxed{x = 3,\ y = 2,\ z = 1}$

49.
(1) $2x + y = 4$
(2) $x - z = 2$
(3) $y + z = 1$

Add (2) and (3):

$$\begin{array}{rl} (2) & x \qquad - z = 2 \\ (3) & \underline{\qquad y + z = 1} \\ (4) & x + y \qquad = 3 \end{array}$$

Solve the system of two equations and two unknowns formed by equations (1) and (4):

$$\begin{array}{l} 2x + y = 4 \Rightarrow \times(-1) \\ \underline{x + y = 3 \Rightarrow} \end{array} \quad \begin{aligned} -2x - y &= -4 \\ \underline{x + y} &\underline{= \ 3} \\ -x &= -1 \\ x &= \ 1 \end{aligned} \qquad \begin{aligned} x + y &= 3 \\ 1 + y &= 3 \\ y &= 2 \end{aligned} \qquad \begin{aligned} y + z &= 1 \\ 2 + z &= 1 \\ z &= -1 \end{aligned}$$

Solution: $\boxed{x = 1,\ y = 2,\ z = -1}$

50.
(1) $3x + y + z = 0$
(2) $2x - y + z = 0$
(3) $2x + y + z = 0$

Add (1) and (2):

$$\begin{array}{rl} (1) & 3x + y + z = 0 \\ (2) & \underline{2x - y + z = 0} \\ (4) & 5x \qquad + 2z = 0 \end{array}$$

Add equations (2) and (3):

$$\begin{array}{rl} (2) & 2x - y + z = 0 \\ (3) & \underline{2x + y + z = 0} \\ (5) & 4x \qquad + 2z = 0 \end{array}$$

Solve the system of two equations and two unknowns formed by equations (4) and (5):

$$\begin{array}{l} 5x + 2z = 0 \Rightarrow \times(-1) \\ \underline{4x + 2z = 0 \Rightarrow} \end{array} \quad \begin{aligned} -5x - 2z &= 0 \\ \underline{4x + 2z} &\underline{= 0} \\ -x &= 0 \\ x &= 0 \end{aligned} \qquad \begin{aligned} 4x + 2z &= 0 \\ 4(0) + 2z &= 0 \\ 2z &= 0 \\ z &= 0 \end{aligned} \qquad \begin{aligned} 3x + y + z &= 0 \\ 3(0) + y + 0 &= 9 \\ y &= 0 \end{aligned}$$

Solution: $\boxed{x = 0,\ y = 0,\ z = 0}$

51.
(1) $x + y + z = 6$
(2) $2x + y + 3z = 17$
(3) $x + y + 2z = 11$

Add (1) and $-(2)$:

$$\begin{array}{rl} (1) & x + y + z = 6 \\ -(2) & \underline{-2x - y - 3z = -17} \\ (4) & -x \qquad - 2z = -11 \end{array}$$

Add equations (1) and $-(3)$:

$$\begin{array}{rl} (1) & x + y + z = 6 \\ -(3) & \underline{-x - y - 2z = -11} \\ (5) & -z = -5 \\ & z = 5 \end{array}$$

Solve the system of two equations and two unknowns formed by equations (4) and (5):

$$\begin{aligned} -x - 2z &= -11 \\ -x - 2(5) &= -11 \\ -x &= -1 \\ x &= 1 \end{aligned} \qquad \begin{aligned} x + y + z &= 6 \\ 1 + y + 5 &= 6 \\ y &= 0 \end{aligned}$$

Solution: $\boxed{x = 1,\ y = 0,\ z = 5}$

52.

$$\begin{array}{ll} (1) & x+y+z=3 \\ (2) & 2x+y+z=6 \\ (3) & x+2y+3z=2 \end{array}$$

Add $-(1)$ and (2):

$$\begin{array}{rrcr} -(1) & -x-y-z & = & -3 \\ (2) & 2x+y+z & = & 6 \\ \hline (4) & x & = & 3 \end{array}$$

Add equations $-2\cdot(1)$ and (3):

$$\begin{array}{rrcr} -2\cdot(1) & -2x-2y-2z & = & -6 \\ (3) & x+2y+3z & = & 2 \\ \hline (5) & -x \quad\quad + z & = & -4 \end{array}$$

Solve the system of two equations and two unknowns formed by equations (4) and (5):

$$\begin{array}{rcl} -x+z & = & -4 \\ -3+z & = & -4 \\ z & = & -1 \end{array} \qquad \begin{array}{rcl} x+y+z & = & 3 \\ 3+y+(-1) & = & 3 \\ y & = & 1 \end{array}$$

Solution: $\boxed{x=3,\ y=1,\ z=-1}$

53.

$$\begin{array}{ll} (1) & x+y+z=3 \\ (2) & x+z=2 \\ (3) & 2x+2y+2z=3 \end{array}$$

Add $-2\cdot(1)$ and (3):

$$\begin{array}{rrcr} -2\cdot(1) & -2x-2y-2z & = & -6 \\ (3) & 2x+2y+2z & = & 3 \\ \hline (4) & 0 & \neq & -3 \end{array}$$

No solution; inconsistent system

54.

$$\begin{array}{ll} (1) & x+y+z=3 \\ (2) & x+z=2 \\ (3) & 2x+y+2z=5 \end{array}$$

Add (1) and $-(2)$:

$$\begin{array}{rrcr} (1) & x+y+z & = & 3 \\ -(2) & -x \quad\quad -z & = & -2 \\ \hline (4) & y & = & 1 \end{array}$$

Add equations $-2\cdot(1)$ and (3):

$$\begin{array}{rrcr} -2(1) & -2x-2y-2z & = & -6 \\ (3) & 2x+y+2z & = & 5 \\ \hline (5) & -y & = & -1 \end{array}$$

Since both additions resulted in the same equation, the equations are dependent. Thus, y must equal 1, but x and z can be any real numbers that satisfy the equations. Notice that if the value $y=1$ is substituted into any of the equations, $x+z=2$ is the result. So $y=1$, and x and z must satisfy $x+z=2$. Solution: $z=$ any real number, $y=1$, $x=2-z \Rightarrow \boxed{(2-z,1,z)}$

55.

$$\begin{array}{ll} (1) & x+2y-z=2 \\ (2) & 2x-y=-1 \\ (3) & 3x+y+z=1 \end{array}$$

Add (1) and (3):

$$\begin{array}{rrcr} (1) & x+2y-z & = & 2 \\ (3) & 3x+y+z & = & 1 \\ \hline (4) & 4x+3y & = & 3 \end{array}$$

Solve the system of two equations and two unknowns formed by equations (2) and (4):

$$\begin{array}{rcl} 2x-y & = & -1 \Rightarrow \times(3) \\ 4x+3y & = & 3 \Rightarrow \end{array} \qquad \begin{array}{rcl} 6x-3y & = & -3 \\ 4x+3y & = & 3 \\ \hline 10x & = & 0 \\ x & = & 0 \end{array}$$

$$\begin{array}{rcl} 2x-y & = & -1 \\ 2(0)-y & = & -1 \\ -y & = & -1 \\ y & = & 1 \end{array} \qquad \begin{array}{rcl} 3x+y+z & = & 1 \\ 3(0)+1+z & = & 1 \\ z & = & 0 \end{array}$$

Solution: $\boxed{x=0,\ y=1,\ z=0}$

56.

$$\begin{array}{ll} (1) & x+y=2 \\ (2) & y+z=2 \\ (3) & 3x+3y=2 \end{array}$$

Add $-3\cdot(1)$ and (3):

$$\begin{array}{rrcr} -3\cdot(1) & -3x-3y & = & -6 \\ (3) & 3x+3y & = & 2 \\ \hline (4) & 0 & \neq & -4 \end{array}$$

$\boxed{\text{Inconsistent system} \Rightarrow \text{No solution}}$

57. (1) $3x+4y+2z=4$ (2) $6x-2y+z=4$ (3) $3x-8y-6z=-3$

Add (1) and $2\cdot(2)$:

$$\begin{array}{lrcl} (1) & 3x+4y+2z &=& 4 \\ 2\cdot(2) & 12x-4y+2z &=& 8 \\ \hline (4) & 15x \qquad +4z &=& 12 \end{array}$$

Add equations $2\cdot(1)$ and (3):

$$\begin{array}{lrcl} 2\cdot(1) & 6x+8y+4z &=& 8 \\ (3) & 3x-8y-6z &=& -3 \\ \hline (5) & 9x \qquad -2z &=& 5 \end{array}$$

Solve the system of two equations and two unknowns formed by equations (4) and (5):

$$\begin{array}{ll} 15x+4z=12 \Rightarrow & 15x+4z=12 \\ 9x-2z=\ \ 5 \Rightarrow \times(2) & 18x-4z=10 \\ \hline & 33x \quad =22 \\ & x \quad =\frac{2}{3} \end{array}$$

$$15x+4z=12 \qquad 15\left(\tfrac{2}{3}\right)+4z=12 \qquad 4z=2 \qquad z=\tfrac{1}{2}$$

$$3x+4y+2z=4 \qquad 3\left(\tfrac{2}{3}\right)+4y+2\left(\tfrac{1}{2}\right)=4 \qquad 4y=1 \qquad y=\tfrac{1}{4}$$

Solution: $x=\frac{2}{3}$, $y=\frac{1}{4}$, $z=\frac{1}{2}$

58. (1) $x+y=2$ (2) $y+z=2$ (3) $x-z=0$

Add (1) and $-(2)$:

$$\begin{array}{lrcl} (1) & x+y \qquad &=& 2 \\ -(2) & -x \qquad +z &=& 0 \\ \hline (4) & y+z &=& 2 \end{array}$$

Since (4) is the same as (2), the equations are dependent. Let $z=$ any real number. Then, from (4), $y=2-z$. Finally, substituting for y in (1) yields $x=2-y=2-(2-z)=z$.

Solution: $(z, 2-z, z)$

59. (1) $2x-y-z=0$ (2) $x-2y-z=-1$ (3) $x-y-2z=-1$

Add (1) and $-2\cdot(2)$:

$$\begin{array}{lrcl} (1) & 2x-\ y-\ z &=& 0 \\ -2\cdot(2) & -2x+4y+2z &=& 2 \\ \hline (4) & 3y+\ z &=& 2 \end{array}$$

Add equations (1) and $-2\cdot(3)$:

$$\begin{array}{lrcl} (1) & 2x-\ y-\ z &=& 0 \\ (3) & -2x+2y+4z &=& 2 \\ \hline (5) & y+3z &=& 2 \end{array}$$

Solve the system of two equations and two unknowns formed by equations (4) and (5):

$$\begin{array}{ll} 3y+\ z=2 \Rightarrow & 3y+\ z=\ 2 \\ y+3z=2 \Rightarrow \times(-3) & -3y-9z=-6 \\ \hline & -8z=-4 \\ & z=\ \frac{1}{2} \end{array}$$

$$y+3z=2 \qquad y+3\left(\tfrac{1}{2}\right)=2 \qquad y=\tfrac{1}{2}$$

$$x-y-2z=-1 \qquad x-\tfrac{1}{2}-2\left(\tfrac{1}{2}\right)=-1 \qquad x=\tfrac{1}{2}$$

Solution: $x=\frac{1}{2}$, $y=\frac{1}{2}$, $z=\frac{1}{2}$

60. (1) $x+3y-z=5$ (2) $3x-y+z=2$ (3) $2x+y=1$

Add (1) and (2):

$$\begin{array}{lrcl} (1) & x+3y-z &=& 5 \\ (2) & 3x-\ y+z &=& 2 \\ \hline (4) & 4x+2y \qquad &=& 7 \end{array}$$

Add equations $-2\cdot(3)$ and (4):

$$\begin{array}{lrcl} -2\cdot(3) & -4x-2y &=& -2 \\ (4) & 4x+2y &=& 7 \\ \hline (5) & 0 &\neq& 5 \end{array}$$

No solution

Inconsistent System

61. (1) $(x+y)+(y+z)+(z+x)=6 \Rightarrow 2x+2y+2z=6$

(2) $(x-y)+(y-z)+(z-x)=0 \Rightarrow 0=0$

(3) $x+y+2z=4 \Rightarrow x+y+2z=4$

Add (1) and $-2\cdot(3)$:

$$\begin{array}{lrcl} (1) & 2x+2y+2z &=& 6 \\ -2\cdot(3) & -2x-2y-4z &=& -8 \\ \hline (4) & -2z &=& -2 \\ & z &=& 1 \end{array}$$

Since (2) is always true, the equations are dependent. z must equal 1. Then, from (3), $x+y=2$. Let $y=$ any real #. Then $x=2-y$. Solution: $(2-y, y, 1)$

62. (1) $(x+y)+(y+z)=1 \Rightarrow x+2y+z=1$
(2) $(x+z)+(x+z)=3 \Rightarrow 2x+2z=3$
(3) $(x-y)-(x-z)=-1 \Rightarrow -y+z=-1$

Add $-2\cdot(1)$ and (2):

$$\begin{array}{lrcl} -2\cdot(1) & -2x-4y-2z & = & -2 \\ (2) & 2x \qquad +2z & = & 3 \\ \hline (4) & -4y & = & 1 \\ & y & = & -\frac{1}{4} \end{array}$$

$$\begin{aligned} -y+z&=-1 \\ -(-\tfrac{1}{4})+z&=-1 \\ z&=-\tfrac{5}{4} \end{aligned}$$

$$\begin{aligned} 2x+2z&=3 \\ 2x+2(-\tfrac{5}{4})&=3 \\ 2x&=\tfrac{22}{4} \\ x&=\tfrac{11}{4} \end{aligned}$$

Solution: $x=\frac{11}{4}, y=-\frac{1}{4}, z=-\frac{5}{4}$

63. Let x = acres of corn and let y = acres of soybeans. Then $\begin{cases} (1) & x+y=350 \\ (2) & x=y+100 \end{cases}$

Substitute $x=y+100$ from (2) into (1):

$$\begin{aligned} x+y&=350 \\ y+100+y&=350 \\ 2y&=250 \\ y&=125 \end{aligned}$$

Substitute and solve for x:

$$\begin{aligned} x&=y+100 \\ &=125+100=225 \end{aligned}$$

The farmer should plant 225 acres of corn and 125 acres of soybeans.

64. Let x = the initiation fee and let y = the monthly dues. Then the following system applies:

$$\begin{array}{l} x+7y=3025 \Rightarrow \times(-1) \\ \underline{x+18y=3850} \end{array} \qquad \begin{array}{rcr} -x-7y&=&-3025 \\ x+18y&=&3850 \\ \hline 11y&=&825 \\ y&=&75 \end{array}$$

$$\begin{aligned} x+7y&=3025 \\ x+7(75)&=3025 \\ x&=2500 \end{aligned}$$

The initiation fee is \$2500 and dues are \$75 per month.

65. Let w = width and let l = length. Then $\begin{cases} (1) & 2w+2l=1900 \\ (2) & w=l-250 \end{cases}$

Substitute $w=l-250$ from (2) into (1):

$$\begin{aligned} 2w+2l&=1900 \\ 2(l-250)+2l&=1900 \\ 2l-500+2l&=1900 \\ 4l&=2400 \\ l&=600 \end{aligned}$$

Substitute and solve for w:

$$\begin{aligned} w&=l-250 \\ &=600-250=350 \end{aligned}$$

Area $= lw = (600 \text{ cm})(350 \text{ cm})$

The area is 210,000 cm^2.

66. Let b = speed in still water. Let c = the speed of the current. Then the following system applies:

$$\begin{array}{ll} 3(b+c)=30 & 3b+3c=30 \Rightarrow \times(5) \\ 5(b-c)=30 & \underline{5b-5c=30} \Rightarrow \times(3) \end{array} \qquad \begin{array}{rcr} 15b+15c&=&150 \\ 15b-15c&=&90 \\ \hline 30b&=&240 \\ b&=&8 \end{array}$$

The boat has a speed of 8 kilometers per hour in still water.

67. Let x = grams of 9% alloy. Let y = grams of 84% alloy. Then the following system applies: (note: 34% of 60 is $0.34 \times 60 = 20.4$)

$$\begin{aligned} x + y &= 60 \Rightarrow \times(-9) & -9x - 9y &= -540 \\ 0.09x + 0.84y &= 20.4 \Rightarrow \times(100) & 9x + 84y &= 2040 \\ & & 75y &= 1500 \\ & & y &= 20 \end{aligned}$$

She must use 40 grams of the 9% and 20 grams of the 84% alloy.

68.

$$\begin{aligned} 2w_1 &= 3w_2 & \Rightarrow 2w_1 - 3w_2 &= 0 \Rightarrow \times(-2) & -4w_1 + 6w_2 &= 0 \\ 3w_1 &= 2(w_2 + 5) & \Rightarrow 3w_1 - 2w_2 &= 10 \Rightarrow \times(3) & 9w_1 - 6w_2 &= 30 \\ & & & & 5w_1 &= 30 \\ & & & & w_1 &= 6 \end{aligned}$$

The weights are 6 and 4 pounds.

69.

$$\begin{aligned} 448x &= 112y & \Rightarrow 448x - 112y &= 0 \Rightarrow \times(-1) & -448x + 112y &= 0 \\ 448(x+1) &= 192(y-1) & \Rightarrow 448x - 192y &= -640 \Rightarrow & 448x - 192y &= -640 \\ & & & & -80y &= -640 \\ & & & & y &= 8 \end{aligned}$$

$$\begin{aligned} 448x &= 112y \\ 448x &= 112(8) \\ x &= 2 \end{aligned}$$

The lever has a length of 10 feet.

70.

$$\begin{aligned} a(x+2y) - b(2x - y) &= ax + 2ay - 2bx + by \\ &= (a - 2b)x + (2a + b)y \end{aligned}$$

$$\begin{aligned} a - 2b &= -3 \Rightarrow \times(-2) & -2a + 4b &= 6 & a - 2b &= -3 \\ 2a + b &= 9 & 2a + b &= 9 & a - 2(3) &= -3 \\ & & 5b &= 15 & a &= 3 \\ & & b &= 3 \end{aligned}$$

Solution: $a = 3, b = 3$

71.

$$E(x) = 43.53x + 742.72 \qquad R(x) = 89.95x$$

$$\begin{aligned} E(x) &= R(x) \\ 43.53x + 742.72 &= 89.95x \\ 742.72 &= 46.42x \\ 16 &= x \Rightarrow \end{aligned}$$

Daily production should be 16 pairs.

72.

$$S_1(x) = 326 + 0.035x \qquad S_2(x) = 200 + 0.0425x$$

$$\begin{aligned} S_1(x) &= S_2(x) \\ 326 + 0.035x &= 200 + 0.0425x \\ 126 &= 0.0075x \\ 16{,}800 &= x \end{aligned}$$

The salary would be the same at a sales level of $16,800.

73. Let x = hours at fast food restaurant, y = hours at gas station and z = janitorial hours.

(1) $x = 15$ Substitute $x = 15$ into (2) and (3):

(2) $x + y + z = 30$ (2) $15 + y + z = 30$

(3) $5.7x + 6.3y + 10z = 198.50$ (3) $5.7(15) + 6.3y + 10z = 198.5$

Solve the system of two equations and two unknowns formed by equations (2) and (3):

$$\begin{array}{l} y + z = 15 \Rightarrow \times(-10) \\ 6.3y + 10z = 113 \Rightarrow \times(-3) \end{array} \quad \begin{array}{rcr} -10y - 10z &=& -150 \\ 6.3y + 10z &=& 113 \\ \hline -3.7y &=& -37 \\ y &=& 10 \end{array} \quad \begin{array}{r} y + z = 15 \\ 10 + z = 15 \\ z = 5 \end{array}$$

He spends 15 hours cooking, 10 hours at the gas station and 5 hours doing janitorial work.

74. Let x = amount at 5%, y = amount at 6% and z = amount at 7%.

(1) $x + y + z = 22000$

(2) $y = x + 2000$

(3) $0.05x + 0.06y + 0.07z = 1370$

Add (1) and (2):

$$\begin{array}{lrcr} (1) & x + y + z &=& 22000 \\ (2) & -x + y &=& 2000 \\ \hline (4) & 2y + z &=& 24000 \end{array}$$

Add $-0.05(1)$ and (3):

$$\begin{array}{lrcr} -0.05(1) & -0.05x - 0.05y - 0.05z &=& -1100 \\ (3) & 0.05x + 0.06y + 0.07z &=& 1370 \\ \hline (5) & 0.01y + 0.02z &=& 270 \end{array}$$

Solve the system of two equations and two unknowns formed by equations (4) and (5):

$$\begin{array}{l} 2y + z = 24000 \Rightarrow \\ 0.01y + 0.02z = 270 \Rightarrow \times(100) \end{array} \quad \begin{array}{l} 2y + z = 24000 \Rightarrow \times(-2) \\ y + 2z = 27000 \quad \Rightarrow \end{array} \quad \begin{array}{rcr} -4y - 2z &=& -48000 \\ y + 2z &=& 27000 \\ \hline -3y &=& -21000 \\ y &=& 7000 \end{array}$$

She invested \$5000 at 5%, \$7000 at 6% and \$10,000 at 7%.

75. Let x = # between 0-14, y = # between 15-49 and z = # 50 or over.

(1) $x + y + z = 3$

(2) $x + y = 2.61$

(3) $y + z = 1.95$

Add (1) and $-(2)$:

$$\begin{array}{lrcr} (1) & x + y + z &=& 3 \\ -(2) & -x - y &=& -2.61 \\ \hline & z &=& 0.39 \end{array}$$

Substitute $z = 0.39$ into (3):

$$y + z = 1.95$$
$$y + 0.39 = 1.95$$
$$y = 1.56$$

Substitute $y = 1.56$ into (2):

$$x + y = 2.61$$
$$x + 1.56 = 2.61$$
$$x = 1.05$$

There are 1.05 million between 0-14, 1.56 million between 15-49 and 0.39 million over 50.

76. Points on the parabola: $(0, 0)$, $(10, 22.5)$ and $(40, 0)$. Substitute each into the equation:

$$y = ax^2 + bx + c \qquad y = ax^2 + bx + c \qquad y = ax^2 + bx + c$$
$$0 = a(0)^2 + b(0) + c \qquad 22.5 = a(10)^2 + b(10) + c \qquad 0 = a(40)^2 + b(40) + c$$
$$(1)\ 0 = c \qquad (2)\ 22.5 = 100a + 10b + c \qquad (3)\ 0 = 1600a + 40b + c$$

Substitute $c = 0$ into (2) and (3) and solve the resulting system of equations:

$$\begin{aligned} 100a + 10b &= 22.5 \Rightarrow \times\ (-4) \\ 1600a + 40b &= 0 \end{aligned} \qquad \begin{aligned} -400a - 40b &= -90 \\ 1600a + 40b &= 0 \\ \hline 1200a &= -90 \\ a &= -\tfrac{3}{40} \end{aligned} \qquad \begin{aligned} 1600a + 40b &= 0 \\ 1600(-\tfrac{3}{40}) + 40b &= 0 \\ -120 + 40b &= 0 \\ b &= 3 \end{aligned}$$

Solution: $\boxed{a = -\frac{3}{40}, b = 3, c = 0}$

77. Let $x =$ the smallest angle, $y =$ the middle angle and $z =$ the largest angle.

$$\begin{aligned} (1)\ & x + y + z = 180 \\ (2)\ & z = x + y + 20 \\ (3)\ & z = 3x + 10 \end{aligned}$$

Substitute (3) into (1):
$$\begin{aligned} x + y + 3x + 10 &= 180 \\ 4x + y &= 170 \quad (4) \end{aligned}$$

Substitute (3) and (2):
$$\begin{aligned} 3x + 10 &= x + y + 20 \\ 2x - y &= 10 \quad (5) \end{aligned}$$

Solve the system of two equations and two unknowns formed by equations (4) and (5):

$$\begin{aligned} 4x + y &= 170 \\ 2x - y &= 10 \\ \hline 6x &= 180 \\ x &= 30 \end{aligned} \qquad \begin{aligned} 4x + y &= 170 \\ 4(30) + y &= 170 \\ 120 + y &= 170 \\ y &= 50 \end{aligned} \qquad \begin{aligned} z &= 3x + 10 \\ z &= 3(30) + 10 \\ z &= 90 + 10 \\ z &= 100 \end{aligned}$$

Solution: $\boxed{\text{The angles have measures of } 30°, 50° \text{ and } 100°.}$

78. Points on the parabola: $(0, 0)$, $(8, 12)$ and $(12, 15)$. Substitute each into the equation:

$$y = ax^2 + bx + c \qquad y = ax^2 + bx + c \qquad y = ax^2 + bx + c$$
$$0 = a(0)^2 + b(0) + c \qquad 12 = a(8)^2 + b(8) + c \qquad 15 = a(12)^2 + b(12) + c$$
$$(1)\ 0 = c \qquad (2)\ 12 = 64a + 8b + c \qquad (3)\ 15 = 144a + 12b + c$$

Substitute $c = 0$ into (2) and (3) and solve the resulting system of equations:

$$\begin{aligned} 64a + 8b &= 12 \Rightarrow \times\ (-3) \\ 144a + 12b &= 15 \Rightarrow \times\ (2) \end{aligned} \qquad \begin{aligned} -192a - 24b &= -36 \\ 288a + 24b &= 30 \\ \hline 96a &= -6 \\ a &= -\tfrac{1}{16} \end{aligned} \qquad \begin{aligned} 64a + 8b &= 12 \\ 64(-\tfrac{1}{16}) + 8b &= 12 \\ -4 + 8b &= 12 \\ 8b &= 16 \\ b &= 2 \end{aligned}$$

Solution: $\boxed{a = -\frac{1}{16}, b = 2, c = 0}$

79. **Answers may vary.**

80. **Answers may vary.**

81. **Answers may vary.**

82. **Answers may vary.**

83. **Answers may vary.**

84. **Answers may vary.**

85. $y = 3^x$; points: $(0, 1)$, $(1, 3)$

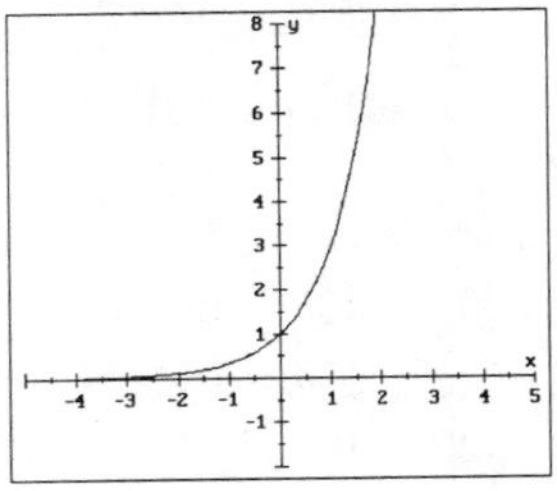

86. $y = \log_2 x$; points: $(1, 0)$, $(2, 1)$

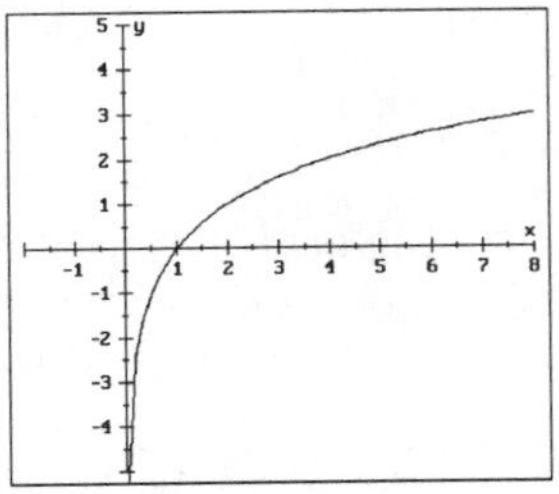

87.
$$\begin{aligned} 3 &= \log_2 x \\ 2^3 &= x \\ 8 &= x \end{aligned}$$

88.
$$\begin{aligned} x &= \log_5 \frac{1}{25} \\ 5^x &= \frac{1}{25} \\ x &= -2 \end{aligned}$$

89.
$$\begin{aligned} \log \frac{x}{y^2 z} &= \log x - \log\left(y^2 z\right) \\ &= \log x - \left(\log y^2 + \log z\right) \\ &= \log x - 2\log y - \log z \end{aligned}$$

90.
$$\begin{aligned} \log xy^z &= \log x + \log y^z \\ &= \log x + z \log y \end{aligned}$$

91. $\log x + 3\log y - \frac{1}{2}\log z = \log x + \log y^3 + \log z^{-1/2} = \log x + \log y^3 + \log \frac{1}{\sqrt{z}} = \log \frac{xy^3}{\sqrt{z}}$

92. $\frac{1}{2}(\log A - 3\log B) = \frac{1}{2}\left(\log A - \log B^3\right) = \frac{1}{2}\log \frac{A}{B^3} = \log \sqrt{\frac{A}{B^3}}$

Exercise 6.2 (page 445)

1. matrix **2.** 3, 5 **3.** coefficient **4.** system, augmented

5. equation **6.** row operations **7.** row equivalent **8.** same solutions

9. interchanged **10.** multiplied **11.** adding, multiple **12.** lead entry

13.
$$\begin{cases} (1) & x + y = 7 \\ (2) & x - 2y = -1 \end{cases} \Rightarrow \begin{cases} (1) & x + y = 7 \\ (2) & -3y = -8 \end{cases} \Rightarrow \begin{cases} (1) & x + y = 7 \\ (2) & y = \frac{8}{3} \end{cases}$$

$-(1) + (2) \Rightarrow (2)$ $\quad -\frac{1}{3}(2) \Rightarrow (2)$

From (2): $y = \frac{8}{3}$

From (1):
$$\begin{aligned} x + y &= 7 \\ x + \frac{8}{3} &= 7 \\ x &= \frac{13}{3} \end{aligned}$$

Solution: $\boxed{x = \frac{13}{3}, y = \frac{8}{3}}$

14. $\begin{cases}(1) & x+3y=8\\(2) & 2x-5y=5\end{cases} \Rightarrow \begin{cases}(1) & x+\ 3y=\ 8\\(2) & -11y=-11\end{cases} \Rightarrow \begin{cases}(1) & x+3y=8\\(2) & y=1\end{cases}$

$-2(1)+(2)\Rightarrow(2)$ $\quad -\frac{1}{11}(2)\Rightarrow(2)$

From (2): $y=1$ From (1): $x+3y=8$, $x+3(1)=8$, $x=5$

Solution: $\boxed{x=5,\ y=1}$

15. $\begin{cases}(1) & x-y=1\\(2) & 2x-y=8\end{cases} \Rightarrow \begin{cases}(1) & x-y=1\\(2) & y=6\end{cases}$

$-2(1)+(2)\Rightarrow(2)$

From (2): $y=6$ From (1): $x-y=1$, $x-6=1$, $x=7$

Solution: $\boxed{x=7,\ y=6}$

16. $\begin{cases}(1) & x-5y=\ 4\\(2) & 2x+3y=21\end{cases} \Rightarrow \begin{cases}(1) & x-\ 5y=\ 4\\(2) & 13y=13\end{cases} \Rightarrow \begin{cases}(1) & x-5y=4\\(2) & y=1\end{cases}$

$-2(1)+(2)\Rightarrow(2)$ $\quad \frac{1}{13}(2)\Rightarrow(2)$

From (2): $y=1$ From (1): $x-5y=4$, $x-5(1)=4$, $x=9$

Solution: $\boxed{x=9,\ y=1}$

17. $\begin{cases}(1) & x+2y-\ z=\ 2\\(2) & x-3y+2z=\ 1\\(3) & x+\ y-3z=-6\end{cases} \Rightarrow \begin{cases}(1) & x+2y-\ z=\ 2\\(2) & -5y+3z=-1\\(3) & -\ y-2z=-8\end{cases} \Rightarrow \begin{cases}(1) & x+2y-\ z=\ 2\\(2) & -5y+\ 3z=-1\\(3) & 13z=\ 39\end{cases} \Rightarrow$

$-(1)+(2)\Rightarrow(2)$
$-(1)+(3)\Rightarrow(3)$ $\quad -5(3)+(2)\Rightarrow(3)$

$\begin{cases}(1) & x+2y-\ z=2\\(2) & y-\frac{3}{5}z=\frac{1}{5}\\(3) & z=3\end{cases}$

$-\frac{1}{5}(2)\Rightarrow(2)$
$\frac{1}{13}(3)\Rightarrow(3)$

From (3): $z=3$

From (2): $y-\dfrac{3}{5}z=\dfrac{1}{5}$

$y-\dfrac{3}{5}(3)=\dfrac{1}{5}$

$y=2$

From (1): $x+2y-z=2$, $x+2(2)-(3)=2$, $x=1$

Solution: $\boxed{x=1,\ y=2,\ z=3}$

18. $\begin{cases}(1)\ x+5y-z=2\\(2)\ x+2y+z=3\\(3)\ x+\ y+z=2\end{cases} \Rightarrow \begin{cases}(1)\ x+5y-\ z=\ \ 2\\(2)\qquad 3y-2z=-1\\(3)\qquad 4y-2z=\ \ 0\end{cases} \Rightarrow \begin{cases}(1)\ x+5y-\ z=\ \ 2\\(2)\qquad y-\frac{2}{3}z=-\frac{1}{3}\\(3)\qquad 4y-2z=\ \ 0\end{cases} \Rightarrow$

$-(2)+(1)\Rightarrow(2)$; $-(3)+(1)\Rightarrow(3)$; $\frac{1}{3}(2)\Rightarrow(2)$

$\begin{cases}(1)\ x+5y-\ z=\ \ 2\\(2)\qquad y-\frac{2}{3}z=-\frac{1}{3}\\(3)\qquad \frac{2}{3}z=\ \ \frac{4}{3}\end{cases} \Rightarrow \begin{cases}(1)\ x+5y-\ z=\ \ 2\\(2)\qquad y-\frac{2}{3}z=-\frac{1}{3}\\(3)\qquad z=\ \ 2\end{cases}$

$-4(2)+(3)\Rightarrow(3)$; $\frac{3}{2}(3)\Rightarrow(3)$

From (3): $z=2$ From (2): $y-\frac{2}{3}z=-\frac{1}{3}$

$y-\frac{2}{3}(2)=-\frac{1}{3}$

$y=1$

From (1): $x+5y-z=2$

$x+5(1)-2=2$

$x=-1$

Solution: $\boxed{x=-1,\ y=1,\ z=2}$

19. $\begin{cases}(1)\ \ x-y-z=-3\\(2)\ 5x+y\qquad=\ \ 6\\(3)\qquad y+z=\ \ 4\end{cases} \Rightarrow \begin{cases}(1)\ x-\ y-\ z=-3\\(2)\qquad 6y+5z=\ 21\\(3)\qquad y+\ z=\ \ 4\end{cases} \Rightarrow \begin{cases}(1)\ x-y-\ z=-3\\(2)\qquad y+\frac{5}{6}z=\ \ \frac{7}{2}\\(3)\qquad -\ z=-3\end{cases} \Rightarrow$

$-5(1)+(2)\Rightarrow(2)$; $\frac{1}{6}(2)\Rightarrow(2)$; $-6(3)+(2)\Rightarrow(3)$

$\begin{cases}(1)\ x-y-\ z=-3\\(2)\qquad y+\frac{5}{6}z=\ \ \frac{7}{2}\\(3)\qquad z=\ \ 3\end{cases} \Rightarrow$

$-(3)\Rightarrow(3)$

From (3): $z=3$

From (2): $y+\frac{5}{6}z=\frac{7}{2}$

$y+\frac{5}{6}(3)=\frac{7}{2}$

$y=1$

From (1): $x-y-z=-3$

$x-(1)-(3)=-3$

$x=1$

Solution: $\boxed{x=1,\ y=1,\ z=3}$

20. $\begin{cases}(1)\ x+y\qquad=1\\(2)\ x\qquad+z=3\\(3)\qquad y+z=2\end{cases} \Rightarrow \begin{cases}(1)\ x+y\qquad=1\\(2)\qquad -y+z=2\\(3)\qquad y+z=2\end{cases} \Rightarrow \begin{cases}(1)\ x+y\qquad=\ \ 1\\(2)\qquad y-z=-2\\(3)\qquad 2z=\ \ 4\end{cases} \Rightarrow$

$-(1)+(2)\Rightarrow(2)$; $-(2)\Rightarrow(2)$; $(2)+(3)\Rightarrow(3)$

$\begin{cases}(1)\ x+y\qquad=\ \ 1\\(2)\qquad y-z=-2\\(3)\qquad z=\ \ 2\end{cases} \Rightarrow$

$\frac{1}{2}(3)\Rightarrow(3)$

From (3): $z=2$

From (2): $y-z=-2$

$y-(2)=-2$

$y=0$

From (1): $x+y=1$

$x+(0)=1$

$x=1$

Solution: $\boxed{x=1,\ y=0,\ z=2}$

21. row echelon form **22.** row echelon form **23.** reduced row echelon form **24.** reduced row echelon form

25. $\left[\begin{array}{cc|c} 2 & 1 & 3 \\ 1 & -3 & 5 \end{array}\right] \Rightarrow \underset{R_1 \Leftrightarrow R_2}{\left[\begin{array}{cc|c} 1 & -3 & 5 \\ 2 & 1 & 3 \end{array}\right]} \Rightarrow \underset{-2R_1 + R_2 \Rightarrow R_2}{\left[\begin{array}{cc|c} 1 & -3 & 5 \\ 0 & 7 & -7 \end{array}\right]} \Rightarrow \underset{\frac{1}{7}R_2 \Rightarrow R_2}{\left[\begin{array}{cc|c} 1 & -3 & 5 \\ 0 & 1 & -1 \end{array}\right]}$

From R_2: $y = -1$ From R_1: $x - 3y = 5$ Solution: $\boxed{x = 2, y = -1}$

$$\begin{aligned} x - 3(-1) &= 5 \\ x + 3 &= 5 \\ x &= 2 \end{aligned}$$

26. $\left[\begin{array}{cc|c} 1 & 2 & -1 \\ 3 & -5 & 19 \end{array}\right] \Rightarrow \underset{-3R_1 + R_2 \Rightarrow R_2}{\left[\begin{array}{cc|c} 1 & 2 & -1 \\ 0 & -11 & 22 \end{array}\right]} \Rightarrow \underset{-\frac{1}{11}R_2 \Rightarrow R_2}{\left[\begin{array}{cc|c} 1 & 2 & -1 \\ 0 & 1 & -2 \end{array}\right]}$

From R_2: $y = -2$ From R_1: $x + 2y = -1$ Solution: $\boxed{x = 3, y = -2}$

$$\begin{aligned} x + 2(-2) &= -1 \\ x &= 3 \end{aligned}$$

27. $\left[\begin{array}{cc|c} 1 & -7 & -2 \\ 5 & -2 & -10 \end{array}\right] \Rightarrow \underset{-5R_1 + R_2 \Rightarrow R_2}{\left[\begin{array}{cc|c} 1 & -7 & -2 \\ 0 & 33 & 0 \end{array}\right]} \Rightarrow \underset{\frac{1}{33}R_2 \Rightarrow R_2}{\left[\begin{array}{cc|c} 1 & -7 & -2 \\ 0 & 1 & 0 \end{array}\right]}$

From R_2: $y = 0$ From R_1: $x - 7y = -2$ Solution: $\boxed{x = -2, y = 0}$

$$\begin{aligned} x - 7(0) &= -2 \\ x &= -2 \end{aligned}$$

28. $\left[\begin{array}{cc|c} 3 & -1 & 3 \\ 2 & 1 & -3 \end{array}\right] \Rightarrow \underset{-\frac{3}{2}R_2 + R_1 \Rightarrow R_2}{\left[\begin{array}{cc|c} 3 & -1 & 3 \\ 0 & -\frac{5}{2} & \frac{15}{2} \end{array}\right]} \Rightarrow \underset{\substack{\frac{1}{3}R_1 \Rightarrow R_1 \\ -\frac{2}{5}R_2 \Rightarrow R_2}}{\left[\begin{array}{cc|c} 1 & -\frac{1}{3} & 1 \\ 0 & 1 & -3 \end{array}\right]}$

From R_2: $y = -3$ From R_1: $x - \frac{1}{3}y = 1$ Solution: $\boxed{x = 0, y = -3}$

$$\begin{aligned} x - \tfrac{1}{3}(-3) &= 1 \\ x + 1 &= 1 \\ x &= 0 \end{aligned}$$

29. $\left[\begin{array}{cc|c} 2 & -1 & 5 \\ 1 & 3 & 6 \end{array}\right] \Rightarrow \underset{R_1 \Leftrightarrow R_2}{\left[\begin{array}{cc|c} 1 & 3 & 6 \\ 2 & -1 & 5 \end{array}\right]} \Rightarrow \underset{-2R_1 + R_2 \Rightarrow R_2}{\left[\begin{array}{cc|c} 1 & 3 & 6 \\ 0 & -7 & -7 \end{array}\right]} \Rightarrow \underset{-\frac{1}{7}R_2 \Rightarrow R_2}{\left[\begin{array}{cc|c} 1 & 3 & 6 \\ 0 & 1 & 1 \end{array}\right]}$

From R_2: $y = 1$ From R_1: $x + 3y = 6$ Solution: $\boxed{x = 3, y = 1}$

$$\begin{aligned} x + 3(1) &= 6 \\ x + 3 &= 6 \\ x &= 3 \end{aligned}$$

30. $\left[\begin{array}{cc|c} 3 & -5 & -25 \\ 2 & 1 & 5 \end{array}\right] \Rightarrow \underset{-\frac{3}{2}R_2 + R_1 \Rightarrow R_2}{\left[\begin{array}{cc|c} 3 & -5 & -25 \\ 0 & -\frac{13}{2} & -\frac{65}{2} \end{array}\right]} \Rightarrow \underset{\substack{\frac{1}{3}R_1 \Rightarrow R_1 \\ -\frac{2}{13}R_2 \Rightarrow R_2}}{\left[\begin{array}{cc|c} 1 & -\frac{5}{3} & -\frac{25}{3} \\ 0 & 1 & 5 \end{array}\right]}$

From R_2: $y = 5$ From R_1: $x - \frac{5}{3}y = -\frac{25}{3}$ Solution: $\boxed{x = 0, y = 5}$

$x - \frac{5}{3}(5) = -\frac{25}{3}$

$x - \frac{25}{3} = -\frac{25}{3}$

$x = 0$

31. $\left[\begin{array}{cc|c} 1 & -2 & 3 \\ -2 & 4 & 6 \end{array}\right] \Rightarrow \underset{2R_1 + R_2 \Rightarrow R_2}{\left[\begin{array}{cc|c} 1 & -2 & 3 \\ 0 & 0 & 12 \end{array}\right]} \Rightarrow$ From R_2, $0x + 0y = 12$. This is impossible.

$\boxed{\text{No solution} \Rightarrow \text{inconsistent system}}$

32. $\left[\begin{array}{cc|c} 2 & -1 & 7 \\ -1 & \frac{1}{3} & -\frac{7}{3} \end{array}\right] \Rightarrow \underset{R_1 \Leftrightarrow -R_2}{\left[\begin{array}{cc|c} 1 & -\frac{1}{3} & \frac{7}{3} \\ 2 & -1 & 7 \end{array}\right]} \Rightarrow \underset{-2R_1 + R_2 \Rightarrow R_2}{\left[\begin{array}{cc|c} 1 & -\frac{1}{3} & \frac{7}{3} \\ 0 & -\frac{1}{3} & \frac{7}{3} \end{array}\right]} \Rightarrow \underset{-3R_2 \Rightarrow R_2}{\left[\begin{array}{cc|c} 1 & -\frac{1}{3} & \frac{7}{3} \\ 0 & 1 & -7 \end{array}\right]}$

From R_2: $y = -7$ From R_1: $x - \frac{1}{3}y = \frac{7}{3}$ Solution: $\boxed{x = 0, y = -7}$

$x - \frac{1}{3}(-7) = \frac{7}{3}$

$x + \frac{7}{3} = \frac{7}{3}$

$x = 0$

33. $\left[\begin{array}{ccc|c} 1 & -1 & 1 & 3 \\ 2 & -1 & 1 & 4 \\ 1 & 2 & -1 & -1 \end{array}\right] \Rightarrow \underset{\substack{-2R_1 + R_2 \Rightarrow R_2 \\ -R_1 + R_3 \Rightarrow R_3}}{\left[\begin{array}{ccc|c} 1 & -1 & 1 & 3 \\ 0 & 1 & -1 & -2 \\ 0 & 3 & -2 & -4 \end{array}\right]} \Rightarrow \underset{-3R_2 + R_3 \Rightarrow R_3}{\left[\begin{array}{ccc|c} 1 & -1 & 1 & 3 \\ 0 & 1 & -1 & -2 \\ 0 & 0 & 1 & 2 \end{array}\right]} \Rightarrow$

From R_3: $z = 2$ From R_1: $x - y + z = 3$

From R_2: $y - z = -2$ $x - (0) + (2) = 3$

$y - (2) = -2$ $x = 1$

$y = 0$ Solution: $\boxed{x = 1, y = 0, z = 2}$

34. $\left[\begin{array}{ccc|c} 2 & 1 & -1 & 1 \\ 1 & 1 & -1 & 0 \\ 3 & 1 & 2 & 2 \end{array}\right] \Rightarrow \underset{\substack{-2R_2 + R_1 \Rightarrow R_2 \\ -3R_2 + R_3 \Rightarrow R_3}}{\left[\begin{array}{ccc|c} 2 & 1 & -1 & 1 \\ 0 & -1 & 1 & 1 \\ 0 & -2 & 5 & 2 \end{array}\right]} \Rightarrow \underset{\substack{-R_2 \Rightarrow R_2 \\ -2R_2 + R_3 \Rightarrow R_3}}{\left[\begin{array}{ccc|c} 2 & 1 & -1 & 1 \\ 0 & 1 & -1 & -1 \\ 0 & 0 & 3 & 0 \end{array}\right]} \Rightarrow \underset{\substack{\frac{1}{3}R_3 \Rightarrow R_3 \\ \frac{1}{2}R_1 \Rightarrow R_1}}{\left[\begin{array}{ccc|c} 1 & \frac{1}{2} & -\frac{1}{2} & \frac{1}{2} \\ 0 & 1 & -1 & -1 \\ 0 & 0 & 1 & 0 \end{array}\right]}$

From (3): $z = 0$ From (1): $x + \frac{1}{2}y - \frac{1}{2}z = \frac{1}{2}$ Solution:

From (2): $y - z = -1$ $x + \frac{1}{2}(-1) - \frac{1}{2}(0) = \frac{1}{2}$ $\boxed{x = 1, y = -1, z = 0}$

$y - (0) = -1$ $x - \frac{1}{2} = \frac{1}{2}$

$y = -1$ $x = 1$

35. $\left[\begin{array}{ccc|c} 1 & 1 & -1 & -1 \\ 3 & 1 & 0 & 4 \\ 0 & 1 & -2 & -4 \end{array}\right] \Rightarrow \left[\begin{array}{ccc|c} 1 & 1 & -1 & -1 \\ 0 & -2 & 3 & 7 \\ 0 & 1 & -2 & -4 \end{array}\right] \Rightarrow \left[\begin{array}{ccc|c} 1 & 1 & -1 & -1 \\ 0 & 1 & -\frac{3}{2} & -\frac{7}{2} \\ 0 & 0 & -1 & -1 \end{array}\right] \Rightarrow \left[\begin{array}{ccc|c} 1 & 1 & -1 & -1 \\ 0 & 1 & -\frac{3}{2} & -\frac{7}{2} \\ 0 & 0 & 1 & 1 \end{array}\right]$

$-3R_1 + R_2 \Rightarrow R_2$ $\quad$ $-\frac{1}{2}R_2 \Rightarrow R_2$, $R_2 + 2R_3 \Rightarrow R_3$ $\quad$ $-R_3 \Rightarrow R_3$

From (3): $z = 1$

From (2): $y - \frac{3}{2}z = -\frac{7}{2}$

$y - \frac{3}{2}(1) = -\frac{7}{2}$

$y = -2$

From (1): $x + y - z = -1$

$x + (-2) - (1) = -1$

$x = 2$

Solution: $\boxed{x = 2, y = -2, z = 1}$

36. $\left[\begin{array}{ccc|c} 3 & 1 & 0 & 7 \\ 1 & 0 & -1 & 0 \\ 0 & 1 & -2 & -8 \end{array}\right] \Rightarrow \left[\begin{array}{ccc|c} 1 & \frac{1}{3} & 0 & \frac{7}{3} \\ 0 & 1 & 3 & 7 \\ 0 & 1 & -2 & -8 \end{array}\right] \Rightarrow \left[\begin{array}{ccc|c} 1 & \frac{1}{3} & 0 & \frac{7}{3} \\ 0 & 1 & 3 & 7 \\ 0 & 0 & 5 & 15 \end{array}\right] \Rightarrow \left[\begin{array}{ccc|c} 1 & \frac{1}{3} & 0 & \frac{7}{3} \\ 0 & 1 & 3 & 7 \\ 0 & 0 & 1 & 3 \end{array}\right]$

$-3R_2 + R_1 \Rightarrow R_2$, $\frac{1}{3}R_1 \Rightarrow R_1$ $\quad$ $-R_3 + R_2 \Rightarrow R_3$ $\quad$ $\frac{1}{5}R_3 \Rightarrow R_3$

From (3): $z = 3$

From (2): $y + 3z = 7$

$y + 3(3) = 7$

$y = -2$

From (1): $x + \frac{1}{3}y = \frac{7}{3}$

$x + \frac{1}{3}(-2) = \frac{7}{3}$

$x = 3$

Solution: $\boxed{x = 3, y = -2, z = 3}$

37. $\left[\begin{array}{ccc|c} 1 & -1 & 1 & 2 \\ 2 & 1 & 1 & 5 \\ 3 & 0 & -4 & -5 \end{array}\right] \Rightarrow \left[\begin{array}{ccc|c} 1 & -1 & 1 & 2 \\ 0 & 3 & -1 & 1 \\ 0 & 3 & -7 & -11 \end{array}\right] \Rightarrow \left[\begin{array}{ccc|c} 1 & -1 & 1 & 2 \\ 0 & 1 & -\frac{1}{3} & \frac{1}{3} \\ 0 & 0 & 6 & 12 \end{array}\right] \Rightarrow$

$-2R_1 + R_2 \Rightarrow R_2$, $-3R_1 + R_3 \Rightarrow R_3$ $\quad$ $\frac{1}{3}R_2 \Rightarrow R_2$, $-R_3 + R_2 \Rightarrow R_3$

$\left[\begin{array}{ccc|c} 1 & -1 & 1 & 2 \\ 0 & 1 & -\frac{1}{3} & \frac{1}{3} \\ 0 & 0 & 1 & 2 \end{array}\right]$

$\frac{1}{6}R_3 \Rightarrow R_3$

From (3): $z = 2$

From (2): $y - \frac{1}{3}z = \frac{1}{3}$

$y - \frac{1}{3}(2) = \frac{1}{3}$

$y = 1$

From (1): $x - y + z = 2$

$x - (1) + (2) = 2$

$x = 1$

Solution: $\boxed{x = 1, y = 1, z = 2}$

38. $\left[\begin{array}{ccc|c} 1 & 0 & 1 & -1 \\ 3 & 1 & 0 & 2 \\ 2 & 1 & 5 & 3 \end{array}\right] \Rightarrow \left[\begin{array}{ccc|c} 1 & 0 & 1 & -1 \\ 0 & 1 & -3 & 5 \\ 0 & 1 & 7 & 5 \end{array}\right] \Rightarrow \left[\begin{array}{ccc|c} 1 & 0 & 1 & -1 \\ 0 & 1 & -3 & 5 \\ 0 & 0 & 4 & 0 \end{array}\right] \Rightarrow \left[\begin{array}{ccc|c} 1 & 0 & 1 & -1 \\ 0 & 1 & -3 & 5 \\ 0 & 0 & 1 & 0 \end{array}\right]$

$-3R_1 + R_2 \Rightarrow R_2$, $-2R_1 + R_3 \Rightarrow R_3$ $\quad$ $-R_2 + R_3 \Rightarrow R_3$ $\quad$ $\frac{1}{4}R_3 \Rightarrow R_3$

From (3): $z = 0$

From (2): $y - 3z = 5$

$y - 3(0) = 5$

$y = 5$

From (1): $x + z = -1$

$x + (0) = -1$

$x = -1$

Solution: $\boxed{x = -1, y = 5, z = 0}$

39. $\left[\begin{array}{ccc|c} 1 & 1 & 2 & 4 \\ -1 & -1 & -3 & -5 \\ 2 & 1 & 1 & 2 \end{array}\right] \Rightarrow \left[\begin{array}{ccc|c} 1 & 1 & 2 & 4 \\ 0 & 0 & -1 & -1 \\ 0 & -1 & -3 & -6 \end{array}\right] \Rightarrow \left[\begin{array}{ccc|c} 1 & 1 & 2 & 4 \\ 0 & -1 & -3 & -6 \\ 0 & 0 & -1 & -1 \end{array}\right] \Rightarrow \left[\begin{array}{ccc|c} 1 & 1 & 2 & 4 \\ 0 & 1 & 3 & 6 \\ 0 & 0 & 1 & 1 \end{array}\right]$

$R_1 + R_2 \Rightarrow R_2$, $-2R_1 + R_3 \Rightarrow R_3$; $R_2 \Leftrightarrow R_3$; $-R_2 \Rightarrow R_2$, $-R_3 \Rightarrow R_3$

From (3): $z = 1$

From (2): $y + 3z = 6$; $y + 3(1) = 6$; $y = 3$

From (1): $x + y + 2z = 4$; $x + (3) + 2(1) = 4$; $x = -1$

Solution: $\boxed{x = -1, y = 3, z = 1}$

40. $\left[\begin{array}{ccc|c} 2 & -1 & 1 & 6 \\ 3 & 1 & -1 & 2 \\ -1 & 3 & -3 & 8 \end{array}\right] \Rightarrow \left[\begin{array}{ccc|c} -1 & 3 & -3 & 8 \\ 3 & 1 & -1 & 2 \\ 2 & -1 & 1 & 6 \end{array}\right] \Rightarrow \left[\begin{array}{ccc|c} -1 & 3 & -3 & 8 \\ 0 & 10 & -10 & 26 \\ 0 & 5 & -5 & 22 \end{array}\right] \Rightarrow$

$R_1 \Leftrightarrow R_3$; $3R_1 + R_2 \Rightarrow R_2$, $2R_1 + R_3 \Rightarrow R_3$

$\left[\begin{array}{ccc|c} -1 & 3 & -3 & 8 \\ 0 & 10 & -10 & 26 \\ 0 & 0 & 0 & -18 \end{array}\right]$

$-2R_3 + R_2 \Rightarrow R_3$

R_3 indicates $0x + 0y + 0z = -18$. This is impossible.

$\boxed{\text{No solution} \Rightarrow \text{inconsistent system}}$

41. $\left[\begin{array}{cc|c} 1 & -2 & 7 \\ 0 & 1 & 3 \end{array}\right] \Rightarrow \left[\begin{array}{cc|c} 1 & 0 & 13 \\ 0 & 1 & 3 \end{array}\right] \Rightarrow$ Solution: $\boxed{x = 13, y = 3}$

$2R_2 + R_1 \Rightarrow R_1$

42. $\left[\begin{array}{cc|c} 1 & -2 & 7 \\ 0 & 1 & 8 \end{array}\right] \Rightarrow \left[\begin{array}{cc|c} 1 & 0 & 23 \\ 0 & 1 & 8 \end{array}\right] \Rightarrow$ Solution: $\boxed{x = 23, y = 8}$

$2R_2 + R_1 \Rightarrow R_1$

43. $\left[\begin{array}{ccc|c} 1 & 2 & -1 & 3 \\ 0 & 1 & 3 & 1 \\ 0 & 0 & 1 & -2 \end{array}\right] \Rightarrow \left[\begin{array}{ccc|c} 1 & 0 & -7 & 1 \\ 0 & 1 & 3 & 1 \\ 0 & 0 & 1 & -2 \end{array}\right] \Rightarrow \left[\begin{array}{ccc|c} 1 & 0 & 0 & -13 \\ 0 & 1 & 0 & 7 \\ 0 & 0 & 1 & -2 \end{array}\right]$ Solution: $\boxed{x = -13, y = 7, z = -2}$

$-2R_2 + R_1 \Rightarrow R_1$; $7R_3 + R_1 \Rightarrow R_1$, $-3R_3 + R_2 \Rightarrow R_2$

44. $\left[\begin{array}{ccc|c} 1 & -3 & 2 & -1 \\ 0 & 1 & -2 & 3 \\ 0 & 0 & 1 & 5 \end{array}\right] \Rightarrow \left[\begin{array}{ccc|c} 1 & 0 & -4 & 8 \\ 0 & 1 & -2 & 3 \\ 0 & 0 & 1 & 5 \end{array}\right] \Rightarrow \left[\begin{array}{ccc|c} 1 & 0 & 0 & 28 \\ 0 & 1 & 0 & 13 \\ 0 & 0 & 1 & 5 \end{array}\right]$ Solution: $\boxed{x = 28, y = 13, z = 5}$

$3R_2 + R_1 \Rightarrow R_1$; $4R_3 + R_1 \Rightarrow R_1$, $2R_3 + R_2 \Rightarrow R_2$

45. $\left[\begin{array}{cc|c} 1 & -1 & 7 \\ 1 & 1 & 13 \end{array}\right] \Rightarrow \left[\begin{array}{cc|c} 1 & -1 & 7 \\ 0 & 2 & 6 \end{array}\right] \Rightarrow \left[\begin{array}{cc|c} 1 & -1 & 7 \\ 0 & 1 & 3 \end{array}\right] \Rightarrow \left[\begin{array}{cc|c} 1 & 0 & 10 \\ 0 & 1 & 3 \end{array}\right]$ Solution: $\boxed{x = 10, y = 3}$

$-R_1 + R_2 \Rightarrow R_2$; $\frac{1}{2}R_2 \Rightarrow R_2$; $R_2 + R_1 \Rightarrow R_1$

46. $$\left[\begin{array}{cc|c}1 & 2 & 7\\ 2 & -1 & -1\end{array}\right] \Rightarrow \underset{-2R_1+R_2\Rightarrow R_2}{\left[\begin{array}{cc|c}1 & 2 & 7\\ 0 & -5 & -15\end{array}\right]} \Rightarrow \underset{-\frac{1}{5}R_2\Rightarrow R_2}{\left[\begin{array}{cc|c}1 & 2 & 7\\ 0 & 1 & 3\end{array}\right]} \Rightarrow \underset{-2R_2+R_1\Rightarrow R_1}{\left[\begin{array}{cc|c}1 & 0 & 1\\ 0 & 1 & 3\end{array}\right]}$$

Solution: $\boxed{x=1, y=3}$

47. $$\left[\begin{array}{cc|c}1 & -\frac{1}{2} & 0\\ 1 & 2 & 0\end{array}\right] \Rightarrow \underset{-R_1+R_2\Rightarrow R_2}{\left[\begin{array}{cc|c}1 & -\frac{1}{2} & 0\\ 0 & \frac{5}{2} & 0\end{array}\right]} \Rightarrow \underset{\frac{2}{5}R_2\Rightarrow R_2}{\left[\begin{array}{cc|c}1 & -\frac{1}{2} & 0\\ 0 & 1 & 0\end{array}\right]} \Rightarrow \underset{\frac{1}{2}R_2+R_1\Rightarrow R_1}{\left[\begin{array}{cc|c}1 & 0 & 0\\ 0 & 1 & 0\end{array}\right]}$$

Solution: $\boxed{x=0, y=0}$

48. $$\left[\begin{array}{cc|c}1 & -1 & 5\\ -1 & \frac{1}{5} & -9\end{array}\right] \Rightarrow \underset{R_1+R_2\Rightarrow R_2}{\left[\begin{array}{cc|c}1 & -1 & 5\\ 0 & -\frac{4}{5} & -4\end{array}\right]} \Rightarrow \underset{-\frac{5}{4}R_2\Rightarrow R_2}{\left[\begin{array}{cc|c}1 & -1 & 5\\ 0 & 1 & 5\end{array}\right]} \Rightarrow \underset{R_2+R_1\Rightarrow R_1}{\left[\begin{array}{cc|c}1 & 0 & 10\\ 0 & 1 & 5\end{array}\right]}$$

Solution: $\boxed{x=10, y=5}$

49. $$\left[\begin{array}{ccc|c}1 & 1 & 2 & 0\\ 1 & 1 & 1 & 2\\ 1 & 0 & 1 & 1\end{array}\right] \Rightarrow \underset{\substack{-R_1+R_2\Rightarrow R_2\\ -R_1+R_3\Rightarrow R_3}}{\left[\begin{array}{ccc|c}1 & 1 & 2 & 0\\ 0 & 0 & -1 & 2\\ 0 & -1 & -1 & 1\end{array}\right]} \Rightarrow \underset{R_2\Leftrightarrow R_3}{\left[\begin{array}{ccc|c}1 & 1 & 2 & 0\\ 0 & -1 & -1 & 1\\ 0 & 0 & -1 & 2\end{array}\right]} \Rightarrow \underset{\substack{-R_2\Rightarrow R_2\\ -R_3\Rightarrow R_3}}{\left[\begin{array}{ccc|c}1 & 1 & 2 & 0\\ 0 & 1 & 1 & -1\\ 0 & 0 & 1 & -2\end{array}\right]}$$

$$\underset{-R_2+R_1\Rightarrow R_1}{\left[\begin{array}{ccc|c}1 & 0 & 1 & 1\\ 0 & 1 & 1 & -1\\ 0 & 0 & 1 & -2\end{array}\right]} \Rightarrow \underset{\substack{-R_3+R_1\Rightarrow R_1\\ -R_3+R_2\Rightarrow R_2}}{\left[\begin{array}{ccc|c}1 & 0 & 0 & 3\\ 0 & 1 & 0 & 1\\ 0 & 0 & 1 & -2\end{array}\right]}$$

Solution: $\boxed{x=3, y=1, z=-2}$

50. $$\left[\begin{array}{ccc|c}1 & 2 & 0 & -3\\ 1 & 4 & 0 & -2\\ 2 & 0 & 1 & -8\end{array}\right] \Rightarrow \underset{\substack{-R_1+R_2\Rightarrow R_2\\ -2R_1+R_3\Rightarrow R_3}}{\left[\begin{array}{ccc|c}1 & 2 & 0 & -3\\ 0 & 2 & 0 & 1\\ 0 & -4 & 1 & -2\end{array}\right]} \Rightarrow \underset{\substack{-R_2+R_1\Rightarrow R_1\\ 2R_2+R_3\Rightarrow R_3}}{\left[\begin{array}{ccc|c}1 & 0 & 0 & -4\\ 0 & 2 & 0 & 1\\ 0 & 0 & 1 & 0\end{array}\right]} \Rightarrow \underset{\frac{1}{2}R_2\Rightarrow R_2}{\left[\begin{array}{ccc|c}1 & 0 & 0 & -4\\ 0 & 1 & 0 & \frac{1}{2}\\ 0 & 0 & 1 & 0\end{array}\right]}$$

Solution: $\boxed{x=-4, y=\frac{1}{2}, z=0}$

51. $$\left[\begin{array}{ccc|c}2 & 1 & -2 & 1\\ -1 & 1 & -3 & 0\\ 4 & 3 & 0 & 4\end{array}\right] \Rightarrow \underset{\substack{R_1+2R_2\Rightarrow R_2\\ -2R_1+R_3\Rightarrow R_3}}{\left[\begin{array}{ccc|c}2 & 1 & -2 & 1\\ 0 & 3 & -8 & 1\\ 0 & 1 & 4 & 2\end{array}\right]} \Rightarrow \underset{\substack{-3R_1+R_2\Rightarrow R_1\\ -3R_3+R_2\Rightarrow R_3}}{\left[\begin{array}{ccc|c}-6 & 0 & -2 & -2\\ 0 & 3 & -8 & 1\\ 0 & 0 & -20 & -5\end{array}\right]} \Rightarrow \underset{-\frac{1}{20}R_3\Rightarrow R_3}{\left[\begin{array}{ccc|c}-6 & 0 & -2 & -2\\ 0 & 3 & -8 & 1\\ 0 & 0 & 1 & \frac{1}{4}\end{array}\right]}$$

$$\underset{\substack{2R_3+R_1\Rightarrow R_1\\ 8R_3+R_2\Rightarrow R_2}}{\left[\begin{array}{ccc|c}-6 & 0 & 0 & -\frac{3}{2}\\ 0 & 3 & 0 & 3\\ 0 & 0 & 1 & \frac{1}{4}\end{array}\right]} \Rightarrow \underset{\substack{-\frac{1}{6}R_1\Rightarrow R_1\\ \frac{1}{3}R_2\Rightarrow R_2}}{\left[\begin{array}{ccc|c}1 & 0 & 0 & \frac{1}{4}\\ 0 & 1 & 0 & 1\\ 0 & 0 & 1 & \frac{1}{4}\end{array}\right]}$$

Solution: $\boxed{x=\frac{1}{4}, y=1, z=\frac{1}{4}}$

52.

$$\left[\begin{array}{ccc|c} 3 & 1 & 0 & 3 \\ 3 & 1 & -1 & 2 \\ 6 & 0 & 1 & 5 \end{array}\right] \Rightarrow \left[\begin{array}{ccc|c} 3 & 1 & 0 & 3 \\ 0 & 0 & -1 & -1 \\ 0 & -2 & 1 & -1 \end{array}\right] \Rightarrow \left[\begin{array}{ccc|c} 3 & 1 & 0 & 3 \\ 0 & -2 & 1 & -1 \\ 0 & 0 & -1 & -1 \end{array}\right] \Rightarrow \left[\begin{array}{ccc|c} 6 & 0 & 1 & 5 \\ 0 & -2 & 1 & -1 \\ 0 & 0 & 1 & 1 \end{array}\right]$$

$-R_1 + R_2 \Rightarrow R_2$, $-2R_1 + R_3 \Rightarrow R_3$; $R_2 \Leftrightarrow R_3$; $2R_1 + R_2 \Rightarrow R_1$, $-R_3 \Rightarrow R_3$

$$\left[\begin{array}{ccc|c} 6 & 0 & 0 & 4 \\ 0 & -2 & 0 & -2 \\ 0 & 0 & 1 & 1 \end{array}\right] \Rightarrow \left[\begin{array}{ccc|c} 1 & 0 & 0 & \frac{2}{3} \\ 0 & 1 & 0 & 1 \\ 0 & 0 & 1 & 1 \end{array}\right]$$

$-R_3 + R_1 \Rightarrow R_1$, $-R_3 + R_2 \Rightarrow R_2$; $\frac{1}{6}R_1 \Rightarrow R_1$, $\frac{1}{2}R_2 \Rightarrow R_2$

Solution: $\boxed{x = \frac{2}{3}, y = 1, z = 1}$

53.

$$\left[\begin{array}{cccc|c} 2 & -2 & 3 & 1 & 2 \\ 1 & 1 & 1 & 1 & 5 \\ -1 & 2 & -3 & 2 & 2 \\ 1 & 1 & 2 & -1 & 4 \end{array}\right] \Rightarrow \left[\begin{array}{cccc|c} 2 & -2 & 3 & 1 & 2 \\ 0 & -4 & 1 & -1 & -8 \\ 0 & 2 & -3 & 5 & 6 \\ 0 & -4 & -1 & 3 & -6 \end{array}\right] \Rightarrow \left[\begin{array}{cccc|c} -4 & 0 & -5 & -3 & -12 \\ 0 & -4 & 1 & -1 & -8 \\ 0 & 0 & -5 & 9 & 4 \\ 0 & 0 & 2 & -4 & -2 \end{array}\right]$$

$-2R_2 + R_1 \Rightarrow R_2$, $2R_3 + R_1 \Rightarrow R_3$, $-2R_4 + R_1 \Rightarrow R_4$; $-2R_1 + R_2 \Rightarrow R_1$, $2R_3 + R_2 \Rightarrow R_3$, $-R_4 + R_2 \Rightarrow R_4$

$$\left[\begin{array}{cccc|c} -4 & 0 & -5 & -3 & -12 \\ 0 & -4 & 1 & -1 & -8 \\ 0 & 0 & -5 & 9 & 4 \\ 0 & 0 & 1 & -2 & -1 \end{array}\right] \Rightarrow \left[\begin{array}{cccc|c} 4 & 0 & 0 & 12 & 16 \\ 0 & -20 & 0 & 4 & -36 \\ 0 & 0 & -5 & 9 & 4 \\ 0 & 0 & 0 & -1 & -1 \end{array}\right] \Rightarrow \left[\begin{array}{cccc|c} 1 & 0 & 0 & 3 & 4 \\ 0 & -5 & 0 & 1 & -9 \\ 0 & 0 & -5 & 9 & 4 \\ 0 & 0 & 0 & 1 & 1 \end{array}\right]$$

$\frac{1}{2}R_4 \Rightarrow R_4$; $-R_1 + R_3 \Rightarrow R_1$, $5R_2 + R_3 \Rightarrow R_2$, $5R_4 + R_3 \Rightarrow R_4$; $\frac{1}{4}R_1 \Rightarrow R_1$, $\frac{1}{4}R_2 \Rightarrow R_2$, $-R_4 \Rightarrow R_4$

$$\Rightarrow \left[\begin{array}{cccc|c} 1 & 0 & 0 & 0 & 1 \\ 0 & -5 & 0 & 0 & -10 \\ 0 & 0 & -5 & 0 & -5 \\ 0 & 0 & 0 & 1 & 1 \end{array}\right] \Rightarrow \left[\begin{array}{cccc|c} 1 & 0 & 0 & 0 & 1 \\ 0 & 1 & 0 & 0 & 2 \\ 0 & 0 & 1 & 0 & 1 \\ 0 & 0 & 0 & 1 & 1 \end{array}\right]$$

$-3R_4 + R_1 \Rightarrow R_1$, $-R_4 + R_2 \Rightarrow R_2$, $-9R_4 + R_3 \Rightarrow R_3$; $-\frac{1}{5}R_2 \Rightarrow R_2$, $-\frac{1}{5}R_3 \Rightarrow R_3$

Solution: $\boxed{x = 1, y = 2, z = 1, t = 1}$

54. $\left[\begin{array}{cccc|c} 1 & 1 & 2 & 1 & 1 \\ 1 & 2 & 1 & 1 & 2 \\ 2 & 1 & 1 & 1 & 4 \\ 1 & 1 & 1 & 2 & 3 \end{array}\right] \Rightarrow \left[\begin{array}{cccc|c} 1 & 1 & 2 & 1 & 1 \\ 0 & 1 & -1 & 0 & 1 \\ 0 & -1 & -3 & -1 & 2 \\ 0 & 0 & -1 & 1 & 2 \end{array}\right] \Rightarrow \left[\begin{array}{cccc|c} 1 & 0 & -1 & 0 & 3 \\ 0 & 1 & -1 & 0 & 1 \\ 0 & 0 & -4 & -1 & 3 \\ 0 & 0 & -1 & 1 & 2 \end{array}\right] \Rightarrow$

$-R_1 + R_2 \Rightarrow R_2$, $-2R_1 + R_3 \Rightarrow R_3$, $-R_1 + R_4 \Rightarrow R_4$; $R_3 + R_1 \Rightarrow R_1$, $R_3 + R_2 \Rightarrow R_3$

$\left[\begin{array}{cccc|c} 1 & 0 & -1 & 0 & 3 \\ 0 & 1 & -1 & 0 & 1 \\ 0 & 0 & 1 & \frac{1}{4} & -\frac{3}{4} \\ 0 & 0 & -1 & 1 & 2 \end{array}\right] \Rightarrow \left[\begin{array}{cccc|c} 1 & 0 & 0 & \frac{1}{4} & \frac{9}{4} \\ 0 & 1 & 0 & \frac{1}{4} & \frac{1}{4} \\ 0 & 0 & 1 & \frac{1}{4} & -\frac{3}{4} \\ 0 & 0 & 0 & \frac{5}{4} & \frac{5}{4} \end{array}\right] \Rightarrow \left[\begin{array}{cccc|c} -5 & 0 & 0 & 0 & -10 \\ 0 & -5 & 0 & 0 & 0 \\ 0 & 0 & -5 & 0 & 5 \\ 0 & 0 & 0 & \frac{5}{4} & \frac{5}{4} \end{array}\right] \Rightarrow$

$-\frac{1}{4}R_3 \Rightarrow R_3$; $R_1 + R_3 \Rightarrow R_1$, $R_2 + R_3 \Rightarrow R_2$, $R_4 + R_3 \Rightarrow R_4$; $-5R_1 + R_4 \Rightarrow R_1$, $-5R_2 + R_4 \Rightarrow R_2$, $-5R_3 + R_4 \Rightarrow R_3$

$-\frac{1}{5}R_1 \Rightarrow R_1$, $-\frac{1}{5}R_2 \Rightarrow R_2$, $-\frac{1}{5}R_3 \Rightarrow R_3$, $\frac{4}{5}R_4 \Rightarrow R_4$ $\left[\begin{array}{cccc|c} 1 & 0 & 0 & 0 & 2 \\ 0 & 1 & 0 & 0 & 0 \\ 0 & 0 & 1 & 0 & -1 \\ 0 & 0 & 0 & 1 & 1 \end{array}\right]$

Solution: $\boxed{x = 2, y = 0, z = -1, t = 1}$

55. $\left[\begin{array}{cccc|c} 1 & 1 & 0 & 1 & 4 \\ 1 & 0 & 1 & 1 & 2 \\ 2 & 2 & 1 & 2 & 8 \\ 1 & -1 & 1 & -1 & -2 \end{array}\right] \Rightarrow \left[\begin{array}{cccc|c} 1 & 1 & 0 & 1 & 4 \\ 0 & 1 & -1 & 0 & 2 \\ 0 & 0 & 1 & 0 & 0 \\ 0 & 2 & -1 & 2 & 6 \end{array}\right] \Rightarrow \left[\begin{array}{cccc|c} 1 & 0 & 1 & 1 & 2 \\ 0 & 1 & -1 & 0 & 2 \\ 0 & 0 & 1 & 0 & 0 \\ 0 & 0 & 1 & 2 & 2 \end{array}\right] \Rightarrow$

$-R_2 + R_1 \Rightarrow R_2$, $-2R_1 + R_3 \Rightarrow R_3$, $-R_4 + R_1 \Rightarrow R_4$; $-R_2 + R_1 \Rightarrow R_1$, $-2R_2 + R_4 \Rightarrow R_4$

$\left[\begin{array}{cccc|c} 1 & 0 & 0 & 1 & 2 \\ 0 & 1 & 0 & 0 & 2 \\ 0 & 0 & 1 & 0 & 0 \\ 0 & 0 & 0 & 2 & 2 \end{array}\right] \Rightarrow \left[\begin{array}{cccc|c} 1 & 0 & 0 & 0 & 1 \\ 0 & 1 & 0 & 0 & 2 \\ 0 & 0 & 1 & 0 & 0 \\ 0 & 0 & 0 & 1 & 1 \end{array}\right]$ Solution: $\boxed{x = 1, y = 2, z = 0, t = 1}$

$-R_3 + R_1 \Rightarrow R_1$, $R_3 + R_2 \Rightarrow R_2$, $-R_3 + R_4 \Rightarrow R_4$; $-\frac{1}{2}R_4 + R_1 \Rightarrow R_1$, $\frac{1}{2}R_4 \Rightarrow R_4$

56. $$\left[\begin{array}{cccc|c} 1 & -1 & 2 & 1 & 3 \\ 3 & -2 & -1 & -1 & 4 \\ 2 & 1 & 2 & -1 & 10 \\ 1 & 2 & 1 & -3 & 8 \end{array}\right] \Rightarrow \left[\begin{array}{cccc|c} 1 & -1 & 2 & 1 & 3 \\ 0 & 1 & -7 & -4 & -5 \\ 0 & 3 & -2 & -3 & 4 \\ 0 & 3 & -1 & -4 & 5 \end{array}\right] \Rightarrow \left[\begin{array}{cccc|c} 1 & 0 & -5 & -3 & -2 \\ 0 & 1 & -7 & -4 & -5 \\ 0 & 0 & 19 & 9 & 19 \\ 0 & 0 & 20 & 8 & 20 \end{array}\right]$$

$-3R_1 + R_2 \Rightarrow R_2$, $-2R_1 + R_3 \Rightarrow R_3$, $-R_1 + R_4 \Rightarrow R_4$

$R_2 + R_1 \Rightarrow R_1$, $-3R_2 + R_3 \Rightarrow R_3$, $-3R_2 + R_4 \Rightarrow R_4$

$$\left[\begin{array}{cccc|c} 1 & 0 & -5 & -3 & -2 \\ 0 & 1 & -7 & -4 & -5 \\ 0 & 0 & 1 & \frac{9}{19} & 1 \\ 0 & 0 & 1 & \frac{2}{5} & 1 \end{array}\right] \Rightarrow \left[\begin{array}{cccc|c} 1 & 0 & 0 & -\frac{12}{19} & 3 \\ 0 & 1 & 0 & -\frac{13}{19} & 2 \\ 0 & 0 & 1 & \frac{9}{19} & 1 \\ 0 & 0 & 0 & \frac{7}{95} & 0 \end{array}\right] \Rightarrow \left[\begin{array}{cccc|c} 1 & 0 & 0 & -\frac{12}{19} & 3 \\ 0 & 1 & 0 & -\frac{13}{19} & 2 \\ 0 & 0 & 1 & \frac{9}{19} & 1 \\ 0 & 0 & 0 & 1 & 0 \end{array}\right] \Rightarrow$$

$\frac{1}{19}R_3 \Rightarrow R_3$, $\frac{1}{20}R_4 \Rightarrow R_4$

$5R_3 + R_1 \Rightarrow R_1$, $7R_3 + R_2 \Rightarrow R_2$, $-R_4 + R_3 \Rightarrow R_4$

$\frac{95}{7}R_4 \Rightarrow R_4$

$$\Rightarrow \left[\begin{array}{cccc|c} 1 & 0 & 0 & 0 & 3 \\ 0 & 1 & 0 & 0 & 2 \\ 0 & 0 & 1 & 0 & 1 \\ 0 & 0 & 0 & 1 & 0 \end{array}\right]$$

$\frac{12}{19}R_4 + R_1 \Rightarrow R_1$, $\frac{13}{19}R_4 + R_2 \Rightarrow R_2$, $-\frac{9}{19}R_4 + R_3 \Rightarrow R_3$

Solution: $\boxed{x = 3, y = 2, z = 1, t = 0}$

57. $$\left[\begin{array}{ccc|c} \frac{1}{3} & \frac{3}{4} & -\frac{2}{3} & -2 \\ 1 & \frac{1}{2} & \frac{1}{3} & 1 \\ \frac{1}{6} & -\frac{1}{8} & -1 & 0 \end{array}\right] \Rightarrow \left[\begin{array}{ccc|c} 1 & \frac{9}{4} & -2 & -6 \\ 6 & 3 & 2 & 6 \\ 4 & -3 & -24 & 0 \end{array}\right] \Rightarrow \left[\begin{array}{ccc|c} 1 & \frac{9}{4} & -2 & -6 \\ 0 & -\frac{21}{2} & 14 & 42 \\ 0 & -12 & -16 & 24 \end{array}\right] \Rightarrow$$

$3R_1 \Rightarrow R_1$, $6R_2 \Rightarrow R_2$, $24R_3 \Rightarrow R_3$

$-6R_1 + R_2 \Rightarrow R_2$, $-4R_1 + R_3 \Rightarrow R_3$

$$\left[\begin{array}{ccc|c} 1 & \frac{9}{4} & -2 & -6 \\ 0 & 1 & -\frac{4}{3} & -4 \\ 0 & 3 & 4 & -6 \end{array}\right] \Rightarrow \left[\begin{array}{ccc|c} 1 & 0 & 1 & 3 \\ 0 & 1 & -\frac{4}{3} & -4 \\ 0 & 0 & 8 & 6 \end{array}\right] \Rightarrow \left[\begin{array}{ccc|c} 1 & 0 & 0 & \frac{9}{4} \\ 0 & 1 & 0 & -3 \\ 0 & 0 & 1 & \frac{3}{4} \end{array}\right]$$

$-\frac{2}{21}R_2 \Rightarrow R_2$, $-\frac{1}{4}R_3 \Rightarrow R_3$

$-\frac{9}{4}R_2 + R_1 \Rightarrow R_1$, $-3R_2 + R_3 \Rightarrow R_3$

$-\frac{1}{8}R_3 + R_1 \Rightarrow R_1$, $\frac{1}{6}R_3 + R_2 \Rightarrow R_2$, $\frac{1}{8}R_3 \Rightarrow R_3$

Solution: $\boxed{x = \frac{9}{4}, y = -3, z = \frac{3}{4}}$

58. $\left[\begin{array}{ccc|c} \frac{1}{4} & 1 & 3 & 1 \\ \frac{1}{2} & -4 & 6 & -1 \\ \frac{1}{3} & -2 & -2 & -1 \end{array}\right] \Rightarrow \left[\begin{array}{ccc|c} 1 & 4 & 12 & 4 \\ 1 & -8 & 12 & -2 \\ 1 & -6 & -6 & -3 \end{array}\right] \Rightarrow \left[\begin{array}{ccc|c} 1 & 4 & 12 & 4 \\ 0 & 12 & 0 & 6 \\ 0 & 10 & 18 & 7 \end{array}\right] \Rightarrow$

$4R_1 \Rightarrow R_1, 2R_2 \Rightarrow R_2$, $3R_3 \Rightarrow R_3$; $-R_2 + R_1 \Rightarrow R_2$, $-R_3 + R_1 \Rightarrow R_3$

$\left[\begin{array}{ccc|c} 1 & 4 & 12 & 4 \\ 0 & 1 & 0 & \frac{1}{2} \\ 0 & 10 & 18 & 7 \end{array}\right] \Rightarrow \left[\begin{array}{ccc|c} 1 & 0 & 12 & 2 \\ 0 & 1 & 0 & \frac{1}{2} \\ 0 & 0 & 18 & 2 \end{array}\right] \Rightarrow \left[\begin{array}{ccc|c} 1 & 0 & 0 & \frac{2}{3} \\ 0 & 1 & 0 & \frac{1}{2} \\ 0 & 0 & 1 & \frac{1}{9} \end{array}\right]$ Solution: $\boxed{x = \frac{2}{3}, y = \frac{1}{2}, z = \frac{1}{9}}$

$\frac{1}{12}R_2 \Rightarrow R_2$; $-4R_2 + R_1 \Rightarrow R_1$, $-10R_2 + R_3 \Rightarrow R_3$; $-\frac{2}{3}R_3 + R_1 \Rightarrow R_1$, $\frac{1}{18}R_3 \Rightarrow R_3$

59. $\left[\begin{array}{ccc|c} \frac{1}{2} & \frac{1}{4} & -1 & 2 \\ \frac{2}{3} & \frac{1}{4} & \frac{1}{2} & \frac{3}{2} \\ \frac{2}{3} & 0 & 1 & -\frac{1}{3} \end{array}\right] \Rightarrow \left[\begin{array}{ccc|c} 1 & \frac{1}{2} & -2 & 4 \\ 8 & 3 & 6 & 18 \\ 2 & 0 & 3 & -1 \end{array}\right] \Rightarrow \left[\begin{array}{ccc|c} 1 & \frac{1}{2} & -2 & 4 \\ 0 & -1 & 22 & -14 \\ 0 & -1 & 7 & -9 \end{array}\right] \Rightarrow$

$2R_1 \Rightarrow R_1, 12R_2 \Rightarrow R_2$, $3R_3 \Rightarrow R_3$; $-8R_1 + R_2 \Rightarrow R_2$, $-2R_1 + R_3 \Rightarrow R_3$

$\left[\begin{array}{ccc|c} 1 & \frac{1}{2} & -2 & 4 \\ 0 & 1 & -22 & 14 \\ 0 & -1 & 7 & -9 \end{array}\right] \Rightarrow \left[\begin{array}{ccc|c} 1 & 0 & 9 & -3 \\ 0 & 1 & -22 & 14 \\ 0 & 0 & -15 & 5 \end{array}\right] \Rightarrow \left[\begin{array}{ccc|c} 1 & 0 & 9 & -3 \\ 0 & 1 & -22 & 14 \\ 0 & 0 & 1 & -\frac{1}{3} \end{array}\right] \Rightarrow$

$-R_2 \Rightarrow R_2$; $-\frac{1}{2}R_2 + R_1 \Rightarrow R_1$, $R_2 + R_3 \Rightarrow R_3$; $-\frac{1}{15}R_3 \Rightarrow R_3$

$\left[\begin{array}{ccc|c} 1 & 0 & 0 & 0 \\ 0 & 1 & 0 & \frac{20}{3} \\ 0 & 0 & 1 & -\frac{1}{3} \end{array}\right]$ Solution: $\boxed{x = 0, y = \frac{20}{3}, z = -\frac{1}{3}}$

$-9R_3 + R_1 \Rightarrow R_1$, $22R_3 + R_2 \Rightarrow R_2$

60. $\left[\begin{array}{ccc|c} \frac{5}{7} & -\frac{1}{3} & 1 & 0 \\ \frac{2}{7} & 1 & \frac{1}{8} & 9 \\ 6 & 4 & -\frac{27}{4} & 20 \end{array}\right] \Rightarrow \left[\begin{array}{ccc|c} 1 & -\frac{7}{15} & \frac{7}{5} & 0 \\ 16 & 56 & 7 & 504 \\ 24 & 16 & -27 & 80 \end{array}\right] \Rightarrow \left[\begin{array}{ccc|c} 1 & -\frac{7}{15} & \frac{7}{5} & 0 \\ 0 & \frac{952}{15} & -\frac{77}{5} & 504 \\ 0 & \frac{408}{15} & -\frac{303}{5} & 80 \end{array}\right] \Rightarrow$

$\frac{7}{5}R_1 \Rightarrow R_1,\ 56R_2 \Rightarrow R_2$, $4R_3 \Rightarrow R_3$; $-16R_1 + R_2 \Rightarrow R_2$, $-24R_1 + R_3 \Rightarrow R_3$

$\left[\begin{array}{ccc|c} 1 & -\frac{7}{15} & \frac{7}{5} & 0 \\ 0 & 1 & -\frac{33}{136} & \frac{135}{17} \\ 0 & 1 & -\frac{303}{136} & \frac{150}{51} \end{array}\right] \Rightarrow \left[\begin{array}{ccc|c} 1 & 0 & \frac{175}{136} & \frac{63}{17} \\ 0 & 1 & -\frac{33}{136} & \frac{135}{17} \\ 0 & 0 & \frac{135}{68} & 5 \end{array}\right] \Rightarrow \left[\begin{array}{ccc|c} 1 & 0 & \frac{175}{136} & \frac{63}{17} \\ 0 & 1 & -\frac{33}{136} & \frac{135}{17} \\ 0 & 0 & 1 & \frac{68}{27} \end{array}\right] \Rightarrow$

$\frac{15}{952}R_2 \Rightarrow R_2$, $\frac{15}{408}R_3 \Rightarrow R_3$; $\frac{7}{15}R_2 + R_1 \Rightarrow R_1$, $-R_3 + R_2 \Rightarrow R_3$; $\frac{68}{135}R_3 \Rightarrow R_3$

$\left[\begin{array}{ccc|c} 1 & 0 & 0 & \frac{427}{918} \\ 0 & 1 & 0 & \frac{2617}{306} \\ 0 & 0 & 1 & \frac{68}{27} \end{array}\right]$ Solution: $x = \frac{427}{918},\ y = \frac{2617}{306},\ z = \frac{68}{27}$

$-\frac{175}{136}R_3 + R_1 \Rightarrow R_1$, $\frac{33}{136}R_3 + R_2 \Rightarrow R_2$

61. $\left[\begin{array}{cc|c} 1 & 1 & -2 \\ 3 & -1 & 6 \\ 2 & 2 & -4 \\ 1 & -1 & 4 \end{array}\right] \Rightarrow \left[\begin{array}{cc|c} 1 & 1 & -2 \\ 0 & -4 & 12 \\ 0 & 0 & 0 \\ 0 & -2 & 6 \end{array}\right] \Rightarrow \left[\begin{array}{cc|c} 1 & 1 & -2 \\ 0 & 1 & -3 \\ 0 & -2 & 6 \\ 0 & 0 & 0 \end{array}\right] \Rightarrow \left[\begin{array}{cc|c} 1 & 0 & 1 \\ 0 & 1 & -3 \\ 0 & 0 & 0 \\ 0 & 0 & 0 \end{array}\right]$

$-3R_1 + R_2 \Rightarrow R_2$, $-2R_1 + R_3 \Rightarrow R_3$, $-R_1 + R_4 \Rightarrow R_4$; $-\frac{1}{4}R_2 \Rightarrow R_2$, $R_3 \Leftrightarrow R_4$; $-R_2 + R_1 \Rightarrow R_1$, $2R_2 + R_3 \Rightarrow R_3$

Solution: $x = 1$, $y = -3$

62. $\left[\begin{array}{cc|c} 1 & -1 & -3 \\ 2 & 1 & -3 \\ 3 & -1 & -7 \\ 4 & 1 & -7 \end{array}\right] \Rightarrow \left[\begin{array}{cc|c} 1 & -1 & -3 \\ 0 & 3 & 3 \\ 0 & 2 & 2 \\ 0 & 5 & 5 \end{array}\right] \Rightarrow \left[\begin{array}{cc|c} 1 & -1 & -3 \\ 0 & 1 & 1 \\ 0 & 2 & 2 \\ 0 & 5 & 5 \end{array}\right] \Rightarrow \left[\begin{array}{cc|c} 1 & 0 & -2 \\ 0 & 1 & 1 \\ 0 & 0 & 0 \\ 0 & 0 & 0 \end{array}\right]$

$-2R_1 + R_2 \Rightarrow R_2$, $-3R_1 + R_3 \Rightarrow R_3$, $-4R_1 + R_4 \Rightarrow R_4$; $\frac{1}{3}R_2 \Rightarrow R_2$, $R_3 \Leftrightarrow R_4$; $R_2 + R_1 \Rightarrow R_1$, $-2R_2 + R_3 \Rightarrow R_3$, $-5R_2 + R_4 \Rightarrow R_4$

Solution: $x = -2$, $y = 1$

63. $\left[\begin{array}{ccc|c} 1 & 2 & 1 & 4 \\ 3 & -1 & -1 & 2 \end{array}\right] \Rightarrow \left[\begin{array}{ccc|c} 1 & 2 & 1 & 4 \\ 0 & -7 & -4 & -10 \end{array}\right] \Rightarrow \left[\begin{array}{ccc|c} 1 & 2 & 1 & 4 \\ 0 & 1 & \frac{4}{7} & \frac{10}{7} \end{array}\right] \Rightarrow \left[\begin{array}{ccc|c} 1 & 0 & -\frac{1}{7} & \frac{8}{7} \\ 0 & 1 & \frac{4}{7} & \frac{10}{7} \end{array}\right]$

$-3R_1 + R_2 \Rightarrow R_2$; $-\frac{1}{7}R_2 \Rightarrow R_2$; $-2R_2 + R_1 \Rightarrow R_1$

From R_1: $x - \frac{1}{7}z = \frac{8}{7}$, $x = \frac{8}{7} + \frac{1}{7}z$

From R_2: $y + \frac{4}{7}z = \frac{10}{7}$, $y = \frac{10}{7} - \frac{4}{7}z$

Solution: $x = \frac{8}{7} + \frac{1}{7}z,\ y = \frac{10}{7} - \frac{4}{7}z$, $z =$ any real number

64. $\left[\begin{array}{ccc|c} 1 & 2 & -3 & -5 \\ 5 & 1 & -1 & -11 \end{array}\right] \Rightarrow \underset{-5R_1+R_2 \Rightarrow R_2}{\left[\begin{array}{ccc|c} 1 & 2 & -3 & -5 \\ 0 & -9 & 14 & 14 \end{array}\right]} \Rightarrow \underset{-\frac{1}{9}R_2 \Rightarrow R_2}{\left[\begin{array}{ccc|c} 1 & 2 & -3 & -5 \\ 0 & 1 & -\frac{14}{9} & -\frac{14}{9} \end{array}\right]} \Rightarrow \underset{-2R_2+R_1 \Rightarrow R_1}{\left[\begin{array}{ccc|c} 1 & 0 & \frac{1}{9} & -\frac{17}{9} \\ 0 & 1 & -\frac{14}{9} & -\frac{14}{9} \end{array}\right]}$

From R_1: $x + \frac{1}{9}z = -\frac{17}{9}$
$x = -\frac{17}{9} - \frac{1}{9}z$

From R_2: $y - \frac{14}{9}z = -\frac{14}{9}$
$y = -\frac{14}{9} + \frac{14}{9}z$

Solution:
$x = -\frac{17}{9} - \frac{1}{9}z$
$y = -\frac{14}{9} + \frac{14}{9}z$
$z =$ any real number

65. $\left[\begin{array}{cccc|c} 1 & 1 & 0 & 0 & 1 \\ 1 & 0 & 1 & 0 & 0 \\ 0 & 1 & 0 & 1 & 0 \end{array}\right] \Rightarrow \underset{-R_2+R_1 \Rightarrow R_2}{\left[\begin{array}{cccc|c} 1 & 1 & 0 & 0 & 1 \\ 0 & 1 & -1 & 0 & 1 \\ 0 & 1 & 0 & 1 & 0 \end{array}\right]} \Rightarrow \underset{\substack{-R_2+R_1 \Rightarrow R_1 \\ -R_2+R_3 \Rightarrow R_3}}{\left[\begin{array}{cccc|c} 1 & 0 & 1 & 0 & 0 \\ 0 & 1 & -1 & 0 & 1 \\ 0 & 0 & 1 & 1 & -1 \end{array}\right]} \Rightarrow$

$\underset{\substack{-R_3+R_1 \Rightarrow R_1 \\ R_3+R_2 \Rightarrow R_2}}{\left[\begin{array}{cccc|c} 1 & 0 & 0 & -1 & 1 \\ 0 & 1 & 0 & 1 & 0 \\ 0 & 0 & 1 & 1 & -1 \end{array}\right]} \Rightarrow$ From R_1: $w - z = 1$, $w = 1 + z$

From R_2: $x + z = 0$, $x = -z$

From R_3: $y + z = -1$, $y = -1 - z$

Solution:
$w = 1 + z$,
$x = -z$,
$y = -1 - z$,
$z =$ any real #

66. $\left[\begin{array}{cccc|c} 1 & 1 & -1 & 1 & 2 \\ 2 & -1 & -2 & 1 & 0 \\ 1 & -2 & -1 & 1 & -1 \end{array}\right] \Rightarrow \underset{\substack{-2R_1+R_2 \Rightarrow R_2 \\ -R_3+R_1 \Rightarrow R_3}}{\left[\begin{array}{cccc|c} 1 & 1 & -1 & 1 & 2 \\ 0 & -3 & 0 & -1 & -4 \\ 0 & 3 & 0 & 0 & 3 \end{array}\right]} \Rightarrow \underset{\substack{3R_1+R_2 \Rightarrow R_1 \\ R_2+R_3 \Rightarrow R_2 \\ \frac{1}{3}R_3 \Rightarrow R_3}}{\left[\begin{array}{cccc|c} 3 & 0 & -3 & 2 & 2 \\ 0 & 0 & 0 & -1 & -1 \\ 0 & 1 & 0 & 0 & 1 \end{array}\right]} \Rightarrow$

$\underset{\substack{2R_2+R_1 \Rightarrow R_1 \\ -R_2 \Rightarrow R_2}}{\left[\begin{array}{cccc|c} 3 & 0 & -3 & 0 & 0 \\ 0 & 0 & 0 & 1 & 1 \\ 0 & 1 & 0 & 0 & 1 \end{array}\right]} \Rightarrow \underset{\frac{1}{3}R_1 \Rightarrow R_1}{\left[\begin{array}{cccc|c} 1 & 0 & -1 & 0 & 0 \\ 0 & 0 & 0 & 1 & 1 \\ 0 & 1 & 0 & 0 & 1 \end{array}\right]}$ From R_1: $w - y = 0$, $w = y$

Solution:
$w = y$, $x = 1$,
$y =$ any real #, $z = 1$

67. $\left[\begin{array}{cc|c} 1 & 1 & 3 \\ 2 & 1 & 1 \\ 3 & 2 & 2 \end{array}\right] \Rightarrow \underset{\substack{-2R_1+R_2 \Rightarrow R_2 \\ -3R_1+R_3 \Rightarrow R_3}}{\left[\begin{array}{cc|c} 1 & 1 & 3 \\ 0 & -1 & -5 \\ 0 & -1 & -7 \end{array}\right]} \Rightarrow \underset{-R_2+R_3 \Rightarrow R_3}{\left[\begin{array}{cc|c} 1 & 1 & 3 \\ 0 & -1 & -5 \\ 0 & 0 & -2 \end{array}\right]}$

R_3 indicates that $0x + 0y = -2$. This is impossible. The system is inconsistent. $\Rightarrow$ no solution

68. $\left[\begin{array}{ccc|c} 1 & 2 & 1 & 4 \\ 1 & -1 & 1 & 1 \\ 2 & 1 & 2 & 2 \\ 3 & 0 & 3 & 6 \end{array}\right] \Rightarrow \left[\begin{array}{ccc|c} 1 & 2 & 1 & 4 \\ 0 & -3 & 0 & -3 \\ 0 & -3 & 0 & -6 \\ 0 & -6 & 0 & -6 \end{array}\right] \Rightarrow \left[\begin{array}{ccc|c} 1 & 2 & 1 & 4 \\ 0 & -3 & 0 & -3 \\ 0 & 0 & 0 & -3 \\ 0 & -6 & 0 & -6 \end{array}\right]$

$-R_1 + R_2 \Rightarrow R_2$, $-2R_1 + R_3 \Rightarrow R_3$, $-3R_1 + R_4 \Rightarrow R_4$; $-R_2 + R_3 \Rightarrow R_3$

R_3 indicates that $0x + 0y + 0z = -3$. This is impossible. The system is inconsistent. $\Rightarrow$ no solution

69. Let $p =$ speed with no wind. Let $w =$ the speed of the wind. Then the following system applies:

$\begin{cases} p + w = 300 \\ p - w = 220 \end{cases}$ $\left[\begin{array}{cc|c} 1 & 1 & 300 \\ 1 & -1 & 220 \end{array}\right] \Rightarrow \left[\begin{array}{cc|c} 1 & 1 & 300 \\ 0 & 2 & 80 \end{array}\right] \Rightarrow \left[\begin{array}{cc|c} 1 & 1 & 300 \\ 0 & 1 & 40 \end{array}\right] \Rightarrow \left[\begin{array}{cc|c} 1 & 0 & 260 \\ 0 & 1 & 40 \end{array}\right]$

$-R_2 + R_1 \Rightarrow R_2$; $\frac{1}{2}R_2 \Rightarrow R_2$; $-R_2 + R_1 \Rightarrow R_1$

The plane has a speed of 260 miles per hour with no wind, so it could travel 1300 miles in 5 hours.

70. Let $T =$ gallons for Triple A. Let $U =$ gallons for UnityAir. Then the following system applies:

$\begin{cases} T + U = 120000 \\ T = 2U \end{cases}$ $\begin{cases} T + U = 120000 \\ T - 2U = 0 \end{cases}$ $\left[\begin{array}{cc|c} 1 & 1 & 120000 \\ 1 & -2 & 0 \end{array}\right] \Rightarrow \left[\begin{array}{cc|c} 1 & 1 & 120000 \\ 0 & 3 & 120000 \end{array}\right] \Rightarrow$

$-R_2 + R_1 \Rightarrow R_2$

$\left[\begin{array}{cc|c} 1 & 1 & 120000 \\ 0 & 1 & 40000 \end{array}\right] \Rightarrow \left[\begin{array}{cc|c} 1 & 0 & 80000 \\ 0 & 1 & 40000 \end{array}\right]$

$\frac{1}{3}R_2 \Rightarrow R_2$; $-R_2 + R_1 \Rightarrow R_1$

Triple A should be allocated 80,000 gallons.

71. Let $d =$ width of a dictionary, $a =$ width of an atlas and $t =$ width of a thesaurus.

$\begin{cases} 3d + 5a + t = 35 \\ 6d + 2t = 35 \\ 2d + 4a + 3t = 35 \end{cases}$ $\left[\begin{array}{ccc|c} 3 & 5 & 1 & 35 \\ 6 & 0 & 2 & 35 \\ 2 & 4 & 3 & 35 \end{array}\right] \Rightarrow \left[\begin{array}{ccc|c} 3 & 5 & 1 & 35 \\ 0 & -10 & 0 & -35 \\ 0 & \frac{2}{3} & \frac{7}{3} & \frac{35}{3} \end{array}\right] \Rightarrow \left[\begin{array}{ccc|c} 3 & 5 & 1 & 35 \\ 0 & 1 & 0 & 3.5 \\ 0 & 2 & 7 & 35 \end{array}\right]$

$-2R_1 + R_2 \Rightarrow R_2$, $-\frac{2}{3}R_1 + R_3 \Rightarrow R_3$; $-\frac{1}{10}R_2 \Rightarrow R_2$, $3R_3 \Rightarrow R_3$

$\Rightarrow \left[\begin{array}{ccc|c} 3 & 0 & 1 & 17.5 \\ 0 & 1 & 0 & 3.5 \\ 0 & 0 & 7 & 28 \end{array}\right] \Rightarrow \left[\begin{array}{ccc|c} 3 & 0 & 0 & 13.5 \\ 0 & 1 & 0 & 3.5 \\ 0 & 0 & 1 & 4 \end{array}\right] \Rightarrow \left[\begin{array}{ccc|c} 1 & 0 & 0 & 4.5 \\ 0 & 1 & 0 & 3.5 \\ 0 & 0 & 1 & 4 \end{array}\right]$

$-5R_2 + R_1 \Rightarrow R_1$, $-2R_2 + R_3 \Rightarrow R_3$; $-\frac{1}{7}R_3 + R_1 \Rightarrow R_1$, $\frac{1}{7}R_3 \Rightarrow R_3$; $\frac{1}{3}R_1 \Rightarrow R_1$

Dictionaries are 4.5 in. wide. Atlases are 3.5 in. wide. Thesauruses are 4 in. wide.

72. Let A, B and C represent the number of copies per minute each copier can make.

$\begin{cases} A + B = 100 \\ A + C = 140 \\ A + B + C = 180 \end{cases}$ $\left[\begin{array}{ccc|c} 1 & 1 & 0 & 100 \\ 1 & 0 & 1 & 140 \\ 1 & 1 & 1 & 180 \end{array}\right] \Rightarrow \left[\begin{array}{ccc|c} 1 & 1 & 0 & 100 \\ 0 & -1 & 1 & 40 \\ 0 & 0 & 1 & 80 \end{array}\right] \Rightarrow$

$-R_1 + R_2 \Rightarrow R_2$, $-R_1 + R_3 \Rightarrow R_3$

$\left[\begin{array}{ccc|c} 1 & 0 & 1 & 140 \\ 0 & 1 & -1 & -40 \\ 0 & 0 & 1 & 80 \end{array}\right] \Rightarrow \left[\begin{array}{ccc|c} 1 & 0 & 0 & 60 \\ 0 & 1 & 0 & 40 \\ 0 & 0 & 1 & 80 \end{array}\right]$

$R_2 + R_1 \Rightarrow R_1$, $-R_2 \Rightarrow R_2$; $-R_3 + R_1 \Rightarrow R_1$, $R_3 + R_2 \Rightarrow R_2$

Copier A can make 60 copies per minute. Copier B can make 40 copies per minute. Copier C can make 80 copies per minute.

73. **Answers may vary.**

74. **Answers may vary.**

75. **Answers may vary.**

76. **Answers may vary.**

77.
$$\left[\begin{array}{ccc|c} 1 & 1 & 1 & 14 \\ 2 & 3 & -2 & -7 \\ 1 & -5 & 1 & 8 \end{array}\right] \Rightarrow \left[\begin{array}{ccc|c} 1 & 1 & 1 & 14 \\ 0 & 1 & -4 & -35 \\ 0 & -6 & 0 & -6 \end{array}\right] \Rightarrow \left[\begin{array}{ccc|c} 1 & 1 & 1 & 14 \\ 0 & -6 & 0 & -6 \\ 0 & 1 & -4 & -35 \end{array}\right] \Rightarrow$$

$-2R_1 + R_2 \Rightarrow R_2$, $-R_1 + R_3 \Rightarrow R_3$; $R_2 \Leftrightarrow R_3$

$$\left[\begin{array}{ccc|c} 1 & 0 & 1 & 13 \\ 0 & -6 & 0 & -6 \\ 0 & 0 & -4 & -36 \end{array}\right] \Rightarrow \left[\begin{array}{ccc|c} 1 & 0 & 0 & 4 \\ 0 & 1 & 0 & 1 \\ 0 & 0 & 1 & 9 \end{array}\right]$$

$\frac{1}{6}R_2 + R_1 \Rightarrow R_1$, $\frac{1}{6}R_2 + R_3 \Rightarrow R_3$; $\frac{1}{4}R_3 + R_1 \Rightarrow R_1$, $-\frac{1}{6}R_2 \Rightarrow R_2$, $-\frac{1}{4}R_3 \Rightarrow R_3$

$x^2 = 4 \Rightarrow \boxed{x = \pm 2}$

$y^2 = 1 \Rightarrow \boxed{y = \pm 1}$

$z^2 = 9 \Rightarrow \boxed{z = \pm 3}$

78.
$$\left[\begin{array}{ccc|c} 5 & 2 & 1 & 22 \\ 1 & 1 & -1 & 5 \\ 3 & -2 & -3 & 10 \end{array}\right] \Rightarrow \left[\begin{array}{ccc|c} 1 & 1 & -1 & 5 \\ 5 & 2 & 1 & 22 \\ 3 & -2 & -3 & 10 \end{array}\right] \Rightarrow \left[\begin{array}{ccc|c} 1 & 1 & -1 & 5 \\ 0 & -3 & 6 & -3 \\ 0 & -5 & 0 & -5 \end{array}\right] \Rightarrow$$

$R_1 \Leftrightarrow R_2$; $-5R_1 + R_2 \Rightarrow R_2$, $-3R_1 + R_3 \Rightarrow R_3$

$$\left[\begin{array}{ccc|c} 1 & 1 & -1 & 5 \\ 0 & -5 & 0 & -5 \\ 0 & -3 & 6 & -3 \end{array}\right] \Rightarrow \left[\begin{array}{ccc|c} 1 & 1 & -1 & 5 \\ 0 & 1 & 0 & 1 \\ 0 & -1 & 2 & -1 \end{array}\right] \Rightarrow \left[\begin{array}{ccc|c} 1 & 0 & -1 & 4 \\ 0 & 1 & 0 & 1 \\ 0 & 0 & 2 & 0 \end{array}\right] \Rightarrow \left[\begin{array}{ccc|c} 1 & 0 & 0 & 4 \\ 0 & 1 & 0 & 1 \\ 0 & 0 & 1 & 0 \end{array}\right]$$

$R_2 \Leftrightarrow R_3$; $-\frac{1}{5}R_2 \Rightarrow R_2$, $\frac{1}{3}R_3 \Rightarrow R_3$; $-R_2 + R_1 \Rightarrow R_1$, $R_2 + R_3 \Rightarrow R_3$; $\frac{1}{2}R_3 + R_1 \Rightarrow R_1$, $\frac{1}{2}R_3 \Rightarrow R_3$

$\sqrt{x} = 4 \Rightarrow \boxed{x = 16}$, $\sqrt{y} = 1 \Rightarrow \boxed{y = 1}$, $\sqrt{z} = 0 \Rightarrow \boxed{z = 0}$

79. $y = mx + b$

80. $y - y_1 = m(x - x_1)$

81. equal

82. perpendicular

83.
$$\begin{aligned} y &= mx + b \\ y &= 2x + 7 \end{aligned}$$

84.
$$\begin{aligned} y - y_1 &= m(x - x_1) \\ y - (-3) &= -3(x - 2) \\ y + 3 &= -3x + 6 \\ y &= -3x + 3 \end{aligned}$$

85. $x = 2$

86. $y = -3$

Exercise 6.3 (page 456)

1. i, j

2. size, equal

3. every element

4. corresponding

5. additive identity

6. multiplicative identity

7. $x = 2, y = 5$

8. $x = 0, y = 2$

9. $x+y=3$
$3+x=4 \Rightarrow x=1$
$5y=10 \Rightarrow y=2$

10. $x+y=-x \qquad x=-1$
$x-y=x-2 \qquad y=2$
$2x=-y$
$3y=8-y$

11. $5A=5\begin{bmatrix}3 & -3\\0 & -2\end{bmatrix}=\begin{bmatrix}15 & -15\\0 & -10\end{bmatrix}$

12. $5A=5\begin{bmatrix}3 & \frac{3}{5}\\0 & -1\end{bmatrix}=\begin{bmatrix}15 & 3\\0 & -5\end{bmatrix}$

13. $5A=5\begin{bmatrix}5 & 15 & -2\\-2 & -5 & 1\end{bmatrix}=\begin{bmatrix}25 & 75 & -10\\-10 & -25 & 5\end{bmatrix}$

14. $5A=5\begin{bmatrix}-3 & 1 & 2\\-8 & -2 & -5\end{bmatrix}=\begin{bmatrix}-15 & 5 & 10\\-40 & -10 & -25\end{bmatrix}$

15. $A+B=\begin{bmatrix}2 & 1 & -1\\-3 & 2 & 5\end{bmatrix}+\begin{bmatrix}-3 & 1 & 2\\-3 & -2 & -5\end{bmatrix}=\begin{bmatrix}-1 & 2 & 1\\-6 & 0 & 0\end{bmatrix}$

16. $A+B=\begin{bmatrix}3 & 2 & 1\\-2 & 3 & -3\\-4 & -2 & -1\end{bmatrix}+\begin{bmatrix}-2 & 6 & -2\\5 & 7 & -1\\-4 & -6 & 7\end{bmatrix}=\begin{bmatrix}1 & 8 & -1\\3 & 10 & -4\\-8 & -8 & 6\end{bmatrix}$

17. $A-B=\begin{bmatrix}-3 & 2 & -2\\-1 & 4 & -5\end{bmatrix}-\begin{bmatrix}3 & -3 & -2\\-2 & 5 & -5\end{bmatrix}=\begin{bmatrix}-6 & 5 & 0\\1 & -1 & 0\end{bmatrix}$

18. $A-B=\begin{bmatrix}2 & 2 & 0\\-2 & 8 & 1\\3 & -3 & -8\end{bmatrix}-\begin{bmatrix}-4 & 3 & 7\\-1 & 2 & 0\\1 & 4 & -1\end{bmatrix}=\begin{bmatrix}6 & -1 & -7\\-1 & 6 & 1\\2 & -7 & -7\end{bmatrix}$

19. $5A+3B=5\begin{bmatrix}3 & 1 & -2\\-4 & 3 & -2\end{bmatrix}+3\begin{bmatrix}1 & -2 & 2\\-5 & -5 & 3\end{bmatrix}=\begin{bmatrix}15 & 5 & -10\\-20 & 15 & -10\end{bmatrix}+\begin{bmatrix}3 & -6 & 6\\-15 & -15 & 9\end{bmatrix}=\begin{bmatrix}18 & -1 & -4\\-35 & 0 & -1\end{bmatrix}$

20. $5A+3B=5\begin{bmatrix}2 & -5\\-5 & 2\end{bmatrix}+3\begin{bmatrix}5 & -2\\2 & -5\end{bmatrix}=\begin{bmatrix}10 & -25\\-25 & 10\end{bmatrix}+\begin{bmatrix}15 & -6\\6 & -15\end{bmatrix}=\begin{bmatrix}25 & -31\\-19 & -5\end{bmatrix}$

21. additive inverse of $A=\begin{bmatrix}-5 & 2 & -7\\5 & 0 & -3\\2 & -3 & 5\end{bmatrix}$

22. additive inverse of $A=\begin{bmatrix}-3 & \frac{2}{3} & 5 & -\frac{1}{2}\end{bmatrix}$

23. $\begin{bmatrix}2 & 3\\3 & -2\end{bmatrix}_{2\times2}\begin{bmatrix}1 & 2\\0 & -2\end{bmatrix}_{2\times2}=\begin{bmatrix}(2)(1)+(3)(0) & (2)(2)+(3)(-2)\\(3)(1)+(-2)(0) & (3)(2)+(-2)(-2)\end{bmatrix}_{2\times2}=\begin{bmatrix}2 & -2\\3 & 10\end{bmatrix}$

24. $\begin{bmatrix}-2 & 3\\3 & -2\end{bmatrix}_{2\times2}\begin{bmatrix}2 & 4\\-5 & 7\end{bmatrix}_{2\times2}=\begin{bmatrix}(-2)(2)+(3)(-5) & (-2)(4)+(3)(7)\\(3)(2)+(-2)(-5) & (3)(4)+(-2)(7)\end{bmatrix}_{2\times2}=\begin{bmatrix}-19 & 13\\16 & -2\end{bmatrix}$

25. $$\begin{bmatrix} -4 & -2 \\ 21 & 0 \end{bmatrix}_{2\times 2} \begin{bmatrix} -5 & 6 \\ 21 & -1 \end{bmatrix}_{2\times 2} = \begin{bmatrix} (-4)(-5)+(-2)(21) & (-4)(6)+(-2)(-1) \\ (21)(-5)+(0)(21) & (21)(6)+(0)(-1) \end{bmatrix}_{2\times 2} = \begin{bmatrix} -22 & -22 \\ -105 & 126 \end{bmatrix}$$

26. $$\begin{bmatrix} -5 & 4 \\ 4 & -5 \end{bmatrix}_{2\times 2} \begin{bmatrix} 6 & -2 \\ 1 & 3 \end{bmatrix}_{2\times 2} = \begin{bmatrix} (-5)(6)+(4)(1) & (-5)(-2)+(4)(3) \\ (4)(6)+(-5)(1) & (4)(-2)+(-5)(3) \end{bmatrix}_{2\times 2} = \begin{bmatrix} -26 & 22 \\ 19 & -23 \end{bmatrix}$$

27. $$\begin{bmatrix} 2 & 1 & 3 \\ 1 & 2 & -1 \\ 0 & 1 & 0 \end{bmatrix}_{3\times 3} \begin{bmatrix} 1 & 2 & 3 \\ 2 & -2 & 1 \\ 0 & 0 & 1 \end{bmatrix}_{3\times 3}$$
$$= \begin{bmatrix} (2)(1)+(1)(2)+(3)(0) & (2)(2)+(1)(-2)+(3)(0) & (2)(3)+(1)(1)+(3)(1) \\ (1)(1)+(2)(2)+(-1)(0) & (1)(2)+(2)(-2)+(-1)(0) & (1)(3)+(2)(1)+(-1)(1) \\ (0)(1)+(1)(2)+(0)(0) & (0)(2)+(1)(-2)+(0)(0) & (0)(3)+(1)(1)+(0)(1) \end{bmatrix}_{3\times 3}$$
$$= \begin{bmatrix} 4 & 2 & 10 \\ 5 & -2 & 4 \\ 2 & -2 & 1 \end{bmatrix}$$

28. $$\begin{bmatrix} 2 & 1 & 1 \\ 1 & 1 & 2 \\ 1 & -2 & -1 \end{bmatrix}_{3\times 3} \begin{bmatrix} 1 & 2 & 3 \\ 1 & 2 & -3 \\ -1 & -1 & 3 \end{bmatrix}_{3\times 3}$$
$$= \begin{bmatrix} (2)(1)+(1)(1)+(1)(-1) & (2)(2)+(1)(2)+(1)(-1) & (2)(3)+(1)(-3)+(1)(3) \\ (1)(1)+(1)(1)+(2)(-1) & (1)(2)+(1)(2)+(2)(-1) & (1)(3)+(1)(-3)+(2)(3) \\ 1(1)+(-2)(1)+(-1)(-1) & 1(2)+(-2)(2)+(-1)(-1) & 1(3)+(-2)(-3)+(-1)(3) \end{bmatrix}$$
$$= \begin{bmatrix} 2 & 5 & 6 \\ 0 & 2 & 6 \\ 0 & -1 & 6 \end{bmatrix}$$

29. $$\begin{bmatrix} 1 & -2 & -3 \\ 2 & 0 & 1 \end{bmatrix}_{2\times 3} \begin{bmatrix} 4 \\ -5 \\ -6 \end{bmatrix}_{3\times 1} = \begin{bmatrix} (1)(4)+(-2)(-5)+(-3)(-6) \\ (2)(4)+(0)(-5)+(1)(-6) \end{bmatrix}_{2\times 1} = \begin{bmatrix} 32 \\ 2 \end{bmatrix}$$

30. $$\begin{bmatrix} 1 \\ -2 \\ -3 \end{bmatrix}_{3\times 1} [4 \quad -5 \quad -6]_{1\times 3} = \begin{bmatrix} (1)(4) & (1)(-5) & (1)(-6) \\ (-2)(4) & (-2)(-5) & (-2)(-6) \\ (-3)(4) & (-3)(-5) & (-3)(-6) \end{bmatrix}_{3\times 3} = \begin{bmatrix} 4 & -5 & -6 \\ -8 & 10 & 12 \\ -12 & 15 & 18 \end{bmatrix}$$

31. $[1 \quad 2 \quad 3]_{1\times 3} \begin{bmatrix} 4 & 5 & 6 \\ 7 & 8 & 9 \end{bmatrix}_{2\times 3}$ $\Rightarrow$ Not possible

32. $$\begin{bmatrix} 2 & 3 & 4 \\ 1 & 2 & 3 \\ -2 & 2 & 2 \end{bmatrix}_{3\times 3} \begin{bmatrix} -1 \\ 2 \\ 3 \end{bmatrix}_{3\times 1} = \begin{bmatrix} (2)(-1)+(3)(2)+(4)(3) \\ (1)(-1)+(2)(2)+(3)(3) \\ (-2)(-1)+(2)(2)+(2)(3) \end{bmatrix}_{3\times 1} = \begin{bmatrix} 16 \\ 12 \\ 12 \end{bmatrix}$$

33. $\begin{bmatrix} 2 & 5 \\ -3 & 1 \\ 0 & -2 \\ 1 & -5 \end{bmatrix}_{4\times 2} \begin{bmatrix} 3 & -2 & 4 \\ -2 & -3 & 1 \end{bmatrix}_{2\times 3}$

$$= \begin{bmatrix} (2)(3)+(5)(-2) & (2)(-2)+(5)(-3) & (2)(4)+(5)(1) \\ (-3)(3)+(1)(-2) & (-3)(-2)+(1)(-3) & (-3)(4)+(1)(1) \\ (0)(3)+(-2)(-2) & (0)(-2)+(-2)(-3) & (0)(4)+(-2)(1) \\ (1)(3)+(-5)(-2) & (1)(-2)+(-5)(-3) & (1)(4)+(-5)(1) \end{bmatrix}_{4\times 3} = \begin{bmatrix} -4 & -19 & 13 \\ -11 & 3 & -11 \\ 4 & 6 & -2 \\ 13 & 13 & -1 \end{bmatrix}$$

34. $\begin{bmatrix} 1 & 4 & 0 & 0 \\ -4 & 1 & 0 & -2 \\ 0 & 0 & 1 & 0 \\ 0 & 2 & 0 & 1 \end{bmatrix}_{4\times 4} \begin{bmatrix} 1 \\ 2 \\ -2 \\ -1 \end{bmatrix}_{4\times 1} = \begin{bmatrix} (1)(1)+(4)(2)+(0)(-2)+(0)(-1) \\ (-4)(1)+(1)(2)+(0)(-2)+(-2)(-1) \\ (0)(1)+(0)(2)+(1)(-2)+(0)(-1) \\ (0)(1)+(2)(2)+(0)(-2)+(1)(-1) \end{bmatrix}_{4\times 1} = \begin{bmatrix} 9 \\ 0 \\ -2 \\ 3 \end{bmatrix}$

35. $AB = \begin{bmatrix} 2.3 & -1.7 & 3.1 \\ -2 & 3.5 & 1 \\ -8 & 4.7 & 9.1 \end{bmatrix} \begin{bmatrix} -2.5 \\ 5.2 \\ -7 \end{bmatrix} = \begin{bmatrix} -36.29 \\ 16.2 \\ -19.26 \end{bmatrix}$

36. $B + C = \begin{bmatrix} -2.5 \\ 5.2 \\ -7 \end{bmatrix} + \begin{bmatrix} -5.8 \\ 2.9 \\ 4.1 \end{bmatrix} = \begin{bmatrix} -8.3 \\ 8.1 \\ -2.9 \end{bmatrix}$

37. $A^2 = \begin{bmatrix} 2.3 & -1.7 & 3.1 \\ -2 & 3.5 & 1 \\ -8 & 4.7 & 9.1 \end{bmatrix} \begin{bmatrix} 2.3 & -1.7 & 3.1 \\ -2 & 3.5 & 1 \\ -8 & 4.7 & 9.1 \end{bmatrix} = \begin{bmatrix} -16.11 & 4.71 & 33.64 \\ -19.6 & 20.35 & 6.4 \\ -100.6 & 72.82 & 62.71 \end{bmatrix}$

38. $AB + C = \begin{bmatrix} 2.3 & -1.7 & 3.1 \\ -2 & 3.5 & 1 \\ -8 & 4.7 & 9.1 \end{bmatrix} \begin{bmatrix} -2.5 \\ 5.2 \\ -7 \end{bmatrix} + \begin{bmatrix} -5.8 \\ 2.9 \\ 4.1 \end{bmatrix} = \begin{bmatrix} -42.09 \\ 19.1 \\ -15.16 \end{bmatrix}$

39. $A(B+C) = \begin{bmatrix} 2 & 3 \\ 1 & 3 \end{bmatrix} \left(\begin{bmatrix} 2 & 1 & -5 \\ 1 & 1 & 2 \end{bmatrix} + \begin{bmatrix} -2 & -1 & 6 \\ 0 & -1 & -1 \end{bmatrix} \right) = \begin{bmatrix} 2 & 3 \\ 1 & 3 \end{bmatrix} \begin{bmatrix} 0 & 0 & 1 \\ 1 & 0 & 1 \end{bmatrix} = \begin{bmatrix} 3 & 0 & 5 \\ 3 & 0 & 4 \end{bmatrix}$

$$AB + AC = \begin{bmatrix} 2 & 3 \\ 1 & 3 \end{bmatrix} \begin{bmatrix} 2 & 1 & -5 \\ 1 & 1 & 2 \end{bmatrix} + \begin{bmatrix} 2 & 3 \\ 1 & 3 \end{bmatrix} \begin{bmatrix} -2 & -1 & 6 \\ 0 & -1 & -1 \end{bmatrix}$$
$$= \begin{bmatrix} 7 & 5 & -4 \\ 5 & 4 & 1 \end{bmatrix} + \begin{bmatrix} -4 & -5 & 9 \\ -2 & -4 & 3 \end{bmatrix} = \begin{bmatrix} 3 & 0 & 5 \\ 3 & 0 & 4 \end{bmatrix}$$

40. $5(6A) = 5\left(6\begin{bmatrix} 2 & 3 \\ 1 & 3 \end{bmatrix}\right) = 5\begin{bmatrix} 12 & 18 \\ 6 & 18 \end{bmatrix} = \begin{bmatrix} 60 & 90 \\ 30 & 90 \end{bmatrix}$

$(5 \cdot 6)A = 30A = 30\begin{bmatrix} 2 & 3 \\ 1 & 3 \end{bmatrix} = \begin{bmatrix} 60 & 90 \\ 30 & 90 \end{bmatrix}$

41. $3(AB) = 3\left(\begin{bmatrix} 2 & 3 \\ 1 & 3 \end{bmatrix}\begin{bmatrix} 2 & 1 & -5 \\ 1 & 1 & 2 \end{bmatrix}\right) = 3\begin{bmatrix} 7 & 5 & -4 \\ 5 & 4 & 1 \end{bmatrix} = \begin{bmatrix} 21 & 15 & -12 \\ 15 & 12 & 3 \end{bmatrix}$

$(3A)B = \left(3\begin{bmatrix} 2 & 3 \\ 1 & 3 \end{bmatrix}\right)\begin{bmatrix} 2 & 1 & -5 \\ 1 & 1 & 2 \end{bmatrix} = \begin{bmatrix} 6 & 9 \\ 3 & 9 \end{bmatrix}\begin{bmatrix} 2 & 1 & -5 \\ 1 & 1 & 2 \end{bmatrix} = \begin{bmatrix} 21 & 15 & -12 \\ 15 & 12 & 3 \end{bmatrix}$

42. $A(DE) = \begin{bmatrix} 2 & 3 \\ 1 & 3 \end{bmatrix}\left(\begin{bmatrix} 1 & 2 \\ 1 & 3 \end{bmatrix}\begin{bmatrix} 1 & -2 \\ 2 & 3 \end{bmatrix}\right) = \begin{bmatrix} 2 & 3 \\ 1 & 3 \end{bmatrix}\begin{bmatrix} 5 & 4 \\ 7 & 7 \end{bmatrix} = \begin{bmatrix} 31 & 29 \\ 26 & 25 \end{bmatrix}$

$(AD)E = \left(\begin{bmatrix} 2 & 3 \\ 1 & 3 \end{bmatrix}\begin{bmatrix} 1 & 2 \\ 1 & 3 \end{bmatrix}\right)\begin{bmatrix} 1 & -2 \\ 2 & 3 \end{bmatrix} = \begin{bmatrix} 5 & 13 \\ 4 & 11 \end{bmatrix}\begin{bmatrix} 1 & -2 \\ 2 & 3 \end{bmatrix} = \begin{bmatrix} 31 & 29 \\ 26 & 25 \end{bmatrix}$

43. $A - BC = \begin{bmatrix} 1 & 3 \\ 2 & 5 \end{bmatrix} - \begin{bmatrix} -1 \\ 3 \end{bmatrix}\begin{bmatrix} 3 & 2 \end{bmatrix} = \begin{bmatrix} 1 & 3 \\ 2 & 5 \end{bmatrix} - \begin{bmatrix} -3 & -2 \\ 9 & 6 \end{bmatrix} = \begin{bmatrix} 4 & 5 \\ -7 & -1 \end{bmatrix}$

44. $AB + B = \begin{bmatrix} 1 & 3 \\ 2 & 5 \end{bmatrix}\begin{bmatrix} -1 \\ 3 \end{bmatrix} + \begin{bmatrix} -1 \\ 3 \end{bmatrix} = \begin{bmatrix} 8 \\ 13 \end{bmatrix} + \begin{bmatrix} -1 \\ 3 \end{bmatrix} = \begin{bmatrix} 7 \\ 16 \end{bmatrix}$

45. $CB - AB = \begin{bmatrix} 3 & 2 \end{bmatrix}\begin{bmatrix} -1 \\ 3 \end{bmatrix} - \begin{bmatrix} 1 & 3 \\ 2 & 5 \end{bmatrix}\begin{bmatrix} -1 \\ 3 \end{bmatrix} = \begin{bmatrix} 3 \end{bmatrix} - \begin{bmatrix} 8 \\ 13 \end{bmatrix} \Rightarrow$ not possible

46. $CAB = \begin{bmatrix} 3 & 2 \end{bmatrix}\begin{bmatrix} 1 & 3 \\ 2 & 5 \end{bmatrix}\begin{bmatrix} -1 \\ 3 \end{bmatrix} = \begin{bmatrix} 7 & 19 \end{bmatrix}\begin{bmatrix} -1 \\ 3 \end{bmatrix} = \begin{bmatrix} 50 \end{bmatrix}$

47. $ABC = \begin{bmatrix} 1 & 3 \\ 2 & 5 \end{bmatrix}\begin{bmatrix} -1 \\ 3 \end{bmatrix}\begin{bmatrix} 3 & 2 \end{bmatrix} = \begin{bmatrix} 8 \\ 13 \end{bmatrix}\begin{bmatrix} 3 & 2 \end{bmatrix} = \begin{bmatrix} 24 & 16 \\ 39 & 26 \end{bmatrix}$

48. $CA + C = \begin{bmatrix} 3 & 2 \end{bmatrix}\begin{bmatrix} 1 & 3 \\ 2 & 5 \end{bmatrix} + \begin{bmatrix} 3 & 2 \end{bmatrix} = \begin{bmatrix} 7 & 19 \end{bmatrix} + \begin{bmatrix} 3 & 2 \end{bmatrix} = \begin{bmatrix} 10 & 21 \end{bmatrix}$

49. $A^2B = \begin{bmatrix} 1 & 3 \\ 2 & 5 \end{bmatrix}\begin{bmatrix} 1 & 3 \\ 2 & 5 \end{bmatrix}\begin{bmatrix} -1 \\ 3 \end{bmatrix} = \begin{bmatrix} 7 & 18 \\ 12 & 31 \end{bmatrix}\begin{bmatrix} -1 \\ 3 \end{bmatrix} = \begin{bmatrix} 47 \\ 81 \end{bmatrix}$

50. $(BC)^2 = \left(\begin{bmatrix} -1 \\ 3 \end{bmatrix}\begin{bmatrix} 3 & 2 \end{bmatrix}\right)^2 = \left(\begin{bmatrix} -3 & -2 \\ 9 & 6 \end{bmatrix}\right)^2 = \begin{bmatrix} -3 & -2 \\ 9 & 6 \end{bmatrix}\begin{bmatrix} -3 & -2 \\ 9 & 6 \end{bmatrix} = \begin{bmatrix} -9 & -6 \\ 27 & 18 \end{bmatrix}$

51. $Q = \begin{bmatrix} 217 & 23 & 319 \\ 347 & 24 & 340 \\ 3 & 97 & 750 \end{bmatrix}, P = \begin{bmatrix} 0.75 \\ 1.00 \\ 1.25 \end{bmatrix}$

$QP = \begin{bmatrix} 217 & 23 & 319 \\ 347 & 24 & 340 \\ 3 & 97 & 750 \end{bmatrix}\begin{bmatrix} 0.75 \\ 1.00 \\ 1.25 \end{bmatrix} = \begin{bmatrix} 584.50 \\ 709.25 \\ 1036.75 \end{bmatrix}\begin{matrix} \text{\$ spent by adult males} \\ \text{\$ spent by adult females} \\ \text{\$ spent by children} \end{matrix}$

52. $\begin{bmatrix} 19 & 23 & 27 \\ 17 & 21 & 22 \\ 21 & 18 & 20 \\ 27 & 25 & 22 \end{bmatrix}\begin{bmatrix} 1.20 & 1.35 \\ 0.75 & 0.85 \\ 3.50 & 3.70 \end{bmatrix} = \begin{bmatrix} 134.55 & 145.10 \\ 113.15 & 122.20 \\ 108.70 & 117.65 \\ 128.15 & 139.10 \end{bmatrix}\begin{matrix} \text{Day/Night costs in Ashtabula} \\ \text{Day/Night costs in Boston} \\ \text{Day/Night costs in Chicago} \\ \text{Day/Night costs in Denver} \end{matrix}$

53. $A^2 = \begin{bmatrix} 0 & 1 & 1 \\ 1 & 0 & 0 \\ 0 & 1 & 0 \end{bmatrix}^2 = \begin{bmatrix} 0 & 1 & 1 \\ 1 & 0 & 0 \\ 0 & 1 & 0 \end{bmatrix}\begin{bmatrix} 0 & 1 & 1 \\ 1 & 0 & 0 \\ 0 & 1 & 0 \end{bmatrix} = \begin{bmatrix} 1 & 1 & 0 \\ 0 & 1 & 1 \\ 1 & 0 & 0 \end{bmatrix}$

54. $A + A^2 = \begin{bmatrix} 0 & 1 & 1 \\ 1 & 0 & 0 \\ 0 & 1 & 0 \end{bmatrix} + \begin{bmatrix} 0 & 1 & 1 \\ 1 & 0 & 0 \\ 0 & 1 & 0 \end{bmatrix}^2 = \begin{bmatrix} 0 & 1 & 1 \\ 1 & 0 & 0 \\ 0 & 1 & 0 \end{bmatrix} + \begin{bmatrix} 1 & 1 & 0 \\ 0 & 1 & 1 \\ 1 & 0 & 0 \end{bmatrix} = \begin{bmatrix} 1 & 2 & 1 \\ 1 & 1 & 1 \\ 1 & 1 & 0 \end{bmatrix}$

The matrix $A + A^2$ contains the number of ways for a message to get from one person to another either directly or through one other person. The only 0 in the matrix is in the location which represents a message from Carl to himself. Thus, everybody is able to receive a letter from everyone else with at most one forwarding.

55. $A^2 = \begin{bmatrix} 0 & 2 & 1 & 0 \\ 2 & 0 & 1 & 0 \\ 1 & 1 & 0 & 2 \\ 0 & 0 & 2 & 0 \end{bmatrix}^2 = \begin{bmatrix} 0 & 2 & 1 & 0 \\ 2 & 0 & 1 & 0 \\ 1 & 1 & 0 & 2 \\ 0 & 0 & 2 & 0 \end{bmatrix}\begin{bmatrix} 0 & 2 & 1 & 0 \\ 2 & 0 & 1 & 0 \\ 1 & 1 & 0 & 2 \\ 0 & 0 & 2 & 0 \end{bmatrix} = \begin{bmatrix} 5 & 1 & 2 & 2 \\ 1 & 5 & 2 & 2 \\ 2 & 2 & 6 & 0 \\ 2 & 2 & 0 & 4 \end{bmatrix}$

A^2 represents the number of ways two cities can be linked through one intermediary.

56. $C^2 = \begin{bmatrix} 0 & 2 & 1 \\ 1 & 0 & 1 \\ 2 & 0 & 0 \end{bmatrix}^2 = \begin{bmatrix} 0 & 2 & 1 \\ 1 & 0 & 1 \\ 2 & 0 & 0 \end{bmatrix}\begin{bmatrix} 0 & 2 & 1 \\ 1 & 0 & 1 \\ 2 & 0 & 0 \end{bmatrix} = \begin{bmatrix} 4 & 0 & 2 \\ 2 & 2 & 1 \\ 0 & 4 & 2 \end{bmatrix}$

C^2 represents the number of ways two centers can be linked through one intermediary.

57. Let $A = \begin{bmatrix} 1 & 1 \\ 1 & 1 \end{bmatrix}$ and $B = \begin{bmatrix} 1 & 0 \\ 0 & 0 \end{bmatrix}$.

$(AB)^2 = \left(\begin{bmatrix} 1 & 1 \\ 1 & 1 \end{bmatrix}\begin{bmatrix} 1 & 0 \\ 0 & 0 \end{bmatrix}\right)^2 = \begin{bmatrix} 1 & 0 \\ 1 & 0 \end{bmatrix}^2 = \begin{bmatrix} 1 & 0 \\ 1 & 0 \end{bmatrix}\begin{bmatrix} 1 & 0 \\ 1 & 0 \end{bmatrix} = \begin{bmatrix} 1 & 0 \\ 1 & 0 \end{bmatrix}$

$A^2B^2 = \begin{bmatrix} 1 & 1 \\ 1 & 1 \end{bmatrix}^2\begin{bmatrix} 1 & 0 \\ 0 & 0 \end{bmatrix}^2 = \begin{bmatrix} 2 & 2 \\ 2 & 2 \end{bmatrix}\begin{bmatrix} 1 & 0 \\ 0 & 0 \end{bmatrix} = \begin{bmatrix} 2 & 0 \\ 2 & 0 \end{bmatrix}$. $(AB)^2 \neq A^2B^2$

58. Let $A = \begin{bmatrix} 1 & 0 \\ 0 & 0 \end{bmatrix}$, $B = \begin{bmatrix} 0 & 1 \\ 1 & 1 \end{bmatrix}$ and $C = \begin{bmatrix} 0 & 1 \\ 1 & 2 \end{bmatrix}$.

$AB = \begin{bmatrix} 1 & 0 \\ 0 & 0 \end{bmatrix}\begin{bmatrix} 0 & 1 \\ 1 & 1 \end{bmatrix} = \begin{bmatrix} 0 & 1 \\ 0 & 0 \end{bmatrix}$; $AC = \begin{bmatrix} 1 & 0 \\ 0 & 0 \end{bmatrix}\begin{bmatrix} 0 & 1 \\ 1 & 2 \end{bmatrix} = \begin{bmatrix} 0 & 1 \\ 0 & 0 \end{bmatrix}$

So $AB = AC$, but $B \neq C$.

59. Let $A = \begin{bmatrix} 1 & 2 \\ 1 & 2 \end{bmatrix}$ and $B = \begin{bmatrix} 2 & 2 \\ -1 & -1 \end{bmatrix}$. $AB = \begin{bmatrix} 1 & 2 \\ 1 & 2 \end{bmatrix}\begin{bmatrix} 2 & 2 \\ -1 & -1 \end{bmatrix} = \begin{bmatrix} 0 & 0 \\ 0 & 0 \end{bmatrix}$

60. Let $A=\begin{bmatrix}1 & 0\\ 0 & 0\end{bmatrix}$ and $B=\begin{bmatrix}0 & 1\\ 0 & 0\end{bmatrix}$.

$$(A+B)(A-B)=\left(\begin{bmatrix}1 & 0\\ 0 & 0\end{bmatrix}+\begin{bmatrix}0 & 1\\ 0 & 0\end{bmatrix}\right)\left(\begin{bmatrix}1 & 0\\ 0 & 0\end{bmatrix}-\begin{bmatrix}0 & 1\\ 0 & 0\end{bmatrix}\right)$$
$$=\begin{bmatrix}1 & 1\\ 0 & 0\end{bmatrix}\begin{bmatrix}1 & -1\\ 0 & 0\end{bmatrix}=\begin{bmatrix}1 & -1\\ 0 & 0\end{bmatrix}$$
$$A^2-B^2=\begin{bmatrix}1 & 0\\ 0 & 0\end{bmatrix}^2-\begin{bmatrix}0 & 1\\ 0 & 0\end{bmatrix}^2=\begin{bmatrix}1 & 0\\ 0 & 0\end{bmatrix}\begin{bmatrix}1 & 0\\ 0 & 0\end{bmatrix}-\begin{bmatrix}0 & 1\\ 0 & 0\end{bmatrix}\begin{bmatrix}0 & 1\\ 0 & 0\end{bmatrix}$$
$$=\begin{bmatrix}1 & 0\\ 0 & 0\end{bmatrix}-\begin{bmatrix}0 & 0\\ 0 & 0\end{bmatrix}=\begin{bmatrix}1 & 0\\ 0 & 0\end{bmatrix}$$

61. $(3x+2)(2x-3)-(2-x)=6x^2-9x+4x-6-2+x=6x^2-4x-8$

62. $\dfrac{x^2+3x-4}{2x+5-(x+1)}=\dfrac{(x-1)(x+4)}{2x+5-x-1}=\dfrac{(x-1)(x+4)}{x+4}=x-1$

63. $\dfrac{1+\frac{1}{x}}{1-\frac{1}{x}}=\dfrac{x\left(1+\frac{1}{x}\right)}{x\left(1-\frac{1}{x}\right)}=\dfrac{x+1}{x-1}$

64. $\dfrac{1-x^{-1}}{1+x^{-1}}=\dfrac{1-\frac{1}{x}}{1+\frac{1}{x}}=\dfrac{x\left(1-\frac{1}{x}\right)}{x\left(1+\frac{1}{x}\right)}=\dfrac{x-1}{x+1}$

65.
$$s=\frac{n(a+l)}{2}$$
$$2s=n(a+l)$$
$$\frac{2s}{n}=a+l$$
$$\frac{2s}{n}-l=a$$

66.
$$y-y_1=m(x-x_1)$$
$$\frac{y-y_1}{m}=x-x_1$$
$$x_1=x-\frac{y-y_1}{m}$$

Exercise 6.4 (page 466)

1. $AB=BA=I$ **2.** is **3.** $[I\mid A^{-1}]$ **4.** $X=A^{-1}B$

5.
$$\left[\begin{array}{cc|cc}3 & -4 & 1 & 0\\ -2 & 3 & 0 & 1\end{array}\right]\Rightarrow\underset{\frac{1}{3}R_1\Rightarrow R_1}{\left[\begin{array}{cc|cc}1 & -\frac{4}{3} & \frac{1}{3} & 0\\ -2 & 3 & 0 & 1\end{array}\right]}\Rightarrow\underset{2R_1+R_2\Rightarrow R_2}{\left[\begin{array}{cc|cc}1 & -\frac{4}{3} & \frac{1}{3} & 0\\ 0 & \frac{1}{3} & \frac{2}{3} & 1\end{array}\right]}\Rightarrow$$
$$\underset{4R_2+R_1\Rightarrow R_1}{\left[\begin{array}{cc|cc}1 & 0 & 3 & 4\\ 0 & \frac{1}{3} & \frac{2}{3} & 1\end{array}\right]}\Rightarrow\underset{3R_2\Rightarrow R_2}{\left[\begin{array}{cc|cc}1 & 0 & 3 & 4\\ 0 & 1 & 2 & 3\end{array}\right]}\Rightarrow\text{Inverse: }\begin{bmatrix}3 & 4\\ 2 & 3\end{bmatrix}$$

6. $\left[\begin{array}{cc|cc} 2 & 3 & 1 & 0 \\ 3 & 5 & 0 & 1 \end{array}\right] \Rightarrow \underset{\frac{1}{2}R_1 \Rightarrow R_1}{\left[\begin{array}{cc|cc} 1 & \frac{3}{2} & \frac{1}{2} & 0 \\ 3 & 5 & 0 & 1 \end{array}\right]} \Rightarrow \underset{-3R_1 + R_2 \Rightarrow R_2}{\left[\begin{array}{cc|cc} 1 & \frac{3}{2} & \frac{1}{2} & 0 \\ 0 & \frac{1}{2} & -\frac{3}{2} & 1 \end{array}\right]} \Rightarrow$

$\underset{-3R_2 + R_1 \Rightarrow R_1}{\left[\begin{array}{cc|cc} 1 & 0 & 5 & -3 \\ 0 & \frac{1}{2} & -\frac{3}{2} & 1 \end{array}\right]} \Rightarrow \underset{2R_2 \Rightarrow R_2}{\left[\begin{array}{cc|cc} 1 & 0 & 5 & -3 \\ 0 & 1 & -3 & 2 \end{array}\right]} \Rightarrow$ Inverse: $\begin{bmatrix} 5 & -3 \\ -3 & 2 \end{bmatrix}$

7. $\left[\begin{array}{cc|cc} 3 & 7 & 1 & 0 \\ 2 & 5 & 0 & 1 \end{array}\right] \Rightarrow \underset{\frac{1}{3}R_1 \Rightarrow R_1}{\left[\begin{array}{cc|cc} 1 & \frac{7}{3} & \frac{1}{3} & 0 \\ 2 & 5 & 0 & 1 \end{array}\right]} \Rightarrow \underset{-2R_1 + R_2 \Rightarrow R_2}{\left[\begin{array}{cc|cc} 1 & \frac{7}{3} & \frac{1}{3} & 0 \\ 0 & \frac{1}{3} & -\frac{2}{3} & 1 \end{array}\right]} \Rightarrow$

$\underset{-7R_2 + R_1 \Rightarrow R_1}{\left[\begin{array}{cc|cc} 1 & 0 & 5 & -7 \\ 0 & \frac{1}{3} & -\frac{2}{3} & 1 \end{array}\right]} \Rightarrow \underset{3R_2 \Rightarrow R_2}{\left[\begin{array}{cc|cc} 1 & 0 & 5 & -7 \\ 0 & 1 & -2 & 3 \end{array}\right]} \Rightarrow$ Inverse: $\begin{bmatrix} 5 & -7 \\ -2 & 3 \end{bmatrix}$

8. $\left[\begin{array}{cc|cc} 1 & -2 & 1 & 0 \\ 2 & -5 & 0 & 1 \end{array}\right] \Rightarrow \underset{-2R_1 + R_2 \Rightarrow R_2}{\left[\begin{array}{cc|cc} 1 & -2 & 1 & 0 \\ 0 & -1 & -2 & 1 \end{array}\right]} \Rightarrow \underset{\substack{-2R_2 + R_1 \Rightarrow R_1 \\ -R_2 \Rightarrow R_2}}{\left[\begin{array}{cc|cc} 1 & 0 & 5 & -2 \\ 0 & 1 & 2 & -1 \end{array}\right]} \Rightarrow$ Inverse: $\begin{bmatrix} 5 & -2 \\ 2 & -1 \end{bmatrix}$

9. $\left[\begin{array}{ccc|ccc} 1 & 0 & 3 & 1 & 0 & 0 \\ -1 & 1 & 3 & 0 & 1 & 0 \\ -2 & 1 & 1 & 0 & 0 & 1 \end{array}\right] \Rightarrow \underset{\substack{R_1 + R_2 \Rightarrow R_2 \\ 2R_1 + R_3 \Rightarrow R_3}}{\left[\begin{array}{ccc|ccc} 1 & 0 & 3 & 1 & 0 & 0 \\ 0 & 1 & 6 & 1 & 1 & 0 \\ 0 & 1 & 7 & 2 & 0 & 1 \end{array}\right]} \Rightarrow \underset{-R_2 + R_3 \Rightarrow R_3}{\left[\begin{array}{ccc|ccc} 1 & 0 & 3 & 1 & 0 & 0 \\ 0 & 1 & 6 & 1 & 1 & 0 \\ 0 & 0 & 1 & 1 & -1 & 1 \end{array}\right]} \Rightarrow$

$\underset{\substack{-3R_3 + R_1 \Rightarrow R_1 \\ -6R_3 + R_2 \Rightarrow R_2}}{\left[\begin{array}{ccc|ccc} 1 & 0 & 0 & -2 & 3 & -3 \\ 0 & 1 & 0 & -5 & 7 & -6 \\ 0 & 0 & 1 & 1 & -1 & 1 \end{array}\right]} \Rightarrow$ Inverse: $\begin{bmatrix} -2 & 3 & -3 \\ -5 & 7 & -6 \\ 1 & -1 & 1 \end{bmatrix}$

10. $\left[\begin{array}{ccc|ccc} 2 & 1 & -1 & 1 & 0 & 0 \\ 2 & 2 & -1 & 0 & 1 & 0 \\ -1 & -1 & 1 & 0 & 0 & 1 \end{array}\right] \Rightarrow \underset{-R_3 \Leftrightarrow R_1}{\left[\begin{array}{ccc|ccc} 1 & 1 & -1 & 0 & 0 & -1 \\ 2 & 2 & -1 & 0 & 1 & 0 \\ 2 & 1 & -1 & 1 & 0 & 0 \end{array}\right]} \Rightarrow \underset{\substack{-2R_1 + R_2 \Rightarrow R_2 \\ -2R_1 + R_3 \Rightarrow R_3}}{\left[\begin{array}{ccc|ccc} 1 & 1 & -1 & 0 & 0 & -1 \\ 0 & 0 & 1 & 0 & 1 & 2 \\ 0 & -1 & 1 & 1 & 0 & 2 \end{array}\right]}$

$\Rightarrow \underset{-R_2 \Leftrightarrow R_3}{\left[\begin{array}{ccc|ccc} 1 & 1 & -1 & 0 & 0 & -1 \\ 0 & 1 & -1 & -1 & 0 & -2 \\ 0 & 0 & 1 & 0 & 1 & 2 \end{array}\right]} \Rightarrow \underset{-R_2 + R_1 \Rightarrow R_1}{\left[\begin{array}{ccc|ccc} 1 & 0 & 0 & 1 & 0 & 1 \\ 0 & 1 & -1 & -1 & 0 & -2 \\ 0 & 0 & 1 & 0 & 1 & 2 \end{array}\right]} \Rightarrow$

$\underset{R_2 + R_3 \Rightarrow R_2}{\left[\begin{array}{ccc|ccc} 1 & 0 & 0 & 1 & 0 & 1 \\ 0 & 1 & 0 & -1 & 1 & 0 \\ 0 & 0 & 1 & 0 & 1 & 2 \end{array}\right]} \Rightarrow$ Inverse $= \begin{bmatrix} 1 & 0 & 1 \\ -1 & 1 & 0 \\ 0 & 1 & 2 \end{bmatrix}$

11. $$\left[\begin{array}{ccc|ccc} 3 & 2 & 1 & 1 & 0 & 0 \\ 1 & 1 & -1 & 0 & 1 & 0 \\ 4 & 3 & 1 & 0 & 0 & 1 \end{array}\right] \Rightarrow \underset{R_1 \Leftrightarrow R_2}{\left[\begin{array}{ccc|ccc} 1 & 1 & -1 & 0 & 1 & 0 \\ 3 & 2 & 1 & 1 & 0 & 0 \\ 4 & 3 & 1 & 0 & 0 & 1 \end{array}\right]} \Rightarrow \underset{\substack{-3R_1 + R_2 \Rightarrow R_2 \\ -4R_1 + R_3 \Rightarrow R_3}}{\left[\begin{array}{ccc|ccc} 1 & 1 & -1 & 0 & 1 & 0 \\ 0 & -1 & 4 & 1 & -3 & 0 \\ 0 & -1 & 5 & 0 & -4 & 1 \end{array}\right]} \Rightarrow$$

$$\underset{-R_2 \Rightarrow R_2}{\left[\begin{array}{ccc|ccc} 1 & 1 & -1 & 0 & 1 & 0 \\ 0 & 1 & -4 & -1 & 3 & 0 \\ 0 & -1 & 5 & 0 & -4 & 1 \end{array}\right]} \Rightarrow \underset{\substack{-R_2 + R_1 \Rightarrow R_1 \\ R_2 + R_3 \Rightarrow R_3}}{\left[\begin{array}{ccc|ccc} 1 & 0 & 3 & 1 & -2 & 0 \\ 0 & 1 & -4 & -1 & 3 & 0 \\ 0 & 0 & 1 & -1 & -1 & 1 \end{array}\right]} \Rightarrow$$

$$\underset{\substack{-3R_3 + R_1 \Rightarrow R_1 \\ 4R_3 + R_2 \Rightarrow R_2}}{\left[\begin{array}{ccc|ccc} 1 & 0 & 0 & 4 & 1 & -3 \\ 0 & 1 & 0 & -5 & -1 & 4 \\ 0 & 0 & 1 & -1 & -1 & 1 \end{array}\right]} \Rightarrow \text{Inverse} = \left[\begin{array}{ccc} 4 & 1 & -3 \\ -5 & -1 & 4 \\ -1 & -1 & 1 \end{array}\right]$$

12. $$\left[\begin{array}{ccc|ccc} -2 & 1 & -3 & 1 & 0 & 0 \\ 2 & 3 & 0 & 0 & 1 & 0 \\ 1 & 0 & 1 & 0 & 0 & 1 \end{array}\right] \Rightarrow \underset{R_3 \Leftrightarrow R_1}{\left[\begin{array}{ccc|ccc} 1 & 0 & 1 & 0 & 0 & 1 \\ 2 & 3 & 0 & 0 & 1 & 0 \\ -2 & 1 & -3 & 1 & 0 & 0 \end{array}\right]} \Rightarrow \underset{\substack{-2R_1 + R_2 \Rightarrow R_2 \\ 2R_1 + R_3 \Rightarrow R_3}}{\left[\begin{array}{ccc|ccc} 1 & 0 & 1 & 0 & 0 & 1 \\ 0 & 3 & -2 & 0 & 1 & -2 \\ 0 & 1 & -1 & 1 & 0 & 2 \end{array}\right]} \Rightarrow$$

$$\underset{R_2 \Leftrightarrow R_3}{\left[\begin{array}{ccc|ccc} 1 & 0 & 1 & 0 & 0 & 1 \\ 0 & 1 & -1 & 1 & 0 & 2 \\ 0 & 3 & -2 & 0 & 1 & -2 \end{array}\right]} \Rightarrow \underset{-3R_2 + R_3 \Rightarrow R_3}{\left[\begin{array}{ccc|ccc} 1 & 0 & 1 & 0 & 0 & 1 \\ 0 & 1 & -1 & 1 & 0 & 2 \\ 0 & 0 & 1 & -3 & 1 & -8 \end{array}\right]} \Rightarrow$$

$$\underset{\substack{-R_3 + R_1 \Rightarrow R_1 \\ R_3 + R_2 \Rightarrow R_2}}{\left[\begin{array}{ccc|ccc} 1 & 0 & 0 & 3 & -1 & 9 \\ 0 & 1 & 0 & -2 & 1 & -6 \\ 0 & 0 & 1 & -3 & 1 & -8 \end{array}\right]} \Rightarrow \text{Inverse} = \left[\begin{array}{ccc} 3 & -1 & 9 \\ -2 & 1 & -6 \\ -3 & 1 & -8 \end{array}\right]$$

13. $$\left[\begin{array}{ccc|ccc} 1 & 3 & 5 & 1 & 0 & 0 \\ 0 & 1 & 6 & 0 & 1 & 0 \\ 1 & 4 & 11 & 0 & 0 & 1 \end{array}\right] \Rightarrow \underset{-R_1 + R_3 \Rightarrow R_3}{\left[\begin{array}{ccc|ccc} 1 & 3 & 5 & 1 & 0 & 0 \\ 0 & 1 & 6 & 0 & 1 & 0 \\ 0 & 1 & 6 & -1 & 0 & 1 \end{array}\right]} \Rightarrow \underset{-R_2 + R_3 \Rightarrow R_3}{\left[\begin{array}{ccc|ccc} 1 & 3 & 5 & 1 & 0 & 0 \\ 0 & 1 & 6 & 0 & 1 & 0 \\ 0 & 0 & 0 & -1 & -1 & 1 \end{array}\right]}$$

Since the original matrix cannot be changed into the identity, there is no inverse matrix.

14. $$\left[\begin{array}{ccc|ccc} 1 & 2 & 3 & 1 & 0 & 0 \\ 4 & 5 & 6 & 0 & 1 & 0 \\ 7 & 8 & 9 & 0 & 0 & 1 \end{array}\right] \Rightarrow \underset{\substack{-4R_1 + R_2 \Rightarrow R_2 \\ -7R_1 + R_3 \Rightarrow R_3}}{\left[\begin{array}{ccc|ccc} 1 & 2 & 3 & 1 & 0 & 0 \\ 0 & -3 & -6 & -4 & 1 & 0 \\ 0 & -6 & -12 & -7 & 0 & 1 \end{array}\right]} \Rightarrow \underset{-2R_2 + R_3 \Rightarrow R_3}{\left[\begin{array}{ccc|ccc} 1 & 2 & 3 & 1 & 0 & 0 \\ 0 & -3 & -6 & -4 & 1 & 0 \\ 0 & 0 & 0 & 1 & -2 & 1 \end{array}\right]}$$

Since the original matrix cannot be changed into the identity, there is no inverse matrix.

15. $\left[\begin{array}{ccc|ccc} 1 & 2 & 3 & 1 & 0 & 0 \\ 0 & 1 & 2 & 0 & 1 & 0 \\ 0 & 0 & 1 & 0 & 0 & 1 \end{array}\right] \Rightarrow \left[\begin{array}{ccc|ccc} 1 & 0 & -1 & 1 & -2 & 0 \\ 0 & 1 & 2 & 0 & 1 & 0 \\ 0 & 0 & 1 & 0 & 0 & 1 \end{array}\right] \Rightarrow \left[\begin{array}{ccc|ccc} 1 & 0 & 0 & 1 & -2 & 1 \\ 0 & 1 & 0 & 0 & 1 & -2 \\ 0 & 0 & 1 & 0 & 0 & 2 \end{array}\right] \Rightarrow$

$-2R_2 + R_1 \Rightarrow R_1$ $\qquad$ $R_3 + R_1 \Rightarrow R_1$, $-2R_3 + R_2 \Rightarrow R_2$

Inverse $= \begin{bmatrix} 1 & -2 & 1 \\ 0 & 1 & -2 \\ 0 & 0 & 1 \end{bmatrix}$

16. $\left[\begin{array}{ccc|ccc} 1 & 2 & 3 & 1 & 0 & 0 \\ 0 & 1 & 1 & 0 & 1 & 0 \\ 0 & -1 & 0 & 0 & 0 & 1 \end{array}\right] \Rightarrow \left[\begin{array}{ccc|ccc} 1 & 2 & 3 & 1 & 0 & 0 \\ 0 & -1 & 0 & 0 & 0 & 1 \\ 0 & 1 & 1 & 0 & 1 & 0 \end{array}\right] \Rightarrow \left[\begin{array}{ccc|ccc} 1 & 0 & 3 & 1 & 0 & 2 \\ 0 & 1 & 0 & 0 & 0 & -1 \\ 0 & 0 & 1 & 0 & 1 & 1 \end{array}\right] \Rightarrow$

$R_2 \Leftrightarrow R_3$ $\qquad$ $2R_2 + R_1 \Rightarrow R_1$, $R_2 + R_3 \Rightarrow R_3$, $-R_2 \Rightarrow R_2$

$\left[\begin{array}{ccc|ccc} 1 & 0 & 0 & 1 & -3 & -1 \\ 0 & 1 & 0 & 0 & 0 & -1 \\ 0 & 0 & 1 & 0 & 1 & 1 \end{array}\right] \Rightarrow$ Inverse $= \begin{bmatrix} 1 & -3 & -1 \\ 0 & 0 & -1 \\ 0 & 1 & 1 \end{bmatrix}$

$-3R_3 + R_1 \Rightarrow R_1$

17. $\left[\begin{array}{ccc|ccc} 1 & 6 & 4 & 1 & 0 & 0 \\ 1 & -2 & -5 & 0 & 1 & 0 \\ 2 & 4 & -1 & 0 & 0 & 1 \end{array}\right] \Rightarrow \left[\begin{array}{ccc|ccc} 1 & 6 & 4 & 1 & 0 & 0 \\ 0 & -8 & -9 & -1 & 1 & 0 \\ 0 & -8 & -9 & -2 & 0 & 1 \end{array}\right] \Rightarrow \left[\begin{array}{ccc|ccc} 1 & 6 & 4 & 1 & 0 & 0 \\ 0 & -8 & -9 & -1 & 1 & 0 \\ 0 & 0 & 0 & -1 & -1 & 1 \end{array}\right]$

$-R_1 + R_2 \Rightarrow R_2$, $-2R_1 + R_3 \Rightarrow R_3$ $\qquad$ $-R_2 + R_3 \Rightarrow R_3$

Since the original matrix cannot be changed into the identity, there is no inverse matrix.

18. $\left[\begin{array}{ccc|ccc} 1 & 1 & 1 & 1 & 0 & 0 \\ 1 & 0 & -1 & 0 & 1 & 0 \\ 1 & 2 & 3 & 0 & 0 & 1 \end{array}\right] \Rightarrow \left[\begin{array}{ccc|ccc} 1 & 1 & 1 & 1 & 0 & 0 \\ 0 & -1 & -2 & -1 & 1 & 0 \\ 0 & 1 & 2 & -1 & 0 & 1 \end{array}\right] \Rightarrow \left[\begin{array}{ccc|ccc} 1 & 1 & 1 & 1 & 0 & 0 \\ 0 & -1 & -2 & -1 & 1 & 0 \\ 0 & 0 & 0 & -2 & 1 & 1 \end{array}\right]$

$-R_1 + R_2 \Rightarrow R_2$, $-R_1 + R_3 \Rightarrow R_3$ $\qquad$ $R_2 + R_3 \Rightarrow R_3$

Since the original matrix cannot be changed into the identity, there is no inverse matrix.

19. Inverse $= \begin{bmatrix} 1 & -2 & 1 & 0 \\ 0 & 1 & -2 & 1 \\ 0 & 0 & 1 & -2 \\ 0 & 0 & 0 & 1 \end{bmatrix}$

20. Inverse $= \begin{bmatrix} 1 & 0 & 0 & 0 \\ -1 & 1 & 0 & 0 \\ 0 & -1 & 1 & 0 \\ 1 & 0 & -2 & 1 \end{bmatrix}$

21. Inverse $= \begin{bmatrix} 8 & -2 & -6 \\ -5 & 2 & 4 \\ 2 & 0 & -2 \end{bmatrix}$

22. Inverse $= \begin{bmatrix} -0.2 & 1.2 & 1.6 \\ -0.2 & -0.8 & -0.4 \\ 0.4 & 1.6 & 2.8 \end{bmatrix}$

23. Inverse $= \begin{bmatrix} -2.5 & 5 & 3 & 5.5 \\ 5.5 & -8 & -6 & -9.5 \\ -1 & 3 & 1 & 3 \\ -5.5 & 9 & 6 & 10.5 \end{bmatrix}$

24. Inverse $= \begin{bmatrix} 1 & 0 & 0 & 0 \\ -2 & 1 & 0 & 0 \\ 1 & -2 & 1 & 0 \\ 0 & 1 & -2 & 1 \end{bmatrix}$

25. $\begin{bmatrix} 3 & -4 \\ -2 & 3 \end{bmatrix}\begin{bmatrix} x \\ y \end{bmatrix} = \begin{bmatrix} 1 \\ 5 \end{bmatrix}$

$$\begin{bmatrix} x \\ y \end{bmatrix} = \begin{bmatrix} 3 & -4 \\ -2 & 3 \end{bmatrix}^{-1}\begin{bmatrix} 1 \\ 5 \end{bmatrix}$$
$$\begin{bmatrix} x \\ y \end{bmatrix} = \begin{bmatrix} 3 & 4 \\ 2 & 3 \end{bmatrix}\begin{bmatrix} 1 \\ 5 \end{bmatrix}$$
$$\begin{bmatrix} x \\ y \end{bmatrix} = \begin{bmatrix} 23 \\ 17 \end{bmatrix}$$

26. $\begin{bmatrix} 3 & -4 \\ -2 & 3 \end{bmatrix}\begin{bmatrix} x \\ y \end{bmatrix} = \begin{bmatrix} -1 \\ 3 \end{bmatrix}$

$$\begin{bmatrix} x \\ y \end{bmatrix} = \begin{bmatrix} 3 & -4 \\ -2 & 3 \end{bmatrix}^{-1}\begin{bmatrix} -1 \\ 3 \end{bmatrix}$$
$$\begin{bmatrix} x \\ y \end{bmatrix} = \begin{bmatrix} 3 & 4 \\ 2 & 3 \end{bmatrix}\begin{bmatrix} -1 \\ 3 \end{bmatrix}$$
$$\begin{bmatrix} x \\ y \end{bmatrix} = \begin{bmatrix} 9 \\ 7 \end{bmatrix}$$

27. $\begin{bmatrix} 3 & -4 \\ -2 & 3 \end{bmatrix}\begin{bmatrix} x \\ y \end{bmatrix} = \begin{bmatrix} 0 \\ 0 \end{bmatrix}$

$$\begin{bmatrix} x \\ y \end{bmatrix} = \begin{bmatrix} 3 & -4 \\ -2 & 3 \end{bmatrix}^{-1}\begin{bmatrix} 0 \\ 0 \end{bmatrix}$$
$$\begin{bmatrix} x \\ y \end{bmatrix} = \begin{bmatrix} 3 & 4 \\ 2 & 3 \end{bmatrix}\begin{bmatrix} 0 \\ 0 \end{bmatrix}$$
$$\begin{bmatrix} x \\ y \end{bmatrix} = \begin{bmatrix} 0 \\ 0 \end{bmatrix}$$

28. $\begin{bmatrix} 3 & -4 \\ -2 & 3 \end{bmatrix}\begin{bmatrix} x \\ y \end{bmatrix} = \begin{bmatrix} -3 \\ -2 \end{bmatrix}$

$$\begin{bmatrix} x \\ y \end{bmatrix} = \begin{bmatrix} 3 & -4 \\ -2 & 3 \end{bmatrix}^{-1}\begin{bmatrix} -3 \\ -2 \end{bmatrix}$$
$$\begin{bmatrix} x \\ y \end{bmatrix} = \begin{bmatrix} 3 & 4 \\ 2 & 3 \end{bmatrix}\begin{bmatrix} -3 \\ -2 \end{bmatrix}$$
$$\begin{bmatrix} x \\ y \end{bmatrix} = \begin{bmatrix} -17 \\ -12 \end{bmatrix}$$

29. $\begin{bmatrix} 2 & 1 & -1 \\ 2 & 2 & -1 \\ -1 & -1 & 1 \end{bmatrix}\begin{bmatrix} x \\ y \\ z \end{bmatrix} = \begin{bmatrix} 2 \\ 4 \\ -1 \end{bmatrix}$

$$\begin{bmatrix} x \\ y \\ z \end{bmatrix} = \begin{bmatrix} 2 & 1 & -1 \\ 2 & 2 & -1 \\ -1 & -1 & 1 \end{bmatrix}^{-1}\begin{bmatrix} 2 \\ 4 \\ -1 \end{bmatrix}$$
$$\begin{bmatrix} x \\ y \\ z \end{bmatrix} = \begin{bmatrix} 1 & 0 & 1 \\ -1 & 1 & 0 \\ 0 & 1 & 2 \end{bmatrix}\begin{bmatrix} 2 \\ 4 \\ -1 \end{bmatrix} = \begin{bmatrix} 1 \\ 2 \\ 2 \end{bmatrix}$$

30. $\begin{bmatrix} 2 & 1 & -1 \\ 2 & 2 & -1 \\ -1 & -1 & 1 \end{bmatrix}\begin{bmatrix} x \\ y \\ z \end{bmatrix} = \begin{bmatrix} 3 \\ -1 \\ 4 \end{bmatrix}$

$$\begin{bmatrix} x \\ y \\ z \end{bmatrix} = \begin{bmatrix} 2 & 1 & -1 \\ 2 & 2 & -1 \\ -1 & -1 & 1 \end{bmatrix}^{-1}\begin{bmatrix} 3 \\ -1 \\ 4 \end{bmatrix}$$
$$\begin{bmatrix} x \\ y \\ z \end{bmatrix} = \begin{bmatrix} 1 & 0 & 1 \\ -1 & 1 & 0 \\ 0 & 1 & 2 \end{bmatrix}\begin{bmatrix} 3 \\ -1 \\ 4 \end{bmatrix} = \begin{bmatrix} 7 \\ -4 \\ 7 \end{bmatrix}$$

31. $$\begin{bmatrix} -2 & 1 & -3 \\ 2 & 3 & 0 \\ 1 & 0 & 1 \end{bmatrix}\begin{bmatrix} x \\ y \\ z \end{bmatrix} = \begin{bmatrix} 2 \\ -3 \\ 5 \end{bmatrix}$$

$$\begin{bmatrix} x \\ y \\ z \end{bmatrix} = \begin{bmatrix} -2 & 1 & -3 \\ 2 & 3 & 0 \\ 1 & 0 & 1 \end{bmatrix}^{-1}\begin{bmatrix} 2 \\ -3 \\ 5 \end{bmatrix}$$

$$\begin{bmatrix} x \\ y \\ z \end{bmatrix} = \begin{bmatrix} 3 & -1 & 9 \\ -2 & 1 & -6 \\ -3 & 1 & -8 \end{bmatrix}\begin{bmatrix} 2 \\ -3 \\ 5 \end{bmatrix} = \begin{bmatrix} 54 \\ -37 \\ -49 \end{bmatrix}$$

32. $$\begin{bmatrix} -2 & 1 & -3 \\ 2 & 3 & 0 \\ 1 & 0 & 1 \end{bmatrix}\begin{bmatrix} x \\ y \\ z \end{bmatrix} = \begin{bmatrix} 5 \\ 1 \\ -2 \end{bmatrix}$$

$$\begin{bmatrix} x \\ y \\ z \end{bmatrix} = \begin{bmatrix} -2 & 1 & -3 \\ 2 & 3 & 0 \\ 1 & 0 & 1 \end{bmatrix}^{-1}\begin{bmatrix} 5 \\ 1 \\ -2 \end{bmatrix}$$

$$\begin{bmatrix} x \\ y \\ z \end{bmatrix} = \begin{bmatrix} 3 & -1 & 9 \\ -2 & 1 & -6 \\ -3 & 1 & -8 \end{bmatrix}\begin{bmatrix} 5 \\ 1 \\ -2 \end{bmatrix} = \begin{bmatrix} -4 \\ 3 \\ 2 \end{bmatrix}$$

33. $$\begin{bmatrix} 5 & 3 \\ -7 & 5 \end{bmatrix}\begin{bmatrix} x \\ y \end{bmatrix} = \begin{bmatrix} 13 \\ -9 \end{bmatrix}$$

$$\begin{bmatrix} x \\ y \end{bmatrix} = \begin{bmatrix} 5 & 3 \\ -7 & 5 \end{bmatrix}^{-1}\begin{bmatrix} 13 \\ -9 \end{bmatrix}$$

$$\begin{bmatrix} x \\ y \end{bmatrix} = \begin{bmatrix} 2 \\ 1 \end{bmatrix}$$

34. $$\begin{bmatrix} 8 & -3 \\ -3 & 2 \end{bmatrix}\begin{bmatrix} x \\ y \end{bmatrix} = \begin{bmatrix} 7 \\ 0 \end{bmatrix}$$

$$\begin{bmatrix} x \\ y \end{bmatrix} = \begin{bmatrix} 8 & -3 \\ -3 & 2 \end{bmatrix}^{-1}\begin{bmatrix} 7 \\ 0 \end{bmatrix}$$

$$\begin{bmatrix} x \\ y \end{bmatrix} = \begin{bmatrix} 2 \\ 3 \end{bmatrix}$$

35. $$\begin{bmatrix} 5 & 2 & 3 \\ 2 & 0 & 5 \\ 3 & 0 & 1 \end{bmatrix}\begin{bmatrix} x \\ y \\ z \end{bmatrix} = \begin{bmatrix} 12 \\ 7 \\ 4 \end{bmatrix}$$

$$\begin{bmatrix} x \\ y \\ z \end{bmatrix} = \begin{bmatrix} 5 & 2 & 3 \\ 2 & 0 & 5 \\ 3 & 0 & 1 \end{bmatrix}^{-1}\begin{bmatrix} 12 \\ 7 \\ 4 \end{bmatrix} = \begin{bmatrix} 1 \\ 2 \\ 1 \end{bmatrix}$$

36. $$\begin{bmatrix} 3 & 2 & -1 \\ 5 & -2 & 0 \\ 3 & 1 & 1 \end{bmatrix}\begin{bmatrix} x \\ y \\ z \end{bmatrix} = \begin{bmatrix} 0 \\ 5 \\ 6 \end{bmatrix}$$

$$\begin{bmatrix} x \\ y \\ z \end{bmatrix} = \begin{bmatrix} 3 & 2 & -1 \\ 5 & -2 & 0 \\ 3 & 1 & 1 \end{bmatrix}^{-1}\begin{bmatrix} 0 \\ 5 \\ 6 \end{bmatrix} = \begin{bmatrix} 1 \\ 0 \\ 3 \end{bmatrix}$$

37. $$\begin{bmatrix} 23 & 27 \\ 21 & 22 \end{bmatrix}\begin{bmatrix} x \\ y \end{bmatrix} = \begin{bmatrix} 127 \\ 108 \end{bmatrix}$$
$$\begin{bmatrix} x \\ y \end{bmatrix} = \begin{bmatrix} 23 & 27 \\ 21 & 22 \end{bmatrix}^{-1}\begin{bmatrix} 127 \\ 108 \end{bmatrix}$$
$$\begin{bmatrix} x \\ y \end{bmatrix} = \begin{bmatrix} 2 \\ 3 \end{bmatrix}$$
2 of model A and 3 of model B can be made.

38. $$AY = \begin{bmatrix} 30 \\ 122 \\ 49 \end{bmatrix}$$
$$A^{-1}AY = IY = Y$$
$$Y = A^{-1}AY = \begin{bmatrix} 1 & 1 & 0 \\ 2 & 3 & 3 \\ 1 & 1 & 1 \end{bmatrix}^{-1}\begin{bmatrix} 30 \\ 122 \\ 49 \end{bmatrix}$$
$$= \begin{bmatrix} 25 \\ 5 \\ 19 \end{bmatrix} \Rightarrow \text{"YES"}$$

39. **Answers may vary.**

40. **Answers may vary.**

41. $$A^2 = \begin{bmatrix} -1 & -1 \\ 1 & 1 \end{bmatrix}\begin{bmatrix} -1 & -1 \\ 1 & 1 \end{bmatrix} = \begin{bmatrix} 0 & 0 \\ 0 & 0 \end{bmatrix}$$

42. $$I - A = \begin{bmatrix} 2 & 1 \\ -1 & 0 \end{bmatrix}, I + A = \begin{bmatrix} 0 & -1 \\ 1 & 2 \end{bmatrix};$$
$$(I - A)(I + A) = \begin{bmatrix} 2 & 1 \\ -1 & 0 \end{bmatrix}\begin{bmatrix} 0 & -1 \\ 1 & 2 \end{bmatrix} = \begin{bmatrix} 1 & 0 \\ 0 & 1 \end{bmatrix}$$
Since the product is the identity, they are inverse matrices.

43. $$\begin{bmatrix} 1 & 0 & 0 \\ -2 & -3 & -2 \\ 3 & 6 & 1 \end{bmatrix}\begin{bmatrix} x \\ y \\ z \end{bmatrix} = \begin{bmatrix} 0 \\ 0 \\ 0 \end{bmatrix}$$
$$\begin{bmatrix} x \\ y \\ z \end{bmatrix} = \begin{bmatrix} 1 & 0 & 0 \\ -2 & -3 & -2 \\ 3 & 6 & 1 \end{bmatrix}^{-1}\begin{bmatrix} 0 \\ 0 \\ 0 \end{bmatrix} = \begin{bmatrix} 0 \\ 0 \\ 0 \end{bmatrix}$$

44. Cannot be solved using inverse matrix.

Solution is $\begin{bmatrix} 0 \\ 0 \\ 0 \end{bmatrix}$.

45. $$AB = AC$$
$$A^{-1}AB = A^{-1}AC$$
$$IB = IC$$
$$B = C$$

46. $$\left[\begin{array}{cc|cc} a & b & 1 & 0 \\ c & d & 0 & 1 \end{array}\right] \Rightarrow \left[\begin{array}{cc|cc} 1 & \frac{b}{a} & \frac{1}{a} & 0 \\ c & d & 0 & 1 \end{array}\right] \Rightarrow \left[\begin{array}{cc|cc} 1 & \frac{b}{a} & \frac{1}{a} & 0 \\ 0 & \frac{ad-bc}{a} & -\frac{c}{a} & 1 \end{array}\right] \Rightarrow$$
$$\tfrac{1}{a}R_1 \Rightarrow R_1 \qquad -cR_1 + R_2 \Rightarrow R_2$$
$$\left[\begin{array}{cc|cc} 1 & \frac{b}{a} & \frac{1}{a} & 0 \\ 0 & 1 & -\frac{c}{ad-bc} & \frac{a}{ad-bc} \end{array}\right] \Rightarrow \left[\begin{array}{cc|cc} 1 & 0 & \frac{d}{ad-bc} & -\frac{b}{ad-bc} \\ 0 & 1 & -\frac{c}{ad-bc} & \frac{a}{ad-bc} \end{array}\right] \Rightarrow \text{Inverse: } \begin{bmatrix} \frac{d}{ad-bc} & -\frac{b}{ad-bc} \\ -\frac{c}{ad-bc} & \frac{a}{ad-bc} \end{bmatrix}$$
$$\tfrac{a}{ad-bc}R_2 \Rightarrow R_2 \qquad -\tfrac{b}{a}R_2 + R_1 \Rightarrow R_1$$
The inverse will be defined if and only if the denominator, $ad - bc$, is not equal to 0.

47. $$\begin{aligned}(I-B)(I+B) &= I^2+IB-BI-B^2\\ &= I+B-B-B^2\\ &= I-B^2\\ &= I-\mathbf{0}=I \Rightarrow \text{Thus, } I-B \text{ and } I+B \text{ are inverses.}\end{aligned}$$

48. $$\begin{aligned}(I-C)\left(I+C+C^2\right) &= I^2+IC+IC^2-CI-C^2-C^3\\ &= I+C+C^2-C-C^2-C^3\\ &= I-C^3\\ &= I-\mathbf{0}=I \Rightarrow \text{Thus, } I-C \text{ and } I+C+C^2 \text{ are inverses.}\end{aligned}$$

49. $y=\dfrac{3x-5}{x^2-4}=\dfrac{3x-5}{(x+2)(x-2)}$
domain: $(-\infty,-2)\cup(-2,2)\cup(2,\infty)$

50. $y=\dfrac{3x-5}{x^2+4}$
domain $=(-\infty,\infty)$

51. $y=\dfrac{3x-5}{\sqrt{x^2+4}}$
domain $=(-\infty,\infty)$

52. $y=\dfrac{3x-5}{\sqrt{x^2-4}}$
domain $=(-\infty,-2)\cup(2,\infty)$

53. $y=x^2$; range $=[0,\infty)$

54. $y=x^3$; range $=(-\infty,\infty)$

55. $y=\log x$; range $=(-\infty,\infty)$

56. $y=2^x$; range $=(0,\infty)$

Exercise 6.5 (page 477)

1. $|A|$, $\det A$

2. $ad-bc$

3. 0

4. $|A|$

5. 0

6. coefficient matrix

7. $$\begin{vmatrix}2 & 1\\ -2 & 3\end{vmatrix}=(2)(3)-(1)(-2)=6-(-2)=8$$

8. $$\begin{vmatrix}-3 & -6\\ 2 & -5\end{vmatrix}=(-3)(-5)-(-6)(2)=15-(-12)=27$$

9. $$\begin{vmatrix}2 & -3\\ -3 & 5\end{vmatrix}=(2)(5)-(-3)(-3)=10-9=1$$

10. $$\begin{vmatrix}5 & 8\\ -6 & -2\end{vmatrix}=(5)(-2)-(8)(-6)=-10-(-48)=38$$

11. $M_{21}=\begin{vmatrix}-2 & 3\\ 8 & 9\end{vmatrix}$

12. $M_{13}=\begin{vmatrix}4 & 5\\ -7 & 8\end{vmatrix}$

13. $M_{33}=\begin{vmatrix}1 & -2\\ 4 & 5\end{vmatrix}$

14. $M_{32}=\begin{vmatrix}1 & 3\\ 4 & -6\end{vmatrix}$

15. $C_{21}=-\begin{vmatrix}-2 & 3\\ 8 & 9\end{vmatrix}$

16. $C_{13}=\begin{vmatrix}4 & 5\\ -7 & 8\end{vmatrix}$

17. $C_{33}=\begin{vmatrix}1 & -2\\ 4 & 5\end{vmatrix}$

18. $C_{32}=-\begin{vmatrix}1 & 3\\ 4 & -6\end{vmatrix}$

19. $$\begin{vmatrix} 2 & -3 & 5 \\ -2 & 1 & 3 \\ 1 & 3 & -2 \end{vmatrix} = 2\begin{vmatrix} 1 & 3 \\ 3 & -2 \end{vmatrix} - (-3)\begin{vmatrix} -2 & 3 \\ 1 & -2 \end{vmatrix} + 5\begin{vmatrix} -2 & 1 \\ 1 & 3 \end{vmatrix}$$
$$= 2(-11) + 3(1) + 5(-7) = -22 + 3 - 35 = -54$$

20. $$\begin{vmatrix} 1 & 3 & 1 \\ -2 & 5 & 3 \\ 3 & -2 & -2 \end{vmatrix} = 1\begin{vmatrix} 5 & 3 \\ -2 & -2 \end{vmatrix} - 3\begin{vmatrix} -2 & 3 \\ 3 & -2 \end{vmatrix} + 1\begin{vmatrix} -2 & 5 \\ 3 & -2 \end{vmatrix}$$
$$= 1(-4) - 3(-5) + 1(-11) = -4 + 15 - 11 = 0$$

21. $$\begin{vmatrix} 1 & -1 & 2 \\ 2 & 1 & 3 \\ 1 & 1 & -1 \end{vmatrix} = 1\begin{vmatrix} 1 & 3 \\ 1 & -1 \end{vmatrix} - (-1)\begin{vmatrix} 2 & 3 \\ 1 & -1 \end{vmatrix} + 2\begin{vmatrix} 2 & 1 \\ 1 & 1 \end{vmatrix}$$
$$= 1(-4) + 1(-5) + 2(1) = -4 - 5 + 2 = -7$$

22. $$\begin{vmatrix} 1 & 3 & 1 \\ 2 & 1 & -1 \\ 2 & -1 & 1 \end{vmatrix} = 1\begin{vmatrix} 1 & -1 \\ -1 & 1 \end{vmatrix} - 3\begin{vmatrix} 2 & -1 \\ 2 & 1 \end{vmatrix} + 1\begin{vmatrix} 2 & 1 \\ 2 & -1 \end{vmatrix}$$
$$= 1(0) - 3(4) + 1(-4) = 0 - 12 - 4 = -16$$

23. $$\begin{vmatrix} 2 & 1 & -1 \\ 1 & 3 & 5 \\ 2 & -5 & 3 \end{vmatrix} = 2\begin{vmatrix} 3 & 5 \\ -5 & 3 \end{vmatrix} - 1\begin{vmatrix} 1 & 5 \\ 2 & 3 \end{vmatrix} + (-1)\begin{vmatrix} 1 & 3 \\ 2 & -5 \end{vmatrix}$$
$$= 2(34) - 1(-7) - 1(-11) = 68 + 7 + 11 = 86$$

24. $$\begin{vmatrix} 3 & 1 & -2 \\ -3 & 2 & 1 \\ 1 & 3 & 0 \end{vmatrix} = 3\begin{vmatrix} 2 & 1 \\ 3 & 0 \end{vmatrix} - 1\begin{vmatrix} -3 & 1 \\ 1 & 0 \end{vmatrix} + (-2)\begin{vmatrix} -3 & 2 \\ 1 & 3 \end{vmatrix}$$
$$= 3(-3) - 1(-1) - 2(-11) = -9 + 1 + 22 = 14$$

25. $$\begin{vmatrix} 0 & 1 & -3 \\ -3 & 5 & 2 \\ 2 & -5 & 3 \end{vmatrix} = 0\begin{vmatrix} 5 & 2 \\ -5 & 3 \end{vmatrix} - 1\begin{vmatrix} -3 & 2 \\ 2 & 3 \end{vmatrix} + (-3)\begin{vmatrix} -3 & 5 \\ 2 & -5 \end{vmatrix}$$
$$= 0 - 1(-13) - 3(5) = 0 + 13 - 15 = -2$$

26. $$\begin{vmatrix} 1 & -7 & -2 \\ -2 & 0 & 3 \\ -1 & 7 & 1 \end{vmatrix} = 1\begin{vmatrix} 0 & 3 \\ 7 & 1 \end{vmatrix} - (-7)\begin{vmatrix} -2 & 3 \\ -1 & 1 \end{vmatrix} + (-2)\begin{vmatrix} -2 & 0 \\ -1 & 7 \end{vmatrix}$$
$$= 1(-21) + 7(1) - 2(-14) = -21 + 7 + 28 = 14$$

27. $\begin{vmatrix} 0 & 0 & 1 & 0 \\ -2 & 1 & 0 & 1 \\ 1 & 0 & 1 & 2 \\ 2 & 0 & 1 & 2 \end{vmatrix} = 0(***) - 0(***) + 1\begin{vmatrix} -2 & 1 & 1 \\ 1 & 0 & 2 \\ 2 & 0 & 2 \end{vmatrix} - 0(***)$

$$= 1\left(-2\begin{vmatrix} 0 & 2 \\ 0 & 2 \end{vmatrix} - 1\begin{vmatrix} 1 & 2 \\ 2 & 2 \end{vmatrix} - 1\begin{vmatrix} 1 & 0 \\ 2 & 0 \end{vmatrix}\right) = -2(0) - 1(-2) - 1(0) = 2$$

28. Expand along 1st column...

$$\begin{vmatrix} 1 & 0 & -2 & 1 \\ 0 & 1 & 0 & 1 \\ 0 & 3 & -1 & 2 \\ 0 & -1 & 0 & 1 \end{vmatrix} = 1\begin{vmatrix} 1 & 0 & 1 \\ 3 & -1 & 2 \\ -1 & 0 & 1 \end{vmatrix} - 0(***) + 0(***) - 0(***)$$

$$= 1\left(1\begin{vmatrix} -1 & 2 \\ 0 & 1 \end{vmatrix} - 0\begin{vmatrix} 3 & 2 \\ -1 & 1 \end{vmatrix} + 1\begin{vmatrix} 3 & -1 \\ -1 & 0 \end{vmatrix}\right) = 1(-1) - 0 + 1(-1) = -2$$

29. $\begin{vmatrix} 1 & 2 & 1 & 3 \\ -2 & 1 & -3 & 1 \\ -1 & 0 & 1 & -2 \\ 2 & -1 & -1 & 3 \end{vmatrix} = \begin{vmatrix} 1 & 2 & 1 & 3 \\ 0 & 0 & -4 & 4 \\ 0 & 2 & 2 & 1 \\ 0 & -5 & -3 & -3 \end{vmatrix} \quad \begin{matrix} \\ R_2 + R_4 \\ R_1 + R_3 \\ -2R_1 + R_4 \end{matrix}$

$$= 1\begin{vmatrix} 0 & -4 & 4 \\ 2 & 2 & 1 \\ -5 & -3 & -3 \end{vmatrix} \quad \text{(expand along first column)}$$

$$= 1\left(0\begin{vmatrix} 2 & 1 \\ -3 & -3 \end{vmatrix} - (-4)\begin{vmatrix} 2 & 1 \\ -5 & -3 \end{vmatrix} + 4\begin{vmatrix} 2 & 2 \\ -5 & -3 \end{vmatrix}\right)$$

$$= 0 + 4(-1) + 4(4) = 12$$

30. $\begin{vmatrix} -1 & 3 & -2 & 5 \\ 2 & 1 & 0 & 1 \\ 1 & 3 & -2 & 5 \\ 2 & -1 & 0 & -1 \end{vmatrix} = \begin{vmatrix} -1 & 3 & -2 & 5 \\ 0 & 7 & -4 & 11 \\ 0 & 6 & -4 & 10 \\ 0 & 5 & -4 & 9 \end{vmatrix} \quad \begin{matrix} \\ 2R_1 + R_2 \\ R_1 + R_3 \\ 2R_1 + R_4 \end{matrix}$

$$= 1\begin{vmatrix} 7 & -4 & 11 \\ 6 & -4 & 10 \\ 5 & -4 & 9 \end{vmatrix} \quad \text{(expand along first column)}$$

$$= 1\left(7\begin{vmatrix} -4 & 11 \\ -4 & 10 \end{vmatrix} - (-4)\begin{vmatrix} 6 & 10 \\ 5 & 9 \end{vmatrix} + 11\begin{vmatrix} 6 & -4 \\ 5 & -4 \end{vmatrix}\right)$$

$$= 7(4) + 4(4) + 11(-4) = 0$$

31. R_1 and R_2 have been switched. This multiplies the determinant by -1. TRUE

32. R_1 has been multiplied by $\frac{1}{2}$. This multiplies the determinant by $\frac{1}{2}$. FALSE

33. R_1 and R_2 have both been multiplied by -1. This multiplies the determinant by -1 twice. FALSE

34. R_1 has been added to R_2. This leaves the determinant unchanged. TRUE

35. R_1 and R_2 have been switched. This multiplies the determinant by -1. However, R_3 has been multiplied by -1, which also multiplies the determinant by -1. Thus, the determinant remains equal to 3.

36. R_1 has been multiplied by 5, which multiplies the determinant by 5. R_3 has been multiplied by 3, which multiplies the determinant by 3. R_2 has been multiplied by -1, which multiplies the determinant by -1. Thus, the determinant $= 5(3)(-1)\cdot 3 = -45$.

37. R_1 has been added to R_3. This leaves the determinant equal to 3.

38. R_1 and R_3 were switched, and then R_2 and the new R_3 were switched. Both switches multiply the determinant by -1. Thus, the determinant remains equal to 3.

39. $$x = \frac{\begin{vmatrix} 7 & 2 \\ -4 & -3 \end{vmatrix}}{\begin{vmatrix} 3 & 2 \\ 2 & -3 \end{vmatrix}} = \frac{-13}{-13} = 1 \quad y = \frac{\begin{vmatrix} 3 & 7 \\ 2 & -4 \end{vmatrix}}{\begin{vmatrix} 3 & 2 \\ 2 & -3 \end{vmatrix}} = \frac{-26}{-13} = 2$$

40. $$x = \frac{\begin{vmatrix} -6 & -5 \\ -1 & 2 \end{vmatrix}}{\begin{vmatrix} 1 & -5 \\ 3 & 2 \end{vmatrix}} = \frac{-17}{17} = -1 \quad y = \frac{\begin{vmatrix} 1 & -6 \\ 3 & -1 \end{vmatrix}}{\begin{vmatrix} 1 & -5 \\ 3 & 2 \end{vmatrix}} = \frac{17}{17} = 1$$

41. $$x = \frac{\begin{vmatrix} 3 & -1 \\ 9 & -7 \end{vmatrix}}{\begin{vmatrix} 1 & -1 \\ 3 & -7 \end{vmatrix}} = \frac{-12}{-4} = 3 \quad y = \frac{\begin{vmatrix} 1 & 3 \\ 3 & 9 \end{vmatrix}}{\begin{vmatrix} 1 & -1 \\ 3 & -7 \end{vmatrix}} = \frac{0}{-4} = 0$$

42. $$x = \frac{\begin{vmatrix} -6 & -1 \\ 0 & 1 \end{vmatrix}}{\begin{vmatrix} 2 & -1 \\ 1 & 1 \end{vmatrix}} = \frac{-6}{3} = -2 \quad y = \frac{\begin{vmatrix} 2 & -6 \\ 1 & 0 \end{vmatrix}}{\begin{vmatrix} 2 & -1 \\ 1 & 1 \end{vmatrix}} = \frac{6}{3} = 2$$

43. $$x = \frac{\begin{vmatrix} 2 & 2 & 1 \\ 2 & -1 & 1 \\ 4 & 1 & 3 \end{vmatrix}}{\begin{vmatrix} 1 & 2 & 1 \\ 1 & -1 & 1 \\ 1 & 1 & 3 \end{vmatrix}} = \frac{-6}{-6} = 1 \quad y = \frac{\begin{vmatrix} 1 & 2 & 1 \\ 1 & 2 & 1 \\ 1 & 4 & 3 \end{vmatrix}}{\begin{vmatrix} 1 & 2 & 1 \\ 1 & -1 & 1 \\ 1 & 1 & 3 \end{vmatrix}} = \frac{0}{-6} = 0 \quad z = \frac{\begin{vmatrix} 1 & 2 & 2 \\ 1 & -1 & 2 \\ 1 & 1 & 4 \end{vmatrix}}{\begin{vmatrix} 1 & 2 & 1 \\ 1 & -1 & 1 \\ 1 & 1 & 3 \end{vmatrix}} = \frac{-6}{-6} = 1$$

44. $x = \dfrac{\begin{vmatrix} -1 & 2 & -1 \\ 1 & 1 & -1 \\ 17 & -3 & -5 \end{vmatrix}}{\begin{vmatrix} 1 & 2 & -1 \\ 2 & 1 & -1 \\ 1 & -3 & -5 \end{vmatrix}} = \dfrac{4}{17}$ $y = \dfrac{\begin{vmatrix} 1 & -1 & -1 \\ 2 & 1 & -1 \\ 1 & 17 & -5 \end{vmatrix}}{\begin{vmatrix} 1 & 2 & -1 \\ 2 & 1 & -1 \\ 1 & -3 & -5 \end{vmatrix}} = \dfrac{-30}{17}$ $z = \dfrac{\begin{vmatrix} 1 & 2 & -1 \\ 2 & 1 & 1 \\ 1 & -3 & 17 \end{vmatrix}}{\begin{vmatrix} 1 & 2 & -1 \\ 2 & 1 & -1 \\ 1 & -3 & -5 \end{vmatrix}} = \dfrac{-39}{17}$

45. $x = \dfrac{\begin{vmatrix} 5 & -1 & 1 \\ 10 & -3 & 2 \\ 0 & 3 & 1 \end{vmatrix}}{\begin{vmatrix} 2 & -1 & 1 \\ 3 & -3 & 2 \\ 1 & 3 & 1 \end{vmatrix}} = \frac{-5}{-5} = 1$ $y = \dfrac{\begin{vmatrix} 2 & 5 & 1 \\ 3 & 10 & 2 \\ 1 & 0 & 1 \end{vmatrix}}{\begin{vmatrix} 2 & -1 & 1 \\ 3 & -3 & 2 \\ 1 & 3 & 1 \end{vmatrix}} = \frac{5}{-5} = -1$ $z = \dfrac{\begin{vmatrix} 2 & -1 & 5 \\ 3 & -3 & 10 \\ 1 & 3 & 0 \end{vmatrix}}{\begin{vmatrix} 2 & -1 & 1 \\ 3 & -3 & 2 \\ 1 & 3 & 1 \end{vmatrix}} = \frac{-10}{-5} = 2$

46. $x = \dfrac{\begin{vmatrix} 2 & -1 & -1 \\ 2 & 1 & 1 \\ -4 & -1 & 1 \end{vmatrix}}{\begin{vmatrix} 1 & -1 & -1 \\ 1 & 1 & 1 \\ -1 & -1 & 1 \end{vmatrix}} = \dfrac{8}{4} = 2$ $y = \dfrac{\begin{vmatrix} 1 & 2 & -1 \\ 1 & 2 & 1 \\ -1 & -4 & 1 \end{vmatrix}}{\begin{vmatrix} 1 & -1 & -1 \\ 1 & 1 & 1 \\ -1 & -1 & 1 \end{vmatrix}} = \dfrac{4}{4} = 1$

$z = \dfrac{\begin{vmatrix} 1 & -1 & 2 \\ 1 & 1 & 2 \\ -1 & -1 & -4 \end{vmatrix}}{\begin{vmatrix} 1 & -1 & -1 \\ 1 & 1 & 1 \\ -1 & -1 & 1 \end{vmatrix}} = \dfrac{-4}{4} = -1$

47. Rewrite system:
$3x + 2y + 3z = 66$
$2x + 6y - z = 36$
$3x + 1y + 6z = 96$

$x = \dfrac{\begin{vmatrix} 66 & 2 & 3 \\ 36 & 6 & -1 \\ 96 & 1 & 6 \end{vmatrix}}{\begin{vmatrix} 3 & 2 & 3 \\ 2 & 6 & -1 \\ 3 & 1 & 6 \end{vmatrix}} = \dfrac{198}{33} = 6$

$y = \dfrac{\begin{vmatrix} 3 & 66 & 3 \\ 2 & 36 & -1 \\ 3 & 96 & 6 \end{vmatrix}}{\begin{vmatrix} 3 & 2 & 3 \\ 2 & 6 & -1 \\ 3 & 1 & 6 \end{vmatrix}} = \dfrac{198}{33} = 6$ $z = \dfrac{\begin{vmatrix} 3 & 2 & 66 \\ 2 & 6 & 36 \\ 3 & 1 & 96 \end{vmatrix}}{\begin{vmatrix} 3 & 2 & 3 \\ 2 & 6 & -1 \\ 3 & 1 & 6 \end{vmatrix}} = \dfrac{396}{33} = 12$

48. Rewrite system:

$$15x + 6y + 10z = 510$$
$$2x + 5y + 2z = 320$$
$$6x + 2y + 3z = 180$$

$$x = \frac{\begin{vmatrix} 510 & 6 & 10 \\ 320 & 5 & 2 \\ 180 & 2 & 3 \end{vmatrix}}{\begin{vmatrix} 15 & 6 & 10 \\ 2 & 5 & 2 \\ 6 & 2 & 3 \end{vmatrix}} = \frac{-590}{-59} = 10$$

$$y = \frac{\begin{vmatrix} 15 & 510 & 10 \\ 2 & 320 & 2 \\ 6 & 180 & 3 \end{vmatrix}}{\begin{vmatrix} 15 & 6 & 10 \\ 2 & 5 & 2 \\ 6 & 2 & 3 \end{vmatrix}} = \frac{-3540}{-59} = 60 \qquad z = \frac{\begin{vmatrix} 15 & 6 & 510 \\ 2 & 5 & 320 \\ 6 & 2 & 180 \end{vmatrix}}{\begin{vmatrix} 15 & 6 & 10 \\ 2 & 5 & 2 \\ 6 & 2 & 3 \end{vmatrix}} = \frac{0}{-59} = 0$$

49.

$$p = \frac{\begin{vmatrix} 0 & -1 & 3 & -1 \\ -1 & 1 & 0 & -1 \\ 2 & 0 & -1 & 0 \\ 7 & -2 & 0 & 3 \end{vmatrix}}{\begin{vmatrix} 2 & -1 & 3 & -1 \\ 1 & 1 & 0 & -1 \\ 3 & 0 & -1 & 0 \\ 1 & -2 & 0 & 3 \end{vmatrix}} = \frac{-15}{-18} = \frac{5}{6} \qquad q = \frac{\begin{vmatrix} 2 & 0 & 3 & -1 \\ 1 & -1 & 0 & -1 \\ 3 & 2 & -1 & 0 \\ 1 & 7 & 0 & 3 \end{vmatrix}}{\begin{vmatrix} 2 & -1 & 3 & -1 \\ 1 & 1 & 0 & -1 \\ 3 & 0 & -1 & 0 \\ 1 & -2 & 0 & 3 \end{vmatrix}} = \frac{-12}{-18} = \frac{2}{3}$$

$$r = \frac{\begin{vmatrix} 2 & -1 & 0 & -1 \\ 1 & 1 & -1 & -1 \\ 3 & 0 & 2 & 0 \\ 1 & -2 & 7 & 3 \end{vmatrix}}{\begin{vmatrix} 2 & -1 & 3 & -1 \\ 1 & 1 & 0 & -1 \\ 3 & 0 & -1 & 0 \\ 1 & -2 & 0 & 3 \end{vmatrix}} = \frac{-9}{-18} = \frac{1}{2} \qquad s = \frac{\begin{vmatrix} 2 & -1 & 3 & 0 \\ 1 & 1 & 0 & -1 \\ 3 & 0 & -1 & 2 \\ 1 & -2 & 0 & 7 \end{vmatrix}}{\begin{vmatrix} 2 & -1 & 3 & -1 \\ 1 & 1 & 0 & -1 \\ 3 & 0 & -1 & 0 \\ 1 & -2 & 0 & 3 \end{vmatrix}} = \frac{-45}{-18} = \frac{5}{2}$$

50.

$$a = \frac{\begin{vmatrix} 8 & 1 & 1 & 1 \\ 7 & 1 & 1 & 2 \\ 3 & 1 & 2 & 3 \\ 4 & 2 & 3 & 4 \end{vmatrix}}{\begin{vmatrix} 1 & 1 & 1 & 1 \\ 1 & 1 & 1 & 2 \\ 1 & 1 & 2 & 3 \\ 1 & 2 & 3 & 4 \end{vmatrix}} = \frac{-7}{-1} = 7 \quad b = \frac{\begin{vmatrix} 1 & 8 & 1 & 1 \\ 1 & 7 & 1 & 2 \\ 1 & 3 & 2 & 3 \\ 1 & 4 & 3 & 4 \end{vmatrix}}{\begin{vmatrix} 1 & 1 & 1 & 1 \\ 1 & 1 & 1 & 2 \\ 1 & 1 & 2 & 3 \\ 1 & 2 & 3 & 4 \end{vmatrix}} = \frac{-5}{-1} = 5$$

$$c = \frac{\begin{vmatrix} 1 & 1 & 8 & 1 \\ 1 & 1 & 7 & 2 \\ 1 & 1 & 3 & 3 \\ 1 & 2 & 4 & 4 \end{vmatrix}}{\begin{vmatrix} 1 & 1 & 1 & 1 \\ 1 & 1 & 1 & 2 \\ 1 & 1 & 2 & 3 \\ 1 & 2 & 3 & 4 \end{vmatrix}} = \frac{3}{-1} = -3 \quad d = \frac{\begin{vmatrix} 1 & 1 & 1 & 8 \\ 1 & 1 & 1 & 7 \\ 1 & 1 & 2 & 3 \\ 1 & 2 & 3 & 4 \end{vmatrix}}{\begin{vmatrix} 1 & 1 & 1 & 1 \\ 1 & 1 & 1 & 2 \\ 1 & 1 & 2 & 3 \\ 1 & 2 & 3 & 4 \end{vmatrix}} = \frac{1}{-1} = -1$$

51.

$$\begin{vmatrix} x & y & 1 \\ 0 & 0 & 1 \\ 4 & 6 & 1 \end{vmatrix} = 0$$

$$x\begin{vmatrix} 0 & 1 \\ 6 & 1 \end{vmatrix} - y\begin{vmatrix} 0 & 1 \\ 4 & 1 \end{vmatrix} + 1\begin{vmatrix} 0 & 0 \\ 4 & 6 \end{vmatrix} = 0$$

$$x(-6) - y(-4) + 1(0) = 0$$

$$-6x + 4y = 0$$

$$3x - 2y = 0$$

52.

$$\begin{vmatrix} x & y & 1 \\ 2 & 3 & 1 \\ 6 & 8 & 1 \end{vmatrix} = 0$$

$$x\begin{vmatrix} 3 & 1 \\ 8 & 1 \end{vmatrix} - y\begin{vmatrix} 2 & 1 \\ 6 & 1 \end{vmatrix} + 1\begin{vmatrix} 2 & 3 \\ 6 & 8 \end{vmatrix} = 0$$

$$x(-5) - y(-4) + 1(-2) = 0$$

$$-5x + 4y - 2 = 0$$

$$5x - 4y = -2$$

53.

$$\begin{vmatrix} x & y & 1 \\ -2 & 3 & 1 \\ 5 & -3 & 1 \end{vmatrix} = 0$$

$$x\begin{vmatrix} 3 & 1 \\ -3 & 1 \end{vmatrix} - y\begin{vmatrix} -2 & 1 \\ 5 & 1 \end{vmatrix} + 1\begin{vmatrix} -2 & 3 \\ 5 & -3 \end{vmatrix} = 0$$

$$x(6) - y(-7) + 1(-9) = 0$$

$$6x + 7y - 9 = 0$$

$$6x + 7y = 9$$

54.

$$\begin{vmatrix} x & y & 1 \\ 1 & -2 & 1 \\ -4 & 3 & 1 \end{vmatrix} = 0$$

$$x\begin{vmatrix} -2 & 1 \\ 3 & 1 \end{vmatrix} - y\begin{vmatrix} 1 & 1 \\ -4 & 1 \end{vmatrix} + 1\begin{vmatrix} 1 & -2 \\ -4 & 3 \end{vmatrix} = 0$$

$$x(-5) - y(5) + 1(-5) = 0$$

$$-5x - 5y - 5 = 0$$

$$x + y = -1$$

55. $$\pm\frac{1}{2}\begin{vmatrix} 0 & 0 & 1 \\ 12 & 0 & 1 \\ 12 & 5 & 1 \end{vmatrix} = \pm\frac{1}{2}(60)$$

$= 30$ square units

56. $$\pm\frac{1}{2}\begin{vmatrix} 0 & 0 & 1 \\ 0 & 5 & 1 \\ 12 & 5 & 1 \end{vmatrix} = \pm\frac{1}{2}(-60)$$

$= 30$ square units

57. $\pm\frac{1}{2}\begin{vmatrix} 2 & 3 & 1 \\ 10 & 8 & 1 \\ 0 & 20 & 1 \end{vmatrix} = \pm\frac{1}{2}(146)$
$= 73$ square units

58. $\pm\frac{1}{2}\begin{vmatrix} 1 & 1 & 1 \\ 6 & 6 & 1 \\ 2 & 10 & 1 \end{vmatrix} = \pm\frac{1}{2}(40)$
$= 20$ square units

59. $\begin{vmatrix} a & b \\ c & d \end{vmatrix} = ad - bc$

$\begin{vmatrix} b & a \\ d & c \end{vmatrix} = bc - ad = -(ad - bc)$

60. $\begin{vmatrix} a & b \\ c & d \end{vmatrix} = ad - bc$

$\begin{vmatrix} ka & b \\ kc & d \end{vmatrix} = kad - kbc = k(ad - bc)$

61. $\begin{vmatrix} a & b \\ c & d \end{vmatrix} = ad - bc$

$\begin{vmatrix} a & b + ka \\ c & d + kc \end{vmatrix} = a(d + kc) - (b + ka)c = ad + akc - bc - akc = ad - bc$

62. $ax + by = e \Rightarrow \times (-c)$ $\quad -acx - bcy = -ec$
$cx + dy = f \Rightarrow \times a$ $\quad acx + ady = fa$

$$(ad - bc)y = af - ec$$
$$y = \frac{af - ec}{ad - bc}$$

63. $\begin{vmatrix} 3 & x \\ 1 & 2 \end{vmatrix} = \begin{vmatrix} 2 & -1 \\ x & -5 \end{vmatrix}$
$6 - x = -10 + x$
$-2x = -16$
$x = 8$

64. $\begin{vmatrix} 4 & x^2 \\ 1 & -1 \end{vmatrix} = \begin{vmatrix} x & 4 \\ 2 & 3 \end{vmatrix}$
$-4 - x^2 = 3x - 8$
$0 = x^2 + 3x - 4$
$0 = (x - 1)(x + 4)$
$x = 1$ or $x = -4$

65. $\begin{vmatrix} 3 & x & 1 \\ x & 0 & -2 \\ 4 & 0 & 1 \end{vmatrix} = \begin{vmatrix} 2 & x \\ x & 4 \end{vmatrix}$
$-x\begin{vmatrix} x & -2 \\ 4 & 1 \end{vmatrix} = 8 - x^2$
$-x(x + 8) = 8 - x^2$
$-x^2 - 8x = -x^2 + 8$
$x = -1$

66. $$\begin{vmatrix} x & -1 & 2 \\ -2 & x & 3 \\ 4 & -3 & -1 \end{vmatrix} = \begin{vmatrix} 2 & 2 \\ 5 & x \end{vmatrix}$$

$$x\begin{vmatrix} x & 3 \\ -3 & -1 \end{vmatrix} - (-1)\begin{vmatrix} -2 & 3 \\ 4 & -1 \end{vmatrix} + 2\begin{vmatrix} -2 & x \\ 4 & -3 \end{vmatrix} = 2x - 10$$
$$x(-x + 9) + 1(2 - 12) + 2(6 - 4x) = 2x - 10$$
$$-x^2 + 9x - 10 + 12 - 8x = 2x - 10$$
$$0 = x^2 + x - 12$$
$$0 = (x + 4)(x - 3) \Rightarrow x = -4 \text{ or } x = 3$$

67. Let $x =$ \$ invested in HiTech, $y =$ \$ invested in SaveTel, and $z =$ \$ invested in OilCo.

$$\begin{cases} x+y+z=20{,}000 \\ y+z=3x \\ 0.10x+0.05y+0.06z=0.066(20{,}000) \end{cases} \qquad \begin{aligned} x+y+z&=20000 \\ -3x+y+z&=0 \\ 10x+5y+6z&=132000 \end{aligned}$$

$$x=\frac{\begin{vmatrix} 20000 & 1 & 1 \\ 0 & 1 & 1 \\ 132000 & 5 & 6 \end{vmatrix}}{\begin{vmatrix} 1 & 1 & 1 \\ -3 & 1 & 1 \\ 10 & 5 & 6 \end{vmatrix}}=\frac{20000}{4}=5000,\ y=\frac{\begin{vmatrix} 1 & 20000 & 1 \\ -3 & 0 & 1 \\ 10 & 132000 & 6 \end{vmatrix}}{\begin{vmatrix} 1 & 1 & 1 \\ -3 & 1 & 1 \\ 10 & 5 & 6 \end{vmatrix}}=\frac{32000}{4}=8000$$

$$z=\frac{\begin{vmatrix} 1 & 1 & 20000 \\ -3 & 1 & 0 \\ 10 & 5 & 132000 \end{vmatrix}}{\begin{vmatrix} 1 & 1 & 1 \\ -3 & 1 & 1 \\ 10 & 5 & 6 \end{vmatrix}}=\frac{28000}{4}=7000 \Rightarrow$$ He should invest \$5000 in HiTech, \$8000 in SaveTel, and \$7000 in OilCo.

68. Let x, y, and z represent the radii of the circles.

$$\begin{cases} x+y=10 \\ x+z=18 \\ y+z=14 \end{cases} \quad x=\frac{\begin{vmatrix} 10 & 1 & 0 \\ 18 & 0 & 1 \\ 14 & 1 & 1 \end{vmatrix}}{\begin{vmatrix} 1 & 1 & 0 \\ 1 & 0 & 1 \\ 0 & 1 & 1 \end{vmatrix}}=\frac{-14}{-2}=7,\ y=\frac{\begin{vmatrix} 1 & 10 & 0 \\ 1 & 18 & 1 \\ 0 & 14 & 1 \end{vmatrix}}{\begin{vmatrix} 1 & 1 & 0 \\ 1 & 0 & 1 \\ 0 & 1 & 1 \end{vmatrix}}=\frac{-6}{-2}=3$$

$$z=\frac{\begin{vmatrix} 1 & 1 & 10 \\ 1 & 0 & 18 \\ 0 & 1 & 14 \end{vmatrix}}{\begin{vmatrix} 1 & 1 & 0 \\ 1 & 0 & 1 \\ 0 & 1 & 1 \end{vmatrix}}=\frac{-22}{-2}=11 \Rightarrow$$ The radii are 7 yd, 3 yd, and 11 yd.

69. $$\begin{vmatrix} 1 & 3 & 4 \\ 0 & 5 & 2 \\ 0 & 0 & 2 \end{vmatrix}=10$$
$1\cdot 5\cdot 2=10$

70. $$\begin{vmatrix} 2 & 1 & -2 \\ 0 & 3 & 4 \\ 0 & 0 & -1 \end{vmatrix}=-6$$
$2\cdot 3\cdot(-1)=-6$

71. $$\begin{vmatrix} 1 & 2 & 4 & 3 \\ 0 & 2 & 2 & 1 \\ 0 & 0 & 3 & 2 \\ 0 & 0 & 0 & 4 \end{vmatrix}=24$$
$1\cdot 2\cdot 3\cdot 4=24$

72. $$\begin{vmatrix} 2 & 1 & -2 & 1 \\ 0 & 2 & 2 & -1 \\ 0 & 0 & 3 & 1 \\ 0 & 0 & 0 & 2 \end{vmatrix}=24$$
$2\cdot 2\cdot 3\cdot 2=24$

73. **Answers may vary.**

74. **Answers may vary.**

75. **Answers may vary.**

76. **Answers may vary.**

77. yes

78. no

79. $\begin{vmatrix} 2.3 & 5.7 & 6.1 \\ 3.4 & 6.2 & 8.3 \\ 5.8 & 8.2 & 9.2 \end{vmatrix} = 21.468$

80. $\begin{vmatrix} 0.32 & -7.4 & -6.7 \\ 3.3 & 5.5 & -0.27 \\ -8 & -0.13 & 5.47 \end{vmatrix} = -164.716332$

81. $x^2 + 3x - 4 = (x+4)(x-1)$

82. $2x^2 - 5x - 12 = (2x+3)(x-4)$

83. $\begin{aligned} 9x^3 - x &= x(9x^2 - 1) \\ &= x(3x+1)(3x-1) \end{aligned}$

84. $x^2 + 3x + 5$: prime

85. $\dfrac{1}{x-2} + \dfrac{2}{2x-1} = \dfrac{1(2x-1)}{(x-2)(2x-1)} + \dfrac{2(x-2)}{(2x-1)(x-2)} = \dfrac{2x-1+2x-4}{(x-2)(2x-1)} = \dfrac{4x-5}{(x-2)(2x-1)}$

86. $\begin{aligned} \dfrac{2}{x} + \dfrac{3}{x^2} - \dfrac{1}{x-1} = \dfrac{2x(x-1)}{x^2(x-1)} + \dfrac{3(x-1)}{x^2(x-1)} - \dfrac{x^2}{x^2(x-1)} &= \dfrac{2x^2 - 2x + 3x - 3 - x^2}{x^2(x-1)} \\ &= \dfrac{x^2 + x - 3}{x^2(x-1)} \end{aligned}$

87. $\begin{aligned} \dfrac{2}{x^2+1} + \dfrac{1}{x} &= \dfrac{2x}{x(x^2+1)} + \dfrac{x^2+1}{x(x^2+1)} \\ &= \dfrac{x^2+2x+1}{x(x^2+1)} \end{aligned}$

88. $\begin{aligned} \dfrac{2x}{x^2+1} + \dfrac{1}{x} &= \dfrac{2x^2}{x(x^2+1)} + \dfrac{x^2+1}{x(x^2+1)} \\ &= \dfrac{3x^2+1}{x(x^2+1)} \end{aligned}$

Exercise 6.6 (page 486)

1. first-degree, second-degree

2. prime

3.
$$\frac{3x-1}{x(x-1)} = \frac{A}{x} + \frac{B}{x-1}$$
$$\frac{3x-1}{x(x-1)} = \frac{A(x-1)}{x(x-1)} + \frac{Bx}{x(x-1)}$$
$$\frac{3x-1}{x(x-1)} = \frac{Ax - A + Bx}{x(x-1)}$$
$$\frac{3x-1}{x(x-1)} = \frac{(A+B)x - A}{x(x-1)}$$
$$\begin{cases} A + B = 3 \\ -A = -1 \end{cases} \Rightarrow A = 1, B = 2$$
$$\frac{3x-1}{x(x-1)} = \frac{1}{x} + \frac{2}{x-1}$$

4.
$$\frac{4x+6}{x(x+2)} = \frac{A}{x} + \frac{B}{x+2}$$
$$\frac{4x+6}{x(x+2)} = \frac{A(x+2)}{x(x+2)} + \frac{Bx}{x(x+2)}$$
$$\frac{4x+6}{x(x+2)} = \frac{Ax + 2A + Bx}{x(x+2)}$$
$$\frac{4x+6}{x(x+2)} = \frac{(A+B)x + 2A}{x(x+2)}$$
$$\begin{cases} A + B = 4 \\ 2A = 6 \end{cases} \Rightarrow A = 3, B = 1$$
$$\frac{4x+6}{x(x+2)} = \frac{3}{x} + \frac{1}{x+2}$$

5.
$$\frac{2x-15}{x(x-3)} = \frac{A}{x} + \frac{B}{x-3}$$
$$\frac{2x-15}{x(x-3)} = \frac{A(x-3)}{x(x-3)} + \frac{Bx}{x(x-3)}$$
$$\frac{2x-15}{x(x-3)} = \frac{Ax-3A+Bx}{x(x-3)}$$
$$\frac{2x-15}{x(x-3)} = \frac{(A+B)x-3A}{x(x-3)}$$
$$\begin{cases} A+B = 2 \\ -3A = -15 \end{cases} \Rightarrow A=5, B=-3$$
$$\frac{2x-15}{x(x-3)} = \frac{5}{x} - \frac{3}{x-3}$$

6.
$$\frac{5x+21}{x(x+7)} = \frac{A}{x} + \frac{B}{x+7}$$
$$\frac{5x+21}{x(x+7)} = \frac{A(x+7)}{x(x+7)} + \frac{Bx}{x(x+7)}$$
$$\frac{5x+21}{x(x+7)} = \frac{Ax+7A+Bx}{x(x+7)}$$
$$\frac{5x+21}{x(x+7)} = \frac{(A+B)x+7A}{x(x+7)}$$
$$\begin{cases} A+B = 5 \\ 7A = 21 \end{cases} \Rightarrow A=3, B=2$$
$$\frac{5x+21}{x(x+7)} = \frac{3}{x} + \frac{2}{x+7}$$

7.
$$\frac{3x+1}{(x+1)(x-1)} = \frac{A}{x+1} + \frac{B}{x-1}$$
$$\frac{3x+1}{(x+1)(x-1)} = \frac{A(x-1)}{(x+1)(x-1)} + \frac{B(x+1)}{(x+1)(x-1)}$$
$$\frac{3x+1}{(x+1)(x-1)} = \frac{Ax-A+Bx+B}{(x+1)(x-1)}$$
$$\frac{3x+1}{(x+1)(x-1)} = \frac{(A+B)x+(-A+B)}{(x+1)(x-1)}$$
$$\begin{cases} A+B=3 \\ -A+B=1 \end{cases} \Rightarrow A=1, B=2$$
$$\frac{3x+1}{(x+1)(x-1)} = \frac{1}{x+1} + \frac{2}{x-1}$$

8.
$$\frac{9x-3}{(x+1)(x-2)} = \frac{A}{x+1} + \frac{B}{x-2}$$
$$\frac{9x-3}{(x+1)(x-2)} = \frac{A(x-2)}{(x+1)(x-2)} + \frac{B(x+1)}{(x+1)(x-2)}$$
$$\frac{9x-3}{(x+1)(x-2)} = \frac{Ax-2A+Bx+B}{(x+1)(x-2)}$$
$$\frac{9x-3}{(x+1)(x-2)} = \frac{(A+B)x+(-2A+B)}{(x+1)(x-2)}$$
$$\begin{cases} A+B = 9 \\ -2A+B = -3 \end{cases} \Rightarrow A=4, B=5$$
$$\frac{9x-3}{(x+1)(x-2)} = \frac{4}{x+1} + \frac{5}{x-2}$$

9.
$$\frac{-2x+11}{(x+2)(x-3)} = \frac{A}{x+2} + \frac{B}{x-3}$$
$$\frac{-2x+11}{(x+2)(x-3)} = \frac{A(x-3)}{(x+2)(x-3)} + \frac{B(x+2)}{(x+2)(x-3)}$$
$$\frac{-2x+11}{(x+2)(x-3)} = \frac{Ax-3A+Bx+2B}{(x+2)(x-3)}$$
$$\frac{-2x+11}{(x+2)(x-3)} = \frac{(A+B)x+(-3A+2B)}{(x+2)(x-3)}$$
$$\frac{-2x+11}{x^2-x-6} = \frac{-2x+11}{(x+2)(x-3)}$$
$$\begin{cases} A+B=-2 \\ -3A+2B = 11 \end{cases} \Rightarrow A=-3, B=1$$
$$\frac{-2x+11}{(x+2)(x-3)} = \frac{-3}{x+2} + \frac{1}{x-3}$$

10. $\dfrac{7x+2}{(x+2)(x-1)} = \dfrac{A}{x+2} + \dfrac{B}{x-1}$

$\dfrac{7x+2}{x^2+x-2} = \dfrac{7x+2}{(x+2)(x-1)}$

$$\frac{7x+2}{(x+2)(x-1)} = \frac{A(x-1)}{(x+2)(x-1)} + \frac{B(x+2)}{(x+2)(x-1)}$$
$$\frac{7x+2}{(x+2)(x-1)} = \frac{Ax-A+Bx+2B}{(x+2)(x-1)}$$
$$\frac{7x+2}{(x+2)(x-1)} = \frac{(A+B)x+(-A+2B)}{(x+2)(x-1)}$$

$$\begin{cases} A+\ \ B=7 \\ -A+2B=2 \end{cases} \Rightarrow A=4,\ B=3$$
$$\frac{7x+2}{(x+2)(x-1)} = \frac{4}{x+2} + \frac{3}{x-1}$$

11. $\dfrac{3x-23}{(x+3)(x-1)} = \dfrac{A}{x+3} + \dfrac{B}{x-1}$

$\dfrac{3x-23}{x^2+2x-3} = \dfrac{3x-23}{(x+3)(x-1)}$

$$\frac{3x-23}{(x+3)(x-1)} = \frac{A(x-1)}{(x+3)(x-1)} + \frac{B(x+3)}{(x+3)(x-1)}$$
$$\frac{3x-23}{(x+3)(x-1)} = \frac{Ax-A+Bx+3B}{(x+3)(x-1)}$$
$$\frac{3x-23}{(x+3)(x-1)} = \frac{(A+B)x+(-A+3B)}{(x+3)(x-1)}$$

$$\begin{cases} A+\ \ B=\ \ \ 3 \\ -A+3B=-23 \end{cases} \Rightarrow A=8,\ B=-5$$
$$\frac{3x-23}{(x+3)(x-1)} = \frac{8}{x+3} - \frac{5}{x-1}$$

12. $\dfrac{-x-17}{(x+2)(x-3)} = \dfrac{A}{x+2} + \dfrac{B}{x-3}$

$\dfrac{-x-17}{x^2-x-6} = \dfrac{-x-17}{(x+2)(x-3)}$

$$\frac{-x-17}{(x+2)(x-3)} = \frac{A(x-3)}{(x+2)(x-3)} + \frac{B(x+2)}{(x+2)(x-3)}$$
$$\frac{-x-17}{(x+2)(x-3)} = \frac{Ax-3A+Bx+2B}{(x+2)(x-3)}$$
$$\frac{-x-17}{(x+2)(x-3)} = \frac{(A+B)x+(-3A+2B)}{(x+2)(x-3)}$$

$$\begin{cases} A+\ \ B=\ -1 \\ -3A+2B=-17 \end{cases} \Rightarrow A=3,\ B=-4$$
$$\frac{-x-17}{(x+2)(x-3)} = \frac{3}{x+2} - \frac{4}{x-3}$$

13. $\dfrac{9x-31}{2x^2-13x+15} = \dfrac{9x-31}{(2x-3)(x-5)} = \dfrac{A}{2x-3} + \dfrac{B}{x-5}$

$$\frac{9x-31}{(2x-3)(x-5)} = \frac{A(x-5)}{(2x-3)(x-5)} + \frac{B(2x-3)}{(2x-3)(x-5)}$$
$$\frac{9x-31}{(2x-3)(x-5)} = \frac{Ax-5A+2Bx-3B}{(2x-3)(x-5)}$$
$$\frac{9x-31}{(2x-3)(x-5)} = \frac{(A+2B)x+(-5A-3B)}{(2x-3)(x-5)}$$

$$\begin{cases} A+2B=\ \ \ 9 \\ -5A-3B=-31 \end{cases} \Rightarrow A=5,\ B=2 \qquad \frac{9x-31}{(2x-3)(x-5)} = \frac{5}{2x-3} + \frac{2}{x-5}$$

14. $$\frac{-2x-6}{3x^2-7x+2}=\frac{-2x-6}{(3x-1)(x-2)}=\frac{A}{3x-1}+\frac{B}{x-2}$$
$$\frac{-2x-6}{(3x-1)(x-2)}=\frac{A(x-2)}{(3x-1)(x-2)}+\frac{B(3x-1)}{(3x-1)(x-2)}$$
$$\frac{-2x-6}{(3x-1)(x-2)}=\frac{Ax-2A+3Bx-B}{(3x-1)(x-2)}$$
$$\frac{-2x-6}{(3x-1)(x-2)}=\frac{(A+3B)x+(-2A-B)}{(3x-1)(x-2)}$$
$$\begin{cases} A+3B=-2 \\ -2A-\ \ B=-6 \end{cases} \Rightarrow A=4, B=-2 \qquad \frac{-2x-6}{(3x-1)(x-2)}=\frac{4}{3x-1}-\frac{2}{x-2}$$

15. $$\frac{4x^2+4x-2}{x(x^2-1)}=\frac{4x^2+4x-2}{x(x+1)(x-1)}=\frac{A}{x}+\frac{B}{x+1}+\frac{C}{x-1}$$
$$\frac{4x^2+4x-2}{x(x+1)(x-1)}=\frac{A(x+1)(x-1)}{x(x+1)(x-1)}+\frac{Bx(x-1)}{x(x+1)(x-1)}+\frac{Cx(x+1)}{x(x+1)(x-1)}$$
$$\frac{4x^2+4x-2}{x(x+1)(x-1)}=\frac{Ax^2-A+Bx^2-Bx+Cx^2+Cx}{x(x+1)(x-1)}$$
$$\frac{4x^2+4x-2}{x(x+1)(x-1)}=\frac{(A+B+C)x^2+(-B+C)x+(-A)}{x(x+1)(x-1)}$$
$$\begin{cases} A+B+C=\ \ 4 \\ \quad -B+C=\ \ 4 \\ -A \qquad\quad =-2 \end{cases} \Rightarrow \begin{matrix} A=2 \\ B=-1 \\ C=3 \end{matrix} \qquad \frac{4x^2+4x-2}{x(x+1)(x-1)}=\frac{2}{x}-\frac{1}{x+1}+\frac{3}{x-1}$$

16. $$\frac{x^2-6x-13}{(x+2)(x+1)(x-1)}=\frac{A}{x+2}+\frac{B}{x+1}+\frac{C}{x-1}$$
$$=\frac{A(x+1)(x-1)}{(x+2)(x+1)(x-1)}+\frac{B(x+2)(x-1)}{(x+2)(x+1)(x-1)}+\frac{C(x+2)(x+1)}{(x+2)(x+1)(x-1)}$$
$$=\frac{Ax^2-A+Bx^2+Bx-2B+Cx^2+3Cx+2C}{(x+2)(x+1)(x-1)}$$
$$=\frac{(A+B+C)x^2+(B+3C)x+(-A-2B+2C)}{(x+2)(x+1)(x-1)}$$
$$\begin{cases} A+\ B+\ C=\ \ 1 \\ \qquad B+3C=\ -6 \\ -A-2B+2C=-13 \end{cases} \Rightarrow \begin{matrix} A=1 \\ B=3 \\ C=-3 \end{matrix} \qquad \frac{x^2-6x-13}{(x+2)(x+1)(x-1)}=\frac{1}{x+2}+\frac{3}{x+1}-\frac{3}{x-1}$$

17.
$$\begin{aligned}\frac{x^2+x+3}{x(x^2+3)} &= \frac{A}{x}+\frac{Bx+C}{x^2+3}\\ &= \frac{A(x^2+3)}{x(x^2+3)}+\frac{(Bx+C)x}{x(x^2+3)}\\ &= \frac{Ax^2+3A+Bx^2+Cx}{x(x^2+3)}\\ &= \frac{(A+B)x^2+Cx+3A}{x(x^2+3)}\end{aligned}$$

$$\begin{cases} A+B = 1 \\ C = 1 \\ 3A = 3 \end{cases} \Rightarrow \begin{matrix} A=1 \\ B=0 \\ C=1 \end{matrix}$$

$$\frac{x^2+x+3}{x(x^2+3)} = \frac{1}{x}+\frac{1}{x^2+3}$$

18.
$$\begin{aligned}\frac{5x^2+2x+2}{x(x^2+1)} &= \frac{A}{x}+\frac{Bx+C}{x^2+1}\\ &= \frac{A(x^2+1)}{x(x^2+1)}+\frac{(Bx+C)x}{x(x^2+1)}\\ &= \frac{Ax^2+A+Bx^2+Cx}{x(x^2+1)}\\ &= \frac{(A+B)x^2+Cx+A}{x(x^2+1)}\end{aligned}$$

$$\begin{cases} A+B = 5 \\ C = 2 \\ A = 2 \end{cases} \Rightarrow \begin{matrix} A=2 \\ B=3 \\ C=2 \end{matrix}$$

$$\frac{5x^2+2x+2}{x(x^2+1)} = \frac{2}{x}+\frac{3x+2}{x^2+1}$$

19.
$$\frac{3x^2+8x+11}{(x+1)(x^2+2x+3)} = \frac{A}{x+1}+\frac{Bx+C}{x^2+2x+3}$$

$$\frac{3x^2+8x+11}{(x+1)(x^2+2x+3)} = \frac{A(x^2+2x+3)}{(x+1)(x^2+2x+3)}+\frac{(Bx+C)(x+1)}{(x+1)(x^2+2x+3)}$$

$$\frac{3x^2+8x+11}{(x+1)(x^2+2x+3)} = \frac{Ax^2+2Ax+3A+Bx^2+Bx+Cx+C}{(x+1)(x^2+2x+3)}$$

$$\frac{3x^2+8x+11}{(x+1)(x^2+2x+3)} = \frac{(A+B)x^2+(2A+B+C)x+(3A+C)}{(x+1)(x^2+2x+3)}$$

$$\begin{cases} A+B = 3 \\ 2A+B+C = 8 \\ 3A +C = 11 \end{cases} \Rightarrow \begin{matrix} A=3 \\ B=0 \\ C=2 \end{matrix} \qquad \frac{3x^2+8x+11}{(x+1)(x^2+2x+3)} = \frac{3}{x+1}+\frac{2}{x^2+2x+3}$$

20.
$$\frac{-3x^2+x-5}{(x+1)(x^2+2)} = \frac{A}{x+1}+\frac{Bx+C}{x^2+2}$$

$$\frac{-3x^2+x-5}{(x+1)(x^2+2)} = \frac{A(x^2+2)}{(x+1)(x^2+2)}+\frac{(Bx+C)(x+1)}{(x+1)(x^2+2)}$$

$$\frac{-3x^2+x-5}{(x+1)(x^2+2)} = \frac{Ax^2+2A+Bx^2+Bx+Cx+C}{(x+1)(x^2+2)}$$

$$\frac{-3x^2+x-5}{(x+1)(x^2+2)} = \frac{(A+B)x^2+(B+C)x+(2A+C)}{(x+1)(x^2+2)}$$

$$\begin{cases} A+B = -3 \\ B+C = 1 \\ 2A +C = -5 \end{cases} \Rightarrow \begin{matrix} A=-3 \\ B=0 \\ C=1 \end{matrix} \qquad \frac{-3x^2+x-5}{(x+1)(x^2+2)} = \frac{-3}{x+1}+\frac{1}{x^2+2}$$

21. $$\frac{5x^2+9x+3}{x(x+1)^2} = \frac{A}{x} + \frac{B}{x+1} + \frac{C}{(x+1)^2}$$
$$= \frac{A(x+1)^2}{x(x+1)^2} + \frac{Bx(x+1)}{x(x+1)^2} + \frac{Cx}{x(x+1)^2}$$
$$= \frac{Ax^2+2Ax+A+Bx^2+Bx+Cx}{x(x+1)^2}$$
$$= \frac{(A+B)x^2+(2A+B+C)x+A}{x(x+1)^2}$$

$$\begin{cases} A+B \qquad\quad = 5 \\ 2A+B+C = 9 \\ A \qquad\qquad\;\; = 3 \end{cases} \Rightarrow \begin{matrix} A=3 \\ B=2 \\ C=1 \end{matrix} \qquad \frac{5x^2+9x+3}{x(x+1)^2} = \frac{3}{x} + \frac{2}{x+1} + \frac{1}{(x+1)^2}$$

22. $$\frac{2x^2-7x+2}{x(x-1)^2} = \frac{A}{x} + \frac{B}{x-1} + \frac{C}{(x-1)^2}$$
$$= \frac{A(x-1)^2}{x(x-1)^2} + \frac{Bx(x-1)}{x(x-1)^2} + \frac{Cx}{x(x-1)^2}$$
$$= \frac{Ax^2-2Ax+A+Bx^2-Bx+Cx}{x(x-1)^2}$$
$$= \frac{(A+B)x^2+(-2A-B+C)x+A}{x(x-1)^2}$$

$$\begin{cases} A+B \qquad\quad = \;\; 2 \\ -2A-B+C = -7 \\ A \qquad\qquad\;\; = \;\; 2 \end{cases} \Rightarrow \begin{matrix} A=2 \\ B=0 \\ C=-3 \end{matrix} \qquad \frac{2x^2-7x+2}{x(x-1)^2} = \frac{2}{x} - \frac{3}{(x-1)^2}$$

23. $$\frac{-2x^2+x-2}{x^2(x-1)} = \frac{A}{x} + \frac{B}{x^2} + \frac{C}{x-1}$$
$$= \frac{Ax(x-1)}{x^2(x-1)} + \frac{B(x-1)}{x^2(x-1)} + \frac{Cx^2}{x^2(x-1)}$$
$$= \frac{Ax^2-Ax+Bx-B+Cx^2}{x^2(x-1)}$$
$$= \frac{(A+C)x^2+(-A+B)x+(-B)}{x^2(x-1)}$$

$$\begin{cases} A \qquad\quad +C = -2 \\ -A+B \qquad\;\; = \;\; 1 \\ \quad -B \qquad\;\; = -2 \end{cases} \Rightarrow \begin{matrix} A=1 \\ B=2 \\ C=-3 \end{matrix} \qquad \frac{-2x^2+x-2}{x^2(x-1)} = \frac{1}{x} + \frac{2}{x^2} - \frac{3}{x-1}$$

24.
$$\begin{aligned}\frac{x^2+x+1}{x^3} &= \frac{A}{x}+\frac{B}{x^2}+\frac{C}{x^3}\\ &= \frac{Ax^2}{x^3}+\frac{Bx}{x^3}+\frac{C}{x^3}\\ &= \frac{Ax^2+Bx+C}{x^3}\end{aligned}$$

$$\begin{cases} A = 1 \\ B = 1 \\ C = 1 \end{cases} \quad \frac{x^2+x+1}{x^3} = \frac{1}{x}+\frac{1}{x^2}+\frac{1}{x^3}$$

25.
$$\begin{aligned}\frac{3x^2-13x+18}{x(x-3)^2} &= \frac{A}{x}+\frac{B}{x-3}+\frac{C}{(x-3)^2}\\ &= \frac{A(x-3)^2}{x(x-3)^2}+\frac{Bx(x-3)}{x(x-3)^2}+\frac{Cx}{x(x-3)^2}\\ &= \frac{Ax^2-6Ax+9A+Bx^2-3Bx+Cx}{x(x-3)^2}\\ &= \frac{(A+B)x^2+(-6A-3B+C)x+9A}{x(x-3)^2}\end{aligned}$$

$$\begin{cases} A+B = 3 \\ -6A-3B+C = -13 \\ 9A = 18 \end{cases} \Rightarrow \begin{matrix} A=2 \\ B=1 \\ C=2 \end{matrix} \quad \frac{3x^2-13x+18}{x(x-3)^2} = \frac{2}{x}+\frac{1}{x-3}+\frac{2}{(x-3)^2}$$

26.
$$\begin{aligned}\frac{3x^2+13x+20}{x(x+2)^2} &= \frac{A}{x}+\frac{B}{x+2}+\frac{C}{(x+2)^2}\\ &= \frac{A(x+2)^2}{x(x+2)^2}+\frac{Bx(x+2)}{x(x+2)^2}+\frac{Cx}{x(x+2)^2}\\ &= \frac{Ax^2+4Ax+4A+Bx^2+2Bx+Cx}{x(x+2)^2}\\ &= \frac{(A+B)x^2+(4A+2B+C)x+4A}{x(x+2)^2}\end{aligned}$$

$$\begin{cases} A+B = 3 \\ 4A+2B+C = 13 \\ 4A = 20 \end{cases} \Rightarrow \begin{matrix} A=5 \\ B=-2 \\ C=-3 \end{matrix} \quad \frac{3x^2+13x+20}{x(x+2)^2} = \frac{5}{x}-\frac{2}{x+2}-\frac{3}{(x+2)^2}$$

27.
$$\begin{aligned}\frac{x^2-2x-3}{(x-1)^3} &= \frac{A}{x-1}+\frac{B}{(x-1)^2}+\frac{C}{(x-1)^3}\\ &= \frac{A(x-1)^2}{(x-1)^3}+\frac{B(x-1)}{(x-1)^3}+\frac{C}{(x-1)^3}\\ &= \frac{Ax^2-2Ax+A+Bx-B+C}{(x-1)^3}\\ &= \frac{Ax^2+(-2A+B)x+(A-B+C)}{(x-1)^3}\end{aligned}$$

$$\begin{cases} A = 1 \\ -2A+B = -2 \\ A-B+C = -3 \end{cases} \Rightarrow \begin{array}{l} A=1 \\ B=0 \\ C=-4 \end{array} \quad \frac{x^2-2x-3}{(x-1)^3} = \frac{1}{x-1} - \frac{4}{(x-1)^3}$$

28.
$$\begin{aligned}\frac{x^2+8x+18}{(x+3)^3} &= \frac{A}{x+3}+\frac{B}{(x+3)^2}+\frac{C}{(x+3)^3}\\ &= \frac{A(x+3)^2}{(x+3)^3}+\frac{B(x+3)}{(x+3)^3}+\frac{C}{(x+3)^3}\\ &= \frac{Ax^2+6Ax+9A+Bx+3B+C}{(x+3)^3}\\ &= \frac{Ax^2+(6A+B)x+(9A+3B+C)}{(x+3)^3}\end{aligned}$$

$$\begin{cases} A = 1 \\ 6A+B = 8 \\ 9A+3B+C = 18 \end{cases} \Rightarrow \begin{array}{l} A=1 \\ B=2 \\ C=3 \end{array} \quad \frac{x^2+8x+18}{(x+3)^3} = \frac{1}{x+3} + \frac{2}{(x+3)^2} + \frac{3}{(x+3)^3}$$

29.
$$\begin{aligned}\frac{x^3+4x^2+2x+1}{x^2(x^2+x+1)} &= \frac{A}{x}+\frac{B}{x^2}+\frac{Cx+D}{x^2+x+1}\\ &= \frac{Ax(x^2+x+1)}{x^2(x^2+x+1)}+\frac{B(x^2+x+1)}{x^2(x^2+x+1)}+\frac{(Cx+D)x^2}{x^2(x^2+x+1)}\\ &= \frac{Ax^3+Ax^2+Ax+Bx^2+Bx+B+Cx^3+Dx^2}{x^2(x^2+x+1)}\\ &= \frac{(A+C)x^3+(A+B+D)x^2+(A+B)x+B}{x^2(x^2+x+1)}\end{aligned}$$

$$\begin{cases} A + C = 1 \\ A+B+D = 4 \\ A+B = 2 \\ B = 1 \end{cases} \Rightarrow \begin{array}{l} A=1 \\ B=1 \\ C=0 \\ D=2 \end{array} \quad \frac{x^3+4x^2+2x+1}{x^2(x^2+x+1)} = \frac{1}{x} + \frac{1}{x^2} + \frac{2}{x^2+x+1}$$

30. $$\begin{aligned}\frac{3x^3+5x^2+3x+1}{x^2(x^2+x+1)} &= \frac{A}{x}+\frac{B}{x^2}+\frac{Cx+D}{x^2+x+1}\\ &= \frac{Ax(x^2+x+1)}{x^2(x^2+x+1)}+\frac{B(x^2+x+1)}{x^2(x^2+x+1)}+\frac{(Cx+D)x^2}{x^2(x^2+x+1)}\\ &= \frac{Ax^3+Ax^2+Ax+Bx^2+Bx+B+Cx^3+Dx^2}{x^2(x^2+x+1)}\\ &= \frac{(A+C)x^3+(A+B+D)x^2+(A+B)x+B}{x^2(x^2+x+1)}\end{aligned}$$

$$\begin{cases} A \quad +C \quad = 3 \\ A+B \quad +D = 5 \\ A+B \quad = 3 \\ \quad B \quad = 1 \end{cases} \Rightarrow \begin{array}{l} A=2 \\ B=1 \\ C=1 \\ D=2 \end{array} \quad \frac{3x^3+5x^2+3x+1}{x^2(x^2+x+1)} = \frac{2}{x}+\frac{1}{x^2}+\frac{x+2}{x^2+x+1}$$

31. $$\begin{aligned}\frac{4x^3+5x^2+3x+4}{x^2(x^2+1)} &= \frac{A}{x}+\frac{B}{x^2}+\frac{Cx+D}{x^2+1}\\ &= \frac{Ax(x^2+1)}{x^2(x^2+1)}+\frac{B(x^2+1)}{x^2(x^2+1)}+\frac{(Cx+D)x^2}{x^2(x^2+1)}\\ &= \frac{Ax^3+Ax+Bx^2+B+Cx^3+Dx^2}{x^2(x^2+1)}\\ &= \frac{(A+C)x^3+(B+D)x^2+Ax+B}{x^2(x^2+1)}\end{aligned}$$

$$\begin{cases} A \quad +C \quad = 4 \\ \quad B \quad +D = 5 \\ A \quad = 3 \\ \quad B \quad = 4 \end{cases} \Rightarrow \begin{array}{l} A=3 \\ B=4 \\ C=1 \\ D=1 \end{array} \quad \frac{4x^3+5x^2+3x+4}{x^2(x^2+1)} = \frac{3}{x}+\frac{4}{x^2}+\frac{x+1}{x^2+1}$$

32. $$\begin{aligned}\frac{2x^2+1}{x^2(x^2+1)} &= \frac{A}{x}+\frac{B}{x^2}+\frac{Cx+D}{x^2+1}\\ &= \frac{Ax(x^2+1)}{x^2(x^2+1)}+\frac{B(x^2+1)}{x^2(x^2+1)}+\frac{(Cx+D)x^2}{x^2(x^2+1)}\\ &= \frac{Ax^3+Ax+Bx^2+B+Cx^3+Dx^2}{x^2(x^2+1)}\\ &= \frac{(A+C)x^3+(B+D)x^2+Ax+B}{x^2(x^2+1)}\end{aligned}$$

$$\begin{cases} A \quad +C \quad = 0 \\ \quad B \quad +D = 2 \\ A \quad = 0 \\ \quad B \quad = 1 \end{cases} \Rightarrow \begin{array}{l} A=0 \\ B=1 \\ C=0 \\ D=1 \end{array} \quad \frac{2x^2+1}{x^2(x^2+1)} = \frac{1}{x^2}+\frac{1}{x^2+1}$$

33.
$$\begin{aligned}\frac{-x^2-3x-5}{(x+1)(x^2+2)} &= \frac{A}{x+1}+\frac{Bx+C}{x^2+2}\\ &= \frac{A(x^2+2)}{(x+1)(x^2+2)}+\frac{(Bx+C)(x+1)}{(x+1)(x^2+2)}\\ &= \frac{Ax^2+2A+Bx^2+Bx+Cx+C}{(x+1)(x^2+2)}\\ &= \frac{(A+B)x^2+(B+C)x+(2A+C)}{(x+1)(x^2+2)}\end{aligned}$$

$$\begin{cases} A+B = -1 \\ B+C=-3 \\ 2A+C=-5\end{cases} \Rightarrow \begin{matrix} A=-1 \\ B=0 \\ C=-3\end{matrix} \qquad \frac{-x^2-3x-5}{(x+1)(x^2+2)} = \frac{-1}{x+1}-\frac{3}{x^2+2}$$

34.
$$\begin{aligned}\frac{-2x^3+7x^2+6}{x^2(x^2+2)} &= \frac{A}{x}+\frac{B}{x^2}+\frac{Cx+D}{x^2+2}\\ &= \frac{Ax(x^2+2)}{x^2(x^2+2)}+\frac{B(x^2+2)}{x^2(x^2+2)}+\frac{(Cx+D)x^2}{x^2(x^2+2)}\\ &= \frac{Ax^3+2Ax+Bx^2+2B+Cx^3+Dx^2}{x^2(x^2+2)}\\ &= \frac{(A+C)x^3+(B+D)x^2+2Ax+2B}{x^2(x^2+2)}\end{aligned}$$

$$\begin{cases} A+C=-2 \\ B+D=7 \\ 2A=0 \\ 2B=6\end{cases} \Rightarrow \begin{matrix} A=0 \\ B=3 \\ C=-2 \\ D=4\end{matrix} \qquad \frac{-2x^3+7x^2+6}{x^2(x^2+2)} = \frac{3}{x^2}+\frac{-2x+4}{x^2+2}$$

35.
$$\begin{aligned}\frac{x^3+4x^2+3x+6}{(x^2+2)(x^2+x+2)} &= \frac{Ax+B}{x^2+2}+\frac{Cx+D}{x^2+x+2}\\ &= \frac{(Ax+B)(x^2+x+2)}{(x^2+2)(x^2+x+2)}+\frac{(Cx+D)(x^2+2)}{(x^2+2)(x^2+x+2)}\\ &= \frac{Ax^3+Ax^2+2Ax+Bx^2+Bx+2B+Cx^3+2Cx+Dx^2+2D}{(x^2+2)(x^2+x+2)}\\ &= \frac{(A+C)x^3+(A+B+D)x^2+(2A+B+2C)x+(2B+2D)}{(x^2+2)(x^2+x+2)}\end{aligned}$$

$$\begin{cases} A+C=1 \\ A+B+D=4 \\ 2A+B+2C=3 \\ 2B+2D=6\end{cases} \Rightarrow \begin{matrix} A=1 \\ B=1 \\ C=0 \\ D=2\end{matrix} \qquad \frac{x^3+4x^2+3x+6}{(x^2+2)(x^2+x+2)} = \frac{x+1}{x^2+2}+\frac{2}{x^2+x+2}$$

36. $$\frac{x^3+3x^2+2x+4}{(x^2+1)(x^2+x+2)} = \frac{Ax+B}{x^2+1} + \frac{Cx+D}{x^2+x+2}$$
$$= \frac{(Ax+B)(x^2+x+2)}{(x^2+1)(x^2+x+2)} + \frac{(Cx+D)(x^2+1)}{(x^2+1)(x^2+x+2)}$$
$$= \frac{Ax^3+Ax^2+2Ax+Bx^2+Bx+2B+Cx^3+Cx+Dx^2+D}{(x^2+1)(x^2+x+2)}$$
$$= \frac{(A+C)x^3+(A+B+D)x^2+(2A+B+C)x+(2B+D)}{(x^2+1)(x^2+x+2)}$$

$$\begin{cases} A \quad +C = 1 \\ A+B \quad +D=3 \\ 2A+B+C = 2 \\ 2B \quad +D = 4 \end{cases} \Rightarrow \begin{matrix} A=0 \\ B=1 \\ C=1 \\ D=2 \end{matrix} \qquad \frac{x^3+3x^2+2x+4}{(x^2+1)(x^2+x+2)} = \frac{1}{x^2+1} + \frac{x+2}{x^2+x+2}$$

37. $$\frac{2x^4+6x^3+20x^2+22x+25}{x(x^2+2x+5)^2}$$
$$= \frac{A}{x} + \frac{Bx+C}{x^2+2x+5} + \frac{Dx+E}{(x^2+2x+5)^2}$$
$$= \frac{A(x^2+2x+5)^2}{x(x^2+2x+5)^2} + \frac{(Bx+C)(x)(x^2+2x+5)}{x(x^2+2x+5)^2} + \frac{(Dx+E)x}{x(x^2+2x+5)^2}$$
$$= \frac{(A+B)x^4+(4A+2B+C)x^3+(14A+5B+2C+D)x^2+(20A+5C+E)x+(25A)}{x(x^2+2x+5)^2}$$

$$\begin{cases} A+B = 2 \\ 4A+2B+C = 6 \\ 14A+5B+2C+D = 20 \\ 20A \quad +5C \quad +E = 22 \\ 25A = 25 \end{cases} \Rightarrow \begin{matrix} A=1 \\ B=1 \\ C=0 \\ D=1 \\ E=2 \end{matrix}$$

$$\frac{2x^4+6x^3+20x^2+22x+25}{x(x^2+2x+5)^2} = \frac{1}{x} + \frac{x}{x^2+2x+5} + \frac{x+2}{(x^2+2x+5)^2}$$

38. $$\frac{x^3+3x^2+6x+6}{(x^2+1)(x^2+x+5)} = \frac{Ax+B}{x^2+1} + \frac{Cx+D}{x^2+x+5}$$
$$= \frac{(Ax+B)(x^2+x+5)}{(x^2+1)(x^2+x+5)} + \frac{(Cx+D)(x^2+1)}{(x^2+1)(x^2+x+5)}$$
$$= \frac{Ax^3+Ax^2+5Ax+Bx^2+Bx+5B+Cx^3+Cx+Dx^2+D}{(x^2+1)(x^2+x+5)}$$
$$= \frac{(A+C)x^3+(A+B+D)x^2+(5A+B+C)x+(5B+D)}{(x^2+1)(x^2+x+5)}$$

$$\begin{cases} A \quad +C = 1 \\ A+B \quad +D=3 \\ 5A+B+C = 6 \\ 5B \quad +D = 6 \end{cases} \Rightarrow \begin{matrix} A=1 \\ B=1 \\ C=0 \\ D=1 \end{matrix} \qquad \frac{x^3+3x^2+6x+6}{(x^2+1)(x^2+x+5)} = \frac{x+1}{x^2+1} + \frac{1}{x^2+x+5}$$

39. Use long division first: $\frac{x^3}{x^2+3x+2} = x - 3 + \frac{7x+6}{x^2+3x+2} = x - 3 + \frac{7x+6}{(x+1)(x+2)}$

$$\begin{aligned}\frac{7x+6}{(x+1)(x+2)} &= \frac{A}{x+1} + \frac{B}{x+2} \\ &= \frac{A(x+2)}{(x+1)(x+2)} + \frac{B(x+1)}{(x+1)(x+2)} \\ &= \frac{Ax + 2A + Bx + B}{(x+1)(x+2)} \\ &= \frac{(A+B)x + (2A+B)}{(x+1)(x+2)}\end{aligned}$$

$$\begin{cases} A + B = 7 \\ 2A + B = 6 \end{cases} \Rightarrow A = -1, B = 8 \quad x - 3 + \frac{7x+6}{(x+1)(x+2)} = x - 3 - \frac{1}{x+1} + \frac{8}{x+2}$$

40. Use long division first: $\dfrac{2x^3 + 6x^2 + 3x + 2}{x^3 + x^2} = 2 + \dfrac{4x^2 + 3x + 2}{x^3 + x^2} = 2 + \dfrac{4x^2 + 3x + 2}{x^2(x+1)}$

$$\begin{aligned}\frac{4x^2 + 3x + 2}{x^2(x+1)} &= \frac{A}{x} + \frac{B}{x^2} + \frac{C}{x+1} \\ &= \frac{Ax(x+1)}{x^2(x+1)} + \frac{B(x+1)}{x^2(x+1)} + \frac{Cx^2}{x^2(x+1)} \\ &= \frac{Ax^2 + Ax + Bx + B + Cx^2}{x^2(x+1)} \\ &= \frac{(A+C)x^2 + (A+B)x + (B)}{x^2(x+1)}\end{aligned}$$

$$\begin{cases} A \quad\quad + C = 4 \\ A + B \quad\quad = 3 \\ \quad\; B \quad\quad = 2 \end{cases} \Rightarrow \begin{matrix} A = 1 \\ B = 2 \\ C = 3 \end{matrix} \quad 2 + \frac{4x^2 + 3x + 2}{x^2(x+1)} = 2 + \frac{1}{x} + \frac{2}{x^2} + \frac{3}{x+1}$$

41. Use long division first: $\dfrac{3x^3 + 3x^2 + 6x + 4}{3x^3 + x^2 + 3x + 1} = 1 + \dfrac{2x^2 + 3x + 3}{3x^3 + x^2 + 3x + 1} = 1 + \dfrac{2x^2 + 3x + 3}{(3x+1)(x^2+1)}$

$$\begin{aligned}\frac{2x^2 + 3x + 3}{(3x+1)(x^2+1)} &= \frac{A}{3x+1} + \frac{Bx + C}{x^2+1} \\ &= \frac{A(x^2+1)}{(3x+1)(x^2+1)} + \frac{(Bx+C)(3x+1)}{(3x+1)(x^2+1)} \\ &= \frac{Ax^2 + A + 3Bx^2 + Bx + 3Cx + C}{(3x+1)(x^2+1)} \\ &= \frac{(A+3B)x^2 + (B+3C)x + (A+C)}{(3x+1)(x^2+1)}\end{aligned}$$

$$\begin{cases} A + 3B \quad\quad = 2 \\ \quad\quad B + 3C = 3 \\ A \quad\quad + \; C = 3 \end{cases} \Rightarrow \begin{matrix} A = 2 \\ B = 0 \\ C = 1 \end{matrix} \quad 1 + \frac{2x^2 + 3x + 3}{(3x+1)(x^2+1)} = 1 + \frac{2}{3x+1} + \frac{1}{x^2+1}$$

42. Use long division first: $\dfrac{x^4+x^3+3x^2+x+4}{(x^2+1)^2}=1+\dfrac{x^3+x^2+x+3}{(x^2+1)^2}$

$$\begin{aligned}\frac{x^3+x^2+x+3}{(x^2+1)^2}&=\frac{Ax+B}{x^2+1}+\frac{Cx+D}{(x^2+1)^2}\\&=\frac{(Ax+B)(x^2+1)}{(x^2+1)^2}+\frac{(Cx+D)}{(x^2+1)^2}\\&=\frac{Ax^3+Ax+Bx^2+B+Cx+D}{(x^2+1)^2}\\&=\frac{Ax^3+Bx^2+(A+C)x+D}{(x^2+1)^2}\end{aligned}$$

$$\begin{cases}A & =1\\ \quad B & =1\\ A \quad +C & =1\\ \quad B \quad +D & =3\end{cases}\Rightarrow \begin{array}{l}A=1\\B=1\\C=0\\D=2\end{array}\quad 1+\frac{x^3+x^2+x+3}{(x^2+1)^2}=1+\frac{x+1}{x^2+1}+\frac{2}{(x^2+1)^2}$$

43. Use long division first: $\dfrac{x^3+3x^2+2x+1}{x^3+x^2+x}=1+\dfrac{2x^2+x+1}{x^3+x^2+x}=1+\dfrac{2x^2+x+1}{x(x^2+x+1)}$

$$\begin{aligned}\frac{2x^2+x+1}{x(x^2+x+1)}&=\frac{A}{x}+\frac{Bx+C}{x^2+x+1}\\&=\frac{A(x^2+x+1)}{x(x^2+x+1)}+\frac{(Bx+C)x}{x(x^2+x+1)}\\&=\frac{Ax^2+Ax+A+Bx^2+Cx}{x(x^2+x+1)}\\&=\frac{(A+B)x^2+(A+C)x+(A)}{x(x^2+x+1)}\end{aligned}$$

$$\begin{cases}A+B & =2\\ A \quad +C & =1\\ A & =1\end{cases}\Rightarrow \begin{array}{l}A=1\\B=1\\C=0\end{array}\quad 1+\frac{2x^2+x+1}{x(x^2+x+1)}=1+\frac{1}{x}+\frac{x}{x^2+x+1}$$

44. Use long division first: $\dfrac{x^4-x^3+x^2-x+1}{(x^2+1)^2}=1+\dfrac{-x^3-x^2-x}{(x^2+1)^2}$

$$\begin{aligned}\frac{-x^3-x^2-x}{(x^2+1)^2}&=\frac{Ax+B}{x^2+1}+\frac{Cx+D}{(x^2+1)^2}\\&=\frac{(Ax+B)(x^2+1)}{(x^2+1)^2}+\frac{(Cx+D)}{(x^2+1)^2}\\&=\frac{Ax^3+Ax+Bx^2+B+Cx+D}{(x^2+1)^2}\\&=\frac{Ax^3+Bx^2+(A+C)x+D}{(x^2+1)^2}\end{aligned}$$

continued on next page...

44. continued...

$$\frac{-x^3-x^2-x}{(x^2+1)^2}=\frac{Ax^3+Bx^2+(A+C)x+D}{(x^2+1)^2}$$

$$\begin{cases} A & & & = -1 \\ & B & & = -1 \\ A & & +C & = -1 \\ & B & & +D = 0 \end{cases} \Rightarrow \begin{array}{l} A=-1 \\ B=-1 \\ C=0 \\ D=1 \end{array} \quad 1+\frac{-x^3-x^2-x}{(x^2+1)^2}=1+\frac{-x-1}{x^2+1}+\frac{1}{(x^2+1)^2}$$
$$=1-\frac{x+1}{x^2+1}+\frac{1}{(x+1)^2}$$

45. Use long division first: $\frac{2x^4+2x^3+3x^2-1}{(x^2-x)(x^2+1)}=2+\frac{4x^3+x^2+2x-1}{x(x-1)(x^2+1)}$

$$\frac{4x^3+x^2+2x-1}{x(x-1)(x^2+1)}=\frac{A}{x}+\frac{B}{x-1}+\frac{Cx+D}{x^2+1}$$
$$=\frac{A(x-1)(x^2+1)}{x(x-1)(x^2+1)}+\frac{Bx(x^2+1)}{x(x-1)(x^2+1)}+\frac{(Cx+D)(x)(x-1)}{x(x-1)(x^2+1)}$$
$$=\frac{Ax^3-Ax^2+Ax-A+Bx^3+Bx+Cx^3-Cx^2+Dx^2-Dx}{x(x-1)(x^2+1)}$$
$$=\frac{(A+B+C)x^3+(-A-C+D)x^2+(A+B-D)x+(-A)}{x(x-1)(x^2+1)}$$

$$\begin{cases} A+B+C & = 4 \\ -A \quad -C+D & = 1 \\ A+B \quad -D & = 2 \\ -A & = -1 \end{cases} \Rightarrow \begin{array}{l} A=1 \\ B=3 \\ C=0 \\ D=2 \end{array} \quad 2+\frac{4x^3+x^2+2x-1}{x(x-1)(x^2+1)}=2+\frac{1}{x}+\frac{3}{x-1}+\frac{2}{x^2+1}$$

46. Use long division first: $\frac{x^4-x^3+5x^2+x+6}{(x^2+3)(x^2+1)}=1+\frac{-x^3+x^2+x+3}{(x^2+3)(x^2+1)}$

$$\frac{-x^3+x^2+x+3}{(x^2+3)(x^2+1)}=\frac{Ax+B}{x^2+3}+\frac{Cx+D}{x^2+1}$$
$$=\frac{(Ax+B)(x^2+1)}{(x^2+3)(x^2+1)}+\frac{(Cx+D)(x^2+3)}{(x^2+3)(x^2+1)}$$
$$=\frac{Ax^3+Ax+Bx^2+B+Cx^3+3Cx+Dx^2+3D}{(x^2+3)(x^2+1)}$$
$$=\frac{(A+C)x^3+(B+D)x^2+(A+3C)x+(B+3D)}{(x^2+3)(x^2+1)}$$

$$\begin{cases} A & & +C & & = -1 \\ & B & & +D & = 1 \\ A & & +3C & & = 1 \\ & B & & +3D & = 3 \end{cases} \Rightarrow \begin{array}{l} A=-2 \\ B=0 \\ C=1 \\ D=1 \end{array} \quad 1+\frac{-x^3+x^2+x+3}{(x^2+3)(x^2+1)}=1-\frac{2x}{x^2+3}+\frac{x+1}{x^2+1}$$

47. $x^3+1=(x+1)(x^2-x+1)\Rightarrow$ not prime

48. $$\frac{1}{x^3+1} = \frac{1}{(x+1)(x^2-x+1)} = \frac{A}{x+1} + \frac{Bx+C}{x^2-x+1}$$
$$= \frac{A(x^2-x+1)}{(x+1)(x^2-x+1)} + \frac{(Bx+C)(x+1)}{(x+1)(x^2-x+1)}$$
$$= \frac{Ax^2 - Ax + A + Bx^2 + Bx + Cx + C}{(x+1)(x^2-x+1)}$$
$$= \frac{(A+B)x^2 + (-A+B+C)x + (A+C)}{(x+1)(x^2-x+1)}$$

$$\begin{cases} A+B \quad\;\; = 0 \\ -A+B+C = 0 \\ A \qquad\; +C = 1 \end{cases} \Rightarrow \begin{matrix} A = \frac{1}{3} \\ B = -\frac{1}{3} \\ C = \frac{2}{3} \end{matrix} \qquad \frac{1}{x^3+1} = \frac{1}{(x+1)(x^2-x+1)} = \frac{\frac{1}{3}}{x+1} + \frac{-\frac{1}{3}x + \frac{2}{3}}{x^2-x+1}$$

49. $\sqrt{8a^3b} = \sqrt{4a^2}\sqrt{2ab} = 2|a|\sqrt{2ab}$

50. $\sqrt{x^2+6x+9} = \sqrt{(x+3)^2} = |x+3|$

51. $$\sqrt{18x^5} + x^2\sqrt{50x} - 5x^2\sqrt{2x} = \sqrt{9x^4}\sqrt{2x} + x^2\sqrt{25}\sqrt{2x} - 5x^2\sqrt{2x}$$
$$= 3x^2\sqrt{2x} + 5x^2\sqrt{2x} - 5x^2\sqrt{2x} = 3x^2\sqrt{2x}$$

52. $$\frac{\sqrt{x^2y^3}}{\sqrt{xy^5}} = \sqrt{\frac{x^2y^3}{xy^5}} = \sqrt{\frac{x}{y^2}} = \frac{\sqrt{x}}{|y|}$$

53. $$\sqrt{x-5} = x-7$$
$$\left(\sqrt{x-5}\right)^2 = (x-7)^2$$
$$x-5 = x^2 - 14x + 49$$
$$0 = x^2 - 15x + 54$$
$$0 = (x-9)(x-6)$$
$$x = 9 \quad \text{or} \quad x = 6$$
$x = 6$ does not check and is extraneous.

54. $$x-5 = (x-7)^2$$
$$x-5 = x^2 - 14x + 49$$
$$0 = x^2 - 15x + 54$$
$$0 = (x-9)(x-6)$$
$$x = 9 \quad \text{or} \quad x = 6$$

Exercise 6.7 (page 492)

1. half-plane, boundary

2. excluded

3. is not

4. is

5. $2x + 3y < 12$

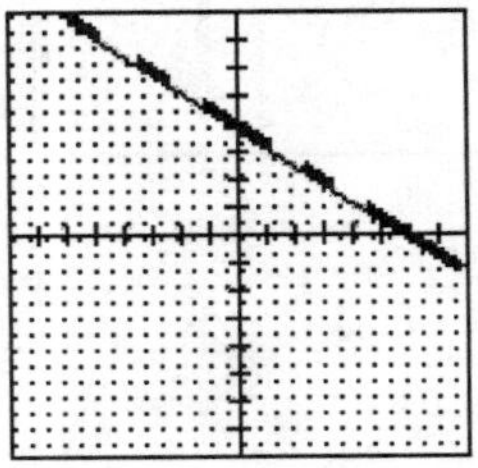

6. $4x - 3y > 6$

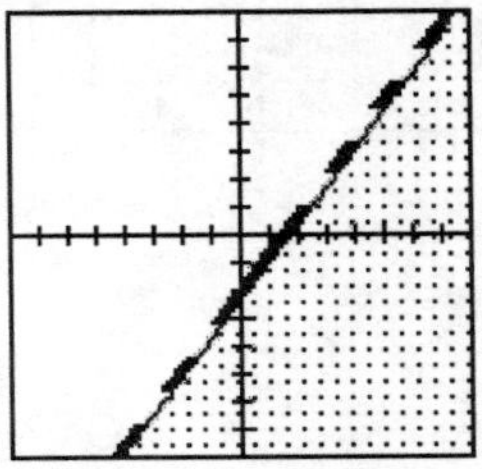

7. $x < 3$

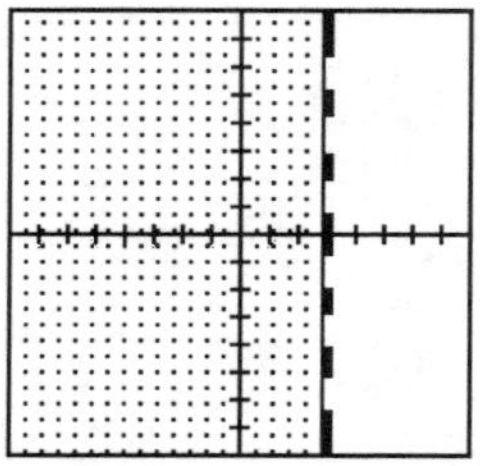

8. $y > -1$

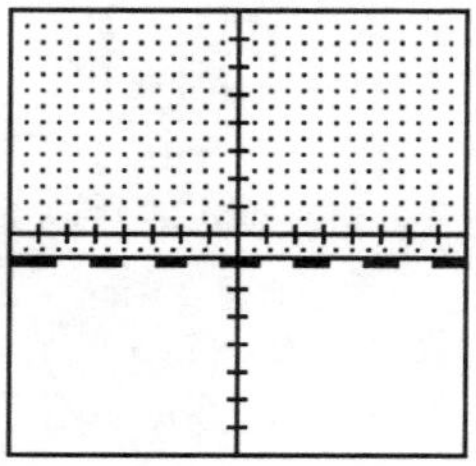

9. $4x - y > 4$

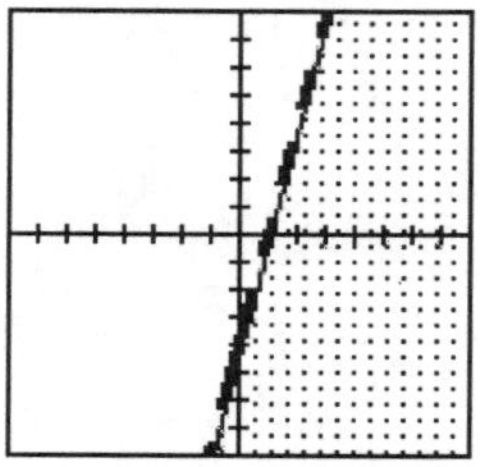

10. $x - 2y < 5$

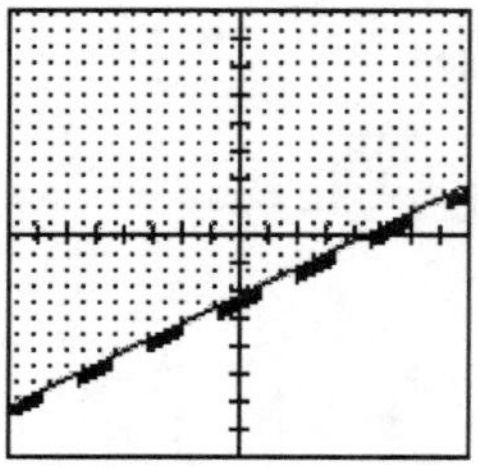

11. $y > 2x$

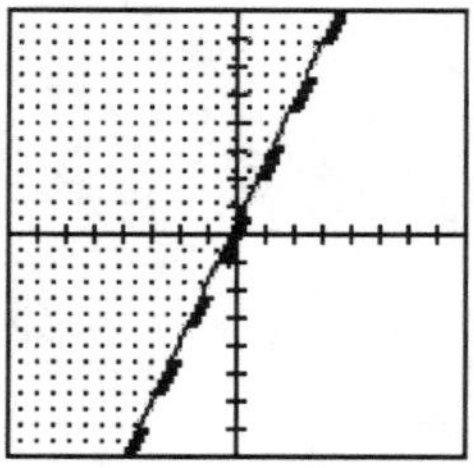

12. $y < 3x$

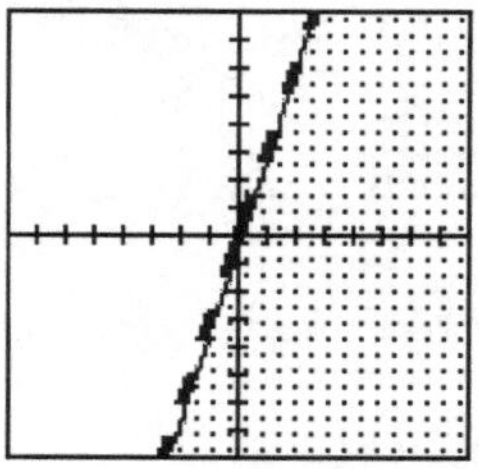

13. $y \leq \frac{1}{2}x + 1$

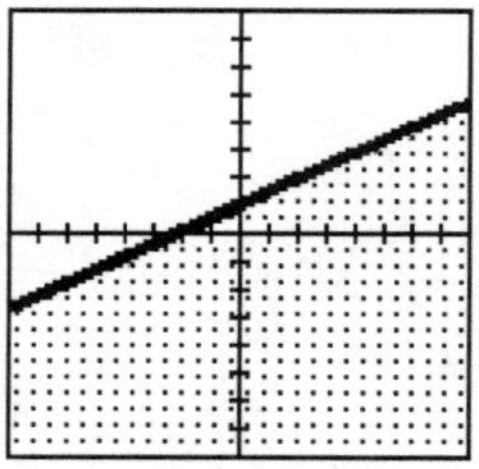

14. $y \geq \frac{1}{3}x - 1$

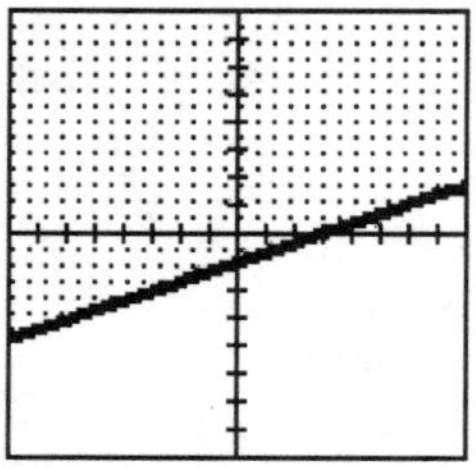

15. $2y \geq 3x - 2$

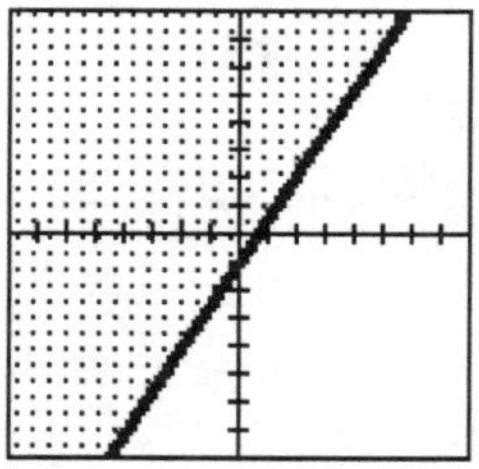

16. $3y \leq 2x + 3$

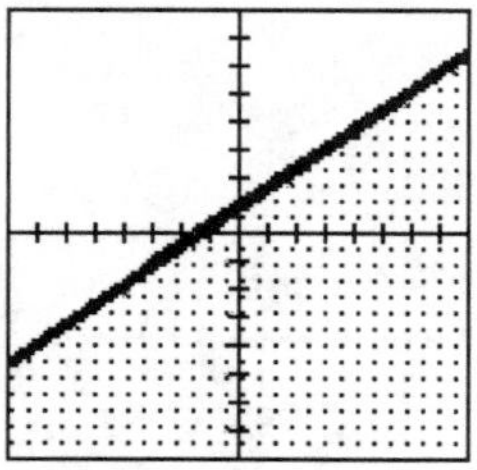

17. $\begin{cases} y < 3 \\ x \geq 2 \end{cases}$

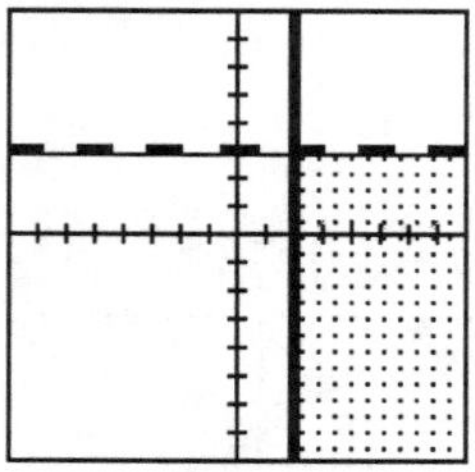

18. $\begin{cases} y \geq -2 \\ x < 0 \end{cases}$

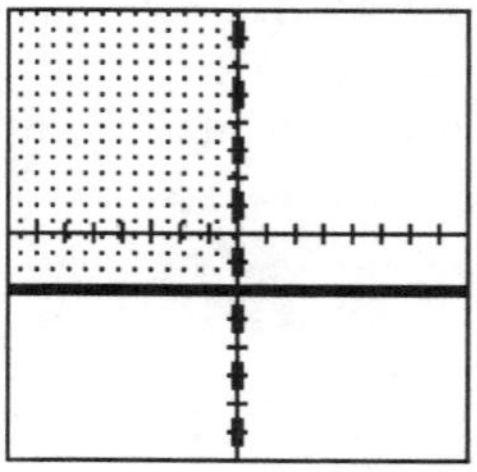

SECTION 6.7

19. $\begin{cases} y \geq 1 \\ x < 2 \end{cases}$

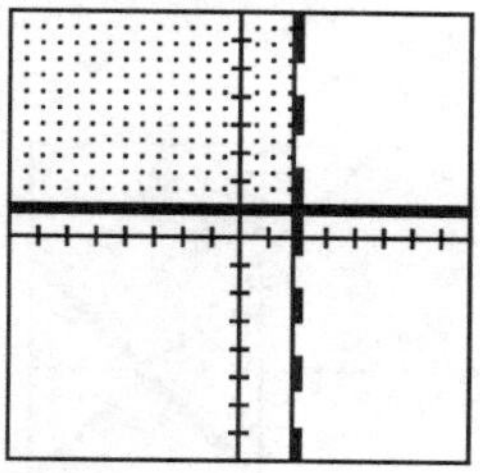

20. $\begin{cases} y \leq -1 \\ x > -1 \end{cases}$

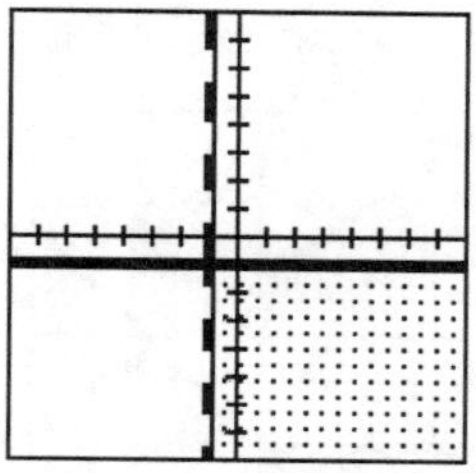

21. $\begin{cases} y \leq x - 2 \\ y \geq 2x + 1 \end{cases}$

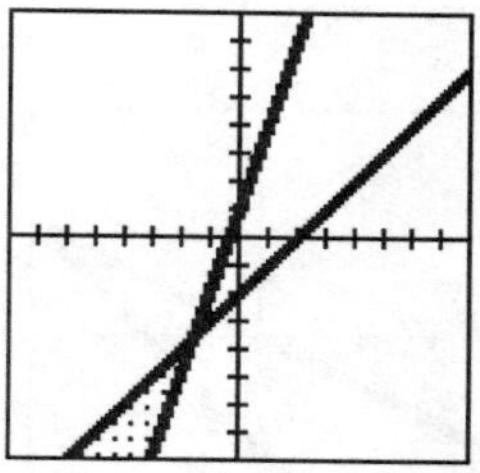

22. $\begin{cases} y < 3x + 2 \\ y < -2x + 3 \end{cases}$

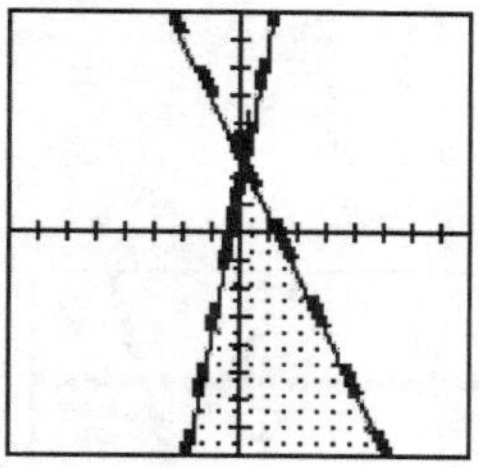

23. $\begin{cases} x + y < 2 \\ x + y \leq 1 \end{cases}$

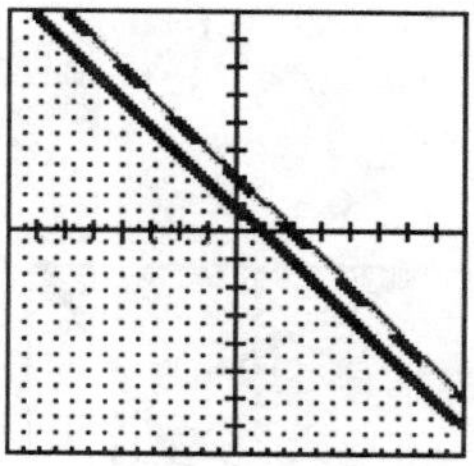

24. $\begin{cases} 3x + 2y \geq 6 \\ x + 3y \leq 2 \end{cases}$

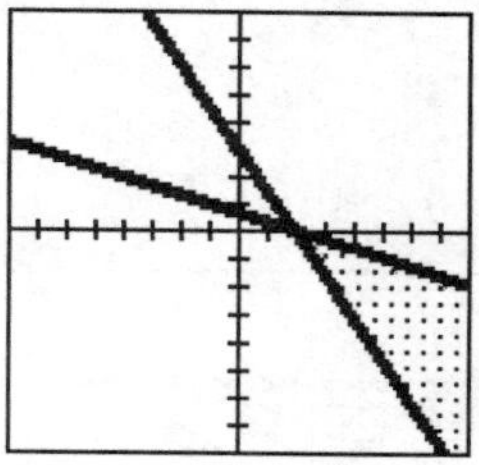

25. $\begin{cases} x + 2y < 3 \\ 2x - 4y < 8 \end{cases}$

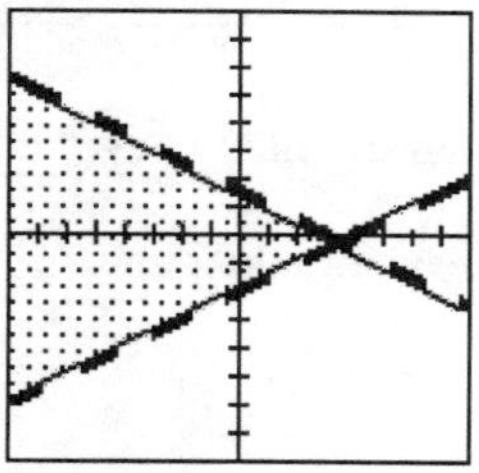

26. $\begin{cases} 3x + y \leq 1 \\ -x + 2y \geq 9 \end{cases}$

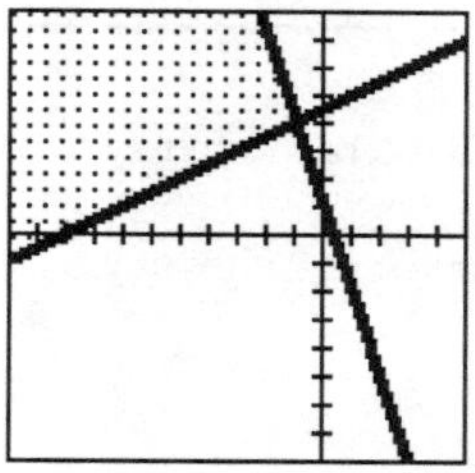

27. $\begin{cases} 2x - 3y \geq 6 \\ 3x + 2y < 6 \end{cases}$

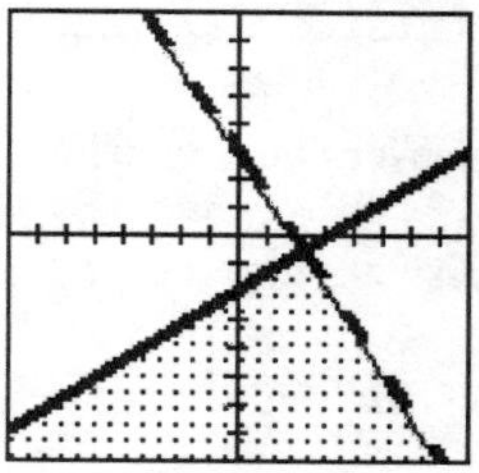

28. $\begin{cases} 4x + 2y \leq 6 \\ 2x - 4y \geq 10 \end{cases}$

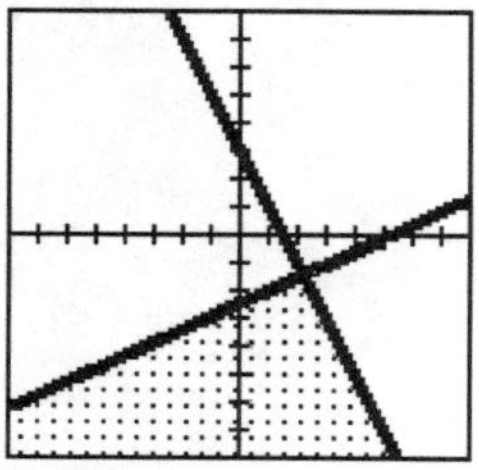

29. $\begin{cases} 2x - y \leq 0 \\ x + 2y \leq 10 \\ y \geq 0 \end{cases}$

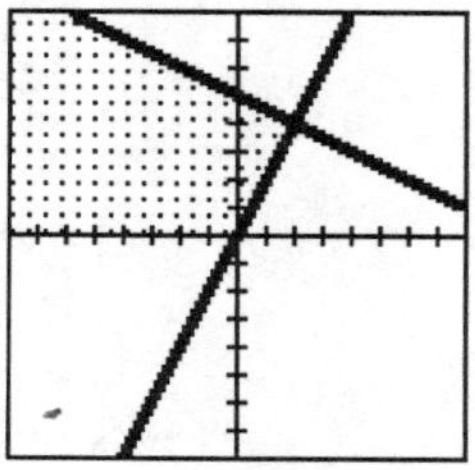

30. $\begin{cases} 3x - 2y \geq 5 \\ 2x + y \geq 8 \\ x \leq 5 \end{cases}$

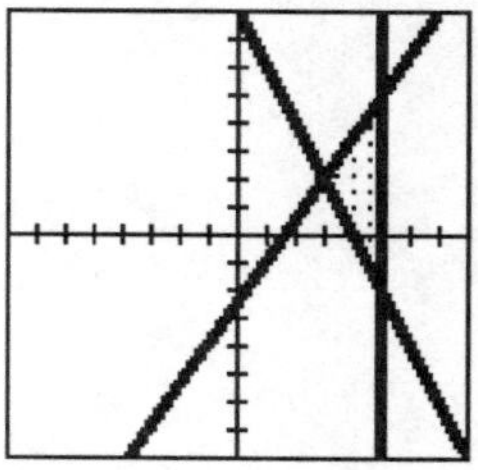

SECTION 6.7

31. $\begin{cases} x - 2y \geq 0 \\ x - y \leq 2 \\ x \geq 0 \end{cases}$

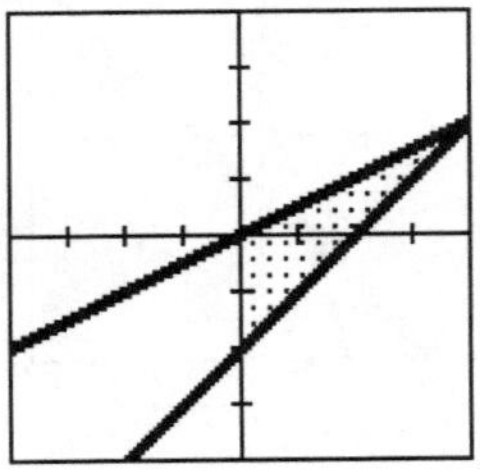

32. $\begin{cases} 2x + 3y \leq 6 \\ x - y \geq 4 \\ y \geq -4 \end{cases}$

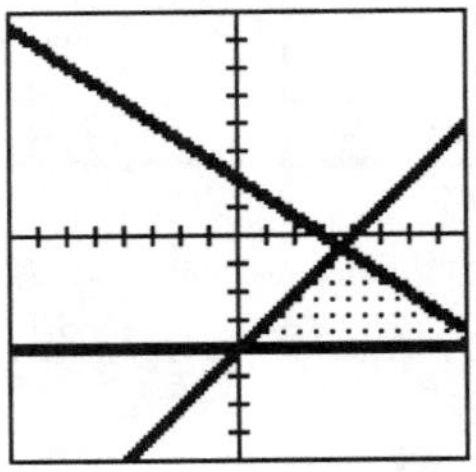

33. $\begin{cases} x + y \leq 4 \\ x - y \leq 4 \\ x \geq 0 \\ y \geq 0 \end{cases}$

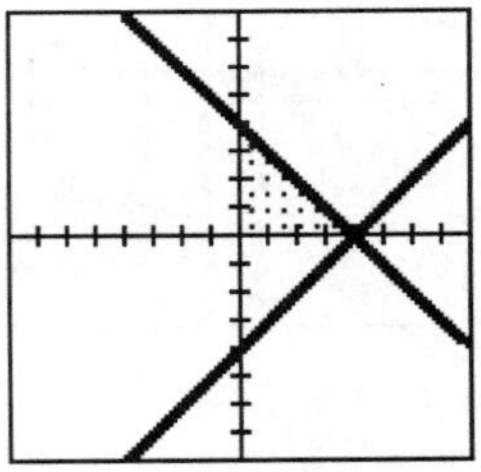

34. $\begin{cases} 2x + 3y \geq 12 \\ 2x - 3y \leq 6 \\ x \geq 0 \\ y \leq 4 \end{cases}$

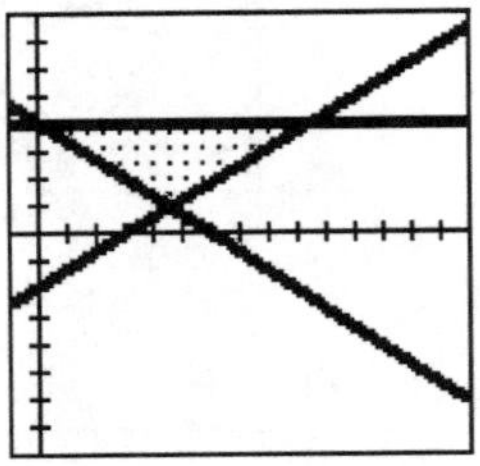

35. $\begin{cases} 3x - 2y \leq 6 \\ x + 2y \leq 10 \\ x \geq 0 \\ y \geq 0 \end{cases}$

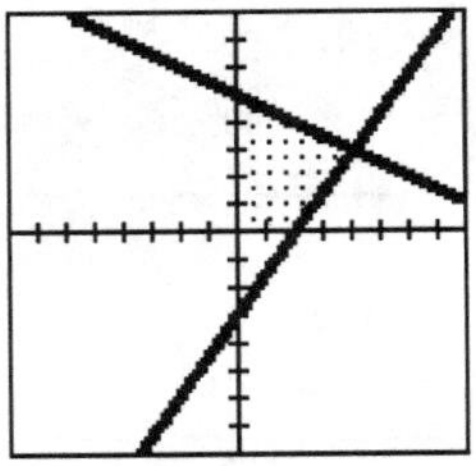

36. $\begin{cases} 3x + 2y \geq 12 \\ 5x - y \leq 15 \\ x \geq 0 \\ y \leq 4 \end{cases}$

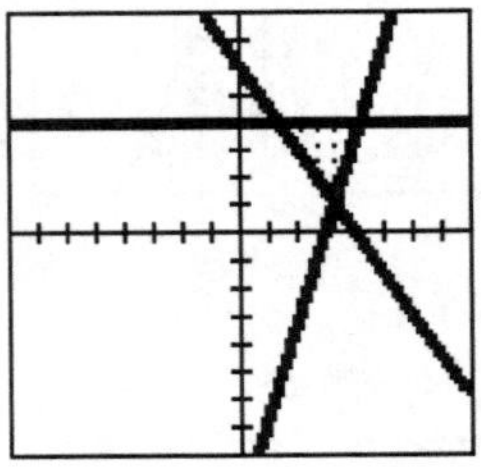

37. **Answers may vary.**

38. **Answers may vary.**

39. **Answers may vary.**

40. **Answers may vary.**

41. **Answers may vary.**

42. **Answers may vary.**

43. one, one

44. zero

45. 0

46. yes

Exercise 6.8 (page 501)

1. constraints **2.** feasible **3.** objective **4.** corner, edge

5.

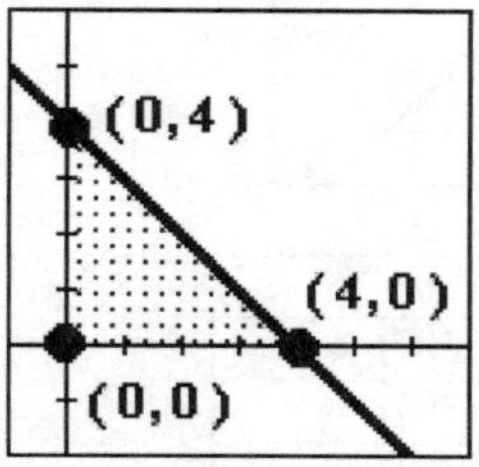

Point	$P = 2x + 3y$
$(0, 0)$	$= 2(0) + 3(0) = 0$
$(0, 4)$	$= 2(0) + 3(4) = 12$
$(4, 0)$	$= 2(4) + 3(0) = 8$

Max: $P = 12$ at $(0, 4)$

6.

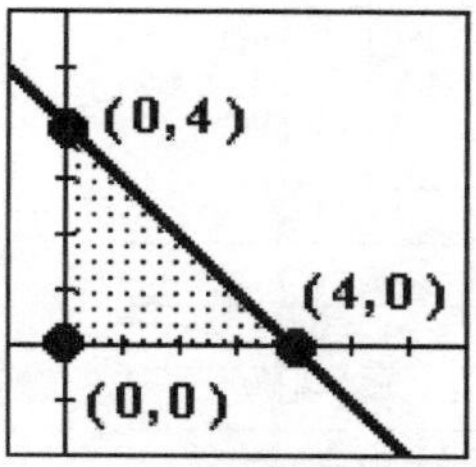

Point	$P = 3x + 2y$
$(0, 0)$	$= 3(0) + 2(0) = 0$
$(0, 4)$	$= 3(0) + 2(4) = 8$
$(4, 0)$	$= 3(4) + 2(0) = 12$

Max: $P = 12$ at $(4, 0)$

7.

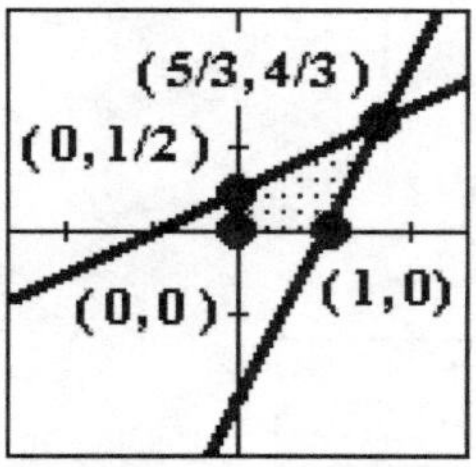

Point	$P = y + \frac{1}{2}x$
$(0, 0)$	$= 0 + \frac{1}{2}(0) = 0$
$\left(0, \frac{1}{2}\right)$	$= \frac{1}{2} + \frac{1}{2}(0) = \frac{1}{2}$
$\left(\frac{5}{3}, \frac{4}{3}\right)$	$= \frac{4}{3} + \frac{1}{2}\left(\frac{5}{3}\right) = \frac{13}{6}$
$(1, 0)$	$= 0 + \frac{1}{2}(1) = \frac{1}{2}$

Max: $P = \frac{13}{6}$ at $\left(\frac{5}{3}, \frac{4}{3}\right)$

8.

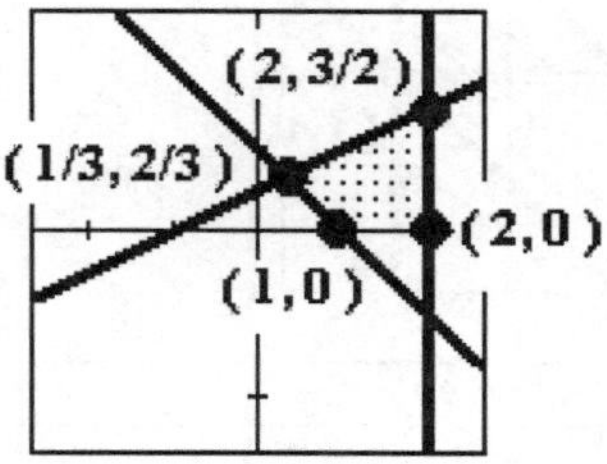

Point	$P = 4y - x$
$(1, 0)$	$= 4(0) - 1 = -1$
$(2, 0)$	$= 4(0) - 2 = -2$
$\left(2, \frac{3}{2}\right)$	$= 4\left(\frac{3}{2}\right) - 2 = 4$
$\left(\frac{1}{3}, \frac{2}{3}\right)$	$= 4\left(\frac{2}{3}\right) - \frac{1}{3} = \frac{7}{3}$

Max: $P = 4$ at $\left(2, \frac{3}{2}\right)$

9.

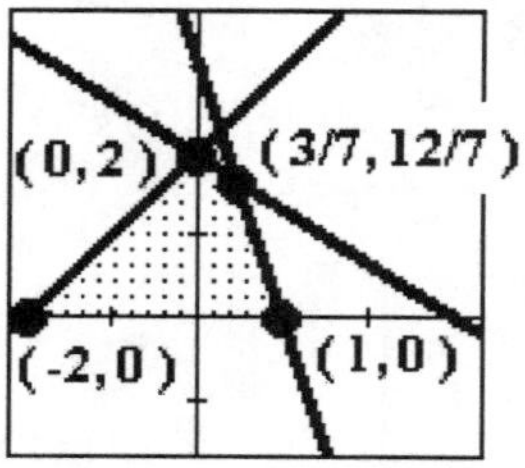

Point	$P = 2x + y$
$(-2, 0)$	$= 2(-2) + 0 = -4$
$(1, 0)$	$= 2(1) + 0 = 2$
$\left(\frac{3}{7}, \frac{12}{7}\right)$	$= 2\left(\frac{3}{7}\right) + \frac{12}{7} = \frac{18}{7}$
$(0, 2)$	$= 2(0) + 2 = 2$

Max: $P = \frac{18}{7}$ at $\left(\frac{3}{7}, \frac{12}{7}\right)$

10.

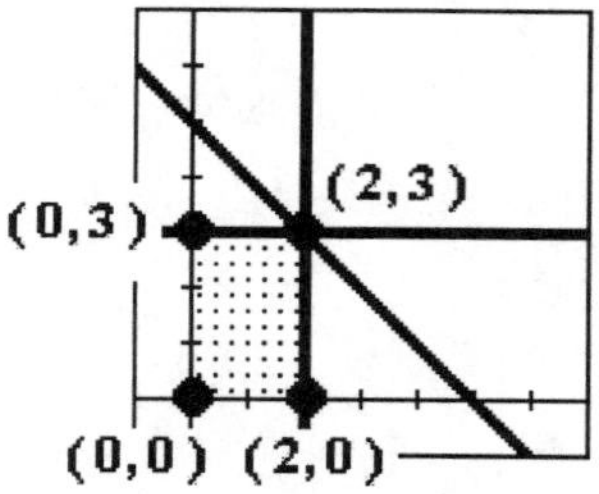

Point	$P = x - 2y$
$(0, 0)$	$= 0 - 2(0) = 0$
$(2, 0)$	$= 2 - 2(0) = 2$
$(2, 3)$	$= 2 - 2(3) = -4$
$(0, 3)$	$= 0 - 2(3) = -6$

Max: $P = 2$ at $(2, 0)$

11.

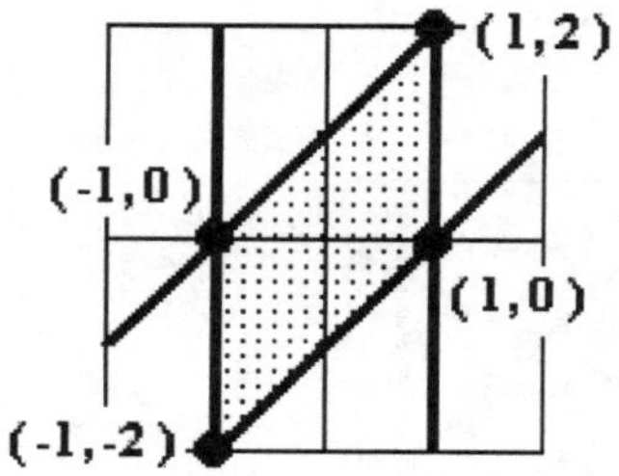

Point	$P = 3x - 2y$
$(1, 0)$	$= 3(1) - 2(0) = 3$
$(1, 2)$	$= 3(1) - 2(2) = -1$
$(-1, 0)$	$= 3(-1) - 2(0) = -3$
$(-1, -2)$	$= 3(-1) - 2(-2) = 1$

Max: $P = 3$ at $(1, 0)$

12.

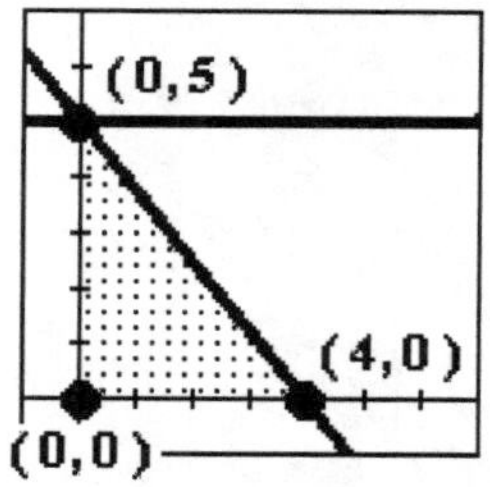

Point	$P = x - y$
$(0, 0)$	$= 0 - 0 = 0$
$(4, 0)$	$= 4 - 0 = 4$
$(0, 5)$	$= 0 - 5 = -5$

Max: $P = 4$ at $(4, 0)$

13.

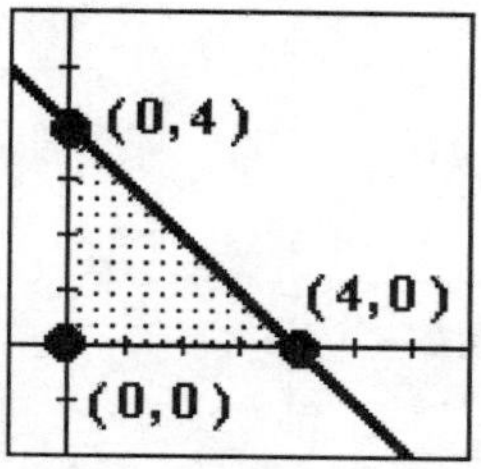

Point	$P = 5x + 12y$
$(0, 0)$	$= 5(0) + 12(0) = 0$
$(0, 4)$	$= 5(0) + 12(4) = 48$
$(4, 0)$	$= 5(4) + 12(0) = 20$

Min: $P = 0$ at $(0, 0)$

14.

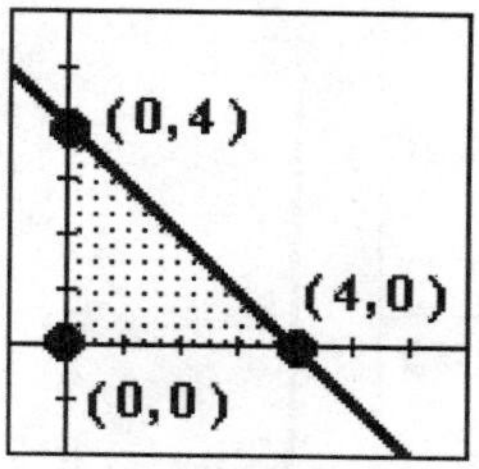

Point	$P = 3x + 6y$
$(0, 0)$	$= 3(0) + 6(0) = 0$
$(0, 4)$	$= 3(0) + 6(4) = 24$
$(4, 0)$	$= 3(4) + 6(0) = 12$

Min: $P = 0$ at $(0, 0)$

15.

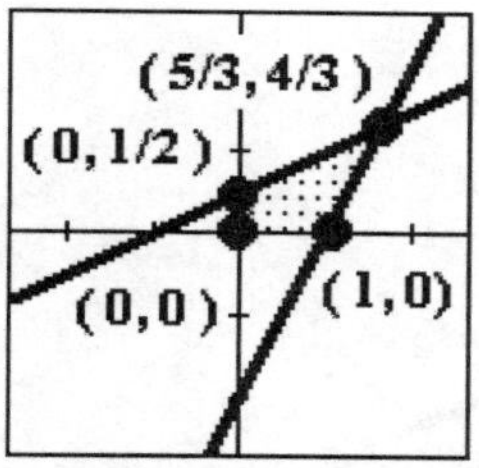

Point	$P = 3y + x$
$(0, 0)$	$= 3(0) + 0 = 0$
$(0, \frac{1}{2})$	$= 3(\frac{1}{2}) + 0 = \frac{3}{2}$
$(\frac{5}{3}, \frac{4}{3})$	$= 3(\frac{4}{3}) + \frac{5}{3} = \frac{17}{3}$
$(1, 0)$	$= 3(0) + 1 = 1$

Min: $P = 0$ at $(0, 0)$

16.

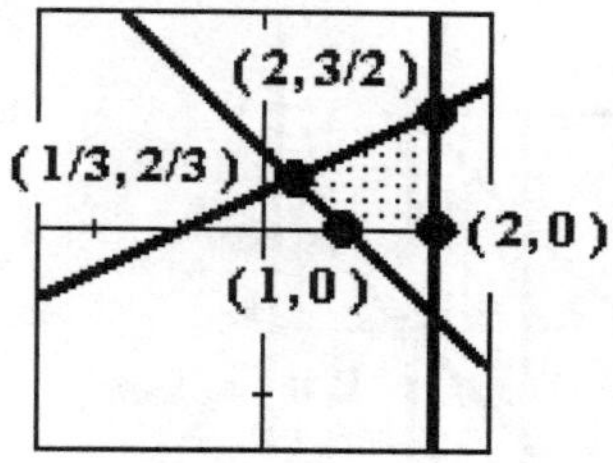

Point	$P = 5y + x$
$(1, 0)$	$= 5(0) + 1 = 1$
$(2, 0)$	$= 5(0) + 2 = 2$
$(2, \frac{3}{2})$	$= 5(\frac{3}{2}) + 2 = \frac{19}{2}$
$(\frac{1}{3}, \frac{2}{3})$	$= 5(\frac{2}{3}) + \frac{1}{3} = \frac{11}{3}$

Min: $P = 1$ at $(1, 0)$

17.

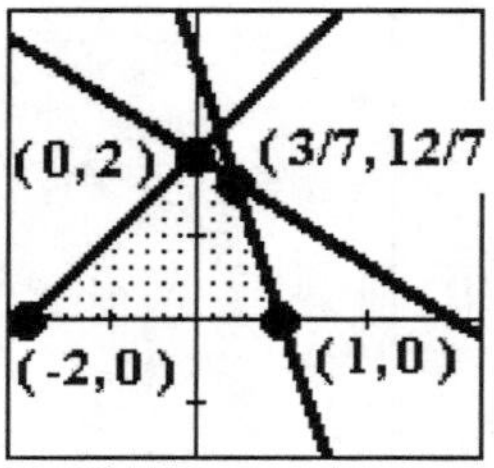

Point	$P = 6x + 2y$
$(-2, 0)$	$= 6(-2) + 2(0) = -12$
$(1, 0)$	$= 6(1) + 2(0) = 6$
$\left(\frac{3}{7}, \frac{12}{7}\right)$	$= 6\left(\frac{3}{7}\right) + 2\left(\frac{12}{7}\right) = 6$
$(0, 2)$	$= 6(0) + 2(2) = 4$

Min: $P = -12$ at $(-2, 0)$

18.

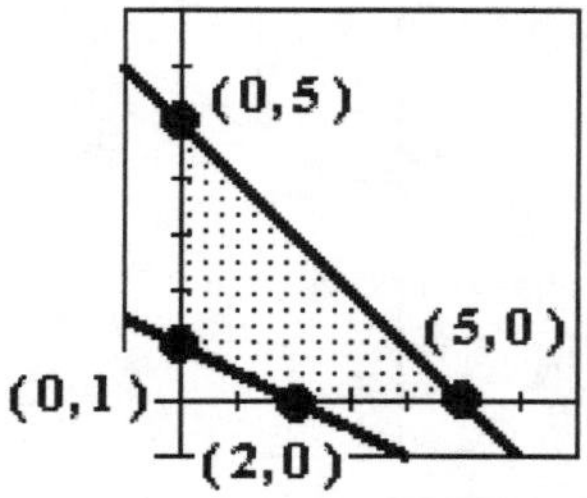

Point	$P = 2y - x$
$(0, 1)$	$= 2(1) - 0 = 2$
$(2, 0)$	$= 2(0) - 2 = -2$
$(5, 0)$	$= 2(0) - 5 = -5$
$(0, 5)$	$= 2(5) - 0 = 10$

Min: $P = -5$ at $(5, 0)$

19.

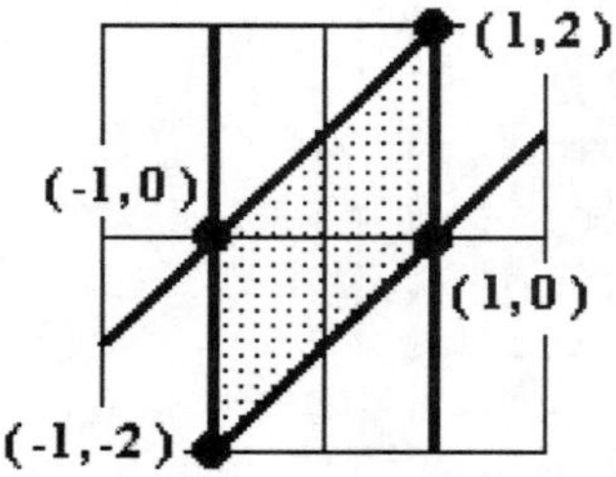

Point	$P = 2x - 2y$
$(1, 0)$	$= 2(1) - 2(0) = 2$
$(1, 2)$	$= 2(1) - 2(2) = -2$
$(-1, 0)$	$= 2(-1) - 2(0) = -2$
$(-1, -2)$	$= 2(-1) - 2(-2) = 2$

Min: $P = -2$ on the edge joining $(1, 2)$ and $(-1, 0)$

20.

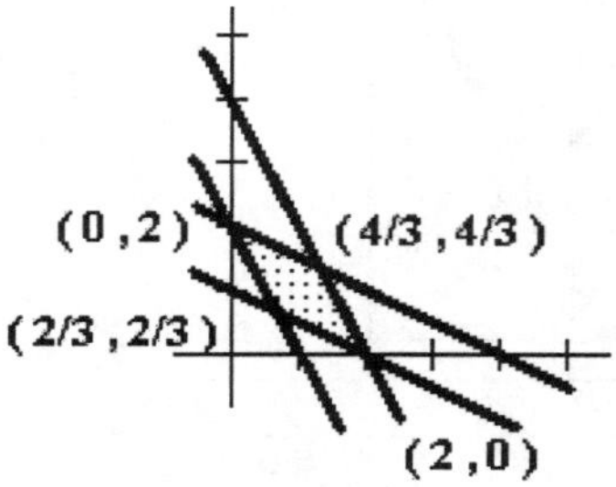

Point	$P = y - 2x$
$\left(\frac{2}{3}, \frac{2}{3}\right)$	$= \frac{2}{3} - 2\left(\frac{2}{3}\right) = -\frac{2}{3}$
$(2, 0)$	$= 0 - 2(2) = -4$
$\left(\frac{4}{3}, \frac{4}{3}\right)$	$= \frac{4}{3} - 2\left(\frac{4}{3}\right) = -\frac{4}{3}$
$(0, 2)$	$= 2 - 2(0) = 2$

Min: $P = -4$ at $(2, 0)$

21. Let x = # tables and y = # chairs.
Maximize $P = 100x + 80y$

subject to $\begin{cases} 2x + 3y \le 42 \\ 6x + 2y \le 42 \\ x \ge 0,\ y \ge 0 \end{cases}$

Point	$P = 100x + 80y$
(7, 0)	$= 100(7) + 80(0) = 700$
(3, 12)	$= 100(3) + 80(12) = 1260$
(0, 14)	$= 100(0) + 80(14) = 1120$
(−1, −2)	$= 2(-1) - 2(-2) = 2$

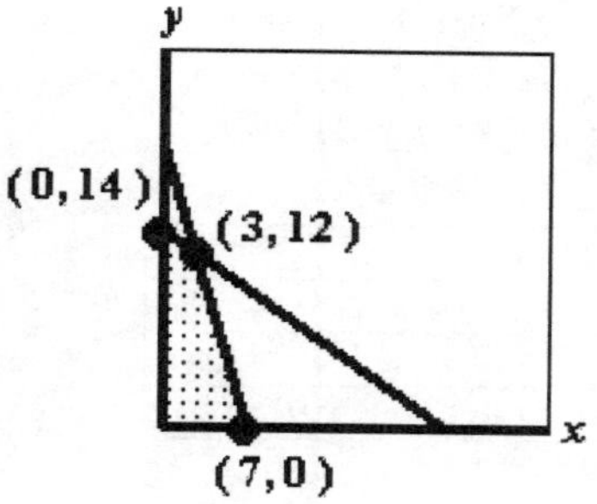

They should make 3 tables and 12 chairs, for a maximum profit of \$1260.

22. Let x = # snowman and y = # Santa Claus ornaments.
Maximize $P = 80x + 64y$

subject to $\begin{cases} 4x + 3y \le 20 \\ 2x + 4y \le 20 \\ x \ge 0,\ y \ge 0 \end{cases}$

Point	$P = 80x + 64y$
(5, 0)	$= 80(5) + 64(0) = 400$
(2, 4)	$= 80(2) + 64(4) = 416$
(0, 5)	$= 80(0) + 64(5) = 320$

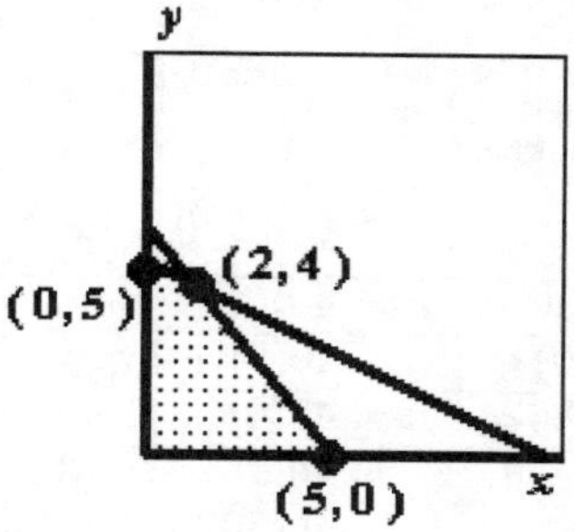

They should make 2 snowman and 4 Santa Claus ornaments, for a maximum profit of \$416.

23. Let x = # IBM and y = # Macintosh.
Maximize $P = 50x + 40y$

subject to $\begin{cases} x + y \le 60 \\ 20 \le x \le 30 \\ 30 \le y \le 50 \end{cases}$

Point	$P = 50x + 40y$
(20, 30)	$= 50(20) + 40(30) = 2200$
(30, 30)	$= 50(30) + 40(30) = 2700$
(20, 40)	$= 50(20) + 40(40) = 2600$

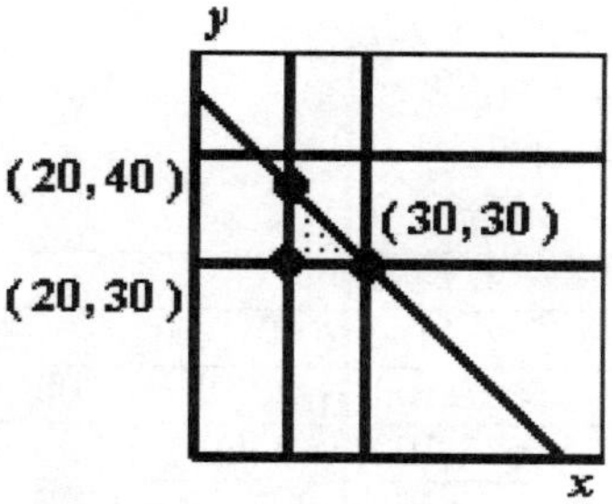

She should stock 30 IBM and 30 Macintosh computers, for a maximum commission of \$2700.

24. Let x = grams of A and y = grams of B.
Minimize $P = 3x + 4y$

subject to $\begin{cases} 3x + 2y \geq 16 \\ 2x + 6y \geq 34 \\ x \geq 0, y \geq 0 \end{cases}$

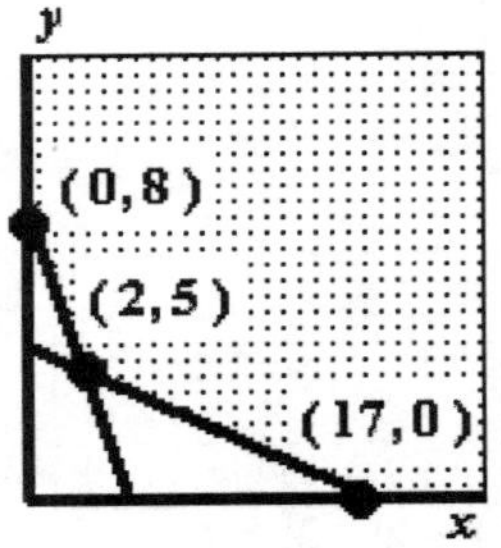

Point	$P = 3x + 4y$
(0, 8)	$= 3(0) + 4(8) = 32$
(2, 5)	$= 3(2) + 4(5) = 26$
(17, 0)	$= 3(17) + 4(0) = 51$

2 grams of A and 5 grams of B should be used, for a minimum cost of 26¢.

25. Let x = # VCRs and y = # TVs.
Maximize $P = 40x + 32y$

subject to $\begin{cases} 3x + 4y \leq 180 \\ 2x + 3y \leq 120 \\ 2x + y \leq 60 \\ x \geq 0, y \geq 0 \end{cases}$

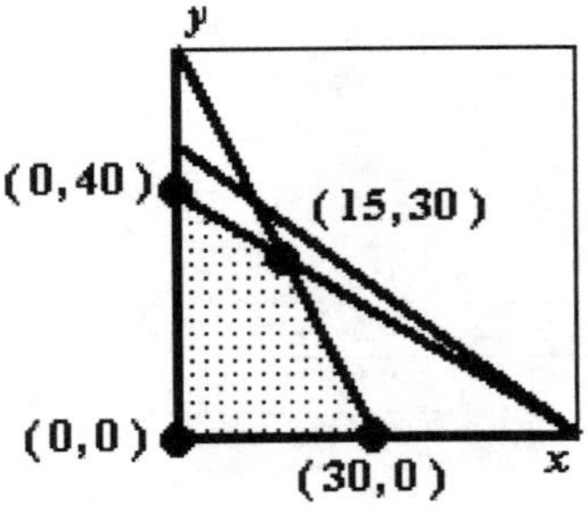

Point	$P = 40x + 32y$
(0, 0)	$= 40(0) + 32(0) = 0$
(0, 40)	$= 40(0) + 32(40) = 1280$
(15, 30)	$= 40(15) + 32(30) = 1560$
(30, 0)	$= 40(30) + 32(0) = 1200$

15 VCRs and 30 TVs should be made, for a maximum profit of \$1560.

26. Let x = # slow chips (2.0) and y = # fast chips (2.8).
Maximize $P = 27x + 20y$

subject to $\begin{cases} y \leq 50, x \leq 100 \\ 3x + 6y \leq 360 \\ x \geq 0, y \geq 0 \end{cases}$

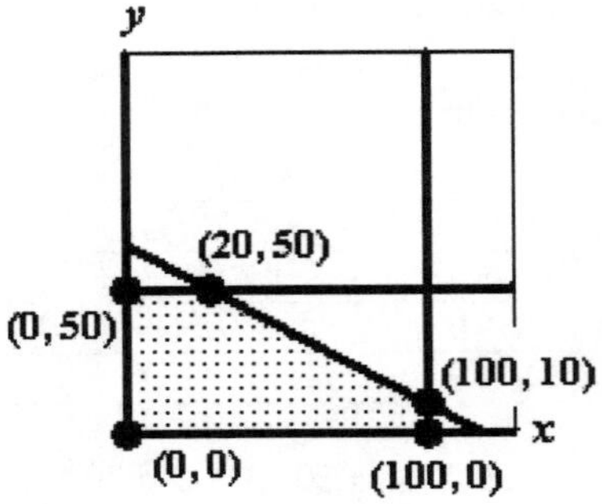

Point	$P = 27x + 20y$
(0, 0)	$= 27(0) + 20(0) = 0$
(100, 0)	$= 27(100) + 20(0) = 2700$
(100, 10)	$= 27(100) + 20(10) = 2900$
(20, 50)	$= 27(20) + 20(50) = 1540$
(0, 50)	$= 27(0) + 20(50) = 1000$

100 slow chips and 10 fast chips should be made, for a maximum profit of \$2900.

27. Let $x = \$$ in stocks and $y = \$$ in bonds.
Maximize $P = 0.09x + 0.07y$

subject to $\begin{cases} x + y \le 200000 \\ x \ge 100000 \\ y \ge 50000 \end{cases}$

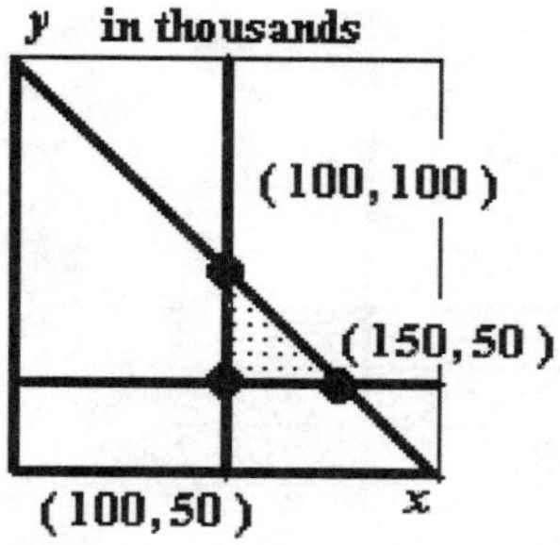

Point	$P = 0.09x + 0.07y$
(100000, 50000)	$= 12500$
(150000, 50000)	$= 17000$
(100000, 100000)	$= 16000$

She should invest \$150,000 in stocks and \$50,000 in bonds, for a maximum return of \$17,000.

28. Let $x =$ acres of beans and $y =$ acres of flowers.
Maximize $P = 1600x + 2000y$

subject to $\begin{cases} 8x + 12y \le 100{,}000 \\ x - 3y \ge 0 \\ 250x + 300y \le 3{,}000{,}000 \\ x \ge 0 . y \ge 0 \end{cases}$

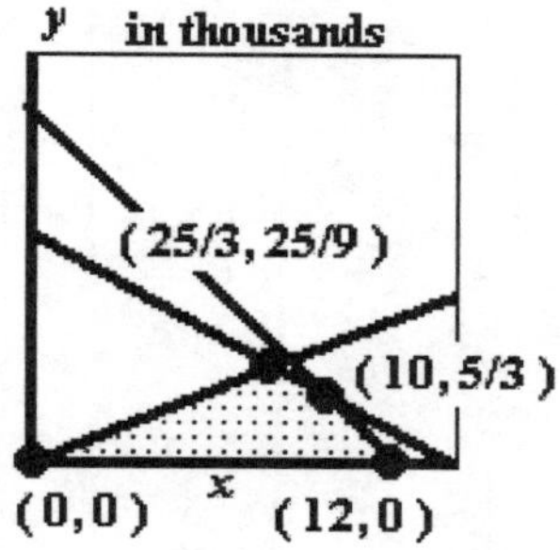

Point	$P = 1600x + 2000y$
(0, 0)	$= 0$
(12000, 0)	$= 19{,}200{,}000$
$\left(10000, \frac{5000}{3}\right)$	$= 19{,}333{,}333$
$\left(\frac{25000}{3}, \frac{25000}{9}\right)$	$= 18{,}888{,}889$

The country should plant 10,000 acres of beans and 1667 acres of flowers, for a maximum profit of \$19,333,333.

29. Let $x = \#$ buses and $y = \#$ trucks.
Minimize $P = 350x + 200y$

subject to $\begin{cases} 40x + 10y \ge 100 \\ 3x + 6y \ge 18 \\ x \ge 0, y \ge 0 \end{cases}$

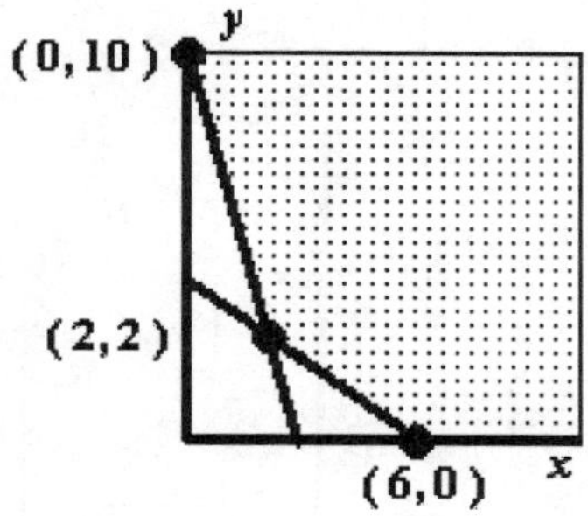

Point	$P = 350x + 200y$
(0, 10)	$= 350(0) + 200(10) = 2000$
(2, 2)	$= 350(2) + 200(2) = 1100$
(6, 0)	$= 350(6) + 200(0) = 2100$

2 buses and 2 trucks should be rented, for a minimum cost of \$1100.

30. Let $x =$ barrels of Fantasy and $y =$ barrels of Excess.
Maximize $P = 500x + 400y$

subject to $\begin{cases} 4x + 4y \le 16 \\ 3x + 2y \le 18 \\ x \ge 0, y \ge 0 \end{cases}$

Point	$P = 500x + 400y$
$(0, 0)$	$= 500(0) + 400(0) = 0$
$(0, 4)$	$= 500(0) + 400(4) = 1600$
$(4, 0)$	$= 500(4) + 400(0) = 2000$

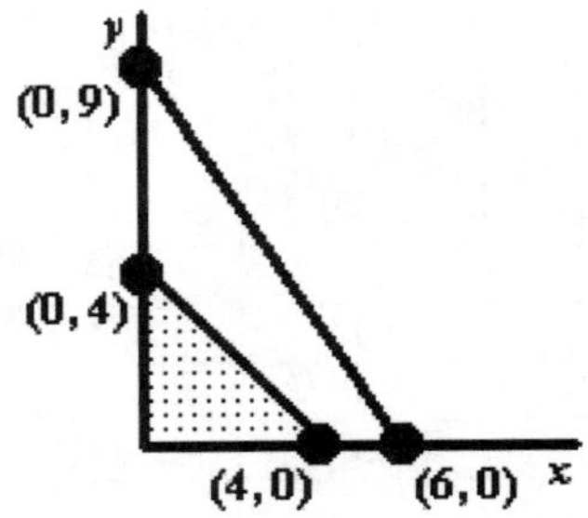

4 barrels of Fantasy and 0 barrels of Excess should be made, for a maximum profit of \$2000.

31. **Answers may vary.**

32. **Answers may vary.**

33.
$$\begin{bmatrix} 1 & 2 & 3 \\ 1 & -2 & 3 \\ 0 & 2 & -3 \\ 2 & 0 & 6 \end{bmatrix} \Rightarrow \underset{\substack{-R_1 + R_2 \Rightarrow R_2 \\ -2R_1 + R_4 \Rightarrow R_4}}{\begin{bmatrix} 1 & 2 & 3 \\ 0 & -4 & 0 \\ 0 & 2 & -3 \\ 0 & -4 & 0 \end{bmatrix}} \Rightarrow \underset{\substack{-\frac{1}{4}R_2 \Rightarrow R_2 \\ -R_4 + R_2 \Rightarrow R_4}}{\begin{bmatrix} 1 & 2 & 3 \\ 0 & 1 & 0 \\ 0 & 2 & -3 \\ 0 & 0 & 0 \end{bmatrix}} \Rightarrow \underset{\substack{-2R_2 + R_1 \Rightarrow R_1 \\ -2R_2 + R_3 \Rightarrow R_3}}{\begin{bmatrix} 1 & 0 & 3 \\ 0 & 1 & 0 \\ 0 & 0 & -3 \\ 0 & 0 & 0 \end{bmatrix}} \Rightarrow \underset{\substack{R_3 + R_1 \Rightarrow R_1 \\ -\frac{1}{3}R_3 \Rightarrow R_3}}{\begin{bmatrix} 1 & 0 & 0 \\ 0 & 1 & 0 \\ 0 & 0 & 1 \\ 0 & 0 & 0 \end{bmatrix}}$$

34.
$$\begin{bmatrix} 1 & 3 & -2 & 1 \\ 3 & 9 & -3 & 2 \end{bmatrix} \Rightarrow \underset{-3R_1 + R_2 \Rightarrow R_2}{\begin{bmatrix} 1 & 3 & -2 & 1 \\ 0 & 0 & 3 & -1 \end{bmatrix}} \Rightarrow \underset{\frac{1}{3}R_2 \Rightarrow R_2}{\begin{bmatrix} 1 & 3 & -2 & 1 \\ 0 & 0 & 1 & -\frac{1}{3} \end{bmatrix}} \Rightarrow \underset{2R_2 + R_1 \Rightarrow R_1}{\begin{bmatrix} 1 & 3 & 0 & \frac{1}{3} \\ 0 & 0 & 1 & -\frac{1}{3} \end{bmatrix}}$$

35. $\left(\frac{1}{3} - 3y, y, -\frac{1}{3}\right)$

36.
$$\left[\begin{array}{ccc|ccc} 7 & 2 & 5 & 1 & 0 & 0 \\ 3 & 1 & 2 & 0 & 1 & 0 \\ 3 & 1 & 3 & 0 & 0 & 1 \end{array}\right] \Rightarrow \underset{-2R_2 + R_1 \Rightarrow R_1}{\left[\begin{array}{ccc|ccc} 1 & 0 & 1 & 1 & -2 & 0 \\ 3 & 1 & 2 & 0 & 1 & 0 \\ 3 & 1 & 3 & 0 & 0 & 1 \end{array}\right]} \Rightarrow \underset{\substack{-3R_1 + R_2 \Rightarrow R_2 \\ -3R_1 + R_3 \Rightarrow R_3}}{\left[\begin{array}{ccc|ccc} 1 & 0 & 1 & 1 & -2 & 0 \\ 0 & 1 & -1 & -3 & 7 & 0 \\ 0 & 1 & 0 & -3 & 6 & 1 \end{array}\right]} \Rightarrow$$

$$\underset{R_2 \Leftrightarrow R_3}{\left[\begin{array}{ccc|ccc} 1 & 0 & 1 & 1 & -2 & 0 \\ 0 & 1 & 0 & -3 & 6 & 1 \\ 0 & 1 & -1 & -3 & 7 & 0 \end{array}\right]} \Rightarrow \underset{-R_3 + R_2 \Rightarrow R_3}{\left[\begin{array}{ccc|ccc} 1 & 0 & 1 & 1 & -2 & 0 \\ 0 & 1 & 0 & -3 & 6 & 1 \\ 0 & 0 & 1 & 0 & -1 & 1 \end{array}\right]} \Rightarrow$$

$$\underset{-R_3 + R_1 \Rightarrow R_1}{\left[\begin{array}{ccc|ccc} 1 & 0 & 0 & 1 & -1 & -1 \\ 0 & 1 & 0 & -3 & 6 & 1 \\ 0 & 0 & 1 & 0 & -1 & 1 \end{array}\right]} \Rightarrow \text{Inverse} = \begin{bmatrix} 1 & -1 & -1 \\ -3 & 6 & 1 \\ 0 & -1 & 1 \end{bmatrix}$$

Chapter 6 Summary (page 505)

1. **a.** $\begin{cases} 2x - y = -1 \\ x + y = 7 \end{cases}$

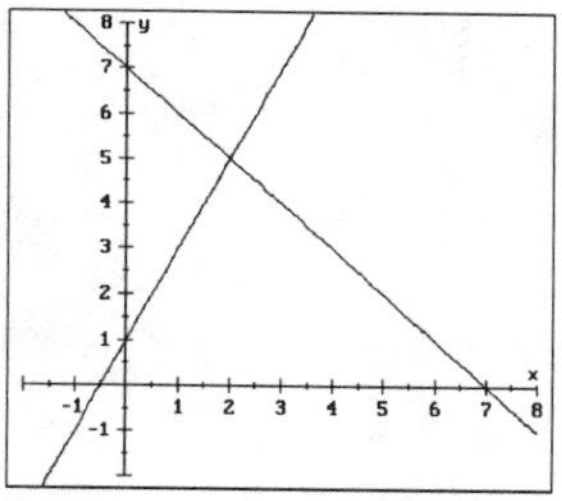

solution: (2, 5)

b. $\begin{cases} 5x + 2y = 1 \\ 2x - y = -5 \end{cases}$

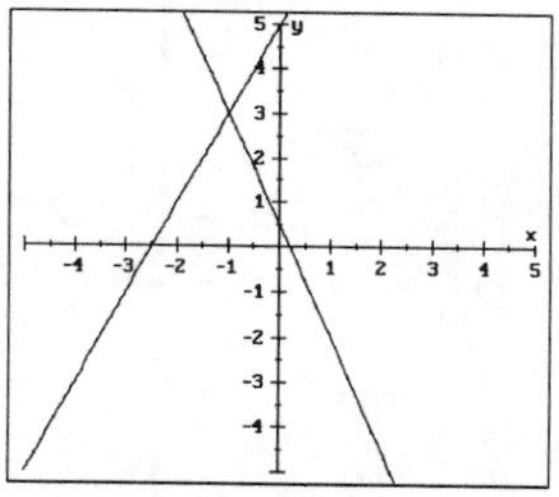

solution: (−1, 3)

c. $\begin{cases} y = 5x + 7 \\ x = y - 7 \end{cases}$

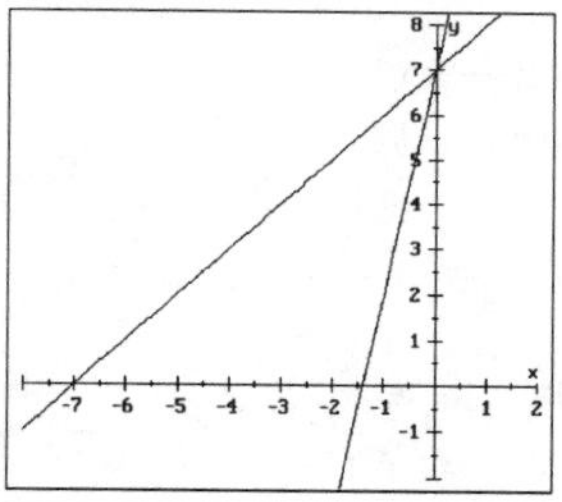

solution: (0, 7)

2. **a.** $\begin{cases} (1) \quad 2y + x = 0 \\ (2) \quad x = y + 3 \end{cases}$

Substitute $x = y + 3$ into (1):

$$2y + x = 0$$
$$2y + (y + 3) = 0$$
$$3y + 3 = 0$$
$$3y = -3$$
$$y = -1$$

Substitute and solve for x:

$x = y + 3$

$x = -1 + 3 = 2$

$\boxed{x = 2, y = -1}$

b. $\begin{cases} (1) \quad 2x + y = -3 \\ (2) \quad x - y = 3 \end{cases}$

Substitute $x = y + 3$ into (1):

$$2x + y = -3$$
$$2(y + 3) + y = -3$$
$$2y + 6 + y = -3$$
$$3y = -9$$
$$y = -3$$

Substitute and solve for x:

$x = y + 3$

$x = -3 + 3 = 0$

$\boxed{x = 0, y = -3}$

c. $\begin{cases} (1) & \dfrac{x+y}{2}+\dfrac{x-y}{3}=1 \\ (2) & y=3x-2 \end{cases}$

Substitute $y = 3x - 2$ into (1):

$$\begin{aligned} \frac{x+3x-2}{2}+\frac{x-(3x-2)}{3} &= 1 \\ \frac{4x-2}{2}+\frac{-2x+2}{3} &= 1 \\ 3(4x-2)+2(-2x+2) &= 6 \\ 12x-6-4x+4 &= 6 \\ 8x &= 8 \\ x &= 1 \end{aligned}$$

Substitute and solve for y:

$$\begin{aligned} y &= 3x-2 \\ y &= 3(1)-2 = 1 \end{aligned}$$

$\boxed{x = 1, y = 1}$

3. **a.**

$$\begin{array}{l} x+5y=\ \ 7 \\ \underline{3x+\ y=-7} \Rightarrow \times\ (-5) \end{array} \quad \begin{array}{r} x+5y=\ 7 \\ \underline{-15x-5y=\ 35} \\ -14x \quad = 42 \\ x \quad = -3 \end{array} \quad \begin{array}{r} x+5y=7 \\ -3+5y=7 \\ 5y=10 \\ y=2 \end{array}$$

Solution: $\boxed{x=-3, y=2}$

b.

$$\begin{array}{l} 2x+3y=\ \ 11 \Rightarrow \times\ (3) \\ \underline{3x-7y=-41} \Rightarrow \times\ (-2) \end{array} \quad \begin{array}{r} 6x+\ 9y=\ 33 \\ \underline{-6x+14y=\ 82} \\ 23y=115 \\ y=\ \ 5 \end{array} \quad \begin{array}{r} 2x+3y=11 \\ 2x+3(5)=11 \\ 2x=-4 \\ x=-2 \end{array}$$

Solution: $\boxed{x=-2, y=5}$

c.

$$\begin{array}{l} 2(x+y)-x=0 \Rightarrow \\ \underline{3(x+y)+2y=1} \Rightarrow \end{array} \begin{array}{l} x+2y=0 \Rightarrow \\ \underline{3x+5y=1} \Rightarrow \end{array} \begin{array}{r} -3x-\ 6y=\ 0 \\ \underline{3x+\ 5y=\ 1} \\ -y=\ 1 \\ y=-1 \end{array} \quad \begin{array}{r} x+2y=0 \\ x+2(-1)=0 \\ x=2 \end{array}$$

Solution: $\boxed{\begin{array}{l} x=2 \\ y=-1 \end{array}}$

4. **a.**

$$\begin{array}{ll} (1) & 3x+2y-z=2 \\ (2) & x+y-z=0 \\ (3) & 2x+3y-z=1 \end{array}$$

Add (1) and $-(2)$:

$$\begin{array}{lr} (1) & 3x+2y-z=2 \\ -(2) & \underline{-x-\ y+z=0} \\ (4) & 2x+\ y \quad =2 \end{array}$$

Add equations (1) and $-(3)$:

$$\begin{array}{lr} (1) & 3x+2y-z=\ \ 2 \\ -(3) & \underline{-2x-3y+z=-1} \\ (5) & x-\ y \quad =\ \ 1 \end{array}$$

Solve the system of two equations and two unknowns formed by equations (4) and (5):

$$\begin{array}{r} 2x+y=2 \\ \underline{x-y=1} \\ 3x \quad =3 \\ x \quad =1 \end{array} \quad \begin{array}{r} 2x+y=2 \\ 2(1)+y=2 \\ y=0 \end{array} \quad \begin{array}{r} x+y-z=0 \\ 1+0-z=0 \\ -z=-1 \\ z=1 \end{array}$$

Solution: $\boxed{x=1, y=0, z=1}$

b.

$$\begin{array}{ll} (1) & 5x - y + z = 3 \\ (2) & 3x + y + 2z = 2 \\ (3) & x + y = 2 \end{array}$$

Add (1) and (2):

$$\begin{array}{lrl} (1) & 5x - y + z &= 3 \\ (2) & 3x + y + 2z &= 2 \\ \hline (4) & 8x \quad + 3z &= 5 \end{array}$$

Add equations (1) and (3):

$$\begin{array}{lrl} (1) & 5x - y + z &= 3 \\ (3) & x + y &= 2 \\ \hline (5) & 6x \quad + z &= 5 \end{array}$$

Solve the system of two equations and two unknowns formed by equations (4) and (5):

$$\begin{array}{rl} 8x + 3z &= 5 \\ 6x + z &= 5 \Rightarrow \times\ (-3) \end{array} \qquad \begin{array}{rl} 8x + 3z &= 5 \\ -18x - 3z &= -15 \\ \hline -10x &= -10 \\ x &= 1 \end{array} \qquad \begin{array}{rl} 6x + z &= 5 \\ 6(1) + z &= 5 \\ z &= -1 \end{array} \qquad \begin{array}{rl} x + y &= 2 \\ 1 + y &= 2 \\ y &= 1 \end{array}$$

Solution: $\boxed{x = 1, y = 1, z = -1}$

c.

$$\begin{array}{ll} (1) & 2x - y + z = 1 \\ (2) & x - y + 2z = 3 \\ (3) & x - y + z = 1 \end{array}$$

Add (1) and −(2):

$$\begin{array}{lrl} (1) & 2x - y + z &= 1 \\ -(2) & -x + y - 2z &= -3 \\ \hline (4) & x \quad - z &= -2 \end{array}$$

Add equations (1) and −(3):

$$\begin{array}{lrl} (1) & 2x - y + z &= 1 \\ -(3) & -x + y - z &= -1 \\ \hline (5) & x &= 0 \end{array}$$

Solve the system of two equations and two unknowns formed by equations (4) and (5):

$$\begin{array}{rl} x - z &= -2 \\ 0 - z &= -2 \\ z &= 2 \end{array} \qquad \begin{array}{rl} x - y + z &= 1 \\ 0 - y + 2 &= 1 \\ -y &= -1 \\ y &= 1 \end{array}$$

Solution: $\boxed{x = 0, y = 1, z = 2}$

5. Let x = cost of fake fur and let y = cost of leather. Then $\begin{cases} (1) & 25x + 15y = 9300 \\ (2) & 10x + 30y = 12600 \end{cases}$

$$\begin{array}{rl} 25x + 15y &= 9300 \Rightarrow \times\ (-2) \\ 10x + 30y &= 12600 \end{array} \qquad \begin{array}{rl} -50x + 30y &= -18600 \\ 10x + 30y &= 12600 \\ \hline -40x &= -6000 \\ x &= 150 \end{array} \qquad \begin{array}{rl} 25x + 15y &= 9300 \\ 25(150) + 15y &= 9300 \\ 15y &= 5550 \\ y &= 370 \end{array}$$

The fake fur coats cost \$150 while the leather coats cost \$370. The cost will be \$10,400.

6. Let x = # adult tickets, y = # senior tickets and z = # children tickets.

$$\begin{array}{ll} (1) & x + y + z = 1800 \\ (2) & 5x + 4y + 2.5z = 7425 \\ (3) & y + z = 900 \end{array}$$

Add −4(1) and (2):

$$\begin{array}{lrl} -4(1) & -4x - 4y - 4z &= -7200 \\ (2) & 5x + 4y + 2.5z &= 7425 \\ \hline (4) & x \quad - 1.5z &= 225 \end{array}$$

Add equations (1) and −(3):

$$\begin{array}{lrl} (1) & x + y + z &= 1800 \\ -(3) & - y - z &= -900 \\ \hline (5) & x &= 900 \end{array}$$

Solve the system of two equations and two unknowns formed by equations (4) and (5):

$$\begin{array}{rl} x - 1.5z &= 225 \\ 900 - 1.5z &= 225 \\ -1.5z &= -675 \\ z &= 450 \end{array} \qquad \begin{array}{rl} y + z &= 900 \\ y + 450 &= 900 \\ y &= 450 \end{array}$$

There were 900 adult tickets, 450 senior tickets, and 450 children's tickets sold.

7. **a.** $\begin{bmatrix} 2 & 5 & | & 7 \\ 3 & -1 & | & 2 \end{bmatrix} \Rightarrow \begin{bmatrix} 1 & -6 & | & -5 \\ 3 & -1 & | & 2 \end{bmatrix} \Rightarrow \begin{bmatrix} 1 & -6 & | & -5 \\ 0 & 17 & | & 17 \end{bmatrix} \Rightarrow \begin{bmatrix} 1 & -6 & | & -5 \\ 0 & 1 & | & 1 \end{bmatrix} \Rightarrow$

$-R_1 + R_2 \Rightarrow R_1 \quad -3R_1 + R_2 \Rightarrow R_2 \quad \frac{1}{17}R_2 \Rightarrow R_2$

$\begin{bmatrix} 1 & 0 & | & 1 \\ 0 & 1 & | & 1 \end{bmatrix}$ Solution: $\boxed{x = 1, y = 1}$

$6R_2 + R_1 \Rightarrow R_1$

b. $\begin{bmatrix} 1 & 3 & -1 & | & 8 \\ 2 & 1 & -2 & | & 11 \\ 1 & -1 & 5 & | & -8 \end{bmatrix} \Rightarrow \begin{bmatrix} 1 & 3 & -1 & | & 8 \\ 0 & -5 & 0 & | & -5 \\ 0 & -4 & 6 & | & -16 \end{bmatrix} \Rightarrow \begin{bmatrix} 1 & 3 & -1 & | & 8 \\ 0 & 1 & 0 & | & 1 \\ 0 & -4 & 6 & | & -16 \end{bmatrix} \Rightarrow$

$-2R_1 + R_2 \Rightarrow R_2 \quad -\frac{1}{5}R_2 \Rightarrow R_2$

$-R_1 + R_3 \Rightarrow R_3$

$\begin{bmatrix} 1 & 0 & -1 & | & 5 \\ 0 & 1 & 0 & | & 1 \\ 0 & 0 & 6 & | & -12 \end{bmatrix} \Rightarrow \begin{bmatrix} 1 & 0 & 0 & | & 3 \\ 0 & 1 & 0 & | & 1 \\ 0 & 0 & 1 & | & -2 \end{bmatrix}$ Solution: $\boxed{x = 3, y = 1, z = -2}$

$-3R_2 + R_1 \Rightarrow R_1 \quad \frac{1}{6}R_3 + R_1 \Rightarrow R_1$

$4R_2 + R_3 \Rightarrow R_3 \quad \frac{1}{6}R_3 \Rightarrow R_3$

c. $\begin{bmatrix} 1 & 3 & 1 & | & 3 \\ 2 & -1 & 1 & | & -11 \\ 3 & 2 & 3 & | & 2 \end{bmatrix} \Rightarrow \begin{bmatrix} 1 & 3 & 1 & | & 3 \\ 0 & -7 & -1 & | & -17 \\ 0 & -7 & 0 & | & -7 \end{bmatrix} \Rightarrow \begin{bmatrix} 1 & 3 & 1 & | & 3 \\ 0 & 1 & 0 & | & 1 \\ 0 & -7 & -1 & | & -17 \end{bmatrix} \Rightarrow$

$-2R_1 + R_2 \Rightarrow R_2 \quad R_2 \Leftrightarrow -\frac{1}{7}R_3$

$-3R_1 + R_3 \Rightarrow R_3$

$\begin{bmatrix} 1 & 0 & 1 & | & 0 \\ 0 & 1 & 0 & | & 1 \\ 0 & 0 & -1 & | & -10 \end{bmatrix} \Rightarrow \begin{bmatrix} 1 & 0 & 0 & | & -10 \\ 0 & 1 & 0 & | & 1 \\ 0 & 0 & 1 & | & 10 \end{bmatrix}$ Solution: $\boxed{x = -10, y = 1, z = 10}$

$-3R_2 + R_1 \Rightarrow R_1 \quad R_3 + R_1 \Rightarrow R_1$

$7R_2 + R_3 \Rightarrow R_3 \quad -R_3 \Rightarrow R_3$

d. $\begin{bmatrix} 1 & 1 & 1 & | & 4 \\ 3 & -2 & -2 & | & -3 \\ 4 & -1 & -1 & | & 0 \end{bmatrix} \Rightarrow \begin{bmatrix} 1 & 1 & 1 & | & 4 \\ 0 & -5 & -5 & | & -15 \\ 0 & -5 & -5 & | & -16 \end{bmatrix} \Rightarrow \begin{bmatrix} 1 & 1 & 1 & | & 4 \\ 0 & -5 & -5 & | & -15 \\ 0 & 0 & 0 & | & -1 \end{bmatrix}$

$-3R_1 + R_2 \Rightarrow R_2 \quad -R_2 + R_3 \Rightarrow R_3$

$-4R_1 + R_3 \Rightarrow R_3$

The last row indicates $0x + 0y + 0z = -1$. This is impossible. $\Rightarrow$ no solution

8. $-4 = x, x = -4, 0 = x + 4, x + 7 = y \Rightarrow \boxed{x = -4, y = 3}$

9. **a.** $\begin{bmatrix} 3 & 2 & 1 \\ 3 & 2 & 1 \end{bmatrix} + \begin{bmatrix} -2 & 1 & 3 \\ 1 & -2 & 1 \end{bmatrix} = \begin{bmatrix} 1 & 3 & 4 \\ 4 & 0 & 2 \end{bmatrix}$

b. $\begin{bmatrix} 2 & 3 & 5 \\ 1 & -2 & 4 \\ 2 & 1 & -2 \end{bmatrix} - \begin{bmatrix} 0 & -2 & 1 \\ 3 & 4 & -2 \\ 6 & -4 & 1 \end{bmatrix} = \begin{bmatrix} 2 & 5 & 4 \\ -2 & -6 & 6 \\ -4 & 5 & -3 \end{bmatrix}$

c. $\begin{bmatrix} 1 & -2 \\ -3 & 1 \end{bmatrix}\begin{bmatrix} 2 & 3 \\ -1 & 2 \end{bmatrix} = \begin{bmatrix} 4 & -1 \\ -7 & -7 \end{bmatrix}$

d. $\begin{bmatrix} -2 & 3 & 5 \\ 1 & -2 & -3 \end{bmatrix}\begin{bmatrix} 2 & 1 \\ -1 & 2 \\ -2 & 3 \end{bmatrix} = \begin{bmatrix} -17 & 19 \\ 10 & -12 \end{bmatrix}$

e. $[1 \quad -3 \quad 2]\begin{bmatrix} 2 \\ 1 \\ 3 \end{bmatrix} = [5]$

f. $\begin{bmatrix} 1 \\ 2 \\ 1 \\ 5 \end{bmatrix}[2 \quad -1 \quad 1 \quad 3] = \begin{bmatrix} 2 & -1 & 1 & 3 \\ 4 & -2 & 2 & 6 \\ 2 & -1 & 1 & 3 \\ 10 & -5 & 5 & 15 \end{bmatrix}$

g. $\begin{bmatrix} 1 & -5 & 3 \\ 2 & 1 & -1 \end{bmatrix}\begin{bmatrix} 2 \\ -2 \\ 3 \end{bmatrix}\begin{bmatrix} 1 & -1 \\ -1 & 3 \end{bmatrix}\begin{bmatrix} 1 \\ -2 \end{bmatrix} = \begin{bmatrix} 21 \\ -1 \end{bmatrix}\begin{bmatrix} 1 & -1 \\ -1 & 3 \end{bmatrix}\begin{bmatrix} 1 \\ -2 \end{bmatrix} \Rightarrow$ undefined

h. $[1 \quad -3 \quad 2]\begin{bmatrix} 2 \\ 1 \\ -5 \end{bmatrix} + [1 \quad -3]\begin{bmatrix} 2 \\ 5 \end{bmatrix} = [-11] + [-13] = [-24]$

i. $\left(\begin{bmatrix} 1 & -3 \\ 3 & 1 \end{bmatrix} + \begin{bmatrix} -1 & 3 \\ 1 & 1 \end{bmatrix}\right)\begin{bmatrix} 1 \\ -5 \end{bmatrix} = \begin{bmatrix} 0 & 0 \\ 4 & 2 \end{bmatrix}\begin{bmatrix} 1 \\ -5 \end{bmatrix} = \begin{bmatrix} 0 \\ -6 \end{bmatrix}$

10. a. $\left[\begin{array}{cc|cc} 2 & 3 & 1 & 0 \\ 3 & 5 & 0 & 1 \end{array}\right] \Rightarrow \underset{\frac{1}{2}R_1 \Rightarrow R_1}{\left[\begin{array}{cc|cc} 1 & \frac{3}{2} & \frac{1}{2} & 0 \\ 3 & 5 & 0 & 1 \end{array}\right]} \Rightarrow \underset{-3R_1 + R_2 \Rightarrow R_2}{\left[\begin{array}{cc|cc} 1 & \frac{3}{2} & \frac{1}{2} & 0 \\ 0 & \frac{1}{2} & -\frac{3}{2} & 1 \end{array}\right]} \Rightarrow$

$\underset{-3R_2 + R_1 \Rightarrow R_1}{\left[\begin{array}{cc|cc} 1 & 0 & 5 & -3 \\ 0 & \frac{1}{2} & -\frac{3}{2} & 1 \end{array}\right]} \Rightarrow \underset{2R_2 \Rightarrow R_2}{\left[\begin{array}{cc|cc} 1 & 0 & 5 & -3 \\ 0 & 1 & -3 & 2 \end{array}\right]} \Rightarrow$ Inverse: $\begin{bmatrix} 5 & -3 \\ -3 & 2 \end{bmatrix}$

b. $\left[\begin{array}{ccc|ccc} 1 & 0 & 0 & 1 & 0 & 0 \\ 2 & 0 & -2 & 0 & 1 & 0 \\ 1 & 2 & 2 & 0 & 0 & 1 \end{array}\right] \Rightarrow \underset{R_2 \Leftrightarrow R_3}{\left[\begin{array}{ccc|ccc} 1 & 0 & 0 & 1 & 0 & 0 \\ 1 & 2 & 2 & 0 & 0 & 1 \\ 2 & 0 & -2 & 0 & 1 & 0 \end{array}\right]} \Rightarrow \underset{\substack{-R_1 + R_2 \Rightarrow R_2 \\ -2R_1 + R_3 \Rightarrow R_3}}{\left[\begin{array}{ccc|ccc} 1 & 0 & 0 & 1 & 0 & 0 \\ 0 & 2 & 2 & -1 & 0 & 1 \\ 0 & 0 & -2 & -2 & 1 & 0 \end{array}\right]} \Rightarrow$

$\underset{R_2 + R_3 \Rightarrow R_3}{\left[\begin{array}{ccc|ccc} 1 & 0 & 0 & 1 & 0 & 0 \\ 0 & 2 & 0 & -3 & 1 & 1 \\ 0 & 0 & -2 & -2 & 1 & 0 \end{array}\right]} \Rightarrow \underset{\substack{\frac{1}{2}R_2 \Rightarrow R_2 \\ -\frac{1}{2}R_3 \Rightarrow R_3}}{\left[\begin{array}{ccc|ccc} 1 & 0 & 0 & 1 & 0 & 0 \\ 0 & 1 & 0 & -\frac{3}{2} & \frac{1}{2} & \frac{1}{2} \\ 0 & 0 & 1 & 1 & -\frac{1}{2} & 0 \end{array}\right]}$: Inverse $= \begin{bmatrix} 1 & 0 & 0 \\ -\frac{3}{2} & \frac{1}{2} & \frac{1}{2} \\ 1 & -\frac{1}{2} & 0 \end{bmatrix}$

c. $\left[\begin{array}{ccc|ccc}1&0&8&1&0&0\\3&7&6&0&1&0\\1&2&3&0&0&1\end{array}\right] \Rightarrow \left[\begin{array}{ccc|ccc}1&0&8&1&0&0\\0&7&-18&-3&1&0\\0&2&-5&-1&0&1\end{array}\right] \Rightarrow$

$$-3R_1 + R_2 \Rightarrow R_2$$
$$-R_1 + R_3 \Rightarrow R_3$$

$\left[\begin{array}{ccc|ccc}1&0&8&1&0&0\\0&1&-\frac{18}{7}&-\frac{3}{7}&\frac{1}{7}&0\\0&2&-5&-1&0&1\end{array}\right] \Rightarrow \left[\begin{array}{ccc|ccc}1&0&8&1&0&0\\0&1&-\frac{18}{7}&-\frac{3}{7}&\frac{1}{7}&0\\0&0&\frac{1}{7}&-\frac{1}{7}&-\frac{2}{7}&1\end{array}\right] \Rightarrow$

$\frac{1}{7}R_2 \Rightarrow R_2$ $\qquad -2R_2 + R_3 \Rightarrow R_3$

$\left[\begin{array}{ccc|ccc}1&0&0&9&16&-56\\0&1&0&-3&-5&18\\0&0&1&-1&-2&7\end{array}\right] \Rightarrow$ Inverse $= \begin{bmatrix}9&16&-56\\-3&-5&18\\-1&-2&7\end{bmatrix}$

$$-56R_3 + R_1 \Rightarrow R_1$$
$$18R_3 + R_2 \Rightarrow R_2$$
$$7R_3 \Rightarrow R_3$$

d. $\left[\begin{array}{ccc|ccc}4&4&1&1&0&0\\1&1&1&0&1&0\\-1&-1&0&0&0&1\end{array}\right] \Rightarrow \left[\begin{array}{ccc|ccc}1&1&1&0&1&0\\4&4&1&1&0&0\\-1&-1&0&0&0&1\end{array}\right] \Rightarrow$

$$R_1 \Leftrightarrow R_2$$

$\left[\begin{array}{ccc|ccc}1&1&1&0&1&0\\0&0&-3&1&-4&0\\0&0&1&0&1&1\end{array}\right] \Rightarrow \left[\begin{array}{ccc|ccc}1&1&1&0&1&0\\0&0&0&1&-1&3\\0&0&1&0&1&1\end{array}\right]$: No inverse

$-4R_1 + R_2 \Rightarrow R_2$ $\qquad 3R_3 + R_2 \Rightarrow R_2$

$R_1 + R_3 \Rightarrow R_3$

11. a. $\begin{bmatrix}4&-1&2\\1&1&2\\1&0&1\end{bmatrix}\begin{bmatrix}x\\y\\z\end{bmatrix} = \begin{bmatrix}0\\1\\0\end{bmatrix}$

$$\begin{bmatrix}x\\y\\z\end{bmatrix} = \begin{bmatrix}4&-1&2\\1&1&2\\1&0&1\end{bmatrix}^{-1}\begin{bmatrix}0\\1\\0\end{bmatrix}$$

$$\begin{bmatrix}x\\y\\z\end{bmatrix} = \begin{bmatrix}1&1&-4\\1&2&-6\\-1&-1&5\end{bmatrix}\begin{bmatrix}0\\1\\0\end{bmatrix} = \begin{bmatrix}1\\2\\-1\end{bmatrix}$$

b. $$\begin{bmatrix}1&3&1&3\\1&4&1&3\\0&1&1&0\\1&2&-1&2\end{bmatrix}\begin{bmatrix}w\\x\\y\\z\end{bmatrix}=\begin{bmatrix}1\\2\\1\\1\end{bmatrix}$$

$$\begin{bmatrix}w\\x\\y\\z\end{bmatrix}=\begin{bmatrix}1&3&1&3\\1&4&1&3\\0&1&1&0\\1&2&-1&2\end{bmatrix}^{-1}\begin{bmatrix}1\\2\\1\\1\end{bmatrix}$$

$$\begin{bmatrix}w\\x\\y\\z\end{bmatrix}=\begin{bmatrix}3&-5&5&3\\-1&1&0&0\\1&-1&1&0\\0&1&-2&-1\end{bmatrix}\begin{bmatrix}1\\2\\1\\1\end{bmatrix}=\begin{bmatrix}1\\1\\0\\-1\end{bmatrix}$$

12 a. $$\begin{vmatrix}3&-2\\1&-3\end{vmatrix}=(3)(-3)-(-2)(1)=-9+2=-7$$

b. $$\begin{vmatrix}1&-2&3\\2&-1&3\\1&-1&0\end{vmatrix}=1\begin{vmatrix}-1&3\\-1&0\end{vmatrix}-(-2)\begin{vmatrix}2&3\\1&0\end{vmatrix}+3\begin{vmatrix}2&-1\\1&-1\end{vmatrix}$$
$$=1(3)+2(-3)+3(-1)=3-6-3=-6$$

c. $$\begin{vmatrix}1&3&-1\\1&2&1\\1&0&2\end{vmatrix}=1\begin{vmatrix}2&1\\0&2\end{vmatrix}-3\begin{vmatrix}1&1\\1&2\end{vmatrix}+(-1)\begin{vmatrix}1&2\\1&0\end{vmatrix}$$
$$=1(4)-3(1)-1(-2)=4-3+2=3$$

d. Expand along 3rd row...

$$\begin{vmatrix}1&2&3&4\\-1&3&-3&2\\0&0&0&-1\\3&3&4&3\end{vmatrix}=0(***)-0(***)+0(***)-(-1)\begin{vmatrix}1&2&3\\-1&3&-3\\3&3&4\end{vmatrix}$$
$$=1\left(1\begin{vmatrix}3&-3\\3&4\end{vmatrix}-2\begin{vmatrix}-1&-3\\3&4\end{vmatrix}+3\begin{vmatrix}-1&3\\3&3\end{vmatrix}\right)$$
$$=1(21)-2(5)+3(-12)=-25$$

13. a. $$x=\frac{\begin{vmatrix}-5&3\\-4&1\end{vmatrix}}{\begin{vmatrix}1&3\\-2&1\end{vmatrix}}=\frac{7}{7}=1\quad y=\frac{\begin{vmatrix}1&-5\\-2&-4\end{vmatrix}}{\begin{vmatrix}1&3\\-2&1\end{vmatrix}}=\frac{-14}{7}=-2$$

b. $$x = \frac{\begin{vmatrix} -1 & -1 & 1 \\ -4 & -1 & 3 \\ -1 & -3 & 1 \end{vmatrix}}{\begin{vmatrix} 1 & -1 & 1 \\ 2 & -1 & 3 \\ 1 & -3 & 1 \end{vmatrix}} = \frac{2}{2} = 1 \qquad y = \frac{\begin{vmatrix} 1 & -1 & 1 \\ 2 & -4 & 3 \\ 1 & -1 & 1 \end{vmatrix}}{\begin{vmatrix} 1 & -1 & 1 \\ 2 & -1 & 3 \\ 1 & -3 & 1 \end{vmatrix}} = \frac{0}{2} = 0$$

$$z = \frac{\begin{vmatrix} 1 & -1 & -1 \\ 2 & -1 & -4 \\ 1 & -3 & -1 \end{vmatrix}}{\begin{vmatrix} 1 & -1 & 1 \\ 2 & -1 & 3 \\ 1 & -3 & 1 \end{vmatrix}} = \frac{-4}{2} = -2$$

c. $$x = \frac{\begin{vmatrix} 7 & -3 & 1 \\ -9 & 1 & -3 \\ 3 & 1 & 1 \end{vmatrix}}{\begin{vmatrix} 1 & -3 & 1 \\ 1 & 1 & -3 \\ 1 & 1 & 1 \end{vmatrix}} = \frac{16}{16} = 1 \qquad y = \frac{\begin{vmatrix} 1 & 7 & 1 \\ 1 & -9 & -3 \\ 1 & 3 & 1 \end{vmatrix}}{\begin{vmatrix} 1 & -3 & 1 \\ 1 & 1 & -3 \\ 1 & 1 & 1 \end{vmatrix}} = \frac{-16}{16} = -1$$

$$z = \frac{\begin{vmatrix} 1 & -3 & 7 \\ 1 & 1 & -9 \\ 1 & 1 & 3 \end{vmatrix}}{\begin{vmatrix} 1 & -3 & 1 \\ 1 & 1 & -3 \\ 1 & 1 & 1 \end{vmatrix}} = \frac{48}{16} = 3$$

d. $$w = \frac{\begin{vmatrix} 4 & 1 & -1 & 1 \\ 4 & 1 & 0 & 1 \\ 0 & 1 & 2 & 1 \\ 2 & 0 & 1 & 1 \end{vmatrix}}{\begin{vmatrix} 1 & 1 & -1 & 1 \\ 2 & 1 & 0 & 1 \\ 0 & 1 & 2 & 1 \\ 1 & 0 & 1 & 1 \end{vmatrix}} = \frac{-4}{-4} = 1 \qquad x = \frac{\begin{vmatrix} 1 & 4 & -1 & 1 \\ 2 & 4 & 0 & 1 \\ 0 & 0 & 2 & 1 \\ 1 & 2 & 1 & 1 \end{vmatrix}}{\begin{vmatrix} 1 & 1 & -1 & 1 \\ 2 & 1 & 0 & 1 \\ 0 & 1 & 2 & 1 \\ 1 & 0 & 1 & 1 \end{vmatrix}} = \frac{0}{-4} = 0$$

$$y = \frac{\begin{vmatrix} 1 & 1 & 4 & 1 \\ 2 & 1 & 4 & 1 \\ 0 & 1 & 0 & 1 \\ 1 & 0 & 2 & 1 \end{vmatrix}}{\begin{vmatrix} 1 & 1 & -1 & 1 \\ 2 & 1 & 0 & 1 \\ 0 & 1 & 2 & 1 \\ 1 & 0 & 1 & 1 \end{vmatrix}} = \frac{4}{-4} = -1 \qquad z = \frac{\begin{vmatrix} 1 & 1 & -1 & 4 \\ 2 & 1 & 0 & 4 \\ 0 & 1 & 2 & 0 \\ 1 & 0 & 1 & 2 \end{vmatrix}}{\begin{vmatrix} 1 & 1 & -1 & 1 \\ 2 & 1 & 0 & 1 \\ 0 & 1 & 2 & 1 \\ 1 & 0 & 1 & 1 \end{vmatrix}} = \frac{-8}{-4} = 2$$

14. a. $\begin{vmatrix} 3a & 3b & 3c \\ d & e & f \\ g & h & i \end{vmatrix} = 3\begin{vmatrix} a & b & c \\ d & e & f \\ g & h & i \end{vmatrix} = 21$

b. $\begin{vmatrix} a & b & c \\ d+g & e+h & f+i \\ g & h & i \end{vmatrix} = 7$

15. a.
$$\begin{aligned}\frac{7x+3}{x(x+1)} &= \frac{A}{x} + \frac{B}{x+1} \\ &= \frac{A(x+1)}{x(x+1)} + \frac{Bx}{x(x+1)} \\ &= \frac{Ax + A + Bx}{x(x+1)} \\ &= \frac{(A+B)x + A}{x(x+1)}\end{aligned}$$

$$\begin{cases} A + B = 7 \\ A \qquad = 3 \end{cases} \Rightarrow \begin{matrix} A = 3 \\ B = 4 \end{matrix} \quad \frac{7x+3}{x(x+1)} = \frac{3}{x} + \frac{4}{x+1}$$

b.
$$\begin{aligned}\frac{4x^3 + x^2 + 3x + 2}{x^2(x^2+1)} &= \frac{A}{x} + \frac{B}{x^2} + \frac{Cx+D}{x^2+1} \\ &= \frac{Ax(x^2+1)}{x^2(x^2+1)} + \frac{B(x^2+1)}{x^2(x^2+1)} + \frac{(Cx+D)x^2}{x^2(x^2+1)} \\ &= \frac{Ax^3 + Ax + Bx^2 + B + Cx^3 + Dx^2}{x^2(x^2+1)} \\ &= \frac{(A+C)x^3 + (B+D)x^2 + Ax + B}{x^2(x^2+1)}\end{aligned}$$

$$\begin{cases} A \quad + C \quad = 4 \\ \quad B \quad + D = 1 \\ A \qquad\quad = 3 \\ \quad B \qquad = 2 \end{cases} \Rightarrow \begin{matrix} A = 3 \\ B = 2 \\ C = 1 \\ D = -1 \end{matrix} \quad \frac{4x^3 + x^2 + 3x + 2}{x^2(x^2+1)} = \frac{3}{x} + \frac{2}{x^2} + \frac{x-1}{x^2+1}$$

c.
$$\begin{aligned}\frac{x^2+5}{x(x^2+x+5)} &= \frac{A}{x} + \frac{Bx+C}{x^2+x+5} \\ &= \frac{A(x^2+x+5)}{x(x^2+x+5)} + \frac{(Bx+C)x}{x(x^2+x+5)} \\ &= \frac{Ax^2 + Ax + 5A + Bx^2 + Cx}{x(x^2+x+5)} \\ &= \frac{(A+B)x^2 + (A+C)x + (5A)}{x(x^2+x+5)}\end{aligned}$$

$$\begin{cases} A + B \qquad = 1 \\ A \qquad + C = 0 \\ 5A \qquad\quad = 5 \end{cases} \Rightarrow \begin{matrix} A = 1 \\ B = 0 \\ C = -1 \end{matrix} \quad \frac{x^2+5}{x(x^2+x+5)} = \frac{1}{x} - \frac{1}{x^2+x+5}$$

d.

$$\begin{aligned}\frac{x^2+1}{(x+1)^3} &= \frac{A}{x+1}+\frac{B}{(x+1)^2}+\frac{C}{(x+1)^3}\\ &= \frac{A(x+1)^2}{(x+1)^3}+\frac{B(x+1)}{(x+1)^3}+\frac{C}{(x+1)^3}\\ &= \frac{Ax^2+2Ax+A+Bx+B+C}{(x+1)^3}\\ &= \frac{Ax^2+(2A+B)x+(A+B+C)}{(x+1)^3}\end{aligned}$$

$$\begin{cases} A = 1 \\ 2A+B = 0 \\ A+B+C = 1\end{cases} \Rightarrow \begin{matrix} A=1 \\ B=-2 \\ C=2\end{matrix} \qquad \frac{x^2+1}{(x+1)^3} = \frac{1}{x+1}-\frac{2}{(x+1)^2}+\frac{2}{(x+1)^3}$$

16. a. $\begin{cases} 3x+2y \le 6 \\ x-y > 3\end{cases}$

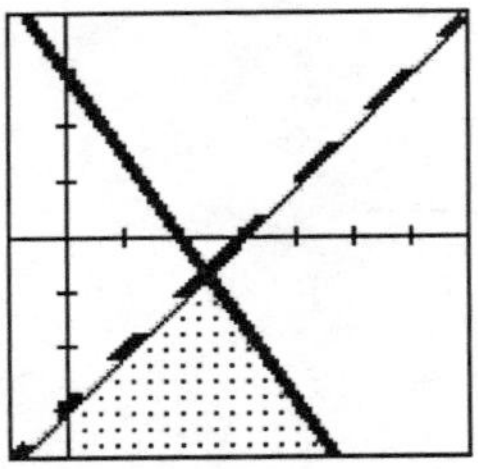

b. $\begin{cases} y \le x^2+1 \\ y \ge x^2-1\end{cases}$

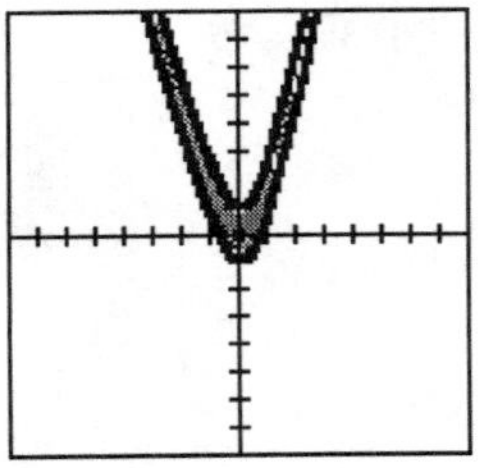

17. a.

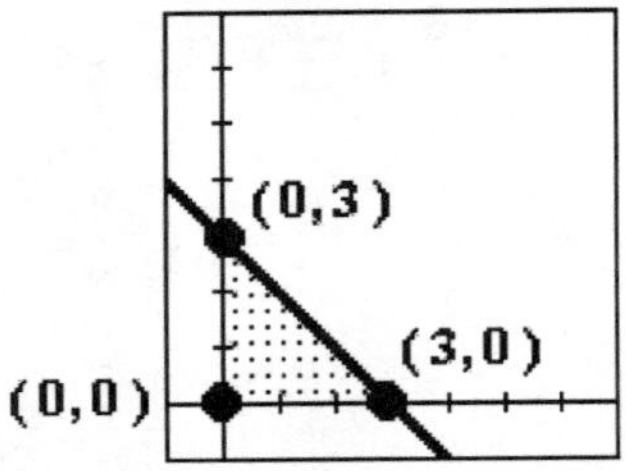

Point	$P = 2x + y$
(0, 0)	$= 2(0) + 0 = 0$
(0, 3)	$= 2(0) + 3 = 3$
(3, 0)	$= 2(3) + 0 = 6$

Max: $P = 6$ at (3, 0)

b.

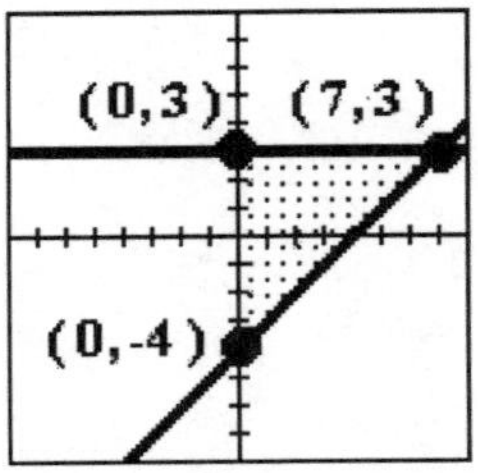

Point	$P = 2x - 3y$
(0, 3)	$= 2(0) - 3(3) = -9$
(7, 3)	$= 2(7) - 3(3) = 5$
(0, −4)	$= 2(0) - 3(-4) = 12$

Max: $P = 12$ at (0, −4)

c.

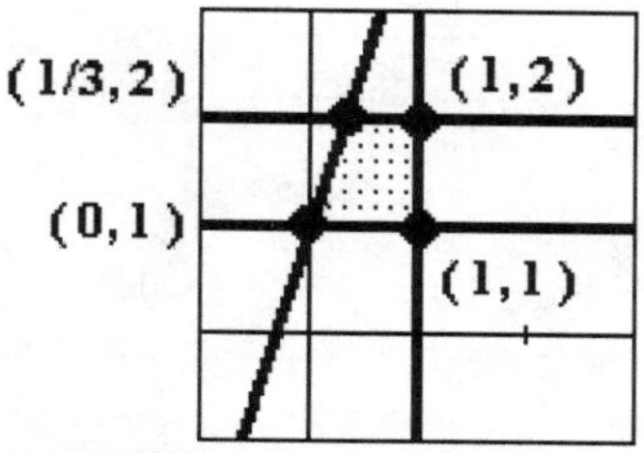

Point	$P = 3x - y$
$(0, 1)$	$= 3(0) - 1 = -1$
$(1, 1)$	$= 3(1) - 1 = 2$
$(1, 2)$	$= 3(1) - 2 = 1$
$(\frac{1}{3}, 2)$	$= 3(\frac{1}{3}) - 2 = -1$

Max: $P = 2$ at $(1, 1)$

d.

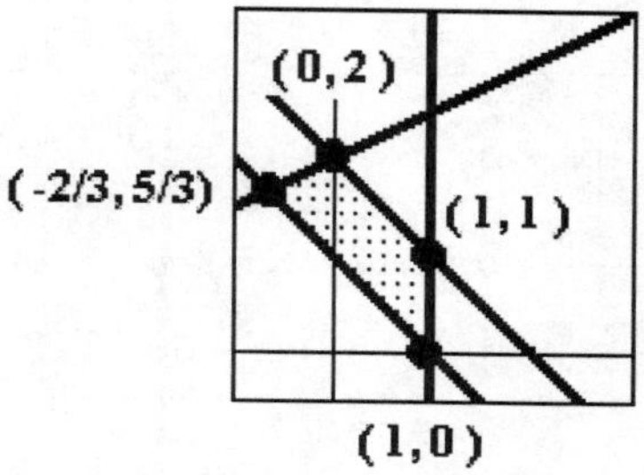

Point	$P = y - 2x$
$(0, 2)$	$= 2 - 2(0) = 2$
$(1, 1)$	$= 1 - 2(1) = -1$
$(1, 0)$	$= 0 - 2(1) = -2$
$(-\frac{2}{3}, \frac{5}{3})$	$= \frac{5}{3} - 2(-\frac{2}{3}) = 3$

Max: $P = 3$ at $\left(-\frac{2}{3}, \frac{5}{3}\right)$

18. Let $x =$ bags of Fertilizer x and $y =$ bags of Fertilizer y.
Maximize $P = 6x + 5y$

subject to $\begin{cases} 6x + 10y \le 20000 \\ 8x + 6y \le 16400 \\ 6x + 4y \le 12000 \\ x \ge 0, y \ge 0 \end{cases}$

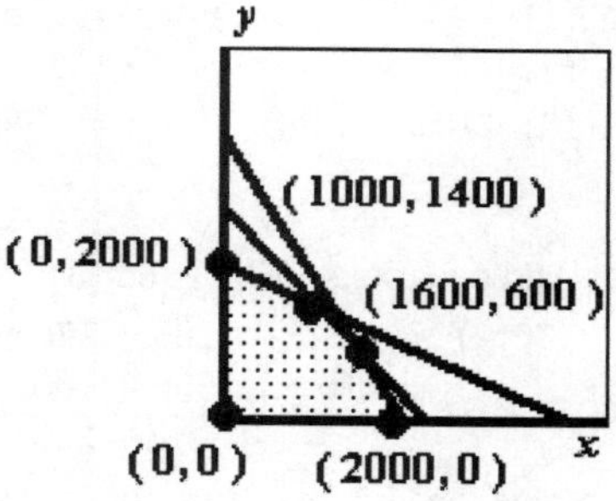

Point	$P = 6x + 5y$
$(0, 0)$	$= 0$
$(0, 2000)$	$= 10000$
$(1000, 1400)$	$= 13000$
$(1600, 600)$	$= 6(1600) + 5(600) = 12600$
$(2000, 0)$	$= 6(2000) + 5(0) = 12000$

1000 bags of x and 1400 bags of y should be made, for a maximum profit of \$12,600.

Chapter 6 Test (page 510)

1. $\begin{cases} x - 3y = -5 \\ 2x - y = 0 \end{cases}$

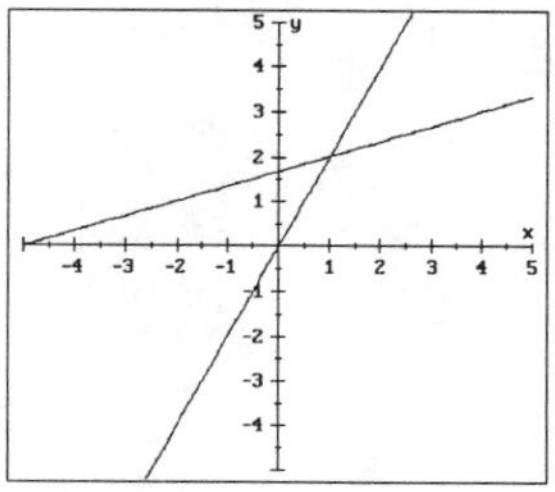

solution: $(1, 2)$

2. $\begin{cases} x = 2y + 5 \\ y = 2x - 4 \end{cases}$

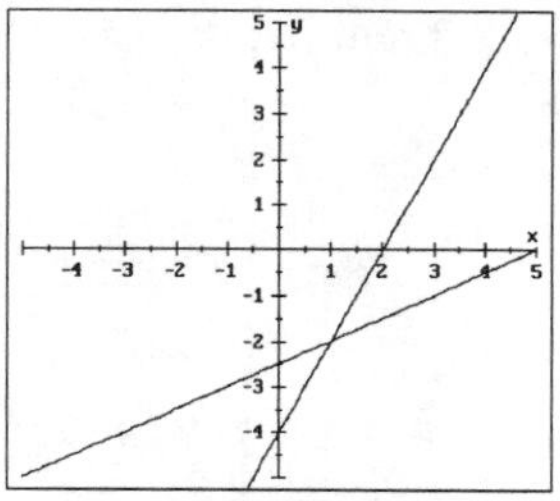

solution: $(1, -2)$

3. $$\begin{array}{l} 3x+\ y=\ 0 \Rightarrow \times\ (5)\\ \underline{2x-5y=17} \end{array} \quad \begin{array}{rl} 15x+5y= & 0\\ \underline{2x-5y=} & \underline{17}\\ 17x \quad = & 17\\ x \quad = & 1 \end{array} \quad \begin{array}{r} 3x+y=0\\ 3(1)+y=0\\ y=-3 \end{array}$$

Solution: $\boxed{x=1,\ y=-3}$

4. $$\begin{array}{l} \dfrac{x+y}{2}+x=\ 7 \Rightarrow 3x+y=\ 14 \Rightarrow\ 3x+\ \ y=14\\ \underline{\dfrac{x-y}{2}-y=-6} \Rightarrow \underline{x-3y=-12} \Rightarrow \underline{-3x+\ 9y=36}\\ \qquad\qquad\qquad\qquad\qquad\qquad\qquad 10y=50\\ \qquad\qquad\qquad\qquad\qquad\qquad\qquad\quad y=\ 5 \end{array} \quad \begin{array}{r} x-3y=-12\\ x-3(5)=-12\\ x=3 \end{array}$$

Solution: $\boxed{\begin{array}{c} x=3\\ y=5 \end{array}}$

5. Let x = liters of 20% solution and y = liters of 45% solution. The following system applies:

$$\begin{array}{l} x+\quad\ y=10 \Rightarrow \times\ (-2)\\ \underline{0.2x+0.45y=\ 3} \Rightarrow \times\ (10) \end{array} \quad \begin{array}{rl} -2x-\quad 2y= & -20\\ \underline{2x+4.5y=} & \underline{30}\\ 2.5y= & 10\\ y= & 4 \end{array}$$

She must use 4 liters of the 45% and 6 liters of the 20% solution.

6. Let x = # from Ace, y = # from Hi-Fi and z = # from CD World.

$$\begin{array}{ll} (1) & x+y+z=175\\ (2) & -x-y+z=25\\ (3) & 170x+165y+160z=28500 \end{array}$$

Add (1) and (2):

$$\begin{array}{lr} (1) & x+y+\ z=175\\ (2) & \underline{-x-y+\ z=\ \ 25}\\ (4) & 2z=200\\ & z=100 \end{array}$$

Add equations 170(2) and (3):

$$\begin{array}{lr} 170(2) & -170x-170y+170z=\ \ 4250\\ (3) & \underline{170x+165y+160z=28500}\\ (5) & -\quad 5y+330z=32750 \end{array}$$

Solve the system of two equations and two unknowns formed by equations (4) and (5):

$$\begin{array}{r} -5y+330z=32750\\ -5y+330(100)=32750\\ -5y=-250\\ y=50 \end{array} \quad \begin{array}{r} x+y+z=175\\ x+50+100=175\\ y=25 \end{array}$$

Ace buys 25 players per month. Hi-Fi buys 50 players per month. CD World buys 100 players per month.

7. $$\left[\begin{array}{cc|c} 3 & -2 & 4\\ 2 & 3 & 7 \end{array}\right] \Rightarrow \underset{-R_2+R_1 \Rightarrow R_1}{\left[\begin{array}{cc|c} 1 & -5 & -3\\ 2 & 3 & 7 \end{array}\right]} \Rightarrow \underset{-2R_1+R_2 \Rightarrow R_2}{\left[\begin{array}{cc|c} 1 & -5 & -3\\ 0 & 13 & 13 \end{array}\right]} \Rightarrow \underset{\frac{1}{13}R_2 \Rightarrow R_2}{\left[\begin{array}{cc|c} 1 & -5 & -3\\ 0 & 1 & 1 \end{array}\right]}$$

From R_2: $y=1$ From R_1: $$\begin{array}{r} x-5y=-3\\ x-5(1)=-3\\ x=2 \end{array}$$

Solution: $\boxed{x=2,\ y=1}$

8. $\left[\begin{array}{ccc|c} 1 & 3 & -1 & 6 \\ 2 & -1 & -2 & -2 \\ 1 & 2 & 1 & 6 \end{array}\right] \Rightarrow \left[\begin{array}{ccc|c} 1 & 3 & -1 & 6 \\ 0 & -7 & 0 & -14 \\ 0 & 1 & -2 & 0 \end{array}\right] \Rightarrow \left[\begin{array}{ccc|c} 1 & 3 & -1 & 6 \\ 0 & 1 & 0 & 2 \\ 0 & 0 & -14 & -14 \end{array}\right] \Rightarrow$

$-2R_1 + R_2 \Rightarrow R_2$ $\quad -\frac{1}{7}R_2 \Rightarrow R_2$

$-R_3 + R_1 \Rightarrow R_3$ $\quad 7R_3 + R_2 \Rightarrow R_3$

$\left[\begin{array}{ccc|c} 1 & 3 & -1 & 6 \\ 0 & 1 & 0 & 2 \\ 0 & 0 & 1 & 1 \end{array}\right]$ From (3): $z = 1$ From (1): $x + 3y - z = 6$

$-\frac{1}{14}R_3 \Rightarrow R_3$ From (2): $y = 2$ $\quad x + 3(2) - (1) = 6$

$x = 1$

Solution: $\boxed{x = 1, y = 2, z = 1}$

9. $\left[\begin{array}{ccc|c} 1 & 2 & 3 & -5 \\ 3 & 1 & -2 & 7 \\ 0 & 1 & -1 & 2 \end{array}\right] \Rightarrow \left[\begin{array}{ccc|c} 1 & 2 & 3 & -5 \\ 0 & -5 & -11 & 22 \\ 0 & 1 & -1 & 2 \end{array}\right] \Rightarrow \left[\begin{array}{ccc|c} 1 & 2 & 3 & -5 \\ 0 & 1 & -1 & 2 \\ 0 & -5 & -11 & 22 \end{array}\right] \Rightarrow$

$-3R_1 + R_2 \Rightarrow R_2$ $\quad R_2 \Leftrightarrow R_3$

$\left[\begin{array}{ccc|c} 1 & 0 & 5 & -9 \\ 0 & 1 & -1 & 2 \\ 0 & 0 & -16 & 32 \end{array}\right] \Rightarrow \left[\begin{array}{ccc|c} 1 & 0 & 5 & -9 \\ 0 & 1 & -1 & 2 \\ 0 & 0 & 1 & -2 \end{array}\right] \Rightarrow \left[\begin{array}{ccc|c} 1 & 0 & 0 & 1 \\ 0 & 1 & 0 & 0 \\ 0 & 0 & 1 & -2 \end{array}\right]$ Solution: $\boxed{\begin{array}{l} x = 1 \\ y = 0 \\ z = -2 \end{array}}$

$-2R_2 + R_1 \Rightarrow R_1$ $\quad -\frac{1}{16}R_3 \Rightarrow R_3$ $\quad -5R_3 + R_1 \Rightarrow R_1$

$5R_2 + R_3 \Rightarrow R_3$ $\quad R_2 + R_3 \Rightarrow R_2$

10. $\left[\begin{array}{ccc|c} 1 & 2 & 1 & 0 \\ 3 & -2 & -2 & 7 \\ 4 & 0 & -1 & 7 \end{array}\right] \Rightarrow \left[\begin{array}{ccc|c} 1 & 2 & 1 & 0 \\ 0 & -8 & -5 & 7 \\ 0 & -8 & -5 & 7 \end{array}\right] \Rightarrow \left[\begin{array}{ccc|c} 1 & 2 & 1 & 0 \\ 0 & 1 & \frac{5}{8} & -\frac{7}{8} \\ 0 & 0 & 0 & 0 \end{array}\right] \Rightarrow$

$-3R_1 + R_2 \Rightarrow R_2$ $\quad -R_2 + R_3 \Rightarrow R_3$

$-4R_1 + R_3 \Rightarrow R_3$ $\quad -\frac{1}{8}R_2 \Rightarrow R_2$

$\left[\begin{array}{ccc|c} 1 & 0 & -\frac{1}{4} & \frac{7}{4} \\ 0 & 1 & \frac{5}{8} & -\frac{7}{8} \\ 0 & 0 & 0 & 0 \end{array}\right] \Rightarrow$ Solution: $\boxed{\begin{array}{l} x = \frac{7}{4} + \frac{1}{4}z \\ y = -\frac{7}{8} - \frac{5}{8}z \\ z = \text{any real number} \end{array}}$ Note: This answer is equivalent to the answer provided in the textbook.

$-2R_2 + R_1 \Rightarrow R_1$

11. $3\begin{bmatrix} 2 & -3 & 5 \\ 0 & 3 & -1 \end{bmatrix} - 5\begin{bmatrix} -2 & 1 & -1 \\ 0 & 3 & 2 \end{bmatrix} = \begin{bmatrix} 6 & -9 & 15 \\ 0 & 9 & -3 \end{bmatrix} - \begin{bmatrix} -10 & 5 & -5 \\ 0 & 15 & 10 \end{bmatrix}$

$= \begin{bmatrix} 16 & -14 & 20 \\ 0 & -6 & -13 \end{bmatrix}$

12. $\begin{bmatrix} 1 & 2 & 3 \end{bmatrix}\begin{bmatrix} 2 & -2 \\ -2 & 2 \\ 1 & 0 \end{bmatrix}\begin{bmatrix} 3 \\ -2 \end{bmatrix} = \begin{bmatrix} 1 & 2 \end{bmatrix}\begin{bmatrix} 3 \\ -2 \end{bmatrix} = \begin{bmatrix} -1 \end{bmatrix}$

13. $\left[\begin{array}{cc|cc} 5 & 19 & 1 & 0 \\ 2 & 7 & 0 & 1 \end{array}\right] \Rightarrow \underset{\frac{1}{5}R_1 \Rightarrow R_1}{\left[\begin{array}{cc|cc} 1 & \frac{19}{5} & \frac{1}{5} & 0 \\ 2 & 7 & 0 & 1 \end{array}\right]} \Rightarrow \underset{-2R_1 + R_2 \Rightarrow R_2}{\left[\begin{array}{cc|cc} 1 & \frac{19}{5} & \frac{1}{5} & 0 \\ 0 & -\frac{3}{5} & -\frac{2}{5} & 1 \end{array}\right]} \Rightarrow$

$\underset{-\frac{5}{3}R_2 \Rightarrow R_1}{\left[\begin{array}{cc|cc} 1 & \frac{19}{5} & \frac{1}{5} & 0 \\ 0 & 1 & \frac{2}{3} & -\frac{5}{3} \end{array}\right]} \Rightarrow \underset{-\frac{19}{5}R_2 + R_1 \Rightarrow R_1}{\left[\begin{array}{cc|cc} 1 & 0 & -\frac{7}{3} & \frac{19}{3} \\ 0 & 1 & \frac{2}{3} & -\frac{5}{3} \end{array}\right]} \Rightarrow$ Inverse: $\begin{bmatrix} -\frac{7}{3} & \frac{19}{3} \\ \frac{2}{3} & -\frac{5}{3} \end{bmatrix}$

14. $\left[\begin{array}{ccc|ccc} -1 & 3 & -2 & 1 & 0 & 0 \\ 4 & 1 & 4 & 0 & 1 & 0 \\ 0 & 3 & -1 & 0 & 0 & 1 \end{array}\right] \Rightarrow \underset{\substack{4R_1 + R_2 \Rightarrow R_2 \\ -R_1 \Rightarrow R_1}}{\left[\begin{array}{ccc|ccc} 1 & -3 & 2 & -1 & 0 & 0 \\ 0 & 13 & -4 & 4 & 1 & 0 \\ 0 & 3 & -1 & 0 & 0 & 1 \end{array}\right]} \Rightarrow$

$\underset{-4R_3 + R_2 \Rightarrow R_2}{\left[\begin{array}{ccc|ccc} 1 & -3 & 2 & -1 & 0 & 0 \\ 0 & 1 & 0 & 4 & 1 & -4 \\ 0 & 3 & -1 & 0 & 0 & 1 \end{array}\right]} \Rightarrow \underset{\substack{3R_2 + R_1 \Rightarrow R_1 \\ -3R_2 + R_3 \Rightarrow R_3}}{\left[\begin{array}{ccc|ccc} 1 & 0 & 2 & 11 & 3 & -12 \\ 0 & 1 & 0 & 4 & 1 & -4 \\ 0 & 0 & -1 & -12 & -3 & 13 \end{array}\right]} \Rightarrow$

$\underset{\substack{2R_3 + R_1 \Rightarrow R_1 \\ -R_3 \Rightarrow R_3}}{\left[\begin{array}{ccc|ccc} 1 & 0 & 0 & -13 & -3 & 14 \\ 0 & 1 & 0 & 4 & 1 & -4 \\ 0 & 0 & 1 & 12 & 3 & -13 \end{array}\right]}$ Inverse: $\begin{bmatrix} -13 & -3 & 14 \\ 4 & 1 & -4 \\ 12 & 3 & -13 \end{bmatrix}$

15. $\begin{bmatrix} 5 & 19 \\ 2 & 7 \end{bmatrix} \begin{bmatrix} x \\ y \end{bmatrix} = \begin{bmatrix} 3 \\ 2 \end{bmatrix}$

$$\begin{bmatrix} x \\ y \end{bmatrix} = \begin{bmatrix} 5 & 19 \\ 2 & 7 \end{bmatrix}^{-1} \begin{bmatrix} 3 \\ 2 \end{bmatrix} = \begin{bmatrix} -\frac{7}{3} & \frac{19}{3} \\ \frac{2}{3} & -\frac{5}{3} \end{bmatrix} \begin{bmatrix} 3 \\ 2 \end{bmatrix} = \begin{bmatrix} \frac{17}{3} \\ -\frac{4}{3} \end{bmatrix}$$

16. $\begin{bmatrix} -1 & 3 & -2 \\ 4 & 1 & 4 \\ 0 & 3 & -1 \end{bmatrix} \begin{bmatrix} x \\ y \\ z \end{bmatrix} = \begin{bmatrix} 1 \\ 3 \\ -1 \end{bmatrix}$

$$\begin{bmatrix} x \\ y \\ z \end{bmatrix} = \begin{bmatrix} -1 & 3 & -2 \\ 4 & 1 & 4 \\ 0 & 3 & -1 \end{bmatrix}^{-1} \begin{bmatrix} 1 \\ 3 \\ -1 \end{bmatrix}$$

$$\begin{bmatrix} x \\ y \\ z \end{bmatrix} = \begin{bmatrix} -13 & -3 & 14 \\ 4 & 1 & -4 \\ 12 & 3 & -13 \end{bmatrix} \begin{bmatrix} 1 \\ 3 \\ -1 \end{bmatrix} = \begin{bmatrix} -36 \\ 11 \\ 34 \end{bmatrix}$$

17. $\begin{vmatrix} 3 & -5 \\ -3 & 1 \end{vmatrix} = (3)(1) - (-5)(-3) = 3 - 15 = -12$

18. $\begin{vmatrix} 3 & 5 & -1 \\ -2 & 3 & -2 \\ 1 & 5 & -3 \end{vmatrix} = 3\begin{vmatrix} 3 & -2 \\ 5 & -3 \end{vmatrix} - 5\begin{vmatrix} -2 & -2 \\ 1 & -3 \end{vmatrix} + (-1)\begin{vmatrix} -2 & 3 \\ 1 & 5 \end{vmatrix}$

$= 3(1) - 5(8) - 1(-13) = 3 - 40 + 13 = -24$

19. $y = \dfrac{\begin{vmatrix} 3 & 3 \\ -3 & 2 \end{vmatrix}}{\begin{vmatrix} 3 & -5 \\ -3 & 1 \end{vmatrix}} = \dfrac{15}{-12} = -\dfrac{5}{4}$

20. $y = \dfrac{\begin{vmatrix} 3 & 2 & -1 \\ -2 & 1 & -2 \\ 1 & 0 & -3 \end{vmatrix}}{\begin{vmatrix} 3 & 5 & -1 \\ -2 & 3 & -2 \\ 1 & 5 & -3 \end{vmatrix}} = \dfrac{-24}{-24} = 1$

21.
$$\begin{aligned} \frac{5x}{(2x-3)(x+1)} &= \frac{A}{2x-3} + \frac{B}{x+1} \\ &= \frac{A(x+1)}{(2x-3)(x+1)} + \frac{B(2x-3)}{(2x-3)(x+1)} \\ &= \frac{Ax + A + 2Bx - 3B}{(2x-3)(x+1)} \\ &= \frac{(A+2B)x + (A-3B)}{(2x-3)(x+1)} \end{aligned}$$

$\begin{cases} A + 2B = 5 \\ A - 3B = 0 \end{cases} \Rightarrow \begin{matrix} A = 3 \\ B = 1 \end{matrix} \quad \dfrac{5x}{(2x-3)(x+1)} = \dfrac{3}{2x-3} + \dfrac{1}{x+1}$

22.
$$\begin{aligned} \frac{3x^2 + x + 2}{x(x^2+2)} &= \frac{A}{x} + \frac{Bx + C}{x^2+2} \\ &= \frac{A(x^2+2)}{x(x^2+2)} + \frac{(Bx+C)x}{x(x^2+2)} \\ &= \frac{Ax^2 + 2A + Bx^2 + Cx}{x(x^2+2)} \\ &= \frac{(A+B)x^2 + Cx + 2A}{x(x^2+2)} \end{aligned}$$

$\begin{cases} A + B = 3 \\ C = 1 \\ 2A = 2 \end{cases} \Rightarrow \begin{matrix} A = 1 \\ B = 2 \\ C = 1 \end{matrix} \quad \dfrac{3x^2 + x + 2}{x(x^2+2)} = \dfrac{1}{x} + \dfrac{2x+1}{x^2+2}$

23. $\begin{cases} x - 3y \geq 3 \\ x + 3y \leq 3 \end{cases}$

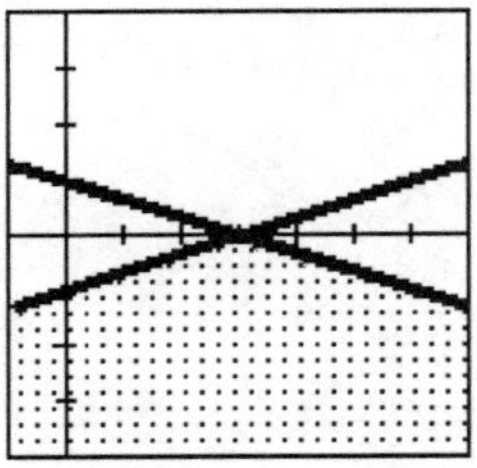

24. $\begin{cases} 3x + 4y \leq 12 \\ 3x + 4y \geq 6 \\ x \geq 0, y \geq 0 \end{cases}$

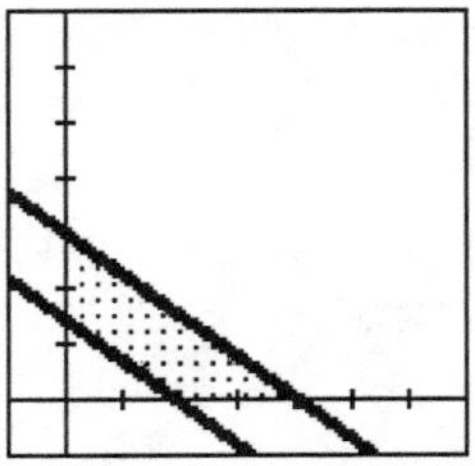

25.

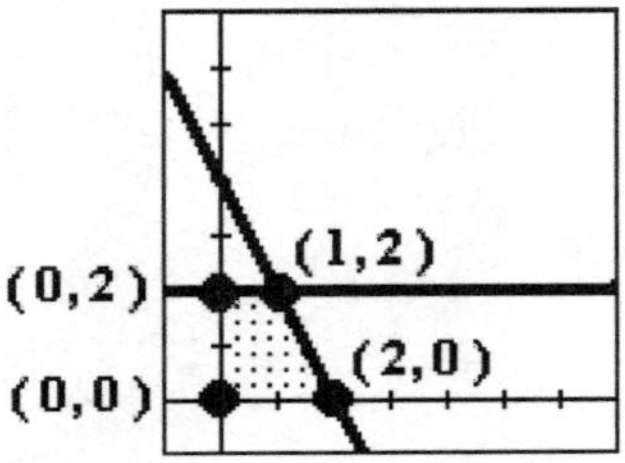

Point	$P = 3x + 2y$
(0, 2)	$= 3(0) + 2(2) = 4$
(1, 2)	$= 3(1) + 2(2) = 7$
(2, 0)	$= 3(2) + 2(0) = 6$
(0, 0)	$= 3(0) + 2(0) = 0$

Max: $P = 7$ at $(1, 2)$

26.

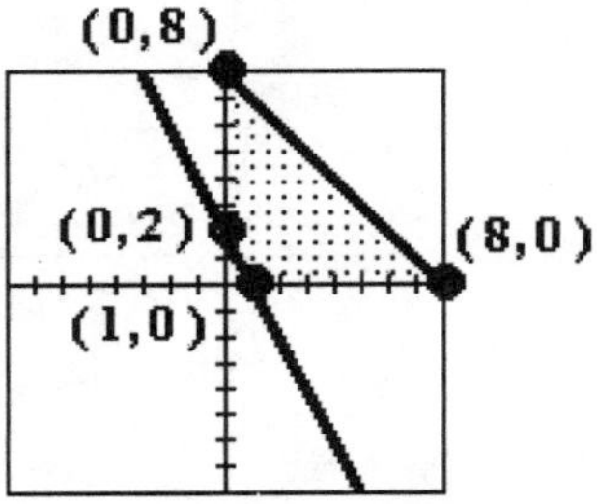

Point	$P = y - x$
(0, 2)	$= 2 - 0 = 2$
(0, 8)	$= 8 - 0 = 8$
(8, 0)	$= 0 - 8 = -8$
(1, 0)	$= 0 - 1 = -1$

Min: $P = -8$ at $(8, 0)$

Exercise 7.1 (page 523)

1. $(2, -5), 3$

2. $(0, 0), 6$

3. $(0, 0), \sqrt{5}$

4. $(9, 0), \sqrt{\frac{7}{2}}$

5. to the left

6. to the right

7. down

8. up

9. directrix, focus

10. $+ Bxy + Cy^2 + Dx + Ey + F$

11. $$\begin{aligned}(x-h)^2 + (y-k)^2 &= r^2\\ (x-0)^2 + (y-0)^2 &= 7^2\\ x^2 + y^2 &= 49\end{aligned}$$

12. $$\begin{aligned}r &= \sqrt{(-3-0)^2 + (2-0)^2} = \sqrt{13}\\ (x-h)^2 + (y-k)^2 &= r^2\\ (x-0)^2 + (y-0)^2 &= \left(\sqrt{13}\right)^2\\ x^2 + y^2 &= 13\end{aligned}$$

13. $$\begin{aligned}r &= \sqrt{(3-2)^2 + (2-(-2))^2} = \sqrt{17}\\ (x-h)^2 + (y-k)^2 &= r^2\\ (x-2)^2 + (y-(-2))^2 &= \left(\sqrt{17}\right)^2\\ (x-2)^2 + (y+2)^2 &= 17\end{aligned}$$

14. $$\begin{aligned}&C\left(\frac{5+(-2)}{2}, \frac{4+(-3)}{2}\right) = C\left(\frac{3}{2}, \frac{1}{2}\right)\\ &r = \sqrt{\left(5-\tfrac{3}{2}\right)^2 + \left(4-\tfrac{1}{2}\right)^2} = \sqrt{\tfrac{49}{2}}\\ &(x-h)^2 + (y-k)^2 = r^2\\ &\left(x-\tfrac{3}{2}\right)^2 + \left(y-\tfrac{1}{2}\right)^2 = \left(\sqrt{\tfrac{49}{2}}\right)^2\\ &\left(x-\tfrac{3}{2}\right)^2 + \left(y-\tfrac{1}{2}\right)^2 = \tfrac{49}{2}\end{aligned}$$

15. $$\begin{array}{ll} 3x + y = 1 \Rightarrow \times\ (3) & 9x + 3y = 3\\ \underline{-2x - 3y = 4} & \underline{-2x - 3y = 4}\\ & 7x \quad = 7\\ & x \quad = 1 \end{array}$$

$$\begin{array}{ll} 3x + y = 1 & \text{Center:}\\ 3(1) + y = 1 & (1, -2)\\ y = -2 & \end{array}$$

$$\begin{aligned}(x-h)^2 + (y-k)^2 &= r^2\\ (x-1)^2 + (y-(-2))^2 &= 6^2\\ (x-1)^2 + (y+2)^2 &= 36\end{aligned}$$

16. $$\begin{array}{ll} x + 2y = \ \ 8 \Rightarrow \times\ (-2) & -2x - 4y = -16\\ \underline{2x - 3y = -5} & \underline{2x - 3y = \ \ -5}\\ & -7y = -21\\ & y = \ \ 3 \end{array}$$

$$\begin{array}{ll} x + 2y = 8 & \text{Center:}\\ x + 2(3) = 8 & (2, 3)\\ x = 2 & \end{array}$$

$$\begin{aligned}(x-h)^2 + (y-k)^2 &= r^2\\ (x-2)^2 + (y-3)^2 &= 8^2\\ (x-2)^2 + (y-3)^2 &= 64\end{aligned}$$

17.
$$x^2 + y^2 = 4$$
$$(x-0)^2 + (y-0)^2 = 2^2$$
$$C(0,0),\ r = 2$$

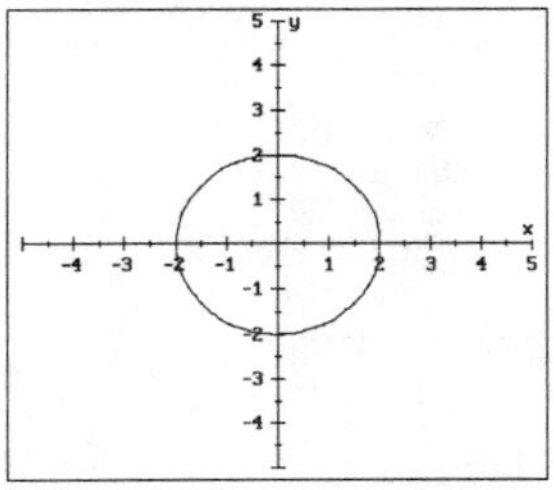

18.
$$x^2 - 2x + y^2 = 15$$
$$x^2 - 2x + 1 + y^2 = 15 + 1$$
$$(x-1)^2 + (y-0)^2 = 4^2$$
$$C(1,0),\ r = 4$$

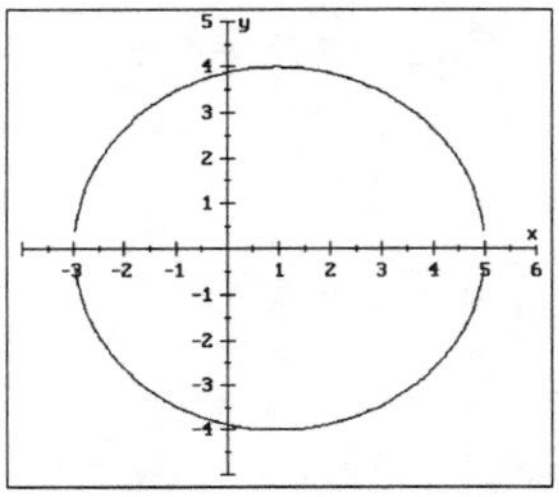

19.
$$3x^2 + 3y^2 - 12x - 6y = 12$$
$$x^2 - 4x + y^2 - 2y = 4$$
$$x^2 - 4x + 4 + y^2 - 2y + 1 = 4 + 4 + 1$$
$$(x-2)^2 + (y-1)^2 = 3^2$$
$$C(2,1),\ r = 3$$

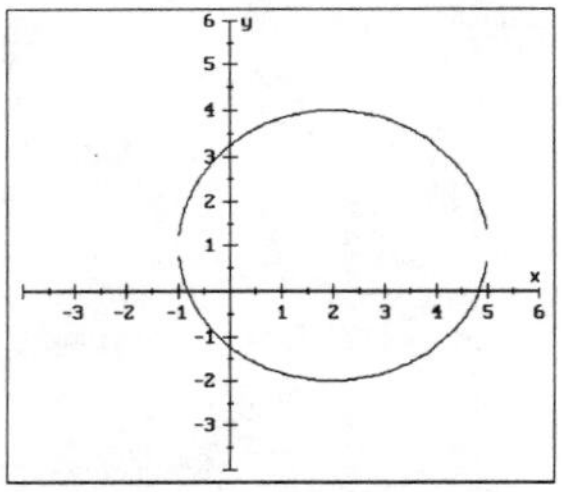

20.
$$2x^2 + 2y^2 + 4x - 8y + 2 = 0$$
$$x^2 + 2x + y^2 - 4y = -1$$
$$x^2 + 2x + 1 + y^2 - 4y + 4 = -1 + 1 + 4$$
$$(x+1)^2 + (y-2)^2 = 2^2$$
$$C(-1,2),\ r = 2$$

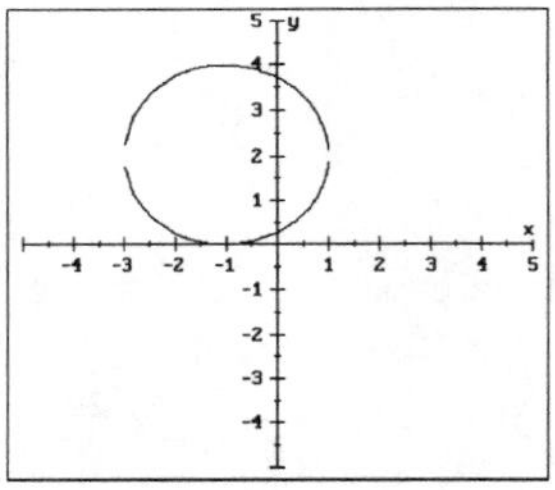

21. Vertical (up), $p = 3$
$$(x-h)^2 = 4p(y-k)$$
$$(x-0)^2 = 4(3)(y-0)$$
$$x^2 = 12y$$

22. Vertical (down), $p = 3$
$$(x-h)^2 = -4p(y-k)$$
$$(x-0)^2 = -4(3)(y-0)$$
$$x^2 = -12y$$

23. Horizontal (left), $p = 3$
$$(y-k)^2 = -4p(x-h)$$
$$(y-0)^2 = -4(3)(x-0)$$
$$y^2 = -12x$$

24. Horizontal (right), $p = 3$
$$(y-k)^2 = 4p(x-h)$$
$$(y-0)^2 = 4(3)(x-0)$$
$$y^2 = 12x$$

25. Vertical (down), $p = 3$
$$(x-h)^2 = -4p(y-k)$$
$$(x-3)^2 = -4(3)(y-5)$$
$$(x-3)^2 = -12(y-5)$$

26. Horizontal (left), $p = 6$
$$(y-k)^2 = -4p(x-h)$$
$$(y-5)^2 = -4(6)(x-3)$$
$$(y-5)^2 = -24(x-3)$$

27. Vertical (down), $p = 7$
$$(x-h)^2 = -4p(y-k)$$
$$(x-3)^2 = -4(7)(y-5)$$
$$(x-3)^2 = -28(y-5)$$

28. Horizontal (right), $p = 3$
$$(y-k)^2 = 4p(x-h)$$
$$(y-5)^2 = 4(3)(x-3)$$
$$(y-5)^2 = 12(x-3)$$

29. $(x-2)^2 = 4p(y-2)$ **OR** $(y-2)^2 = 4p(x-2)$

$$\begin{aligned} (0-2)^2 &= 4p(0-2) \\ 4 &= -8p \\ -\frac{1}{2} &= p \\ -2 &= 4p \\ (x-2)^2 &= -2(y-2) \end{aligned} \qquad \begin{aligned} (0-2)^2 &= 4p(0-2) \\ 4 &= -8p \\ -\frac{1}{2} &= p \\ -2 &= 4p \\ (y-2)^2 &= -2(x-2) \end{aligned}$$

30. $(x-(-2))^2 = 4p(y-(-2))$ **OR** $(y-(-2))^2 = 4p(x-(-2))$

$$\begin{aligned} (0+2)^2 &= 4p(0+2) \\ 4 &= 8p \\ \frac{1}{2} &= p \\ 2 &= 4p \\ (x+2)^2 &= 2(y+2) \end{aligned} \qquad \begin{aligned} (0+2)^2 &= 4p(0+2) \\ 4 &= 8p \\ \frac{1}{2} &= p \\ 2 &= 4p \\ (y+2)^2 &= 2(x+2) \end{aligned}$$

31. $(x-(-4))^2 = 4p(y-6)$ **OR** $(y-6)^2 = 4p(x-(-4))$

$$\begin{aligned} (0+4)^2 &= 4p(3-6) \\ 16 &= -12p \\ -\frac{4}{3} &= p \\ -\frac{16}{3} &= 4p \\ (x+4)^2 &= -\tfrac{16}{3}(y-6) \end{aligned} \qquad \begin{aligned} (3-6)^2 &= 4p(0+4) \\ 9 &= 16p \\ \frac{9}{16} &= p \\ \frac{9}{4} &= 4p \\ (y-6)^2 &= \tfrac{9}{4}(x+4) \end{aligned}$$

32. $(x-(-2))^2 = 4p(y-3)$ **OR** $(y-3)^2 = 4p(x-(-2))$

$$\begin{aligned} (0+2)^2 &= 4p(-3-3) \\ 4 &= -24p \\ -\frac{1}{6} &= p \\ -\frac{2}{3} &= 4p \\ (x+2)^2 &= -\tfrac{2}{3}(y-3) \end{aligned} \qquad \begin{aligned} (-3-3)^2 &= 4p(0+2) \\ 36 &= 8p \\ \frac{9}{2} &= p \\ 18 &= 4p \\ (y-3)^2 &= 18(x+2) \end{aligned}$$

33. $(x-6)^2 = 4p(y-8)$ **OR** $(y-8)^2 = 4p(x-6)$

$$\begin{aligned} (5-6)^2 &= 4p(10-8) \\ 1 &= 8p \\ \frac{1}{8} &= p \\ \frac{1}{2} &= 4p \\ (x-6)^2 &= \tfrac{1}{2}(y-8) \end{aligned} \qquad \begin{aligned} (10-8)^2 &= 4p(5-6) \\ 4 &= -4p \\ -1 &= p \\ -4 &= 4p \\ (y-8)^2 &= -4(x-6) \end{aligned}$$

Check to see which equation is satisfied by (5, 6) as well. Answer: $(y-8)^2 = -4(x-6)$

34. $(x-2)^2 = 4p(y-3)$ **OR** $(y-3)^2 = 4p(x-2)$

$(1-2)^2 = 4p(\frac{13}{4}-3)$ $\quad$ $(\frac{13}{4}-3)^2 = 4p(1-2)$

$1 = p$ $\quad$ $\frac{1}{16} = -4p$

$4 = 4p$ $\quad$ $-\frac{1}{16} = 4p$

$(x-2)^2 = 4(y-3)$ $\quad$ $(y-3)^2 = -\frac{1}{16}(x-2)$

Check to see which equation is satisfied by $\left(-1, \frac{21}{4}\right)$ as well. Answer: $(x-2)^2 = 4(y-3)$

35. $(x-3)^2 = 4p(y-1)$ **OR** $(y-1)^2 = 4p(x-3)$

$(4-3)^2 = 4p(3-1)$ $\quad$ $(3-1)^2 = 4p(4-3)$

$1 = 8p$ $\quad$ $4 = 4p$

$\frac{1}{8} = p$ $\quad$ $(y-1)^2 = 4(x-3)$

$\frac{1}{2} = 4p$

$(x-3)^2 = \frac{1}{2}(y-1)$

Check to see which equation is satisfied by (2, 3) as well. Answer: $(x-3)^2 = \frac{1}{2}(y-1)$

36. $(x-(-4))^2 = 4p(y-(-2))$ **OR** $(y-(-2))^2 = 4p(x-(-4))$

$(-3+4)^2 = 4p(0+2)$ $\quad$ $(0+2)^2 = 4p(-3+4)$

$1 = 8p$ $\quad$ $4 = 4p$

$\frac{1}{2} = 4p$ $\quad$ $(y+2)^2 = 4(x+4)$

$(x+4)^2 = \frac{1}{2}(y+2)$

Check to see which equation is satisfied by $\left(\frac{9}{4}, 3\right)$ as well. Answer: $(y+2)^2 = 4(x+4)$

37.

$$y = x^2 + 4x + 5$$
$$y - 5 = x^2 + 4x$$
$$y - 5 + 4 = x^2 + 4x + 4$$
$$y - 1 = (x+2)^2$$

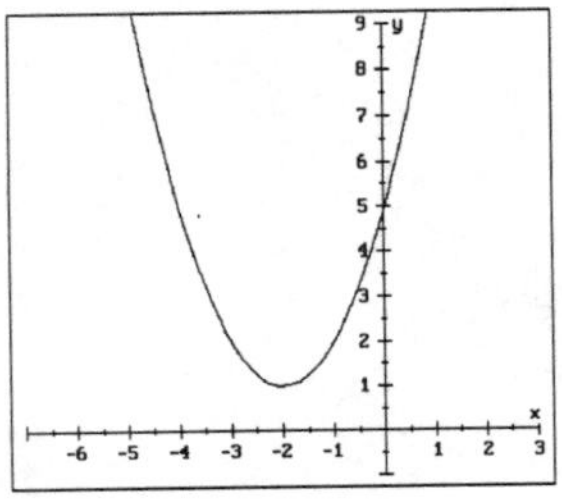

38.

$$2x^2 - 12x - 7y = 10$$
$$x^2 - 6x = \tfrac{7}{2}y + 5$$
$$x^2 - 6x + 9 = \tfrac{7}{2}y + 5 + 9$$
$$(x-3)^2 = \tfrac{7}{2}y + 14$$
$$(x-3)^2 = \tfrac{7}{2}(y+4)$$

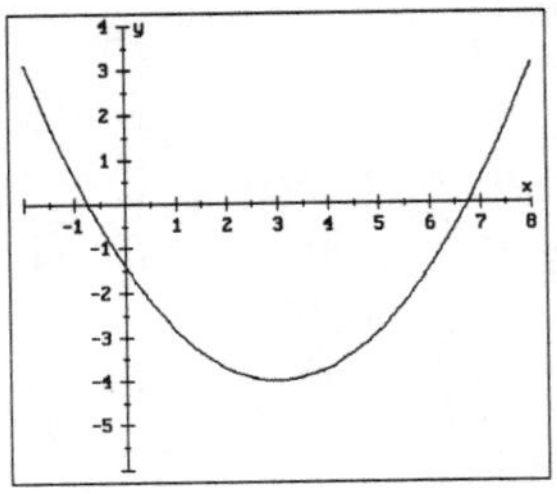

39.
$$\begin{aligned} y^2 + 4x - 6y &= -1 \\ y^2 - 6y &= -4x - 1 \\ y^2 - 6y + 9 &= -4x - 1 + 9 \\ (y-3)^2 &= -4x + 8 \\ (y-3)^2 &= -4(x-2) \end{aligned}$$

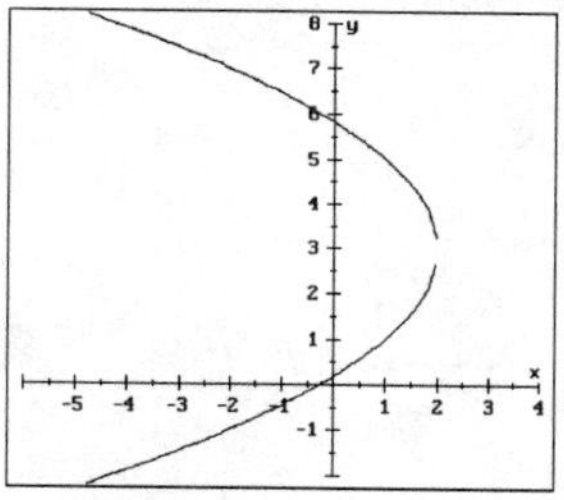

40.
$$\begin{aligned} x^2 - 2y - 2x &= -7 \\ x^2 - 2x &= 2y - 7 \\ x^2 - 2x + 1 &= 2y - 7 + 1 \\ (x-1)^2 &= 2y - 6 \\ (x-1)^2 &= 2(y-3) \end{aligned}$$

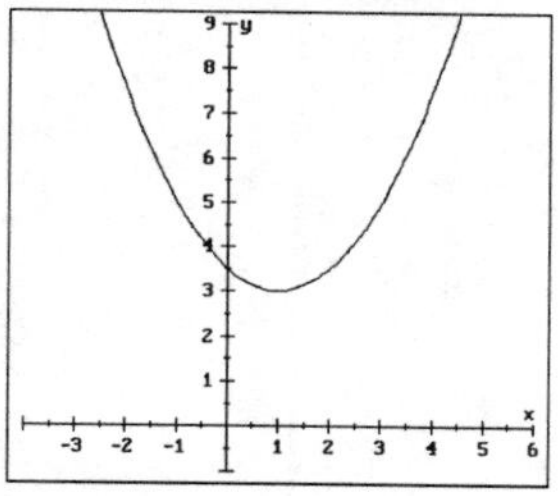

41.
$$\begin{aligned} y^2 + 2x - 2y &= 5 \\ y^2 - 2y &= -2x + 5 \\ y^2 - 2y + 1 &= -2x + 5 + 1 \\ (y-1)^2 &= -2x + 6 \\ (y-1)^2 &= -2(x-3) \end{aligned}$$

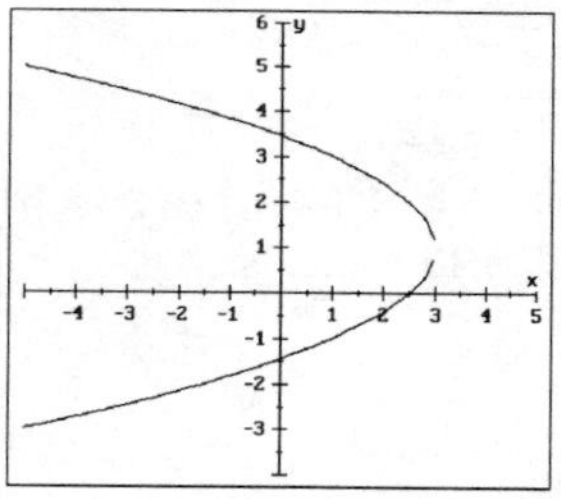

42.
$$\begin{aligned} y^2 - 4y &= -8x + 20 \\ y^2 - 4y + 4 &= -8x + 20 + 4 \\ (y-2)^2 &= -8x + 24 \\ (y-2)^2 &= -8(x-3) \end{aligned}$$

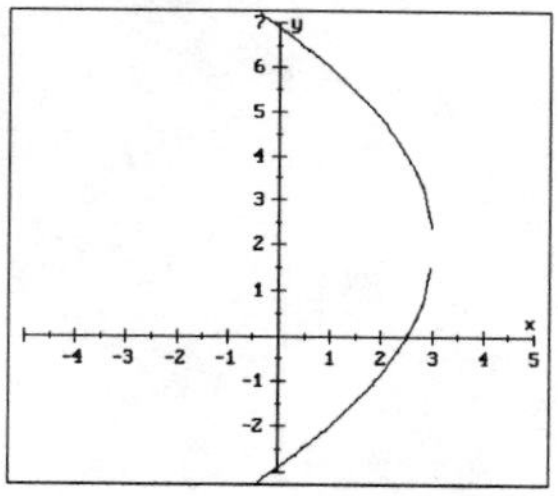

43.
$$\begin{aligned} x^2 - 6y + 22 &= -4x \\ x^2 + 4x &= 6y - 22 \\ x^2 + 4x + 4 &= 6y - 22 + 4 \\ (x+2)^2 &= 6y - 18 \\ (x+2)^2 &= 6(y-3) \end{aligned}$$

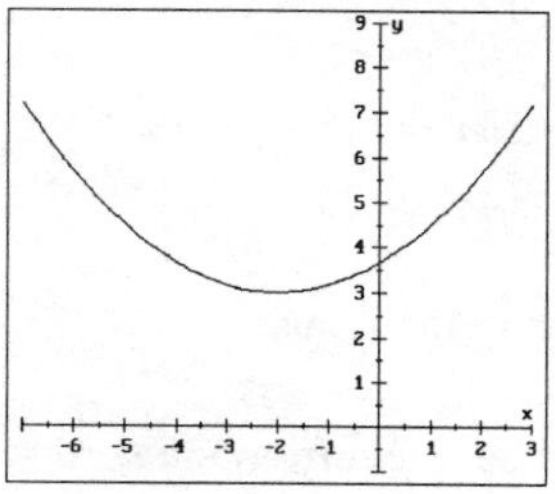

44.
$$\begin{aligned} 4y^2 - 4y + 16x &= 7 \\ y^2 - y &= -4x + \tfrac{7}{4} \\ y^2 - y + \tfrac{1}{4} &= -4x + \tfrac{7}{4} + \tfrac{1}{4} \\ \left(y - \tfrac{1}{2}\right)^2 &= -4x + 2 \\ \left(y - \tfrac{1}{2}\right)^2 &= -4\left(x - \tfrac{1}{2}\right) \end{aligned}$$

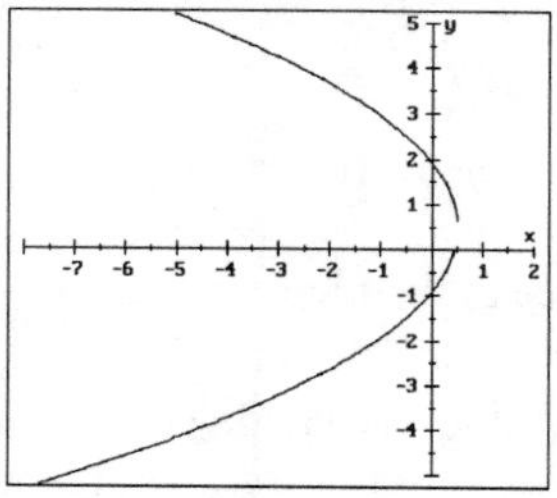

45. $4x^2 - 4x + 32y = 47$

$$x^2 - x = -8y + \tfrac{47}{4}$$
$$x^2 - x + \tfrac{1}{4} = -8y + \tfrac{47}{4} + \tfrac{1}{4}$$
$$\left(x - \tfrac{1}{2}\right)^2 = -8y + 12$$
$$\left(x - \tfrac{1}{2}\right)^2 = -8\left(y - \tfrac{3}{2}\right)$$

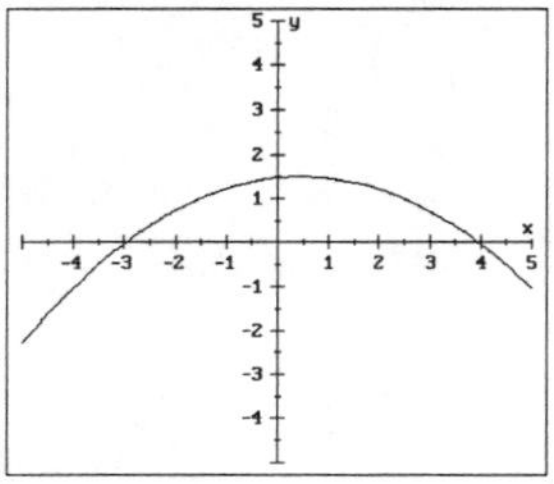

46. $4y^2 - 16x + 17 = 20y$

$$y^2 - 5y = 4x - \tfrac{17}{4}$$
$$y^2 - 5y + \tfrac{25}{4} = 4x - \tfrac{17}{4} + \tfrac{25}{4}$$
$$\left(y - \tfrac{5}{2}\right)^2 = 4x + 2$$
$$\left(y - \tfrac{5}{2}\right)^2 = 4\left(x + \tfrac{1}{2}\right)$$

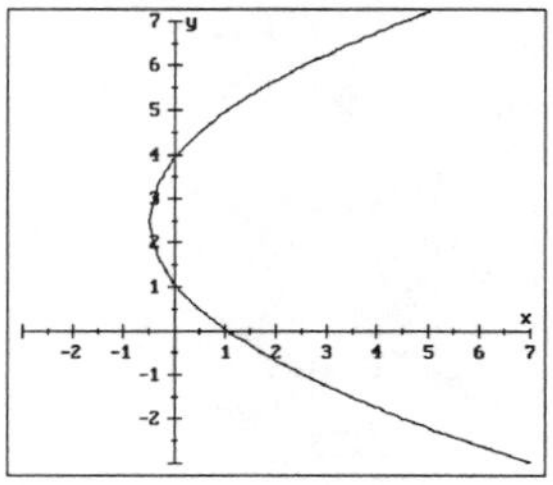

47. Check the coordinates:

$x^2 + y^2 = 50^2 + 70^2$
$= 2500 + 4900 = 7400$

$7400 < 8100$, so the city can receive.

48. Check the coordinates:

$x^2 + y^2 = (-4)^2 + (-5)^2$
$= 16 + 25 = 41$

Since $41 > 36$, the siren cannot be heard.

49. Graph both circles: $\begin{cases} x^2 + y^2 = 1600 \\ x^2 + (y - 35)^2 = 625 \end{cases}$

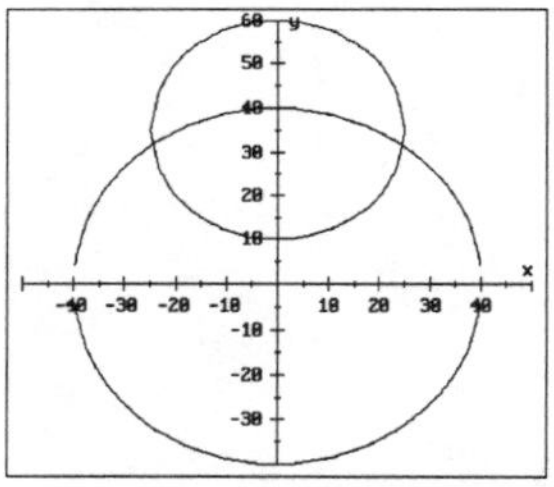

The point farthest from the transmitter (0, 0) is the point (0, 60). The greatest distance is 60 miles.

50. distance $= \sqrt{(15-0)^2 + (36-0)^2}$
$= \sqrt{225 + 1296} = \sqrt{1521} = 39$

Since the distance is 39 feet, the ripples will reach the seagull in 13 seconds.

51. $C(4, 0)$, $r = 4$

$(x - h)^2 + (y - k)^2 = r^2$
$(x - 4)^2 + (y - 0)^2 = 4^2$
$(x - 4)^2 + y^2 = 16$

52. $C(5, 14)$, $r = 5$

$(x - h)^2 + (y - k)^2 = r^2$
$(x - 5)^2 + (y - 14)^2 = 5^2$
$(x - 5)^2 + (y - 14)^2 = 25$

53. Find the distance to the focus:

$4p = 8 \Rightarrow p = 2$

It will be hottest 2 feet from the vertex.

54. Find the distance to the focus:

$4p = 12 \Rightarrow p = 3$

The light should be 3 feet from the vertex.

55. The vertex is (0, 0), while (15, −10) is on the curve (vertical parabola):

$$(x-h)^2 = 4p(y-k)$$
$$(15-0)^2 = 4p(-10-0)$$
$$225 = -40p$$
$$-\tfrac{45}{2} = 4p \Rightarrow x^2 = -\tfrac{45}{2}y$$

56. The vertex is (0, 0), while (1, 3) is on the curve (horizontal parabola):

$$(y-k)^2 = 4p(x-h)$$
$$(3-0)^2 = 4p(1-0)$$
$$9 = 4p$$
$$\tfrac{9}{4} = p \Rightarrow d = \tfrac{9}{4} \text{ feet}$$

57. $\boxed{\text{Income}} = \boxed{\text{Price}} \cdot \boxed{\text{\# rented}}$

$$y = -45\left(\tfrac{n}{32} - \tfrac{1}{2}\right)n$$
$$y = -\tfrac{45}{32}n^2 + \tfrac{45}{2}n$$
$$-\tfrac{32}{45}y = n^2 - 16n$$
$$-\tfrac{32}{45}y + 64 = n^2 - 16n + 64$$
$$-\tfrac{32}{45}y + 64 = (n-8)^2$$

She should build 8 cabins.

58.

$$s = -16t^2 + 80\sqrt{3}t$$
$$-\tfrac{1}{16}s = t^2 - 5\sqrt{3}t$$
$$-\tfrac{1}{16}s + \tfrac{75}{4} = t^2 - 5\sqrt{3}t + \tfrac{75}{4}$$
$$-\tfrac{1}{16}(s-300) = \left(t - \tfrac{5\sqrt{3}}{2}\right)^2$$

The maximum height is 300 feet.

59. Place the vertex at (0, 0), with the focus at $(1, 0) \Rightarrow p = 1, 4p = 4$.

$$(y-k)^2 = 4p(x-h)$$
$$y^2 = 4x$$

Let $x = 10$: $\quad y^2 = 4x$

$$y^2 = 4(10) \Rightarrow y = \pm\sqrt{40}$$

The width $= 2\sqrt{40} \approx 12.6$ cm.

60. The vertex is (0, 15), while (450, 120) is on the curve (vertical parabola):

$$(x-h)^2 = 4p(y-k)$$
$$(450-0)^2 = 4p(120-15)$$
$$202{,}500 = 420p$$
$$\tfrac{13{,}500}{7} = 4p \Rightarrow x^2 = \tfrac{13{,}500}{7}(y-15)$$

61. The vertex is (0, 0), while (315, −630) is on the curve (vertical parabola):

$$(x-h)^2 = 4p(y-k)$$
$$(315-0)^2 = 4p(-630-0)$$
$$99{,}225 = -2520p$$
$$-\tfrac{19845}{504} = p \Rightarrow 4p = -\tfrac{19845}{126}$$

Let $y = -430$:

$$x^2 = -\tfrac{19845}{126}y$$
$$x^2 = -\tfrac{19845}{126}(-430)$$
$$x = \pm\sqrt{-\tfrac{19845}{126}(-430)}$$
$$x \approx \pm 260$$

The width is about 520 feet.

62. The equation is $(x-h)^2 = 4p(y-k)$. From the figure, $h = 0$. Also, the points (4, 0) and (3, 5)are on the graph:

$$x^2 = 4p(y-k) \qquad x^2 = 4p(y-k)$$
$$4^2 = 4p(0-k) \qquad 3^2 = 4p(5-k)$$
$$16 = -4pk \qquad 9 = 20p - 4pk$$
$$-4 = pk$$

Substituting: $\quad 9 = 20p - 4pk$

$$9 = 20p - 4(-4)$$
$$-\tfrac{7}{20} = p \Rightarrow k = \tfrac{80}{7}$$

The maximum height is $\dfrac{80}{7}$ meters.

63.

$$\begin{aligned} (y-2)^2 &= 8(x-1) \\ y^2-4y+4 &= 8x-8 \\ y^2-8x-4y+12 &= 0 \\ 0x^2+0xy+y^2-8x-4y+12 &= 0 \end{aligned}$$

64.

$$\begin{aligned} (x+2)^2+(y-5)^2 &= 36 \\ x^2+4x+4+y^2-10y+25 &= 36 \\ x^2+0xy+y^2+4x-10y-7 &= 0 \end{aligned}$$

65.

$$\begin{aligned} (x-h)^2+(y-k)^2 &= r^2 \\ (0-h)^2+(8-k)^2 &= r^2 \\ h^2+64-16k+k^2 &= r^2 \\ h^2+k^2-r^2 &= 16k-64 \end{aligned}$$

$$\begin{aligned} (x-h)^2+(y-k)^2 &= r^2 \\ (5-h)^2+(3-k)^2 &= r^2 \\ 25-10h+h^2+9-6k+k^2 &= r^2 \\ h^2+k^2-r^2 &= 10h+6k-34 \end{aligned}$$

$$\begin{aligned} (x-h)^2+(y-k)^2 &= r^2 \\ (4-h)^2+(6-k)^2 &= r^2 \\ 16-8h+h^2+36-12k+k^2 &= r^2 \\ h^2+k^2-r^2 &= 8h+12k-52 \end{aligned}$$

$$\begin{cases} 16k-64 = 10h+6k-34 & \Rightarrow \quad 10k-10h = 30 \\ 16k-64 = 8h+12k-52 & \Rightarrow \quad 4k-8h = 12 \end{cases} \Rightarrow k=3,\ h=0$$

Substitute into one of the above equations to get $r = 5$. Circle: $x^2+(y-3)^2 = 25$

66.

$$\begin{aligned} (x-h)^2+(y-k)^2 &= r^2 \\ (-2-h)^2+(0-k)^2 &= r^2 \\ 4+4h+h^2+k^2 &= r^2 \\ h^2+k^2-r^2 &= -4h-4 \end{aligned}$$

$$\begin{aligned} (x-h)^2+(y-k)^2 &= r^2 \\ (2-h)^2+(8-k)^2 &= r^2 \\ 4-4h+h^2+64-16k+k^2 &= r^2 \\ h^2+k^2-r^2 &= 4h+16k-68 \end{aligned}$$

$$\begin{aligned} (x-h)^2+(y-k)^2 &= r^2 \\ (5-h)^2+(-1-k)^2 &= r^2 \\ 25-10h+h^2+1+2k+k^2 &= r^2 \\ h^2+k^2-r^2 &= 10h-2k-26 \end{aligned}$$

$$\begin{cases} -4h-4 = 4h+16k-68 & \Rightarrow \quad -8h-16k = -64 \\ -4h-4 = 10h-2k-26 & \Rightarrow \quad -14h+2k = -22 \end{cases} \Rightarrow h=2,\ k=3$$

Substitute into one of the above equations to get $r = 5$. Circle: $(x-2)^2+(y-3)^2 = 25$

67.

$$\begin{aligned} y &= ax^2+bx+c \\ 8 &= a(1)^2+b(1)+c \\ 8 &= a+b+c \end{aligned}$$

$$\begin{aligned} y &= ax^2+bx+c \\ -1 &= a(-2)^2+b(-2)+c \\ -1 &= 4a-2b+c \end{aligned}$$

$$\begin{aligned} y &= ax^2+bx+c \\ 15 &= a(2)^2+b(2)+c \\ 15 &= 4a+2b+c \end{aligned}$$

$$\begin{cases} a+b+c = 8 \\ 4a-2b+c = -1 \\ 4a+2b+c = 15 \end{cases} \Rightarrow a=1,\ b=4,\ c=3 \Rightarrow y = x^2+4x+3$$

68.

$$y = ax^2 + bx + c \qquad y = ax^2 + bx + c \qquad y = ax^2 + bx + c$$
$$-3 = a(1)^2 + b(1) + c \qquad 12 = a(-2)^2 + b(-2) + c \qquad 3 = a(-1)^2 + b(-1) + c$$
$$-3 = a + b + c \qquad 12 = 4a - 2b + c \qquad 3 = a - b + c$$

$$\begin{cases} a + b + c = -3 \\ 4a - 2b + c = 12 \\ a - b + c = 3 \end{cases} \Rightarrow a = 2,\ b = -3,\ c = -2 \Rightarrow y = 2x^2 - 3x - 2$$

69. The stone hits the ground when $s = 0$:
$0 = -16t^2 + 128t$
$0 = -16t(t - 8)$
It hits the ground after 8 seconds.
Find s when $t = x$:
$s = -16x^2 + 128x$

Find s when $t = 8 - x$:
$$\begin{aligned} s &= -16(8 - x)^2 + 128(8 - x) \\ &= -16(64 - 16x + x^2) + 1024 - 128x \\ &= -1024 + 256x - 16x^2 + 1024 - 128x \\ &= -16x^2 + 128x \end{aligned}$$

70. The maximum height occurs at the vertex:
$$\begin{aligned} s &= -16t^2 + 128t \\ -\tfrac{1}{16}s &= t^2 - 8t \\ -\tfrac{1}{16}s + 16 &= t^2 - 8t + 16 \\ -\tfrac{1}{16}s + 16 &= (t - 4)^2 \end{aligned}$$

The maximum height occurs after 4 seconds, which is half the time of 8 seconds (found in **#69**) it takes the stone to hit the ground.

71. $x^2 + 4x + \boxed{4}$

72. $y^2 - 12y + \boxed{36}$

73. $x^2 - 7x + \boxed{\frac{49}{4}}$

74. $y^2 + 11y + \boxed{\frac{121}{4}}$

75.
$$\begin{aligned} x^2 + 4x &= 5 \\ x^2 + 4x - 5 &= 0 \\ (x + 5)(x - 1) &= 0 \\ x = -5 \text{ or } x &= 1 \end{aligned}$$

76.
$$\begin{aligned} y^2 - 12y &= 13 \\ y^2 - 12y - 13 &= 0 \\ (y + 1)(y - 13) &= 0 \\ y = -1 \text{ or } y &= 13 \end{aligned}$$

77.
$$\begin{aligned} x^2 - 7x - 18 &= 0 \\ (x + 2)(x - 9) &= 0 \\ x = -2 \text{ or } x &= 9 \end{aligned}$$

78.
$$\begin{aligned} y^2 + 11y &= -18 \\ y^2 + 11y + 18 &= 0 \\ (y + 2)(y + 9) &= 0 \\ y = -2 \text{ or } y &= -9 \end{aligned}$$

Exercise 7.2 (page 535)

1. sum, constant

2. focus

3. vertices

4. minor

5. $(a, 0)$, $(-a, 0)$

6. $b^2 = a^2 - c^2$

7. $2a = 26 \Rightarrow$ String: 26 inches long
$2b = 10 \Rightarrow b = 5$
$b^2 = a^2 - c^2$
$5^2 = 13^2 - c^2 \Rightarrow c = 12$
Thumbtacks: $2c = 24$ inches apart

8. $2a = 20 \Rightarrow$ String: 20 cm long
$2b = 12 \Rightarrow b = 6$
$b^2 = a^2 - c^2$
$6^2 = 10^2 - c^2 \Rightarrow c = 8$
Thumbtacks: $2c = 16$ cm apart

9. $c = 3,\ a = 5$; horizontal
$b^2 = a^2 - c^2$
$= 25 - 9 = 16$
$$\frac{x^2}{25} + \frac{y^2}{16} = 1$$

10. $c = 4,\ a = 7$; vertical
$b^2 = a^2 - c^2$
$= 49 - 16 = 33$
$$\frac{x^2}{33} + \frac{y^2}{49} = 1$$

11. $c = 1,\ b = \frac{4}{3}$; vertical
$a^2 = b^2 + c^2$
$= \frac{16}{9} + 1 = \frac{25}{9}$
$$\frac{x^2}{16/9} + \frac{y^2}{25/9} = 1$$
$$\frac{9x^2}{16} + \frac{9y^2}{25} = 1$$

12. $c = 1,\ b = \frac{4}{3}$; horizontal
$a^2 = b^2 + c^2$
$= \frac{16}{9} + 1 = \frac{25}{9}$
$$\frac{x^2}{25/9} + \frac{y^2}{16/9} = 1$$
$$\frac{9x^2}{25} + \frac{9y^2}{16} = 1$$

13. $c = 3,\ a = 4$; vertical
$b^2 = a^2 - c^2$
$= 16 - 9 = 7$
$$\frac{x^2}{7} + \frac{y^2}{16} = 1$$

14. $c = 5,\ a = 6$; horizontal
$b^2 = a^2 - c^2$
$= 36 - 25 = 11$
$$\frac{x^2}{36} + \frac{y^2}{11} = 1$$

15. vertical
$$\frac{(x-3)^2}{4} + \frac{(y-4)^2}{9} = 1$$

16. $a = 6$, vertical
$$\frac{(x-3)^2}{4} + \frac{(y-4)^2}{36} = 1$$

17. horizontal
$$\frac{(x-3)^2}{9} + \frac{(y-4)^2}{4} = 1$$

18. $a = 5$, horizontal
$$\frac{(x-3)^2}{25} + \frac{(y-4)^2}{4} = 1$$

19. Center: $(3, 4)$, $b = 4$, $c = 5$, horizontal
$a^2 = b^2 + c^2 = 16 + 25 = 41$
$$\frac{(x-3)^2}{41} + \frac{(y-4)^2}{16} = 1$$

20. Center: $(6, 5)$, $b = 3$, $c = 2$, horizontal
$a^2 = b^2 + c^2 = 9 + 4 = 13$
$$\frac{(x-6)^2}{13} + \frac{(y-5)^2}{9} = 1$$

21. Center: $(0, 4)$, $c = 4$, $a = 6$, horizontal
$b^2 = a^2 - c^2 = 36 - 16 = 20$
$$\frac{x^2}{36} + \frac{(y-4)^2}{20} = 1$$

22. $a = 6$, $c = 2$, vertical
$b^2 = a^2 - c^2 = 36 - 4 = 32$
$$\frac{(x+4)^2}{32} + \frac{(y-5)^2}{36} = 1$$

23. Center: $(0, 0)$, $c = 6$, $a = 10$, horizontal

$b^2 = a^2 - c^2 = 100 - 36 = 64$

$$\frac{x^2}{100} + \frac{y^2}{64} = 1$$

24. Center: $(0, 0)$, $a = 2$, $b^2 = 2$, horizontal

$$\frac{x^2}{4} + \frac{y^2}{2} = 1$$

25. $\dfrac{x^2}{25} + \dfrac{y^2}{49} = 1$

Center: $(0, 0)$, $a = 7$, $b = 5$, vertical

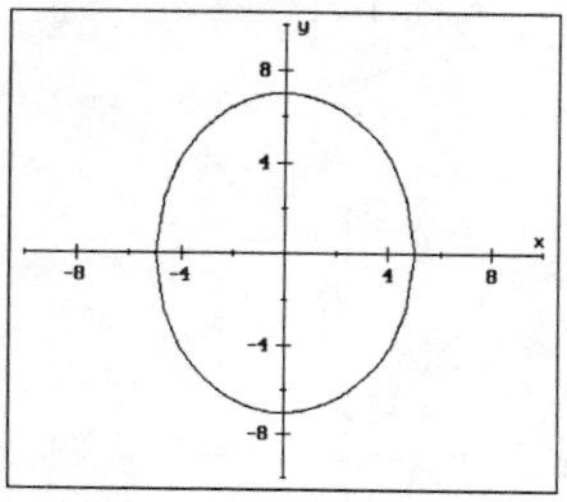

26. $4x^2 + y^2 = 4$

$$\frac{4x^2}{4} + \frac{y^2}{4} = \frac{4}{4}$$

$$\frac{x^2}{1} + \frac{y^2}{4} = 1$$

Center: $(0, 0)$, $a = 2$, $b = 1$, vertical

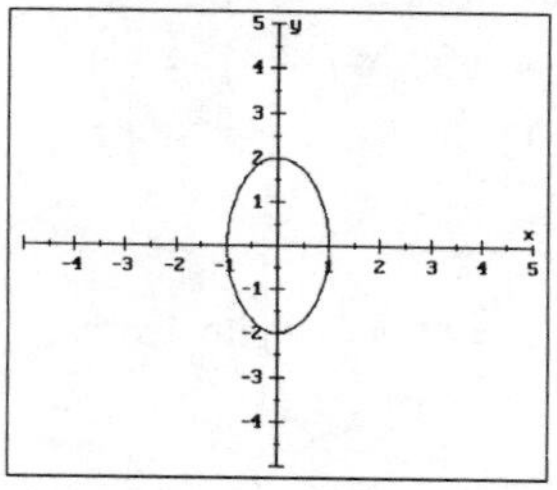

27. $\dfrac{x^2}{16} + \dfrac{(y+2)^2}{36} = 1$

Center: $(0, -2)$, $a = 6$, $b = 4$, vertical

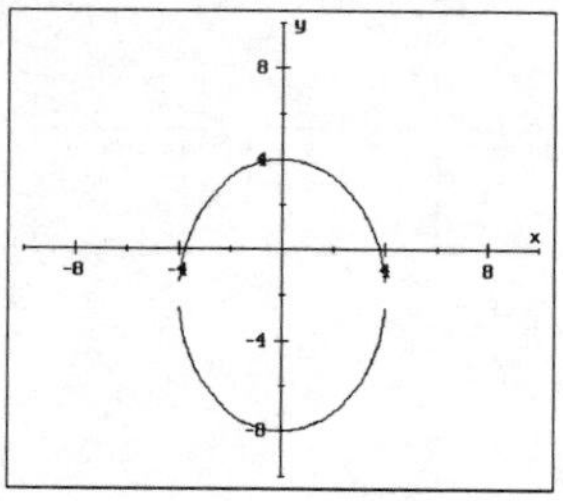

28. $(x-1)^2 + \dfrac{4y^2}{25} = 4$

$$\frac{(x-1)^2}{4} + \frac{4y^2}{4(25)} = \frac{4}{4}$$

$$\frac{(x-1)^2}{4} + \frac{y^2}{25} = 1$$

Center: $(1, 0)$, $a = 5$, $b = 2$, vertical

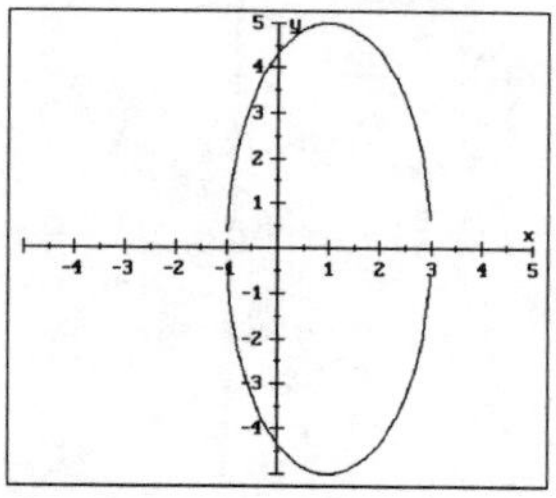

29.

$$\begin{aligned} x^2 + 4y^2 - 4x + 8y + 4 &= 0 \\ x^2 - 4x + 4(y^2 + 2y) &= -4 \\ x^2 - 4x + 4 + 4(y^2 + 2y + 1) &= -4 + 4 + 4 \\ (x-2)^2 + 4(y+1)^2 &= 4 \\ \frac{(x-2)^2}{4} + \frac{(y+1)^2}{1} &= 1 \end{aligned}$$

Center: $(2, -1)$, $a = 2$, $b = 1$, horizontal

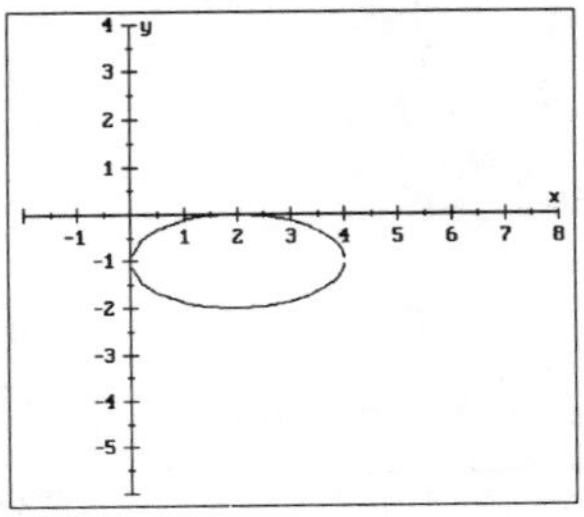

30.

$$\begin{aligned} x^2 + 4y^2 - 2x - 16y &= -13 \\ x^2 - 2x + 4(y^2 - 4y) &= -13 \\ x^2 - 2x + 1 + 4(y^2 - 4y + 4) &= -13 + 1 + 16 \\ (x-1)^2 + 4(y-2)^2 &= 4 \\ \frac{(x-1)^2}{4} + \frac{(y-2)^2}{1} &= 1 \end{aligned}$$

Center: $(1, 2)$, $a = 2$, $b = 1$, horizontal

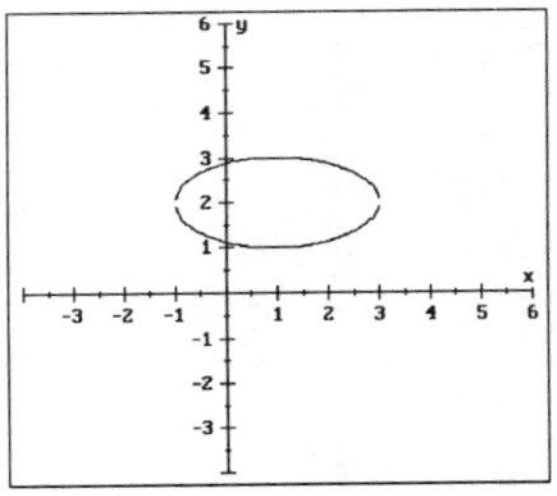

31.

$$\begin{aligned} 16x^2 + 25y^2 - 160x - 200y + 400 &= 0 \\ 16(x^2 - 10x) + 25(y^2 - 8y) &= -400 \\ 16(x^2 - 10x + 25) + 25(y^2 - 8y + 16) &= -400 + 400 + 400 \\ 16(x-5)^2 + 25(y-4)^2 &= 400 \\ \frac{(x-5)^2}{25} + \frac{(y-4)^2}{16} &= 1 \end{aligned}$$

Center: $(5, 4)$, $a = 5$, $b = 4$, horizontal

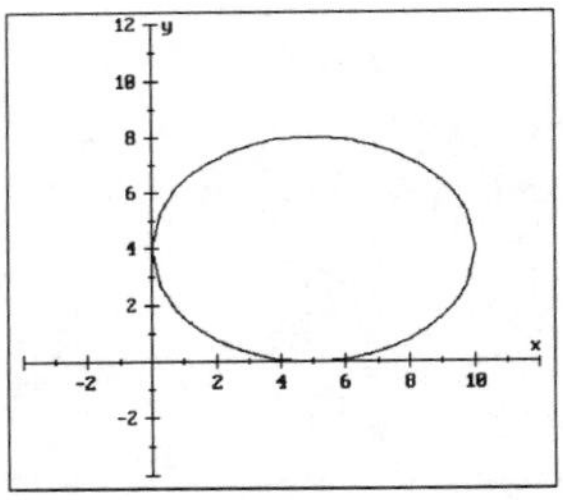

32.

$$\begin{aligned} 3x^2 + 2y^2 + 7x - 6y &= -1 \\ 3\left(x^2 + \tfrac{7}{3}x\right) + 2(y^2 - 3y) &= -1 \\ 3\left(x^2 + \tfrac{7}{3}x + \tfrac{49}{36}\right) + 2\left(y^2 - 3y + \tfrac{9}{4}\right) &= -1 + \tfrac{49}{12} + \tfrac{9}{2} \\ 3\left(x + \tfrac{7}{6}\right)^2 + 2\left(y - \tfrac{3}{2}\right)^2 &= \tfrac{91}{12} \\ \frac{\left(x + \frac{7}{6}\right)^2}{91/36} + \frac{\left(y - \frac{3}{2}\right)^2}{91/24} &= 1 \end{aligned}$$

Center: $\left(-\frac{7}{6}, \frac{3}{2}\right)$, $a = \sqrt{\frac{91}{36}}$, $b = \sqrt{\frac{91}{24}}$, vertical

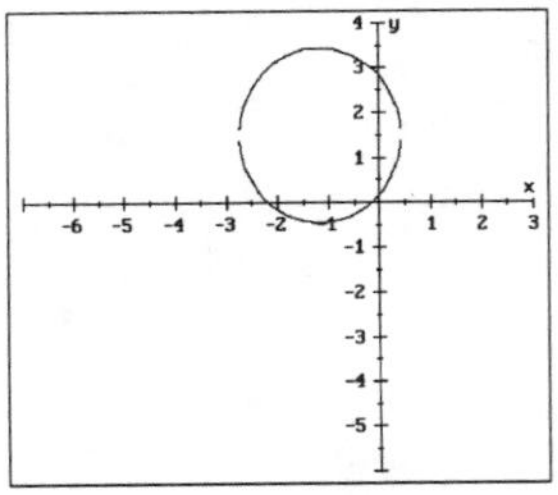

33. The farthest distance $= a + c$:

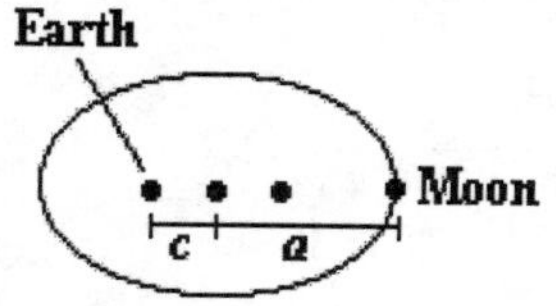

$$a = \frac{378000}{2} = 189000$$
$$\frac{c}{a} = \frac{11}{200}$$
$$c = \frac{11a}{200} = 10395$$
distance $= a + c =$ 199,395 miles

34. $a = 5, b = 5$

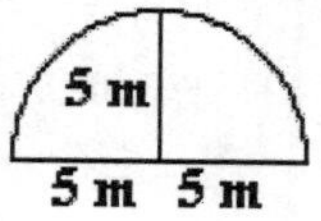

$$\frac{x^2}{25} + \frac{y^2}{25} = 1$$

35. $a = 50, b = 30$

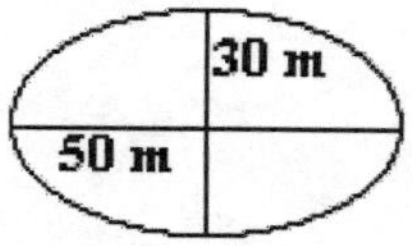

$$\frac{x^2}{2500} + \frac{y^2}{900} = 1$$

$$c^2 = a^2 - b^2 = 2500 - 900 = 1600$$
$$c = 40$$

$$\frac{40^2}{2500} + \frac{y^2}{900} = 1$$
$$\frac{y^2}{900} = \frac{900}{2500}$$
$$\frac{y}{30} = \pm\frac{30}{50}$$
$$y = \pm 18$$
The focal width is 36 meters.

36. Using the Pythagorean Theorem:

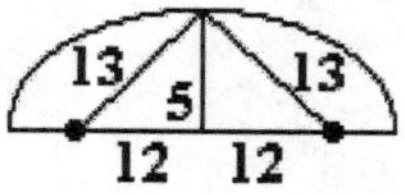

The distance is 26 meters.

37. $a = 24, b = 12$
$$\frac{x^2}{144} + \frac{y^2}{576} = 1$$
$$\frac{x^2}{144} + \frac{y^2}{576} = 1$$
$$\frac{x^2}{144} + \frac{(-12)^2}{576} = 1$$
$$\frac{x^2}{144} = \pm\frac{432}{576} \Rightarrow x \approx \pm 10.4 \Rightarrow \text{The width is about 20.8 inches.}$$

38. $a = 36, b = 15$
$$\frac{x^2}{1296} + \frac{y^2}{225} = 1$$
$$\frac{x^2}{1296} + \frac{y^2}{225} = 1$$
$$\frac{16^2}{1296} + \frac{y^2}{225} = 1$$
$$\frac{y^2}{225} = \pm\frac{1040}{1296} \Rightarrow y \approx \pm 13.45 \Rightarrow \text{The width is about 26.9 inches.}$$

39. $FB = \sqrt{(c-0)^2 + (0-b)^2} = \sqrt{c^2 + b^2} = \sqrt{a^2} = |a| = a \ (a \geq 0)$

40. The equation of the ellipse is $\frac{x^2}{a^2} + \frac{y^2}{b^2} = 1$.
P is a point on the ellipse, so solve for y^2:

$$\frac{x^2}{a^2} + \frac{y^2}{b^2} = 1$$
$$\frac{y^2}{b^2} = 1 - \frac{x^2}{a^2}$$
$$y^2 = b^2\left(1 - \frac{x^2}{a^2}\right)$$

$$\begin{aligned} FP &= \sqrt{(c-x)^2 + (0-y)^2} \\ &= \sqrt{(c-x)^2 + y^2} \\ &= \sqrt{(c-x)^2 + b^2\left(1 - \frac{x^2}{a^2}\right)} \\ &= \sqrt{(c-x)^2 + (a^2 - c^2)\left(1 - \frac{x^2}{a^2}\right)} \\ &= \sqrt{c^2 - 2cx + x^2 + a^2 - x^2 - c^2 + \frac{c^2}{a^2}x^2} \\ &= \sqrt{a^2 - 2cx + \frac{c^2}{a^2}x^2} \\ &= \sqrt{\left(a - \frac{c}{a}x\right)^2} = a - \frac{c}{a}x \end{aligned}$$

41. The equation of the ellipse is $\frac{x^2}{a^2} + \frac{y^2}{b^2} = 1$.
Let $x = c$ and solve for y^2:

$$\frac{x^2}{a^2} + \frac{y^2}{b^2} = 1$$
$$\frac{c^2}{a^2} + \frac{y^2}{b^2} = 1$$
$$\begin{aligned} y^2 &= b^2\left(1 - \frac{c^2}{a^2}\right) \\ &= b^2\left(1 - \frac{a^2 - b^2}{a^2}\right) \\ &= b^2\left(1 - 1 + \frac{b^2}{a^2}\right) = \frac{b^4}{a^2} \end{aligned}$$

Thus, $y = \pm\sqrt{\frac{b^4}{a^2}} = \pm\frac{b^2}{a}$.
The coordinates of A' and A are $\left(c, \frac{b^2}{a}\right)$ and $\left(c, -\frac{b^2}{a}\right)$. Therefore, the focal width is $\frac{2b^2}{a}$.

42. By the result of **#40**, the distance between a point $P(x, y)$ on the ellipse and a focus $F(c, 0)$ is $D = a - \frac{c}{a}x$. Since P is a point on the ellipse, x must take on values from $-a$ to a. To make D as small as possible, x must be positive and as large as possible. This occurs when $x = a$. If $x = a$, then point P is actually at point V.

43. Let the origin be at the midpoint of the line segment between the two thumbtacks and let the x-axis be parallel to that segment. Then $2a = 6$, so $a = 3$. Also, $2c = 2$, so $c = 1$. Find b:
$b^2 = a^2 - c^2 = 3^2 - 1^2 = 8$. The equation is $\frac{x^2}{a^2} + \frac{y^2}{b^2} = 1$, or $\frac{x^2}{9} + \frac{y^2}{8} = 1$.

44. Consider the following diagram:

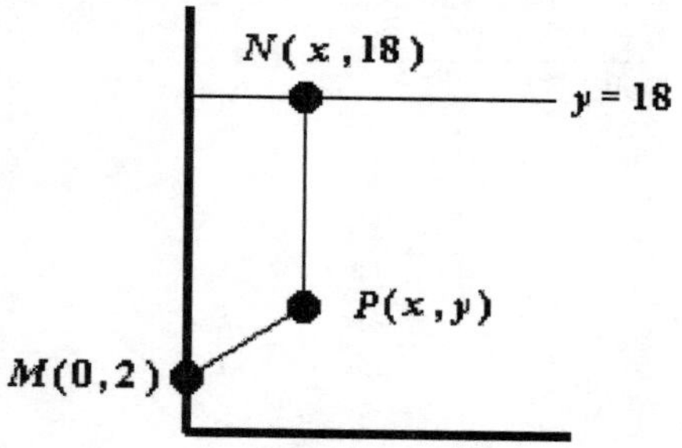

$$PM = \tfrac{1}{3}PN$$
$$\sqrt{(x-0)^2+(y-2)^2} = \tfrac{1}{3}\sqrt{(x-x)^2+(y-18)^2}$$
$$x^2+(y-2)^2 = \tfrac{1}{9}\left[0+(y-18)^2\right]$$
$$x^2+y^2-4y+4 = \tfrac{1}{9}(y-18)^2$$
$$9x^2+9y^2-36y+36 = y^2-36y+324$$
$$9x^2+8y^2 = 288$$
$$\frac{x^2}{32}+\frac{y^2}{36} = 1$$

45. **Answers may vary.**

46. **Answers may vary.**

47. $AB = \begin{bmatrix} 3 & -1 & 2 \\ 0 & 2 & -1 \\ 3 & 1 & 1 \end{bmatrix}\begin{bmatrix} 1 & 2 \\ 2 & 0 \\ -1 & 1 \end{bmatrix} = \begin{bmatrix} -1 & 8 \\ 5 & -1 \\ 4 & 7 \end{bmatrix}$

48. $B+C = \begin{bmatrix} 1 & 2 \\ 2 & 0 \\ -1 & 1 \end{bmatrix} + \begin{bmatrix} 0 & 1 \\ -1 & 1 \\ -2 & 0 \end{bmatrix} = \begin{bmatrix} 1 & 3 \\ 1 & 1 \\ -3 & 1 \end{bmatrix}$

49. $5B-2C = 5\begin{bmatrix} 1 & 2 \\ 2 & 0 \\ -1 & 1 \end{bmatrix} - 2\begin{bmatrix} 0 & 1 \\ -1 & 1 \\ -2 & 0 \end{bmatrix} = \begin{bmatrix} 5 & 10 \\ 10 & 0 \\ -5 & 5 \end{bmatrix} - \begin{bmatrix} 0 & 2 \\ -2 & 2 \\ -4 & 0 \end{bmatrix} = \begin{bmatrix} 5 & 8 \\ 12 & -2 \\ -1 & 5 \end{bmatrix}$

50. $AC+B = \begin{bmatrix} 3 & -1 & 2 \\ 0 & 2 & -1 \\ 3 & 1 & 1 \end{bmatrix}\begin{bmatrix} 0 & 1 \\ -1 & 1 \\ -2 & 0 \end{bmatrix} + \begin{bmatrix} 1 & 2 \\ 2 & 0 \\ -1 & 1 \end{bmatrix} = \begin{bmatrix} -3 & 2 \\ 0 & 2 \\ -3 & 4 \end{bmatrix} + \begin{bmatrix} 1 & 2 \\ 2 & 0 \\ -1 & 1 \end{bmatrix} = \begin{bmatrix} -2 & 4 \\ 2 & 2 \\ -4 & 5 \end{bmatrix}$

51. $\begin{bmatrix} -1 & -2 \\ -2 & 0 \\ 1 & -1 \end{bmatrix}$

52. The matrix is not square, so the inverse does not exist.

Exercise 7.3 (page 544)

1. difference, constant

2. focus

3. $(a, 0), (-a, 0)$

4. $(0, a), (0, -a)$

5. transverse axis

6. $b^2 = c^2 - a^2$

7. $a = 5$, $c = 7$; horizontal
$$b^2 = c^2 - a^2 = 49 - 25 = 24$$
$$\frac{x^2}{25} - \frac{y^2}{24} = 1$$

8. $a = 2$, $c = 3$; horizontal
$$b^2 = c^2 - a^2 = 9 - 4 = 5$$
$$\frac{x^2}{4} - \frac{y^2}{5} = 1$$

9. $a = 2$, $b = 3$; horizontal
$$\frac{(x-2)^2}{4} - \frac{(y-4)^2}{9} = 1$$

10. $a = 2, c = 3$; horizontal

$$b^2 = c^2 - a^2 = 9 - 4 = 5$$

$$\frac{(x+1)^2}{4} - \frac{(y-3)^2}{5} = 1$$

11. $a = 3$; vertical

$$\frac{(y-3)^2}{9} - \frac{(x-5)^2}{b^2} = 1$$

$$\frac{(8-3)^2}{9} - \frac{(1-5)^2}{b^2} = 1$$

$$\frac{25}{9} - \frac{16}{b^2} = 1$$

$$-\frac{16}{b^2} = -\frac{16}{9}$$

$$b^2 = 9$$

$$\frac{(y-3)^2}{9} - \frac{(x-5)^2}{9} = 1$$

12. Center: $(0, 0)$, $c = 10$, $a = 8$; vertical

$$b^2 = c^2 - a^2 = 100 - 64 = 36$$

$$\frac{y^2}{64} - \frac{x^2}{36} = 1$$

13. Center: $(0, 0)$, $a = 3$, $c = 5$; vertical

$$b^2 = c^2 - a^2 = 25 - 9 = 16$$

$$\frac{y^2}{9} - \frac{x^2}{16} = 1$$

14. $c = 4, a = 2$; horizontal

$$b^2 = c^2 - a^2 = 16 - 4 = 12$$

$$\frac{x^2}{4} - \frac{y^2}{12} = 1$$

15. $$\frac{(x-1)^2}{4} - \frac{(y+3)^2}{16} = 1$$

OR

$$\frac{(y+3)^2}{4} - \frac{(x-1)^2}{16} = 1$$

16. $c = 6, a = 2$; horizontal

$$b^2 = c^2 - a^2 = 36 - 4 = 32$$

$$\frac{(x-1)^2}{4} - \frac{(y-4)^2}{32} = 1$$

17. $$\frac{x^2}{a^2} - \frac{y^2}{b^2} = 1$$

$$\frac{4^2}{a^2} - \frac{2^2}{b^2} = 1$$

$$\frac{16}{a^2} - \frac{4}{b^2} = 1$$

$$\frac{16}{a^2} = 1 + \frac{4}{b^2}$$

$$\frac{64}{a^2} = 4 + \frac{16}{b^2}$$

$$\frac{x^2}{a^2} - \frac{y^2}{b^2} = 1$$

$$\frac{8^2}{a^2} - \frac{(-6)^2}{b^2} = 1$$

$$\frac{64}{a^2} - \frac{36}{b^2} = 1$$

$$\frac{64}{a^2} - \frac{36}{b^2} = 1$$

$$4 + \frac{16}{b^2} - \frac{36}{b^2} = 1$$

$$3 = \frac{20}{b^2}$$

$$b^2 = \frac{20}{3}$$

$$a^2 = 10$$

$$\frac{x^2}{10} - \frac{3y^2}{20} = 1$$

18.

$$\frac{(x-3)^2}{a^2} - \frac{(y+1)^2}{b^2} = 1$$
$$\frac{(0-3)^2}{a^2} - \frac{(-1+1)^2}{b^2} = 1$$
$$\frac{9}{a^2} = 1$$
$$9 = a^2$$

$$\frac{(x-3)^2}{9} - \frac{(y+1)^2}{b^2} = 1$$
$$\frac{\left(3+\frac{3\sqrt{5}}{2}-3\right)^2}{9} - \frac{(0+1)^2}{b^2} = 1$$
$$\frac{5}{4} - \frac{1}{b^2} = 1$$
$$\frac{1}{4} = \frac{1}{b^2}$$
$$4 = b^2$$

$$\frac{(x-3)^2}{9} - \frac{(y+1)^2}{4} = 1$$

19.

$$4(x-1)^2 - 9(y+2)^2 = 36$$
$$\frac{4(x-1)^2}{36} - \frac{9(y+2)^2}{36} = \frac{36}{36}$$
$$\frac{(x-1)^2}{9} - \frac{(y+2)^2}{4} = 1$$

$a = 3$, $b = 2$

Area $= (2a)(2b) = (6)(4) = 24$

20.

$$x^2 - y^2 - 4x - 6y = 6$$
$$x^2 - 4x - \left(y^2 + 6y\right) = 6$$
$$x^2 - 4x + 4 - \left(y^2 + 6y + 9\right) = 6 + 4 - 9$$
$$(x-2)^2 - (y+3)^2 = 1$$
$$\frac{(x-2)^2}{1} - \frac{(y+3)^2}{1} = 1$$

$a = 1$, $b = 1$

Area $= (2a)(2b) = (2)(2) = 4$

21.

$$x^2 + 6x - y^2 + 2y = -11$$
$$x^2 + 6x - \left(y^2 - 2y\right) = -11$$
$$x^2 + 6x + 9 - \left(y^2 - 2y + 1\right) = -11 + 9 - 1$$
$$(x+3)^2 - (y-1)^2 = -3$$
$$\frac{(x+3)^2}{-3} - \frac{(y-1)^2}{-3} = 1$$
$$\frac{(y-1)^2}{3} - \frac{(x+3)^2}{3} = 1 \Rightarrow a = \sqrt{3},\ b = \sqrt{3};\ \text{Area} = (2a)(2b) = \left(2\sqrt{3}\right)\left(2\sqrt{3}\right) = 12$$

22.

$$9x^2 - 4y^2 = 18x + 24y + 63$$
$$9\left(x^2 - 2x\right) - 4\left(y^2 + 6y\right) = 63$$
$$9\left(x^2 - 2x + 1\right) - 4\left(y^2 + 6y + 9\right) = 63 + 9 - 36$$
$$9(x-1)^2 - 4(y+3)^2 = 36$$
$$\frac{9(x-1)^2}{36} - \frac{4(y+3)^2}{36} = \frac{36}{36}$$
$$\frac{(x-1)^2}{4} - \frac{(y+3)^2}{9} = 1 \Rightarrow a = 2,\ b = 3;\ \text{Area} = (2a)(2b) = (4)(6) = 24$$

23. $(2a)(2b) = 36$

$4(2b) = 36$

$b = \frac{9}{2}$

$$\frac{(x+2)^2}{4} - \frac{4(y+4)^2}{81} = 1$$

OR

$$\frac{(y+4)^2}{4} - \frac{4(x+2)^2}{81} = 1$$

24. $(2a)(2b) = 24$

$(2a)(12) = 24$

$a = 1$

$$\frac{(x-3)^2}{1} - \frac{(y+5)^2}{36} = 1$$

OR

$$\frac{(y+5)^2}{1} - \frac{(x-3)^2}{36} = 1$$

25. Center: $(0, 0)$, $a = 6$, $b = \frac{5}{4}$

$$\frac{x^2}{6^2} - \frac{y^2}{\left(\frac{5}{4}\right)^2} = 1$$

$$\frac{x^2}{36} - \frac{16y^2}{25} = 1$$

26. $a = 3$, $c = 5$; horizontal

$b^2 = c^2 - a^2$

$= 25 - 9 = 16$

$$\frac{x^2}{9} - \frac{y^2}{16} = 1$$

27. $\frac{x^2}{9} - \frac{y^2}{4} = 1$

Center: $(0, 0)$, $a = 3$, $b = 2$, horizontal

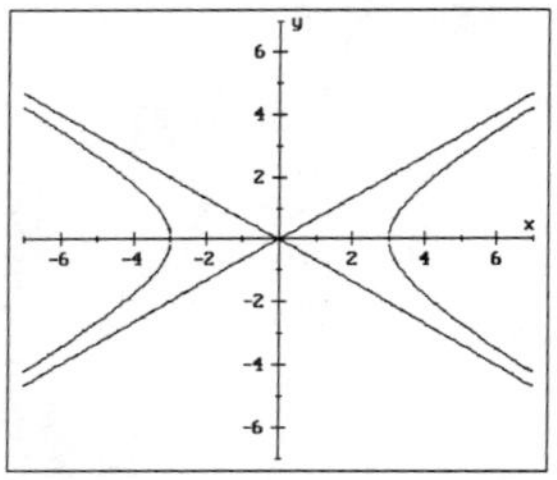

28. $\frac{y^2}{4} - \frac{x^2}{9} = 1$

Center: $(0, 0)$, $a = 2$, $b = 3$, vertical

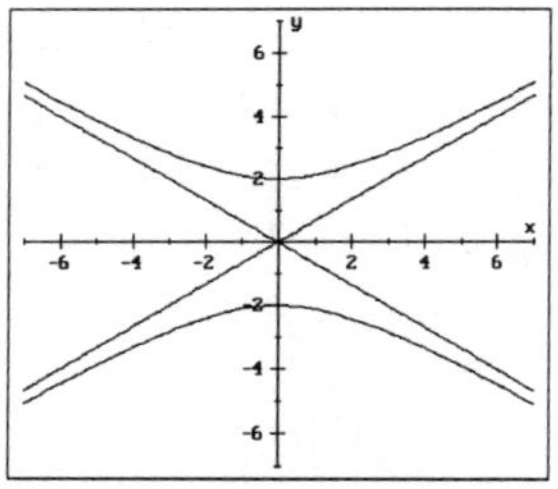

29. $4x^2 - 3y^2 = 36$

$$\frac{4x^2}{36} - \frac{3y^2}{36} = \frac{36}{36}$$

$$\frac{x^2}{9} - \frac{y^2}{12} = 1$$

Center: $(0, 0)$, $a = 3$, $b = 2\sqrt{3}$, horizontal

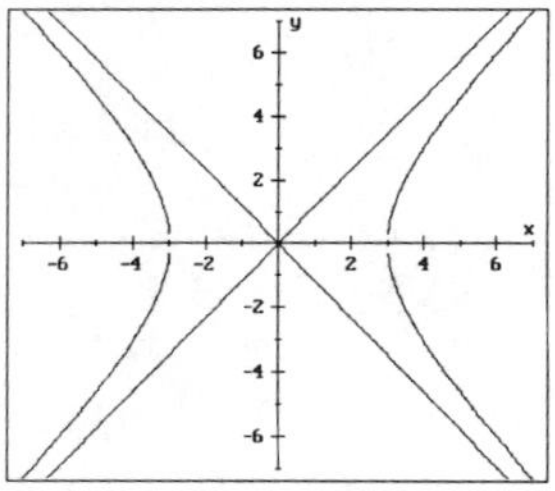

30. $3x^2 - 4y^2 = 36$

$$\frac{3x^2}{36} - \frac{4y^2}{36} = \frac{36}{36}$$

$$\frac{x^2}{12} - \frac{y^2}{9} = 1$$

Center: $(0, 0)$, $a = 2\sqrt{3}$, $b = 3$, horizontal

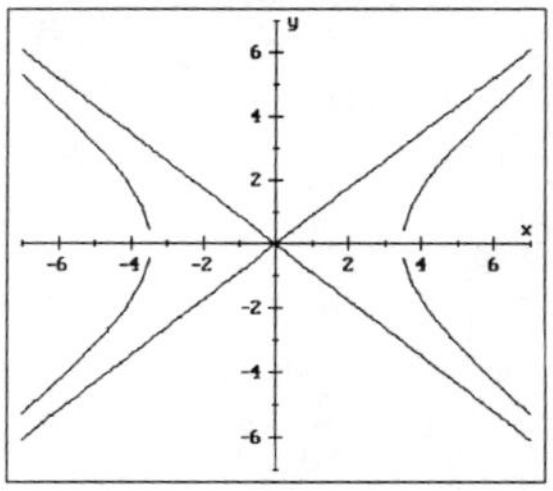

31. $y^2 - x^2 = 1$

$$\frac{y^2}{1} - \frac{x^2}{1} = 1$$

Center: $(0, 0)$, $a = 1$, $b = 1$, vertical

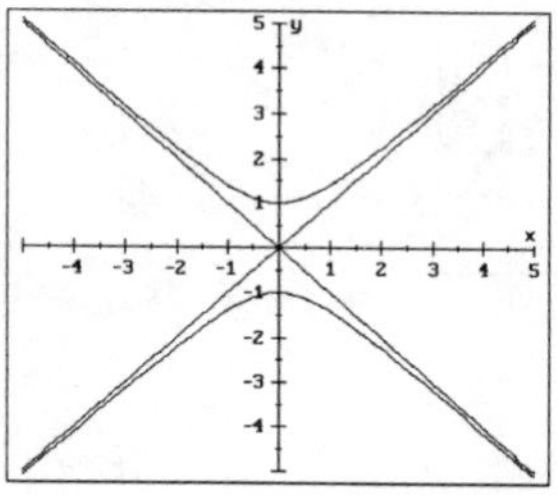

32. $9(y+2)^2 - 4(x-1)^2 = 36$

$$\frac{9(y+2)^2}{36} - \frac{4(x-1)^2}{36} = \frac{36}{36}$$

$$\frac{(y+2)^2}{4} - \frac{(x-1)^2}{9} = 1$$

Center: $(1, -2)$, $a = 2$, $b = 3$, vertical

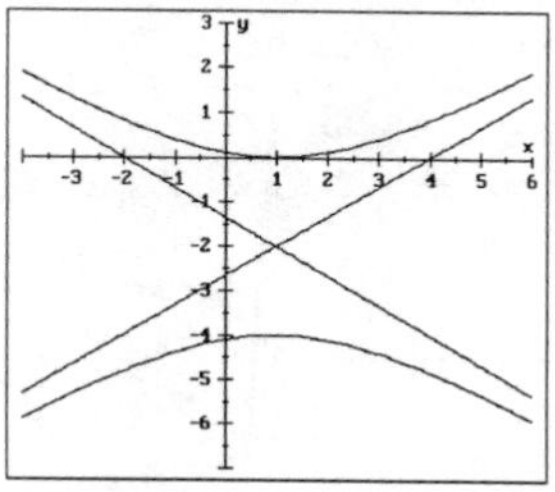

33.

$$4x^2 - 2y^2 + 8x - 8y = 8$$
$$4(x^2 + 2x) - 2(y^2 + 4y) = 8$$
$$4(x^2 + 2x + 1) - 2(y^2 + 4y + 4) = 8 + 4 - 8$$
$$4(x+1)^2 - 2(y+2)^2 = 4$$
$$\frac{4(x+1)^2}{4} - \frac{2(y+2)^2}{4} = \frac{4}{4}$$
$$\frac{(x+1)^2}{1} - \frac{(y+2)^2}{2} = 1$$

Center: $(-1, -2)$, $a = 1$, $b = \sqrt{2}$, horizontal

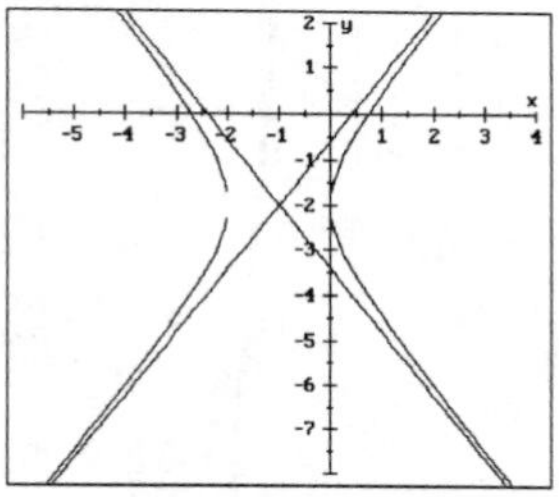

34.

$$x^2 - y^2 - 4x - 6y = 6$$
$$x^2 - 4x - (y^2 + 6y) = 6$$
$$x^2 - 4x + 4 - (y^2 + 6y + 9) = 6 + 4 - 9$$
$$(x-2)^2 - (y+3)^2 = 1$$
$$\frac{(x-2)^2}{1} - \frac{(y+3)^2}{1} = 1$$

Center: $(2, -3)$, $a = 1$, $b = 1$, horizontal

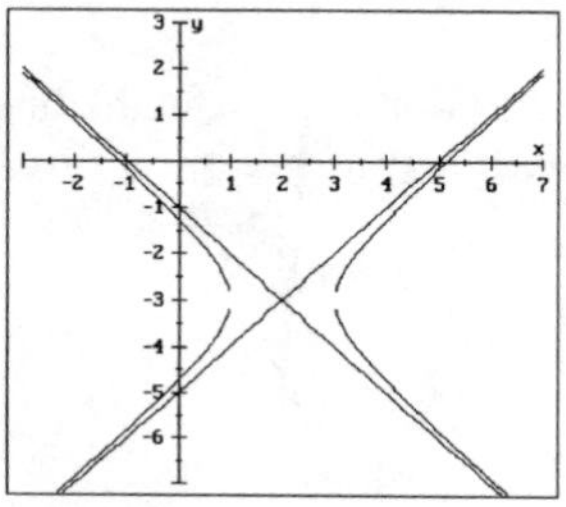

35.

$$y^2 - 4x^2 + 6y + 32x = 59$$
$$y^2 + 6y - 4(x^2 - 8x) = 59$$
$$y^2 + 6y + 9 - 4(x^2 - 8x + 16) = 59 + 9 - 64$$
$$(y+3)^2 - 4(x-4)^2 = 4$$
$$\frac{(y+3)^2}{4} - \frac{(x-4)^2}{1} = 1$$

Center: $(4, -3)$, $a = 2$, $b = 1$, vertical

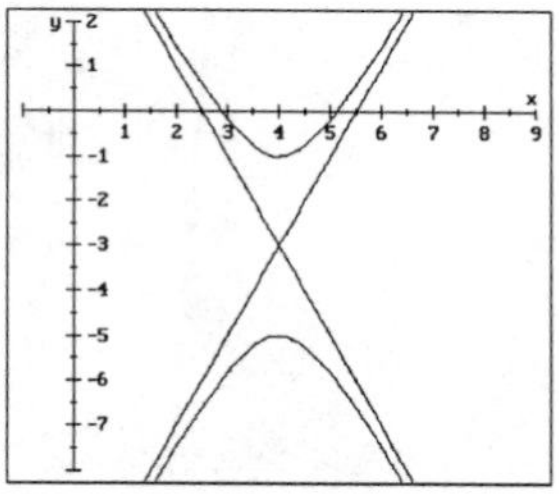

36.

$$\begin{aligned} x^2 + 6x - y^2 + 2y &= -11 \\ x^2 + 6x - (y^2 - 2y) &= -11 \\ x^2 + 6x + 9 - (y^2 - 2y + 1) &= -11 + 9 - 1 \\ (x+3)^2 - (y-1)^2 &= -3 \\ \frac{(x+3)^2}{-3} - \frac{(y-1)^2}{-3} &= 1 \\ \frac{(y-1)^2}{3} - \frac{(x+3)^2}{3} &= 1 \end{aligned}$$

Center: $(-3, 1)$, $a = \sqrt{3}$, $b = \sqrt{3}$, vertical

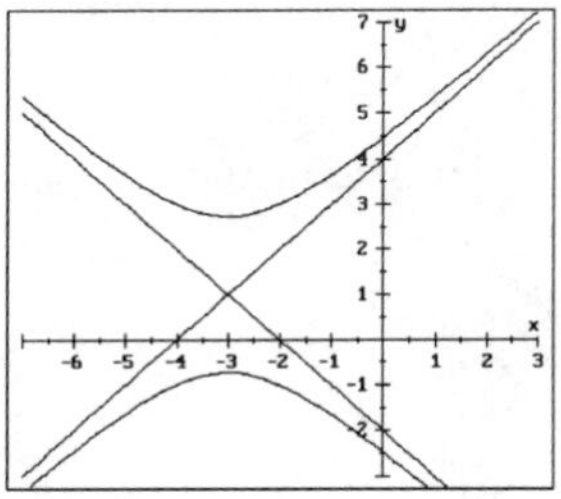

37. $-xy = 6$

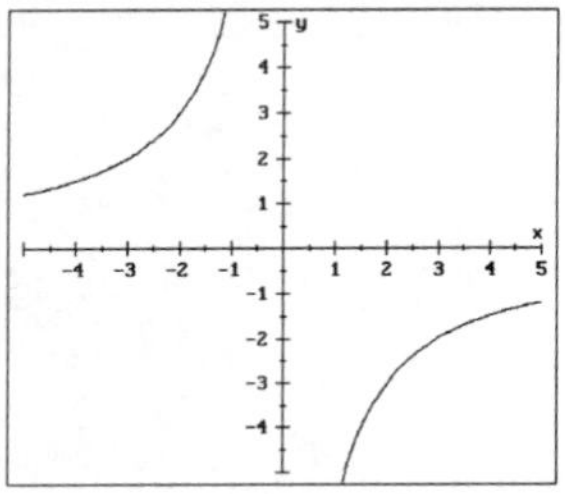

38. $xy = 20$

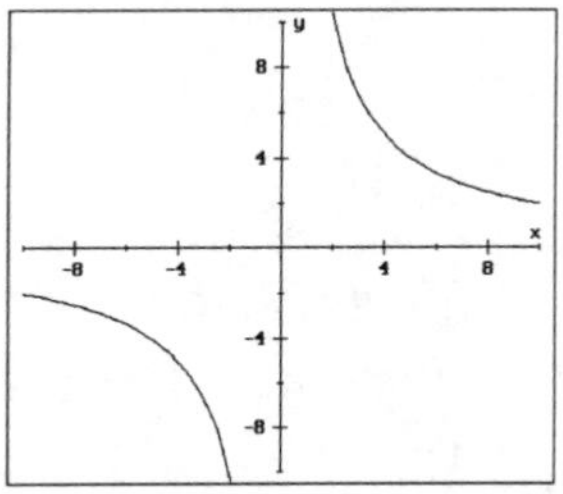

39. Foci: $(-2, 1)$, $(8, 1)$
Center: $(3, 1)$, $c = 5$
$2a = 6 \Rightarrow a = 3, b = 4$

$$\frac{(x-3)^2}{9} - \frac{(y-1)^2}{16} = 1$$

40. Foci: $(3, -1)$, $(3, 5)$
Center: $(3, 2)$, $c = 3$

$$2a = 5 \Rightarrow a = \frac{5}{2}, b = \frac{\sqrt{11}}{2}$$

$$\frac{4(y-2)^2}{25} - \frac{4(x-3)^2}{11} = 1$$

41. The distance between the point (x, y) and the line $x = -2$ is the difference between the y-coordinates, or $y - (-2) = y + 2$.

$$\begin{aligned} \sqrt{(x-0)^2 + (y-3)^2} &= \frac{3}{2}(y+2) \\ x^2 + (y-3)^2 &= \frac{9}{4}(y+2)^2 \\ 4x^2 + 4(y-3)^2 &= 9(y+2)^2 \\ 4x^2 + 4(y^2 - 6y + 9) &= 9(y^2 + 4y + 4) \\ 4x^2 - 5y^2 - 60y &= 0 \end{aligned}$$

42. The distance between the point (x, y) and the line $y = -3$ is the difference between the x-coordinates, or $x - (-3) = x + 3$.

$$\sqrt{(x-5)^2 + (y-4)^2} = \frac{5}{3}(x+3)$$
$$(x-5)^2 + (y-4)^2 = \frac{25}{9}(x+3)^2$$
$$9(x-5)^2 + 9(y-4)^2 = 25(x+3)^2$$
$$9(x^2 - 10x + 25) + 9(y^2 - 8y + 16) = 25(x^2 + 6x + 9)$$
$$9x^2 - 90x + 225 + 9y^2 - 72y + 144 = 25x^2 + 150x + 225$$
$$9y^2 - 72y - 16x^2 - 240x + 144 = 0$$
$$9(y^2 - 8y) - 16(x^2 + 15x) = -144$$
$$9(y^2 - 8y + 16) - 16\left(x^2 + 15x + \frac{225}{4}\right) = -144 + 144 - 900$$
$$9(y-4)^2 - 16\left(x + \tfrac{15}{2}\right)^2 = -900$$
$$16\left(x + \tfrac{15}{2}\right)^2 - 9(y-4)^2 = 900$$
$$\frac{4\left(x + \frac{15}{2}\right)^2}{225} - \frac{(y-4)^2}{100} = 1$$

43. $a = 100{,}000{,}000$
$c = 200{,}000{,}000$
$$\frac{x^2}{100{,}000{,}000^2} + \frac{y^2}{200{,}000{,}000^2} = 1$$

44. The point $(10, 1 \times 10^{-4})$ is on the graph.
$$y = \frac{k}{x}$$
$$1 \times 10^{-4} = \frac{k}{10}$$
$$1 \times 10^{-3} = k$$

45. $2a = 24 \Rightarrow a = 12$
$c = 13 \Rightarrow b = 5$
$$\frac{x^2}{144} - \frac{y^2}{25} = 1$$

46. $2a = 12 \Rightarrow a = 6$
$c = 10 \Rightarrow b = 8$
$$\frac{x^2}{36} - \frac{y^2}{64} = 1$$

47. **Answers may vary.**

48. **Answers may vary.**

49. **Answers may vary.**

50. **Answers may vary.**

51.
$$f(x) = 3x - 2$$
$$y = 3x - 2$$
$$x = 3y - 2$$
$$x + 2 = 3y$$
$$\frac{x+2}{3} = y \Rightarrow f^{-1}(x) = \frac{x+2}{3}$$

52.
$$f(x) = \frac{x+1}{x}$$
$$y = \frac{x+1}{x}$$
$$x = \frac{y+1}{y}$$
$$xy = y + 1$$
$$xy - y = 1$$
$$y(x-1) = 1$$
$$y = \frac{1}{x-1} \Rightarrow f^{-1}(x) = \frac{1}{x-1}$$

53.
$$\begin{aligned} f(x) &= \frac{5x}{x+2} \\ y &= \frac{5x}{x+2} \\ x &= \frac{5y}{y+2} \\ x(y+2) &= 5y \\ xy+2x &= 5y \\ 2x &= 5y-xy \\ 2x &= y(5-x) \\ \frac{2x}{5-x} &= y \Rightarrow f^{-1}(x) = \frac{2x}{5-x} \end{aligned}$$

54.
$$\begin{aligned} f(x) &= x \\ y &= x \\ x &= y \Rightarrow f^{-1}(x) = x \end{aligned}$$

55. $f(g(x)) = f\left((x+1)^2\right) = \left((x+1)^2\right)^2 + 1 = (x+1)^4 + 1$

56. $g(f(x)) = g(x^2+1) = (x^2+1+1)^2 = (x^2+2)^2$

57. $f(f(x)) = f(x^2+1) = (x^2+1)^2 + 1$

58. $g(g(x)) = g\left((x+1)^2\right) = \left((x+1)^2+1\right)^2$

Exercise 7.4 (page 550)

1. graphs

2. graphically, algebraically

3. $\begin{cases} 8x^2 + 32y^2 = 256 \\ x = 2y \end{cases}$

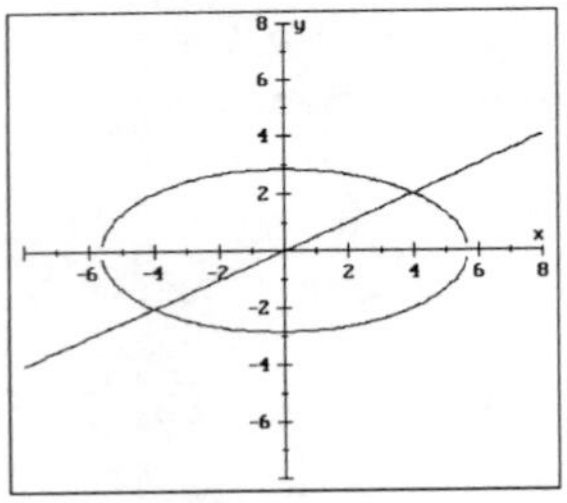

$(4, 2), (-4, 2)$

4. $\begin{cases} x^2 + y^2 = 2 \\ x + y = 2 \end{cases}$

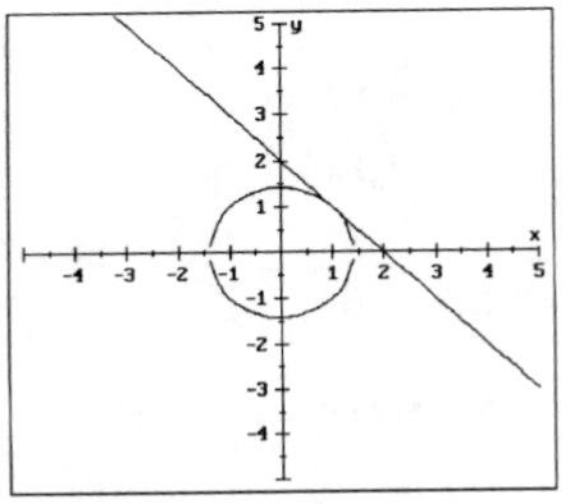

$(1, 1)$

5. $\begin{cases} x^2 + y^2 = 90 \\ y = x^2 \end{cases}$

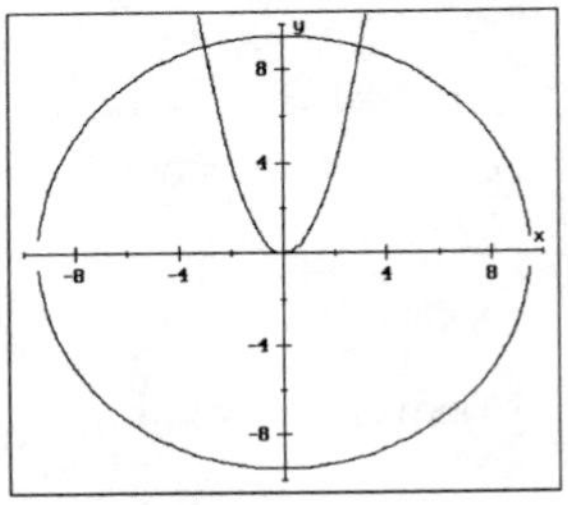

$(3, 9), (-3, 9)$

6. $\begin{cases} x^2 + y^2 = 5 \\ x + y = 3 \end{cases}$

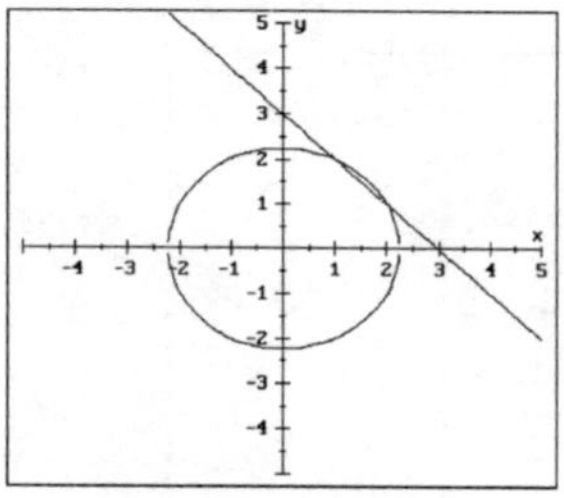

$(1, 2), (2, 1)$

7. $\begin{cases} x^2 + y^2 = 25 \\ 12x^2 + 64y^2 = 768 \end{cases}$

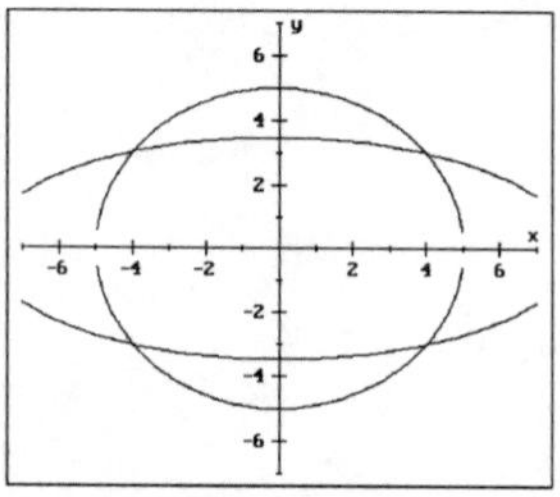

$(-4, 3), (4, 3)$
$(-4, -3), (4, -3)$

8. $\begin{cases} x^2 + y^2 = 13 \\ y = x^2 - 1 \end{cases}$

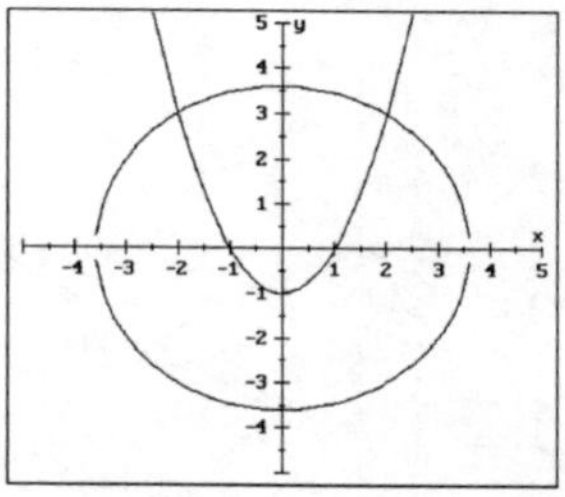

$(-2, 3), (2, 3)$

9. $\begin{cases} x^2 - 13 = -y^2 \\ y = 2x - 4 \end{cases}$

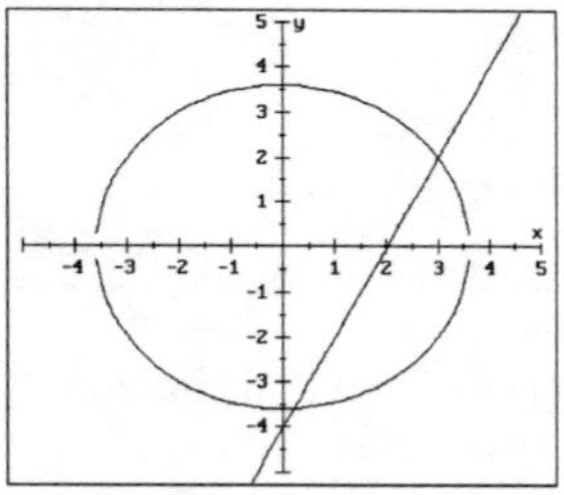

$\left(\frac{1}{5}, -\frac{18}{5}\right), (3, 2)$

10. $\begin{cases} x^2 + y^2 = 20 \\ y = x^2 \end{cases}$

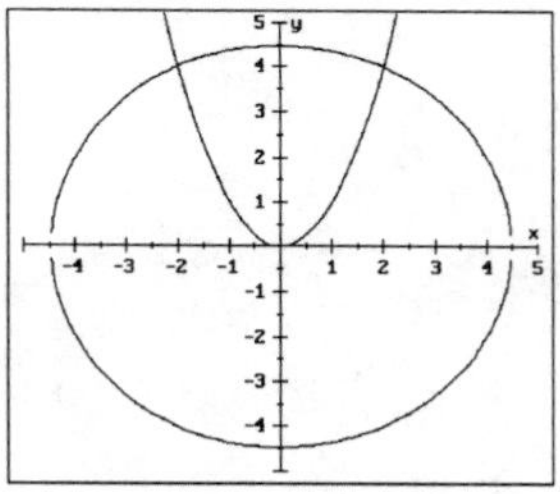

$(2, 4), (-2, 4)$

11. $\begin{cases} x^2 - 6x - y = -5 \\ x^2 - 6x + y = -5 \end{cases}$

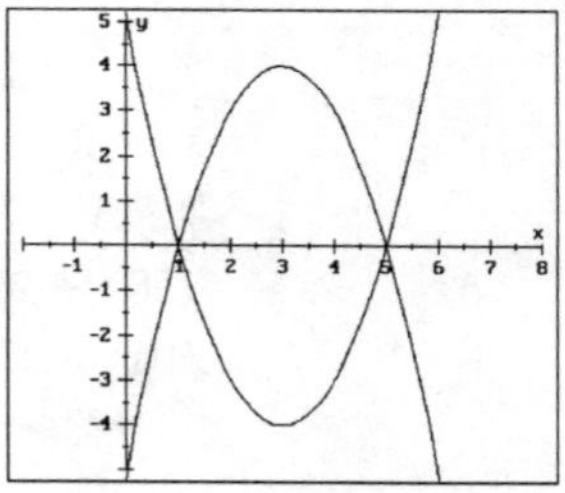

$(1, 0), (5, 0)$

12. $\begin{cases} x^2 - y^2 = -5 \\ 3x^2 + 2y^2 = 30 \end{cases}$

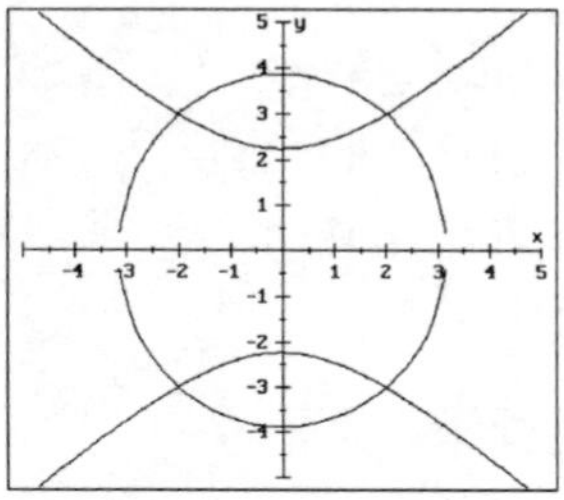

$(-2, 3), (2, 3)$
$(-2, -3), (2, -3)$

13. $\begin{cases} y = x + 1 \\ y = x^2 + x \end{cases}$

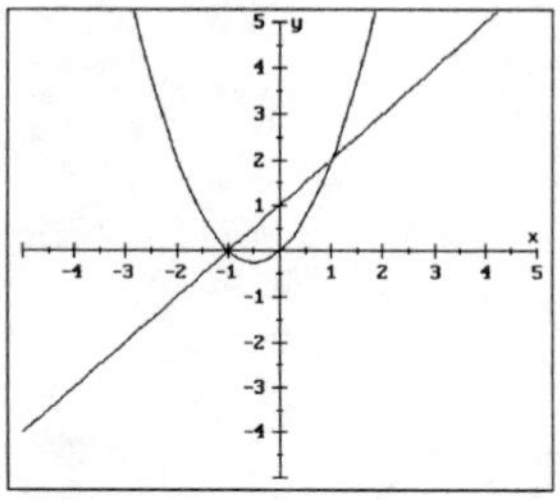

$(1, 2), (-1, 0)$

14. $\begin{cases} y = 6 - x^2 \\ y = x^2 - x \end{cases}$

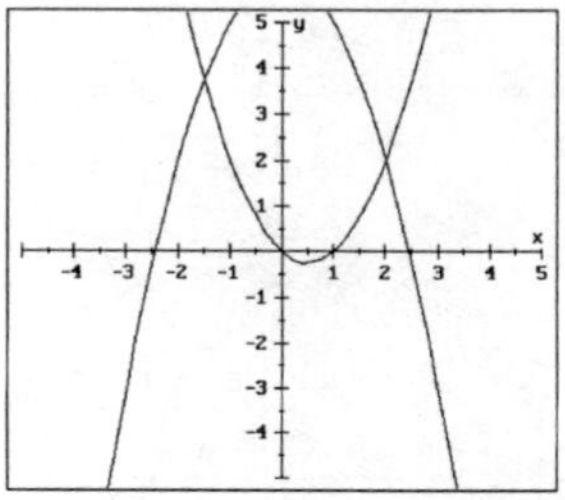

$(2, 2), (-1.5, 3.75)$

15. $\begin{cases} 6x^2 + 9y^2 = 10 & \Rightarrow\ y = \pm\sqrt{\frac{10-6x^2}{9}} \\ 3y - 2x = 0 & \Rightarrow\ y = \frac{2}{3}x \end{cases}$

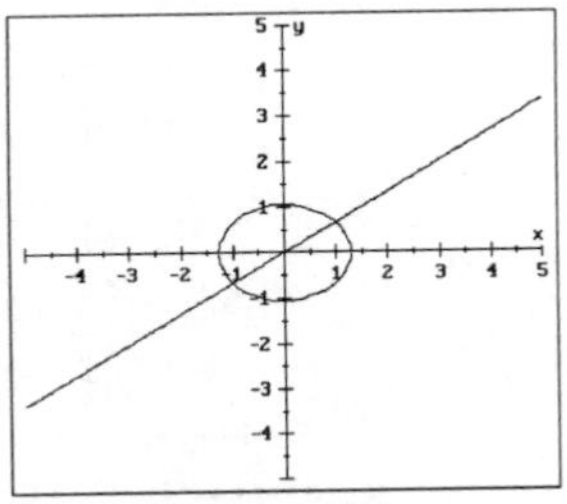

$(1, 0.67), (-1, -0.67)$

16. $\begin{cases} x^2 + y^2 = 68 & \Rightarrow\ y = \pm\sqrt{68 - x^2} \\ y^2 - 3x^2 = 4 & \Rightarrow\ y = \pm\sqrt{4 + 3x^2} \end{cases}$

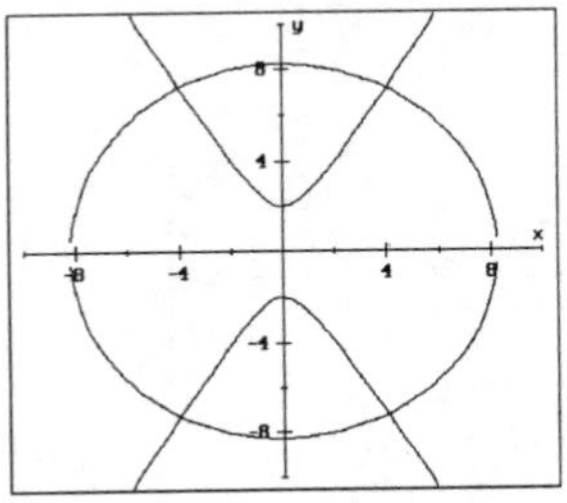

$(4, 7.2), (4, -7.2), (-4, 7.2), (-4, -7.2)$

17.

$$5x + 3y = 15 \Rightarrow y = \frac{15 - 5x}{3}$$
$$25x^2 + 9y^2 = 225$$
$$25x^2 + 9\left(\frac{15 - 5x}{3}\right)^2 = 225$$
$$25x^2 + (15 - 5x)^2 = 225$$
$$25x^2 + 225 - 150x + 25x^2 = 225$$
$$50x^2 - 150x = 0$$
$$50x(x - 3) = 0$$

$x = 0$	$x = 3$
$y = \frac{15 - 5(0)}{3} = 5$	$y = \frac{15 - 5(3)}{3} = 0$
$(0, 5)$	$(3, 0)$

18.

$$y = x^2 \Rightarrow x^2 = y$$
$$x^2 + y^2 = 20$$
$$y + y^2 = 20$$
$$y^2 + y - 20 = 0$$
$$(y - 4)(y + 5) = 0$$

$y = 4$	$y = -5$
$4 = x^2 \Rightarrow x = \pm 2$	$-5 = x^2$
$(2, 4), (-2, 4)$	no real solutions

19.

$$x + y = 2 \Rightarrow y = 2 - x$$
$$x^2 + y^2 = 2$$
$$x^2 + (2 - x)^2 = 2$$
$$x^2 + 4 - 4x + x^2 = 2$$
$$2x^2 - 4x + 2 = 0$$
$$2(x - 1)(x - 1) = 0$$

$x = 1$
$y = 2 - 1 = 1$
$(1, 1)$

20.

$$x^2 + y^2 = 36 \Rightarrow x^2 = 36 - y^2$$
$$49x^2 + 36y^2 = 1764$$
$$49(36 - y^2) + 36y^2 = 1764$$
$$1764 - 49y^2 + 36y^2 = 1764$$
$$-13y^2 = 0$$

$y = 0$
$x^2 = 36 - 0^2 \Rightarrow x = \pm 6$
$(6, 0), (-6, 0)$

21.

$$x + y = 3 \Rightarrow y = 3 - x$$
$$x^2 + y^2 = 5$$
$$x^2 + (3 - x)^2 = 5$$
$$x^2 + 9 - 6x + x^2 = 5$$
$$2x^2 - 6x + 4 = 0$$
$$2(x - 1)(x - 2) = 0$$

$x = 1$	$x = 2$
$y = 3 - 1 = 2$	$y = 3 - 2 = 1$
$(1, 2)$	$(2, 1)$

22.

$$x^2 - x - y = 2 \Rightarrow y = x^2 - x - 2$$
$$4x - 3y = 0$$
$$4x - 3(x^2 - x - 2) = 0$$
$$4x - 3x^2 + 3x + 6 = 0$$
$$3x^2 - 7x - 6 = 0$$
$$(3x + 2)(x - 3) = 0$$

$x = -\frac{2}{3}$	$x = 3$
$y = \left(-\frac{2}{3}\right)^2 - \left(-\frac{2}{3}\right) - 2$	$y = 3^2 - 3 - 2$
$= -\frac{8}{9}$	$= 4$
$\left(-\frac{2}{3}, -\frac{8}{9}\right)$	$(3, 4)$

23.

$$y = x^2 - 1 \Rightarrow x^2 = y + 1$$
$$x^2 + y^2 = 13$$
$$y + 1 + y^2 = 13$$
$$y^2 + y - 12 = 0$$
$$(y - 3)(y + 4) = 0$$

$y = 3$	$y = -4$
$3 + 1 = x^2 \Rightarrow x = \pm 2$	$-4 + 1 = x^2$
$(2, 3), (-2, 3)$	no real solutions

24.

$$x^2 + y^2 = 25 \Rightarrow x^2 = 25 - y^2$$
$$2x^2 - 3y^2 = 5$$
$$2(25 - y^2) - 3y^2 = 5$$
$$50 - 2y^2 - 3y^2 = 5$$
$$45 = 5y^2$$
$$9 = y^2$$

$y = 3$	$y = -3$
$x^2 = 25 - 3^2 \Rightarrow x = \pm 4$	$x^2 = 25 - (-3)^2 \Rightarrow x = \pm 4$
$(4, 3), (-4, 3)$	$(4, -3), (-4, -3)$

25.

$$y = x^2 \Rightarrow x^2 = y$$
$$x^2 + y^2 = 30$$
$$y + y^2 = 30$$
$$y^2 + y - 30 = 0$$
$$(y - 5)(y + 6) = 0$$

$y = 5$	$y = -6$
$5 = x^2 \Rightarrow x = \pm\sqrt{5}$	$-6 = x^2$
$\left(\sqrt{5}, 5\right), \left(-\sqrt{5}, 5\right)$	no real solutions

26.

$$x^2 + y^2 = 9 \Rightarrow x^2 = 9 - y^2$$
$$9x^2 - 7y^2 = 81$$
$$9(9 - y^2) - 7y^2 = 81$$
$$81 - 9y^2 - 7y^2 = 81$$
$$-16y^2 = 0$$

$y = 0$
$x^2 = 9 - 0^2 \Rightarrow x = \pm 3$
$(3, 0), (-3, 0)$

27.

$$\begin{aligned} x^2 + y^2 &= 13 \\ x^2 - y^2 &= 5 \\ \hline 2x^2 &= 18 \\ x^2 &= 9 \\ x &= \pm 3 \end{aligned} \qquad \begin{aligned} x^2 + y^2 &= 13 \\ 9 + y^2 &= 13 \\ y^2 &= 4 \\ y &= \pm 2 \end{aligned}$$

$(3, 2), (-3, 2), (3, -2), (-3, -2)$

28.

$$\begin{aligned} 2x^2 + y^2 &= 6 \\ x^2 - y^2 &= 3 \\ \hline 3x^2 &= 9 \\ x^2 &= 3 \\ x &= \pm\sqrt{3} \end{aligned} \qquad \begin{aligned} 2x^2 + y^2 &= 6 \\ 2(3) + y^2 &= 6 \\ y^2 &= 0 \\ y &= 0 \end{aligned}$$

$\left(\sqrt{3}, 0\right), \left(-\sqrt{3}, 0\right)$

29.
$$\begin{array}{rcl} x^2+y^2 &=& 20 \\ x^2-y^2 &=& -12 \\ \hline 2x^2 &=& 8 \\ x^2 &=& 4 \\ x &=& \pm 2 \end{array} \qquad \begin{aligned} x^2+y^2&=20\\ 4+y^2&=20\\ y^2&=16\\ y&=\pm 4\end{aligned}$$
$(2, 4), (-2, 4), (2, -4), (-2, -4)$

30.
$$\begin{aligned} xy = -\tfrac{9}{2} \Rightarrow y &= -\tfrac{9}{2x} \\ 3x+2y &= 6 \\ 3x + 2\left(-\frac{9}{2x}\right) &= 6 \\ 3x - \frac{9}{x} &= 6 \\ 3x^2 - 6x - 9 &= 0 \\ 3(x-3)(x+1) &= 0 \end{aligned}$$
$$\begin{array}{c} x=3 \\ \hline y = -\frac{9}{2(3)} = -\frac{3}{2} \\ \left(3, -\frac{3}{2}\right) \end{array} \qquad \begin{array}{c} x=-1 \\ \hline y = -\frac{9}{2(-1)} = \frac{9}{2} \\ \left(-1, \frac{9}{2}\right) \end{array}$$

31.
$$\begin{aligned} y = x^2 - 10 \Rightarrow x^2 &= y + 10 \\ y^2 &= 40 - x^2 \\ y^2 &= 40 - y - 10 \\ y^2 + y - 30 &= 0 \\ (y-5)(y+6) &= 0 \end{aligned}$$
$$\begin{array}{c} y=5 \\ \hline x^2 = 5+10 \Rightarrow x = \pm\sqrt{15} \\ \left(\sqrt{15}, 5\right), \left(-\sqrt{15}, 5\right) \end{array} \qquad \begin{array}{c} y=-6 \\ \hline x^2 = -6+10 \Rightarrow x = \pm 2 \\ (2, -6), (-2, -6) \end{array}$$

32.
$$\begin{array}{rcl} x^2 - 6x - y &=& -5 \\ x^2 - 6x + y &=& -5 \\ \hline 2x^2 - 12x &=& -10 \\ 2(x-1)(x-5) &=& 0 \end{array}$$
$$\begin{array}{c} x=1 \\ \hline y = x^2 - 6x + 5 = 0 \\ (1, 0) \end{array} \qquad \begin{array}{c} x=5 \\ \hline y = x^2 - 6x + 5 = 0 \\ (5, 0) \end{array}$$

33.
$$\begin{aligned} y = x^2 - 4 \Rightarrow x^2 &= y + 4 \\ x^2 - y^2 &= -16 \\ y + 4 - y^2 &= -16 \\ y^2 - y - 20 &= 0 \\ (y-5)(y+4) &= 0 \end{aligned}$$
$$\begin{array}{c} y=5 \\ \hline x^2 = 5+4 \Rightarrow x = \pm 3 \\ (3, 5), (-3, 5) \end{array} \qquad \begin{array}{c} y=-4 \\ \hline x^2 = -4+4 \Rightarrow x = 0 \\ (0, -4) \end{array}$$

34.
$$\begin{array}{rcl} 6x^2 + 8y^2 &=& 182 \\ 8x^2 - 3y^2 &=& 24 \\ \hline \\ 18x^2 + 24y^2 &=& 546 \\ 64x^2 - 24y^2 &=& 192 \\ \hline 82x^2 &=& 738 \\ x^2 &=& 9 \\ x &=& \pm 3 \end{array} \qquad \begin{aligned} 6x^2 + 8y^2 &= 182 \\ 6(9) + 8y^2 &= 182 \\ 8y^2 &= 128 \\ y^2 &= 16 \\ y &= \pm 4 \end{aligned}$$
$(3, 4), (-3, 4), (3, -4), (-3, -4)$

35.
$$\begin{array}{rcl} x^2 - y^2 &=& -5 \\ 3x^2 + 2y^2 &=& 30 \\ \hline \\ 2x^2 - 2y^2 &=& -10 \\ 3x^2 + 2y^2 &=& 30 \\ \hline 5x^2 &=& 20 \\ x^2 &=& 4 \\ x &=& \pm 2 \end{array} \qquad \begin{aligned} 3x^2 + 2y^2 &= 30 \\ 3(4) + 2y^2 &= 30 \\ 2y^2 &= 18 \\ y^2 &= 9 \\ y &= \pm 3 \end{aligned}$$
$(2, 3), (-2, 3), (2, -3), (-2, -3)$

36.
$$\begin{aligned} \tfrac{1}{x}+\tfrac{1}{y} &= 5 \\ \tfrac{1}{x}-\tfrac{1}{y} &= -3 \\ \hline \tfrac{2}{x} &= 2 \\ x &= 1 \end{aligned} \qquad \begin{aligned} \tfrac{1}{x}+\tfrac{1}{y} &= 5 \\ \tfrac{1}{1}+\tfrac{1}{y} &= 5 \\ \tfrac{1}{y} &= 4 \\ y &= \tfrac{1}{4} \end{aligned}$$
$$\left(1, \tfrac{1}{4}\right)$$

37.
$$\begin{aligned} \tfrac{1}{x}+\tfrac{2}{y} &= 1 \\ \tfrac{2}{x}-\tfrac{1}{y} &= \tfrac{1}{3} \\ \hline \end{aligned} \qquad \begin{aligned} \tfrac{1}{x}+\tfrac{2}{y} &= 1 \\ \tfrac{4}{x}-\tfrac{2}{y} &= \tfrac{2}{3} \\ \hline \tfrac{5}{x} &= \tfrac{5}{3} \\ x &= 3 \end{aligned} \qquad \begin{aligned} \tfrac{1}{x}+\tfrac{2}{y} &= 1 \\ \tfrac{1}{3}+\tfrac{2}{y} &= 1 \\ \tfrac{2}{y} &= \tfrac{2}{3} \\ y &= 3 \end{aligned}$$
$$(3, 3)$$

38.
$$\begin{aligned} \tfrac{1}{x}+\tfrac{3}{y} &= 4 \\ \tfrac{2}{x}-\tfrac{1}{y} &= 7 \\ \hline \end{aligned} \qquad \begin{aligned} \tfrac{1}{x}+\tfrac{3}{y} &= 4 \\ \tfrac{6}{x}-\tfrac{3}{y} &= 21 \\ \hline \tfrac{7}{x} &= 25 \\ x &= \tfrac{7}{25} \end{aligned} \qquad \begin{aligned} \tfrac{1}{x}+\tfrac{3}{y} &= 4 \\ \tfrac{1}{7/25}+\tfrac{3}{y} &= 4 \\ \tfrac{3}{y} &= \tfrac{3}{7} \\ y &= 7 \Rightarrow \left(\tfrac{7}{25}, 7\right) \end{aligned}$$

39.
$$\begin{aligned} 3y^2 &= xy \\ 3y^2 - xy &= 0 \\ y(3y-x) &= 0 \\ y = 0 &\text{ or } x = 3y \end{aligned}$$

$y = 0$:
$$\begin{aligned} 2x^2 + xy - 84 &= 0 \\ 2x^2 + x(0) - 84 &= 0 \\ 2x^2 &= 84 \\ x^2 &= 42 \\ x &= \pm\sqrt{42} \end{aligned}$$
$$\left(\sqrt{42}, 0\right), \left(-\sqrt{42}, 0\right)$$

$x = 3y$:
$$\begin{aligned} 2x^2 + xy - 84 &= 0 \\ 2(3y)^2 + (3y)y - 84 &= 0 \\ 18y^2 + 3y^2 - 84 &= 0 \\ 21y^2 &= 84 \\ y^2 = 4 &\Rightarrow y = \pm 2 \end{aligned}$$
$$(6, 2), (-6, -2)$$

40.
$$\begin{aligned} x^2 + y^2 = 10 &\Rightarrow x^2 = 10 - y^2 \\ 2x^2 - 3y^2 &= 5 \\ 2\left(10 - y^2\right) - 3y^2 &= 5 \\ 20 - 2y^2 - 3y^2 &= 5 \\ 15 &= 5y^2 \\ 3 &= y^2 \end{aligned}$$

$y = \sqrt{3}$:
$$\begin{aligned} x^2 &= 10 - \left(\sqrt{3}\right)^2 \\ x^2 &= 7 \\ x &= \pm\sqrt{7} \end{aligned}$$
$$\left(\sqrt{7}, \sqrt{3}\right), \left(-\sqrt{7}, \sqrt{3}\right)$$

$y = -\sqrt{3}$:
$$\begin{aligned} x^2 &= 10 - \left(-\sqrt{3}\right)^2 \\ x^2 &= 7 \\ x &= \pm\sqrt{7} \end{aligned}$$
$$\left(\sqrt{7}, -\sqrt{3}\right), \left(-\sqrt{7}, -\sqrt{3}\right)$$

41.
$$\begin{aligned} xy = \tfrac{1}{6} &\Rightarrow y = \tfrac{1}{6x} \\ y + x &= 5xy \\ \frac{1}{6x} + x &= \frac{5x}{6x} \\ 1 + 6x^2 &= 5x \\ 6x^2 - 5x + 1 &= 0 \\ (2x-1)(3x-1) &= 0 \end{aligned}$$

$x = \frac{1}{2}$: $y = \dfrac{1}{6(1/2)} = \dfrac{1}{3}$, $\left(\tfrac{1}{2}, \tfrac{1}{3}\right)$

$x = \frac{1}{3}$: $y = \dfrac{1}{6(1/3)} = \dfrac{1}{2}$, $\left(\tfrac{1}{3}, \tfrac{1}{2}\right)$

42.
$$\begin{aligned} xy = \tfrac{1}{12} &\Rightarrow y = \tfrac{1}{12x} \\ y + x &= 7xy \\ \frac{1}{12x} + x &= \frac{7x}{12x} \\ 1 + 12x^2 &= 7x \\ 12x^2 - 7x + 1 &= 0 \\ (4x-1)(3x-1) &= 0 \end{aligned}$$

$x = \frac{1}{4}$: $y = \dfrac{1}{12(1/4)} = \dfrac{1}{3}$, $\left(\tfrac{1}{4}, \tfrac{1}{3}\right)$

$x = \frac{1}{3}$: $y = \dfrac{1}{12(1/3)} = \dfrac{1}{4}$, $\left(\tfrac{1}{3}, \tfrac{1}{4}\right)$

43. Let x = width and y = length.

$$\begin{cases} xy = 63 \\ 2x + 2y = 32 \end{cases}$$

$xy = 63 \Rightarrow y = \frac{63}{x}$

$$2x + 2y = 32$$
$$2x + 2\left(\frac{63}{x}\right) = 32$$
$$2x^2 + 126 = 32x$$
$$2x^2 - 32x + 126 = 0$$
$$2(x-9)(x-7) = 0$$

$x = 9$	$x = 7$
$y = \frac{63}{9} = 7$	$y = \frac{63}{7} = 9$

The dimensions are 9 cm by 7 cm.

44. Let x = Grant's principal.

	I	P	r
Grant	225	x	$\frac{225}{x}$
Jeff	240	$x + 500$	$\frac{240}{x+500}$

$\boxed{\text{Jeff's rate}} = \boxed{\text{Grant's rate}} - 0.01$

$$\frac{240}{x+500} = \frac{225}{x} - 0.01$$
$$240x = 225(x+500) - 0.01x(x+500)$$
$$0.01x^2 + 20x - 112{,}500 = 0$$
$$x^2 + 2000x - 11{,}250{,}000 = 0$$
$$(x-2500)(x+4500) = 0$$

$x - 2500 = 0$ **or** $x + 4500 = 0$

$x = 2500$ $\quad x = -4500 \Rightarrow$ Grant invested \$2500 at 9% interest.

45. Let x = Carol's principal.

	I	P	r
Carol	67.50	x	$\frac{67.50}{x}$
John	94.50	$x + 150$	$\frac{94.50}{x+150}$

$\boxed{\text{John's rate}} = \boxed{\text{Carol's rate}} + 0.015$

$$\frac{94.50}{x+150} = \frac{67.50}{x} + 0.015$$
$$94.5x = 67.5(x+150) + 0.015x(x+150)$$
$$0.015x^2 - 24.75x + 10{,}125 = 0$$
$$x^2 - 1650x + 675{,}000 = 0$$
$$(x-750)(x-900) = 0$$

$x - 750 = 0$ **or** $x - 900 = 0$ Carol invested either \$750 at 9% or

$x = 750$ $\quad x = 900 \Rightarrow$ she invested \$900 at 7.5% interest.

46. Let r = Jim's rate. Then his brother's rate is $r - 17$.

	Rate	Time	Dist.
Jim's trip	r	$\frac{306}{r}$	306
Brother's trip	$r - 17$	$\frac{306}{r-17}$	306

$\boxed{\text{Jim's time}} = \boxed{\text{Brother's time}} - 1.5$

$$\frac{306}{r} = \frac{306}{r-17} - 1.5$$
$$306(r-17) = 306r - 1.5r(r-17)$$
$$1.5r^2 - 25.5r - 5202 = 0$$
$$r^2 - 17r - 3468 = 0$$
$$(r-68)(r+51) = 0$$

$r - 68 = 0$ **or** $r + 51 = 0$

$r = 68$ $\quad r = -51$ Jim drove 68 miles per hour for 4.5 hours.

47. $\begin{cases} x = 2y \\ (x-120)^2 + y^2 = 100^2 \end{cases}$

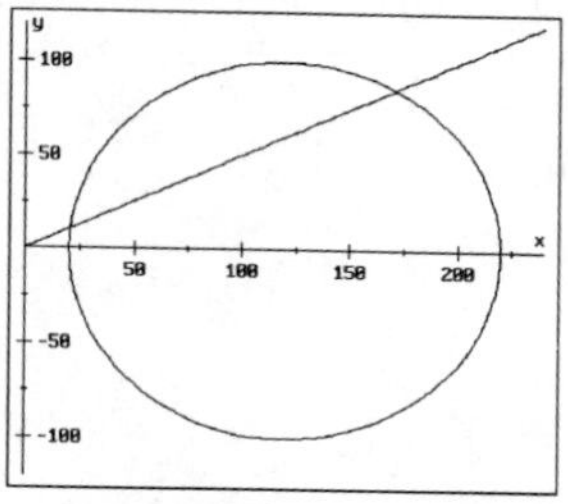

The x-coordinate of the point where the line crosses the circle closest to the origin has the approximate coordinates $(20.5, 10.25)$. The distance to the origin is about 23 miles.

48. $\begin{cases} x = 2y \\ (x-120)^2 + y^2 = 100^2 \end{cases}$

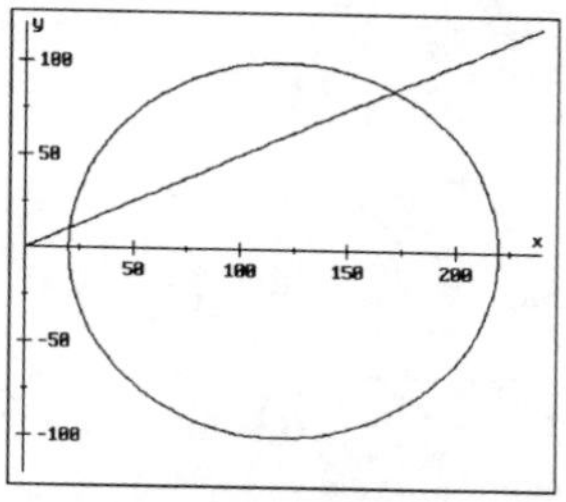

The x-coordinate of the point where the line crosses the circle farthest from the origin has the approximate coordinates $(171.5, 85.7)$. The distance to the point found in **#47** is about 169 miles.

49. **Answers may vary.**

50. **Answers may vary.**

51. **Answers may vary.**

52. **Answers may vary.**

53. **Answers may vary.**

54. **Answers may vary.**

55. $y = \dfrac{3x+1}{x-1}$
Vertical: $x = 1$
Horizontal: $y = 3$
Slant: none

56. $y = \dfrac{x^2+3}{x-1}$
Vertical: $x = 1$
Horizontal: none
Slant: $y = x + 1$

57. $y = \dfrac{3x+1}{x^2-1}$
Vertical: $x = 1, x = -1$
Horizontal: $y = 0$
Slant: none

58. $y = \dfrac{x^2+3}{x^2+1}$
Vertical: none
Horizontal: $y = 1$
Slant: none

59. $y = \dfrac{3x^2+5}{5x^2+3}$
y-axis

60. $y = \dfrac{3x^3+5}{5x^2+3}$
none

61. $y = \dfrac{3x^3}{5x^2+3}$
origin

62. $y^2 = \dfrac{3x^4+8}{2x^2-5}$
y-axis

Chapter 7 Summary (page 554)

1. **a.**
$$(x-h)^2 + (y-k)^2 = r^2$$
$$(x-0)^2 + (y-0)^2 = 4^2$$
$$x^2 + y^2 = 16$$

b.
$$r = \sqrt{(6-0)^2 + (8-0)^2} = 10$$
$$(x-h)^2 + (y-k)^2 = r^2$$
$$(x-0)^2 + (y-0)^2 = 10^2$$
$$x^2 + y^2 = 100$$

c.
$$\begin{aligned}(x-h)^2+(y-k)^2&=r^2\\(x-3)^2+(y-(-2))^2&=5^2\\(x-3)^2+(y+2)^2&=25\end{aligned}$$

d.
$$\begin{aligned}r&=\sqrt{(-2-1)^2+(4-0)^2}=5\\(x-h)^2+(y-k)^2&=r^2\\(x-(-2))^2+(y-4)^2&=5^2\\(x+2)^2+(y-4)^2&=25\end{aligned}$$

e.
$$\begin{aligned}&C\left(\frac{-2+12}{2},\frac{4+16}{2}\right)=C(5,10)\\&r=\sqrt{(12-5)^2+(16-10)^2}=\sqrt{85}\\&(x-h)^2+(y-k)^2=r^2\\&(x-5)^2+(y-10)^2=\left(\sqrt{85}\right)^2\\&(x-5)^2+(y-10)^2=85\end{aligned}$$

f.
$$\begin{aligned}&C\left(\frac{-3+7}{2},\frac{-6+10}{2}\right)=C(2,2)\\&r=\sqrt{(7-2)^2+(10-2)^2}=\sqrt{89}\\&(x-h)^2+(y-k)^2=r^2\\&(x-2)^2+(y-2)^2=\left(\sqrt{89}\right)^2\\&(x-2)^2+(y-2)^2=89\end{aligned}$$

2. **a.**
$$\begin{aligned}x^2+y^2-6x+4y&=3\\x^2-6x+y^2+4y&=3\\x^2-6x+9+y^2+4y+4&=3+9+4\\(x-3)^2+(y+2)^2&=16\end{aligned}$$

b.
$$\begin{aligned}x^2+4x+y^2-10y&=-13\\x^2+4x+4+y^2-10y+25&=-13+4+25\\(x+2)^2+(y-5)^2&=16\end{aligned}$$

3. **a.** Horizontal
$$\begin{aligned}(y-0)^2&=4p(x-0)\\(4-0)^2&=4p(-8-0)\\16&=-32p\\-2&=4p\\y^2&=-2x\end{aligned}$$

b. Vertical
$$\begin{aligned}(x-0)^2&=4p(y-0)\\(-8-0)^2&=4p(4-0)\\64&=16p\\16&=4p\\x^2&=16y\end{aligned}$$

4. Vertical
$$\begin{aligned}(x+2)^2&=4p(y-3)\\(-4+2)^2&=4p(-8-3)\\4&=4p(-11)\\-\frac{4}{11}&=4p\\(x+2)^2&=-\frac{4}{11}(y-3)\end{aligned}$$

5. **a.**

$$x^2 - 4y - 2x + 9 = 0$$
$$x^2 - 2x = 4y - 9$$
$$x^2 - 2x + 1 = 4y - 9 + 1$$
$$(x-1)^2 = 4(y-2)$$

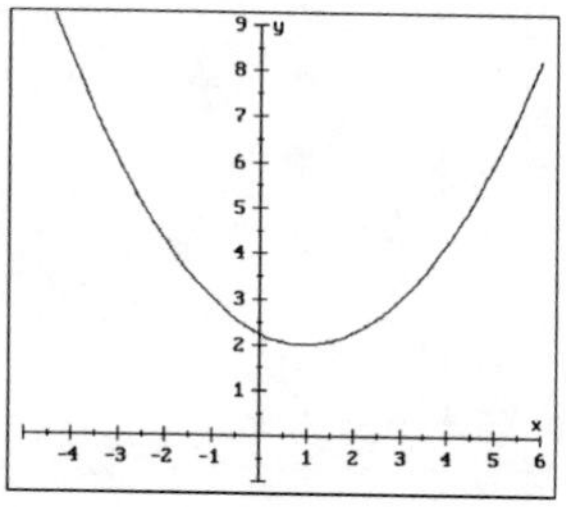

b.

$$y^2 - 6y = 4x - 13$$
$$y^2 - 6y + 9 = 4x - 13 + 9$$
$$(y-3)^2 = 4(x-1)$$

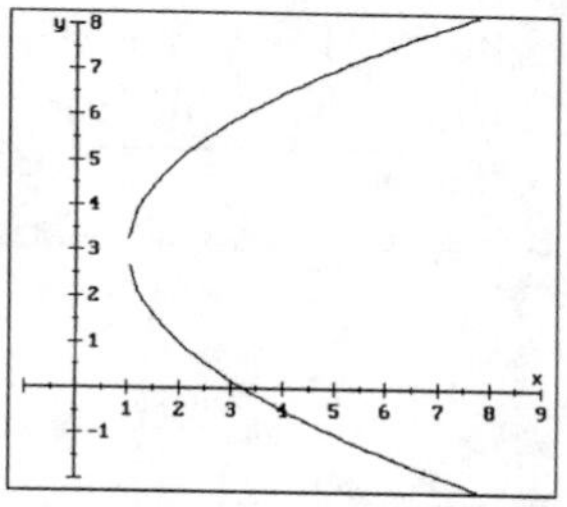

6. $a = 6, b = 4$, horizontal

$$\frac{x^2}{36} + \frac{y^2}{16} = 1$$

7. $a = 5, b = 2$, vertical

$$\frac{y^2}{25} + \frac{x^2}{4} = 1$$

8. $a = 4, b = 3$, horizontal $\Rightarrow \dfrac{(x+2)^2}{16} + \dfrac{(y-3)^2}{9} = 1$

9.

$$4x^2 + y^2 - 16x + 2y = -13$$
$$4\left(x^2 - 4x\right) + y^2 + 2y = -13$$
$$4\left(x^2 - 4x + 4\right) + y^2 + 2y + 1 = -13 + 16 + 1$$
$$4(x-2)^2 + (y+1)^2 = 4$$
$$\frac{(x-2)^2}{1} + \frac{(y+1)^2}{4} = 1$$

Center: $(2, -1)$, $a = 2$, $b = 1$, vertical

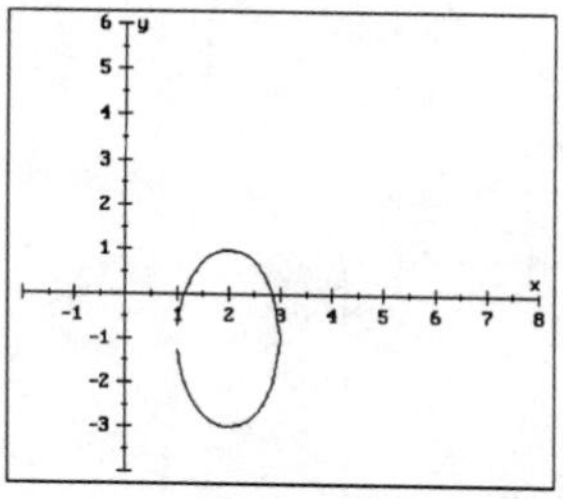

10. $a = 2, c = 4$; horizontal

$b^2 = c^2 - a^2 = 16 - 4 = 12$

$$\frac{x^2}{4} - \frac{y^2}{12} = 1$$

11. $a = 3, c = 5$; vertical

$b^2 = c^2 - a^2 = 25 - 9 = 16$

$$\frac{y^2}{9} - \frac{x^2}{16} = 1$$

12. $C(0, 3)$, $a = 3, c = 5$; horizontal

$b^2 = c^2 - a^2 = 25 - 9 = 16$

$$\frac{x^2}{9} - \frac{(y-3)^2}{16} = 1$$

13. $C(3, 0)$, $a = 3, c = 5$; vertical

$b^2 = c^2 - a^2 = 25 - 9 = 16$

$$\frac{y^2}{9} - \frac{(x-3)^2}{16} = 1$$

14. $y = \pm\dfrac{b}{a}x \Rightarrow y = \pm\dfrac{4}{5}x$

15.
$$\begin{aligned} 9x^2 - 4y^2 - 16y - 18x &= 43 \\ 9(x^2 - 2x) - 4(y^2 + 4y) &= 43 \\ 9(x^2 - 2x + 1) - 4(y^2 + 4y + 4) &= 43 + 9 - 16 \\ 9(x-1)^2 - 4(y+2)^2 &= 36 \\ \frac{(x-1)^2}{4} - \frac{(y+2)^2}{9} &= 1 \end{aligned}$$
Center: $(1, -2)$, $a = 2$, $b = 3$, horizontal

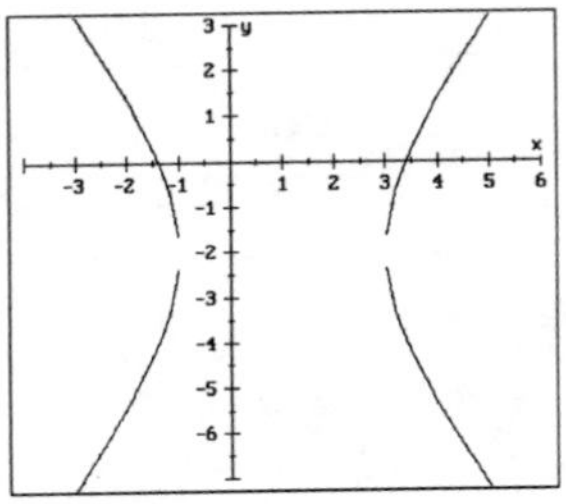

16. $4xy = 1$

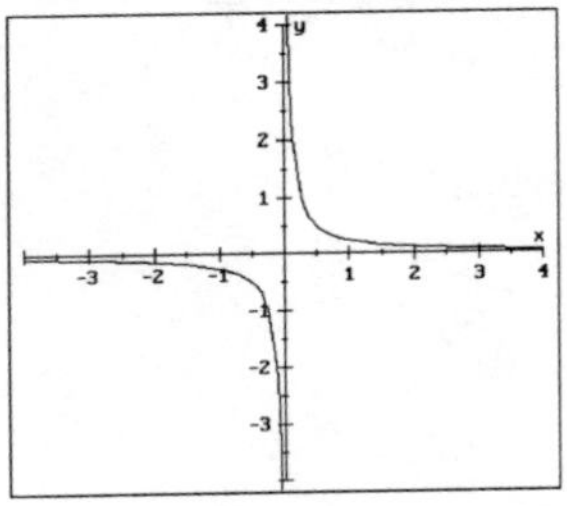

17. $\begin{cases} x^2 + y^2 = 16 \\ y = x + 4 \end{cases}$

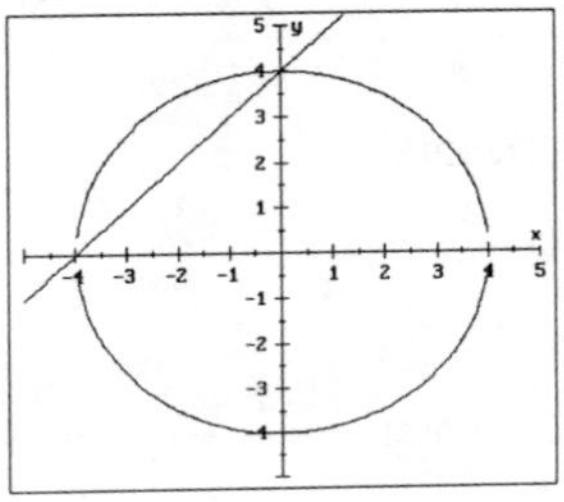

$(-4, 0), (0, 4)$

18. $\begin{cases} 3x^2 + y^2 = 52 \\ x^2 - y^2 = 12 \end{cases}$

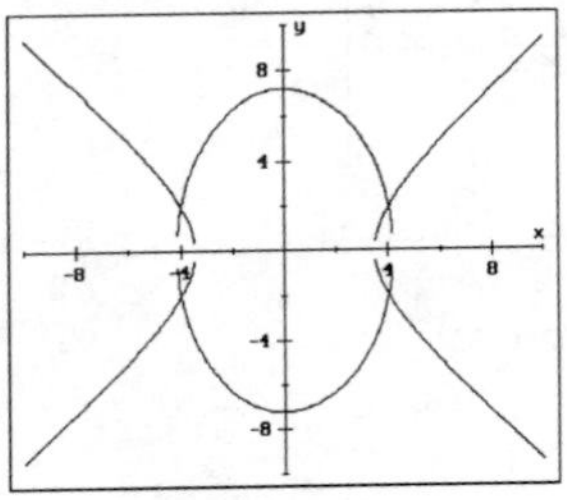

$(-4, 2), (4, 2), (-4, -2), (4, -2)$

19. $\begin{cases} \dfrac{x^2}{16} + \dfrac{y^2}{12} = 1 \\ x^2 - \dfrac{y^2}{3} = 1 \end{cases}$

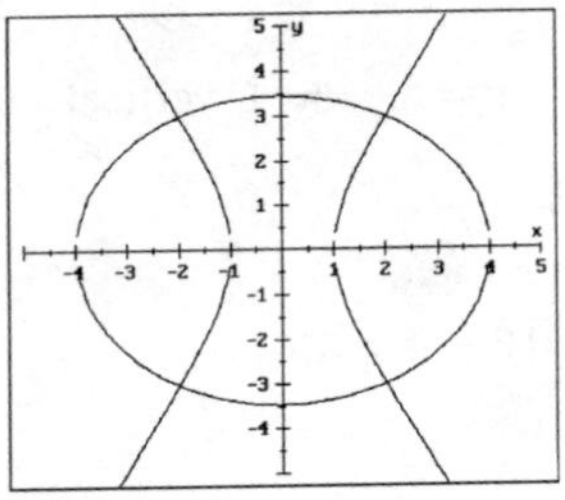

$(-2, 3), (2, 3), (-2, -3), (2, -3)$

20.
$$\begin{array}{rcl} 3x^2 + y^2 &=& 52 \\ x^2 - y^2 &=& 12 \\ \hline 4x^2 &=& 64 \\ x^2 &=& 16 \\ x &=& \pm 4 \end{array} \qquad \begin{aligned} 3x^2 + y^2 &= 52 \\ 3(16) + y^2 &= 52 \\ y^2 &= 4 \\ y &= \pm 2 \end{aligned}$$
$(4, 2), (-4, 2), (4, -2), (-4, -2)$

21. $-\sqrt{3}y + 4\sqrt{3} = 3x \Rightarrow x = \dfrac{-\sqrt{3}y + 4\sqrt{3}}{3}$

$$x^2 + y^2 = 16$$
$$\left(\frac{-\sqrt{3}y + 4\sqrt{3}}{3}\right)^2 + y^2 = 16$$
$$3y^2 - 24y + 48 + 9y^2 = 144$$
$$12y^2 - 24y - 96 = 0$$
$$12(y-4)(y+2) = 0$$

$$\underline{\quad y = 4 \quad}$$
$$x = \frac{-\sqrt{3}(4) + 4\sqrt{3}}{3} = 0 \Rightarrow (0, 4)$$

$$\underline{\quad y = -2 \quad}$$
$$x = \frac{-\sqrt{3}(-2) + 4\sqrt{3}}{3} = 2\sqrt{3} \Rightarrow \left(2\sqrt{3}, -2\right)$$

22.
$$\frac{x^2}{16} + \frac{y^2}{12} = 1$$
$$x^2 - \frac{y^2}{3} = 1$$
$$3x^2 + 4y^2 = 48$$
$$3x^2 - y^2 = 3$$
$$5y^2 = 45$$

$$5y^2 = 45$$
$$y^2 = 9$$
$$y = \pm 3$$

$$3x^2 - y^2 = 3$$
$$3x^2 - 9 = 3$$
$$3x^2 = 12$$
$$x^2 = 4$$
$$x = \pm 2 \Rightarrow (2, 3), (-2, 3), (2, -3), (-2, -3)$$

Chapter 7 Test (page 558)

1.
$$(x-h)^2 + (y-k)^2 = r^2$$
$$(x-2)^2 + (y-3)^2 = 3^2$$
$$(x-2)^2 + (y-3)^2 = 9$$

2.
$$C\left(\frac{-2+6}{2}, \frac{-2+8}{2}\right) = C(2, 3)$$
$$r = \sqrt{(6-2)^2 + (8-3)^2} = \sqrt{41}$$
$$(x-h)^2 + (y-k)^2 = r^2$$
$$(x-2)^2 + (y-3)^2 = \left(\sqrt{41}\right)^2$$
$$(x-2)^2 + (y-3)^2 = 41$$

3.
$$r = \sqrt{(7-2)^2 + (7-(-5))^2} = 13$$
$$(x-h)^2 + (y-k)^2 = r^2$$
$$(x-2)^2 + (y-(-5))^2 = 13^2$$
$$(x-2)^2 + (y+5)^2 = 169$$

4.
$$x^2 + y^2 - 4x + 6y + 4 = 0$$
$$x^2 - 4x + y^2 + 6y = -4$$
$$x^2 - 4x + 4 + y^2 + 6y + 9 = -4 + 4 + 9$$
$$(x-2)^2 + (y+3)^2 = 9$$
$$C(2, -3), r = 3$$

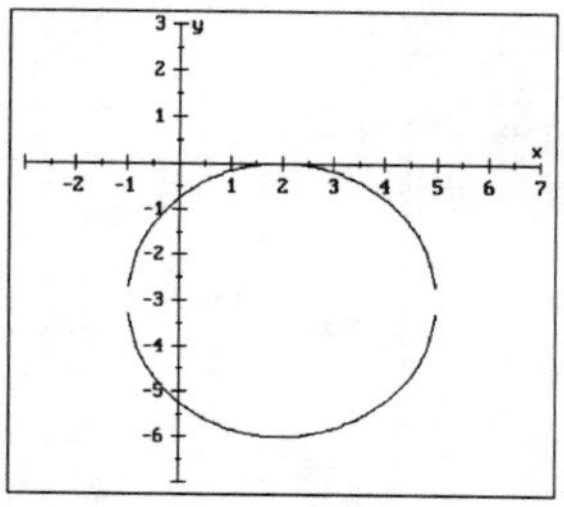

CHAPTER 7 TEST

5. Vertical (up), $p = 4$

$$(x-h)^2 = 4p(y-k)$$
$$(x-3)^2 = 4(4)(y-2)$$
$$(x-3)^2 = 16(y-2)$$

6. Horizontal

$$(y+6)^2 = 4p(x-4)$$
$$(-4+6)^2 = 4p(3-4)$$
$$4 = -4p$$
$$-4 = 4p$$
$$(y+6)^2 = -4(x-4)$$

7. $(x-2)^2 = 4p(y+3)$ **OR** $(y+3)^2 = 4p(x-2)$

$$(0-2)^2 = 4p(0+3) \qquad (0+3)^2 = 4p(0-2)$$
$$4 = 4p(3) \qquad 9 = 4p(-2)$$
$$\frac{4}{3} = 4p \qquad -\frac{9}{2} = 4p$$
$$(x-2)^2 = \tfrac{4}{3}(y+3) \qquad (y+3)^2 = -\tfrac{9}{2}(x-2)$$

8.

$$x^2 - 6x - 8y = 7$$
$$x^2 - 6x = 8y + 7$$
$$x^2 - 6x + 9 = 8y + 7 + 9$$
$$(x-3)^2 = 8(y+2)$$

Vertex: $(3, -2)$, vertical

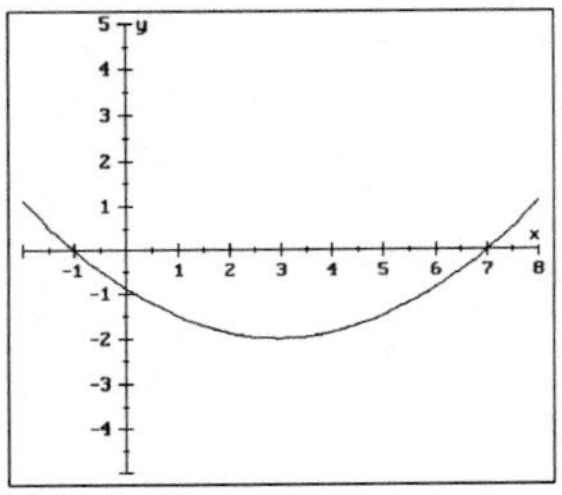

9. $a = 10$, $c = 6$, horizontal

$$b^2 = a^2 - c^2$$
$$= 100 - 36 = 64$$
$$\frac{x^2}{100} + \frac{y^2}{64} = 1$$

10. $b = 12$, $c = 5$, horizontal

$$a^2 = b^2 + c^2$$
$$= 144 + 25 = 169$$
$$\frac{x^2}{169} + \frac{y^2}{144} = 1$$

11. $a = 6$, $b = 2$, vertical

$$\frac{x^2}{4} + \frac{y^2}{36} = 1$$

12.

$$9x^2 + 4y^2 - 18x - 16y - 11 = 0$$
$$9\left(x^2 - 2x\right) + 4\left(y^2 - 4y\right) = 11$$
$$9\left(x^2 - 2x + 1\right) + 4\left(y^2 - 4y + 4\right) = 11 + 9 + 16$$
$$9(x-1)^2 + 4(y-2)^2 = 36$$
$$\frac{(x-1)^2}{4} + \frac{(y-2)^2}{9} = 1$$

Center: $(1, 2)$, $a = 3$, $b = 2$, vertical

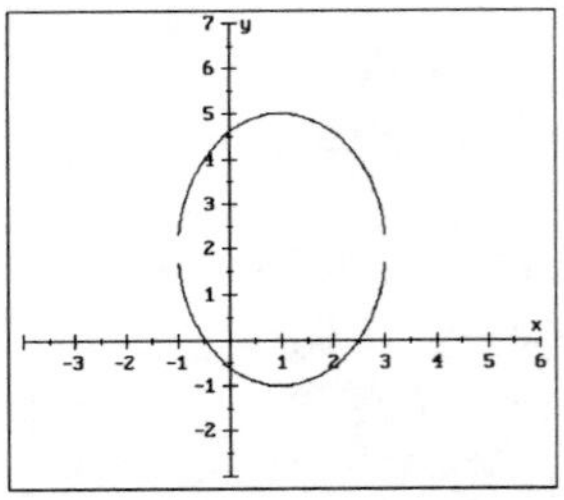

13. $a = 5, c = 13$; horizontal
$$b^2 = c^2 - a^2$$
$$= 169 - 25 = 144$$
$$\frac{x^2}{25} - \frac{y^2}{144} = 1$$

14. $C(0, 0), a = 6, c = \frac{13}{2}$
horizontal
$$b^2 = c^2 - a^2$$
$$= \frac{169}{4} - 36 = \frac{25}{4}$$
$$\frac{x^2}{36} - \frac{4y^2}{25} = 1$$

15. $a = 8, c = 10$; horizontal
$$b^2 = c^2 - a^2$$
$$= 100 - 64 = 36$$
$$\frac{(x-2)^2}{64} - \frac{(y+1)^2}{36} = 1$$

16.
$$x^2 - 4y^2 + 16y = 8$$
$$x^2 - 4(y^2 - 4y) = 8$$
$$x^2 - 4(y^2 - 4y + 4) = 8 - 16$$
$$x^2 - 4(y-2)^2 = -8$$
$$\frac{(y-2)^2}{2} - \frac{x^2}{8} = 1$$
Center: $(0, 2), a = \sqrt{2}, b = \sqrt{8}$, vertical

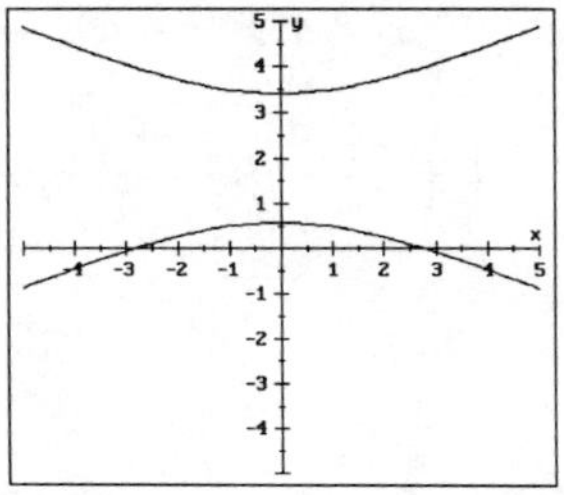

17.
$$y = x^2 - 3 \Rightarrow x^2 = y + 3$$
$$x^2 + y^2 = 23$$
$$y + 3 + y^2 = 23$$
$$y^2 + y - 20 = 0$$
$$(y-4)(y+5) = 0$$

$y = 4$
$$4 + 3 = x^2 \Rightarrow x = \pm\sqrt{7}$$
$$\left(\sqrt{7}, 4\right), \left(-\sqrt{7}, 4\right)$$

$y = -5$
$$-5 + 3 = x^2$$
no real solutions

18.
$$x^2 + y^2 = 27 \Rightarrow x^2 = 27 - y^2$$
$$2x^2 - 3y^2 = 9$$
$$2(27 - y^2) - 3y^2 = 9$$
$$54 - 2y^2 - 3y^2 = 9$$
$$45 = 5y^2$$
$$9 = y^2$$

$y = 3$
$$x^2 = 27 - 3^2 \Rightarrow x = \pm 3\sqrt{2}$$
$$\left(3\sqrt{2}, 3\right), \left(-3\sqrt{2}, 3\right)$$

$y = -3$
$$x^2 = 27 - (-3)^2 \Rightarrow x = \pm 3\sqrt{2}$$
$$\left(3\sqrt{2}, -3\right), \left(-3\sqrt{2}, -3\right)$$

19.
$$y^2 - 4y - 6x - 14 = 0$$
$$y^2 - 4y = 6x + 14$$
$$y^2 - 4x + 4 = 6x + 14 + 4$$
$$(y-2)^2 = 6(x+3) \Rightarrow \text{Parabola}$$

20.
$$2x^2 + 3y^2 - 4x + 12y + 8 = 0$$
$$2(x^2 - 2x) + 3(y^2 + 4y) = -8$$
$$2(x^2 - 2x + 1) + 3(y^2 + 4y + 4) = -8 + 2 + 12$$
$$2(x-1)^2 + 3(y+2)^2 = 6$$
$$\frac{(x-1)^2}{3} + \frac{(y+2)^2}{2} = 1 \Rightarrow \text{ellipse}$$

Cumulative Review Exercises (page 560)

1. $64^{2/3} = \left(64^{1/3}\right)^2 = 4^2 = 16$

2. $8^{-1/3} = \dfrac{1}{8^{1/3}} = \dfrac{1}{2}$

3. $\dfrac{y^{2/3}y^{5/3}}{y^{1/3}} = \dfrac{y^{7/3}}{y^{1/3}} = y^{6/3} = y^2$

4. $\dfrac{x^{5/3}x^{1/2}}{x^{3/4}} = \dfrac{x^{13/6}}{x^{3/4}} = x^{34/24} = x^{17/12}$

5. $\left(x^{2/3} - x^{1/3}\right)\left(x^{2/3} + x^{1/3}\right) = x^{4/3} + x^{3/3} - x^{3/3} - x^{2/3} = x^{4/3} - x^{2/3}$

6. $\left(x^{-1/2} + x^{1/2}\right)^2 = \left(x^{-1/2} + x^{1/2}\right)\left(x^{-1/2} + x^{1/2}\right) = x^{-2/2} + x^0 + x^0 + x^{2/2} = \dfrac{1}{x} + 2 + x$

7. $\sqrt[3]{-27x^3} = \sqrt[3]{(-3x)^3} = -3x$

8. $\sqrt{48t^3} = \sqrt{16t^2}\sqrt{3t} = 4t\sqrt{3t}$

9. $\sqrt[3]{\dfrac{128x^4}{2x}} = \sqrt[3]{64x^3} = 4x$

10. $\sqrt{x^2 + 6x + 9} = \sqrt{(x+3)^2} = x + 3$

11. $\sqrt{50} - \sqrt{8} + \sqrt{32} = 5\sqrt{2} - 2\sqrt{2} + 4\sqrt{2} = 7\sqrt{2}$

12. $-3\sqrt[4]{32} - 2\sqrt[4]{162} + 5\sqrt[4]{48} = -3 \cdot 2\sqrt[4]{2} - 2 \cdot 3\sqrt[4]{2} + 5 \cdot 2\sqrt[4]{3} = -12\sqrt[4]{2} + 10\sqrt[4]{3}$

13. $3\sqrt{2}\left(2\sqrt{3} - 4\sqrt{12}\right) = 6\sqrt{6} - 12\sqrt{24} = 6\sqrt{6} - 12 \cdot 2\sqrt{6} = -18\sqrt{6}$

14. $\dfrac{5}{\sqrt[3]{x}} = \dfrac{5\sqrt[3]{x^2}}{\sqrt[3]{x}\sqrt[3]{x^2}} = \dfrac{5\sqrt[3]{x^2}}{x}$

15.
$$\begin{aligned} \frac{\sqrt{x}+2}{\sqrt{x}-1} &= \frac{\left(\sqrt{x}+2\right)\left(\sqrt{x}+1\right)}{\left(\sqrt{x}-1\right)\left(\sqrt{x}+1\right)} \\ &= \frac{x + 3\sqrt{x} + 2}{x - 1} \end{aligned}$$

16. $\sqrt[6]{x^3y^3} = \left(x^3y^3\right)^{1/6} = x^{3/6}y^{3/6} = x^{1/2}y^{1/2} = (xy)^{1/2} = \sqrt{xy}$

17.
$$\begin{aligned} 5\sqrt{x+2} &= x + 8 \\ \left(5\sqrt{x+2}\right)^2 &= (x+8)^2 \\ 25(x+2) &= x^2 + 16x + 64 \\ 25x + 50 &= x^2 + 16x + 64 \\ 0 &= x^2 - 9x + 14 \\ 0 &= (x-2)(x-7) \end{aligned}$$
$x = 2$ or $x = 7$ (both check)

18.
$$\begin{aligned} \sqrt{x} + \sqrt{x+2} &= 2 \\ \sqrt{x+2} &= 2 - \sqrt{x} \\ \left(\sqrt{x+2}\right)^2 &= \left(2 - \sqrt{x}\right)^2 \\ x + 2 &= 4 - 4\sqrt{x} + x \\ 4\sqrt{x} &= 2 \\ \left(4\sqrt{x}\right)^2 &= 2^2 \\ 16x &= 4 \\ x &= \frac{1}{4} \end{aligned}$$

19.
$$\begin{aligned} 2x^2+x-3&=0\\ x^2+\frac{1}{2}x&=\frac{3}{2}\\ x^2+\frac{1}{2}x+\frac{1}{16}&=\frac{24}{16}+\frac{1}{16}\\ \left(x+\tfrac{1}{4}\right)^2&=\tfrac{25}{16}\\ x+\tfrac{1}{4}&=\pm\tfrac{5}{4}\\ x&=-\tfrac{1}{4}\pm\tfrac{5}{4}\\ x=1 \text{ or } x&=-\tfrac{3}{2}\end{aligned}$$

20. $3x^2+4x-1=0 \Rightarrow a=3, b=4, c=-1$
$$\begin{aligned} x&=\frac{-b\pm\sqrt{b^2-4ac}}{2a}\\ &=\frac{-4\pm\sqrt{4^2-4(3)(-1)}}{2(3)}\\ &=\frac{-4\pm\sqrt{16+12}}{6}\\ &=\frac{-4\pm\sqrt{28}}{6}=\frac{-2\pm\sqrt{7}}{3}\end{aligned}$$

21. $(3+5i)+(4-3i)=3+5i+4-3i=7+2i$

22. $(7-4i)-(12+3i)=7-4i-12-3i=-5-7i$

23. $(2-3i)(2+3i)=4+6i-6i-9i^2=4-9(-1)=4+9=13+0i$

24. $(3+i)(3-3i)=9-9i+3i-3i^2=9-6i-3(-1)=9-6i+3=12-6i$

25. $(3-2i)-(4+i)^2=3-2i-\left(16+8i+i^2\right)=3-2i-(15+8i)=3-2i-15-8i$
$=-12-10i$

26. $\dfrac{5}{3-i}=\dfrac{5(3+i)}{(3-i)(3+i)}=\dfrac{5(3+i)}{9-i^2}=\dfrac{5(3+i)}{10}=\dfrac{3+i}{2}=\dfrac{3}{2}+\dfrac{1}{2}i$

27. $|3+2i|=\sqrt{3^2+2^2}=\sqrt{13}$

28. $|5-6i|=\sqrt{5^2+(-6)^2}=\sqrt{61}$

29. $2x^2+4x=k \Rightarrow 2x^2+4x-k=0$
$a=2, b=4, c=-k$: Set $b^2-4ac=0$.
$$\begin{aligned} b^2-4ac&=0\\ 4^2-4(2)(-k)&=0\\ 16+8k&=0\\ k&=-2\end{aligned}$$

30. $y=\dfrac{1}{2}x^2-x+1$: $a=\dfrac{1}{2}, b=-1, c=1$
$$x=-\frac{b}{2a}=-\frac{-1}{2\left(\frac{1}{2}\right)}=1$$
$$y=\frac{1}{2}(1)^2-1+1=\frac{1}{2}$$

31.
$x^2-x-6>0$
$(x+2)(x-3)>0$
factors = 0: $x=-2, x=3$
intervals: $(-\infty,-2), (-2,3), (3,\infty)$

interval	test number	value of x^2-x-6
$(-\infty,-2)$	-3	$+6$
$(-2,3)$	0	-6
$(3,\infty)$	4	$+6$

Solution: $(-\infty,-2)\cup(3,\infty)$

32.
$x^2-x-6\le 0$
$(x+2)(x-3)\le 0$
factors = 0: $x=-2, x=3$
intervals: $(-\infty,-2), (-2,3), (3,\infty)$

interval	test number	value of x^2-x-6
$(-\infty,-2)$	-3	$+6$
$(-2,3)$	0	-6
$(3,\infty)$	4	$+6$

Solution: $[-2,3]$

33. $f(-1) = 3(-1)^2 + 2 = 3 + 2 = 5$

34. $$\begin{aligned}(g \circ f)(2) = g(f(2)) &= g\big(3(2)^2 + 2\big)\\ &= g(14)\\ &= 2(14) - 1 = 27\end{aligned}$$

35. $$\begin{aligned}(f \circ g)(x) &= f(g(x))\\ &= f(2x-1)\\ &= 3(2x-1)^2 + 2\\ &= 3\big(4x^2 - 4x + 1\big) + 2\\ &= 12x^2 - 12x + 3 + 2\\ &= 12x^2 - 12x + 5\end{aligned}$$

36. $$\begin{aligned}(g \circ f)(x) &= g(f(x))\\ &= g\big(3x^2 + 2\big)\\ &= 2\big(3x^2 + 2\big) - 1\\ &= 6x^2 + 4 - 1\\ &= 6x^2 + 3\end{aligned}$$

37. $y = \log_2 x \Rightarrow 2^y = x$

38. $3^b = a \Rightarrow \log_3 a = b$

39. $\log_x 25 = 2 \Rightarrow x^2 = 25 \Rightarrow x = 5$

40. $\log_5 125 = x \Rightarrow 5^x = 125 \Rightarrow x = 3$

41. $\log_3 x = -3 \Rightarrow 3^{-3} = x \Rightarrow x = \dfrac{1}{27}$

42. $\log_5 x = 0 \Rightarrow 5^0 = x \Rightarrow x = 1$

43. $y = \log_2 x$; inverse: $y = 2^x$

44. $\log_{10} 10^x = x$, so $y = x$.

45. $\log 98 = \log(14 \cdot 7) = \log 14 + \log 7 = 1.1461 + 0.8451 = 1.9912$

46. $\log 2 = \log \dfrac{14}{7} = \log 14 - \log 7 = 1.1461 - 0.8451 = 0.3010$

47. $\log 49 = \log 7^2 = 2 \log 7 = 2(0.8451) = 1.6902$

48. $$\begin{aligned}\log \frac{7}{5} = \log \frac{7}{10/2} = \log 7 - \log \frac{10}{2} = \log 7 - (\log 10 - \log 2) &= \log 7 - \log 10 + \log 2\\ &= 0.8451 - 1 + 0.3010 = 0.1461\end{aligned}$$

49. $$\begin{aligned}2^{x+2} &= 3^x\\ \log 2^{x+2} &= \log 3^x\\ (x+2)\log 2 &= x \log 3\\ x\log 2 + 2\log 2 &= x\log 3\\ 2\log 2 &= x\log 3 - x\log 2\\ 2\log 2 &= x(\log 3 - \log 2)\\ \frac{2\log 2}{\log 3 - \log 2} &= x\end{aligned}$$

50. $$\begin{aligned}2\log 5 + \log x - \log 4 &= 2\\ \log 5^2 + \log x - \log 4 &= 2\\ \log \frac{25x}{4} &= 2\\ 10^2 &= \frac{25x}{4}\\ 400 &= 25x\\ 16 &= x\end{aligned}$$

51. $$\begin{aligned}A &= A_0\left(1 + \frac{r}{k}\right)^{kt}\\ &= 9000\left(1 + \frac{-0.12}{1}\right)^{1(9)}\\ &\approx \$2848.31\end{aligned}$$

52. $\log_6 8 = \dfrac{\log 8}{\log 6} \approx 1.16056$

CUMULATIVE REVIEW EXERCISES

53. $\begin{cases} 2x + y = 5 \\ x - 2y = 0 \end{cases}$

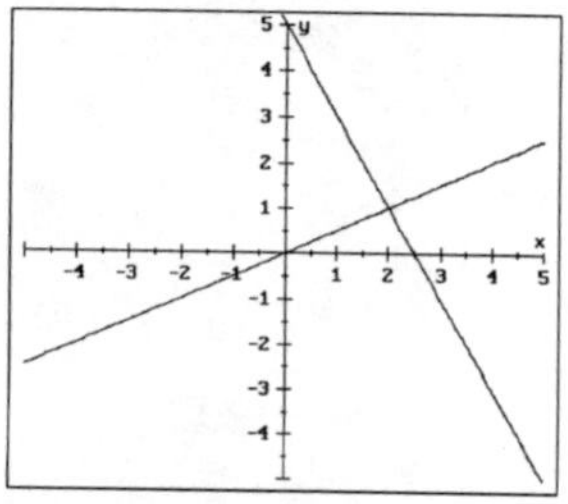

solution: (2, 1)

54. $\begin{cases} (1) & 3x + y = 4 \\ (2) & 2x - 3y = -1 \end{cases}$

Substitute $y = -3x + 4$ from (1) into (2):

$$\begin{aligned} 2x - 3y &= -1 \\ 2x - 3(-3x + 4) &= -1 \\ 2x + 9x - 12 &= -1 \\ 11x &= 11 \\ x &= 1 \end{aligned}$$

Substitute and solve for y:

$y = -3x + 4 = -3(1) + 4 = 1$

$\boxed{x = 1, y = 1}$

55.

$$\begin{array}{l} x + 2y = -2 \\ \underline{2x - y = 6} \Rightarrow \times\ 2 \end{array} \qquad \begin{array}{rcl} x + 2y &=& -2 \\ \underline{4x - 2y} &=& \underline{12} \\ 5x &=& 10 \\ x &=& 2 \end{array} \qquad \begin{array}{r} 2x - y = 6 \\ 2(2) - y = 6 \\ -y = 2 \\ y = -2 \end{array}$$

Solution: $\boxed{x = 2, y = -2}$

56.

$$\begin{array}{l} \frac{x}{10} + \frac{y}{5} = \frac{1}{2} \Rightarrow \times 10 \\ \underline{\frac{x}{2} - \frac{y}{5} = \frac{13}{10}} \Rightarrow \times 10 \end{array} \qquad \begin{array}{rcl} x + 2y &=& 5 \\ 5x - 2y &=& 13 \\ \hline 6x &=& 18 \\ x &=& 3 \end{array} \qquad \begin{array}{r} x + 2y = 5 \\ 3 + 2y = 5 \\ 2y = 2 \\ y = 1 \end{array}$$

Solution: $\boxed{x = 3, y = 1}$

57. $\begin{vmatrix} 3 & -2 \\ 1 & -1 \end{vmatrix} = 3(-1) - (-2)1$

$= -3 + 2 = -1$

58. $y = \dfrac{\begin{vmatrix} 4 & -1 \\ 3 & -7 \end{vmatrix}}{\begin{vmatrix} 4 & -3 \\ 3 & 4 \end{vmatrix}} = \dfrac{-25}{25} = -1$

59. $$\begin{bmatrix} x \\ y \\ z \end{bmatrix} = \begin{bmatrix} 1 & 1 & 1 \\ 2 & -1 & -1 \\ 1 & -2 & 1 \end{bmatrix}^{-1} \begin{bmatrix} 1 \\ -4 \\ 4 \end{bmatrix} = \begin{bmatrix} \frac{1}{3} & \frac{1}{3} & 0 \\ \frac{1}{3} & 0 & -\frac{1}{3} \\ \frac{1}{3} & -\frac{1}{3} & \frac{1}{3} \end{bmatrix} \begin{bmatrix} 1 \\ -4 \\ 4 \end{bmatrix} = \begin{bmatrix} -1 \\ -1 \\ 3 \end{bmatrix}$$

60. $$\begin{bmatrix} x \\ y \\ z \end{bmatrix} = \begin{bmatrix} 1 & 2 & 3 \\ 3 & 2 & 1 \\ 2 & 3 & 1 \end{bmatrix}^{-1} \begin{bmatrix} 6 \\ 6 \\ 6 \end{bmatrix} = \begin{bmatrix} -\frac{1}{12} & \frac{7}{12} & -\frac{1}{3} \\ -\frac{1}{12} & -\frac{5}{12} & \frac{2}{3} \\ \frac{5}{12} & \frac{1}{12} & -\frac{1}{3} \end{bmatrix} \begin{bmatrix} 6 \\ 6 \\ 6 \end{bmatrix} = \begin{bmatrix} 1 \\ 1 \\ 1 \end{bmatrix}$$

Exercise 8.1 (page 568)

1. power

2. degree

3. first

4. exponents

5. $7 \cdot 6 \cdot 5 \cdot 4 \cdot 3 \cdot 2 \cdot 1$

6. 1

7. $(n-1)!$

8. $11 - 7 + 1 = 5$

9. $4! = 4 \cdot 3 \cdot 2 \cdot 1 = 24$

10. $-5! = -(5 \cdot 4 \cdot 3 \cdot 2 \cdot 1) = -120$

11. $3! \cdot 6! = 6 \cdot 720 = 4320$

12. $0! \cdot 7! = 1 \cdot 5040 = 5040$

13. $6! + 6! = 720 + 720 = 1440$

14. $5! - 2! = 120 - 2 = 118$

15. $\dfrac{9!}{12!} = \dfrac{9!}{12 \cdot 11 \cdot 10 \cdot 9!} = \dfrac{1}{1320}$

16. $\dfrac{8!}{5!} = \dfrac{8 \cdot 7 \cdot 6 \cdot 5!}{5!} = 8 \cdot 7 \cdot 6 = 336$

17. $\dfrac{5! \cdot 7!}{9!} = \dfrac{5! \cdot 7!}{9 \cdot 8 \cdot 7!} = \dfrac{120}{72} = \dfrac{5}{3}$

18. $\dfrac{3! \cdot 5! \cdot 7!}{1!8!} = \dfrac{3! \cdot 5! \cdot 7!}{8 \cdot 7!} = \dfrac{720}{8} = 90$

19. $\dfrac{18!}{6!(18-6)!} = \dfrac{18!}{6! \cdot 12!} = \dfrac{18 \cdot 17 \cdot 16 \cdot 15 \cdot 14 \cdot 13 \cdot 12!}{6! \cdot 12!} = \dfrac{13{,}366{,}080}{720} = 18{,}564$

20. $\dfrac{15!}{9!(15-9)!} = \dfrac{15!}{9! \cdot 6!} = \dfrac{15 \cdot 14 \cdot 13 \cdot 12 \cdot 11 \cdot 10 \cdot 9!}{9! \cdot 6!} = \dfrac{3{,}603{,}600}{720} = 5005$

21. $(a+b)^3 = a^3 + \dfrac{3!}{1!2!}a^2b + \dfrac{3!}{2!1!}ab^2 + b^3 = a^3 + 3a^2b + 3ab^2 + b^3$

22. $(a+b)^4 = a^4 + \dfrac{4!}{1!3!}a^3b + \dfrac{4!}{2!2!}a^2b^2 + \dfrac{4!}{3!1!}ab^3 + b^4 = a^4 + 4a^3b + 6a^2b^2 + 4ab^3 + b^4$

23. $$(a-b)^5 = a^5 + \frac{5!}{1!4!}a^4(-b) + \frac{5!}{2!3!}a^3(-b)^2 + \frac{5!}{3!2!}a^2(-b)^3 + \frac{5!}{4!1!}a(-b)^4 + (-b)^5$$
$$= a^5 - 5a^4b + 10a^3b^2 - 10a^2b^3 + 5ab^4 - b^5$$

24. $$(x-y)^4 = x^4 + \frac{4!}{1!3!}x^3(-y) + \frac{4!}{2!2!}x^2(-y)^2 + \frac{4!}{3!1!}x(-y)^3 + (-y)^4$$
$$= x^4 - 4x^3y + 6x^2y^2 - 4xy^3 + y^4$$

25. $(2x+y)^3 = (2x)^3 + \dfrac{3!}{1!2!}(2x)^2y + \dfrac{3!}{2!1!}(2x)y^2 + y^3 = 8x^3 + 12x^2y + 6xy^2 + y^3$

26. $(x+2y)^3 = x^3 + \dfrac{3!}{1!2!}x^2(2y) + \dfrac{3!}{2!1!}x(2y)^2 + (2y)^3 = x^3 + 6x^2y + 12xy^2 + 8y^3$

27. $(x-2y)^3 = x^3 + \frac{3!}{1!2!}x^2(-2y) + \frac{3!}{2!1!}x(-2y)^2 + (-2y)^3 = x^3 - 6x^2y + 12xy^2 - 8y^3$

28. $(2x-y)^3 = (2x)^3 + \frac{3!}{1!2!}(2x)^2(-y) + \frac{3!}{2!1!}(2x)(-y)^2 + (-y)^3 = 8x^3 - 12x^2y + 6xy^2 - y^3$

29. $(2x+3y)^4 = (2x)^4 + \frac{4!}{1!3!}(2x)^3(3y) + \frac{4!}{2!2!}(2x)^2(3y)^2 + \frac{4!}{3!1!}(2x)(3y)^3 + (3y)^4$
$= 16x^4 + 96x^3y + 216x^2y^2 + 216xy^3 + 81y^4$

30. $(2x-3y)^4 = (2x)^4 + \frac{4!}{1!3!}(2x)^3(-3y) + \frac{4!}{2!2!}(2x)^2(-3y)^2 + \frac{4!}{3!1!}(2x)(-3y)^3 + (-3y)^4$
$= 16x^4 - 96x^3y + 216x^2y^2 - 216xy^3 + 81y^4$

31. $(x-2y)^4 = x^4 + \frac{4!}{1!3!}x^3(-2y) + \frac{4!}{2!2!}x^2(-2y)^2 + \frac{4!}{3!1!}x(-2y)^3 + (-2y)^4$
$= x^4 - 8x^3y + 24x^2y^2 - 32xy^3 + 16y^4$

32. $(x+2y)^4 = x^4 + \frac{4!}{1!3!}x^3(2y) + \frac{4!}{2!2!}x^2(2y)^2 + \frac{4!}{3!1!}x(2y)^3 + (2y)^4$
$= x^4 + 8x^3y + 24x^2y^2 + 32xy^3 + 16y^4$

33. $(x-3y)^5 = x^5 + \frac{5!}{1!4!}x^4(-3y) + \frac{5!}{2!3!}x^3(-3y)^2 + \frac{5!}{3!2!}x^2(-3y)^3 + \frac{5!}{4!1!}x(-3y)^4 + (-3y)^5$
$= x^5 - 15x^4y + 90x^3y^2 - 270x^2y^3 + 405xy^4 - 243y^5$

34. $(3x-y)^5$
$= (3x)^5 + \frac{5!}{1!4!}(3x)^4(-y) + \frac{5!}{2!3!}(3x)^3(-y)^2 + \frac{5!}{3!2!}(3x)^2(-y)^3 + \frac{5!}{4!1!}(3x)(-y)^4 + (-y)^5$
$= 243x^5 - 405x^4y + 270x^3y^2 - 90x^2y^3 + 15xy^4 - y^5$

35. $\left(\frac{x}{2}+y\right)^4 = \left(\frac{x}{2}\right)^4 + \frac{4!}{1!3!}\left(\frac{x}{2}\right)^3 y + \frac{4!}{2!2!}\left(\frac{x}{2}\right)^2 y^2 + \frac{4!}{3!1!}\left(\frac{x}{2}\right)y^3 + y^4$
$= \frac{1}{16}x^4 + \frac{1}{2}x^3y + \frac{3}{2}x^2y^2 + 2xy^3 + y^4$

36. $\left(x+\frac{y}{2}\right)^4 = x^4 + \frac{4!}{1!3!}x^3\left(\frac{y}{2}\right) + \frac{4!}{2!2!}x^2\left(\frac{y}{2}\right)^2 + \frac{4!}{3!1!}x\left(\frac{y}{2}\right)^3 + \left(\frac{y}{2}\right)^4$
$= x^4 + 2x^3y + \frac{3}{2}x^2y^2 + \frac{1}{2}xy^3 + \frac{1}{16}y^4$

37. The 3rd term will involve b^2.
$\frac{4!}{2!2!}a^2b^2 = 6a^2b^2$

38. The 2nd term will involve $(-b)^1$.
$\frac{4!}{3!1!}a^3(-b) = -4a^3b$

39. The 5th term will involve b^4.

$$\frac{7!}{3!4!}a^3b^4 = 35a^3b^4$$

40. The 4th term will involve b^3.

$$\frac{5!}{2!3!}a^2b^3 = 10a^2b^3$$

41. The 6th term will involve $(-b)^5$.

$$\frac{5!}{0!5!}a^0(-b)^5 = -b^5$$

42. The 7th term will involve $(-b)^6$.

$$\frac{8!}{2!6!}a^2(-b)^6 = 28a^2b^6$$

43. The 5th term will involve b^4.

$$\frac{17!}{13!4!}a^{13}b^4 = 2380a^{13}b^4$$

44. The 3rd term will involve $(-b)^2$.

$$\frac{12!}{10!2!}a^{10}(-b)^2 = 66a^{10}b^2$$

45. The 2nd term will involve $\left(-\sqrt{2}\right)^1$.

$$\frac{4!}{3!1!}a^3\left(-\sqrt{2}\right)^1 = -4\sqrt{2}\,a^3$$

46. The 3rd term will involve $\left(-\sqrt{3}\right)^2$.

$$\frac{8!}{6!2!}a^6\left(-\sqrt{3}\right)^2 = 84\,a^6$$

47. The 5th term will involve $\left(\sqrt{3}b\right)^4$.

$$\frac{9!}{5!4!}a^5\left(\sqrt{3}b\right)^4 = 1134a^5b^4$$

48. The 4th term will involve $(-b)^3$.

$$\frac{7!}{4!3!}\left(\sqrt{2}a\right)^4(-b)^3 = -140\,a^4b^3$$

49. The 3rd term will involve y^2.

$$\frac{4!}{2!2!}\left(\frac{x}{2}\right)^2y^2 = \frac{3}{2}x^2y^2$$

50. The 3rd term will involve $\left(\frac{n}{2}\right)^2$.

$$\frac{8!}{6!2!}m^6\left(\frac{n}{2}\right)^2 = 7m^6n^2$$

51. The 10th term will involve $\left(-\frac{s}{2}\right)^9$.

$$\frac{11!}{2!9!}\left(\frac{r}{2}\right)^2\left(-\frac{s}{2}\right)^9 = -\frac{55}{2048}r^2s^9$$

52. The 6th term will involve $\left(-\frac{q}{2}\right)^5$.

$$\frac{9!}{4!5!}\left(\frac{p}{2}\right)^4\left(-\frac{q}{2}\right)^5 = -\frac{63}{256}p^4q^5$$

53. The 4th term will involve b^3.

$$\frac{n!}{(n-3)!3!}a^{n-3}b^3$$

54. The 5th term will involve $(-b)^4$.

$$\frac{n!}{(n-4)!4!}a^{n-4}(-b)^4 = \frac{n!}{(n-4)!4!}a^{n-4}b^4$$

55. The rth term will involve b^{r-1}.

$$\frac{n!}{(n-r+1)!(r-1)!}a^{n-r+1}b^{r-1}$$

56. The $(r+1)$th term will involve b^r.

$$\frac{n!}{(n-r)!(r)!}a^{n-r}b^r$$

57. **Answers may vary.**

58. **Answers may vary.**

59. Each term will contain $a^n\left(-\frac{1}{a}\right)^{10-n}$, or $a^n\left(-a^{n-10}\right)$. The constant term will occur when this product is equal to 1, or when the sum of the exponents equals 0.
$n+n-10=0 \Rightarrow n=5$
$\frac{10!}{5!5!}a^5\left(-\frac{1}{a}\right)^5=-252$

60. Each term will contain $x^n\left(\frac{1}{x}\right)^{9-n}$, or $x^n\left(x^{n-9}\right)$. The x^5 term will occur when the sum of the exponents equals 5.
$n+n-9=5 \Rightarrow n=7$
$\frac{9!}{7!2!}x^7\left(\frac{1}{x}\right)^2=36x^5$

61. $\frac{n!}{0!(n-0)!}=\frac{n!}{0!n!}=\frac{n!}{1\cdot n!}=1$

62. $\frac{n!}{n!(n-n)!}=\frac{n!}{n!0!}=\frac{n!}{n!\cdot 1}=1$

63. **Answers may vary.**

64. **Answers may vary.**

65. **Answers may vary.**

66. **Answers may vary.**

67. $3x^3y^2z^4-6xyz^5+15x^2yz^2=3xyz^2(x^2yz^2-2z^3+5x)$

68. $3z^2-15tz+12t^2=3(z^2-5tz+4t^2)=3(z-4t)(z-t)$

69. $a^4-b^4=(a^2+b^2)(a^2-b^2)=(a^2+b^2)(a+b)(a-b)$

70. $3r^4-36r^3-135r^2=3r^2(r^2-12r-45)=3r^2(r-15)(r+3)$

71. $\frac{\frac{1}{x}+\frac{1}{3}}{\frac{1}{x}-\frac{1}{3}}=\frac{3x\left(\frac{1}{x}+\frac{1}{3}\right)}{3x\left(\frac{1}{x}-\frac{1}{3}\right)}=\frac{3+x}{3-x}$

72. $\frac{x-\frac{1}{y}}{y-\frac{1}{x}}=\frac{xy\left(x-\frac{1}{y}\right)}{xy\left(y-\frac{1}{x}\right)}=\frac{x^2y-x}{xy^2-y}=\frac{x(xy-1)}{y(xy-1)}=\frac{x}{y}$

Exercise 8.2 (page 575)

1. domain

2. series

3. Summation notation

4. sum

5. 6

6. $\sum_{k=1}^{5}(3k)=3\sum_{k=1}^{5}k$

7. $5c$

8. sum

9. $f(1)=5(1)(1-1)=0$ $f(2)=5(2)(2-1)=10$ $f(3)=5(3)(3-1)=30$
$f(4)=5(4)(4-1)=60$ $f(5)=5(5)(5-1)=100$ $f(6)=5(6)(6-1)=150$

10. $f(1)=1\left(\frac{1-1}{2}\right)\left(\frac{1-2}{3}\right)=0$ $f(2)=2\left(\frac{2-1}{2}\right)\left(\frac{2-2}{3}\right)=0$ $f(3)=3\left(\frac{3-1}{2}\right)\left(\frac{3-2}{3}\right)=1$
$f(4)=4\left(\frac{4-1}{2}\right)\left(\frac{4-2}{3}\right)=4$ $f(5)=5\left(\frac{5-1}{2}\right)\left(\frac{5-2}{3}\right)=10$ $f(6)=6\left(\frac{6-1}{2}\right)\left(\frac{6-2}{3}\right)=20$

11. 1, 6, 11, 16, ... Add 5 to get the next term. The next term is 21.

12. 1, 8, 27, 64, ... Each term is a perfect cube. The next term is $5^3 = 125$.

13. a, $a+d$, $a+2d$, $a+3d$, ... Add d to get the next term. The next term is $a+4d$.

14. a, ar, ar^2, ar^3, ... Multiply by r to get the next term. The next term is ar^4.

15. 1, 3, 6, 10, ... The difference between terms increases by 1 each time. The next term is $10+5=15$.

16. 20, 17, 13, 8, ... The difference between terms increases 1 each time. The next term is $8-6=2$.

17. $1+2+3+4+5=15$

18. $2+4+6+8+10=30$

19. $3+3+3+3+3=15$

20. $4+4+4+4+4=20$

21. $2\left(\frac{1}{3}\right)^1+2\left(\frac{1}{3}\right)^2+2\left(\frac{1}{3}\right)^3+2\left(\frac{1}{3}\right)^4+2\left(\frac{1}{3}\right)^5=\frac{2}{3}+\frac{2}{9}+\frac{2}{27}+\frac{2}{81}+\frac{2}{243}=\frac{242}{243}$

22. $(-1)^n=-1+1+(-1)+1+(-1)=-1$

23. $[3(1)-2]+[3(2)-2]+[3(3)-2]+[3(4)-2]+[3(5)-2]=1+4+7+10+13=35$

24. $[2(1)+1]+[2(2)+1]+[2(3)+1]+[2(4)+1]+[2(5)+1]=3+5+7+9+11=35$

25.
$a_1=3$
$a_2=2a_1+1=2(3)+1=7$
$a_3=2a_2+1=2(7)+1=15$
$a_4=2a_3+1=2(15)+1=31$

26.
$a_1=-5$
$a_2=-a_1-3=-(-5)-3=2$
$a_3=-a_2-3=-(2)-3=-5$
$a_4=-a_3-3=-(-5)-3=2$

27.
$a_1=-4$
$a_2=\frac{a_1}{2}=\frac{-4}{2}=-2$
$a_3=\frac{a_2}{2}=\frac{-2}{2}=-1$
$a_4=\frac{a_3}{2}=\frac{-1}{2}=-\frac{1}{2}$

28.
$a_1=0$
$a_2=2a_1^2=2(0)^2=0$
$a_3=2a_2^2=2(0)^2=0$
$a_4=2a_3^2=2(0)^2=0$

29.
$a_1=k$
$a_2=a_1^2=k^2$
$a_3=a_2^2=\left(k^2\right)^2=k^4$
$a_4=a_3^2=\left(k^4\right)^2=k^8$

30.
$a_1=3$
$a_2=ka_1=3k$
$a_3=ka_2=k(3k)=3k^2$
$a_4=ka_3=k\left(3k^2\right)=3k^3$

31.
$a_1=8$
$a_2=\frac{2a_1}{k}=\frac{2(8)}{k}=\frac{16}{k}$
$a_3=\frac{2a_2}{k}=\frac{2\left(\frac{16}{k}\right)}{k}=\frac{32}{k^2}$
$a_4=\frac{2a_3}{k}=\frac{2\left(\frac{32}{k^2}\right)}{k}=\frac{64}{k^3}$

32.
$a_1=m$
$a_2=\frac{a_1^2}{m}=\frac{m^2}{m}=m$
$a_3=\frac{a_2^2}{m}=\frac{m^2}{m}=m$
$a_4=\frac{a_3^2}{m}=\frac{m^2}{m}=m$

33. alternating

34. not alternating

35. not alternating

36. alternating

37. $\sum_{k=1}^{5}2k=2\sum_{k=1}^{5}k=2(1+2+3+4+5)=2(15)=30$

38. $\sum_{k=3}^{6} 3k = 3\sum_{k=3}^{6} k = 3(3+4+5+6) = 3(18) = 54$

39. $\sum_{k=3}^{4} (-2k^2) = -2\sum_{k=3}^{4} k^2 = -2(3^2+4^2) = -2(25) = -50$

40. $\sum_{k=1}^{100} 5 = 100(5) = 500$

41. $\sum_{k=1}^{5} (3k-1) = 3\sum_{k=1}^{5} k - \sum_{k=1}^{5} 1 = 3(1+2+3+4+5) - 5(1) = 3(15) - 5 = 40$

42. $$\sum_{n=2}^{5} (n^2+3n) = \sum_{n=2}^{5} n^2 + 3\sum_{n=2}^{5} n = (2^2+3^2+4^2+5^2) + 3(2+3+4+5)$$
$$= (4+9+16+25) + 3(14) = 54 + 42 = 96$$

43. $\sum_{k=1}^{1000} \frac{1}{2} = 1000\left(\frac{1}{2}\right) = 500$

44. $\sum_{x=4}^{5} \frac{2}{x} = \frac{2}{4} + \frac{2}{5} = \frac{1}{2} + \frac{2}{5} = \frac{5}{10} + \frac{4}{10} = \frac{9}{10}$

45. $\sum_{x=3}^{4} \frac{1}{x} = \frac{1}{3} + \frac{1}{4} = \frac{4}{12} + \frac{3}{12} = \frac{7}{12}$

46. $$\sum_{x=2}^{6} (3x^2+2x) - 3\sum_{x=2}^{6} x^2 = \sum_{x=2}^{6} (3x^2+2x) - \sum_{x=2}^{6} 3x^2$$
$$= \sum_{x=2}^{6} 2x = 2\sum_{x=2}^{6} x = 2(2+3+4+5+6) = 2(20) = 40$$

47. $$\sum_{x=1}^{4} (4x+1)^2 - \sum_{x=1}^{4} (4x-1)^2 = \sum_{x=1}^{4} (16x^2+8x+1) - \sum_{x=1}^{4} (16x^2-8x+1)$$
$$= \sum_{x=1}^{4} 16x = 16\sum_{x=1}^{4} x = 16(1+2+3+4) = 16(10) = 160$$

48. $$\sum_{x=0}^{10} (2x-1)^2 + 4\sum_{x=0}^{10} x(1-x) = \sum_{x=0}^{10} (4x^2-4x+1) + 4\sum_{x=0}^{10} (x-x^2)$$
$$= \sum_{x=0}^{10} (4x^2-4x+1) + \sum_{x=0}^{10} (4x-4x^2) = \sum_{x=0}^{10} 1 = 11(1) = 11$$

49. $$\sum_{x=6}^{8}(5x-1)^2+\sum_{x=6}^{8}(10x-1)=\sum_{x=6}^{8}(25x^2-10x+1)+\sum_{x=6}^{8}(10x-1)$$
$$=\sum_{x=6}^{8}(25x^2)=25\sum_{x=6}^{8}x^2=25(6^2+7^2+8^2)=3725$$

50. $$\sum_{x=2}^{7}(3x+1)^2-3\sum_{x=2}^{7}x(3x+2)=\sum_{x=2}^{7}(9x^2+6x+1)-3\sum_{x=2}^{7}(3x^2+2x)$$
$$=\sum_{x=2}^{7}(9x^2+6x+1)-\sum_{x=2}^{7}(9x^2+6x)=\sum_{x=2}^{7}1=1(6)=6$$

51. **Answers may vary.**

52. **Answers may vary.**

53. **Answers may vary.**

54. **Answers may vary.**

55. $$\frac{8}{12}=\frac{4}{x}$$
$$8x=48$$
$$x=6\text{ cm}$$

56. $$\frac{9}{21}=\frac{12}{x}$$
$$9x=252$$
$$x=28\text{ m}$$

57. $$AB^2+BC^2=AC^2$$
$$24^2+10^2=AC^2$$
$$676=AC^2$$
$$26\text{ ft.}=AC$$

58. $$AB^2+BC^2=AC^2$$
$$3^2+x^2=7^2$$
$$9+x^2=49$$
$$x^2=40$$
$$x=\sqrt{40}=2\sqrt{10}\text{ in.}$$

Exercise 8.3 (page 580)

1. $(n-1)d$

2. first, difference, number

3. $l=a+(n-1)d$

4. $S=\dfrac{n(a+l)}{2}$

5. Arithmetic means

6. $s=16t^2$

7. 1, 3, 5, 7, 9, 11

8. −12, −17, −22, −27, −32, −37

9. $$n\text{th term}=a+(n-1)d$$
$$2=5+(3-1)d$$
$$2=5+2d$$
$$-3=2d$$
$$-\frac{3}{2}=d\Rightarrow 5,\frac{7}{2},2,\frac{1}{2},-1,-\frac{5}{2}$$

10. $$n\text{th term}=a+(n-1)d$$
$$12=4+(5-1)d$$
$$12=4+4d$$
$$8=4d$$
$$2=d\Rightarrow 4,6,8,10,12,14$$

11. $n\text{th term} = a + (n-1)d$

$$24 = a + (7-1)\frac{5}{2}$$
$$24 = a + 6\left(\frac{5}{2}\right)$$
$$24 = a + 15$$
$$9 = a \Rightarrow 9, \frac{23}{2}, 14, \frac{33}{2}, 19, \frac{43}{2}$$

12. $n\text{th term} = a + (n-1)d$

$$-49 = a + (20-1)(-3)$$
$$-49 = a + 19(-3)$$
$$-49 = a - 57$$
$$8 = a \Rightarrow 8, 5, 2, -1, -4, -7$$

13. $n\text{th term} = a + (n-1)d$

$$= 6 + (40-1)8$$
$$= 6 + 39(8) = 6 + 312 = 318$$

14. $n\text{th term} = a + (n-1)d$

$$= 50 + (35-1)(-6)$$
$$= 50 + 34(-6) = 50 - 204 = -154$$

15. $n\text{th term} = a + (n-1)d$

$$28 = -2 + (6-1)d$$
$$28 = -2 + 5d$$
$$30 = 5d \Rightarrow d = 6$$

16. $n\text{th term} = a + (n-1)d$

$$-42 = a + (7-1)(-6)$$
$$-42 = a + 6(-6)$$
$$-42 = a - 36 \Rightarrow a = -6$$

17. $n\text{th term} = a + (n-1)d$

$$= -8 + (55-1)7$$
$$= -8 + 54(7) = -8 + 378 = 370$$

18. 2nd term: $-4 = a + d$ 3rd term: $6 = a + 2d$

Solve the system: $\begin{cases} a + d = -4 \\ a + 2d = 6 \end{cases}$

$a = -14$, $d = 10$

37th term $= -14 + 36(10) = 346$

19. 5th term: $14 = a + 4d$ 2nd term: $5 = a + d$

Solve the system: $\begin{cases} a + 4d = 14 \\ a + d = 5 \end{cases}$

$a = 2$, $d = 3$

15th term $= 2 + 14(3) = 44$

20. 4th term: $13 = a + 3d$ 2nd term: $3 = a + d$

Solve the system: $\begin{cases} a + 3d = 13 \\ a + d = 3 \end{cases}$

$a = -2$, $d = 5$

24th term $= -2 + 23(5) = 113$

21. $a = 10$, 5th term $= 20$

$$20 = 10 + 4d$$
$$10 = 4d$$
$$\frac{5}{2} = d \Rightarrow 10, \frac{25}{2}, 15, \frac{35}{2}, 20$$

22. $a = 5$, 7th term $= 15$

$$15 = 5 + 6d$$
$$10 = 6d$$
$$\frac{5}{3} = d \Rightarrow 5, \frac{20}{3}, \frac{25}{3}, 10, \frac{35}{3}, \frac{40}{3}, 15$$

23. $a = -7$, 6th term $= \dfrac{2}{3}$

$$\frac{2}{3} = -7 + 5d$$
$$\frac{23}{3} = 5d$$
$$\frac{23}{15} = d \Rightarrow -7, -\frac{82}{15}, -\frac{59}{15}, -\frac{12}{5}, -\frac{13}{15}, \frac{2}{3}$$

24. $a = -11$, 5th term $= -2$

$$-2 = -11 + 4d$$
$$9 = 4d$$
$$\frac{9}{4} = d \Rightarrow -11, -\frac{35}{4}, -\frac{13}{2}, -\frac{17}{4}, -2$$

25. $a = 5, d = 2$

$$l = a + (n-1)d = 5 + 14(2) = 33$$
$$S = \frac{n(a+l)}{2} = \frac{15(5+33)}{2} = 285$$

26. $a = -3, d = -1$

$$l = a + (n-1)d = -3 + 9(-1) = -12$$
$$S = \frac{n(a+l)}{2} = \frac{10(-3+(-12))}{2} = -75$$

27. $a = \dfrac{27}{2}, d = \dfrac{3}{2}$

$$l = a + (n-1)d = \frac{27}{2} + 19\left(\frac{3}{2}\right) = 42$$
$$S = \frac{n(a+l)}{2} = \frac{20\left(\frac{27}{2} + 42\right)}{2} = 555$$

28. $a = 1, d = \dfrac{2}{3}$

$$l = a + (n-1)d = 1 + 9\left(\frac{2}{3}\right) = 7$$
$$S = \frac{n(a+l)}{2} = \frac{10(1+7)}{2} = 40$$

29. $d = \dfrac{1}{2}$, 25th term $= 10$

$$10 = a + 24\left(\frac{1}{2}\right)$$
$$10 = a + 12 \Rightarrow a = -2$$
$$l = a + (n-1)d = -2 + 29\left(\frac{1}{2}\right) = \frac{25}{2}$$
$$S = \frac{n(a+l)}{2} = \frac{30\left(-2 + \frac{25}{2}\right)}{2} = 157\frac{1}{2}$$

30. $a = 2$, 15th term $= 86$

$$86 = 2 + 14d$$
$$84 = 14d \Rightarrow d = 6$$
$$l = a + (n-1)d = 2 + 99(6) = 596$$
$$S = \frac{n(a+l)}{2} = \frac{100(2+596)}{2} = 29{,}900$$

31. $a = 1, d = 1, n = l = 200$

$$S = \frac{n(a+l)}{2} = \frac{200(1+200)}{2} = 20{,}100$$

32. $a = 1, d = 1, n = l = 1000$

$$S = \frac{n(a+l)}{2} = \frac{1000(1+1000)}{2} = 500{,}500$$

33. $a = 5000, d = -200, n = 13$

Note: $n = 13$ occurs at the <u>beginning</u> of the 13th month, right after the 12th payment has been made

$$\begin{aligned}\text{13th term} &= a + (n-1)d \\ &= 5000 + 12(-200) \\ &= \$2600\end{aligned}$$

34. $a = 5500, d = -105, n = 49$

Note: $n = 49$ occurs at the <u>beginning</u> of the 49th month, right after the 48th payment has been made

$$\begin{aligned}\text{49th term} &= a + (n-1)d \\ &= 5500 + 48(-105) \\ &= \$460\end{aligned}$$

35. $a = \frac{1}{2}$, 51st term $= 6\frac{3}{4} = \frac{27}{4}$

51st term $= a + (n-1)d$

$$\frac{27}{4} = \frac{1}{2} + 50d$$

$$\frac{25}{4} = 50d \Rightarrow d = \frac{1}{8}$$

The distance increased $\frac{1}{8}$ mile per day.

36. $a = 237{,}500$; $d = 150{,}000$;

10th term $= a + (n-1)d$
$= 237{,}500 + 9(150{,}000)$
$= \$1{,}587{,}500$

37. 10th term $= a + (n-1)d$
$= 16 + 9(32)$
$= 304$ feet

38. 3rd term $= a + (n-1)d$
$= 16 + 2(32)$
$= 80$ feet

39. $1 + 2 + 3 + \cdots + 20$

$a = 1, d = 1, n = l = 20$

$$S = \frac{n(a+l)}{2} = \frac{20(1+20)}{2} = 210 \text{ logs}$$

40. $24 + 25 + 26 + \cdots$

$a = 24, d = 1, n = 30$

$l = a + (n-1)d = 24 + 29(1) = 53$

$$S = \frac{n(a+l)}{2} = \frac{30(24+53)}{2} = 1155 \text{ seats}$$

41. **Answers may vary.**

42. **Answers may vary.**

43. **Answers may vary.**

44. **Answers may vary.**

45.
$$x + \sqrt{x+3} = 9$$
$$\sqrt{x+3} = 9 - x$$
$$\left(\sqrt{x+3}\right)^2 = (9-x)^2$$
$$x + 3 = 81 - 18x + x^2$$
$$0 = x^2 - 19x + 78$$
$$0 = (x-6)(x-13)$$
$$x = 6 \text{ or } x = 13$$

$x = 13$ does not check and is extraneous.

46.
$$\frac{x+3}{x} + \frac{x-3}{5} = 2$$
$$5x\left(\frac{x+3}{x} + \frac{x-3}{5}\right) = 5x(2)$$
$$5(x+3) + x(x-3) = 10x$$
$$5x + 15 + x^2 - 3x = 10x$$
$$x^2 - 8x + 15 = 0$$
$$(x-3)(x-5) = 0$$
$$x = 3 \text{ or } x = 5$$

47.
$$\frac{1}{x} + \frac{2}{x^2} + \frac{1}{x^3} = 0$$
$$x^3\left(\frac{1}{x} + \frac{2}{x^2} + \frac{1}{x^3}\right) = x^3(0)$$
$$x^2 + 2x + 1 = 0$$
$$(x+1)(x+1) = 0$$
$$x = -1$$

48.
$$x + 3\sqrt{x} - 10 = 0$$
$$3\sqrt{x} = 10 - x$$
$$\left(3\sqrt{x}\right)^2 = (10-x)^2$$
$$9x = 100 - 20x + x^2$$
$$0 = x^2 - 29x + 100$$
$$0 = (x-25)(x-4)$$
$$x = 25 \text{ or } x = 4$$

$x = 25$ does not check and is extraneous.

49.
$$x^4 - 1 = 0$$
$$(x^2+1)(x^2-1) = 0$$
$$x^2 + 1 = 0 \quad \textbf{OR} \quad x^2 - 1 = 0$$
$$x^2 = -1 \qquad x^2 = 1$$
$$x = \pm\sqrt{-1} \qquad x = \pm\sqrt{1}$$
$$x = \pm i \qquad x = \pm 1$$

50.
$$x^4 - 29x^2 + 100 = 0$$
$$(x^2 - 25)(x^2 - 4) = 0$$
$$(x+5)(x-5)(x+2)(x-2) = 0$$
$$x = \pm 5, x = \pm 2$$

Exercise 8.4 (page 587)

1. r^{n-1}

2. first, ratio, number

3. $l = ar^{n-1}$

4. $S_n = \dfrac{a - ar^n}{1-r}, \ r \neq 1$

5. Geometric means

6. $S = \dfrac{a}{1-r}$

7. 10, 20, 40, 80

8. −3, −6, −12, −24

9. −2, −6, −18, −54

10. 64, 32, 16, 8

11. $3, 3\sqrt{2}, 6, 6\sqrt{2}$

12. $2, 2\sqrt{3}, 6, 6\sqrt{3}$

13.
$$n\text{th term} = ar^{n-1}$$
$$54 = 2r^3$$
$$27 = r^3$$
$$3 = r \Rightarrow 2, 6, 18, 54$$

14.
$$n\text{th term} = ar^{n-1}$$
$$4 = a\left(\frac{1}{2}\right)^2$$
$$4 = \frac{1}{4}a$$
$$16 = a \Rightarrow 16, 8, 4, 2$$

15. $a = \frac{1}{4}, r = 4;$ 6th term $= ar^{n-1} = \left(\frac{1}{4}\right)4^5 = 256$

16.
$$\text{2nd term} = ar^1 \qquad ar^3 = 5$$
$$0.2 = ar^1 \qquad ar \cdot r^2 = 5$$
$$\text{4th term} = ar^3 \qquad 0.2r^2 = 5$$
$$5 = ar^3 \qquad r^2 = 25$$
$$r = \pm 5$$

$$r = 5:\ a = \frac{0.2}{r} = \frac{0.2}{5} = \frac{1}{25}$$
$$r = -5:\ a = \frac{0.2}{r} = \frac{0.2}{-5} = -\frac{1}{25}$$
$$\text{8th term} = ar^7 = \frac{1}{25}(5)^7 = 3125$$
$$\text{8th term} = ar^7 = -\frac{1}{25}(-5)^7 = 3125$$

17.
$$\text{2nd term} = ar^1 \qquad ar^2 = -18$$
$$6 = ar^1 \qquad ar \cdot r = -18$$
$$\text{3rd term} = ar^2 \qquad 6r = -18$$
$$-18 = ar^2 \qquad r = -3$$

$$r = -3:\ a = \frac{6}{r} = \frac{6}{-3} = -2$$
$$\text{4th term} = ar^7 = -2(-3)^4 = -162$$

18. 2nd term $= ar^1$

$3 = ar^1$

4th term $= ar^3$

$\frac{1}{3} = ar^3$

$ar^3 = \frac{1}{3}$

$ar \cdot r^2 = \frac{1}{3}$

$3r^2 = \frac{1}{3}$

$r^2 = \frac{1}{9}$

$r = \pm\frac{1}{3}$

$r = \frac{1}{3}$: $a = \frac{3}{r} = \frac{3}{1/3} = 9$

$r = -\frac{1}{3}$: $a = \frac{3}{r} = \frac{3}{-1/3} = -9$

6th term $= ar^5 = 9\left(\frac{1}{3}\right)^5 = \frac{1}{27}$

6th term $= ar^5 = -9\left(-\frac{1}{3}\right)^5 = \frac{1}{27}$

19. 5th term $= ar^4$

$20 = 10r^4$

$2 = r^4$

$\sqrt[4]{2} = r$ (problem specifies positive)

$10, 10\sqrt[4]{2}, 10\sqrt{2}, 10\sqrt[4]{8}, 20$

20. 7th term $= ar^6$

$5 = -5r^6$

$-1 = r^6$

r is not a real number $\Rightarrow$ not possible

21. 6th term $= ar^5$

$2048 = 2r^5$

$1024 = r^4$

$4 = r$

2, 8, 32, 128, 512, 2048

22. 5th term $= ar^4$

$2 = 162r^4$

$\frac{1}{81} = r^4$

$\pm\frac{1}{3} = r$

162, −54, 18, −6, 2 or 162, 54, 18, 6, 2

23. $a = 4, r = 2, n = 5$

$$S = \frac{a - ar^n}{1 - r} = \frac{4 - 4(2)^5}{1 - 2} = \frac{-124}{-1} = 124$$

24. $a = 9, r = 3, n = 6$

$$S = \frac{a - ar^n}{1 - r} = \frac{9 - 9(3)^6}{1 - 3} = \frac{-6552}{-2} = 3276$$

25. $a = 2, r = -3, n = 10$

$$S = \frac{a - ar^n}{1 - r} = \frac{2 - 2(-3)^{10}}{1 - (-3)} = \frac{-118{,}096}{4} = -29{,}524$$

26. $a = \frac{1}{8}, r = 2, n = 12$

$$S = \frac{a - ar^n}{1 - r} = \frac{\frac{1}{8} - \frac{1}{8}(2)^{12}}{1 - 2} = \frac{-\frac{4095}{8}}{-1} = \frac{4095}{8}$$

27. $a = 3, r = \frac{3}{2}, n = 6$

$$S = \frac{a - ar^n}{1 - r} = \frac{3 - 3\left(\frac{3}{2}\right)^6}{1 - \frac{3}{2}} = \frac{-\frac{1995}{64}}{-\frac{1}{2}} = \frac{1995}{32}$$

28. $a = 12, r = -\frac{1}{2}, n = 6$

$$S = \frac{a - ar^n}{1 - r} = \frac{12 - 12\left(-\frac{1}{2}\right)^6}{1 - \left(-\frac{1}{2}\right)} = \frac{\frac{189}{16}}{\frac{3}{2}} = \frac{63}{8}$$

29. $a = 6, r = \frac{2}{3}$

$$S = \frac{a}{1-r} = \frac{6}{1-\frac{2}{3}} = \frac{6}{\frac{1}{3}} = 18$$

30. $a = 8, r = \frac{1}{2}$

$$S = \frac{a}{1-r} = \frac{8}{1-\frac{1}{2}} = \frac{8}{\frac{1}{2}} = 16$$

31. $a = 12, r = -\frac{1}{2}$

$$S = \frac{a}{1-r} = \frac{12}{1-\left(-\frac{1}{2}\right)} = \frac{12}{\frac{3}{2}} = 8$$

32. $a = 1, r = \frac{1}{3}$

$$S = \frac{a}{1-r} = \frac{1}{1-\frac{1}{3}} = \frac{1}{\frac{2}{3}} = \frac{3}{2}$$

33. $a = \frac{5}{10} = \frac{1}{2}, r = \frac{1}{10}$

$$S = \frac{a}{1-r} = \frac{\frac{1}{2}}{1-\frac{1}{10}} = \frac{\frac{1}{2}}{\frac{9}{10}} = \frac{5}{9}$$

34. $a = \frac{6}{10} = \frac{3}{5}, r = \frac{1}{10}$

$$S = \frac{a}{1-r} = \frac{\frac{3}{5}}{1-\frac{1}{10}} = \frac{\frac{3}{5}}{\frac{9}{10}} = \frac{2}{3}$$

35. $a = \frac{25}{100} = \frac{1}{4}, r = \frac{1}{100}$

$$S = \frac{a}{1-r} = \frac{\frac{1}{4}}{1-\frac{1}{100}} = \frac{\frac{1}{4}}{\frac{99}{100}} = \frac{25}{99}$$

36. $a = \frac{37}{100}, r = \frac{1}{100}$

$$S = \frac{a}{1-r} = \frac{\frac{37}{100}}{1-\frac{1}{100}} = \frac{\frac{37}{100}}{\frac{99}{100}} = \frac{37}{99}$$

37. $a = 623, r = 1.10$

9th term $= ar^8 = 623(1.1)^8$

≈ 1335 students

professors $= \frac{1335}{60} \approx 22.25$

23 professors will be needed.

38. $a = 10, r = 0.95$

14th term $= ar^{13} = 10(0.95)^{13}$

≈ 5.13 meters

39. $a = 1000, r = 1 + \frac{0.0675}{365}, n = 365$

$$ar^{365} = 1000\left(1 + \frac{0.0675}{365}\right)^{365}$$

$\approx \$1069.82$

The interest will be \$69.82.

40. $a = 1, r = 2, n = 10 \cdot 2 = 20$

$ar^{20} = 1(2)^{20} = 1{,}048{,}576$

41. $a = c, r = 0.80, n = 5 \Rightarrow ar^5 = c(0.80)^5 = 0.32768c$, or about $\frac{1}{3}c$

42.

$7\frac{1}{2}\%$ compounded annually	$7\frac{1}{4}\%$ compounded daily
$a = 1000, r = 1 + \frac{0.075}{1}, n = 1$	$a = 1000, r = 1 + \frac{0.0725}{365}, n = 365$
$ar^1 = 1000(1.075)^1$ $= \$1075$	$ar^1 = 1000\left(1 + \frac{0.0725}{365}\right)^{365}$ $\approx \$1075.19 \Rightarrow$ Better investment

43. $a = 5 \times 10^9, r = 2, n = 34$
$ar^{34} = 5 \times 10^9(2)^{34} \approx 8.6 \times 10^{19}$

44. $a = 1300, r = 1 + \frac{0.07}{1}, n = 17$
$ar^{17} = 1300(1.07)^{17}$
$\approx \$4106.46$

45. $a = 50{,}000;\ r = 1.06, n = 22$
$ar^{22} = 50{,}000(1.06)^{22}$
$\approx \$180{,}176.87$

46. $a = 1000, r = 1 + \frac{0.07}{1}, n = 10$
$ar^{10} = 1000(1.07)^{10}$
$\approx \$1967.15$

47. $a = 1000, r = 1 + \frac{0.07}{4}, n = 40$
$ar^{40} = 1000\left(1 + \frac{0.07}{4}\right)^{40}$
$\approx \$2001.60$

48. $a = 1000, r = 1 + \frac{0.07}{12}, n = 120$
$ar^{120} = 1000\left(1 + \frac{0.07}{12}\right)^{120}$
$\approx \$2009.66$

49. $a = 1000, r = 1 + \frac{0.07}{365}, n = 3650$
$ar^{3650} = 1000\left(1 + \frac{0.07}{365}\right)^{3650}$
$\approx \$2013.62$

50. $a = 1000, r = 1 + \frac{0.07}{8760}, n = 87600$
$ar^{87600} = 1000\left(1 + \frac{0.07}{8760}\right)^{87600}$
$\approx \$2013.75$

51. $a = 2000, r = 1 + \frac{0.11}{4}, n = 180$
$ar^{180} = 2000\left(1 + \frac{0.11}{4}\right)^{180}$
$\approx \$264{,}094.58$

52. Since the bacteria double in 5 minutes, it will take 5 minutes for one bacterium to become two bacteria. It will then take 2 hours for the two bacteria to fill the dish, for a total of 2 hours and 5 minutes.

53. $a = 1, r = 2, n = 64$
$S = \frac{a - ar^n}{1 - r} = \frac{1 - 1(2)^{64}}{1 - 2}$
$\approx 1.8447 \times 10^{19}$ grains

54. $\frac{1.8447 \times 10^{19}}{500,000} = 3.689 \times 10^{13}$ bushels

55. **Answers may vary.**

56. **Answers may vary.**

57. $(3 + 2i) + (2 - 5i) = 3 + 2i + 2 - 5i = 5 - 3i$

58. $(7 + 8i) - (2 - 5i) = 7 + 8i - 2 + 5i = 5 + 13i$

59. $(3 + i)(3 - i) = 9 - 3i + 3i - i^2 = 9 - (-1) = 10 + 0i$

60. $\left(3 + \sqrt{3}i\right)\left(3 - \sqrt{3}i\right) = 9 - 3\sqrt{3}i + 3\sqrt{3}i - 3i^2 = 9 - 3(-1) = 12 + 0i$

61. $\dfrac{2+3i}{2-i} = \dfrac{(2+3i)(2+i)}{(2-i)(2+i)} = \dfrac{4+2i+6i+3i^2}{4-i^2} = \dfrac{4+8i+3(-1)}{4-(-1)} = \dfrac{1+8i}{5} = \dfrac{1}{5} + \dfrac{8}{5}i$

62. $(7+3i)^2 = (7+3i)(7+3i) = 49+21i+21i+9i^2 = 49+42i+9(-1) = 40+42i$

63. $i^{127} = i^{124}i^3 = (i^4)^{31}i^3 = 1^{31}i^3 = i^3 = -i$

64. $i^{-127} = \dfrac{1}{i^{127}} = \dfrac{1 \cdot i}{i^{127} \cdot i} = \dfrac{i}{i^{128}} = \dfrac{i}{(i^4)^{42}} = \dfrac{i}{1^{42}} = \dfrac{i}{1} = i$

Exercise 8.5 (page 593)

1. two **2.** $n=1$ **3.** $n=k+1$ **4.** hypothesis

5.

$n=1$:
$$5(1) \stackrel{?}{=} \frac{5(1)(1+1)}{2}$$
$$5 = 5$$

$n=2$:
$$5+5(2) \stackrel{?}{=} \frac{5(2)(2+1)}{2}$$
$$15 \stackrel{?}{=} \frac{10(3)}{2}$$
$$15 = 15$$

$n=3$:
$$5+10+5(3) \stackrel{?}{=} \frac{5(3)(3+1)}{2}$$
$$30 \stackrel{?}{=} \frac{15(4)}{2}$$
$$30 = 30$$

$n=4$:
$$5+10+15+5(4) \stackrel{?}{=} \frac{5(4)(4+1)}{2}$$
$$50 \stackrel{?}{=} \frac{20(5)}{2}$$
$$50 = 50$$

6.

$n=1$:
$$1^2 \stackrel{?}{=} \frac{1(1+1)(2(1)+1)}{6}$$
$$1 \stackrel{?}{=} \frac{1(2)(3)}{6}$$
$$1 = 1$$

$n=2$:
$$1^2+2^2 \stackrel{?}{=} \frac{2(2+1)(2(2)+1)}{6}$$
$$5 \stackrel{?}{=} \frac{2(3)(5)}{6}$$
$$5 = 5$$

$n=3$:
$$1^2+2^2+3^2 \stackrel{?}{=} \frac{3(3+1)(2(3)+1)}{6}$$
$$14 \stackrel{?}{=} \frac{3(4)(7)}{6}$$
$$14 = 14$$

$n=4$:
$$1^2+2^2+3^2+4^2 \stackrel{?}{=} \frac{4(4+1)(2(4)+1)}{6}$$
$$30 \stackrel{?}{=} \frac{4(5)(9)}{6}$$
$$30 = 30$$

7.

$n = 1$

$$3(1) + 4 \stackrel{?}{=} \frac{1(3(1) + 11)}{2}$$
$$7 \stackrel{?}{=} \frac{1(14)}{2}$$
$$7 = 7$$

$n = 2$

$$7 + 3(2) + 4 \stackrel{?}{=} \frac{2(3(2) + 11)}{2}$$
$$17 \stackrel{?}{=} \frac{2(17)}{2}$$
$$17 = 17$$

$n = 3$

$$7 + 10 + 3(3) + 4 \stackrel{?}{=} \frac{3(3(3) + 11)}{2}$$
$$30 \stackrel{?}{=} \frac{3(20)}{2}$$
$$30 = 30$$

$n = 4$

$$7 + 10 + 13 + 3(4) + 4 \stackrel{?}{=} \frac{4(3(4) + 11)}{2}$$
$$46 \stackrel{?}{=} \frac{4(23)}{2}$$
$$46 = 46$$

8.

$n = 1$

$$1(1 + 2) \stackrel{?}{=} \frac{1}{6}(1 + 1)(2(1) + 7)$$
$$3 \stackrel{?}{=} \frac{1}{6}(2)(9)$$
$$3 = 3$$

$n = 2$

$$3 + 2(2 + 2) \stackrel{?}{=} \frac{1}{6}(2 + 1)(2(2) + 7)$$
$$11 \stackrel{?}{=} \frac{2}{6}(3)(11)$$
$$11 = 11$$

$n = 3$

$$3 + 8 + 3(3 + 2) \stackrel{?}{=} \frac{3}{6}(3 + 1)(2(3) + 7)$$
$$26 \stackrel{?}{=} \frac{3}{6}(4)(13)$$
$$26 = 26$$

$n = 4$

$$3 + 8 + 15 + 4(4 + 2) \stackrel{?}{=} \frac{4}{6}(4 + 1)(2(4) + 7)$$
$$50 \stackrel{?}{=} \frac{4}{6}(5)(15)$$
$$50 = 50$$

9.

Check $n = 1$: $2 \stackrel{?}{=} 1(1 + 1)$ True for $n = 1$
$2 = 2$

Assume for $n = k$: $2 + 4 + 6 + \cdots + 2k = k(k + 1)$

Show for $n = k + 1$: $\boxed{2 + 4 + 6 + \cdots + 2k} + 2(k + 1) = \boxed{k(k + 1)} + 2(k + 1)$

$$2 + 4 + 6 + \cdots + 2(k + 1) = k^2 + k + 2k + 2$$
$$2 + 4 + 6 + \cdots + 2(k + 1) = k^2 + 3k + 2$$
$$2 + 4 + 6 + \cdots + 2(k + 1) = (k + 1)(k + 2)$$

Since this is what results when $n = k + 1$ in the formula, we have shown that the formula works for $n = k + 1$ if it works for $n = k$.

10.

Check $n = 1$: $2(1) - 1 \stackrel{?}{=} 1^2$ True for $n = 1$

$1 = 1$

Assume for $n = k$: $1 + 3 + 5 + \cdots + (2k - 1) = k^2$

Show for $n = k + 1$: $\boxed{1 + 3 + 5 + \cdots + (2k - 1)} + 2(k + 1) - 1 = \boxed{k^2} + 2(k + 1) - 1$

$$1 + 3 + 5 + \cdots + [2(k + 1) - 1] = k^2 + 2k + 2 - 1$$
$$1 + 3 + 5 + \cdots + [2(k + 1) - 1] = k^2 + 2k + 1$$
$$1 + 3 + 5 + \cdots + [2(k + 1) - 1] = (k + 1)^2$$

Since this is what results when $n = k + 1$ in the formula, we have shown that the formula works for $n = k + 1$ if it works for $n = k$.

11.

Check $n = 1$: $4(1) - 1 \stackrel{?}{=} 1(2(1) + 1)$ True for $n = 1$

$3 = 3$

Assume for $n = k$ and show for $n = k + 1$:

$$3 + 7 + 11 + \cdots + (4k - 1) = k(2k + 1)$$
$$\boxed{3 + 7 + 11 + \cdots + (4k - 1)} + 4(k + 1) - 1 = \boxed{k(2k + 1)} + 4(k + 1) - 1$$
$$3 + 7 + 11 + \cdots + [4(k + 1) - 1] = 2k^2 + k + 4k + 4 - 1$$
$$3 + 7 + 11 + \cdots + [4(k + 1) - 1] = 2k^2 + 5k + 3$$
$$3 + 7 + 11 + \cdots + [4(k + 1) - 1] = (k + 1)(2k + 3)$$
$$3 + 7 + 11 + \cdots + [4(k + 1) - 1] = (k + 1)(2(k + 1) + 1)$$

Since this is what results when $n = k + 1$ in the formula, we have shown that the formula works for $n = k + 1$ if it works for $n = k$.

12.

Check $n = 1$: $4(1) \stackrel{?}{=} 2(1)(1 + 1)$ True for $n = 1$

$4 = 4$

Assume for $n = k$ and show for $n = k + 1$:

$$4 + 8 + 12 + \cdots + 4k = 2k(k + 1)$$
$$\boxed{4 + 8 + 12 + \cdots + 4k} + 4(k + 1) = \boxed{2k(k + 1)} + 4(k + 1)$$
$$4 + 8 + 12 + \cdots + 4(k + 1) = 2k^2 + 2k + 4k + 4$$
$$4 + 8 + 12 + \cdots + 4(k + 1) = 2k^2 + 6k + 4$$
$$4 + 8 + 12 + \cdots + 4(k + 1) = (2k + 2)(k + 2)$$
$$4 + 8 + 12 + \cdots + 4(k + 1) = 2(k + 1)(k + 2)$$

Since this is what results when $n = k + 1$ in the formula, we have shown that the formula works for $n = k + 1$ if it works for $n = k$.

13.

Check $n = 1$: $14 - 4(1) \stackrel{?}{=} 12(1) - 2(1)^2$ True for $n = 1$

$10 = 10$

Assume for $n = k$ and show for $n = k + 1$:

$$10 + 6 + 2 + \cdots + (14 - 4k) = 12k - 2k^2$$

$$\boxed{10 + 6 + 2 + \cdots + (14 - 4k)} + 14 - 4(k+1) = \boxed{12k - 2k^2} + 14 - 4(k+1)$$

$$10 + 6 + 2 + \cdots + (14 - 4(k+1)) = 12k - 2k^2 + 14 - 4k - 4$$

$$10 + 6 + 2 + \cdots + (14 - 4(k+1)) = 12k + 12 - 2k^2 - 4k - 2$$

$$10 + 6 + 2 + \cdots + (14 - 4(k+1)) = 12(k+1) - 2\left(k^2 + 2k + 1\right)$$

$$10 + 6 + 2 + \cdots + (14 - 4(k+1)) = 12(k+1) - 2(k+1)^2$$

Since this is what results when $n = k + 1$ in the formula, we have shown that the formula works for $n = k + 1$ if it works for $n = k$.

14.

Check $n = 1$: $10 - 2(1) \stackrel{?}{=} 9(1) - (1)^2$ True for $n = 1$

$8 = 8$

Assume for $n = k$ and show for $n = k + 1$:

$$8 + 6 + 4 + \cdots + (10 - 2k) = 9k - k^2$$

$$\boxed{8 + 6 + 4 + \cdots + (10 - 2k)} + 10 - 2(k+1) = \boxed{9k - k^2} + 10 - 2(k+1)$$

$$8 + 6 + 4 + \cdots + (10 - 2(k+1)) = 9k - k^2 + 10 - 2k - 2$$

$$8 + 6 + 4 + \cdots + (10 - 2(k+1)) = 9k + 9 - k^2 - 2k - 1$$

$$8 + 6 + 4 + \cdots + (10 - 2(k+1)) = 9(k+1) - \left(k^2 + 2k + 1\right)$$

$$8 + 6 + 4 + \cdots + (10 - 2(k+1)) = 9(k+1) - (k+1)^2$$

Since this is what results when $n = k + 1$ in the formula, we have shown that the formula works for $n = k + 1$ if it works for $n = k$.

15.

Check $n = 1$: $3(1) - 1 \stackrel{?}{=} \frac{1(3(1)+1)}{2}$ True for $n = 1$

$2 = 2$

Assume for $n = k$ and show for $n = k + 1$:

$$2 + 5 + 8 + \cdots + (3k - 1) = \frac{k(3k+1)}{2}$$

$$\boxed{2 + 5 + 8 + \cdots + (3k - 1)} + 3(k+1) - 1 = \boxed{\frac{k(3k+1)}{2}} + 3(k+1) - 1$$

$$2 + 5 + 8 + \cdots + (3(k+1) - 1) = \frac{k(3k+1)}{2} + \frac{2 \cdot (3(k+1) - 1)}{2}$$

$$2 + 5 + 8 + \cdots + (3(k+1) - 1) = \frac{3k^2 + k + 6k + 6 - 2}{2}$$

$$2 + 5 + 8 + \cdots + (3(k+1) - 1) = \frac{3k^2 + 7k + 4}{2}$$

$$2 + 5 + 8 + \cdots + (3(k+1) - 1) = \frac{(k+1)(3k+4)}{2}$$

$$2 + 5 + 8 + \cdots + (3(k+1) - 1) = \frac{(k+1)(3(k+1)+1)}{2}$$

Since this is what results when $n = k + 1$ in the formula, we have shown that the formula works for $n = k + 1$ if it works for $n = k$.

16.

Check $n = 1$: $3(1) \stackrel{?}{=} \frac{3(1)(1+1)}{2}$ True for $n = 1$

$3 = 3$

Assume for $n = k$ and show for $n = k + 1$:

$$3 + 6 + 9 + \cdots + 3k = \frac{3k(k+1)}{2}$$

$$\boxed{3 + 6 + 9 + \cdots + 3k} + 3(k+1) = \boxed{\frac{3k(k+1)}{2}} + 3(k+1)$$

$$3 + 6 + 9 + \cdots + 3(k+1) = \frac{3k(k+1)}{2} + \frac{2 \cdot 3(k+1)}{2}$$

$$3 + 6 + 9 + \cdots + 3(k+1) = \frac{3(k+1)k + 3(k+1) \cdot 2}{2}$$

$$3 + 6 + 9 + \cdots + 3(k+1) = \frac{3(k+1)(k+2)}{2}$$

Since this is what results when $n = k + 1$ in the formula, we have shown that the formula works for $n = k + 1$ if it works for $n = k$.

17.

Check $n = 1$: $1^2 \stackrel{?}{=} \frac{1(1+1)(2(1)+1)}{6}$ True for $n = 1$ $1 = 1$
Assume for $n = k$ and show for $n = k+1$: $1^2 + 2^2 + 3^2 + \cdots + k^2 = \frac{k(k+1)(2k+1)}{6}$ $\boxed{1^2 + 2^2 + 3^2 + \cdots + k^2} + (k+1)^2 = \boxed{\frac{k(k+1)(2k+1)}{6}} + (k+1)^2$ $1^2 + 2^2 + 3^2 + \cdots + (k+1)^2 = \frac{(2k^2+k)(k+1)}{6} + \frac{6(k+1)(k+1)}{6}$ $1^2 + 2^2 + 3^2 + \cdots + (k+1)^2 = \frac{(2k^2+k+6(k+1))(k+1)}{6}$ $1^2 + 2^2 + 3^2 + \cdots + (k+1)^2 = \frac{(2k^2+7k+6)(k+1)}{6}$ $1^2 + 2^2 + 3^2 + \cdots + (k+1)^2 = \frac{(2k+3)(k+2)(k+1)}{6}$ $1^2 + 2^2 + 3^2 + \cdots + (k+1)^2 = \frac{(k+1)(k+2)(2k+3)}{6}$
Since this is what results when $n = k+1$ in the formula, we have shown that the formula works for $n = k+1$ if it works for $n = k$.

18.

Check $n = 1$: $1 \stackrel{?}{=} 1^2$ True for $n = 1$
Assume for $n = k$ and show for $n = k+1$: $1 + 2 + 3 + \cdots + (k-1) + k + (k-1) + \cdots + 1 = k^2$ $\boxed{1 + 2 + 3 + \cdots + k} + (k+1) + k + \boxed{(k-1) + \cdots + 1} = \boxed{k^2} + k + k + 1$ $1 + 2 + 3 + \cdots + k + (k+1) + k + \cdots + 1 = k^2 + 2k + 1$ $1 + 2 + 3 + \cdots + k + (k+1) + k + \cdots + 1 = (k+1)^2$
Since this is what results when $n = k+1$ in the formula, we have shown that the formula works for $n = k+1$ if it works for $n = k$.

19. Check $n = 1$: $\frac{5}{3}(1) - \frac{4}{3} \stackrel{?}{=} 1\left(\frac{5}{6}(1) - \frac{1}{2}\right)$ True for $n = 1$

$$\frac{1}{3} = \frac{1}{3}$$

Assume for $n = k$ and show for $n = k + 1$:

$$\frac{1}{3} + 2 + \frac{11}{3} + \cdots + \left(\frac{5}{3}k - \frac{4}{3}\right) = k\left(\frac{5}{6}k - \frac{1}{2}\right)$$

$$\boxed{\frac{1}{3} + 2 + \frac{11}{3} + \cdots + \left(\frac{5}{3}k - \frac{4}{3}\right)} + \left(\frac{5}{3}(k+1) - \frac{4}{3}\right) = \boxed{k\left(\frac{5}{6}k - \frac{1}{2}\right)} + \left(\frac{5}{3}(k+1) - \frac{4}{3}\right)$$

$$\frac{1}{3} + 2 + \frac{11}{3} + \cdots + \left(\frac{5}{3}(k+1) - \frac{4}{3}\right) = \frac{5}{6}k^2 - \frac{1}{2}k + \frac{5}{3}k + \frac{5}{3} - \frac{4}{3}$$

$$\frac{1}{3} + 2 + \frac{11}{3} + \cdots + \left(\frac{5}{3}(k+1) - \frac{4}{3}\right) = \frac{5}{6}k^2 + \frac{7}{6}k + \frac{1}{3}$$

$$\frac{1}{3} + 2 + \frac{11}{3} + \cdots + \left(\frac{5}{3}(k+1) - \frac{4}{3}\right) = (k+1)\left(\frac{5}{6}k + \frac{1}{3}\right)$$

$$\frac{1}{3} + 2 + \frac{11}{3} + \cdots + \left(\frac{5}{3}(k+1) - \frac{4}{3}\right) = (k+1)\left(\frac{5}{6}k + \frac{5}{6} - \frac{1}{2}\right)$$

$$\frac{1}{3} + 2 + \frac{11}{3} + \cdots + \left(\frac{5}{3}(k+1) - \frac{4}{3}\right) = (k+1)\left(\frac{5}{6}(k+1) - \frac{1}{2}\right)$$

Since this is what results when $n = k + 1$ in the formula, we have shown that the formula works for $n = k + 1$ if it works for $n = k$.

20. Check $n=1$: $\frac{1}{1\cdot 2} \stackrel{?}{=} \frac{1}{1+1}$ True for $n=1$

$$\frac{1}{2}=\frac{1}{2}$$

Assume for $n=k$ and show for $n=k+1$:

$$\frac{1}{1\cdot 2}+\frac{1}{2\cdot 3}+\frac{1}{3\cdot 4}+\cdots+\frac{1}{k(k+1)}=\frac{k}{k+1}$$

$$\boxed{\frac{1}{1\cdot 2}+\frac{1}{2\cdot 3}+\frac{1}{3\cdot 4}+\cdots+\frac{1}{k(k+1)}}+\frac{1}{(k+1)(k+2)}=\boxed{\frac{k}{k+1}}+\frac{1}{(k+1)(k+2)}$$

$$\frac{1}{1\cdot 2}+\frac{1}{2\cdot 3}+\frac{1}{3\cdot 4}+\cdots+\frac{1}{(k+1)(k+2)}=\frac{k(k+2)+1}{(k+1)(k+2)}$$

$$\frac{1}{1\cdot 2}+\frac{1}{2\cdot 3}+\frac{1}{3\cdot 4}+\cdots+\frac{1}{(k+1)(k+2)}=\frac{k^2+2k+1}{(k+1)(k+2)}$$

$$\frac{1}{1\cdot 2}+\frac{1}{2\cdot 3}+\frac{1}{3\cdot 4}+\cdots+\frac{1}{(k+1)(k+2)}=\frac{(k+1)^2}{(k+1)(k+2)}$$

$$\frac{1}{1\cdot 2}+\frac{1}{2\cdot 3}+\frac{1}{3\cdot 4}+\cdots+\frac{1}{(k+1)(k+2)}=\frac{k+1}{k+2}$$

Since this is what results when $n=k+1$ in the formula, we have shown that the formula works for $n=k+1$ if it works for $n=k$.

21. Check $n=1$: $\left(\frac{1}{2}\right)^1 \stackrel{?}{=} 1-\left(\frac{1}{2}\right)^1$ True for $n=1$

$$\frac{1}{2}=\frac{1}{2}$$

Assume for $n=k$ and show for $n=k+1$:

$$\frac{1}{2}+\frac{1}{4}+\frac{1}{8}+\cdots+\left(\frac{1}{2}\right)^k=1-\left(\frac{1}{2}\right)^k$$

$$\boxed{\frac{1}{2}+\frac{1}{4}+\frac{1}{8}+\cdots+\left(\frac{1}{2}\right)^k}+\left(\frac{1}{2}\right)^{k+1}=\boxed{1-\left(\frac{1}{2}\right)^k}+\left(\frac{1}{2}\right)^{k+1}$$

$$\frac{1}{2}+\frac{1}{4}+\frac{1}{8}+\cdots+\left(\frac{1}{2}\right)^{k+1}=1-2\left(\frac{1}{2}\right)\left(\frac{1}{2}\right)^k+\left(\frac{1}{2}\right)^{k+1}$$

$$\frac{1}{2}+\frac{1}{4}+\frac{1}{8}+\cdots+\left(\frac{1}{2}\right)^{k+1}=1-2\left(\frac{1}{2}\right)^{k+1}+\left(\frac{1}{2}\right)^{k+1}$$

$$\frac{1}{2}+\frac{1}{4}+\frac{1}{8}+\cdots+\left(\frac{1}{2}\right)^{k+1}=1-\left(\frac{1}{2}\right)^{k+1}$$

Since this is what results when $n=k+1$ in the formula, we have shown that the formula works for $n=k+1$ if it works for $n=k$.

22. Check $n = 1$: $\frac{1}{3}\left(\frac{2}{3}\right)^{1-1} \stackrel{?}{=} 1 - \left(\frac{2}{3}\right)^{1}$ True for $n = 1$

$$\frac{1}{3} = \frac{1}{3}$$

Assume for $n = k$ and show for $n = k + 1$:

$$\frac{1}{3} + \frac{2}{9} + \frac{4}{27} + \cdots + \frac{1}{3}\left(\frac{2}{3}\right)^{k-1} = 1 - \left(\frac{2}{3}\right)^{k}$$

$$\boxed{\frac{1}{3} + \frac{2}{9} + \frac{4}{27} + \cdots + \frac{1}{3}\left(\frac{2}{3}\right)^{k-1}} + \frac{1}{3}\left(\frac{2}{3}\right)^{k} = \boxed{1 - \left(\frac{2}{3}\right)^{k}} + \frac{1}{3}\left(\frac{2}{3}\right)^{k}$$

$$\frac{1}{3} + \frac{2}{9} + \frac{4}{27} + \cdots + \frac{1}{3}\left(\frac{2}{3}\right)^{k} = 1 - \frac{3}{2}\left(\frac{2}{3}\right)\left(\frac{2}{3}\right)^{k} + \frac{3}{2}\left(\frac{2}{3}\right)\left(\frac{1}{3}\right)\left(\frac{2}{3}\right)^{k}$$

$$\frac{1}{3} + \frac{2}{9} + \frac{4}{27} + \cdots + \frac{1}{3}\left(\frac{2}{3}\right)^{k} = 1 - \frac{3}{2}\left(\frac{2}{3}\right)^{k+1} + \frac{1}{2}\left(\frac{2}{3}\right)^{k+1}$$

$$\frac{1}{3} + \frac{2}{9} + \frac{4}{27} + \cdots + \frac{1}{3}\left(\frac{2}{3}\right)^{k} = 1 - \left(\frac{2}{3}\right)^{k+1}$$

Since this is what results when $n = k + 1$ in the formula, we have shown that the formula works for $n = k + 1$ if it works for $n = k$.

23. Check $n = 1$: $2^{1-1} \stackrel{?}{=} 2^1 - 1$ True for $n = 1$

$$1 = 1$$

Assume for $n = k$ and show for $n = k + 1$:

$$2^0 + 2^1 + 2^2 + \cdots + 2^{k-1} = 2^k - 1$$

$$\boxed{2^0 + 2^1 + 2^2 + \cdots + 2^{k-1}} + 2^k = \boxed{2^k - 1} + 2^k$$

$$2^0 + 2^1 + 2^2 + \cdots + 2^k = 2 \cdot 2^k - 1$$

$$2^0 + 2^1 + 2^2 + \cdots + 2^k = 2^{k+1} - 1$$

Since this is what results when $n = k + 1$ in the formula, we have shown that the formula works for $n = k + 1$ if it works for $n = k$.

24.

Check $n = 1$: $1^3 \stackrel{?}{=} \left[\frac{1(1+1)}{2}\right]^2$ True for $n = 1$

$1 = 1$

Assume for $n = k$ and show for $n = k + 1$:

$$1^3 + 2^3 + 3^3 + \cdots + k^3 = \left[\frac{k(k+1)}{2}\right]^2$$

$$\boxed{1^3 + 2^3 + 3^3 + \cdots + k^3} + (k+1)^3 = \boxed{\left[\frac{k(k+1)}{2}\right]^2} + (k+1)^3$$

$$1^3 + 2^3 + 3^3 + \cdots + (k+1)^3 = \frac{k^2(k+1)^2 + 4(k+1)^3}{4}$$

$$1^2 + 2^2 + 3^2 + \cdots + (k+1)^2 = \frac{(k+1)^2[k^2 + 4(k+1)]}{4}$$

$$1^2 + 2^2 + 3^2 + \cdots + (k+1)^2 = \frac{(k+1)^2(k+2)^2}{4}$$

Since this is what results when $n = k + 1$ in the formula, we have shown that the formula works for $n = k + 1$ if it works for $n = k$.

25.

Check $n = 1$: $x - y$ is a factor of $x^1 - y^1$. True for $n = 1$

Assume for $n = k$ and show for $n = k + 1$:

Thus, we assume that $x^k - y^k = (x - y)(\text{SOMETHING})$.

$$\begin{aligned} x^{k+1} - y^{k+1} &= x^{k+1} - xy^k + xy^k - y^{k+1} \\ &= x(x^k - y^k) + y^k(x - y) \\ &= x(x - y)(\text{SOMETHING}) + y^k(x - y) \\ &= (x - y)\left[x(\text{SOMETHING}) + y^k\right] \end{aligned}$$

We have shown that $x - y$ is a factor of $x^{k+1} - y^{k+1}$ if it is a factor of $x^k - y^k$.

26.

Check $n = 1$: $1 < 2^1$ True for $n = 1$

Assume for $n = k$ and show for $n = k + 1$:

Certainly, $2^k + 1 < 2^k + 2 < 2^k + 2^k$.

$k < 2^k$

$k + 1 < 2^k + 1 < 2^k + 2^k = 2 \cdot 2^k = 2^{k+1}$

$k + 1 < 2^{k+1}$

We have shown that $k + 1 < 2^{k+1}$ if $k < 2^k$.

27. The formula is true for $n = 3$, since a triangle has $180° = (3 - 2) \cdot 180°$. Next, assume that a polygon with k sides has an angle sum of $(k - 2) \cdot 180°$. Take a polygon with $k + 1$ sides. Consider two adjacent sides with a common endpoint. Connect the endpoints which are NOT common to both sides. The figure is now a polygon with k sides with a triangle adjacent to it.

$$\boxed{\begin{array}{c}\text{Sum of angles of}\\(k+1)\text{-sided polygon}\end{array}} = \boxed{\begin{array}{c}\text{Sum of angles of}\\k\text{-sided polygon}\end{array}} + \boxed{\begin{array}{c}\text{Sum of angles of}\\\text{triangle}\end{array}}$$
$$= (k-2)\cdot 180° + 180° = (k-1)\cdot 180° = [(k+1)-2]\cdot 180°$$

Thus, the formula works for $n = k + 1$ if it works for $n = k$.

28. The formula works for $n = 1$ and $n = 2$, but it does not work for $n = 3$. Therefore, it does not work for all natural numbers.

29. Assume for $n = k$ and show for $n = k + 1$:

$$1 + 2 + 3 + \cdots + k = \tfrac{k}{2}(k+1) + 1$$
$$\boxed{1 + 2 + 3 + \cdots + k} + (k+1) = \boxed{\tfrac{k}{2}(k+1) + 1} + (k+1)$$
$$1 + 2 + 3 + \cdots + (k+1) = \tfrac{1}{2}k(k+1) + (k+1) + 2$$
$$1 + 2 + 3 + \cdots + (k+1) = \tfrac{1}{2}(k+1)(k+2)$$
$$1 + 2 + 3 + \cdots + (k+1) = \tfrac{(k+1)}{2}(k+2)$$

The formula works for $n = k + 1$ if it works for $n = k$. However, the formula does not work for $n = 1$. Thus, the formula does not work for all natural numbers.

30.

Check $n = 1$: $1 + 1 = 1 + 1$ True for $n = 1$
Assume for $n = k$ and show for $n = k + 1$: $k + 1 = 1 + k$ $k + 1 + 1 = 1 + k + 1$ $k + 1 + 1 = 1 + 1 + k$ $(k + 1) + 1 = 1 + (1 + k)$
We have shown that the formula works for $n = k + 1$ if it works for $n = k$.

31.

Check $n = 1$: $7^1 - 1 = 7 - 1 = 6$ True for $n = 1$ Thus, $7^1 - 1$ is divisible by 6.
Assume for $n = k$ and show for $n = k + 1$: $7^k - 1$ is divisible by 6, so $7^k - 1 = 6 \cdot x$, where x is some natural number. Then $7^{k+1} - 1 = 7^k \cdot 7 - 1 = (6x + 1) \cdot 7 - 1 = 42x + 6 = 6(7x + 1)$ Thus, $7^{k+1} - 1$ is divisible by 6.
We have shown that $7^{k+1} - 1$ is divisible by 6 if $7^k - 1$ is divisible by 6.

32.

Check $n = 2$: $1 + 2(2) < 3^2$ True for $n = 2$

$5 < 9$

Assume for $n = k$ and show for $n = k + 1$:

Certainly, $3^k + 2 = 3^k + 1 + 1 < 3^k + 3^k + 3^k$.

$$1 + 2k < 3^k$$

$$1 + 2k + 2 < 3^k + 2 < 3^k + 3^k + 3^k = 3 \cdot 3^k = 3^{k+1}$$

$$1 + 2(k + 1) < 3^{k+1}$$

We have shown that $1 + 2(k + 1) < 3^{k+1}$ if $1 + 2k < 3^k$.

33.

Check $n = 1$: $1 + r^1 \stackrel{?}{=} \dfrac{1 - r^2}{1 - r}$ True for $n = 1$

$$1 + r \stackrel{?}{=} \frac{(1 + r)(1 - r)}{1 - r}$$

$$1 + r = 1 + r$$

Assume for $n = k$ and show for $n = k + 1$:

$$1 + r + r^2 + r^3 + \cdots + r^k = \frac{1 - r^{k+1}}{1 - r}$$

$$\boxed{1 + r + r^2 + r^3 + \cdots + r^k} + r^{k+1} = \boxed{\frac{1 - r^{k+1}}{1 - r}} + r^{k+1}$$

$$1 + r + r^2 + r^3 + \cdots + r^{k+1} = \frac{1 - r^{k+1} + r^{k+1}(1 - r)}{1 - r}$$

$$1 + r + r^2 + r^3 + \cdots + r^{k+1} = \frac{1 - r^{k+1} + r^{k+1} - r^{k+2}}{1 - r}$$

$$1 + r + r^2 + r^3 + \cdots + r^{k+1} = \frac{1 - r^{(k+1)+1}}{1 - r}$$

Since this is what results when $n = k + 1$ in the formula, we have shown that the formula works for $n = k + 1$ if it works for $n = k$.

34. Check $n=1$: $a+(1-1)d \stackrel{?}{=} \frac{1(a+(a+(1-1)d))}{2}$ True for $n=1$

$a=a$

Assume for $n=k$ and show for $n=k+1$:

$$a+(a+d)+(a+2d)+\cdots+a+(k-1)d = \frac{k(a+(a+(k-1)d))}{2}$$
$$= \frac{2ak+k^2d-kd}{2}$$
$$\boxed{a+(a+d)+(a+2d)+\cdots+a+(k-1)d}+a+kd = \boxed{\frac{2ak+k^2d-kd}{2}}+a+kd$$
$$a+(a+d)+(a+2d)+\cdots+(a+kd) = \frac{2ak+k^2d-kd+2a+2kd}{2}$$
$$a+(a+d)+(a+2d)+\cdots+(a+kd) = \frac{2a(k+1)+k^2d+kd}{2}$$
$$a+(a+d)+(a+2d)+\cdots+(a+kd) = \frac{2a(k+1)+kd(k+1)}{2}$$
$$a+(a+d)+(a+2d)+\cdots+(a+kd) = \frac{(k+1)(2a+kd)}{2}$$
$$a+(a+d)+(a+2d)+\cdots+(a+kd) = \frac{(k+1)(a+(a+kd))}{2}$$

Since this is what results when $n=k+1$ in the formula, we have shown that the formula works for $n=k+1$ if it works for $n=k$.

35. Check $n=1$: $a^m a^1 = a^m \cdot a = a^{m+1}$, by definition True for $n=1$

Assume for $n=k$ and show for $n=k+1$:

$$a^m a^k = a^{m+k}$$
$$a^m a^k a = a^{m+k} a$$
$$a^m a^{k+1} = a^{m+k+1}$$
$$a^m a^{k+1} = a^{m+(k+1)}$$

We have shown that the formula works for $n=k+1$ if it works for $n=k$.

36. Check $n=1$: $(a^m)^1 = a^m = a^{m\cdot 1}$ True for $n=1$

Assume for $n=k$ and show for $n=k+1$:

$$(a^m)^k = a^{mk}$$
$$(a^m)^k a^m = a^{mk} a^m$$
$$(a^m)^{k+1} = a^{mk+m}$$
$$(a^m)^{k+1} = a^{m(k+1)}$$

We have shown that the formula works for $n=k+1$ if it works for $n=k$.

37. $3x + 4y \leq 12$

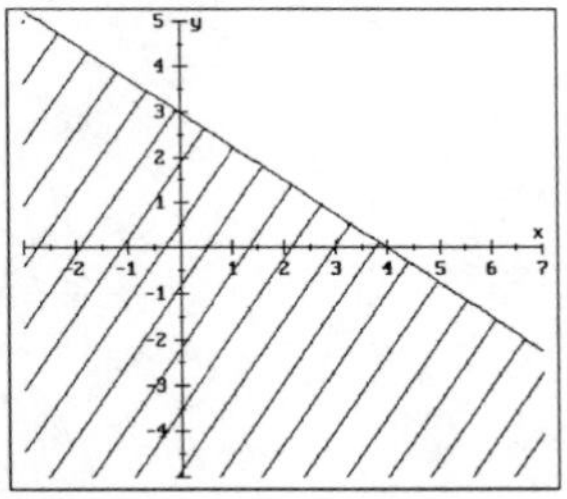

38. $4x - 3y < 12$

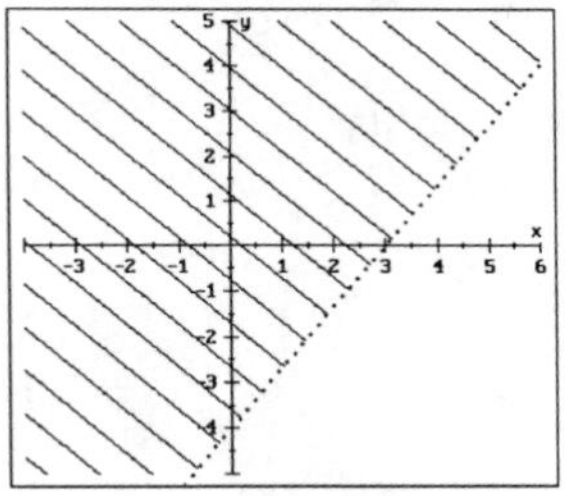

39. $2x + y > 5$

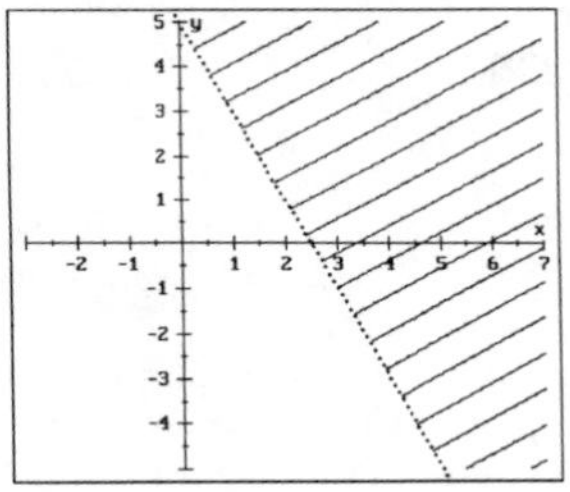

40. $x + 3y \geq 7$

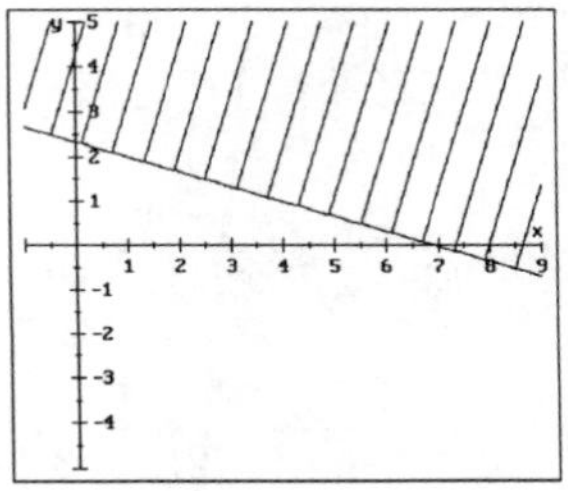

Exercise 8.6 (page 601)

1. $6 \cdot 4 = 24$

2. permutation

3. $\dfrac{n!}{(n-r)!}$

4. $n!$

5. 1

6. $(n-1)!$

7. $\dfrac{n!}{r!(n-r)!}$

8. $\dbinom{n}{r}$

9. 1

10. 1

11. $\dfrac{n!}{a! \cdot b! \cdots}$

12. combinations, permutations

13. $P(7,4) = \dfrac{7!}{(7-4)!} = \dfrac{7!}{3!} = \dfrac{7 \cdot 6 \cdot 5 \cdot 4 \cdot 3!}{3!} = 7 \cdot 6 \cdot 5 \cdot 4 = 840$

14. $P(8,3) = \dfrac{8!}{(8-3)!} = \dfrac{8!}{5!} = \dfrac{8 \cdot 7 \cdot 6 \cdot 5!}{5!} = 8 \cdot 7 \cdot 6 = 336$

15. $C(7,4) = \dfrac{7!}{4!(7-4)!} = \dfrac{7!}{4!3!} = \dfrac{7 \cdot 6 \cdot 5 \cdot 4!}{4!3!} = \dfrac{7 \cdot 6 \cdot 5}{3 \cdot 2 \cdot 1} = 35$

16. $C(8,3) = \dfrac{8!}{3!(8-3)!} = \dfrac{8!}{3!5!} = \dfrac{8 \cdot 7 \cdot 6 \cdot 5!}{3!5!} = \dfrac{8 \cdot 7 \cdot 6}{3 \cdot 2 \cdot 1} = 56$

17. $P(5,5) = \dfrac{5!}{(5-5)!} = \dfrac{5!}{0!} = \dfrac{5!}{1} = 5 \cdot 4 \cdot 3 \cdot 2 \cdot 1 = 120$

18. $P(5,0) = \dfrac{5!}{(5-0)!} = \dfrac{5!}{5!} = 1$

19. $\dbinom{5}{4} = \dfrac{5!}{4!(5-4)!} = \dfrac{5 \cdot 4!}{4!1!} = \dfrac{5}{1} = 5$

20. $\dbinom{8}{4} = \dfrac{8!}{4!(8-4)!} = \dfrac{8 \cdot 7 \cdot 6 \cdot 5 \cdot 4!}{4!4!} = \dfrac{8 \cdot 7 \cdot 6 \cdot 5}{4 \cdot 3 \cdot 2 \cdot 1} = 70$

21. $\dbinom{5}{0} = \dfrac{5!}{0!(5-0)!} = \dfrac{5!}{0!5!} = \dfrac{1}{1} = 1$

22. $\dbinom{5}{5} = \dfrac{5!}{5!(5-5)!} = \dfrac{5!}{5!0!} = \dfrac{1}{1} = 1$

23. $P(5,4) \cdot C(5,3) = \dfrac{5!}{(5-4)!} \cdot \dfrac{5!}{3!(5-3)!} = \dfrac{5!}{1!} \cdot \dfrac{5!}{3!2!} = 120 \cdot 10 = 1200$

24. $P(3,2) \cdot C(4,3) = \dfrac{3!}{(3-2)!} \cdot \dfrac{4!}{3!(4-3)!} = \dfrac{3!}{1!} \cdot \dfrac{4!}{3!1!} = 6 \cdot 4 = 24$

25. $\dbinom{5}{3}\dbinom{4}{3}\dbinom{3}{3} = \dfrac{5!}{3!(5-3)!} \cdot \dfrac{4!}{3!(4-3)!} \cdot \dfrac{3!}{3!(3-3)!} = 10 \cdot 4 \cdot 1 = 40$

26. $\dbinom{5}{5}\dbinom{6}{6}\dbinom{7}{7}\dbinom{8}{8} = 1 \cdot 1 \cdot 1 \cdot 1 = 1$

27. $\dbinom{68}{66} = \dfrac{68!}{66!(68-66)!} = \dfrac{68 \cdot 67 \cdot 66!}{66!2!} = \dfrac{68 \cdot 67}{2 \cdot 1} = 2278$

28. $\dbinom{100}{99} = \dfrac{100!}{99!(100-99)!} = \dfrac{100 \cdot 99!}{99!1!} = 100$

29. $8 \cdot 6 \cdot 3 = 144$

30. $9 \cdot 10 \cdot 10 \cdot 10 \cdot 10 \cdot 10 = 900{,}000$

31. $8 \cdot 10 \cdot 10 \cdot 10 \cdot 10 \cdot 10 \cdot 10 = 8{,}000{,}000$

32. $6! = 720$

33. Consider the e and the r to be a block that cannot be divided, say x. Then the problem becomes finding the number of ways to rearrange the letters in the word $numbx$. This can be done in 5!, or 120 ways. For each of these possibilities, the e and the r could be reversed, doubling the number of possibilities. The answer is $2 \cdot 120$, or 240 ways.

34. The total number of ways, without restrictions, of rearranging the letters is 6!, or 720. Since there are 240 ways of rearranging the letters so that the e and the r ARE next to each other (see **#33**), then there are $720 - 240$, or 480 ways of rearranging the letters so that the e and the r are NOT next to each other.

SECTION 8.6

35. The word must appear as $\square\, L\, U\, \square\, \square$, where one of the Fs must appear in each box. This can be done in 3!, or 6 ways.

36. The word must appear as $F\, \square\, \square\, B\, L\, \square$, where one of the Es must appear in each box. This can be done in 3!, or 6 ways.

37. $8! = 40{,}320$

38. The line might look like this:

5	5	4	4	3	3	2	2	1	1
W	M	W	M	W	M	W	M	W	M

Then there would be $5 \cdot 5 \cdot 4 \cdot 4 \cdot 3 \cdot 3 \cdot 2 \cdot 2 \cdot 1 \cdot 1 = 14{,}400$ ways. However, the line could start with a man instead of a woman, so there are $2 \cdot 14{,}400 = 28{,}800$ possible arrangements.

39. The line will look like this:

5	4	3	2	1	5	4	3	2	1
M	M	M	M	M	W	W	W	W	W

Then there are $5 \cdot 4 \cdot 3 \cdot 2 \cdot 1 \cdot 5 \cdot 4 \cdot 3 \cdot 2 \cdot 1 = 14{,}400$ arrangements.

40. The line will look like this:

5	4	3	2	1	5	4	3	2	1
W	W	W	W	W	M	M	M	M	M

Then there are $5 \cdot 4 \cdot 3 \cdot 2 \cdot 1 \cdot 5 \cdot 4 \cdot 3 \cdot 2 \cdot 1 = 14{,}400$ arrangements.

41. $P(30, 3) = \dfrac{30!}{27!} = 24{,}360$

42. $P(100, 3) = \dfrac{100!}{97!} = 970{,}200$

43. $(8 - 1)! = 7! = 5040$

44. $(7 - 1)! = 6! = 720$

45. Consider the two people who must sit together as a single person, so that there are 5 "people" who must be arranged in a circle. This can be done in $(5 - 1)! = 4! = 24$ ways. However, the two people who have been seated next to each other could be switched, so that the number of arrangements is doubled. There are $2 \cdot 24 = 48$ possible arrangements.

46. Without restrictions, 6 people can be seated at a round table in $(6 - 1)! = 5! = 120$ ways. Since there are 48 ways to sit the 6 people so that 2 MUST be together (see **#45**), there are $120 - 48$, or 72 ways of seating the people so that the 2 are NOT seated next to each other.

47. Consider Sally and John as a single person and Martha and Peter as a single person, so that there are 5 "people" who must be arranged in a circle. This can be done in $(5 - 1)! = 4! = 24$ ways. However, each group of 2 people could be switched, so that the number of arrangements will equal $2 \cdot 2 \cdot 24$, or 96.

48. Consider the three people as a single person, so that there 6 "people" who must be arranged in a circle. This can be done in $(6-1)! = 5! = 120$ ways. However, the group of three people can be rearranged in 3!, or 6 ways, so the total number of arrangements is $6 \cdot 120$, or 720.

49. $\binom{10}{4} = \frac{10!}{4!6!} = 210$

50. $\binom{24}{6} = \frac{24!}{6!18!} = 134{,}596$

51. $4! = 24$

52. $\binom{20}{7} = \frac{20!}{7!13!} = 77{,}520$

53. $7! = 5040$

54. $\frac{6!}{3!2!1!} = 60$

55. $25 \cdot 24 \cdot 9 \cdot 9 \cdot 8 \cdot 7 = 2{,}721{,}600$

56. $\binom{7}{5} = 21$

57. $\binom{6}{3}\binom{8}{3} = 20 \cdot 56 = 1120$

58. $\binom{11}{3}\binom{18}{3} = 165 \cdot 816 = 134{,}640$

59. $\binom{12}{4}\binom{10}{3} = 495 \cdot 120 = 59{,}400$

60. $\binom{10}{5}\binom{8}{2} = 252 \cdot 28 = 7056$

61. $\underset{\text{H}}{\underline{17}} \cdot \underset{\text{W}}{\underline{16}} = 272$

62. There are a total of 7!, or 5040 ways to arrange the people without restrictions. Count the number of arrangements with the two people together. To do this, consider them as one person, so that there are 6!, or 720 arrangements. This needs to be doubled, since the two people considered as a group can switch places. Then there are 1440 arrangements with the two people together. The number of arrangements in which they are NOT together is $5040 - 1440 = 3600$.

63. $\binom{8}{2} = 28$

64. $\binom{10}{2} = 45$

65. $\binom{10}{5} = 252$

66. $\binom{25}{9} = 2{,}042{,}975$

67. $\binom{30}{5} = 142{,}506$

68. $\binom{20}{3}\binom{30}{3} = 1140 \cdot 4060 = 4{,}628{,}400$

69. $\binom{12}{10} = 66$

70. Pick 5 of the 10 as true: $\binom{10}{5} = 252$

71. $C(n, n) = \frac{n!}{n!(n-n)!} = \frac{n!}{n!0!} = \frac{n!}{n!} = 1$

72. $C(n, 0) = \frac{n!}{0!n!} = \frac{n!}{n!} = 1$

73. $\binom{n}{n-r} = \frac{n!}{(n-r)!(n-(n-r))!} = \frac{n!}{(n-r)!r!} = \frac{n!}{r!(n-r)!} = \binom{n}{r}$

74. **Answers may vary.**

75. **Answers may vary.**

76. **Answers may vary.**

77. $\log_x 16 = 4$
$x^4 = 16 \Rightarrow x = 2$

78. $\log_\pi x = \frac{1}{2}$
$x = \pi^{1/2} = \sqrt{\pi}$

79. $\log_{\sqrt{7}} 49 = x$
$\left(\sqrt{7}\right)^x = 49 \Rightarrow x = 4$

80. $\log_x \frac{1}{2} = -\frac{1}{3} \Rightarrow x^{-1/3} = \frac{1}{2} \Rightarrow x = 8$

81. true

82. false

83. true

84. false

Exercise 8.7 (page 608)

1. experiment

2. sample space

3. $\frac{n(E)}{n(S)}$

4. $P(A) \cdot P(B|A)$

5. $\{(1, H), (2, H), (3, H), (4, H), (5, H), (6, H), (1, T), (2, T), (3, T), (4, T), (5, T), (6, T)\}$

6. $\{(H, H, H), (H, H, T), (H, T, H), (H, T, T), (T, H, H), (T, H, T), (T, T, H), (T, T, T)\}$

7. $\{A, B, C, D, E, F, G, H, I, J, K, L, M, N, O, P, Q, R, S, T, U, V, W, X, Y, Z\}$

8. $\{0, 1, 2, 3, 4, 5, 6, 7, 8, 9\}$

9. $\frac{1}{6}$

10. $\frac{2}{6} = \frac{1}{3}$

11. $\frac{4}{6} = \frac{2}{3}$

12. $\frac{3}{6} = \frac{1}{2}$

13. $\frac{19}{42}$

14. $\frac{42}{42} = 1$

15. $\frac{13}{42}$

16. $\frac{9+2}{42} = \frac{11}{42}$

17. $\frac{3}{8}$

18. $\frac{2}{8} = \frac{1}{4}$

19. $\frac{0}{8} = 0$

20. $\frac{1}{8}$

21. rolls of 4: $\{(1, 3), (2, 2), (3, 1)\}$
Probability $= \frac{3}{36} = \frac{1}{12}$

22. $\frac{\text{\# diamonds}}{\text{\# cards}} = \frac{13}{52} = \frac{1}{4}$

23. $\frac{\text{\# aces}}{\text{\# cards}} \cdot \frac{\text{\# aces}}{\text{\# cards}} = \frac{4}{52} \cdot \frac{4}{52} = \frac{1}{169}$

24. $\frac{\text{\# aces}}{\text{\# cards}} \cdot \frac{\text{\# aces}}{\text{\# cards}} = \frac{4}{52} \cdot \frac{3}{51} = \frac{1}{221}$

25. $\frac{\text{\# red}}{\text{\# eggs}} = \frac{5}{12}$

26. $\frac{\text{\# ways to get 2 red eggs}}{\text{total \# ways to get 2 eggs}} = \frac{\binom{5}{2}}{\binom{12}{2}} = \frac{10}{66} = \frac{5}{33}$

27. $\dfrac{\text{\# ways to get 13 cards of the same suit}}{\text{\# ways to get 13 cards from the deck of 52}} = \dfrac{4 \cdot \binom{13}{13}}{\binom{52}{13}} = \dfrac{4}{6.350136 \times 10^{11}} \approx 6.3 \times 10^{-12}$

28. $\dfrac{\text{\# ways to get 6 diamonds}}{\text{\# ways to get 6 cards from the deck of 52}} = \dfrac{\binom{13}{6}}{\binom{52}{6}} = \dfrac{1716}{20{,}358{,}520} = \dfrac{33}{391{,}510}$

29. impossible $\Rightarrow 0$

30. $\dfrac{\text{\# ways to get 5 clubs}}{\text{\# ways to get 5 cards from the 26 black cards}} = \dfrac{\binom{13}{5}}{\binom{26}{5}} = \dfrac{1287}{65780} = \dfrac{9}{460}$

31. $\dfrac{\text{\# face cards}}{\text{\# cards in deck}} = \dfrac{12}{52} = \dfrac{3}{13}$

32. $\dfrac{\text{\# ways to get 6 cards from the 12 face cards}}{\text{\# ways to get 6 cards from the deck of 52}} = \dfrac{\binom{12}{6}}{\binom{52}{6}} = \dfrac{924}{20{,}358{,}520} = \dfrac{33}{727{,}090}$

33. $\dfrac{\text{\# ways to get 5 orange}}{\text{\# ways to get 5 cubes}} = \dfrac{\binom{5}{5}}{\binom{6}{5}} = \dfrac{1}{6}$

34. rolls of 4: $\{(1, 1, 2), (1, 2, 1), (2, 1, 1)\}$
Probability $= \dfrac{3}{216} = \dfrac{1}{72}$

35. rolls of 11: (1, 4, 6), (1, 5, 5), (1, 6, 4), (2, 3, 6), (2, 4, 5), (2, 5, 4), (2, 6, 3), (3, 2, 6), (3, 3, 5) (3, 4, 4), (3, 5, 3), (3, 6, 2), (4, 1, 6), (4, 2, 5), (4, 3, 4), (4, 4, 3), (4, 5, 2), (4, 6, 1), (5, 1, 5), (5, 2, 4), (5, 3, 3), (5, 4, 2), (5, 5, 1), (6, 1, 4), (6, 2, 3), (6, 3, 2), (6, 4, 1)
Probability $= \dfrac{27}{216} = \dfrac{1}{8}$

36. $\dfrac{\binom{8}{5}}{\binom{18}{5}} = \dfrac{56}{8568} = \dfrac{1}{153}$

37. $\dfrac{\binom{5}{3}}{2^5} = \dfrac{10}{32} = \dfrac{5}{16}$

38. $\dfrac{\binom{5}{5}}{2^5} = \dfrac{1}{32}$

39. $SSSS, SSSF, SSFS, SSFF, SFSS, SFSF, SFFS, SFFF,$
$FSSS, FSSF, FSFS, FSFF, FFSS, FFSF, FFFS, FFFF$

40. $\dfrac{1}{16}$

41. $\dfrac{1}{4}$

42. $\dfrac{3}{8}$

43. $\dfrac{1}{4}$

44. $\dfrac{1}{16}$

45. 1

46. $\dfrac{176}{282} = \dfrac{88}{141}$

47. $\dfrac{32}{119}$

48. $\dfrac{15}{71}$

49. $\dfrac{\binom{8}{4}}{\binom{10}{4}} = \dfrac{70}{210} = \dfrac{1}{3}$

50. $\dfrac{\binom{5}{3}}{\binom{9}{3}} = \dfrac{10}{84} = \dfrac{5}{42}$

51. $$\begin{aligned} P(A \cap B) &= P(A) \cdot P(B|A) \\ &= 0.3(0.6) = 0.18 \end{aligned}$$

52. $$\begin{aligned} P(A \cap B) &= P(A) \cdot P(B|A) \\ 0.3 &= P(A)(0.6) \\ 0.5 &= P(A) \end{aligned}$$

53. $$\begin{aligned} P(A \cap B) &= P(A) \cdot P(B|A) \\ &= 0.2(0.7) = 0.14 \end{aligned}$$

54. $$\begin{aligned} P(A \cap B) &= P(A) \cdot P(B|A) \\ &= 0.40(0.85) \\ &= 0.34 = 34\% \end{aligned}$$

55. $$\begin{aligned} P(A \cap B) &= P(A) \cdot P(B|A) \\ 0.25 &= 0.75P(B|A) \\ 0.33 &\approx P(B|A) \\ 33\% &\approx P(B|A) \end{aligned}$$

56. $$\begin{aligned} P(A \cap B) &= P(A) \cdot P(B|A) \\ &= 0.4(0.7) = 0.28 \end{aligned}$$

57. **Answers may vary.**

58. **Answers may vary.**

59. $$|x+3| = 7$$
$$x + 3 = 7 \quad \textbf{OR} \quad x + 3 = -7$$
$$x = 4 \qquad\qquad x = -10$$

60. $$|3x-2| = |2x-3|$$
$$3x - 2 = 2x - 3 \quad \textbf{OR} \quad 3x - 2 = -(2x-3)$$
$$x = -1 \qquad\qquad 3x - 2 = -2x + 3$$
$$5x = 5$$
$$x = 1$$

61. $$\begin{aligned} |x-3| &< 7 \\ -7 < x - 3 &< 7 \\ -4 < \ x \ &< 10 \end{aligned}$$

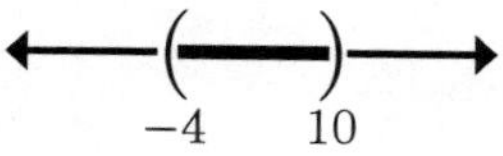

62. $$\begin{aligned} |3x-2| &\ge |2x-3| \\ \sqrt{(3x-2)^2} &\ge \sqrt{(2x-3)^2} \\ 9x^2 - 12x + 4 &\ge 4x^2 - 12x + 9 \\ 5x^2 - 5 &\ge 0 \\ 5(x+1)(x-1) &\ge 0 \end{aligned}$$

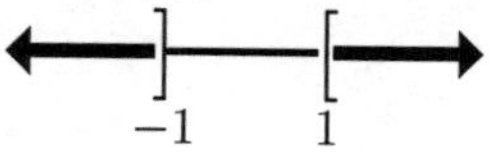

Exercise 8.8 (page 613)

1. compound

2. $P(A) + P(B) - P(A \cap B)$

3. mutually exclusive

4. not A

5. $1 - P(A)$

6. $P(B) = P(B|A)$

7. $P(A) \cdot P(B)$

8. independent

9. $\frac{26}{52} = \frac{1}{2}$

10. $\frac{4}{52} = \frac{1}{13}$

11. $\frac{26}{52} + \frac{4}{52} - \frac{2}{52} = \frac{7}{13}$

12. $\frac{26}{52} + \frac{12}{52} - \frac{6}{52} = \frac{8}{13}$

13. $\frac{4}{52} \cdot \frac{3}{51} = \frac{1}{221}$

14. 0

15. $\frac{13}{52} \cdot \frac{25}{51} = \frac{25}{204}$

16. $\frac{13}{52} \cdot \frac{13}{51} = \frac{13}{204}$

17. $\frac{6}{36} + \frac{5}{36} = \frac{11}{36}$

18. $\frac{4}{36} + \frac{18}{36} = \frac{22}{36} = \frac{11}{18}$

19. $\frac{3}{36} + \frac{18}{36} = \frac{21}{36} = \frac{7}{12}$

20. $\frac{1}{36} + \frac{0}{36} = \frac{1}{36}$

21. $\frac{7}{16} + \frac{3}{16} = \frac{10}{16} = \frac{5}{8}$

22. $\frac{6}{16} = \frac{3}{8}$

23. $1 - \frac{3}{16} = \frac{13}{16}$

24. $1 - \left(\frac{7}{16} + \frac{3}{16}\right) = \frac{3}{8}$

25. $\frac{7}{16} \cdot \frac{6}{16} = \frac{21}{128}$

26. You need to consider that either color may be drawn first

$$\underbrace{\tfrac{3}{16}}_{\text{Blue}} \cdot \underbrace{\tfrac{6}{15}}_{\text{Green}} + \underbrace{\tfrac{6}{16}}_{\text{Green}} \cdot \underbrace{\tfrac{3}{15}}_{\text{Blue}} = \frac{36}{240} = \frac{3}{20}$$

27. $$\underbrace{\tfrac{9}{16}}_{\text{Not beige}} \cdot \underbrace{\tfrac{8}{15}}_{\text{Not beige}} \cdot \underbrace{\tfrac{7}{14}}_{\text{Not beige}} = \frac{504}{3360} = \frac{3}{20}$$

28. $\frac{1}{6} \cdot \frac{4}{52} = \frac{1}{78}$

29. $\frac{7}{7} \cdot \frac{1}{7} \cdot \frac{1}{7} = \frac{1}{49}$

30. $1 - \frac{1}{49} = \frac{48}{49}$

31. $\frac{365}{365} \cdot \frac{364}{365} \cdot \frac{363}{365} \cdot \frac{362}{365} \cdot \frac{361}{365} \approx 0.973$

32. $1 - 0.973 = 0.027$

33. $\frac{1}{4} + \frac{2}{5} - \frac{1}{4} \cdot \frac{2}{5} = \frac{5 + 8 - 2}{20} = \frac{11}{20}$

34. $\frac{1}{4} \cdot \frac{1}{4} \cdot \frac{1}{4} \cdot \frac{1}{4} \cdot \frac{1}{4} = \frac{1}{1024}$

35. $\frac{1}{2} \cdot \frac{1}{3} \cdot \frac{3}{4} = \frac{1}{8}$

36. $\frac{1}{2} \cdot \frac{2}{3} \cdot \frac{1}{4} = \frac{1}{12}$

37. $\frac{1}{2} \cdot \frac{2}{3} \cdot \frac{1}{4} + \frac{1}{2} \cdot \frac{1}{3} \cdot \frac{1}{4} + \frac{1}{2} \cdot \frac{2}{3} \cdot \frac{3}{4} = \frac{2}{24} + \frac{1}{24} + \frac{6}{24} = \frac{9}{24} = \frac{3}{8}$

38. $\frac{1}{2} \cdot \frac{1}{3} \cdot \frac{1}{4} + \frac{1}{2} \cdot \frac{2}{3} \cdot \frac{3}{4} + \frac{1}{2} \cdot \frac{1}{3} \cdot \frac{3}{4} = \frac{1}{24} + \frac{6}{24} + \frac{3}{24} = \frac{10}{24} = \frac{5}{12}$

39. $\frac{2}{3} \cdot \frac{1}{2} \cdot \frac{1}{6} + \frac{2}{3} \cdot \frac{1}{2} \cdot \frac{5}{6} + \frac{1}{3} \cdot \frac{1}{2} \cdot \frac{5}{6} = \frac{2}{36} + \frac{10}{36} + \frac{5}{36} = \frac{17}{36}$

40. $0.80 + 0.60 - 0.45 = 0.95$

41. $P(A) = 0.05,\ P(H|A) = 0.40 \Rightarrow P(A \cap \overline{H}) = P(A) \cdot P(\overline{H}|A) = 0.05(0.60) = 0.03$

42. $\frac{\binom{8}{3}}{\binom{15}{3}} = \frac{56}{455} = \frac{8}{65}$

43. **Answers may vary.**

44. **Answers may vary.**

45.

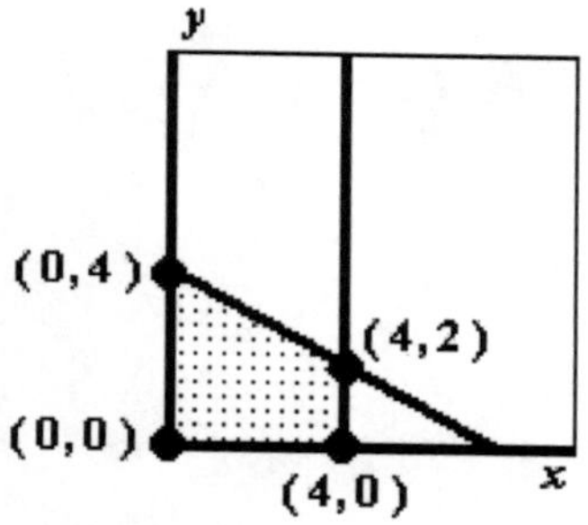

Point	$P = 2x + y$
(0, 0)	$= 2(0) + 0 = 0$
(0, 4)	$= 2(0) + 4 = 4$
(4, 2)	$= 2(4) + 2 = 10$
(4, 0)	$= 2(4) + 0 = 8$

Max: $P = 10$ at (4, 2)

46.

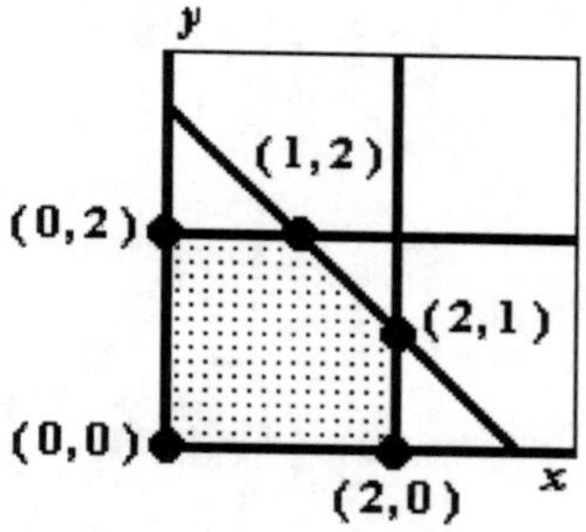

Point	$P = 3x - y$
(0, 0)	$= 3(0) - 0 = 0$
(0, 2)	$= 3(0) - 2 = -2$
(1, 2)	$= 3(1) - 2 = 1$
(2, 1)	$= 3(2) - 1 = 5$
(2, 0)	$= 3(2) - 0 = 6$

Max: $P = 6$ at (2, 0)

Exercise 8.9 (page 617)

1. odds for an event

2. odds against an event

3. $\frac{1}{1+4} = \frac{1}{5}$

4. $P_1x_1 + P_2x_2 + \cdots + P_nx_n$

5. $\frac{6}{36} = \frac{1}{6}$

6. $\frac{\frac{1}{6}}{\frac{5}{6}} = \frac{1}{5} = 1$ to 5

7. $\frac{\frac{5}{6}}{\frac{1}{6}} = \frac{5}{1} = 5$ to 1

8. $\frac{3}{6} = \frac{1}{2}$

9. $\frac{\frac{1}{2}}{\frac{1}{2}} = \frac{1}{1} = 1$ to 1

10. $\frac{\frac{1}{2}}{\frac{1}{2}} = \frac{1}{1} = 1$ to 1

11. $\frac{5}{36}$

12. $\frac{\frac{5}{36}}{\frac{31}{36}} = \frac{5}{31} = 5$ to 31

13. $\frac{\frac{31}{36}}{\frac{5}{36}} = \frac{31}{5} = 31$ to 5

14. $\frac{1}{2}$

15. $\frac{\frac{1}{2}}{\frac{1}{2}} = \frac{1}{1} = 1$ to 1

16. $\frac{\frac{1}{2}}{\frac{1}{2}} = \frac{1}{1} = 1$ to 1

17. $\frac{\frac{4}{52}}{\frac{48}{52}} = \frac{1}{12} = 1$ to 12

18. $\frac{\frac{26}{52}}{\frac{26}{52}} = \frac{1}{1} = 1$ to 1

19. $\frac{\frac{12}{52}}{\frac{40}{52}} = \frac{3}{10} = 3$ to 10

20. $\frac{\frac{39}{52}}{\frac{13}{52}} = \frac{3}{1} = 3$ to 1

21. $\frac{5}{5+2} = \frac{5}{7}$

22. 2 to 5

23. 1 to 90

24. $\frac{\frac{6}{36}}{\frac{30}{36}} = \frac{1}{5} = 1$ to 5

25. $P(\text{4 heads}) = \frac{1}{2}\cdot\frac{1}{2}\cdot\frac{1}{2}\cdot\frac{1}{2} = \frac{1}{16}$

odds against $= \frac{\frac{15}{16}}{\frac{1}{16}} = \frac{15}{1} = 15$ to 1

26. $P(\text{4 girls}) = \frac{1}{2}\cdot\frac{1}{2}\cdot\frac{1}{2}\cdot\frac{1}{2} = \frac{1}{16}$

odds in favor $= \frac{\frac{1}{16}}{\frac{15}{16}} = \frac{1}{15} = 1$ to 15

27. $\frac{1}{8+1} = \frac{1}{9}$

28. $\frac{1}{1+1} = \frac{1}{2}$

29. Expected winnings $= \frac{4}{52}(5) + \frac{4}{52}(4) + \frac{44}{52}(0) = \frac{36}{52} \approx \$0.69 \Rightarrow$ not worth playing

30. Expected winnings $= \frac{2}{1000}(800) = \$1.60 \Leftarrow$ fair price

31. $P(\text{3 boys}) = \frac{1}{2}\cdot\frac{1}{2}\cdot\frac{1}{2}\cdot\frac{1}{2} = \frac{1}{8} \Rightarrow$ odds against $= \frac{\frac{7}{8}}{\frac{1}{8}} = \frac{7}{1} = 7$ to 1

32. $P(\text{5 heads}) = \frac{\binom{5}{5}}{2^5} = \frac{1}{32}$, $P(\text{4 heads}) = \frac{\binom{5}{4}}{2^5} = \frac{5}{32}$, $P(\text{3 heads}) = \frac{\binom{5}{3}}{2^5} = \frac{10}{32}$

$P(\text{at least 3 heads}) = \frac{1}{32} + \frac{5}{32} + \frac{10}{32} = \frac{1}{2} \Rightarrow$ odds in favor $= \frac{\frac{1}{2}}{\frac{1}{2}} = \frac{1}{1} = 1$ to 1

33. $P(\text{5 heads}) = \frac{\binom{5}{5}}{2^5} = \frac{1}{32}$, $P(\text{4 heads}) = \frac{\binom{5}{4}}{2^5} = \frac{5}{32}$, $P(\text{3 heads}) = \frac{\binom{5}{3}}{2^5} = \frac{10}{32}$

Expected winnings $= \frac{1}{32}(5) + \frac{5}{32}(4) + \frac{10}{32}(3) \approx \$1.72 \Leftarrow$ fair price

34. $P(\text{double 6}) = \frac{1}{36}$, $P(\text{double 1}) = \frac{1}{36}$

Expected winnings $= \frac{1}{36}(10) + \frac{1}{36}(1) \approx \$0.31 \Leftarrow$ fair price

35. Expected value $= \frac{4}{52}(1) + \frac{12}{52}(10) + \frac{4}{52}(2) + \frac{4}{52}(3) + \cdots + \frac{4}{52}(10) \approx 6.54$

36. Expected value $= \frac{1}{36}(2) + \frac{2}{36}(3) + \frac{3}{36}(4) + \frac{4}{36}(5) + \frac{5}{36}(6) + \frac{6}{36}(7) + \frac{5}{36}(8) + \frac{4}{36}(9) + \frac{3}{36}(10) + \frac{2}{36}(11) + \frac{1}{36}(12) = \frac{252}{36} = 7$

37. $\binom{8}{7}\cdot\left(\frac{1}{5}\right)^7\cdot\frac{4}{5} = \frac{32}{390{,}625}$

38. 32 to 390,593

39. **Answers may vary.**

40. $\frac{0.0000000372}{1} = \frac{1}{26{,}881{,}720} \Rightarrow$ The odds against are 26,881,720 to 1.

41. $3x - 2y = 9$
$-2y = -3x + 9$
$y = \frac{3}{2}x - \frac{9}{2}$
$m = \frac{3}{2}$
Use $m = -\frac{2}{3}$.

$y - y_1 = m(x - x_1)$
$y - 1 = -\frac{2}{3}(x - 1)$
$3y - 3 = -2(x - 1)$
$3y - 3 = -2x + 2$
$\boxed{2x + 3y = 5}$

42. $(x-3)^2 = 4p(y+2)$
$(0-3)^2 = 4p(0+2)$
$9 = 8p$
$\frac{9}{2} = 4p$
$(x-3)^2 = \frac{9}{2}(y+2)$

OR

$(y+2)^2 = 4p(x-3)$
$(0+2)^2 = 4p(0-3)$
$4 = -12p$
$-\frac{4}{3} = 4p$
$(y+2)^2 = -\frac{4}{3}(x-3)$

43. $C(3, 5), r = 5 \Rightarrow (x-3)^2 + (y-5)^2 = 25$

44.
$$2x^2 + 4y^2 + 12x - 24y + 46 = 0$$
$$2(x^2 + 6x) + 4(y^2 - 6y) = -46$$
$$2(x^2 + 6x + 9) + 4(y^2 - 6y + 9) = -46 + 18 + 36$$
$$2(x+3)^2 + 4(y-3)^2 = 8$$
$$\frac{(x+3)^2}{4} + \frac{(y-3)^2}{2} = 1 \Rightarrow \text{ellipse}$$

Chapter 8 Summary (page 620)

1. **a.** $6! = 6 \cdot 5 \cdot 4 \cdot 3 \cdot 2 \cdot 1 = 720$

b. $7! \cdot 0! \cdot 1! \cdot 3! = 5040 \cdot 1 \cdot 1 \cdot 6 = 30{,}240$

c. $\frac{8!}{7!} = \frac{8 \cdot 7!}{7!} = 8$

d. $\frac{5! \cdot 7! \cdot 8!}{6! \cdot 9!} = \frac{5! \cdot 7 \cdot 6! \cdot 8!}{6! \cdot 9 \cdot 8!} = \frac{5! \cdot 7}{9} = \frac{280}{3}$

2. **a.** $(x+y)^3 = x^3 + \frac{3!}{1!2!}x^2y + \frac{3!}{2!1!}xy^2 + y^3 = x^3 + 3x^2y + 3xy^2 + y^3$

b. $(p+q)^4 = p^4 + \frac{4!}{1!3!}p^3q + \frac{4!}{2!2!}p^2q^2 + \frac{4!}{3!1!}pq^3 + q^4 = p^4 + 4p^3q + 6p^2q^2 + 4pq^3 + q^4$

c. $(a-b)^5 = a^5 + \frac{5!}{1!4!}a^4(-b) + \frac{5!}{2!3!}a^3(-b)^2 + \frac{5!}{3!2!}a^2(-b)^3 + \frac{5!}{4!1!}a(-b)^4 + (-b)^5$
$= a^5 - 5a^4b + 10a^3b^2 - 10a^2b^3 + 5ab^4 - b^5$

d. $(2a-b)^3 = (2a)^3 + \frac{3!}{1!2!}(2a)^2(-b) + \frac{3!}{2!1!}(2a)(-b)^2 + (-b)^3 = 8a^3 - 12a^2b + 6ab^2 - b^3$

3. **a.** The 4th term will involve b^3.

$\dfrac{8!}{5!3!}a^5b^3 = 56a^5b^3$

b. The 3rd term will involve $(-y)^2$.

$\dfrac{5!}{3!2!}(2x)^3(-y)^2 = 80x^3y^2$

c. The 7th term will involve $(-y)^6$.

$\dfrac{9!}{3!6!}x^3(-y)^6 = 84x^3y^6$

d. The 4th term will involve 7^3.

$\dfrac{6!}{3!3!}(4x)^3 7^3 = 439{,}040x^3$

4. **a.** $4^3 - 1 = 63$

b. $\dfrac{4^2+2}{2} = \dfrac{18}{2} = 9$

5. **a.**

$a_1 = 5$
$a_2 = 3a_1 + 2 = 3(5) + 2 = 17$
$a_3 = 3a_2 + 2 = 3(17) + 2 = 53$
$a_4 = 3a_3 + 2 = 3(53) + 2 = 161$

b.

$a_1 = -2$
$a_2 = 2a_1^2 = 2(-2)^2 = 8$
$a_3 = 2a_2^2 = 2(8)^2 = 128$
$a_4 = 2a_3^2 = 2(128)^2 = 32{,}768$

6. **a.** $\displaystyle\sum_{k=1}^{4} 3k^2 = 3\sum_{k=1}^{4} k^2 = 3(1^2 + 2^2 + 3^2 + 4^2) = 3(30) = 90$

b. $\displaystyle\sum_{k=1}^{10} 6 = 10(6) = 60$

c. $\displaystyle\sum_{k=5}^{8}(k^3 + 3k^2) = \sum_{k=5}^{8} k^3 + 3\sum_{k=5}^{8} k^2 = (5^3 + 6^3 + 7^3 + 8^3) + 3(5^2 + 6^2 + 7^2 + 8^2)$

$= 1718$

d. $\displaystyle\sum_{k=1}^{30}\left(\frac{3}{2}k - 12\right) - \frac{3}{2}\sum_{k=1}^{30} k = \frac{3}{2}\sum_{k=1}^{30} k - \sum_{k=1}^{30} 12 - \frac{3}{2}\sum_{k=1}^{30} k = -\sum_{k=1}^{30} 12 = -360$

7. **a.**

$a = 5, d = 4$
29th term $= a + (n-1)d$
$= 5 + (29-1)4 = 117$

b.

$a = 8, d = 7$
40th term $= a + (n-1)d$
$= 8 + (40-1)7 = 281$

c.

$a = 6, d = -7$
15th term $= a + (n-1)d$
$= 6 + (15-1)(-7) = -92$

d.

$a = \frac{1}{2}, d = -2$
35th term $= a + (n-1)d$
$= \frac{1}{2} + (35-1)(-2) = -\frac{135}{2}$

8.

$a = 2$, 5th term $= 8$
$8 = 2 + 4d$
$6 = 4d$
$\dfrac{3}{2} = d \Rightarrow 2, \dfrac{7}{2}, 5, \dfrac{13}{2}, 8$

9.

$a = 10$, 7th term $= 100$
$100 = 10 + 6d$
$90 = 6d$
$15 = d \Rightarrow 10, 25, 40, 55, 70, 85, 100$

10. **a.** $a = 5, d = 4$

$l = a + (n-1)d = 5 + 39(4) = 161$

$S = \frac{n(a+l)}{2} = \frac{40(5+161)}{2} = 3320$

b. $a = 8, d = 7$

$l = a + (n-1)d = 8 + 39(7) = 281$

$S = \frac{n(a+l)}{2} = \frac{40(8+281)}{2} = 5780$

c. $a = 6, d = -7$

$l = a + (n-1)d = 6 + 39(-7) = -267;\ S = \frac{n(a+l)}{2} = \frac{40(6-267)}{2} = -5220$

d. $a = \frac{1}{2}, d = -2$

$l = a + (n-1)d = \frac{1}{2} + 39(-2) = -\frac{155}{2};\ S = \frac{n(a+l)}{2} = \frac{40\left(\frac{1}{2} - \frac{155}{2}\right)}{2} = -1540$

11. **a.** $a = 81, r = \frac{1}{3}$

11th term $= ar^{n-1} = 81\left(\frac{1}{3}\right)^{10} = \frac{1}{729}$

b. $a = 2, r = 3$

9th term $= ar^{n-1} = 2(3)^8 = 13{,}122$

c. $a = 9, r = \frac{1}{2}$

15th term $= ar^{n-1} = 9\left(\frac{1}{2}\right)^{14} = \frac{9}{16{,}384}$

d. $a = 8, r = -\frac{1}{5}$

7th term $= ar^{n-1} = 8\left(-\frac{1}{5}\right)^6 = \frac{8}{15{,}625}$

12. 5th term $= ar^4$

$8 = 2r^4$

$4 = r^4$

$\pm\sqrt[4]{4} = r \Rightarrow r = \pm\sqrt{2}$

Use $r = +\sqrt{2}$:

$2, 2\sqrt{2}, 4, 4\sqrt{2}, 8$

13. 6th term $= ar^5$

$64 = -2r^5$

$-32 = r^5$

$-2 = r$

$-2, 4, -8, 16, -32, 64$

14. 3rd term $= ar^2$

$64 = 4r^2$

$16 = r^2 \Rightarrow r = 4$ (problem specifies positive) $\Rightarrow 4, 16, 64$

15. **a.** $a = 81, r = \frac{1}{3}, n = 8$

$$S = \frac{a - ar^n}{1-r} = \frac{81 - 81\left(\frac{1}{3}\right)^8}{1 - \frac{1}{3}} = \frac{81 - \frac{1}{81}}{\frac{2}{3}} = \frac{3280}{27}$$

b. $a = 2, r = 3, n = 8$

$$S = \frac{a - ar^n}{1-r} = \frac{2 - 2(3)^8}{1-3} = \frac{-13{,}120}{-2} = 6560$$

c. $a = 9, r = \frac{1}{2}, n = 8$

$$S = \frac{a - ar^n}{1-r} = \frac{9 - 9\left(\frac{1}{2}\right)^8}{1 - \frac{1}{2}} = \frac{\frac{2295}{256}}{\frac{1}{2}} = \frac{2295}{128}$$

d. $a = 8, r = -\frac{1}{5}, n = 8$

$$S = \frac{a - ar^n}{1-r} = \frac{8 - 8\left(-\frac{1}{5}\right)^8}{1 - \left(-\frac{1}{5}\right)} = \frac{\frac{3{,}124{,}992}{390{,}625}}{\frac{6}{5}} = \frac{520{,}832}{78{,}125}$$

16. $a = \frac{1}{3}, r = 3, n = 8$

$$S = \frac{a - ar^n}{1 - r} = \frac{\frac{1}{3} - \frac{1}{3}(3)^8}{1 - 3}$$
$$= \frac{-\frac{6560}{3}}{-2} = \frac{3280}{3}$$

17. 7th term $= ar^6$
$$= 2\sqrt{2}\left(\sqrt{2}\right)^6$$
$$= 16\sqrt{2}$$

18. **a.** $a = \frac{1}{3}, r = \frac{1}{2}$
$$S = \frac{a}{1 - r} = \frac{\frac{1}{3}}{1 - \frac{1}{2}} = \frac{\frac{1}{3}}{\frac{1}{2}} = \frac{2}{3}$$

b. $a = \frac{1}{5}, r = -\frac{2}{3}$
$$S = \frac{a}{1 - r} = \frac{\frac{1}{5}}{1 - \left(-\frac{2}{3}\right)} = \frac{\frac{1}{5}}{\frac{5}{3}} = \frac{3}{25}$$

c. $a = \frac{1}{3}, r = \frac{3}{2} > 1 \Rightarrow$ no sum

d. $a = \frac{1}{2}, r = \frac{1}{2}$
$$S = \frac{a}{1 - r} = \frac{\frac{1}{2}}{1 - \frac{1}{2}} = \frac{\frac{1}{2}}{\frac{1}{2}} = 1$$

19. **a.** $a = \frac{3}{10}, r = \frac{1}{10}$
$$S = \frac{a}{1 - r} = \frac{\frac{3}{10}}{1 - \frac{1}{10}} = \frac{\frac{3}{10}}{\frac{9}{10}} = \frac{1}{3}$$

b. $a = \frac{9}{10}, r = \frac{1}{10}$
$$S = \frac{a}{1 - r} = \frac{\frac{9}{10}}{1 - \frac{1}{10}} = \frac{\frac{9}{10}}{\frac{9}{10}} = 1$$

c. $a = \frac{17}{100}, r = \frac{1}{100}$
$$S = \frac{a}{1 - r} = \frac{\frac{17}{100}}{1 - \frac{1}{100}} = \frac{\frac{17}{100}}{\frac{99}{100}} = \frac{17}{99}$$

d. $a = \frac{45}{100}, r = \frac{1}{100}$
$$S = \frac{a}{1 - r} = \frac{\frac{45}{100}}{1 - \frac{1}{100}} = \frac{\frac{45}{100}}{\frac{99}{100}} = \frac{5}{11}$$

20. $a = 3000, r = 1 + \frac{0.0775}{365}, n = 2190$
$$ar^{365} = 3000\left(1 + \frac{0.0775}{365}\right)^{2190}$$
$$\approx \$4775.81$$
The amount will be \$4775.81.

21. $a = 4000, r = 1.05, n = 10$

$ar^{10} = 4000(1.05)^{10} \approx 6516$ in 10 years

$ar^{-5} = 4000(1.05)^{-5} \approx 3134$ 5 years ago

22. $a = 10{,}000;\ r = 0.90;\ ar^{10} = 10{,}000(0.90)^{10} \approx \$3486.78$ in 10 years

23.

$n = 1$

$$1^3 \stackrel{?}{=} \frac{1^2(1+1)^2}{4}$$
$$1 = 1$$

$n = 2$

$$1^3 + 2^3 \stackrel{?}{=} \frac{2^2(2+1)^2}{4}$$
$$9 \stackrel{?}{=} \frac{4(9)}{4}$$
$$9 = 9$$

$n = 3$

$$1^3 + 2^3 + 3^3 \stackrel{?}{=} \frac{3^2(3+1)^2}{4}$$
$$36 \stackrel{?}{=} \frac{9(16)}{4}$$
$$36 = 36$$

$n = 4$

$$1^3 + 2^3 + 3^3 + 4^3 \stackrel{?}{=} \frac{4^2(4+1)^2}{4}$$
$$100 \stackrel{?}{=} \frac{16(25)}{4}$$
$$100 = 100$$

24. Check $n = 1$: $1^3 = \frac{1^2(1+1)^2}{4}$ True for $n = 1$

$$1 = 1$$

Assume for $n = k$ and show for $n = k + 1$:

$$1^3 + 2^3 + 3^3 + \cdots + k^3 = \frac{k^2(k+1)^2}{4}$$
$$\boxed{1^3 + 2^3 + 3^3 + \cdots + k^3} + (k+1)^3 = \boxed{\frac{k^2(k+1)^2}{4}} + (k+1)^3$$
$$1^3 + 2^3 + 3^3 + \cdots + (k+1)^3 = \frac{k^2(k+1)^2 + 4(k+1)^3}{4}$$
$$1^2 + 2^2 + 3^2 + \cdots + (k+1)^2 = \frac{(k+1)^2[k^2 + 4(k+1)]}{4}$$
$$1^2 + 2^2 + 3^2 + \cdots + (k+1)^2 = \frac{(k+1)^2(k+2)^2}{4}$$

Since this is what results when $n = k + 1$ in the formula, we have shown that the formula works for $n = k + 1$ if it works for $n = k$.

25. **a.** $P(8, 5) = \frac{8!}{(8-5)!} = \frac{8!}{3!} = 8 \cdot 7 \cdot 6 \cdot 5 \cdot 4 = 6720$

b. $C(7, 4) = \frac{7!}{4!(7-4)!} = \frac{7!}{4!3!} = \frac{7 \cdot 6 \cdot 5 \cdot 4!}{4! \cdot 3 \cdot 2 \cdot 1} = 35$

c. $0! \cdot 1! = 1 \cdot 1 = 1$

d. $P(10, 2) \cdot C(10, 2) = \frac{10!}{8!} \cdot \frac{10!}{2!8!} = 90 \cdot 45 = 4050$

e. $P(8, 6) \cdot C(8, 6) = \frac{8!}{2!} \cdot \frac{8!}{6!2!} = 20{,}160 \cdot 28 = 564{,}480$

f. $C(8,5)\cdot C(6,2)=\dfrac{8!}{5!3!}\cdot\dfrac{6!}{2!4!}=56\cdot 15=840$

g. $C(7,5)\cdot P(4,0)=\dfrac{7!}{5!2!}\cdot\dfrac{4!}{4!}=21\cdot 1=21$

h. $C(12,10)\cdot C(11,0)=\dfrac{12!}{10!2!}\cdot\dfrac{11!}{0!11!}=66\cdot 1=66$

i. $\dfrac{P(8,5)}{C(8,5)}=\dfrac{6720}{56}=120$

j. $\dfrac{C(8,5)}{C(13,5)}=\dfrac{56}{1287}$

k. $\dfrac{C(6,3)}{C(10,3)}=\dfrac{20}{120}=\dfrac{1}{6}$

l. $\dfrac{C(13,5)}{C(52,5)}=\dfrac{1287}{2{,}598{,}960}=\dfrac{33}{66{,}640}$

26. Consider each set of two people who must sit together as a single person, so that there are 8 "people" who must be arranged in a circle. This can be done in $(8-1)!=7!=5040$ ways. However, each pair seated next to each other could be switched, so that the number of arrangements is multiplied by 4. There are $4\cdot 5040=20{,}160$ possible arrangements.

27. $\dfrac{9!}{2!2!}=90{,}720$

28.

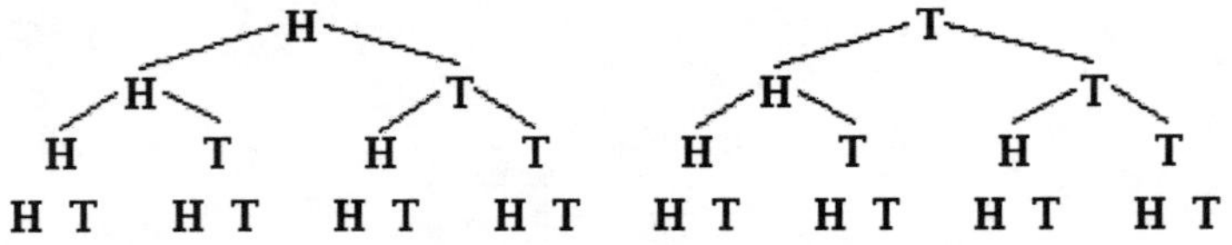

29. $\binom{4}{3}\binom{4}{2}=4\cdot 6=24$

30. $\dfrac{\binom{4}{3}\binom{4}{2}}{\binom{52}{5}}=\dfrac{24}{2{,}598{,}960}=\dfrac{1}{108{,}290}$

31. $1-\dfrac{1}{108{,}290}=\dfrac{108{,}289}{108{,}290}$

32. $\dfrac{\binom{4}{4}\binom{4}{4}\binom{4}{4}\binom{4}{1}}{\binom{52}{13}}\approx\dfrac{4}{6.35\times 10^{11}}\approx 6.3\times 10^{-12}$

33. $\dfrac{\binom{8}{3}\binom{6}{2}}{\binom{14}{5}}=\dfrac{840}{2002}=\dfrac{60}{143}$

34. $\dfrac{13+13}{52}=\dfrac{1}{2}$

35. $\dfrac{26+4-2}{52}=\dfrac{7}{13}$

36. $\dfrac{1}{\binom{52}{5}}=\dfrac{1}{2{,}598{,}960}$

37. $\dfrac{4\binom{13}{13}}{\binom{52}{13}}\approx\dfrac{4}{6.35\times 10^{11}}$

38. Use the tree diagram in **#28**. $\Rightarrow \dfrac{15}{16}$

39. $P(2 \text{ or spade}) = P(2) + P(\text{spade}) - P(2 \text{ and spade}) = \frac{4}{52} + \frac{13}{52} - \frac{1}{52} = \frac{16}{52} = \frac{4}{13}$

40. $\# \text{ cured} = 0.83(800) = 664$ people
$\# \text{ not cured} = 800 - 664 = 136$

41. $\dfrac{\frac{1}{8}}{\frac{7}{8}} = \dfrac{1}{7} = 1$ to 7

42. $P(4 \text{ girls}) = \dfrac{1}{2} \cdot \dfrac{1}{2} \cdot \dfrac{1}{2} \cdot \dfrac{1}{2} = \dfrac{1}{16}$
odds in favor $= \dfrac{\frac{1}{16}}{\frac{15}{16}} = \dfrac{1}{15} = 1$ to 15

43. $P(\text{neither}) = \dfrac{1}{6} \cdot \dfrac{1}{4} = \dfrac{1}{24}$
odds $= \dfrac{\frac{1}{24}}{\frac{23}{24}} = \dfrac{1}{23} = 1$ to 23

44. $P(\text{not graduate}) = \dfrac{10}{10+11} = \dfrac{10}{21} \Rightarrow P(\text{graduate}) = \dfrac{11}{21}$

45. $P(4 \text{ heads}) = \dfrac{\binom{4}{4}}{2^4} = \dfrac{1}{16}$, $P(3 \text{ heads}) = \dfrac{\binom{4}{3}}{2^4} = \dfrac{4}{16}$, $P(2 \text{ heads}) = \dfrac{\binom{4}{2}}{2^4} = \dfrac{6}{16}$
$P(1 \text{ heads}) = \dfrac{\binom{4}{1}}{2^4} = \dfrac{4}{16}$, $P(0 \text{ heads}) = \dfrac{\binom{4}{0}}{2^4} = \dfrac{1}{16}$
Expected value $= 4\left(\dfrac{1}{16}\right) + 3\left(\dfrac{4}{16}\right) + 2\left(\dfrac{6}{16}\right) + 1\left(\dfrac{4}{16}\right) + 0\left(\dfrac{1}{16}\right) = \dfrac{32}{16} = \$2.00$

46. Each addend represents the number of ways of selecting a subset from the set, starting with subsets of size 0, size 1, size 2, and so on until size n. Thus, when added together, the sum represents the total number of subsets (of all size), or 2^n.

Chapter 8 Test (page 624)

1. $3! \cdot 0! \cdot 4! \cdot 1! = 6 \cdot 1 \cdot 24 \cdot 1 = 144$

2. $\dfrac{2! \cdot 4! \cdot 6! \cdot 8!}{3! \cdot 5! \cdot 7!} = 2! \cdot \dfrac{4!}{3!} \cdot \dfrac{6!}{5!} \cdot \dfrac{8!}{7!}$
$= 2 \cdot 4 \cdot 6 \cdot 8 = 384$

3. The 2nd term will involve $(2y)^1$.
$\dfrac{5!}{4!1!} x^4 (2y)^1 = 10x^4 y$

4. The 7th term will involve $(-b)^6$.
$\dfrac{8!}{2!6!} (2a)^2 (-b)^6 = 112a^2b^6$

5. $\sum_{k=1}^{3} (4k+1) = 4\sum_{k=1}^{3} k + \sum_{k=1}^{3} 1 = 4(1+2+3) + 3(1) = 24 + 3 = 27$

6. $\sum_{k=2}^{4} (3k-21) = 3\sum_{k=2}^{4} k - \sum_{k=2}^{4} 21 = 3(2+3+4) - 3(21) = 27 - 63 = -36$

7. $a = 2, d = 3$
$l = a + (n-1)d = 2 + 9(3) = 29$
$S = \dfrac{n(a+l)}{2} = \dfrac{10(2+29)}{2} = 155$

8. $a = 5, d = -4$
$l = a + (n-1)d = 5 + 9(-4) = -31$
$S = \dfrac{n(a+l)}{2} = \dfrac{10(5-31)}{2} = -130$

9. $a = 4$, 5th term $= 24$

$24 = 4 + 4d$

$20 = 4d$

$5 = d \Rightarrow 4, 9, 14, 19, 24$

10. 4th term $= ar^3$

$-54 = -2r^3$

$27 = r^3$

$3 = r \Rightarrow -2, -6, -18, -54$

11. $a = \frac{1}{4}, r = 2, n = 10$

$$S = \frac{a - ar^n}{1 - r} = \frac{\frac{1}{4} - \frac{1}{4}(2)^{10}}{1 - 2} = \frac{-\frac{1023}{4}}{-1} = \frac{1023}{4} = 255.75$$

12. $a = 6, r = \frac{1}{3}, n = 10$

$$S = \frac{a - ar^n}{1 - r} = \frac{6 - 6\left(\frac{1}{3}\right)^{10}}{1 - \frac{1}{3}} = \frac{\frac{354{,}288}{59{,}049}}{\frac{2}{3}} = \frac{177{,}144}{19{,}683} \approx 9$$

13. $a = c;\ r = 0.75$

$ar^3 = c(0.75)^3 \approx \$0.42c$ in 3 years

14. $a = c;\ r = 1.10$

$ar^4 = c(1.10)^4 \approx \$1.46c$ in 4 years

15.

Check $n = 1$: $3 = \frac{1}{2}(1)(1 + 5)$ True for $n = 1$

$3 = 3$

Assume for $n = k$ and show for $n = k + 1$:

$$3 + 4 + 5 + \cdots + (k + 2) = \frac{1}{2}k(k + 5)$$

$$\boxed{3 + 4 + 5 + \cdots + (k + 2)} + ((k + 1) + 2) = \boxed{\frac{1}{2}k(k + 5)} + ((k + 1) + 2)$$

$$3 + 4 + 5 + \cdots + ((k + 1) + 2) = \frac{1}{2}k^2 + \frac{7}{2}k + 3$$

$$3 + 4 + 5 + \cdots + ((k + 1) + 2) = \frac{1}{2}\left(k^2 + 7k + 6\right)$$

$$3 + 4 + 5 + \cdots + ((k + 1) + 2) = \frac{1}{2}(k + 1)(k + 6) = \frac{1}{2}(k + 1)((k + 1) + 5)$$

Since this is what results when $n = k + 1$ in the formula, we have shown that the formula works for $n = k + 1$ if it works for $n = k$.

16. $8 \cdot 10 \cdot 10 \cdot 10 \cdot 10 \cdot 10 = 800{,}000$

17. $P(7, 2) = \frac{7!}{5!} = 42$

18. $P(4, 4) = \frac{4!}{0!} = 24$

19. $C(8, 2) = \frac{8!}{2!6!} = 28$

20. $C(12, 0) = \frac{12!}{0!12!} = 1$

21. $4!4! = 576$

22. $(6 - 1)! = 5! = 120$

23. $\frac{5!}{2!} = 60$

24. $\{(H,H,H),(H,H,T),(H,T,H),(H,T,T),(T,H,H),(T,H,T),(T,T,H),(T,T,T)\}$

25. $\frac{1}{6}$

26. $\frac{4+4}{52}=\frac{2}{13}$

27. $\frac{\binom{13}{5}}{\binom{52}{5}}=\frac{429}{866{,}320}$

28. $\frac{\binom{5}{2}}{2^5}=\frac{10}{32}=\frac{5}{16}$

29. $0.30+0.80-0.70=0.40$
$=40\%$

30. $1-0.1=0.9$

31. $\frac{26+12-6}{52}=\frac{8}{13}$

32. $\frac{2+18}{36}=\frac{5}{9}$

33. $\frac{3}{3+1}=\frac{3}{4}$

34. Expected winnings $=\frac{1}{6}(4)+\frac{1}{6}(2)+\frac{4}{6}(0)=\$1.00 \Leftarrow$ fair price

Exercise 9.1 (page 635)

1. interest

2. compound

3. annual

4. principal, present

5. future

6. percent

7. interest

8. nominal

9. periodic rate

10. conversion

11. principal, periodic rate,
frequency of compounding, number of years

12. future value, periodic rate,
frequency of compounding, number of years

13. effective

14. 10

15. $P=1200,\ i=0.08,\ k=1,\ n=1$
$FV=P(1+i)^{kn}$
$=1200(1+0.08)^{1\cdot 1}\approx \$1296$

16. $P=1200,\ i=0.08,\ k=1,\ n=3$
$FV=P(1+i)^{kn}$
$=1200(1+0.08)^{1\cdot 3}\approx \$1511.65$

17. $P=1200,\ i=0.08,\ k=1,\ n=5$
$FV=P(1+i)^{kn}$
$=1200(1+0.08)^{1\cdot 5}\approx \$1763.19$

18. $P=1200,\ i=0.08,\ k=1,\ n=20$
$FV=P(1+i)^{kn}$
$=1200(1+0.08)^{1\cdot 20}\approx \$5593.15$

19. $P=1200,\ i=0.03,\ k=1,\ n=10$
$FV=P(1+i)^{kn}$
$=1200(1+0.03)^{1\cdot 10}\approx \$1612.70$

20. $P=1200,\ i=0.05,\ k=1,\ n=10$
$FV=P(1+i)^{kn}$
$=1200(1+0.05)^{1\cdot 10}\approx \$1954.67$

21. $P=1200,\ i=0.09,\ k=1,\ n=10$
$FV=P(1+i)^{kn}$
$=1200(1+0.09)^{1\cdot 10}\approx \$2840.84$

22. $P=1200,\ i=0.12,\ k=1,\ n=10$
$FV=P(1+i)^{kn}$
$=1200(1+0.12)^{1\cdot 10}\approx \$3727.02$

23. $P = 1200,\ i = \frac{0.06}{2},\ k = 2,\ n = 15$
$FV = P(1+i)^{kn}$
$= 1200\left(1 + \frac{0.06}{2}\right)^{2\cdot 15} \approx \$2912.71$

24. $P = 1200,\ i = \frac{0.06}{4},\ k = 4,\ n = 15$
$FV = P(1+i)^{kn}$
$= 1200\left(1 + \frac{0.06}{4}\right)^{4\cdot 15} \approx \$2931.86$

25. $P = 1200,\ i = \frac{0.06}{12},\ k = 12,\ n = 15$
$FV = P(1+i)^{kn}$
$= 1200\left(1 + \frac{0.06}{12}\right)^{12\cdot 15} \approx \$2944.91$

26. $P = 1200,\ i = \frac{0.06}{365},\ k = 365,\ n = 15$
$FV = P(1+i)^{kn}$
$= 1200\left(1 + \frac{0.06}{365}\right)^{365\cdot 15} \approx \$2951.31$

27. $k = 4,\ i = \frac{0.06}{4}$
$R = (1+i)^k - 1$
$= \left(1 + \frac{0.06}{4}\right)^4 - 1$
$\approx 0.0614 = 6.14\%$

28. $k = 12,\ i = \frac{0.08}{12}$
$R = (1+i)^k - 1$
$= \left(1 + \frac{0.08}{12}\right)^{12} - 1$
$\approx 0.0830 = 8.30\%$

29. $k = 2,\ i = \frac{0.095}{2}$
$R = (1+i)^k - 1$
$= \left(1 + \frac{0.095}{2}\right)^2 - 1$
$\approx 0.0973 = 9.73\%$

30. $k = 360,\ i = \frac{0.10}{360}$
$R = (1+i)^k - 1$
$= \left(1 + \frac{0.10}{360}\right)^{360} - 1$
$\approx 0.1052 = 10.52\%$

31. $FV = 20{,}000;\ i = \frac{0.06}{2},\ k = 2,\ n = 6$
$PV = FV(1+i)^{-kn}$
$= 20{,}000\left(1 + \frac{0.06}{2}\right)^{-2\cdot 6}$
$\approx \$14{,}027.60$

32. $FV = 20{,}000;\ i = \frac{0.08}{4},\ k = 4,\ n = 6$
$PV = FV(1+i)^{-kn}$
$= 20{,}000\left(1 + \frac{0.08}{4}\right)^{-4\cdot 6}$
$\approx \$12{,}434.43$

33. $FV = 20{,}000;\ i = \frac{0.09}{12},\ k = 12,\ n = 6$
$PV = FV(1+i)^{-kn}$
$= 20{,}000\left(1 + \frac{0.09}{12}\right)^{-12\cdot 6}$
$\approx \$11{,}678.47$

34. $FV = 20{,}000;\ i = \frac{0.07}{360},\ k = 360,\ n = 6$
$PV = FV(1+i)^{-kn}$
$= 20{,}000\left(1 + \frac{0.07}{360}\right)^{-360\cdot 6}$
$\approx \$13{,}141.47$

35. $P = 7000,\ i = \frac{0.06}{4},\ k = 4,\ n = 18$
$FV = P(1+i)^{kn}$
$= 7000\left(1 + \frac{0.06}{4}\right)^{4\cdot 18} \approx \$20{,}448.11$

36. $P = 5700,\ i = \frac{0.08}{12},\ k = 12,\ n = 6$
$FV = P(1+i)^{kn}$
$= 5700\left(1 + \frac{0.08}{12}\right)^{12\cdot 6} \approx \$9196.96$

37. $P = 147{,}500;\ i = \frac{0.075}{2},\ k = 2,\ n = 12$
$FV = P(1+i)^{kn}$
$= 147{,}500\left(1 + \frac{0.075}{2}\right)^{2\cdot 12} \approx \$356{,}867.13$

38. $P = 3,\ i = \frac{0.0873}{2},\ k = 2,\ n = 8$
$FV = P(1+i)^{kn}$
$= 3\left(1 + \frac{0.0873}{2}\right)^{2\cdot 8} \approx \$5.943$ million

39. $P = 137{,}000;\ i = \frac{0.11}{1},\ k = 1,\ n = 4$
$FV = P(1+i)^{kn}$
$= 137{,}000\left(1 + \frac{0.11}{1}\right)^{1\cdot 4} \approx \$207{,}976$

40. $P = 47{,}000;\ i = \frac{0.085}{1},\ k = 1,\ n = 5$
$FV = P(1+i)^{kn}$
$= 47{,}000\left(1 + \frac{0.085}{1}\right)^{1\cdot 5} \approx \$70{,}672$

41. $P = 4.3$, $i = \frac{0.072}{1}$, $k = 1$, $n = 10$

$FV = P(1+i)^{kn}$

$= 4.3\left(1 + \frac{0.072}{1}\right)^{1 \cdot 10} \approx \$8.62$ million ft^3

42.

Bank One	Bank Two
$k = 4$, $i = \frac{0.0435}{4}$	$k = 12$, $i = \frac{0.043}{12}$
$R = (1+i)^k - 1$	$R = (1+i)^k - 1$
$= \left(1 + \frac{0.0435}{4}\right)^4 - 1$	$= \left(1 + \frac{0.043}{12}\right)^{12} - 1$
$\approx 0.0442 = 4.42\%$	$\approx 0.0439 = 4.39\%$

Bank One provides the better growth.

43.

NOW account	Money Market
$k = 4$, $i = \frac{0.072}{4}$	$k = 12$, $i = \frac{0.069}{12}$
$R = (1+i)^k - 1$	$R = (1+i)^k - 1$
$= \left(1 + \frac{0.072}{4}\right)^4 - 1$	$= \left(1 + \frac{0.069}{12}\right)^{12} - 1$
$\approx 0.0740 = 7.40\%$	$\approx 0.0712 = 7.12\%$

44.

CD	Passbook
$k = 2$, $i = \frac{0.062}{2}$	$k = 4$, $i = \frac{0.0525}{4}$
$R = (1+i)^k - 1$	$R = (1+i)^k - 1$
$= \left(1 + \frac{0.062}{2}\right)^2 - 1$	$= \left(1 + \frac{0.0525}{4}\right)^4 - 1$
$\approx 0.0630 = 6.30\%$	$\approx 0.0535 = 5.35\%$

45. $P = 1230$, $i = \frac{0.12}{360}$, $k = 360$, $n = 0.25$

$FV = P(1+i)^{kn}$

$= 1230\left(1 + \frac{0.12}{360}\right)^{360(0.25)} \approx \$1267.45$

46. $P = 2570$, $i = \frac{0.114}{12}$, $k = 12$, $n = 0.75$

$FV = P(1+i)^{kn}$

$= 2570\left(1 + \frac{0.114}{12}\right)^{12(0.75)} \approx \$2798.27$

47. $FV = 4200$; $i = \frac{0.0575}{12}$, $k = 12$, $n = 1.5$

$PV = FV(1+i)^{-kn}$

$= 4200\left(1 + \frac{0.0575}{12}\right)^{-12(1.5)}$

$\approx \$3853.73$

48. $FV = 2780$; $i = \frac{0.076}{4}$, $k = 4$, $n = 1.5$

$PV = FV(1+i)^{-kn}$

$= 2780\left(1 + \frac{0.076}{4}\right)^{-4(1.5)}$

$\approx \$2483.13$

49.

First ten years

$P = 12{,}000$; $i = \frac{0.075}{12}$, $k = 12$, $n = 10$

$FV = P(1+i)^{kn}$

$= 12{,}000\left(1 + \frac{0.075}{12}\right)^{12(10)} \approx \$25{,}344.78$

Next four years

$P = 37{,}344.78$; $i = \frac{0.075}{12}$, $k = 12$, $n = 4$

$FV = P(1+i)^{kn}$

$= 37{,}344.78\left(1 + \frac{0.075}{12}\right)^{12(4)} \approx \$50{,}363.14$

50. First five years

$P = 1100;\ i = \frac{0.10}{12},\ k = 12,\ n = 5$

$FV = P(1+i)^{kn}$

$= 1100\left(1 + \frac{0.10}{12}\right)^{12(5)} \approx \$1809.84$

Next five years

$P = 1809.84;\ i = \frac{0.08}{2},\ k = 2,\ n = 5$

$FV = P(1+i)^{kn}$

$= 1809.84\left(1 + \frac{0.08}{2}\right)^{2(5)} \approx \$2679.01$

51. **Answers may vary.**

52. **Answers may vary.**

53. $\frac{x^2 - 2x - 15}{2x^2 - 9x - 5} = \frac{(x-5)(x+3)}{(2x+1)(x-5)} = \frac{x+3}{2x+1}$

54. $3x(x^2 - 5) - (x^3 - 2x) = 3x^3 - 15x - x^3 + 2x = 2x^3 - 13x$

55. $\frac{(3-x)(x+3)}{-x^2+9} = \frac{(3-x)(x+3)}{9-x^2} = \frac{(3-x)(x+3)}{(3+x)(3-x)} = 1$

56. $-\sqrt{x^2 - 6x + 9} = -\sqrt{(x-3)^2} = -(x-3) = -x+3$

Exercise 9.2 (page 640)

1. annuities

2. end

3. payments, interest

4. term

5. regular deposit, periodic rate, frequency of compounding, number of years

6. sinking

7. $P = 100,\ i = \frac{0.06}{1},\ k = 1,\ n = 10$

$$FV = \frac{P\left[(1+i)^{kn} - 1\right]}{i} = \frac{100\left[\left(1 + \frac{0.06}{1}\right)^{1 \cdot 10} - 1\right]}{\frac{0.06}{1}} \approx \$1318.08$$

8. $P = 100,\ i = \frac{0.06}{1},\ k = 1,\ n = 5$

$$FV = \frac{P\left[(1+i)^{kn} - 1\right]}{i} = \frac{100\left[\left(1 + \frac{0.06}{1}\right)^{1 \cdot 5} - 1\right]}{\frac{0.06}{1}} \approx \$563.71$$

9. $P = 100,\ i = \frac{0.06}{1},\ k = 1,\ n = 3$

$$FV = \frac{P\left[(1+i)^{kn} - 1\right]}{i} = \frac{100\left[\left(1 + \frac{0.06}{1}\right)^{1 \cdot 3} - 1\right]}{\frac{0.06}{1}} \approx \$318.36$$

10. $P = 100,\ i = \frac{0.06}{1},\ k = 1,\ n = 20$

$$FV = \frac{P\left[(1+i)^{kn} - 1\right]}{i} = \frac{100\left[\left(1 + \frac{0.06}{1}\right)^{1 \cdot 20} - 1\right]}{\frac{0.06}{1}} \approx \$3678.56$$

11. $P = 100, i = \frac{0.04}{1}, k = 1, n = 10$

$$FV = \frac{P\left[(1+i)^{kn} - 1\right]}{i} = \frac{100\left[\left(1 + \frac{0.04}{1}\right)^{1\cdot 10} - 1\right]}{\frac{0.04}{1}} \approx \$1200.61$$

12. $P = 100, i = \frac{0.07}{1}, k = 1, n = 10$

$$FV = \frac{P\left[(1+i)^{kn} - 1\right]}{i} = \frac{100\left[\left(1 + \frac{0.07}{1}\right)^{1\cdot 10} - 1\right]}{\frac{0.07}{1}} \approx \$1381.64$$

13. $P = 100, i = \frac{0.095}{1}, k = 1, n = 10$

$$FV = \frac{P\left[(1+i)^{kn} - 1\right]}{i} = \frac{100\left[\left(1 + \frac{0.095}{1}\right)^{1\cdot 10} - 1\right]}{\frac{0.095}{1}} \approx \$1556.03$$

14. $P = 100, i = \frac{0.085}{1}, k = 1, n = 10$

$$FV = \frac{P\left[(1+i)^{kn} - 1\right]}{i} = \frac{100\left[\left(1 + \frac{0.085}{1}\right)^{1\cdot 10} - 1\right]}{\frac{0.085}{1}} \approx \$1483.51$$

15. $P = 100, i = \frac{0.08}{2}, k = 2, n = 15$

$$FV = \frac{P\left[(1+i)^{kn} - 1\right]}{i} = \frac{100\left[\left(1 + \frac{0.08}{2}\right)^{2\cdot 15} - 1\right]}{\frac{0.08}{2}} \approx \$5608.49$$

16. $P = 100, i = \frac{0.08}{4}, k = 4, n = 15$

$$FV = \frac{P\left[(1+i)^{kn} - 1\right]}{i} = \frac{100\left[\left(1 + \frac{0.08}{4}\right)^{4\cdot 15} - 1\right]}{\frac{0.08}{4}} \approx \$11{,}405.15$$

17. $P = 100, i = \frac{0.08}{12}, k = 12, n = 15$

$$FV = \frac{P\left[(1+i)^{kn} - 1\right]}{i} = \frac{100\left[\left(1 + \frac{0.08}{12}\right)^{12\cdot 15} - 1\right]}{\frac{0.08}{12}} \approx \$34{,}603.82$$

18. $P = 100, i = \frac{0.08}{1}, k = 1, n = 15$

$$FV = \frac{P\left[(1+i)^{kn} - 1\right]}{i} = \frac{100\left[\left(1 + \frac{0.08}{1}\right)^{1\cdot 15} - 1\right]}{\frac{0.08}{1}} \approx \$2715.21$$

19. $FV = 20{,}000;\ i = \frac{0.04}{1}, k = 1, n = 10$

$$P = \frac{FVi}{(1+i)^{kn} - 1} = \frac{20{,}000\left(\frac{0.04}{1}\right)}{\left(1 + \frac{0.04}{1}\right)^{1\cdot 10} - 1} \approx \$1665.81$$

20. $FV = 20{,}000;\ i = \frac{0.06}{4}, k = 4, n = 10$

$$P = \frac{FVi}{(1+i)^{kn} - 1} = \frac{20{,}000\left(\frac{0.06}{4}\right)}{\left(1 + \frac{0.06}{4}\right)^{4\cdot 10} - 1} \approx \$368.54$$

21. $FV = 20{,}000;\ i = \frac{0.09}{2}, k = 2, n = 10$

$$P = \frac{FVi}{(1+i)^{kn} - 1} = \frac{20{,}000\left(\frac{0.09}{2}\right)}{\left(1 + \frac{0.09}{2}\right)^{2\cdot 10} - 1} \approx \$637.52$$

22. $FV = 20{,}000;\ i = \frac{0.08}{12}, k = 12, n = 10$

$$P = \frac{FVi}{(1+i)^{kn} - 1} = \frac{20{,}000\left(\frac{0.08}{12}\right)}{\left(1 + \frac{0.08}{12}\right)^{12\cdot 10} - 1} \approx \$109.32$$

23. $P = 200, i = \frac{0.06}{12}, k = 12, n = 1$

$$FV = \frac{P\left[(1+i)^{kn} - 1\right]}{i} = \frac{200\left[\left(1 + \frac{0.06}{12}\right)^{12\cdot 1} - 1\right]}{\frac{0.06}{12}} \approx \$2467.11$$

24. $P = 1300, i = \frac{0.065}{4}, k = 4, n = 21$

$$FV = \frac{P\left[(1+i)^{kn} - 1\right]}{i} = \frac{1300\left[\left(1 + \frac{0.065}{4}\right)^{4\cdot 21} - 1\right]}{\frac{0.065}{4}} \approx \$229{,}839.59$$

25. $P = 135{,}000;\ i = \frac{0.087}{12}, k = 12, n = 20$

$$FV = \frac{P\left[(1+i)^{kn} - 1\right]}{i} = \frac{135{,}000\left[\left(1 + \frac{0.087}{12}\right)^{12\cdot 20} - 1\right]}{\frac{0.087}{12}} \approx \$86{,}803{,}923.58$$

26. $P = 25, i = \frac{0.075}{12}, k = 12, n = 11$

$$FV = \frac{P\left[(1+i)^{kn} - 1\right]}{i} = \frac{25\left[\left(1 + \frac{0.075}{12}\right)^{12\cdot 11} - 1\right]}{\frac{0.075}{12}} \approx \$5104.12$$

27. $FV = 750{,}000;\ i = \frac{0.0975}{12}, k = 12, n = 2.5$

$$P = \frac{FVi}{(1+i)^{kn} - 1} = \frac{750{,}000\left(\frac{0.0975}{12}\right)}{\left(1 + \frac{0.0975}{12}\right)^{12\cdot 2.5} - 1} \approx \$22{,}177.71$$

28. $FV = 500{,}000;\ i = \frac{0.085}{12}, k = 12, n = 25$

$$P = \frac{FVi}{(1+i)^{kn} - 1} = \frac{500{,}000\left(\frac{0.085}{12}\right)}{\left(1 + \frac{0.085}{12}\right)^{12\cdot 25} - 1} \approx \$484.47$$

29.

Bank A

$FV = 10{,}000;\ i = \frac{0.055}{1}, k = 1, n = 20$

$$P = \frac{FVi}{(1+i)^{kn} - 1} = \frac{10{,}000\left(\frac{0.055}{1}\right)}{\left(1 + \frac{0.055}{1}\right)^{1\cdot 20} - 1} \approx \$286.79 \text{ per year}$$

Bank B

$FV = 10{,}000;\ i = \frac{0.0535}{12}, k = 12, n = 20$

$$P = \frac{FVi}{(1+i)^{kn} - 1} = \frac{10{,}000\left(\frac{0.0535}{12}\right)}{\left(1 + \frac{0.0535}{12}\right)^{12\cdot 20} - 1} \approx \$23.36 \text{ per month, or } \$280.32 \text{ per year}$$

Bank B requires the lower annual contributions.

30. $FV = 47{,}000;\ i = \frac{0.102}{12}, k = 12, n = 12$

$$P = \frac{FVi}{(1+i)^{kn} - 1} = \frac{47{,}000\left(\frac{0.102}{12}\right)}{\left(1 + \frac{0.102}{12}\right)^{12 \cdot 12} - 1} \approx \$167.63$$

31.

First 15 years

$P = 100, i = \frac{0.08}{12}, k = 12, n = 15$

$$FV = \frac{P\left[(1+i)^{kn} - 1\right]}{i} = \frac{100\left[\left(1 + \frac{0.08}{12}\right)^{12 \cdot 15} - 1\right]}{\frac{0.08}{12}} \approx \$34.603.82$$

Next 15 years

$P = 34{,}603.82, i = \frac{0.08}{12}, k = 12, n = 15$

$$FV = P(1+i)^{kn} = 34{,}603.82\left(1 + \frac{0.08}{12}\right)^{12 \cdot 15} \approx \$114{,}432.12$$

32. $P = 200, i = \frac{0.08}{12}, k = 12, n = 15$

$$FV = \frac{P\left[(1+i)^{kn} - 1\right]}{i} = \frac{200\left[\left(1 + \frac{0.08}{12}\right)^{12 \cdot 15} - 1\right]}{\frac{0.08}{12}} \approx \$69{,}207.64$$

33.

Last 5 years

$FV = 13{,}500;\ i = \frac{0.09}{1}, k = 1, n = 5$

$$PV = FV(1+i)^{-kn} = 13{,}500\left(1 + \frac{0.09}{1}\right)^{-1(5)} \approx \$8774.07$$

First 5 years

$FV = 8774.07;\ i = \frac{0.09}{1}, k = 1, n = 5$

$$P = \frac{FVi}{(1+i)^{kn} - 1} = \frac{8774.07\left(\frac{0.09}{1}\right)}{\left(1 + \frac{0.09}{1}\right)^{1 \cdot 5} - 1} \approx \$1466.08 \text{ per year}$$

34. **Answers may vary.**

35.

$$\begin{aligned} \frac{2(5x - 12)}{x} &= 8 \\ 2(5x - 12) &= 8x \\ 10x - 24 &= 8x \\ 2x &= 24 \\ x &= 12 \end{aligned}$$

36.

$$\begin{aligned} \frac{2(5x - 12)}{x} &= x \\ 2(5x - 12) &= x^2 \\ 0 &= x^2 - 10x + 24 \\ 0 &= (x-4)(x-6) \\ x = 4 &\quad \text{or} \quad x = 6 \end{aligned}$$

37.

$$\begin{aligned} \sqrt{2x+3} &= 3 \\ \left(\sqrt{2x+3}\right)^2 &= 3^2 \\ 2x + 3 &= 9 \\ 2x &= 6 \\ x &= 3 \end{aligned}$$

38.

$$\begin{aligned} \sqrt{2x+3} &= x \\ \left(\sqrt{2x+3}\right)^2 &= x^2 \\ 2x + 3 &= x^2 \\ 0 &= x^2 - 2x - 3 \\ 0 &= (x-3)(x+1) \end{aligned}$$

$\boxed{x = 3}$ or $x = -1$ (extraneous)

Exercise 9.3 (page 646)

1. present value **2.** present value **3.** promissory note

4. installments **5.** amortizing **6.** mortgage

7. $P = 3500, k = 1, i = \frac{0.0525}{1}, n = 25$

$$PV = \frac{P\left[1-(1+i)^{-kn}\right]}{i} = \frac{3500\left[1-\left(1+\frac{0.0525}{1}\right)^{-1\cdot 25}\right]}{\frac{0.0525}{1}} \approx \$48{,}116.14$$

8. $P = 375, k = 2, i = \frac{0.0492}{2}, n = 10$

$$PV = \frac{P\left[1-(1+i)^{-kn}\right]}{i} = \frac{375\left[1-\left(1+\frac{0.0492}{2}\right)^{-2\cdot 10}\right]}{\frac{0.0492}{2}} \approx \$5868.09$$

9. $A = 25{,}000;\ k = 12, i = \frac{0.12}{12}, n = 15$

$$P = \frac{Ai}{1-(1+i)^{-kn}} = \frac{25{,}000\left(\frac{0.12}{12}\right)}{1-\left(1+\frac{0.12}{12}\right)^{-12\cdot 15}} \approx \$300.04$$

10. $A = 1750;\ k = 12, i = \frac{0.19}{12}, n = 1.5$

$$P = \frac{Ai}{1-(1+i)^{-kn}} = \frac{1750\left(\frac{0.19}{12}\right)}{1-\left(1+\frac{0.19}{12}\right)^{-12\cdot 1.5}} \approx \$112.50$$

11. $P = 700, k = 4, i = \frac{0.0625}{4}, n = 15$

$$PV = \frac{P\left[1-(1+i)^{-kn}\right]}{i} = \frac{700\left[1-\left(1+\frac{0.0625}{4}\right)^{-4\cdot 15}\right]}{\frac{0.0625}{4}} \approx \$27{,}128.43$$

12. $P = 15{,}000;\ k = 12, i = \frac{0.092}{12}, n = 20$

$$PV = \frac{P\left[1-(1+i)^{-kn}\right]}{i} = \frac{15{,}000\left[1-\left(1+\frac{0.092}{12}\right)^{-12\cdot 20}\right]}{\frac{0.092}{12}} \approx \$1{,}643{,}603.78$$

13. $P = 12{,}000;\ k = 1, i = \frac{0.085}{1}, n = 15$

$$PV = \frac{P\left[1-(1+i)^{-kn}\right]}{i} = \frac{12{,}000\left[1-\left(1+\frac{0.085}{1}\right)^{-1\cdot 15}\right]}{\frac{0.085}{1}} \approx \$99{,}650.84$$

14. $P = 5000, k = 4, i = \frac{0.0766666667}{4}, n = 25$

$$PV = \frac{P\left[1-(1+i)^{-kn}\right]}{i} = \frac{5000\left[1-\left(1+\frac{0.0766666667}{4}\right)^{-4\cdot 25}\right]}{\frac{0.0766666667}{4}} \approx \$221{,}794.27$$

15. $A = 21{,}700;\ k = 12, i = \dfrac{0.084}{12}, n = 4$

$$P = \frac{Ai}{1-(1+i)^{-kn}} = \frac{21{,}700\left(\frac{0.084}{12}\right)}{1-\left(1+\frac{0.084}{12}\right)^{-12\cdot 4}} \approx \$533.84$$

16. Refer to **#15**. Total payments $= 48 \cdot 533.84 = \$25{,}624.32$

17.

15-year

$A = 130{,}000;\ k = 12, i = \dfrac{0.12}{12}, n = 15$

$$P = \frac{Ai}{1-(1+i)^{-kn}} = \frac{130{,}000\left(\frac{0.12}{12}\right)}{1-\left(1+\frac{0.12}{12}\right)^{-12\cdot 15}} \approx \$1560.22$$

20-year

$A = 130{,}000;\ k = 12, i = \dfrac{0.11}{12}, n = 20$

$$P = \frac{Ai}{1-(1+i)^{-kn}} = \frac{130{,}000\left(\frac{0.11}{12}\right)}{1-\left(1+\frac{0.11}{12}\right)^{-12\cdot 20}} \approx \$1341.84$$

18. Refer to **#17**

15-year	20-year
Total $= 180 \cdot 1560.22 = \$280{,}839.60$	Total $= 240 \cdot 1341.84 = \$322{,}041.60$

19.

From 55 to 80

$P = 5000;\ k = 12, i = \frac{0.0875}{12}, n = 25$

$$PV = \frac{P\left[1-(1+i)^{-kn}\right]}{i} = \frac{5000\left[1-\left(1+\frac{0.0875}{12}\right)^{-12\cdot 25}\right]}{\frac{0.0875}{12}} \approx \$608{,}166.24$$

From 20 to 55

$FV = 608{,}166.24;\ i = \frac{0.0875}{12}, k = 12, n = 35$

$$P = \frac{FVi}{(1+i)^{kn}-1} = \frac{608{,}166.24\left(\frac{0.0875}{12}\right)}{\left(1+\frac{0.0875}{12}\right)^{12\cdot 35}-1} \approx \$220.13$$

20. **a.** $$FV = \frac{1000\left[\left(1+\frac{0.08}{1}\right)^{1\cdot 10}-1\right]}{\frac{0.08}{1}} \approx \$14{,}486.56$$

$$FV = 14{,}486.56\left(1+\frac{0.08}{1}\right)^{1(10)} \approx 31{,}275.40$$

b. $$FV = \frac{500\left[\left(1+\frac{0.08}{1}\right)^{1\cdot 20}-1\right]}{\frac{0.08}{1}} \approx \$22{,}880.98$$

c. $$FV = \frac{2000\left[\left(1+\frac{0.08}{1}\right)^{1\cdot 10}-1\right]}{\frac{0.08}{1}} \approx \$28{,}973.12$$

d. $$FV = 8000\left(1+\frac{0.08}{1}\right)^{1(20)} \approx \$37{,}287.66$$ ⇐ Best FV, so best option

21. First ten years

$$FV = \frac{500\left[\left(1+\frac{0.0725}{4}\right)^{4\cdot 10}-1\right]}{\frac{0.0725}{4}} \approx \$29{,}003.32$$

Next ten years (2 parts)

$$FV = \frac{1500\left[\left(1+\frac{0.0725}{4}\right)^{4\cdot 10}-1\right]}{\frac{0.0725}{4}} \approx \$87{,}009.96$$

$$FV = 29{,}003.32\left(1+\frac{0.0725}{4}\right)^{4(10)} \approx \$59{,}496.55$$

Total $= \$87{,}009.96 + \$59{,}496.55 = \$146{,}506.51$

22. First five years

$$FV = \frac{150\left[\left(1+\frac{0.05}{12}\right)^{12\cdot 5}-1\right]}{\frac{0.05}{12}} \approx \$10{,}200.91$$

Next five years (2 parts)

$$FV = \frac{150\left[\left(1+\frac{0.065}{12}\right)^{12\cdot 5}-1\right]}{\frac{0.065}{12}} \approx \$10{,}601.10$$

$$FV = 10{,}200.91\left(1+\frac{0.065}{12}\right)^{12(5)} \approx \$14{,}106.00$$

Total $= \$10{,}601.10 + \$14{,}106.00 = \$24{,}707.10$

23. $\dfrac{6\sqrt{30}}{3\sqrt{5}} = \dfrac{6}{3}\cdot\dfrac{\sqrt{30}}{\sqrt{5}} = 2\sqrt{\dfrac{30}{5}} = 2\sqrt{6}$

24. $\dfrac{6}{\sqrt{7}-2} = \dfrac{6\left(\sqrt{7}+2\right)}{\left(\sqrt{7}-2\right)\left(\sqrt{7}+2\right)} = \dfrac{6\left(\sqrt{7}+2\right)}{7-4} = \dfrac{6\left(\sqrt{7}+2\right)}{3} = 2\left(\sqrt{7}+2\right)$

25. $3\sqrt{5x}+5\sqrt{20x} = 3\sqrt{5x}+5\sqrt{4}\sqrt{5x} = 3\sqrt{5x}+10\sqrt{5x} = 13\sqrt{5x}$

26. $\sqrt{\dfrac{x^3y^5}{x^5y^6}} = \sqrt{\dfrac{1}{x^2y}} = \dfrac{1}{x\sqrt{y}} = \dfrac{1\sqrt{y}}{x\sqrt{y}\sqrt{y}} = \dfrac{\sqrt{y}}{xy}$

Chapter 9 Summary (page 649)

1. $FV = 2000\left(1+\dfrac{0.09}{1}\right)^{1\cdot 5} \approx \$3077.25$

2. $FV = 2350\left(1+\dfrac{0.14}{360}\right)^{360(1/6)} \approx \$2405.47$

3. $FV = 2000\left(1+\dfrac{0.076}{4}\right)^{4\cdot 16} \approx \$6670.80$

4. BigBank: $R = \left(1+\dfrac{0.063}{4}\right)^{4} - 1 = 0.0645$ BestBank: $R = \left(1+\dfrac{0.0621}{365}\right)^{365} - 1 = 0.0641$

BigBank has the better return.

5. $PV = 7900\left(1 + \dfrac{0.0575}{2}\right)^{-2\cdot 6}$
$\approx \$5622.23$

6. $FV = \dfrac{500\left[\left(1 + \frac{0.05}{1}\right)^{1\cdot 13} - 1\right]}{\frac{0.05}{1}}$
$\approx \$8856.49$

7. $FV = \dfrac{150\left[\left(1 + \frac{0.08}{12}\right)^{12\cdot 20} - 1\right]}{\frac{0.08}{12}}$
$\approx \$88{,}353.06$

8. $P = \dfrac{40{,}700\left(\frac{0.075}{12}\right)}{\left(1 + \frac{0.075}{12}\right)^{12\cdot 7} - 1} \approx \$369.89$

9. $PV = \dfrac{250\left[1 - \left(1 + \frac{0.065}{2}\right)^{-2\cdot 20}\right]}{\frac{0.065}{2}}$
$\approx \$5552.11$

10. $PV = \dfrac{50{,}000\left[1 - \left(1 + \frac{0.096}{1}\right)^{-1\cdot 20}\right]}{\frac{0.096}{1}}$
$\approx \$437{,}563.50$

11. $P = \dfrac{150{,}500\left(\frac{0.1075}{12}\right)}{1 - \left(1 + \frac{0.1075}{12}\right)^{-12\cdot 15}} \approx \$1687.03$; Total paid $= 1687.03 \cdot 180 = \$303{,}665.40$

12. $P = \dfrac{150{,}500\left(\frac{0.1075}{12}\right)}{1 - \left(1 + \frac{0.1075}{12}\right)^{-12\cdot 30}} \approx \$1404.89$; Total paid $= 1404.89 \cdot 360 = \$505{,}760.40$

Chapter 9 Test (page 651)

1. compound

2. periodic

3. effective

4. annual

5. annuities

6. sinking fund

7. present value

8. amortizing

9. $FV = 1300\left(1 + \frac{0.05}{1}\right)^{1\cdot 10} \approx \$2117.56$

10. $FV = 1300\left(1 + \frac{0.05}{12}\right)^{12\cdot 10} \approx \$2141.11$

11. $R = \left(1 + \frac{0.05}{12}\right)^{12} - 1 = 0.05116$
$= 5.116\%$

12. $PV = 5000\left(1 + \frac{0.07}{4}\right)^{-4\cdot 10} \approx \$2498.00$

13. $FV = \dfrac{700\left[\left(1 + \frac{0.073}{12}\right)^{12\cdot 5} - 1\right]}{\frac{0.073}{12}}$
$\approx \$50{,}506.10$

14. $P = \dfrac{8000\left(\frac{0.065}{12}\right)}{\left(1 + \frac{0.065}{12}\right)^{12\cdot 5} - 1} \approx \$113.20$

15. $PV = \dfrac{1000\left[1 - \left(1 + \frac{0.068}{12}\right)^{-12\cdot 15}\right]}{\frac{0.068}{12}}$
$\approx \$112{,}652.71$

16. $P = \dfrac{90{,}000\left(\frac{0.0895}{12}\right)}{1 - \left(1 + \frac{0.0895}{12}\right)^{-12\cdot 15}} \approx \$910.16$

Cumulative Review Exercises (page 652)

1. $\begin{cases} 2x + y = 8 \\ x - 2y = -1 \end{cases}$

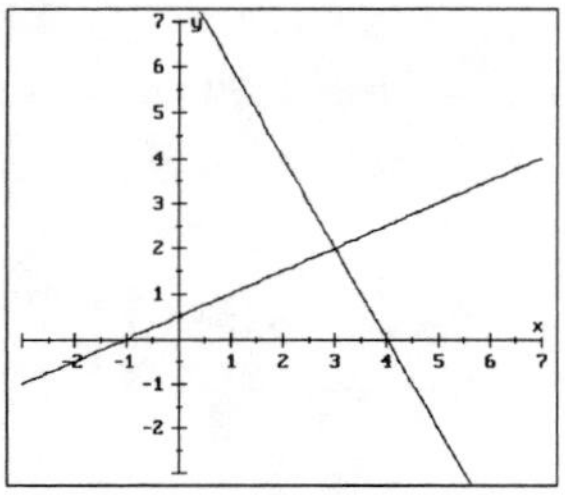

(3, 2)

2. $\begin{cases} 3x = -y + 2 \\ y + x - 4 = -2x \end{cases}$

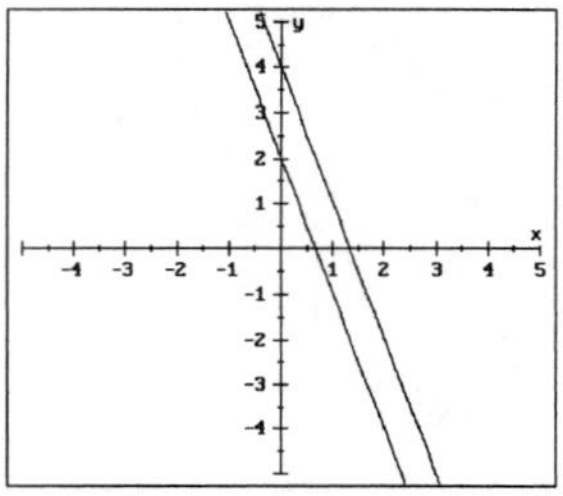

no solution, inconsistent system

3.
$$\begin{array}{l} 5x = 3y + 12 \Rightarrow 5x - 3y = 12 \Rightarrow 5x - 3y = 12 \\ \underline{2x - 3y = 3 \qquad \Rightarrow 2x - 3y = 3} \Rightarrow \underline{-2x + 3y = -3} \\ \qquad\qquad\qquad\qquad\qquad\qquad\quad 3x \qquad = 9 \\ \qquad\qquad\qquad\qquad\qquad\qquad\quad x \qquad = 3 \end{array}$$
$$\begin{aligned} 2x - 3y &= 3 \\ 2(3) - 3y &= 3 \\ -3y &= -3 \\ y &= 1 \end{aligned}$$

Solution: $\boxed{x = 3, y = 1}$

4. $\begin{bmatrix} x \\ y \\ z \end{bmatrix} = \begin{bmatrix} 2 & 1 & -1 \\ 1 & -1 & 1 \\ 1 & 1 & -3 \end{bmatrix}^{-1} \begin{bmatrix} 7 \\ 2 \\ 2 \end{bmatrix} = \begin{bmatrix} 3 \\ 2 \\ 1 \end{bmatrix}$

5. $\left[\begin{array}{ccc|c} 2 & 1 & -1 & 0 \\ 1 & -1 & 1 & 3 \\ 1 & 1 & -3 & -5 \end{array}\right] \Rightarrow \underset{R_1 \Leftrightarrow R_3}{\left[\begin{array}{ccc|c} 1 & 1 & -3 & -5 \\ 1 & -1 & 1 & 3 \\ 2 & 1 & -1 & 0 \end{array}\right]} \Rightarrow \underset{\substack{-R_1 + R_2 \Rightarrow R_2 \\ -2R_1 + R_3 \Rightarrow R_3}}{\left[\begin{array}{ccc|c} 1 & 1 & -3 & -5 \\ 0 & -2 & 4 & 8 \\ 0 & -1 & 5 & 10 \end{array}\right]} \Rightarrow$

$\underset{\substack{\frac{1}{2}R_2 + R_1 \Rightarrow R_1 \\ -\frac{1}{2}R_2 + R_3 \Rightarrow R_3 \\ -\frac{1}{2}R_2 \Rightarrow R_2}}{\left[\begin{array}{ccc|c} 1 & 0 & -1 & -1 \\ 0 & 1 & -2 & -4 \\ 0 & 0 & 3 & 6 \end{array}\right]} \Rightarrow \underset{\substack{\frac{1}{3}R_3 + R_1 \Rightarrow R_1 \\ \frac{2}{3}R_3 + R_2 \Rightarrow R_2 \\ \frac{1}{3}R_3 \Rightarrow R_3}}{\left[\begin{array}{ccc|c} 1 & 0 & 0 & 1 \\ 0 & 1 & 0 & 0 \\ 0 & 0 & 1 & 2 \end{array}\right]}$ Solution: $\boxed{x = 1, y = 0, z = 2}$

6. $\left[\begin{array}{cccc|c} 2 & -2 & 3 & 1 & 2 \\ 1 & 1 & 1 & 1 & 5 \\ -1 & 2 & -3 & 2 & 2 \\ 1 & 1 & 2 & -1 & 4 \end{array}\right] \Rightarrow \left[\begin{array}{cccc|c} 2 & -2 & 3 & 1 & 2 \\ 0 & -4 & 1 & -1 & -8 \\ 0 & 2 & -3 & 5 & 6 \\ 0 & -4 & -1 & 3 & -6 \end{array}\right] \Rightarrow \left[\begin{array}{cccc|c} -4 & 0 & -5 & -3 & -12 \\ 0 & -4 & 1 & -1 & -8 \\ 0 & 0 & -5 & 9 & 4 \\ 0 & 0 & 2 & -4 & -2 \end{array}\right]$

$-2R_2 + R_1 \Rightarrow R_2$, $2R_3 + R_1 \Rightarrow R_3$, $-2R_4 + R_1 \Rightarrow R_4$

$-2R_1 + R_2 \Rightarrow R_1$, $2R_3 + R_2 \Rightarrow R_3$, $-R_4 + R_2 \Rightarrow R_4$

$\left[\begin{array}{cccc|c} -4 & 0 & -5 & -3 & -12 \\ 0 & -4 & 1 & -1 & -8 \\ 0 & 0 & -5 & 9 & 4 \\ 0 & 0 & 1 & -2 & -1 \end{array}\right] \Rightarrow \left[\begin{array}{cccc|c} 4 & 0 & 0 & 12 & 16 \\ 0 & -20 & 0 & 4 & -36 \\ 0 & 0 & -5 & 9 & 4 \\ 0 & 0 & 0 & -1 & -1 \end{array}\right] \Rightarrow \left[\begin{array}{cccc|c} 1 & 0 & 0 & 3 & 4 \\ 0 & -5 & 0 & 1 & -9 \\ 0 & 0 & -5 & 9 & 4 \\ 0 & 0 & 0 & 1 & 1 \end{array}\right]$

$\frac{1}{2}R_4 \Rightarrow R_4$

$-R_1 + R_3 \Rightarrow R_1$, $5R_2 + R_3 \Rightarrow R_2$, $5R_4 + R_3 \Rightarrow R_4$

$\frac{1}{4}R_1 \Rightarrow R_1$, $\frac{1}{4}R_2 \Rightarrow R_2$, $-R_4 \Rightarrow R_4$

$\Rightarrow \left[\begin{array}{cccc|c} 1 & 0 & 0 & 0 & 1 \\ 0 & -5 & 0 & 0 & -10 \\ 0 & 0 & -5 & 0 & -5 \\ 0 & 0 & 0 & 1 & 1 \end{array}\right] \Rightarrow \left[\begin{array}{cccc|c} 1 & 0 & 0 & 0 & 1 \\ 0 & 1 & 0 & 0 & 2 \\ 0 & 0 & 1 & 0 & 1 \\ 0 & 0 & 0 & 1 & 1 \end{array}\right]$

$-3R_4 + R_1 \Rightarrow R_1$, $-R_4 + R_2 \Rightarrow R_2$, $-9R_4 + R_3 \Rightarrow R_3$

$-\frac{1}{5}R_2 \Rightarrow R_2$, $-\frac{1}{5}R_3 \Rightarrow R_3$

Solution: $\boxed{x = 1, y = 2, z = 1, t = 1}$

7. $\begin{bmatrix} 2 & 1 \\ 1 & 4 \end{bmatrix} + \begin{bmatrix} -1 & 2 \\ 2 & 3 \end{bmatrix} = \begin{bmatrix} 1 & 3 \\ 3 & 7 \end{bmatrix}$

8. $\begin{bmatrix} -1 & 2 \\ 2 & 3 \end{bmatrix} - \begin{bmatrix} 2 & 1 \\ 1 & 4 \end{bmatrix} = \begin{bmatrix} -3 & 1 \\ 1 & -1 \end{bmatrix}$

9. $\begin{bmatrix} 2 & 1 \\ 1 & 4 \end{bmatrix}\begin{bmatrix} 2 & 0 & -1 \\ -1 & 2 & 2 \end{bmatrix} = \begin{bmatrix} 3 & 2 & 0 \\ -2 & 8 & 7 \end{bmatrix}$

10. $\begin{bmatrix} -1 & 2 \\ 2 & 3 \end{bmatrix}^2 + 2\begin{bmatrix} 2 & 1 \\ 1 & 4 \end{bmatrix} = \begin{bmatrix} -1 & 2 \\ 2 & 3 \end{bmatrix}\begin{bmatrix} -1 & 2 \\ 2 & 3 \end{bmatrix} + \begin{bmatrix} 4 & 2 \\ 2 & 8 \end{bmatrix} = \begin{bmatrix} 5 & 4 \\ 4 & 13 \end{bmatrix} + \begin{bmatrix} 4 & 2 \\ 2 & 8 \end{bmatrix} = \begin{bmatrix} 9 & 6 \\ 6 & 21 \end{bmatrix}$

11. $\left[\begin{array}{cc|cc} 2 & 6 & 1 & 0 \\ 2 & 4 & 0 & 1 \end{array}\right] \Rightarrow \left[\begin{array}{cc|cc} 1 & 3 & \frac{1}{2} & 0 \\ 2 & 4 & 0 & 1 \end{array}\right] \Rightarrow \left[\begin{array}{cc|cc} 1 & 3 & \frac{1}{2} & 0 \\ 0 & -2 & -1 & 1 \end{array}\right] \Rightarrow$

$\frac{1}{2}R_1 \Rightarrow R_1$ $\quad -2R_1 + R_2 \Rightarrow R_2$

$\left[\begin{array}{cc|cc} 1 & 3 & \frac{1}{2} & 0 \\ 0 & 1 & \frac{1}{2} & -\frac{1}{2} \end{array}\right] \Rightarrow \left[\begin{array}{cc|cc} 1 & 0 & -1 & \frac{3}{2} \\ 0 & 1 & \frac{1}{2} & -\frac{1}{2} \end{array}\right] \Rightarrow$ Inverse: $\begin{bmatrix} -1 & \frac{3}{2} \\ \frac{1}{2} & -\frac{1}{2} \end{bmatrix}$

$-\frac{1}{2}R_2 \Rightarrow R_2$ $\quad -3R_2 + R_1 \Rightarrow R_1$

12. $\left[\begin{array}{ccc|ccc} 1 & -1 & 1 & 1 & 0 & 0 \\ 1 & 4 & 0 & 0 & 1 & 0 \\ 2 & 4 & 1 & 0 & 0 & 1 \end{array}\right] \Rightarrow \left[\begin{array}{ccc|ccc} 1 & -1 & 1 & 1 & 0 & 0 \\ 0 & 5 & -1 & -1 & 1 & 0 \\ 0 & 6 & -1 & -2 & 0 & 1 \end{array}\right] \Rightarrow \left[\begin{array}{ccc|ccc} 1 & -1 & 1 & 1 & 0 & 0 \\ 0 & 1 & 0 & -1 & -1 & 1 \\ 0 & 6 & -1 & -2 & 0 & 1 \end{array}\right]$

$-R_1 + R_2 \Rightarrow R_2$, $-2R_2 + R_3 \Rightarrow R_3$; $-R_2 + R_3 \Rightarrow R_2$

$\Rightarrow \left[\begin{array}{ccc|ccc} 1 & 0 & 1 & 0 & -1 & 1 \\ 0 & 1 & 0 & -1 & -1 & 1 \\ 0 & 0 & -1 & 4 & 6 & -5 \end{array}\right] \Rightarrow \left[\begin{array}{ccc|ccc} 1 & 0 & 0 & 4 & 5 & -4 \\ 0 & 1 & 0 & -1 & -1 & 1 \\ 0 & 0 & 1 & -4 & -6 & 5 \end{array}\right] \Rightarrow \text{Inv} = \begin{bmatrix} 4 & 5 & -4 \\ -1 & -1 & 1 \\ -4 & -6 & 5 \end{bmatrix}$

$R_2 + R_1 \Rightarrow R_1$, $-6R_2 + R_3 \Rightarrow R_3$; $R_3 + R_1 \Rightarrow R_1$, $-R_3 \Rightarrow R_3$

13. $\begin{vmatrix} -3 & 5 \\ 4 & 7 \end{vmatrix} = (-3)(7) - (5)(4) = -21 - 20 = -41$

14. $\begin{vmatrix} 2 & -3 & 2 \\ 0 & 1 & -1 \\ 1 & -2 & 1 \end{vmatrix} = 2\begin{vmatrix} 1 & -1 \\ -2 & 1 \end{vmatrix} - (-3)\begin{vmatrix} 0 & -1 \\ 1 & 1 \end{vmatrix} + 2\begin{vmatrix} 0 & 1 \\ 1 & -2 \end{vmatrix}$

$= 2(-1) + 3(1) + 2(-1) = -2 + 3 - 2 = -1$

15. $x = \dfrac{\begin{vmatrix} 11 & 3 \\ 24 & 5 \end{vmatrix}}{\begin{vmatrix} 4 & 3 \\ -2 & 5 \end{vmatrix}}$

16. $y = \dfrac{\begin{vmatrix} 4 & 11 \\ -2 & 24 \end{vmatrix}}{\begin{vmatrix} 4 & 3 \\ -2 & 5 \end{vmatrix}}$

17.
$$\begin{aligned} \frac{-x+1}{(x+1)(x+2)} &= \frac{A}{x+1} + \frac{B}{x+2} \\ &= \frac{A(x+2)}{(x+1)(x+2)} + \frac{B(x+1)}{(x+1)(x+2)} \\ &= \frac{Ax + 2A + Bx + B}{(x+1)(x+2)} \\ &= \frac{(A+B)x + (2A+B)}{(x+1)(x+2)} \end{aligned}$$

$\begin{cases} A + B = -1 \\ 2A + B = 1 \end{cases} \Rightarrow A = 2, B = -3$

$\dfrac{-x+1}{(x+1)(x+2)} = \dfrac{2}{x+1} - \dfrac{3}{x+2}$

18.
$$\begin{aligned} \frac{x-4}{(2x-5)^2} &= \frac{A}{2x-5} + \frac{B}{(2x-5)^2} \\ &= \frac{A(2x-5)}{(2x-5)^2} + \frac{B}{(2x-5)^2} \\ &= \frac{2Ax - 5A + B}{(2x-5)^2} \\ &= \frac{2Ax + (-5A+B)}{(2x-5)^2} \end{aligned}$$

$\begin{cases} 2A = 1 \\ -5A + B = -4 \end{cases} \Rightarrow \begin{array}{l} A = \frac{1}{2} \\ B = -\frac{3}{2} \end{array}$

$\dfrac{x-4}{(2x-5)^2} = \dfrac{\frac{1}{2}}{2x-5} - \dfrac{\frac{3}{2}}{(2x-5)^2}$

47.

Check $n = 1$: $3(1) + 1 \overset{?}{=} \dfrac{1(3(1)+5)}{2}$ True for $n = 1$ $4 = 4$
Assume for $n = k$ and show for $n = k + 1$: $$4+7+10+\cdots+(3k+1) = \frac{k(3k+5)}{2}$$ $$\boxed{4+7+10+\cdots+(3k+1)} + 3(k+1)+1 = \boxed{\frac{k(3k+5)}{2}} + 3(k+1)+1$$ $$4+7+10+\cdots+(3(k+1)+1) = \frac{k(3k+5)}{2} + \frac{2\cdot(3(k+1)+1)}{2}$$ $$4+7+10+\cdots+(3(k+1)+1) = \frac{3k^2+5k+6k+6+2}{2}$$ $$4+7+10+\cdots+(3(k+1)+1) = \frac{3k^2+11k+8}{2}$$ $$4+7+10+\cdots+(3(k+1)+1) = \frac{(k+1)(3k+8)}{2}$$ $$4+7+10+\cdots+(3(k+1)+1) = \frac{(k+1)(3(k+1)+5)}{2}$$
Since this is what results when $n = k + 1$ in the formula, we have shown that the formula works for $n = k + 1$ if it works for $n = k$.

48. Expected winnings $= \dfrac{4}{52}(100) + \dfrac{4}{52}(10) + \dfrac{44}{52}(0) \approx \$8.46 \Leftarrow$ fair price

49. $PV = 10{,}000\left(1 + \dfrac{0.085}{1}\right)^{-1\cdot 12}$
$\approx \$3757.02$

50. $P = \dfrac{110{,}000\left(\frac{0.0875}{12}\right)}{1 - \left(1 + \frac{0.0875}{12}\right)^{-12\cdot 20}} \approx \$972.08$